**Volume 2** Topics 5–8

## Authors

**Robert Q. Berry, III**
Professor of Mathematics Education, Department of Curriculum, Instruction and Special Education, University of Virginia, Charlottesville, Virginia

**Zachary Champagne**
Assistant in Research
Florida Center for Research in Science, Technology, Engineering, and Mathematics (FCR-STEM)
Jacksonville, Florida

**Eric Milou**
Professor of Mathematics
Rowan University,
Glassboro, New Jersey

**Jane F. Schielack**
Professor Emerita
Department of Mathematics
Texas A&M University,
College Station, Texas

**Jonathan A. Wray**
Mathematics Supervisor,
Howard County Public Schools,
Ellicott City, Maryland

**Randall I. Charles**
Professor Emeritus
Department of Mathematics
San Jose State University
San Jose, California

**Francis (Skip) Fennell**
Professor Emeritus of Education and Graduate and Professional Studies,
McDaniel College
Westminster, Maryland

D1283332

Pearson

Boston, Massachusetts  Chandler, Arizona
Glenview, Illinois  New York, New York

## Mathematician Reviewers

**Gary Lippman, Ph.D.**
Professor Emeritus
Mathematics and Computer Science
California State University, East Bay
Hayward, California

**Karen Edwards, Ph.D.**
Mathematics Lecturer
Arlington, MA

## Additional Reviewers

**Kristine Peterfeso**
Teacher Middle School Math,
Palm Beach County School District

**Tamala Ferguson**
Math Curriculum Coach,
School District of Osceola County

**Melissa Nelson**
Math Coach and Assessment
Coordinator, St. Lucie Public Schools

This work is solely for the use of instructors and administrators for the purpose of teaching courses and assessing student learning. Unauthorized dissemination, publication or sale of the work, in whole or in part (including posting on the internet) will destroy the integrity of the work and is strictly prohibited.

Pearson K12 Learning LLC. 221 River Street, Hoboken, NJ 07030

© 2021 Pearson K12 Learning LLC. All Rights Reserved. Printed in the United States of America.

This publication is protected by copyright, and permission should be obtained from the publisher prior to any prohibited reproduction, storage in a retrieval system, or transmission in any form or by any means, electronic, mechanical, photocopying, recording, or otherwise. For information regarding permissions, request forms and the appropriate contacts within the K12 Learning Rights Management group, please visit www.pearsonschool.com or email K12LearningPermissions@pearson.com

Attributions of third party content appear on page A1 which constitutes an extension of this copyright page.

PEARSON, ALWAYS LEARNING, and **envision**® are exclusive trademarks owned by Pearson Education, Inc. or its affiliates in the US and/or other countries.

Common Core State Standards: Copyright© 2010. National Governors Association Center for Best Practices and Council of Chief State School Officers. All rights reserved.

*ExamView*® is a registered trademark of Turning Technologies, LLC. Used under license.

Unless otherwise indicated herein, any third party trademarks that may appear in this work are the property of their respective owners and any references to third party trademarks, logos or other trade dress are for demonstrative or descriptive purposes only. Such references are not intended to imply any sponsorship, endorsement, authorization, or promotion of Pearson's products by the owners of such marks, or any relationship between the owner and Pearson Education, Inc. or its affiliates, authors, licensees or distributors.

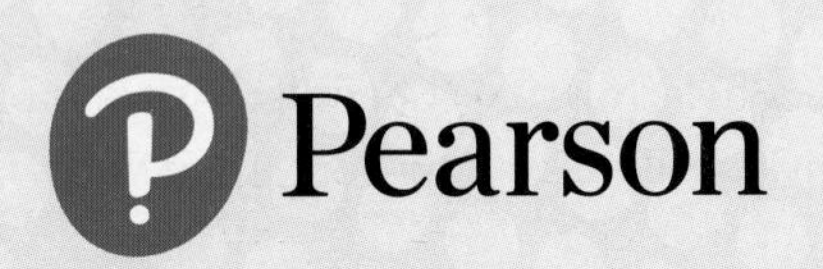


ISBN-13: 978-1-41-826934-0
ISBN-10: 1-41-826934-4
1 19

# DIGITAL RESOURCES

Go Online

Digital

## Additional Digital Resources

**ETEXT**
**Teacher's Edition eText** includes all pages from the Teacher's Edition plus access to printable resources and the digital glossary.

**VIDEOS**
**Professional Development Videos** include a **Topic Overview Video** that is presented by the authors and provides important information about the topic. **Listen and Look For Lesson Videos** provide helpful information for teaching particular lessons, as well as **Classroom Videos** that show the program in action.

**ACTIVITY**
**Today's Challenge** for each topic is a set of 5 problems on separate screens that use the same data. They can be projected in class or assigned electronically to individuals. A Teacher's Guide with a page for each problem is available online.

**ASSESSMENT**
**Online assessments** are auto scored and include: Grade-Level Readiness Test, Progress Monitoring Assessments, Topic Readiness Assessments, Lesson Quizzes, Mid-Topic Assessments, Topic Assessments, Topic Performance Tasks, Cumulative/Benchmark Assessments, and Grade-Level Practice Tests.

All print resources are also available online as eText pages or PDF files.

# Content Overview

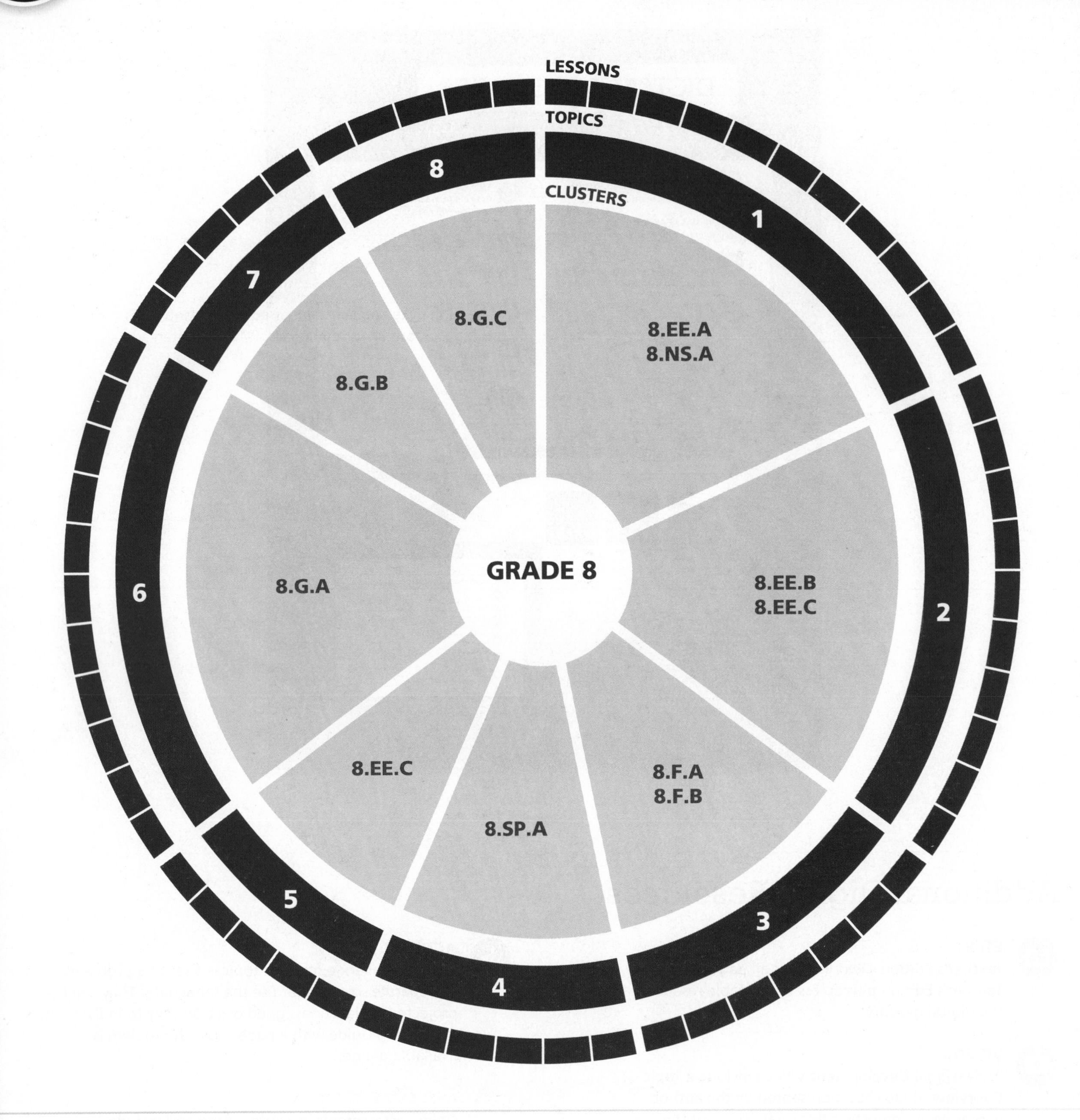


## Common Core Domains

**8.NS** THE NUMBER SYSTEM
**8.EE** EXPRESSIONS AND EQUATIONS
**8.F** FUNCTIONS
**8.G** GEOMETRY
**8.SP** STATISTICS AND PROBABILITY

**FOCUS COHERENCE RIGOR**

Content is developed with focus, coherence, and rigor. The attention to rigor reflects the balances of conceptual understanding, procedural skill and fluency, and applications in the Common Core Standards. See each Topic Overview.

| TOPIC | FOCUS ON CLUSTERS |
|---|---|
| **1 Real Numbers** | **8.EE.A** Work with radicals and integer exponents. (Major Content)<br>**8.NS.A** Know that there are numbers that are not rational, and approximate them by rational numbers. (Supporting Content) |
| **2 Analyze and Solve Linear Equations** | **8.EE.B** Understand the connections between proportional relationships, lines, and linear equations. (Major Content)<br>**8.EE.C** Analyze and solve linear equations and pairs of simultaneous linear equations. (Major Content) |
| **3 Use Functions to Model Relationships** | **8.F.A** Define, evaluate, and compare functions. (Major Content)<br>**8.F.B** Use functions to model relationships between quantities. (Major Content) |
| **4 Investigate Bivariate Data** | **8.SP.A** Investigate patterns of association in bivariate data. (Supporting Content) |
| **5 Analyze and Solve Systems of Linear Equations** | **8.EE.C** Analyze and solve linear equations and pairs of simultaneous linear equations. (Major Content) |
| **6 Congruence and Similarity** | **8.G.A** Understand congruence and similarity using physical models, transparencies, or geometry software. (Major Content) |
| **7 Understand and Apply the Pythagorean Theorem** | **8.G.B** Understand and apply the Pythagorean Theorem. (Major Content) |
| **8 Solve Problems Involving Surface Area and Volume** | **8.G.C** Solve real-world and mathematical problems involving volume of cylinders, cones, and spheres. (Additional Content) |

**Cross-Cluster Connections** See the Coherence section on each Topic and Lesson Overview page for information about connections between the clusters in **enVision**® Mathematics.

# Real Numbers



## TOPIC 1 FOCUSES ON

**8.EE.A** Work with radicals and integer exponents.

**8.NS.A** Know that there are numbers that are not rational, and approximate them by rational numbers.

## TOPIC 1 OVERVIEW

# Analyze and Solve Linear Equations

## TOPIC 2 FOCUSES ON

**8.EE.B** Understand the connections between proportional relationships, lines, and linear equations.

**8.EE.C** Analyze and solve linear equations and pairs of simultaneous linear equations.

## TOPIC 2 OVERVIEW

# Use Functions to Model Relationships

### TOPIC 3 FOCUSES ON

**8.F.A** Define, evaluate, and compare functions.

**8.F.B** Use functions to model relationships between quantities.

### TOPIC 3 OVERVIEW

# Investigate Bivariate Data

## TOPIC 4 FOCUSES ON

**8.SP.A** Investigate patterns of association in bivariate data.

## TOPIC 4 OVERVIEW

TOPIC 5 FOCUSES ON

**8.EE.A** Analyze and solve linear equations and pairs of simultaneous linear equations.

TOPIC 5 OVERVIEW



TOPIC 5

# Analyze and Solve Systems of Linear Equations

# Congruence and Similarity

## TOPIC 6 FOCUSES ON

**8.G.A** Understand congruence and similarity using physical models, transparencies, or geometry software.

## TOPIC 6 OVERVIEW

TOPIC 7 FOCUSES ON

**8.G.B** Understand and apply the Pythagorean Theorem.

TOPIC 7 OVERVIEW



TOPIC 7

# Understand and Apply the Pythagorean Theorem

TOPIC 8

# Solve Problems Involving Surface Area and Volume

## TOPIC 8 FOCUSES ON

**8.G.C** Solve real-world and mathematical problems involving volume of cylinders, cones, and spheres.

## TOPIC 8 OVERVIEW

# Common Core State Standards

## THE NUMBER SYSTEM

8.NS.A **Know that there are numbers that are not rational, and approximate them by rational numbers.** (Supporting Cluster)

8.NS.A.1 Know that numbers that are not rational are called irrational. Understand informally that every number has a decimal expansion; for rational numbers show that the decimal expansion repeats eventually, and convert a decimal expansion which repeats eventually into a rational number.

8.NS.A.2 Use rational approximations of irrational numbers to compare the size of irrational numbers, locate them approximately on a number line diagram, and estimate the value of expressions (e.g., $\pi^2$)

## EXPRESSIONS & EQUATIONS

8.EE.A **Work with radicals and integer exponents.** (Major Cluster)

8.EE.A.1 Know and apply the properties of integer exponents to generate equivalent numerical expressions.

8.EE.A.2 Use square root and cube root symbols to represent solutions to equations of the form $x^2 = p$ and $x^3 = p$, where $p$ is a positive rational number. Evaluate square roots of small perfect squares and cube roots of small perfect cubes. Know that $\sqrt{2}$ is irrational.

8.EE.A.3 Use numbers expressed in the form of a single digit times an integer power of 10 to estimate very large or very small quantities, and to express how many times as much one is than the other.

8.EE.A.4 Perform operations with numbers expressed in scientific notation, including problems where both decimal and scientific notation are used. Use scientific notation and choose units of appropriate size for measurements of very large or very small quantities (e.g., use millimeters per year for seafloor spreading). Interpret scientific notation that has been generated by technology.

8.EE.B **Understand the connections between proportional relationships, lines, and linear equations.** (Major Cluster)

8.EE.B.5 Graph proportional relationships, interpreting the unit rate as the slope of the graph. Compare two different proportional relationships represented in different ways.

8.EE.B.6 Use similar triangles to explain why the slope $m$ is the same between any two distinct points on a non-vertical line in the coordinate plane; derive the equation $y = mx$ for a line through the origin and the equation $y = mx + b$ for a line intercepting the vertical axis at $b$.

8.EE.C **Analyze and solve linear equations and pairs of simultaneous linear equations.** (Major Cluster)

8.EE.C.7 Solve linear equations in one variable.

8.EE.C.7a Give examples of linear equations in one variable with one solution, infinitely many solutions, or no solutions. Show which of these possibilities is the case by successively transforming the given equation into simpler forms, until an equivalent equation of the form $x = a$, $a = a$,or $a = b$ results (where $a$ and $b$ are different numbers).

8.EE.C.7b Solve linear equations with rational number coefficients, including equations whose solutions require expanding expressions using the distributive property and collecting like terms.

8.EE.C.8 Analyze and solve pairs of simultaneous linear equations.

8.EE.C.8a Understand that solutions to a system of two linear equations in two variables correspond to points of intersection of their graphs, because points of intersection satisfy both equations simultaneously.

8.EE.C.8b Solve systems of two linear equations in two variables algebraically, and estimate solutions by graphing the equations. Solve simple cases by inspection.

8.EE.C.8c Solve real-world and mathematical problems leading to two linear equations in two variables.

Go Online

Digital

## FUNCTIONS

**8.F.A Define, evaluate, and compare functions.** (Major Cluster)

**8.F.A.1** Understand that a function is a rule that assigns to each input exactly one output. The graph of a function is the set of ordered pairs consisting of an input and the corresponding output.[1]

**8.F.A.2** Compare properties of two functions each represented in a different way (algebraically, graphically, numerically in tables, or by verbal descriptions).

**8.F.A.3** Interpret the equation $y = mx + b$ as defining a linear function, whose graph is a straight line; give examples of functions that are not linear.

**8.F.B Use functions to model relationships between quantities.** (Major Cluster)

**8.F.B.4** Construct a function to model a linear relationship between two quantities. Determine the rate of change and initial value of the function from a description of a relationship or from two $(x, y)$ values, including reading these from a table or from a graph. Interpret the rate of change and initial value of a linear function in terms of the situation it models, and in terms of its graph or a table of values.

**8.F.B.5** Describe qualitatively the functional relationship between two quantities by analyzing a graph (e.g., where the function is increasing or decreasing, linear or nonlinear). Sketch a graph that exhibits the qualitative features of a function that has been described verbally.

[1]*Function notation is not required for Grade 8.*

## GEOMETRY

**8.G.A Understand congruence and similarity using physical models, transparencies, or geometry software.** (Major Cluster)

**8.G.A.1** Verify experimentally the properties of rotations, reflections, and translations:

**8.G.A.1a** Lines are taken to lines, and line segments to line segments of the same length.

**8.G.A.1b** Angles are taken to angles of the same measure.

**8.G.A.1c** Parallel lines are taken to parallel lines.

**8.G.A.2** Understand that a two-dimensional figure is congruent to another if the second can be obtained from the first by a sequence of rotations, reflections, and translations; given two congruent figures, describe a sequence that exhibits the congruence between them.

**8.G.A.3** Describe the effect of dilations, translations, rotations, and reflections on two-dimensional figures using coordinates.

**8.G.A.4** Understand that a two-dimensional figure is similar to another if the second can be obtained from the first by a sequence of rotations, reflections, translations, and dilations; given two similar two-dimensional figures, describe a sequence that exhibits the similarity between them.

**8.G.A.5** Use informal arguments to establish facts about the angle sum and exterior angle of triangles, about the angles created when parallel lines are cut by a transversal, and the angle-angle criterion for similarity of triangles.

**8.G.B Understand and apply the Pythagorean Theorem.** (Major Cluster)

**8.G.B.6** Explain a proof of the Pythagorean Theorem and its converse.

**8.G.B.7** Apply the Pythagorean Theorem to determine unknown side lengths in right triangles in real-world and mathematical problems in two and three dimensions.

**8.G.B.8** Apply the Pythagorean Theorem to find the distance between two points in a coordinate system.

**8.G.C Solve real-world and mathematical problems involving volume of cylinders, cones, and spheres.** (Additional Cluster)

**8.G.C.9** Know the formulas for the volumes of cones, cylinders, and spheres and use them to solve real-world and mathematical problems.

## STATISTICS & PROBABILITY

**8.SP.A Investigate patterns of association in bivariate data.** (Supporting Cluster)

**8.SP.A.1** Construct and interpret scatter plots for bivariate measurement data to investigate patterns of association between two quantities. Describe patterns such as clustering, outliers, positive or negative association, linear association, and nonlinear association.

**8.SP.A.2** Know that straight lines are widely used to model relationships between two quantitative variables. For scatter plots that suggest a linear association, informally fit a straight line, and informally assess the model fit by judging the closeness of the data points to the line.

**8.SP.A.3** Use the equation of a linear model to solve problems in the context of bivariate measurement data, interpreting the slope and intercept.

**8.SP.A.4** Understand that patterns of association can also be seen in bivariate categorical data by displaying frequencies and relative frequencies in a two-way table. Construct and interpret a two-way table summarizing data on two categorical variables collected from the same subjects. Use relative frequencies calculated for rows or columns to describe possible association between the two variables.

Go Online

## STANDARDS FOR MATHEMATICAL PRACTICE

**MP.1 Make sense of problems and persevere in solving them.**

Mathematically proficient students start by explaining to themselves the meaning of a problem and looking for entry points to its solution. They analyze givens, constraints, relationships, and goals. They make conjectures about the form and meaning of the solution and plan a solution pathway rather than simply jumping into a solution attempt. They consider analogous problems, and try special cases and simpler forms of the original problem in order to gain insight into its solution. They monitor and evaluate their progress and change course if necessary. Older students might, depending on the context of the problem, transform algebraic expressions or change the viewing window on their graphing calculator to get the information they need. Mathematically proficient students can explain correspondences between equations, verbal descriptions, tables, and graphs or draw diagrams of important features and relationships, graph data, and search for regularity or trends. Younger students might rely on using concrete objects or pictures to help conceptualize and solve a problem. Mathematically proficient students check their answers to problems using a different method, and they continually ask themselves, "Does this make sense?" They can understand the approaches of others to solving complex problems and identify correspondences between different approaches.

**MP.2 Reason abstractly and quantitatively.**

Mathematically proficient students make sense of quantities and their relationships in problem situations. They bring two complementary abilities to bear on problems involving quantitative relationships: the ability to decontextualize—to abstract a given situation and represent it symbolically and manipulate the representing symbols as if they have a life of their own, without necessarily attending to their referents—and the ability to contextualize, to pause as needed during the manipulation process in order to probe into the referents for the symbols involved. Quantitative reasoning entails habits of creating a coherent representation of the problem at hand; considering the units involved; attending to the meaning of quantities, not just how to compute them; and knowing and flexibly using different properties of operations and objects.

**MP.3 Construct viable arguments and critique the reasoning of others.**

Mathematically proficient students understand and use stated assumptions, definitions, and previously established results in constructing arguments. They make conjectures and build a logical progression of statements to explore the truth of their conjectures. They are able to analyze situations by breaking them into cases, and can recognize and use counterexamples. They justify their conclusions, communicate them to others, and respond to the arguments of others. They reason inductively about data, making plausible arguments that take into account the context from which the data arose. Mathematically proficient students are also able to compare the effectiveness of two plausible arguments, distinguish correct logic or reasoning from that which is flawed, and—if there is a flaw in an argument—explain what it is. Elementary students can construct arguments using concrete referents such as objects, drawings, diagrams, and actions. Such arguments can make sense and be correct, even though they are not generalized or made formal until later grades. Later, students learn to determine domains to which an argument applies. Students at all grades can listen or read the arguments of others, decide whether they make sense, and ask useful questions to clarify or improve the arguments.

**MP.4 Model with mathematics.**

Mathematically proficient students can apply the mathematics they know to solve problems arising in everyday life, society, and the workplace. In early grades, this might be as simple as writing an addition equation to describe a situation. In middle grades, a student might apply proportional reasoning to plan a school event or analyze a problem in the community. By high school, a student might use geometry to solve a design problem or use a function to describe how one quantity of interest depends on another. Mathematically proficient students who can apply what they know are comfortable making assumptions and approximations to simplify a complicated situation, realizing that these may need revision later. They are able to identify important quantities in a practical situation and map their relationships using such tools as diagrams, two-way tables, graphs, flowcharts and formulas. They can analyze those relationships mathematically to draw conclusions. They routinely interpret their mathematical results in the context of the situation and reflect on whether the results make sense, possibly improving the model if it has not served its purpose.

**MP.5 Use appropriate tools strategically.**

Mathematically proficient students consider the available tools when solving a mathematical problem. These tools might include pencil and paper, concrete models, a ruler, a protractor, a calculator, a spreadsheet, a computer algebra system, a statistical package, or dynamic geometry software. Proficient students are sufficiently familiar with tools appropriate for their grade or course to make sound decisions about when each of these tools might be helpful, recognizing both the insight to be gained and their limitations. For example, mathematically proficient high school students analyze graphs of functions and solutions generated using a graphing calculator. They detect possible errors by strategically using estimation and other mathematical knowledge. When making mathematical models, they know that technology can enable them to visualize the results of varying assumptions, explore consequences, and compare predictions with data. Mathematically proficient students at various grade levels are able to identify relevant external mathematical resources, such as digital content located on a website, and use them to pose or solve problems. They are able to use technological tools to explore and deepen their understanding of concepts.

**MP.6 Attend to precision.**

Mathematically proficient students try to communicate precisely to others. They try to use clear definitions in discussion with others and in their own reasoning. They state the meaning of the symbols they choose, including using the equal sign consistently and appropriately. They are careful about specifying units of measure, and labeling axes to clarify the correspondence with quantities in a problem. They calculate accurately and efficiently, express numerical answers with a degree of precision appropriate for the problem context. In the elementary grades, students give carefully formulated explanations to each other. By the time they reach high school they have learned to examine claims and make explicit use of definitions.

**MP.7 Look for and make use of structure.**

Mathematically proficient students look closely to discern a pattern or structure. Young students, for example, might notice that three and seven more is the same amount as seven and three more, or they may sort a collection of shapes according to how many sides the shapes have. Later, students will see $7 \times 8$ equals the well remembered $7 \times 5 + 7 \times 3$, in preparation for learning about the distributive property. In the expression $x^2 + 9x + 14$, older students can see the 14 as $2 \times 7$ and the 9 as $2 + 7$. They recognize the significance of an existing line in a geometric figure and can use the strategy of drawing an auxiliary line for solving problems. They also can step back for an overview and shift perspective. They can see complicated things, such as some algebraic expressions, as single objects or as being composed of several objects. For example, they can see $5 - 3(x - y)^2$ as 5 minus a positive number times a square and use that to realize that its value cannot be more than 5 for any real numbers $x$ and $y$.

**MP.8 Look for and express regularity in repeated reasoning.**

Mathematically proficient students notice if calculations are repeated, and look both for general methods and for shortcuts. Upper elementary students might notice when dividing 25 by 11 that they are repeating the same calculations over and over again, and conclude they have a repeating decimal. By paying attention to the calculation of slope as they repeatedly check whether points are on the line through (1, 2) with slope 3, middle school students might abstract the equation $\frac{(y - 2)}{(x - 1)} = 3$. Noticing the regularity in the way terms cancel when expanding $(x - 1)(x + 1)$, $(x - 1)(x^2 + x + 1)$, and $(x - 1)(x^3 + x^2 + x + 1)$ might lead them to the general formula for the sum of a geometric series. As they work to solve a problem, mathematically proficient students maintain oversight of the process, while attending to the details. They continually evaluate the reasonableness of their intermediate results.

Go Online

Digital

## Common Core State Standards
### Standards for Mathematical Practice

**MP.1** Make sense of problems and persevere in solving them.

**Mathematically proficient students:**
- can explain the meaning of a problem
- look for entry points to begin solving a problem
- analyze givens, constraints, relationships, and goals
- make conjectures about the solution
- plan a solution pathway
- think of similar problems, and try simpler forms of the problem
- evaluate their progress toward a solution and change pathways if necessary
- can explain similarities and differences between different representations
- check their solutions to problems.

**MP.2** Reason abstractly and quantitatively.

**Mathematically proficient students:**
- make sense of quantities and their relationships in problem situations:
  - They *decontextualize*—create a coherent representation of a problem situation using numbers, variables, and symbols; and
  - They *contextualize* – attend to the meaning of numbers, variables, and symbols in the problem situation
- know and use different properties of operations to solve problems.

**MP.3** Construct viable arguments and critique the reasoning of others.

**Mathematically proficient students:**
- use definitions and problem solutions when constructing arguments
- make conjectures about the solutions to problems
- build a logical progression of statements to support their conjectures and justify their conclusions
- analyze situations and recognize and use counterexamples
- reason inductively about data, making plausible arguments that take into account the context from which the data arose
- listen or read the arguments of others, and decide whether they make sense
- respond to the arguments of others
- compare the effectiveness of two plausible arguments
- distinguish correct logic or reasoning from flawed, and—if there is a flaw in an argument—explain what it is
- ask useful questions to clarify or improve arguments of others.

F14

**MP.4** Model with mathematics.

**Mathematically proficient students:**
- can develop a representation—drawing, diagram, table, graph, expression, equation–to model a problem situation
- make assumptions and approximations to simplify a complicated situation
- identify important quantities in a practical situation and map their relationships using a range of tools
- analyze relationships mathematically to draw conclusions
- interpret mathematical results in the context of the situation and propose improvements to the model as needed.

**MP.5** Use appropriate tools strategically.

**Mathematically proficient students:**
- consider appropriate tools when solving a mathematical problem
- make sound decisions about when each of these tools might be helpful
- identify relevant mathematical resources, and use them to pose or solve problems
- use tools and technology to explore and deepen their understanding of concepts.

**MP.6** Attend to precision.

**Mathematically proficient students:**
- communicate precisely to others
- use clear definitions in discussions with others and in their own reasoning
- state the meaning of the symbols they use
- specify units of measure, and label axes to clarify their correspondence with quantities in a problem
- calculate accurately and efficiently
- express numerical answers with a degree of precision appropriate for the problem context.

**MP.7** Look for and make use of structure.

**Mathematically proficient students:**
- look closely at a problem situation to identify a pattern or structure
- can step back from a solution pathway and shift perspective
- can see complex representations, such as some algebraic expressions, as single objects or as being composed of several objects.

**MP.8** Look for and express regularity in repeated reasoning.

**Mathematically proficient students:**
- notice if calculations are repeated, and look both for general methods and for shortcuts
- maintain oversight of the process as they work to solve a problem, while also attending to the details
- continually evaluate the reasonableness of their intermediate results.

F15

## Introducing the Handbook

The **Math Practices and Problem Solving Handbook** is available online.

This handbook can be used at the beginning of the year and at any teachable moment. Explain to students that the handbook will help them become good math thinkers and good math problem solvers.

The Standards for Mathematical Practice are involved in all aspects of mathematics.

## Introducing the Math Practices

Use pages F14–F23 to review with students the Standards for Mathematical Practice. These standards represent the habits of mind, processes, and dispositions that proficient math thinkers have and use. Encourage students to refer back to these pages any time during the year.

Use the descriptions for each practice and the following rubric to evaluate a student's overall proficiency with the Math Practices.

| Math Practices Proficiency Rubric | |
|---|---|
| 4 | **Exemplary** The student exhibits all of the behaviors. |
| 3 | **Proficient** The student exhibits most of the behaviors. |
| 2 | **Emerging** The student exhibits about half of the behaviors. |
| 1 | **Needs Improvement** The student exhibits less than half of the behaviors. |

TOPIC 5

# Analyze and Solve Systems of Linear Equations

## Math Background Focus

### Solve Systems of Linear Equations Graphically

- **Analyze Graphs of Linear Systems** In Lesson 5-1, students relate the number of solutions to a linear system to the slopes and $y$-intercepts of the graphed lines. They see that a solution is any ordered pair that makes all equations in the system true. Students then apply these skills to systems of linear equations that represent real-world situations.

The system of equations $\begin{matrix} 6x + 2y = 12 \\ 12x + 4y = 24 \end{matrix}$ represents the situation.

Write each equation in slope-intercept form.

| | |
|---|---|
| $6x + 2y = 12$ | $12x + 4y = 24$ |
| $2y = -6x + 12$ | $4y = -12x + 24$ |
| $y = -3x + 6$ | $y = -3x + 6$ |

The equations represent the same line. Every $(x, y)$ pair on the line is a solution.

Corey and Winnie bought the same amount of cheese and tomatoes.

- **Graph Linear Systems** In Lesson 5-2, students graph systems of linear equations and see that the relationship of the two lines represents the solution. Students interpret the meaning of the relationship to a given scenario.

**STEP 2** Graph the system.

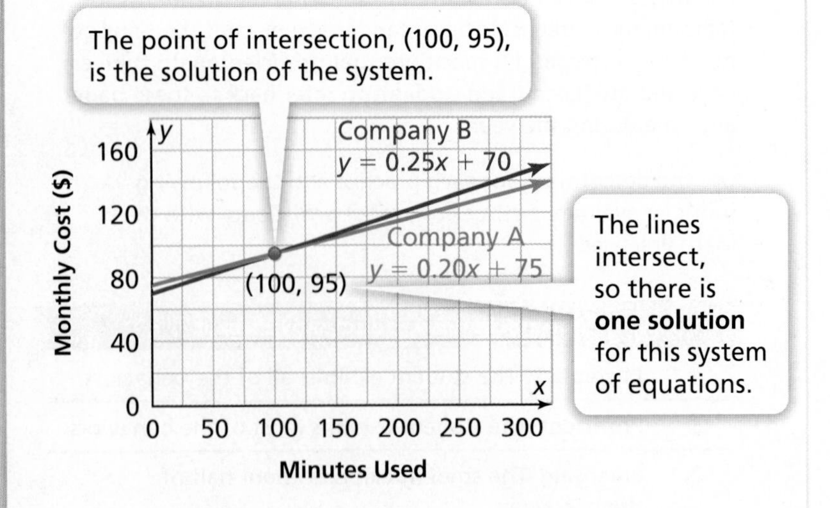


If Li uses 100 minutes, both plans cost $95. She could choose either plan.
If Li uses fewer than 100 minutes, she should choose Company B.
If Li uses more than 100 minutes, she should choose Company A.

### Solve Systems of Linear Equations Algebraically

- **Solve by Substitution** In Lesson 5-3, students write systems of linear equations that describe the relationship between two variables. They learn to solve the system by solving one equation for one variable, and then substituting the solution into the other equation. Students then solve the second equation, which now contains only one variable. They use the solution to the system of equations to answer a given question.

**STEP 1** Write a system of linear equations to represent the situation. Let $x$ equal the number of hours and $y$ equal Seiko's cost.

$$y = 14x$$
$$y = \frac{1}{2}(28x + 15)$$

**STEP 2** Use substitution to solve one of the equations for one variable.

$$14x = \frac{1}{2}(28x + 15)$$
$$14x = 14x + 7.50$$
$$0 \neq 7.50$$

Substitute $14x$ for $y$ in the second equation.

The result is not a true statement, so the system has no solution. There is no number of hours for which Seiko's cost is the same at both studios.

Go Online

- **Solve by Elimination** In Lesson 5-4, students extend the skill of writing a system of linear equations to systems that can be solved using elimination. The goal is to eliminate one of the variables, creating a new equation in one variable. Students first learn to use addition and subtraction to eliminate one variable. They then multiply one or both equations to create opposites, and add to eliminate a variable.

The difference of the length and width of the rectangle is 3 centimeters. What are the length and width of the rectangle?

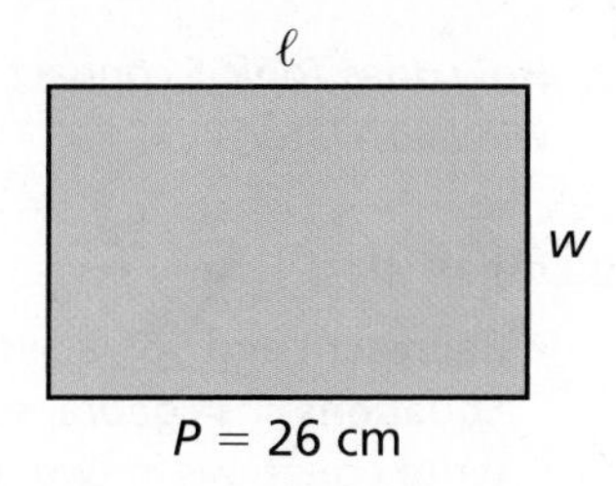


**STEP 1** Write a system of equations to relate the length and width.

$$2\ell + 2w = 26$$
$$\ell - w = 3$$

**STEP 2** Eliminate one variable. The coefficients of $\ell$ and $w$ are not the same or opposites. Multiply one or both of the equations so that the variables are the same or opposites.

$$\begin{array}{r} 2\ell + 2w = 26 \\ + \; 2\ell - 2w = 6 \\ \hline 4\ell + 0 = 32 \\ \ell = 8 \end{array}$$

Multiply each term of the second equation by 2 so that the $w$ terms are opposites.

**STEP 3** Solve for the other variable.

$$\ell - w = 3$$
$$8 - w = 3$$
$$w = 5$$

The length of the rectangle is 8 centimeters and the width is 5 centimeters.

# Advanced Concepts for the Teacher

- **Operations on Systems of Equations** Solving a system of linear equations is finding the set of all values for the variables that makes all equations in the system simultaneously true. When solving systems of equations using elimination, the goal is to use Properties of Equality to generate equivalent systems of equations that have the same solution set.

Consider the system below.

$$\begin{cases} ax + by = c \\ dx - by = g \end{cases}$$

The first equation tells you that $ax + by = c$, so you can add $ax + by$ to one side of the second equation and $c$ to the other side of the second equation, and the solution set of the second equation will not change.

$$\begin{cases} ax + by = c \\ dx - by + ax + by = g + c \end{cases}$$

In this case, the result is a new system with the same solution set where the $y$ variable has been eliminated from the second equation.

$$\begin{cases} ax + by = c \\ (d + a)\,x = g + c \end{cases}$$

- **Strategy in Solving Systems of Equations** Often, the strategy chosen for solving a system of equation is based solely on the form in which the equations are given. One example is always choosing to use graphing if both equations are in the form $y = ax + b$.

The strategy for solving a problem should be considered thoughtfully. Although the equations may be written in a form that suggests the use of a specific strategy, but the problem may be solved more efficiently using a different strategy.

Consider the following system of equations.

$$\begin{cases} y = \frac{1}{5}x - \frac{3}{5} \\ y = -\frac{1}{3}x + \frac{2}{3} \end{cases}$$

Each equation is written in the form $y = mx + b$, which suggests solving by graphing or substitution. However, the equations contain fractions that could be easily removed by multiplying each side by a common denominator.

$$\begin{cases} 5y = x - 3 \\ 3y = -x + 2 \end{cases}$$

The result is a system of equations that can be easily solved by elimination, without rewriting them in standard form $Ax + By = C$.

# Math Background Coherence

Students learn best when concepts are connected throughout the curriculum. This coherence is achieved within clusters, across clusters, across domains, and across grade levels.

## Look Back

*How does Topic 5 connect to what students learned earlier?*

### Grade 7

- **Expressions and Equations** In Grade 7, students learned to write expressions to represent situations, and to solve one-step and two-step equations.

### Earlier in Grade 8

- **Solve Equations** In Topic 2, students reviewed how to solve one-step, two-step, and multi-step equations, and extended their understanding to include equations with real number coefficients. Students gained experience with equations that had zero, one, or infinitely many solutions. They also graphed linear equations, and found equations to match given line graphs.

## Topic 5

*How is content connected within Topic 5?*

- **Solve Systems of Linear Equations** Students are introduced to three different methods for finding the solution to a linear system. In Lesson 5-1, students analyze graphs of linear systems to determine the number of solutions to the system. Students progress into Lesson 5-2 where they graph a linear system, determine any intersection points, and check their solutions. In Lessons 5-3 and 5-4, students learn two different algebraic procedures for finding the solution of a linear system using substitution or elimination.

  **The perimeter of a photo frame is 36 inches. The length is 2 inches greater than the width. What are the dimensions of the frame?**

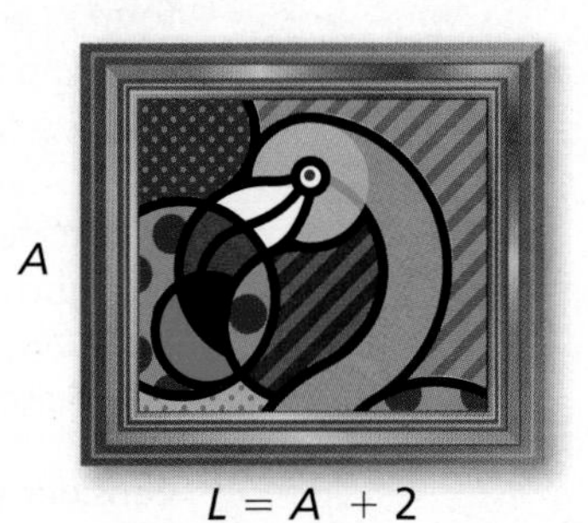


## Look Ahead

*How does Topic 5 connect to what students will learn later?*

### Algebra

- **Represent and Solve Systems of Equations** In Algebra, students will write equations in two or more variables to represent relationships between quantities, and graph the equations of the coordinate plane. They will continue to work with systems of equations solving simple systems of one linear equation and one quadratic equation in two variables both graphically and algebraically.

Go Online

Video

# Math Background Rigor

A rigorous curriculum emphasizes conceptual understanding, procedural skill and fluency, and applications.

## Conceptual Understanding

- **Identifying the Number of Solutions of a System of Equations** Students understand that by comparing the slopes and the *y*-intercepts of the equations in a system of equations they can identify the number of solutions to the system. They also recognize that when the equations are graphed, the relationship of the graphed lines visually represents the solution.

  Consider the following system of equations.

  $y = -3x + 6$

  $y = 3x - 12$

  **PART A**

  Which of the following statements are true about the system? Select all that apply.

  - ☐ The graph of the system is a pair of lines that do not intersect.
  - ☐ The graph of the system is a pair of lines that intersect at exactly one point.
  - ☐ The graph of the system is a pair of lines that intersect in every point.
  - ☐ The system has no solution.
  - ☐ The system has 1 solution.
  - ☐ The system has infinitely many solutions.

- **Solve Systems Algebraically** Students understand that substitution and elimination are methods they can employ to arrive at an equation with one variable that they can use to solve a system of equations. They recognize that substitution is a good method to use when one of the equations can be solved easily for one variable. They recognize that elimination is a good method to use when like variables have the same or opposite coefficients, or when multiplying the variables will create the same or opposite coefficients.

**Construct Arguments** Consider the system of equations. Would you solve this system by substitution or by elimination? Explain.

$$1\frac{3}{4}x + y = 2\frac{3}{16}$$

$$\frac{1}{4}x - y = -1\frac{11}{16}$$

## Procedural Skill and Fluency

- **Solve Algebraically Using Substitution** Students will become proficient in solving one equation in a system of equations for one of its variables, substituting the solution into the other equation, and solving to find the second variable.
- **Solve Algebraically Using Elimination** Students will become proficient in adding and subtracting equations to eliminate a variable. They will also multiply equations by constants to create opposite terms, which can be eliminated.

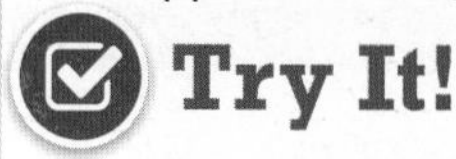

### Try It!

Brandon took a 50-question exam worth a total of 160 points. There were *x* two-point questions and *y* five-point questions. How many of each type of question were on the exam?

$$x + y = 50$$

$$2x + 5y = 160$$

**Convince Me!** How do you know which equation to solve for one of the variables and in which equation to substitute?

## Applications

- **Real-World Situations** Students apply what they are learning to represent many situations. Some problems that are very difficult to answer using arithmetic are relatively easy when using a system of equations.

Two trains, Train A and Train B, weigh a total of 312 tons. Train A is heavier than Train B. The difference in their weights is 170 tons. Use elimination to solve the system of equations to find the weight of each train.

$$a + b = 312$$

$$a - b = 170$$

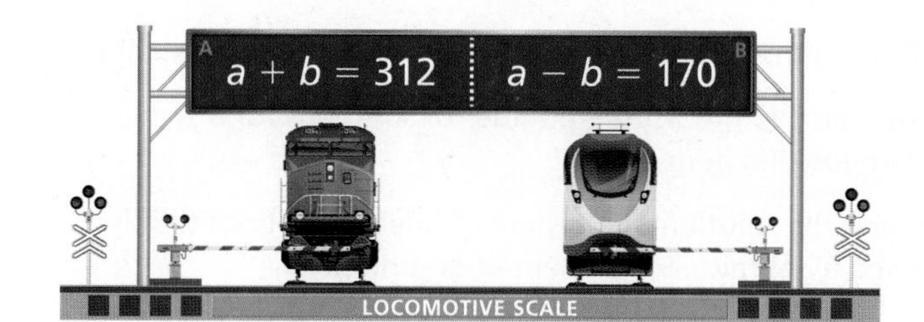

# Math Practices

The math practices and processes describe the behaviors and thinking habits that mathematically proficient students demonstrate when actively engaged in mathematics work. Opportunities for engagement in the practices and to develop expertise with these important behaviors and thinking habits exist throughout the topic and program. Here we focus on mathematical reasoning and explaining.

As students solve linear systems of equations, look for these behaviors to assess and identify students who demonstrate proficiency with mathematical reasoning and explaining.

| Math Practices Within Topic 5 Lessons | |
|---|---|
| **Reason abstractly and quantitatively.** (MP.2) | **Look for and make use of structure.** (MP.7) |
| Mathematically proficient students: | Mathematically proficient students: |
| • Analyze the graphs of the linear equations to determine the number of solutions of the system of equations. | • Apply inverse operations to solve linear equations algebraically. |
| • Understand the intersection of the graphs of two linear equations as the solution to that system of linear equations. | • Look for the overall structure of slopes and *y*-intercepts of equations in a linear system to predict the number of solutions to the system. |
| • Attend to the meaning of the solution of a system of linear equations as the value or values that are true for both equations in the system. | • See linear systems with one solution as having a specific value for each variable that makes the system true at only one point. |
| • Create a logical representation of problems in graphical form. | • Analyze systems of linear equations to develop efficient solution strategies. |

Help students become more proficient with mathematical reasoning and explanation.

If students do not understand how to solve systems of linear equations, then use these questioning strategies to help them develop reasoning and explaining skills as they solve problems throughout the topic.

**Q:** What do the slopes and *y*-intercepts of the equations tell you?

**Q:** How can you predict the number of solutions for a system when looking at its graph?

**Q:** How is the solution of a system of linear equations that is solved algebraically represented graphically?

**Q:** Could we have used another method to solve this system? Explain.

**Q:** What do you notice when you graph a system of linear equations with one solution?

**Q:** What patterns do you find in systems of linear equations that are easier to solve using substitution?

**Q:** What patterns do you find in systems of linear equations that are easier to solve using elimination?

**Q:** What parts of the two equations can you simplify first?

# Topic Readiness Assessment

Go Online

Assess

Topic Readiness Assessment Masters

Name ______________________

Topic **5**
Readiness Assessment

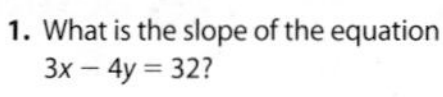

**1.** What is the slope of the equation $3x - 4y = 32$?

Ⓐ $-\frac{3}{4}$ ● $\frac{3}{4}$

Ⓑ $-8$ Ⓓ $8$

**2.** Write an equation in standard form that has a slope of $-\frac{5}{2}$ and $y$-intercept of $-2$.

$5x + 2y = -4$

**3.** Write the equation of a line with slope 4 that passes through the point (3.5, 5) in slope-intercept form.

$y = 4x - 9$

**4.** What is the equation of the line shown in the graph?

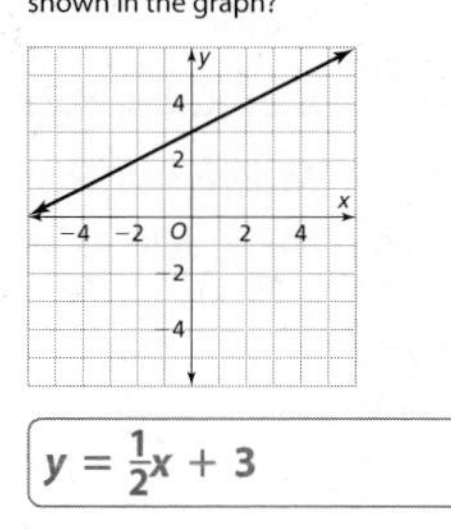

$y = \frac{1}{2}x + 3$

**5.** Which is the graph of $y = -4x + 4$?

Ⓐ

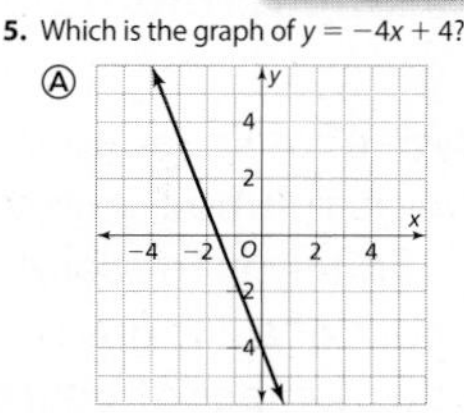

Ⓑ

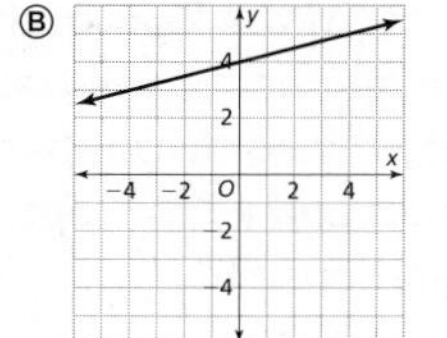

Ⓒ

●

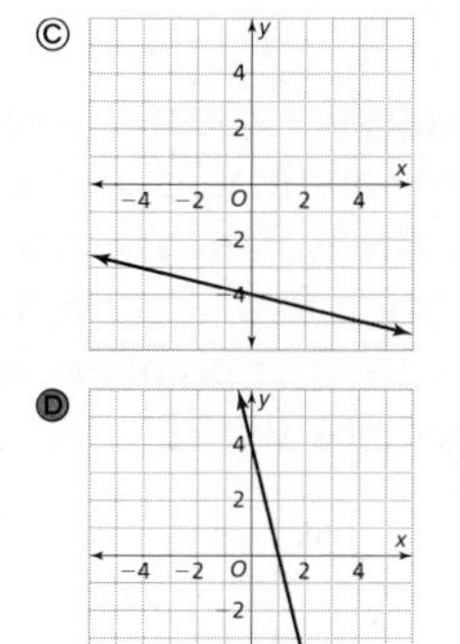

Readiness Assessment 1 of 2

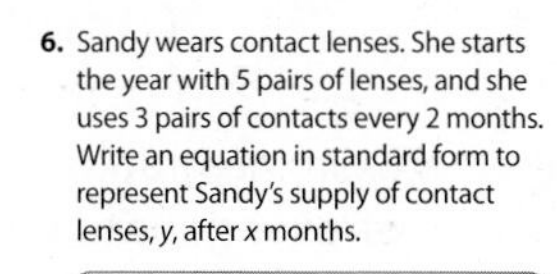

**6.** Sandy wears contact lenses. She starts the year with 5 pairs of lenses, and she uses 3 pairs of contacts every 2 months. Write an equation in standard form to represent Sandy's supply of contact lenses, $y$, after $x$ months.

$2y + 3x = 10$

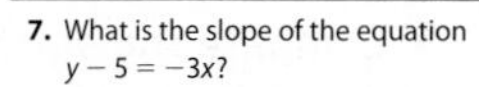

**7.** What is the slope of the equation $y - 5 = -3x$?

Ⓐ 5 ● −3

Ⓑ 3 Ⓓ −8

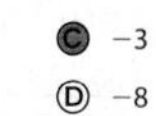

**8.** Write an equation in slope-intercept form for the line that goes through points (1.4, 0) and (1, −2).

$y = 5x - 7$

**9.** What is the equation of the line shown in the graph, in standard form?

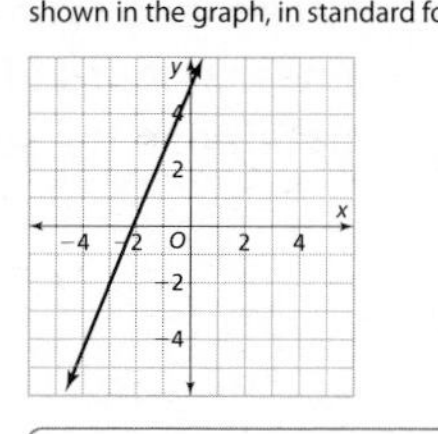

$7x - 3y = -15$

Readiness Assessment

2 of 2

**10.** Which equation is shown in the graph?

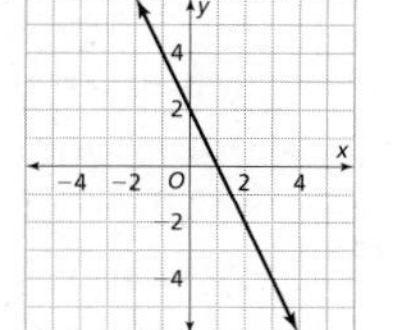

● $3y + 6x = 6$ Ⓒ $-3y - 6x = 6$

Ⓑ $3x - 6y = 6$ Ⓓ $-3x + 6y = 6$

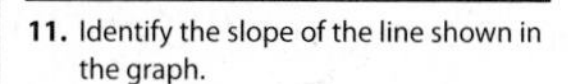

**11.** Identify the slope of the line shown in the graph.

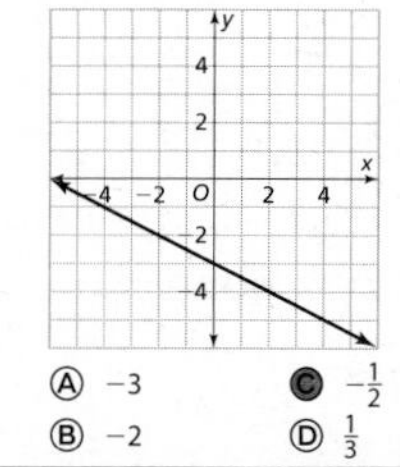

Ⓐ −3 ● $-\frac{1}{2}$

Ⓑ −2 Ⓓ $\frac{1}{3}$

**12.** Kerry is skateboarding down a hill. The top of the hill is 4 feet above street level, and after traveling 3 yards, her height is 2 ft. Let $y$ represent her height above street level, in feet, and $x$ represent the distance she has traveled, in yards. Write an equation to represent Kerry's height, in slope-intercept form.

$y = -\frac{2}{3}x + 4$

Assess students' understanding of prerequisite concepts and skills using the Topic Readiness Assessment.

You may opt to have students take the automatically scored Topic Readiness Assessment online.

## Scoring Guide

| Score | Recommendations |
|---|---|
| Greater Than 85% | Assign the corresponding MDIS for items answered incorrectly. Use Enrichment activities with the student during the topic. |
| 70%–85% | Assign the corresponding MDIS for items answered incorrectly. Monitor the student during Step 1 and Try It! parts of the lessons for personalized remediation needs. |
| Less Than 70% | Assign the corresponding MDIS for items answered incorrectly. Assign appropriate intervention lessons available online. |

## RtI Item Analysis for Diagnosis and Remediation

| Item | DOK | MDIS | Standard |
|---|---|---|---|
| 1 | 2 | K52, K50 | 8.F.B.4 |
| 2 | 3 | K52 | 8.F.B.4 |
| 3 | 3 | K52 | 8.F.B.4 |
| 4 | 3 | K49 | 8.F.B.4 |
| 5 | 2 | K49 | 8.F.B.5 |
| 6 | 3 | K52 | 8.F.B.4 |
| 7 | 2 | K52, K50 | 8.F.B.4 |
| 8 | 3 | K52 | 8.F.B.4 |
| 9 | 3 | K49 | 8.F.B.4 |
| 10 | 2 | K49 | 8.F.B.5 |
| 11 | 2 | K49, K50 | 8.F.B.5 |
| 12 | 3 | K52 | 8.F.B.4 |

TOPIC 5

# Topic Planner

## Analyze and Solve Systems of Linear Equations

| Lesson | Vocabulary | Objective | Essential Understanding | Standard |
|---|---|---|---|---|
| **5-1** Estimate Solutions by Inspection | system of linear equations, solution of a system of linear equations | • Examine graphs of linear systems of equations to determine the number of solutions, based on number of intersection points.<br>• Compare the equations in a linear system to look for a relationship between the number of solutions and the slopes and *y*-intercepts of the equations. | A system of linear equations can have no solution, one solution, or infinitely many solutions. The number of solutions is based on the number of intersection points of the lines in the system. The number of solutions can be determined by comparing the slopes and *y*-intercepts of the equations. | 8.EE.C.8b, 8.EE.C.8c<br>**Mathematical Practices**<br>MP.2, MP.3, MP.7, MP.8 |
| **5-2** Solve Systems by Graphing | none | • Create and examine graphs of linear systems of equations to determine the solution. | Systems of equations can have zero solutions, one solution, or infinitely many solutions. The solution to a linear system is the point or points at which the lines intersect. | 8.EE.C.8a, 8.EE.C.8c<br>**Mathematical Practices**<br>MP.2, MP.3, MP.4 |

## Lesson Resources

Digital

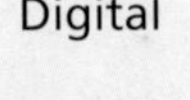
Print

**Student's Edition**

**Additional Practice Workbook**

**Teaching Resources**
- Reteach to Build Understanding
- Additional Vocabulary Support
- Build Mathematical Literacy
- Enrichment

**Assessment Resources**
- Lesson Quiz

Digital

**Digital Lesson Courseware**
- Today's Challenge
- Visual Learning Animation Plus
- Key Concept
- Additional Examples
- 3-Act Mathematical Modeling
- Online Practice powered by MathXL for School
- Adaptive Practice
- Virtual Nerd Video Tutorials
- Animated Glossary
- Digital Math Tools
- Online Math Games

**Lesson Support for Teachers**
- Listen and Look For PD Lesson Video

The suggested pacing for each lesson is 2 days for a 45-minute math class and 1 day for a 90-minute class.

Go Online

Digital

| Lesson | Vocabulary | Objective | Essential Understanding | Standard |
|---|---|---|---|---|
| **5-3** Solve Systems by Substitution | none | • Understand how substitution can be used to solve a linear system of equations.<br>• Apply this understanding to solve a system of linear equations with one solution, no solutions, or infinitely many solutions. | Substitution is a useful method for solving a system of linear equations. It is accomplished by rewriting an equation for one variable in terms of the other, and substituting that expression into the other equation and then solving. | 8.EE.C.8b, 8.EE.C.8c<br>**Mathematical Practices** MP.2, MP.3, MP.6, MP.8 |
| **5-4** Solve Systems by Elimination | none | • Understand how the process of elimination can be used to solve a system of linear equations with no solution, one solution, or infinitely many solutions.<br>• Apply this understanding to solve mathematical and real-world problems. | Elimination can be used to solve a system of linear equations by adding or subtracting the equations to eliminate one variable. The resulting equation can be solved for the remaining variable or used to determine if there is no solution or an infinite number of solutions. | 8.EE.C.8b, 8.EE.C.8c<br>**Mathematical Practices** MP.3, MP.4, MP.7 |
| 3-Act Mathematical Modeling: Ups and Downs | none | • Use mathematical modeling to represent a problem situation and to propose a solution.<br>• Test and verify the appropriateness of their math models.<br>• Explain why the results from their mathematical models may not align exactly to the problem situation. | Many real-world problem situations can be represented with a mathematical model, but that model may not represent a real-world situation exactly. | 8.EE.C.8, 8.SP.A.3, 8.F.B.4<br>**Mathematical Practices** MP.4 |

# Topic Resources

Digital

Print

### Student's Edition
- Review What You Know
- Language Development Activity
- Mid-Topic Checkpoint and Performance Task
- Topic Review
- Fluency Practice Activity
- enVision® STEM Project
- Pick a Project

### Assessment Resources
- Topic Readiness Assessment
- Mid-Topic Assessment
- Topic Assessment
- Topic Performance Task

Digital

### Topic Support for Students
- Math Practice Animations
- enVision® STEM Project
- 3-Act Mathematical Modeling Lesson

### Topic Support for Teachers
- Topic Overview Video
- ExamView Test Generator

# Analyze and Solve Systems of Linear Equations

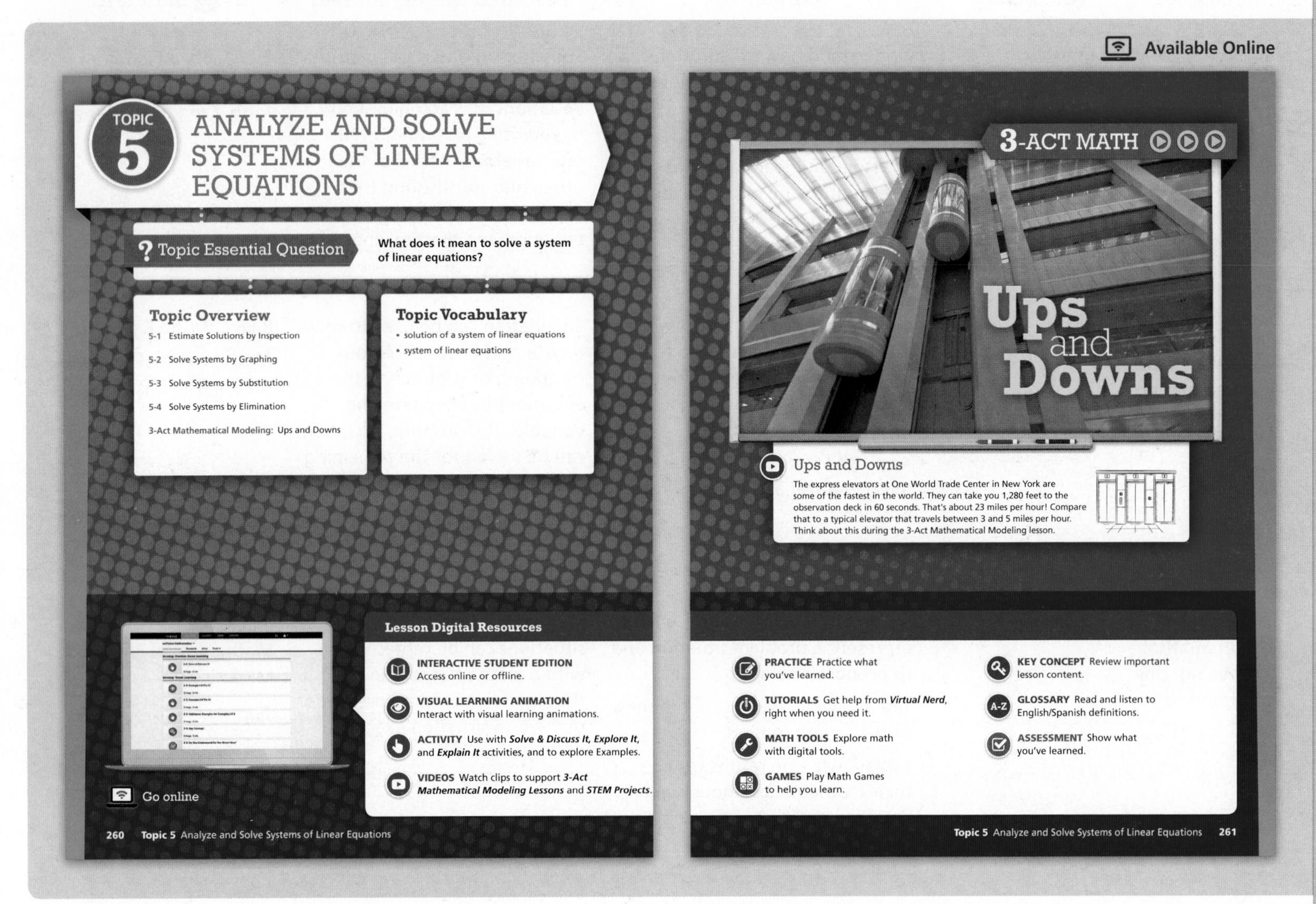
Available Online

TOPIC 5 ANALYZE AND SOLVE SYSTEMS OF LINEAR EQUATIONS

? Topic Essential Question

What does it mean to solve a system of linear equations?

**Topic Overview**

5-1 Estimate Solutions by Inspection
5-2 Solve Systems by Graphing
5-3 Solve Systems by Substitution
5-4 Solve Systems by Elimination
3-Act Mathematical Modeling: Ups and Downs

**Topic Vocabulary**

- solution of a system of linear equations
- system of linear equations

Go online

**Lesson Digital Resources**

INTERACTIVE STUDENT EDITION Access online or offline.

VISUAL LEARNING ANIMATION Interact with visual learning animations.

ACTIVITY Use with *Solve & Discuss It, Explore It,* and *Explain It* activities, and to explore Examples.

VIDEOS Watch clips to support *3-Act Mathematical Modeling Lessons* and *STEM Projects*.

260 Topic 5 Analyze and Solve Systems of Linear Equations

3-ACT MATH

Ups and Downs

Ups and Downs

The express elevators at One World Trade Center in New York are some of the fastest in the world. They can take you 1,280 feet to the observation deck in 60 seconds. That's about 23 miles per hour! Compare that to a typical elevator that travels between 3 and 5 miles per hour. Think about this during the 3-Act Mathematical Modeling lesson.

PRACTICE Practice what you've learned.

TUTORIALS Get help from *Virtual Nerd,* right when you need it.

MATH TOOLS Explore math with digital tools.

GAMES Play Math Games to help you learn.

KEY CONCEPT Review important lesson content.

GLOSSARY Read and listen to English/Spanish definitions.

ASSESSMENT Show what you've learned.

Topic 5 Analyze and Solve Systems of Linear Equations 261

## Topic Essential Question

**What does it mean to solve a system of linear equations?**

Revisit the Topic Essential Question throughout the topic. See the Teacher's Edition for the Topic Review for notes about answering the question.

## 3-Act Mathematical Modeling

**Generate excitement about the upcoming 3-Act Mathematical Modeling lesson by having students read about the math modeling problem for this topic.**

See the Teacher's Edition lesson support for notes about how to use the lesson video in your classroom.

TOPIC 5 enVision® STEM Project

Go Online

Video

# Daily Grind

In this project, students investigate the science behind the coffee industry. Students will analyze the factors involved in growing and producing coffee and the effects of coffee growth practices on the economy and environment.

### What's the Math?

Students write and solve equations and systems of equations to evaluate aspects of the coffee farming industry and calculate how to create and price a coffee blend.

### What's the Science?

Students gather evidence and interpret data to describe how resource availability and environmental factors influence the growth of coffee. They will also learn about the effects of the coffee growing and harvesting processes on the environment.

### What's the Engineering and Technology?

Students think like engineers as they gather, analyze, synthesize, and present data in clear and understandable ways. Students learn about how engineering advances have affected the coffee industry and use this analysis to develop a coffee blend with desired characteristics.

### Introduce the Project

Present the project by having students discuss what they know about coffee. The questions below can be used to guide the discussion.

**Q:** How is coffee grown? [Sample answer: Coffee beans come from the seeds of the fruit that grows on coffee plants.]

**Q:** Where is coffee grown? Why do you think it's grown there? [Sample answer: In fields or forests of tropical climates. It is grown there because coffee plants need warm climates to thrive.]

**Q:** Which country produces the most coffee? Which three countries consume the most coffee? [Brazil; United States, Brazil, and Germany]

**Q:** Since two of the three highest coffee consuming countries cannot produce their own coffee, how does this impact the coffee industry? [Sample answer: Coffee must be shipped long distances from where it is harvested. Such long distance shipping creates additional costs and environmental impacts.]

**Q:** How can farmers minimize the environmental impact of their coffee farms? [Sample answer: Use sustainable methods that minimize chemical use.]

You can launch this project any time after Topic 5.

Show the Topic 5 STEM video to generate interest in the project.

Teacher resources that provide students with project details and support are available online.

**enVision STEM Project Video** is available online.

TOPIC 5 enVision STEM Project

Did You Know?

After the Boston Tea Party of 1773, many Americans **switched to drinking coffee** rather than tea because drinking tea was considered unpatriotic.

Although Brazil is the largest coffee-producing nation in the world, Americans combine to drink 0.2% more coffee each year than Brazilians. The third ranked nation for total **coffee consumption**, Germany, consumes approximately 44% as much coffee as either the United States or Brazil.

**The United States consumes the most coffee by total weight**, but Americans do not drink the most coffee per capita. People in northern European countries like Finland, Norway, and Holland drink more than twice as much coffee as their American counterparts each day.



In some coffee-producing nations, millions of acres of forest are cleared to make space for coffee farming. **Sustainable farms** grow coffee plants in natural growing conditions without chemicals and with minimal waste.

Coffee beans are actually **seeds** that are harvested from cherries that grow on coffee plants in **tropical climates**.

Your Task: Daily Grind

Coffee roasters create coffee blends by mixing specialty coffees with less expensive coffees in order to create unique coffees, reduce costs, and provide customers with consistent flavor. You and your classmates will explore coffee blends while considering the environmental and economical impact of the coffee trade.

262 Topic 5 enVision STEM Project

### Common Core Content Standards

8.EE.C.8

### Mathematical Practices Standards

MP.1, MP.2, MP.3, MP.6

### Next Generation Science Standards

MS-LS1-5, MS-LS2-1, MS-ESS3-3, MS-ESS3-4

# Get Ready!

Go Online

Glossary

## Review What You Know!

Assign the Review What You Know to activate prior knowledge and practice the prerequisite skills needed for success in this topic.

Encourage students to work independently or with a partner. Use these questioning strategies to help them get started.

### Identifying Slope and $y$-Intercept

**Q:** How can you identify the slope and $y$-intercept of a line by analyzing its equation? [Sample answer: If the equation is solved for $y$, the coefficient of $x$ is the slope and the constant is the $y$-intecept.]

### Graphing Linear Equations

**Q:** Explain how to graph a linear equation using the $y$-intercept and the slope. [Sample answer: Plot a point at the known $y$-intercept. Slope is the rate of change of the line and can be represented as a fraction. The numerator of the fraction is the vertical change and the denominator is the horizontal change.]

### Solving Equations for Variables

**Q:** How do you solve for a variable? [Sample answer: Combine like terms, and then use inverse operations to isolate the variable.]

### Item Analysis for Diagnosis and Remediation

| Item | MDIS | Standard |
|---|---|---|
| 1 | K50 | 8.EE.B.5 |
| 2 | N2 | 8.EE.B.7a |
| 3 | K52 | 8.EE.B.6 |
| 4 | K52 | 8.EE.B.6 |
| 5–7 | K50, K52 | 8.EE.B.6 |
| 8–9 | K49 | 8.EE.B.5 |
| 10–12 | K52 | 8.EE.B.7b |

Available Online

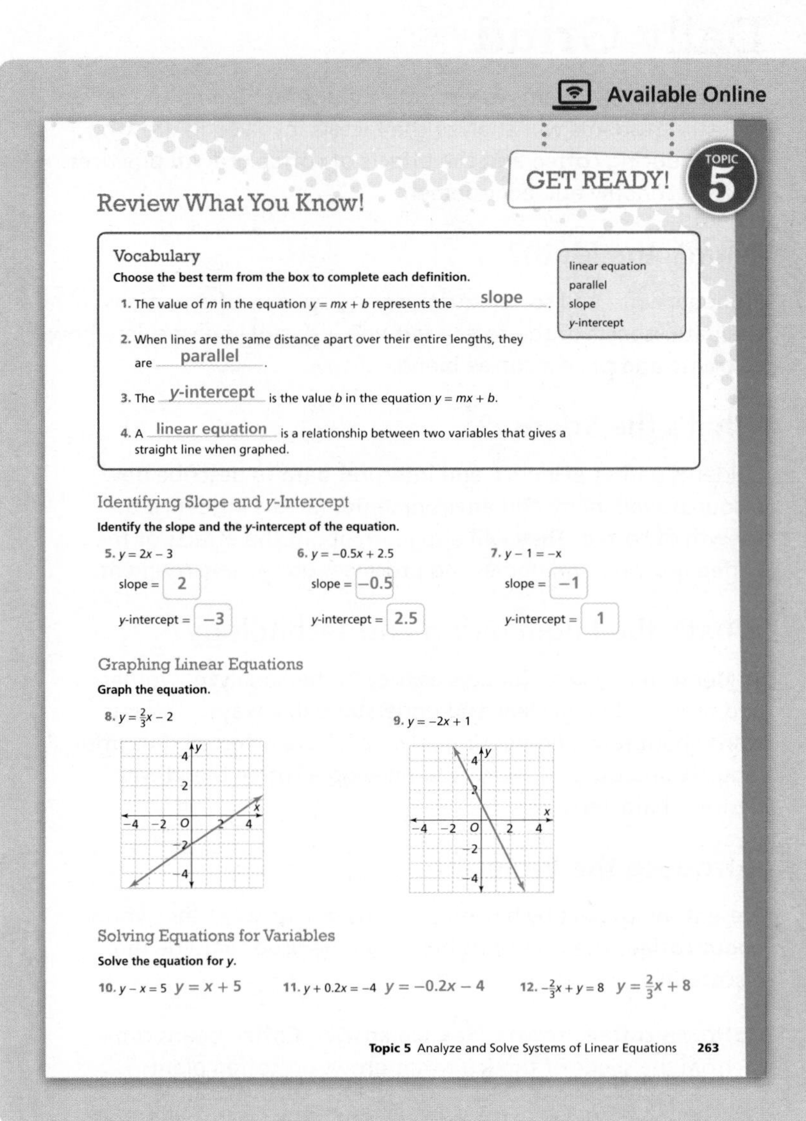

GET READY! TOPIC 5

Review What You Know!

Vocabulary

Choose the best term from the box to complete each definition.

linear equation
parallel
slope
$y$-intercept

1. The value of $m$ in the equation $y = mx + b$ represents the slope.
2. When lines are the same distance apart over their entire lengths, they are parallel.
3. The $y$-intercept is the value $b$ in the equation $y = mx + b$.
4. A linear equation is a relationship between two variables that gives a straight line when graphed.

Identifying Slope and $y$-Intercept

Identify the slope and the $y$-intercept of the equation.

5. $y = 2x - 3$ slope = 2 $y$-intercept = −3
6. $y = -0.5x + 2.5$ slope = −0.5 $y$-intercept = 2.5
7. $y - 1 = -x$ slope = −1 $y$-intercept = 1

Graphing Linear Equations

Graph the equation.

8. $y = \frac{2}{3}x - 2$
9. $y = -2x + 1$

Solving Equations for Variables

Solve the equation for $y$.

10. $y - x = 5$ $y = x + 5$
11. $y + 0.2x = -4$ $y = -0.2x - 4$
12. $-\frac{2}{3}x + y = 8$ $y = \frac{2}{3}x + 8$

Topic 5 Analyze and Solve Systems of Linear Equations 263

## Vocabulary Review

You may choose to strengthen vocabulary with the following activity.

- Have students work individually or in pairs to complete a poster with the definition and one or two representations for all four vocabulary terms. Make sure students have the materials they need to create the posters. These posters would be a good visual aid as students work through the topic.

Go Online

Glossary

# Language Development

Ask students to fill in the fishbone map as they complete each lesson. Have them label each diagonal line with a key term or phrase related to systems of linear equations. Write details that support the key term or phrase on the horizontal lines. Remind students to add additional lines as needed.

**Q:** Why is it important to understand solving systems of linear equations? [Sample answer: Some real-world problems are easier to understand and answer when using a system of equations.]

As students work through each lesson, encourage them to review the details that support systems of linear equations and update their fishbone maps as needed. Revising the details with more pertinent ones may be necessary.

**Q:** How does listing details you have learned during the lesson help you better understand the vocabulary term? [Sample answer: It helps reinforce your understanding of the new vocabulary by providing more than just a definition.]

Remind students to revisit systems of equations and the details supporting them as they progress through the topic.

## Extension for Language Development

Challenge students to use their completed fishbone maps to write a brief summary of the concepts they have learned in this topic.

## Word Wall

To help students comprehend the meaning of *system of linear equations*, assist them in making a word wall. Invite students to write linear equations that represent a system on index cards, and display them under the word phrase *System of Linear Equations*. Remind students that two or more linear equations that use the same variables describe a system of linear equations. Instructions on how to design a word wall are included in the Language Support Handbook.

For additional resources, see the **Language Support Handbook.**

# Pick a Project

Available Online

## Overview

A variety of rich projects is provided for each topic. Students may select the project that is most interesting to them.

| Project | Different Engaging Contexts | Different Activity Modalities | Different Final Products |
|---|---|---|---|
| 5A | Debates | Write | Live debate or video |
| 5B | Diagrams | Draw | Venn diagram |
| 5C | Cell phones | Choose | Advertising pamphlet and analysis |
| 5D | Stained glass | Make | Model |

## Selecting a Project

Introduce each project option with the students. Sharing the resource masters with students might help them choose.

## During the Project

**Pacing** Projects will be completed over a number of lessons. The amount of time students spend on each project will vary. You may wish to let early finishers choose an additional project.

**Grouping** You might have students work independently, with a partner, or in small groups.

**Content** Projects are related to the content of this topic. As students continue their work on projects throughout the topic, new math ideas should be incorporated.

**Project Sharing** Invite students to share their completed projects with a partner, a small group, or with the whole class. Encourage students to discuss how they demonstrated math practices during the project. Provide students an opportunity for reflection by asking what interesting information they learned and what math they used in the project.

**Extensions** Extension suggestions are included for each project.

**Look For** Did students achieve the goal of the project? Did they apply math correctly in the project?

## Project 5A Ⓒ 8.EE.C.8

**Materials** video recorder (optional)

**Guidelines** Students can start writing their speeches after learning about the three methods for solving systems of linear equations.

**Extension** Have students critique the debate. Ask them to write down what they learned about the method their partner or partners chose. Have them include the similarities and differences in both methods.

## Project 5B Ⓒ 8.EE.C.8

**Guidelines** Students should complete their Venn diagrams after learning about all three methods for solving systems of linear equations.

**Extension** Ask students to think about including a circle that represents estimating solutions by inspection on their Venn diagrams. Where would this circle be placed on the diagram? Would this circle overlap with any of the other circles? List similarities and differences between estimating solutions and the other methods of solving.

## Project 5C Ⓒ 8.EE.C.8

**Materials** construction paper, old magazines, markers

**Guidelines** Students can analyze costs and compare cell phone plans after each lesson.

**Extension** Ask students to review the cell phone plan that they did not choose. Ask them to write a paragraph explaining why this choice was not the best. Have them include suggestions that could be made to the company to make this cell phone plan better and more desirable than the other plan.

## Project 5D Ⓒ 8.EE.C.8

**Materials** uncooked spaghetti, construction paper, scissors, glue

**Guidelines** Students can update their designs and do their calculations after each lesson.

**Extension** Ask students how their designs would change if they included one horizontal and one vertical line in their designs. Where would they position the lines, and why?

**Available Online**

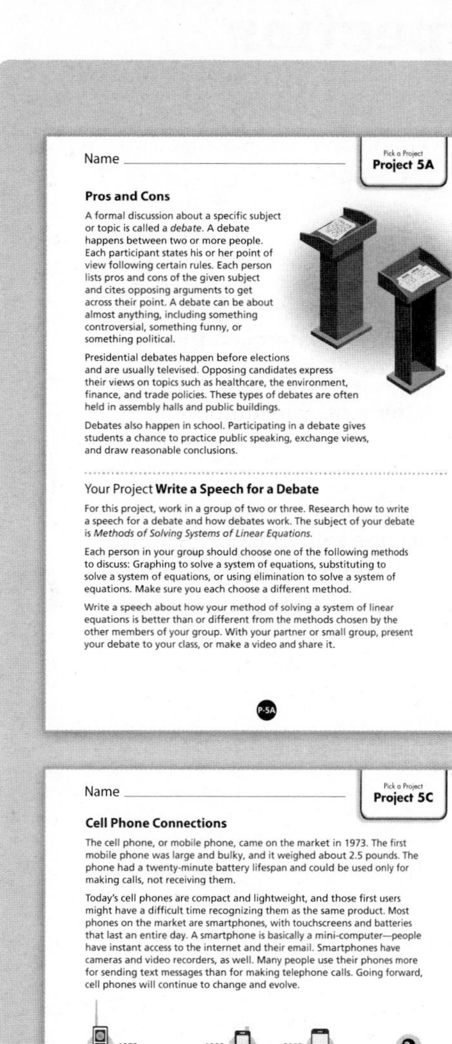

Name ______

Pick a Project
**Project 5A**

**Pros and Cons**

A formal discussion about a specific subject or topic is called a *debate*. A debate happens between two or more people. Each participant states his or her point of view following certain rules. Each person lists pros and cons of the given subject and cites opposing arguments to get across their point. A debate can be about almost anything, including something controversial, something funny, or something political.

Presidential debates happen before elections and are usually televised. Opposing candidates express their views on topics such as healthcare, the environment, finance, and trade policies. These types of debates are often held in assembly halls and public buildings.

Debates also happen in school. Participating in a debate gives students a chance to practice public speaking, exchange views, and draw reasonable conclusions.

Your Project **Write a Speech for a Debate**

For this project, work in a group of two or three. Research how to write a speech for a debate and how debates work. The subject of your debate is *Methods of Solving Systems of Linear Equations.*

Each person in your group should choose one of the following methods to discuss: Graphing to solve a system of equations, substituting to solve a system of equations, or using elimination to solve a system of equations. Make sure you each choose a different method.

Write a speech about how your method of solving a system of linear equations is better than or different from the methods chosen by the other members of your group. With your partner or small group, present your debate to your class, or make a video and share it.

P-5A

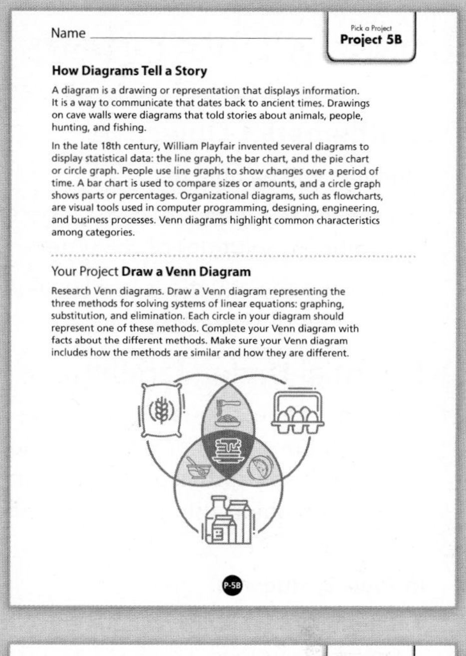

Name ______

Pick a Project
**Project 5B**

**How Diagrams Tell a Story**

A diagram is a drawing or representation that displays information. It is a way to communicate that dates back to ancient times. Drawings on cave walls were diagrams that told stories about animals, people, hunting, and fishing.

In the late 18th century, William Playfair invented several diagrams to display statistical data: the line graph, the bar chart, and the pie chart or circle graph. People use line graphs to show changes over a period of time. A bar chart is used to compare sizes or amounts, and a circle graph shows parts or percentages. Organizational diagrams, such as flowcharts, are visual tools used in computer programming, designing, engineering, and business processes. Venn diagrams highlight common characteristics among categories.

Your Project **Draw a Venn Diagram**

Research Venn diagrams. Draw a Venn diagram representing the three methods for solving systems of linear equations: graphing, substitution, and elimination. Each circle in your diagram should represent one of these methods. Complete your Venn diagram with facts about the different methods. Make sure your Venn diagram includes how the methods are similar and how they are different.

P-5B

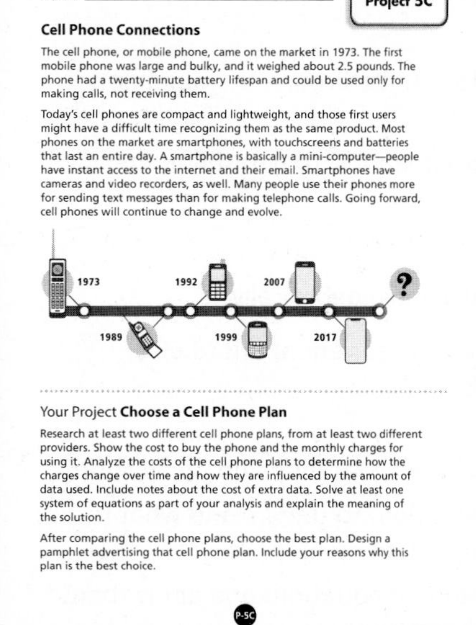

Name ______

Pick a Project
**Project 5C**

**Cell Phone Connections**

The cell phone, or mobile phone, came on the market in 1973. The first mobile phone was large and bulky, and it weighed about 2.5 pounds. The phone had a twenty-minute battery lifespan and could be used only for making calls, not receiving them.

Today's cell phones are compact and lightweight, and those first users might have a difficult time recognizing them as the same product. Most phones on the market are smartphones, with touchscreens and batteries that last an entire day. A smartphone is basically a mini-computer—people have instant access to the internet and their email. Smartphones have cameras and video recorders, as well. Many people use their phones more for sending text messages than for making telephone calls. Going forward, cell phones will continue to change and evolve.



Your Project **Choose a Cell Phone Plan**

Research at least two different cell phone plans, from at least two different providers. Show the cost to buy the phone and the monthly charges for using it. Analyze the costs of the cell phone plans to determine how the charges change over time and how they are influenced by the amount of data used. Include notes about the cost of extra data. Solve at least one system of equations as part of your analysis and explain the meaning of the solution.

After comparing the cell phone plans, choose the best plan. Design a pamphlet advertising that cell phone plan. Include your reasons why this plan is the best choice.

P-5C

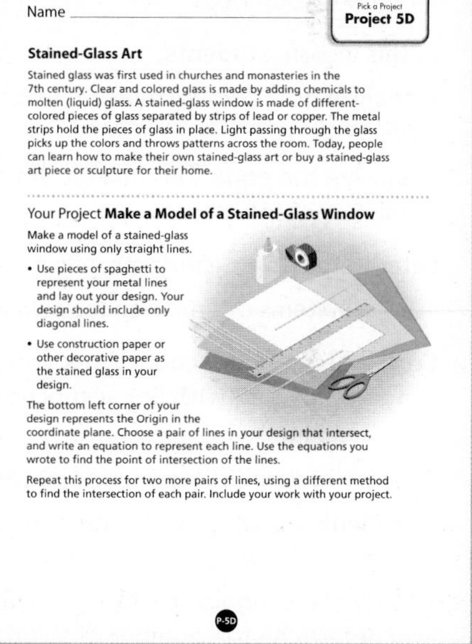

Name ______

Pick a Project
**Project 5D**

**Stained-Glass Art**

Stained glass was first used in churches and monasteries in the 7th century. Clear and colored glass is made by adding chemicals to molten (liquid) glass. A stained-glass window is made of different-colored pieces of glass separated by strips of lead or copper. The metal strips hold the pieces of glass in place. Light passing through the glass picks up the colors and throws patterns across the room. Today, people can learn how to make their own stained-glass art or buy a stained-glass art piece or sculpture for their home.

Your Project **Make a Model of a Stained-Glass Window**

Make a model of a stained-glass window using only straight lines.

- Use pieces of spaghetti to represent your metal lines and lay out your design. Your design should include only diagonal lines.
- Use construction paper or other decorative paper as the stained glass in your design.

The bottom left corner of your design represents the Origin in the coordinate plane. Choose a pair of lines in your design that intersect, and write an equation to represent each line. Use the equations you wrote to find the point of intersection of the lines.

Repeat this process for two more pairs of lines, using a different method to find the intersection of each pair. Include your work with your project.

P-5D

# Scoring Guide

Provide a scoring rubric to students as they begin work on the project.

For students who score Below Expectations on any goal, review the rubric score with them in detail. Encourage them to update their project, or select a different project, to demonstrate their understanding of the mathematics in this topic.

**Sample Scoring Rubric**

| Below Expectations (0–1 point: Explain.) | Meets Goal (2 points) | Above Expectations (3–4 points: Explain.) |
|---|---|---|
| | **Mathematics:** The project accurately demonstrates understanding of a key mathematical concept from the topic. | |
| | **Context:** The mathematics from the topic connects to the project context in a logical and natural way. | |
| | **Presentation:** The directions and guidelines were accurately followed. | |

Go Online

# Lesson 5-1 Estimate Solutions by Inspection

## Lesson Overview

FOCUS

### Mathematics Objective

**Students will be able to:**

✓ examine the graphs of a linear system of equations to determine the number of solutions of the system.

✓ compare the equations in a linear system to determine the number of solutions of the system.

### Essential Understanding

A system of linear equations can have no solution, one solution, or infinitely many solutions. The number of solutions can be determined by comparing the slopes and $y$-intercepts of the equations or by identifying the number of intersection points using graphs of the lines.

COHERENCE

**In Topic 2, students:**

- determined whether an equation with one variable has zero, one, or many solutions.

**In this lesson, students:**

- analyze graphs of systems of linear equations to determine the number of solutions.
- analyze the equations in a system of linear equations, to determine the number of solutions.

**Later in this topic, students will:**

- solve systems of linear equations graphically and algebraically.

**Cross-Cluster Connection** Work with systems of linear equations (8.EE.3) connects to work with linear functions (8.F.2).

RIGOR

This lesson emphasizes a blend of **conceptual understanding** and **application**.

- Students use graphs of systems of linear equations to understand what it means to have zero, one, or infinitely many solutions.
- Students recognize patterns in a linear system of equations and apply them to determine the number of solutions without graphing.

## Language Support

### Lesson Language Objective

Explain how to find the number of solutions of a system of linear equations by inspecting the equations.

Additional resources are available in the **Language Support Handbook**.

## Math Anytime

### Today's Challenge

Use the Topic 5 problems any time during this topic.

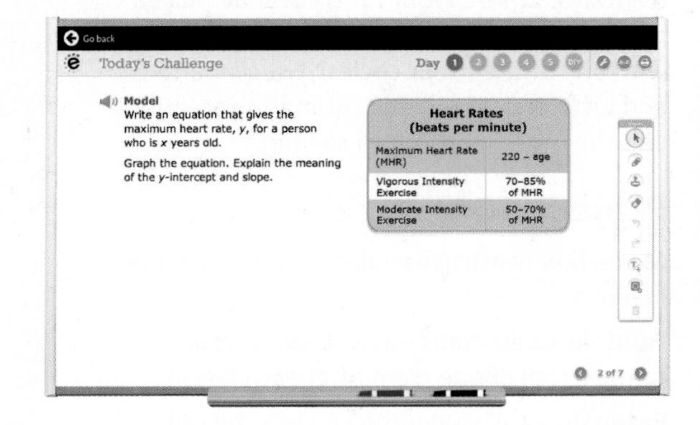


## Mathematics Overview | Common Core Standards

### Content Standards

In this lesson, you will focus on **8.EE.C.8b** and **8.EE.C.8c**.

- **8.EE.C.8b** Solve systems of two linear equations in two variables algebraically, and estimate solutions by graphing the equations. Solve simple cases by inspection.
- **8.EE.C.8c** Solve real-world and mathematical problems leading to two linear equations in two variables.

### Mathematical Practice Standards

**MP.2 Reason Abstractly and Quantitatively**
Throughout this lesson students interpret and determine the number of solutions of a system of linear equations by analyzing graphs and equations.

**MP.7 Look for and Make Use of Structure**
Students look for a relationship between the number of solutions of a system of equations and the slopes and $y$-intercepts of the equations.

STEP 1 | Problem-Based Learning

15-20 min

Go Online

Activity

# Solve & Discuss It!

Formative Assessment

**Purpose** Students explore different ways lines can intersect so they can relate intersections to solutions of systems of linear equations in the Visual Learning Bridge.

## ETP Before — WHOLE CLASS

### 1 Introduce the Problem

Provide graphing paper, colored markers or pencils, and rulers as needed.

### 2 Check for Understanding of the Problem

Engage prior knowledge by asking: What are some properties of lines?

## ETP During — SMALL GROUP

### 3 Observe Students at Work

Observe students while they work, noting the strategies that students use to draw each pair of lines. Students will likely draw lines that intersect in one place quickly but may struggle to determine other ways that lines could intersect. If needed, ask Is it possible that lines could never intersect?

### Early Finishers

How would the problem change if you drew groups of 3 lines? [Answers will vary.]

## ETP After — WHOLE CLASS

### 4 Discuss Solution Strategies and Key Ideas

Have students present their pairs of lines that intersect once. Have them find the slopes of these lines and discuss what they notice; the slopes of each pair of intersecting lines are different. Then have students present their pairs of lines that do not intersect. Have them discuss what they call lines that do not intersect (parallel), and what they notice about the slopes and $y$-intercepts of lines that are parallel; the slopes are the same, but the $y$-intercepts are different.

Lastly, have students present lines that overlap and discuss how these lines are different from lines that never intersect; these lines have the same slope and the same $y$-intercept. Encourage groups to discuss if they think there are any other ways lines could intersect; there is not.

### 5 Consider Instructional Implications

When presenting Example 1, have students identify the three types of intersections they found in the Solve & Discuss It. In the Solve & Discuss It, they identified whether lines would intersect based on the slope and $y$-intercept of the lines. Have students explore how they can use the slope-intercept form of the equation of a line to determine how the graphs of those lines will intersect (or not).

## Analyze Student Work

**Solve and Discuss It!** Activity is available online.

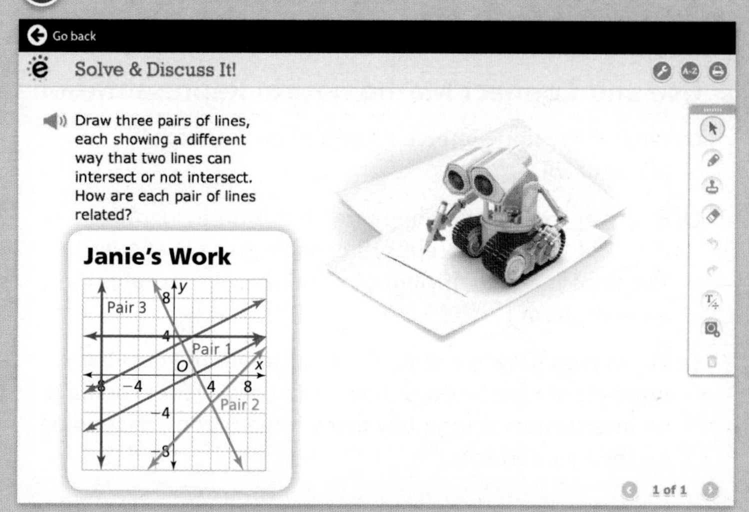


**Janie** graphs three pairs of lines; one pair of lines with no intersection and two pairs of lines with one intersection, one of which is a pair of perpendicular lines.

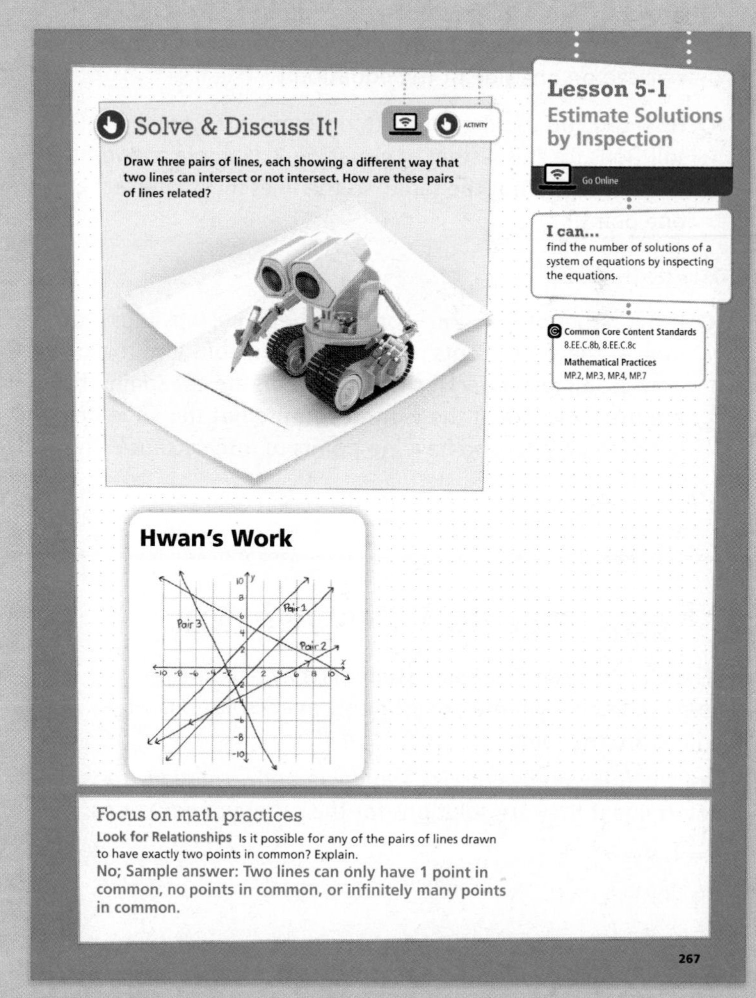


**Hwan** graphs one pair of lines with no intersection and one pair of lines with one intersection. He also graphs a pair of lines that are the same, with infinitely many points of intersection.

# STEP 2 | Visual Learning

Go Online

Visual Learning Assess

## ETP Establish Mathematics Goals to Focus Learning

Engage students in a discussion about the ***Essential Question***. Make sure students know how to put an equation into slope-intercept form and how to identify the slope and $y$-intercept.

## EXAMPLE 1 Relate Solutions of Linear Systems

### ETP Use and Connect Mathematical Representations

**Q:** What is the slope-intercept form of an equation? [$y = mx + b$]

**Q:** How can you use the slope-intercept form to identify the slope and $y$-intercept of the line? [Sample answer: The slope is the coefficient of $x$ and the $y$-intercept is the constant term.]

**Q:** If two lines have the same slope, what are the possible numbers of intersections they could have? [They can have no intersection or infinitely many intersections, depending on their $y$-intercepts.]

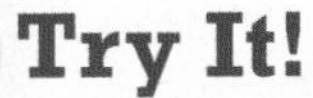

## Try It!

Formative Assessment

### ETP Elicit and Use Evidence of Student Thinking

**Q:** Are both equations in slope-intercept form? Explain. [Yes. Sample answer: Both equations have the variable, $y$, isolated on one side of the equation.]

**Q:** How can you use the slopes to determine the number of solutions for this system of equations? [Sample answer: The slopes are not the same, so the lines must intersect at one point.]

### Convince Me!

**Q:** If the slopes of two equations are the same, why must you look at the $y$-intercepts to tell how many solutions there are? [Sample answer: If the $y$-intercepts are the same, they are the same line. If the $y$-intercepts are not the same, the lines are parallel and have no points of intersection.]

**Visual Learning Animation Plus** is available online.

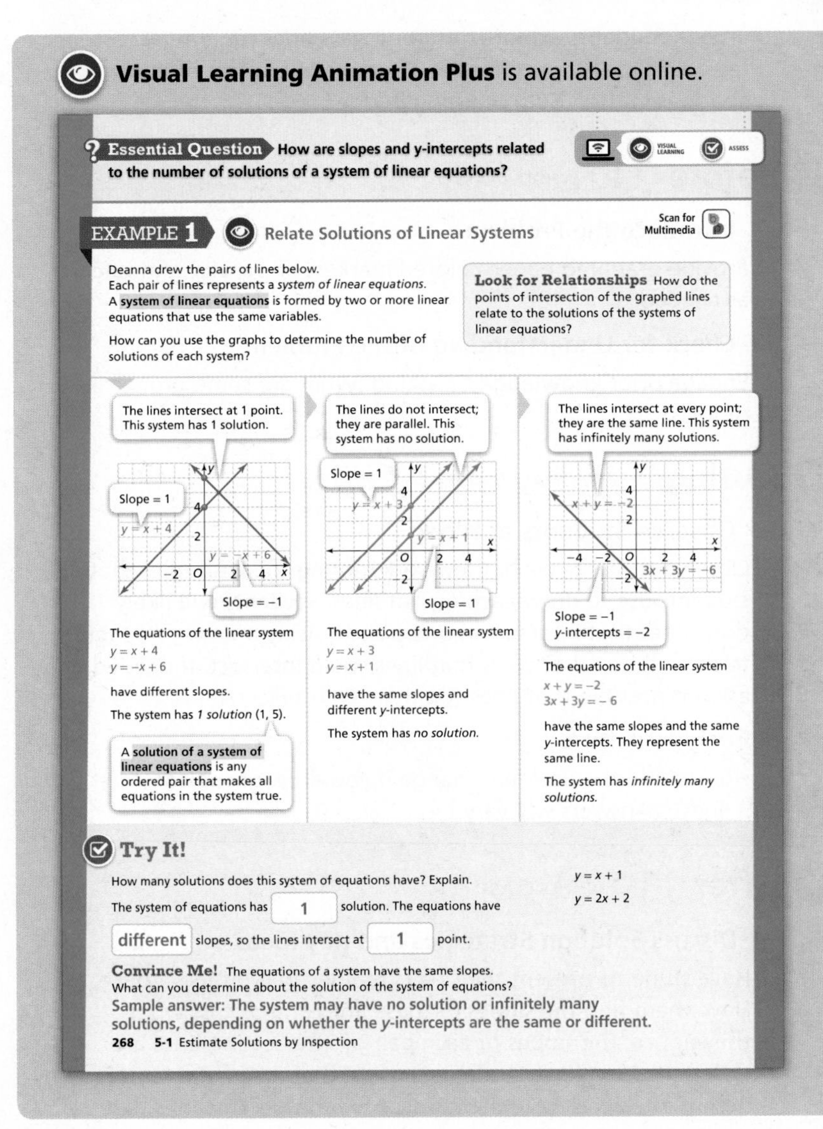
Essential Question How are slopes and y-intercepts related to the number of solutions of a system of linear equations?

EXAMPLE 1 Relate Solutions of Linear Systems

Scan for Multimedia

Deanna drew the pairs of lines below. Each pair of lines represents a *system of linear equations*. A **system of linear equations** is formed by two or more linear equations that use the same variables.

How can you use the graphs to determine the number of solutions of each system?

Look for Relationships How do the points of intersection of the graphed lines relate to the solutions of the systems of linear equations?



The equations of the linear system $y = x + 4$, $y = -x + 6$ have different slopes.

The system has *1 solution* (1, 5).

A **solution of a system of linear equations** is any ordered pair that makes all equations in the system true.

The equations of the linear system $y = x + 3$, $y = x + 1$ have the same slopes and different $y$-intercepts.

The system has *no solution*.

The equations of the linear system $x + y = -2$, $3x + 3y = -6$ have the same slopes and the same $y$-intercepts. They represent the same line.

The system has *infinitely many solutions*.

Try It!

How many solutions does this system of equations have? Explain. $y = x + 1$, $y = 2x + 2$

The system of equations has 1 solution. The equations have different slopes, so the lines intersect at 1 point.

Convince Me! The equations of a system have the same slopes. What can you determine about the solution of the system of equations?

Sample answer: The system may have no solution or infinitely many solutions, depending on whether the $y$-intercepts are the same or different.

268 5-1 Estimate Solutions by Inspection

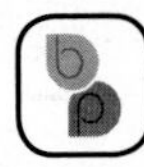

Students can access the ***Visual Learning Animation Plus*** by using the **BouncePages app** to scan this page. Students can download the app for free in their mobile devices' app store.

## Response to Intervention

**USE WITH EXAMPLE 3** Some students may need help understanding why there are infinitely many solutions when the lines are the same.

- Test the following values for $x$ and $y$ in both equations to determine if they are solutions for the system of equations.

  $x = 1, y = 3$

  $x = 0, y = 6$

  $x = 2, y = 0$

  Students should conclude that all of these pairs of values are solutions to both equations.

## Enrichment

**USE WITH EXAMPLE 1** Challenge students to complete the table showing the characteristics and number of solutions for different possibilities of two lines.

| model | slopes | y-intercepts | number of solutions |
|---|---|---|---|
| parallel lines | same | different | zero |
| lines that intersect once | different | same or different | one |
| lines that are the same | same | same | infinitely many |

Go Online

Activity Assess

# EXAMPLE 2 Estimate Solutions of Systems by Inspection

## ETP Pose Purposeful Questions

**Q:** What does the term $5x$ represent? [The cost of $x$ comic books at $5 each.]

**Q:** Why are the slopes the same but the $y$-intercepts different? [Sample answer: The slopes are the same because they bought the same number of comic books that each cost the same amount. The $y$-intercepts are different because they paid different amounts for their action figures.]

# EXAMPLE 3  Estimate More Solutions of Systems by Inspection

##  Pose Purposeful Questions

**Q:** Describe what a graph of these two lines would look like. Explain. [Sample answer: The graph would show the same line. They would be the same line because they have the same slope and $y$-intercept.]

**Q:** What relationship do you notice between $6x + 2y = 12$ and $12x + 4y = 24$? [Sample answer: The second equation is the first equation multiplied by 2. They are the same line.]

#  Try It!  Formative Assessment

##  Elicit and Use Evidence of Student Thinking

**Q:** What could you do to make Part b easier to solve? Explain. [Sample answer: You could write it in slope-intercept form to make it easier to compare the slopes and the $y$-intercepts.]

**Examples and Try Its!** are available online.

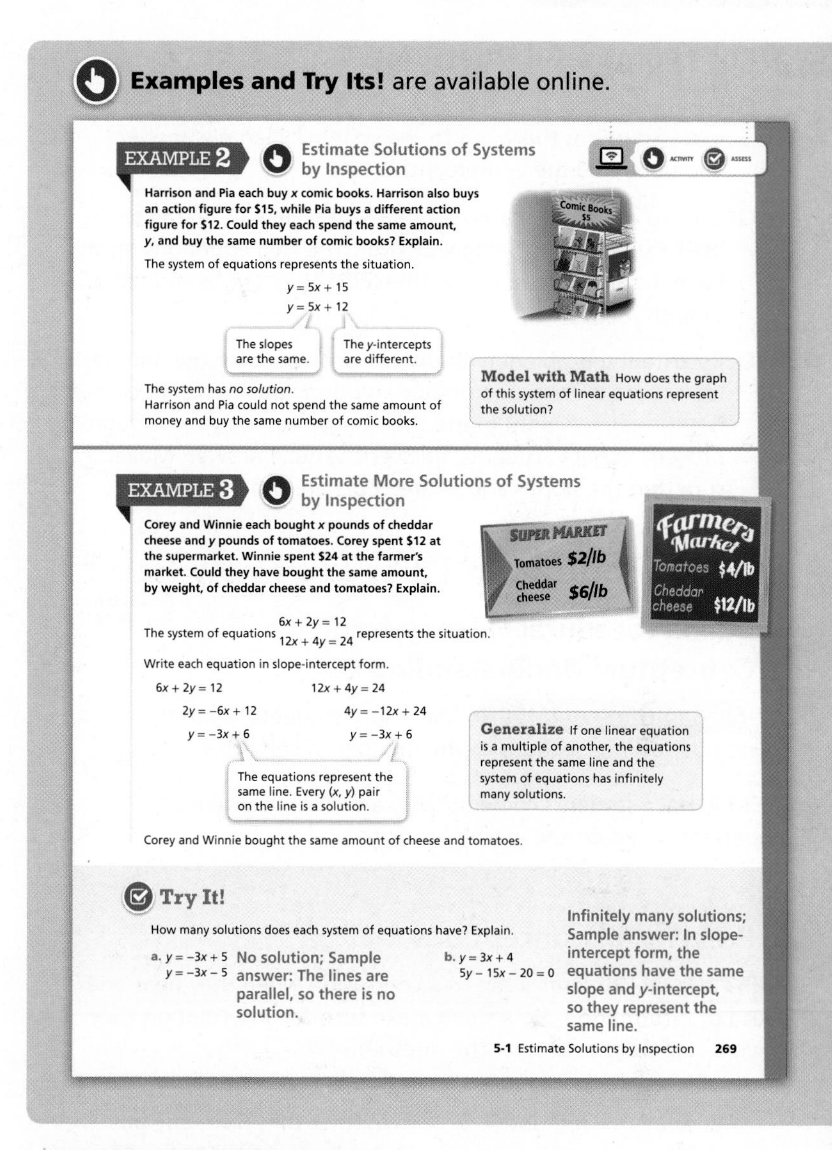

EXAMPLE 2 Estimate Solutions of Systems by Inspection

**Harrison and Pia each buy $x$ comic books. Harrison also buys an action figure for $15, while Pia buys a different action figure for $12. Could they each spend the same amount, $y$, and buy the same number of comic books? Explain.**

The system of equations represents the situation.

$$y = 5x + 15$$
$$y = 5x + 12$$

The slopes are the same. The $y$-intercepts are different.

The system has *no solution*.
Harrison and Pia could not spend the same amount of money and buy the same number of comic books.

**Model with Math** How does the graph of this system of linear equations represent the solution?

EXAMPLE 3 Estimate More Solutions of Systems by Inspection

**Corey and Winnie each bought $x$ pounds of cheddar cheese and $y$ pounds of tomatoes. Corey spent $12 at the supermarket. Winnie spent $24 at the farmer's market. Could they have bought the same amount, by weight, of cheddar cheese and tomatoes? Explain.**

The system of equations $6x + 2y = 12$, $12x + 4y = 24$ represents the situation.

Write each equation in slope-intercept form.

| $6x + 2y = 12$ | $12x + 4y = 24$ |
|---|---|
| $2y = -6x + 12$ | $4y = -12x + 24$ |
| $y = -3x + 6$ | $y = -3x + 6$ |

The equations represent the same line. Every $(x, y)$ pair on the line is a solution.

**Generalize** If one linear equation is a multiple of another, the equations represent the same line and the system of equations has infinitely many solutions.

Corey and Winnie bought the same amount of cheese and tomatoes.

Try It!

How many solutions does each system of equations have? Explain.

a. $y = -3x + 5$, $y = -3x - 5$ No solution; Sample answer: The lines are parallel, so there is no solution.

b. $y = 3x + 4$, $5y - 15x - 20 = 0$ Infinitely many solutions; Sample answer: In slope-intercept form, the equations have the same slope and $y$-intercept, so they represent the same line.

5-1 Estimate Solutions by Inspection 269

ADDITIONAL EXAMPLES

**For additional examples go online.**

# ELL English Language Learners

**ENTERING** See Example 2.

Help English Language Learners summarize the problem by having them complete the following sentences.

**Q:** Explain in your own words what *equation*, *slope*, and *y-intercept* mean.

**Q:** Use these three words in a sentence to describe the equation that models Harrison's purchase. [Sample answer: The slope of the equation is $5x$ and the $y$-intercept is 15.]

**DEVELOPING** See Example 2.

Have students reread the problem, then summarize the known information and the question aloud. Ask students to share their summaries.

**Q:** Explain why $y = 5x + 15$ models Harrison's purchase. [Sample answer: He bought $x$ comics for $5 each, for a cost of $5x$ dollars. He also bought an action figure for $15. The sum of the costs of the comic books and the action figure is equal to the total cost, $y$.]

**EXPANDING** See Example 3.

Have students identify unknown vocabulary words and try to determine what they mean based on the context of the problem and the equation model. Then, have students reread the problem and explain to a partner the steps taken to write each equation in slope-intercept form. Have students edit each other's work then share their summaries.

**Q:** How can you use the slope and the $y$-intercept of each equation to help determine the number of solutions to a system of equations?

Go Online

Key Concept

Assess

Activity

## KEY CONCEPT

### ETP Pose Purposeful Questions

**Q:** What must you look at in two equations to determine how many solutions there are to the system? [Sample answer: The slope and the $y$-intercept]

**Q:** Do two equations have to look exactly alike to be the same line? Explain. [No; Sample answer: The two equations must have the same slope and $y$-intercept. They can be multiples of each other.]

**Q:** Rewrite the problem with different weights for the marbles. Make sure there is one unique solution where each person has the same weight in the their bags. Explain your thought process. [Check students' answers; Sample answer: Make sure that the slopes and $y$-intercepts are different.]

## Do You Understand/Do You Know How?

**Formative** Assessment

### ETP Build Procedural Fluency from Conceptual Understanding

**Essential Question** Make sure students relate the number of intersections to the number of solutions.

**ITEM 4** Have students come up with a different system of equations based on the marble scenario.

### Prevent Misconceptions

**ITEM 2** Some students jump to a conclusion when they hear one piece of information. Help them make sure the information they have is sufficient to answer the question.

**Q:** If you know that two lines have the same slope, is that enough information to know whether they have any points of intersection? Explain. [No; Sample answer: You need to know the $y$-intercepts.]

Available Online

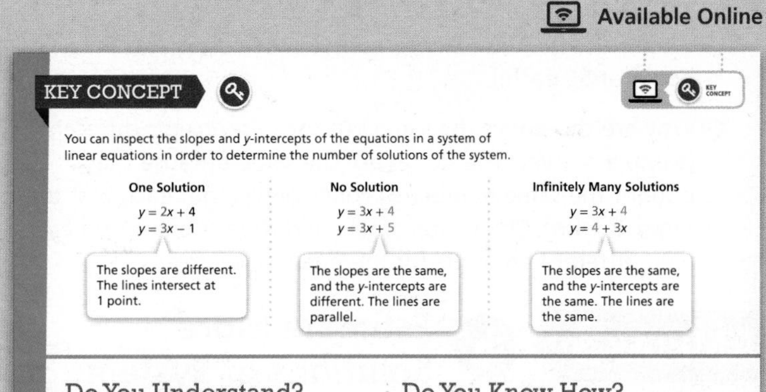
KEY CONCEPT

You can inspect the slopes and $y$-intercepts of the equations in a system of linear equations in order to determine the number of solutions of the system.

| One Solution | No Solution | Infinitely Many Solutions |
|---|---|---|
| $y = 2x + 4$<br>$y = 3x - 1$ | $y = 3x + 4$<br>$y = 3x + 5$ | $y = 3x + 4$<br>$y = 4 + 3x$ |
| The slopes are different. The lines intersect at 1 point. | The slopes are the same, and the $y$-intercepts are different. The lines are parallel. | The slopes are the same, and the $y$-intercepts are the same. The lines are the same. |

#### Do You Understand?

1. **Essential Question** How are slopes and $y$-intercepts related to the number of solutions of a system of linear equations?

   Sample answer: If the slopes of the lines in the system are different, the system will have one solution. If the slopes of the lines in the system are the same, but the $y$-intercepts are different, the system will have no solution. If the slopes of the lines in the system are the same, and the $y$-intercepts are the same, the system will have infinitely many solutions.

2. **Construct Arguments** Macy says that any time the equations in a system have the same $y$-intercept, the system has infinitely many solutions. Is Macy correct? Explain.

   No; Sample answer: If the two lines have the same $y$-intercepts, but different slopes, the system will only have one solution.

3. **Use Structure** How can you determine the number of solutions of a system of linear equations by inspecting its equations?

   Sample answer: Rewrite the equations in slope-intercept form, and compare the slopes and $y$-intercepts. If the slopes and $y$-intercepts are the same, there are infinitely many solutions. If the slopes are the same and the $y$-intercepts differ, there is no solution. If the slopes differ, there is one solution.

#### Do You Know How?

4. Kyle has $x$ 3-ounce blue marbles and a 5-ounce green marble. Lara has $x$ 5-ounce green marbles and a 3-ounce blue marble. Is it possible for Kyle and Lara to have the same number of green marbles and the same total bag weight, $y$? Explain.

   Yes; Sample answer: Kyle's bag weighs $y = 3x + 5$
   Lara's bag weighs $y = 5x + 3$
   Because each equation has a different slope, there is one possible solution, (1, 8), in which Kyle and Lara have the same number of green marbles and the same total bag weight.

5. How many solutions does this system of linear equations have? Explain.

   $$\frac{1}{2}x = y$$
   $$y = \frac{1}{2}x + 3$$

   None; Sample answer: Both equations have a slope of $\frac{1}{2}$, but they have different $y$-intercepts. They are parallel lines that never intersect.

6. How many solutions does this system of linear equations have? Explain.

   $$3y + 6x = 12$$
   $$8x + 4y = 16$$

   Infinitely many solutions; Sample answer: The equations have the same slope, −2, and the same $y$-intercept, 4, so there are infinitely many solutions.

270 **5-1** Estimate Solutions by Inspection

## ADDITIONAL EXAMPLE 2

Help students interpret a system of linear equations with slopes that are rational numbers, but not integers.

Make sure students can reason about the slopes and $y$-intercepts of the equations.

**Q:** What can you determine about the solution from the slopes? Explain. [Sample answer: The slopes are different. The lines will intersect at one point, so there is a solution.]

**Q:** What can you determine about the solution from the $y$-intercepts? Explain. [Sample answer: They will pay the same amount when they do not download any songs. The $y$-intercepts are the same, so the lines will intersect at the point (0, 8.95).]

**Additional Examples** are available online.

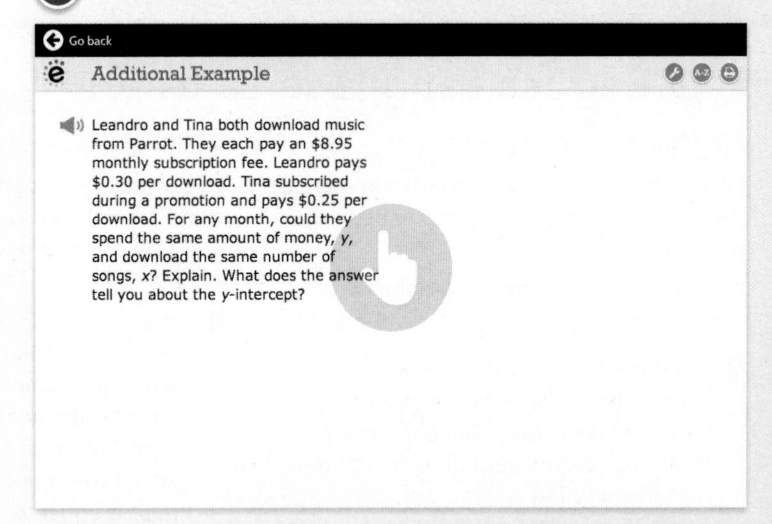
Go back

Additional Example

Leandro and Tina both download music from Parrot. They each pay an $8.95 monthly subscription fee. Leandro pays $0.30 per download. Tina subscribed during a promotion and pays $0.25 per download. For any month, could they spend the same amount of money, $y$, and download the same number of songs, $x$? Explain. What does the answer tell you about the $y$-intercept?

**Answer:** The only value of $x$ for which their cost is the same is 0. The $y$-intercept is (0, 8.95), and is the only point of intersection.

Go Online

 Practice  Tutorials   Math Tools

# Practice & Problem Solving  

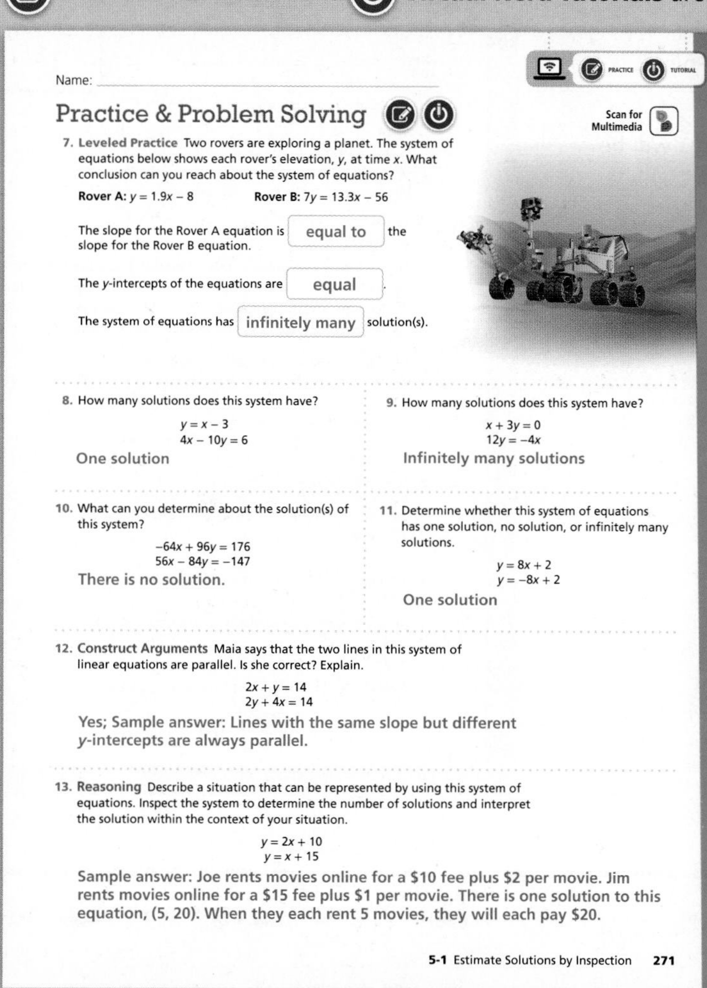

Name: ______

## Practice & Problem Solving

PRACTICE TUTORIAL

Scan for Multimedia

7. **Leveled Practice** Two rovers are exploring a planet. The system of equations below shows each rover's elevation, $y$, at time $x$. What conclusion can you reach about the system of equations?

**Rover A:** $y = 1.9x - 8$ **Rover B:** $7y = 13.3x - 56$

The slope for the Rover A equation is [equal to] the slope for the Rover B equation.

The $y$-intercepts of the equations are [equal].

The system of equations has [infinitely many] solution(s).

8. How many solutions does this system have?

$$y = x - 3$$
$$4x - 10y = 6$$

One solution

9. How many solutions does this system have?

$$x + 3y = 0$$
$$12y = -4x$$

Infinitely many solutions

10. What can you determine about the solution(s) of this system?

$$-64x + 96y = 176$$
$$56x - 84y = -147$$

There is no solution.

11. Determine whether this system of equations has one solution, no solution, or infinitely many solutions.

$$y = 8x + 2$$
$$y = -8x + 2$$

One solution

12. **Construct Arguments** Maia says that the two lines in this system of linear equations are parallel. Is she correct? Explain.

$$2x + y = 14$$
$$2y + 4x = 14$$

Yes; Sample answer: Lines with the same slope but different $y$-intercepts are always parallel.

13. **Reasoning** Describe a situation that can be represented by using this system of equations. Inspect the system to determine the number of solutions and interpret the solution within the context of your situation.

$$y = 2x + 10$$
$$y = x + 15$$

Sample answer: Joe rents movies online for a $10 fee plus $2 per movie. Jim rents movies online for a $15 fee plus $1 per movie. There is one solution to this equation, (5, 20). When they each rent 5 movies, they will each pay $20.



14. **Look for Relationships** Does this system have one solution, no solutions, or infinitely many solutions? Write another system of equations with the same number of solutions that uses the first equation only.

$$12x + 51y = 156$$
$$-8x - 34y = -104$$

Infinitely many solutions; Sample answer: $12x + 51y = 156$ and $4x + 17y = 52$

15. The equations represent the heights, $y$, of the flowers, in inches, after $x$ days. What does the $y$-intercept of each equation represent? Will the flowers ever be the same height? Explain.

$y = 0.7x + 2$ $y = 0.4x + 2$

The $y$-intercept represents the height of each flower when planted. Yes; Sample answer: The flowers are the same height when they are planted.

16. Does this system have one solution, no solution, or an infinite number of solutions?

$$4x + 3y = 8$$
$$8x + 6y = 2$$

No solution

17. **Higher Order Thinking** Under what circumstances does the system of equations $Qx + Ry = S$ and $y = Tx + S$ have infinitely many solutions?

When $T = -Q$ and $R = 1$

## Assessment Practice

18. By inspecting the equations, what can you determine about the solution(s) of this system?

$$12y = 9x + 33$$
$$20y = 15x + 55$$

The system has infinitely many solutions.

19. Choose the statement that correctly describes how many solutions there are for this system of equations.

$$y = \frac{2}{3}x + 3$$
$$y = \frac{5}{4}x + 3$$

Ⓐ Infinitely many solutions because the slopes are equal and the $y$-intercepts are equal

Ⓑ Exactly one solution because the slopes are equal but the $y$-intercepts are NOT equal

Ⓒ No solution because the slopes are equal and the $y$-intercepts are NOT equal

● Exactly one solution because the slopes are NOT equal



## Error Intervention

**ITEM 10** Explain to students that a good way to solve this problem is to put the equations in slope-intercept form. At the appropriate time in the problem discuss with students different strategies for simplifying the fractions.

**Q:** Explain how to solve the first equation for $y$. [First, add $64x$ to both sides. Then, divide both sides by 96. Then simplify the fractions to obtain $y = \frac{2}{3}x + \frac{11}{6}$.]

**Q:** Explain how to solve the second equation for $y$. [First, subtract $56x$ from both sides. Then, divide both sides by –84. Simplify the factions to obtain $y = \frac{2}{3} + \frac{7}{4}$.]

##  Challenge

**ITEM 15** Challenge students to change this system of equations so it has a different solution.

**Q:** Write two new sets of equations in which the plants reach the same height. Try keeping the slopes or the $y$-intercepts the same as in the original problem. [Check students' solutions.]

You may opt to have students complete the automatically scored Practice & Problem Solving items online.

### Item Analysis

| Example | Items | DOK |
|---|---|---|
| 1 | 8, 9, 11 | 1 |
| 2 | 13, 15, 19 | 2 |
| 3 | 7 | 1 |
| | 10, 12, 14, 16, 18 | 2 |
| | 17 | 3 |

# STEP 3 | Assess & Differentiate

Go Online

## Lesson Quiz

Use the student scores on the Lesson Quiz to prescribe differentiated assignments.

**I Intervention** 0–3 Points **O On-Level** 4 Points **A Advanced** 5 Points

You may opt to have students take the Lesson Quiz online. The Lesson Quiz will be automatically scored and appropriate remediation, practice, or enrichment will be assigned based on student performance.

**Lesson Quiz** is available online.

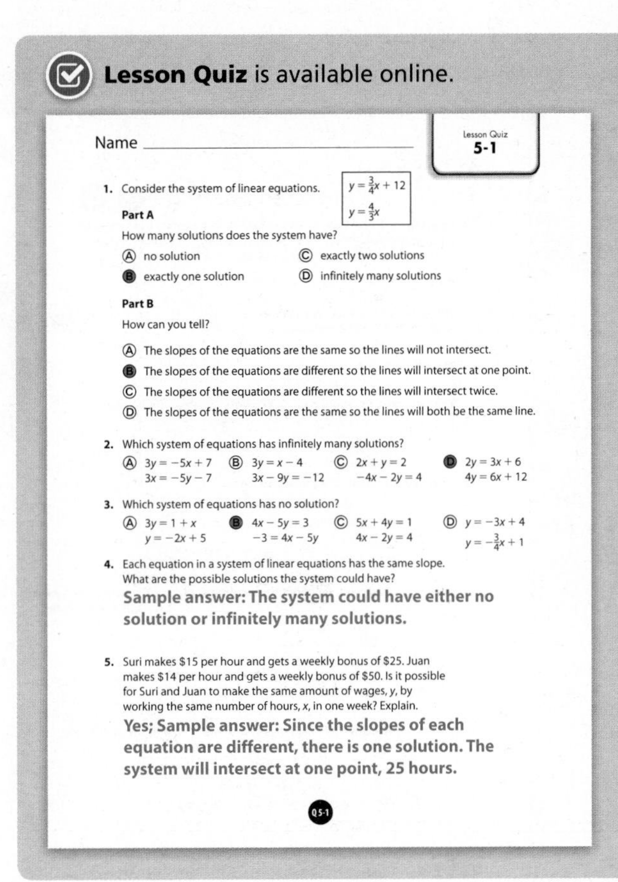

Name ________________ Lesson Quiz 5-1

1. Consider the system of linear equations. $y = \frac{3}{4}x + 12$, $y = \frac{4}{3}x$

   **Part A**

   How many solutions does the system have?

   Ⓐ no solution Ⓒ exactly two solutions
   Ⓑ exactly one solution Ⓓ infinitely many solutions

   **Part B**

   How can you tell?

   Ⓐ The slopes of the equations are the same so the lines will not intersect.
   Ⓑ The slopes of the equations are different so the lines will intersect at one point.
   Ⓒ The slopes of the equations are different so the lines will intersect twice.
   Ⓓ The slopes of the equations are the same so the lines will both be the same line.

2. Which system of equations has infinitely many solutions?

   Ⓐ $3y = -5x + 7$, $3x = -5y - 7$ Ⓑ $3y = x - 4$, $3x - 9y = -12$ Ⓒ $2x + y = 2$, $-4x - 2y = 4$ Ⓓ $2y = 3x + 6$, $4y = 6x + 12$

3. Which system of equations has no solution?

   Ⓐ $3y = 1 + x$, $y = -2x + 5$ Ⓑ $4x - 5y = 3$, $-3 = 4x - 5y$ Ⓒ $5x + 4y = 1$, $4x - 2y = 4$ Ⓓ $y = -3x + 4$, $y = -\frac{3}{4}x + 1$

4. Each equation in a system of linear equations has the same slope. What are the possible solutions the system could have?

   **Sample answer: The system could have either no solution or infinitely many solutions.**

5. Suri makes $15 per hour and gets a weekly bonus of $25. Juan makes $14 per hour and gets a weekly bonus of $50. Is it possible for Suri and Juan to make the same amount of wages, $y$, by working the same number of hours, $x$, in one week? Explain.

   **Yes; Sample answer: Since the slopes of each equation are different, there is one solution. The system will intersect at one point, 25 hours.**

Q5-1

## Video Tutorials

Students can access instructional tutorials using the **Virtual Nerd app**.

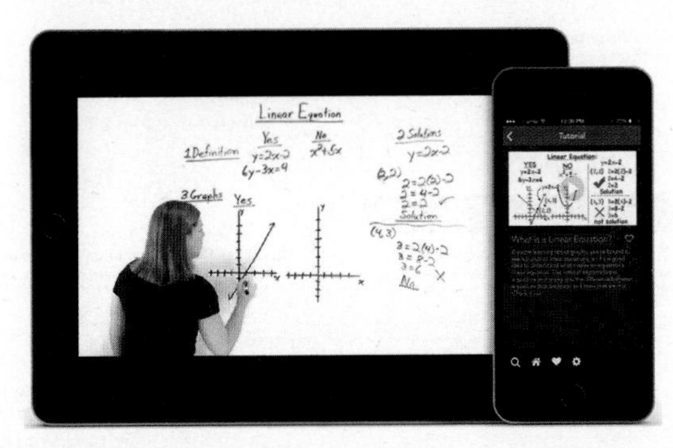

Students can also access the videos using the **BouncePages app** to scan exercise pages marked with this icon. Students can download both apps for free in their mobile devices' app store.

## Differentiated Intervention

**I** = Intervention **O** = On-Level **A** = Advanced

### Reteach to Build Understanding I

Provides scaffolded reteaching for the key lesson concepts.

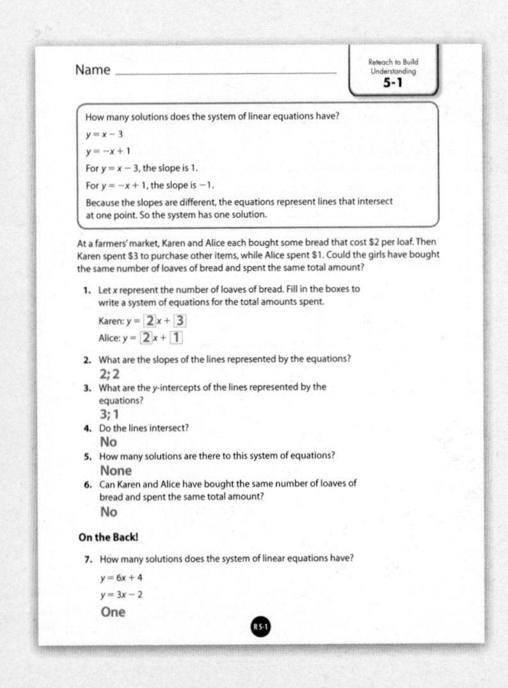

Name ________________ Reteach to Build Understanding 5-1

How many solutions does the system of linear equations have?

$y = x - 3$

$y = -x + 1$

For $y = x - 3$, the slope is 1.

For $y = -x + 1$, the slope is $-1$.

Because the slopes are different, the equations represent lines that intersect at one point. So the system has one solution.

At a farmers' market, Karen and Alice each bought some bread that cost $2 per loaf. Then Karen spent $3 to purchase other items, while Alice spent $1. Could the girls have bought the same number of loaves of bread and spent the same total amount?

1. Let $x$ represent the number of loaves of bread. Fill in the boxes to write a system of equations for the total amounts spent.

   Karen: $y = 2x + 3$

   Alice: $y = 2x + 1$

2. What are the slopes of the lines represented by the equations?

   2; 2

3. What are the $y$-intercepts of the lines represented by the equations?

   3; 1

4. Do the lines intersect?

   No

5. How many solutions are there to this system of equations?

   None

6. Can Karen and Alice have bought the same number of loaves of bread and spent the same total amount?

   No

**On the Back!**

7. How many solutions does the system of linear equations have?

   $y = 6x + 4$

   $y = 3x - 2$

   One

R5-1

### Additional Vocabulary Support I O

Helps students develop and reinforce understanding of key terms and concepts.

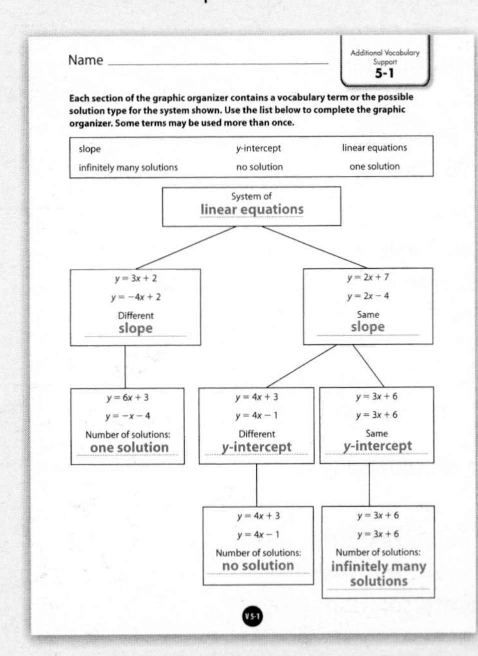

Name ________________ Additional Vocabulary Support 5-1

**Each section of the graphic organizer contains a vocabulary term or the possible solution type for the system shown. Use the list below to complete the graphic organizer. Some terms may be used more than once.**

| slope | y-intercept | linear equations |
|---|---|---|
| infinitely many solutions | no solution | one solution |

System of **linear equations**

- $y = 3x + 2$, $y = -4x + 2$ — Different **slope**
  - $y = 6x + 3$, $y = -x - 4$ — Number of solutions: **one solution**
- $y = 2x + 7$, $y = 2x - 4$ — Same **slope**
  - $y = 4x + 3$, $y = 4x - 1$ — Different **y-intercept**
    - $y = 4x + 3$, $y = 4x - 1$ — Number of solutions: **no solution**
  - $y = 3x + 6$, $y = 3x + 6$ — Same **y-intercept**
    - $y = 3x + 6$, $y = 3x + 6$ — Number of solutions: **infinitely many solutions**

V5-1

### Build Mathematical Literacy I O

Provides support for struggling readers to build mathematical literacy.

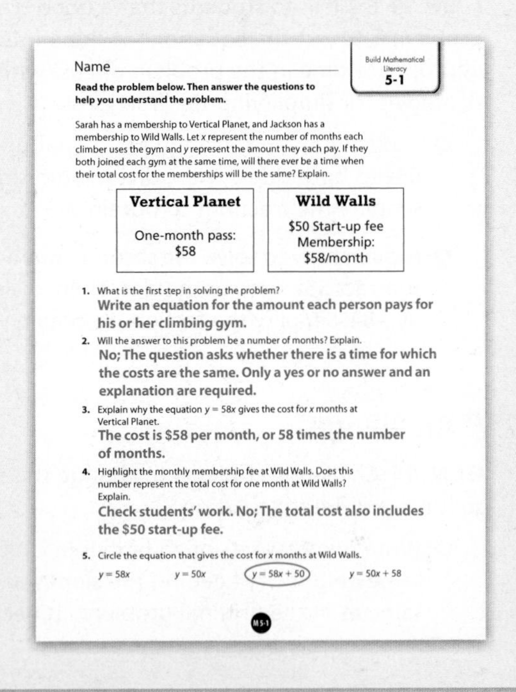

Name ________________ Build Mathematical Literacy 5-1

**Read the problem below. Then answer the questions to help you understand the problem.**

Sarah has a membership to Vertical Planet, and Jackson has a membership to Wild Walls. Let $x$ represent the number of months each climber uses the gym and $y$ represent the amount they each pay. If they both joined each gym at the same time, will there ever be a time when their total cost for the memberships will be the same? Explain.

| Vertical Planet | Wild Walls |
|---|---|
| One-month pass: $58 | $50 Start-up fee Membership: $58/month |

1. What is the first step in solving the problem?

   **Write an equation for the amount each person pays for his or her climbing gym.**

2. Will the answer to this problem be a number of months? Explain.

   **No; The question asks whether there is a time for which the costs are the same. Only a yes or no answer and an explanation are required.**

3. Explain why the equation $y = 58x$ gives the cost for $x$ months at Vertical Planet.

   **The cost is $58 per month, or 58 times the number of months.**

4. Highlight the monthly membership fee at Wild Walls. Does this number represent the total cost for one month at Wild Walls? Explain.

   **Check students' work. No; The total cost also includes the $50 start-up fee.**

5. Circle the equation that gives the cost for $x$ months at Wild Walls.

   $y = 58x$ $y = 50x$ $y = 58x + 50$ (circled) $y = 50x + 58$

M5-1

Go Online

Practice

Worksheets

Math Tools

Math Games

# Additional Practice

You may opt to have students complete the automatically scored Additional Practice items online.

### Item Analysis

| Example | Items | DOK |
|---|---|---|
| 1 | 2, 3, 6 | 1 |
| 2 | 7, 11 | 2 |
| 3 | 1 | 1 |
| | 4, 5, 8, 10 | 2 |
| | 9 | 3 |

**Interactive Practice** is available online.

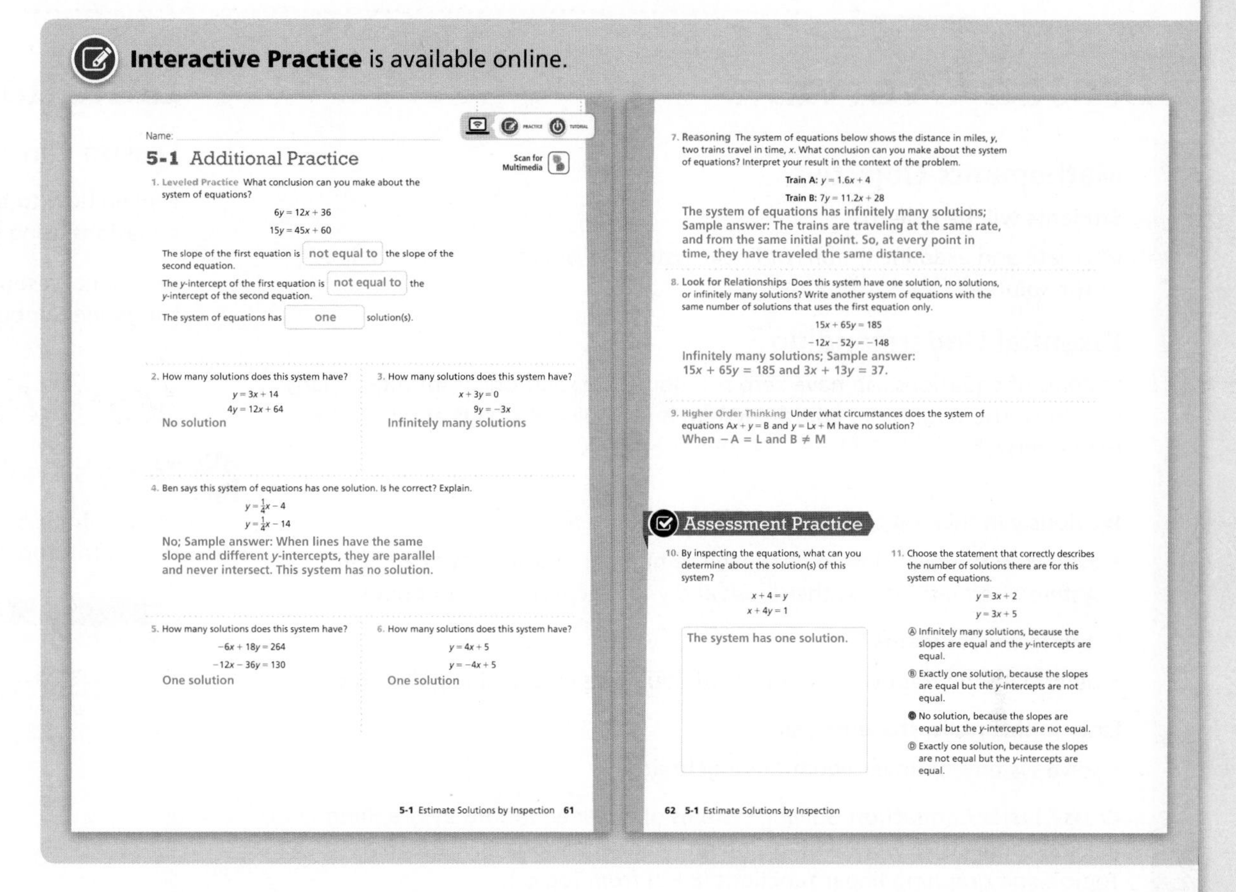

Name:

**5-1** Additional Practice

Scan for Multimedia

1. Leveled Practice What conclusion can you make about the system of equations?

$6y = 12x + 36$
$15y = 45x + 60$

The slope of the first equation is **not equal to** the slope of the second equation.

The $y$-intercept of the first equation is **not equal to** the $y$-intercept of the second equation.

The system of equations has **one** solution(s).

2. How many solutions does this system have?
$y = 3x + 14$
$4y = 12x + 64$
No solution

3. How many solutions does this system have?
$x + 3y = 0$
$9y = -3x$
Infinitely many solutions

4. Ben says this system of equations has one solution. Is he correct? Explain.
$y = \frac{1}{4}x - 4$
$y = \frac{1}{4}x - 14$
No; Sample answer: When lines have the same slope and different $y$-intercepts, they are parallel and never intersect. This system has no solution.

5. How many solutions does this system have?
$-6x + 18y = 264$
$-12x - 36y = 130$
One solution

6. How many solutions does this system have?
$y = 4x + 5$
$y = -4x + 5$
One solution

5-1 Estimate Solutions by Inspection 61

7. Reasoning The system of equations below shows the distance in miles, $y$, two trains travel in time, $x$. What conclusion can you make about the system of equations? Interpret your result in the context of the problem.
Train A: $y = 1.6x + 4$
Train B: $7y = 11.2x + 28$
The system of equations has infinitely many solutions; Sample answer: The trains are traveling at the same rate, and from the same initial point. So, at every point in time, they have traveled the same distance.

8. Look for Relationships Does this system have one solution, no solutions, or infinitely many solutions? Write another system of equations with the same number of solutions that uses the first equation only.
$15x + 65y = 185$
$-12x - 52y = -148$
Infinitely many solutions; Sample answer: $15x + 65y = 185$ and $3x + 13y = 37$.

9. Higher Order Thinking Under what circumstances does the system of equations $Ax + y = B$ and $y = Lx + M$ have no solution?
When $-A = L$ and $B \neq M$

Assessment Practice

10. By inspecting the equations, what can you determine about the solution(s) of this system?
$x + 4 = y$
$x + 4y = 1$
The system has one solution.

11. Choose the statement that correctly describes the number of solutions there are for this system of equations.
$y = 3x + 2$
$y = 3x + 5$
Ⓐ Infinitely many solutions, because the slopes are equal and the $y$-intercepts are equal.
Ⓑ Exactly one solution, because the slopes are equal but the $y$-intercepts are not equal.
● No solution, because the slopes are equal but the $y$-intercepts are not equal.
Ⓓ Exactly one solution, because the slopes are not equal but the $y$-intercepts are equal.

62 5-1 Estimate Solutions by Inspection

# Differentiated Intervention

I = Intervention 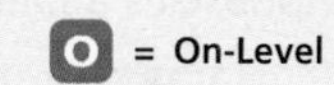 O = On-Level  A = Advanced

## Enrichment O A

Presents engaging problems and activities that extend the lesson concepts.

## Math Tools and Games I O A

Offers additional activities and games to build understanding and fluency.

## Pick a Project and STEM Project I O A

Provides an additional opportunity for students to demonstrate understanding of key mathematical concepts.

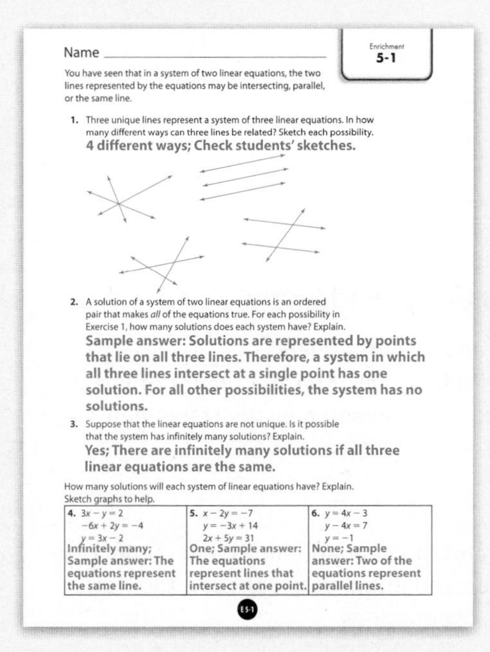

Name

Enrichment 5-1

You have seen that in a system of two linear equations, the two lines represented by the equations may be intersecting, parallel, or the same line.

1. Three unique lines represent a system of three linear equations. In how many different ways can three lines be related? Sketch each possibility.
4 different ways; Check students' sketches.

2. A solution of a system of two linear equations is an ordered pair that makes *all* of the equations true. For each possibility in Exercise 1, how many solutions does each system have? Explain.
Sample answer: Solutions are represented by points that lie on all three lines. Therefore, a system in which all three lines intersect at a single point has one solution. For all other possibilities, the system has no solutions.

3. Suppose that the linear equations are not unique. Is it possible that the system has infinitely many solutions? Explain.
Yes; There are infinitely many solutions if all three linear equations are the same.

How many solutions will each system of linear equations have? Explain. Sketch graphs to help.

| 4. $3x - y = 2$, $-6x + 2y = -4$, $y = 3x - 2$ | 5. $x - 2y = -7$, $y = -3x + 14$, $2x + 5y = 31$ | 6. $y = 4x - 3$, $y - 4x = 7$, $y = -1$ |
|---|---|---|
| Infinitely many; Sample answer: The equations represent the same line. | One; Sample answer: The equations represent lines that intersect at one point. | None; Sample answer: Two of the equations represent parallel lines. |

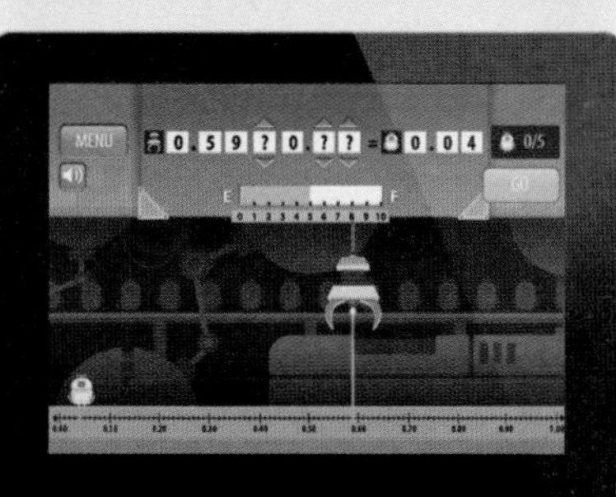

Go Online

Video Activity

# Lesson 5-2 Solve Systems by Graphing

## Lesson Overview

FOCUS

### Mathematics Objective

**Students will be able to:**

✔ create and examine graphs of linear systems of equations to determine the solution.

### Essential Understanding

Systems of equations can have zero solutions, one solution, or infinitely many solutions. The solution to a linear system is the point or points at which the lines intersect.

COHERENCE

**Previously in this topic, students:**

- examined the relationship between the number of solutions of a linear system of equations and the slopes and *y*-intercepts of the equations.

**In this lesson, students:**

- determine the solution to a system of equations by examining the graph.

**Later in this topic, students will:**

- solve systems of linear equations algebraically.

**Cross-Cluster Connection** Solving systems of linear equations by graphing (8.EE.3) connects to work with graphing linear equations (8.EE.2) from Topic 2 and graphing linear functions (8.F.2) from Topic 3.

RIGOR

This lesson emphasizes a blend of **conceptual understanding** and **application.**

- Students will examine graphs of a system of linear equations to determine the solution, understanding that the point(s) of intersection represents the *x*- and *y*-values that are the solution to the system.
- Students will apply their graphical analysis of systems of equations to find the solution(s), if any, at the intersection point(s) of the graphs. They will interpret solutions to linear systems in context.

## Language Support

### Lesson Language Objective

Explain how to find the solution to a system of equations using graphs.

Additional resources are available in the **Language Support Handbook**.

## Math Anytime

### Today's Challenge

Use the Topic 5 problems any time during this topic.

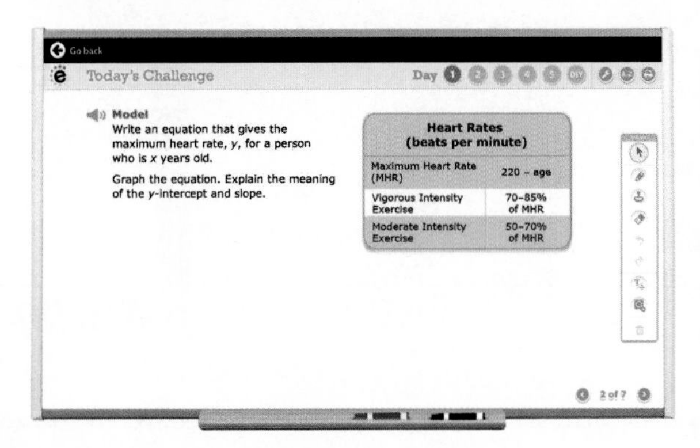


Watch the **Listen and Look For Video** for strategies and habits of mind to look for as students complete work on this lesson.

## Mathematics Overview | Common Core Standards

### Content Standards

In this lesson, you will focus on **8.EE.C.8a** and **8.EE.C.8c**.

- **8.EE.C.8a** Understand that solutions to a system of two linear equations in two variables correspond to points of intersection of their graphs, because points of intersection satisfy both equations simultaneously.
- **8.EE.C.8c** Solve real-world and mathematical problems leading to two linear equations in two variables.

### Mathematical Practice Standards

**MP.2 Reason Abstractly and Quantitatively**
Throughout this lesson students will interpret graphs of linear systems of equations and make meaning by understanding that the solution is the intersection point(s).

**MP.4 Model with Math**
Students work with systems of linear equations that model real-world situations. They use and interpret graphs as a tool for understanding a system of equations.

Go Online

Activity

15-20 min

# STEP 1 | Problem-Based Learning

## Explore It!

Formative Assessment

**Purpose** Students write a system of equations that has a given solution and connect this to solving systems of equations by graphing in the Visual Learning Bridge.

### ETP Before — WHOLE CLASS

**1 Introduce the Problem**

Provide graph paper, as needed.

**2 Check for Understanding of the Problem**

Ask students: Have you and a friend ever taken separate paths to arrive at the same destination?

### ETP During — SMALL GROUP

**3 Observe Students at Work**

Observe students while they work, noting the strategies that students take to determine two lines. Students can draw any two lines that pass through the point (2, 3), but not overlapping lines. If needed, ask How can you use two points to draw a line?

**Early Finishers**

How would the problem change if the library was located at (−1, 3)? [Sample answer: I drew two new lines. One line passes through (−1, 3) and (0, 2) and the other line passes through (−1, 3) and (0, 4). The equations of the lines are $y = x + 4$ and $y = -x + 2$.]

### ETP After — WHOLE CLASS

**4 Discuss Solution Strategies and Key Ideas**

Have students present their graphs and discuss how they chose and drew their lines. Ask students how they could have drawn infinitely many different pairs of lines that intersect at that same point; a line can be defined by two points. You can choose one of those points to always be the point of intersection. Then have them explain how they found the slope and *y*-intercept of their lines. Have students discuss what a system of equations is and how they can use the equations of their two lines to write a system of equations to represent the situation; a system of equations is a set of two or more equations that have the same unknowns.

Have students identify the point of intersection of the lines and discuss its meaning in the context of the problem; the point of intersection is the library and it is the common point on Beth and Dante's paths on their way home.

**5 Consider Instructional Implications**

When presenting Example 1, have students look at their system of equations and the point of intersection in the Explore It. Have students evaluate both Dante and Beth's equations at the intersection point (2, 3) and discuss what they notice; the values of the coordinates, $x = 2$ and $y = 3$, make both equations true. Have them discuss whether they think this point is the only point that makes both equation true; yes, as the lines only intersect once, there is only one solution.

## Analyze Student Work

**Explore It!** Activity is available online.

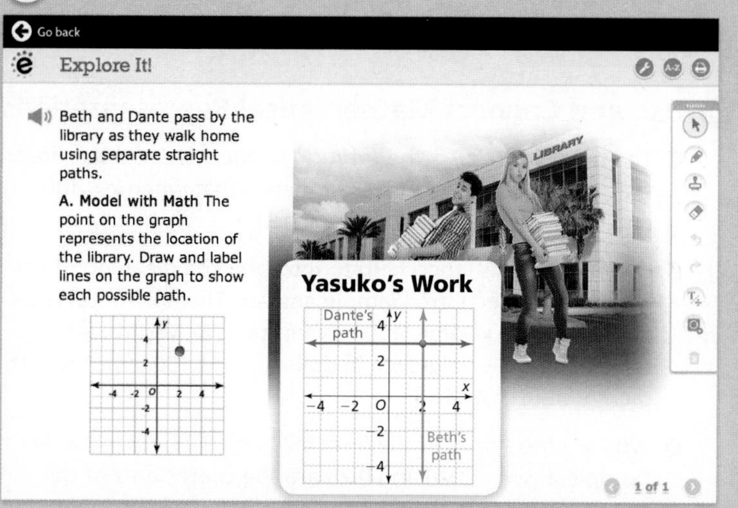


**Yasuko** draws a horizontal and a vertical line that intersect at the library, (2, 3).

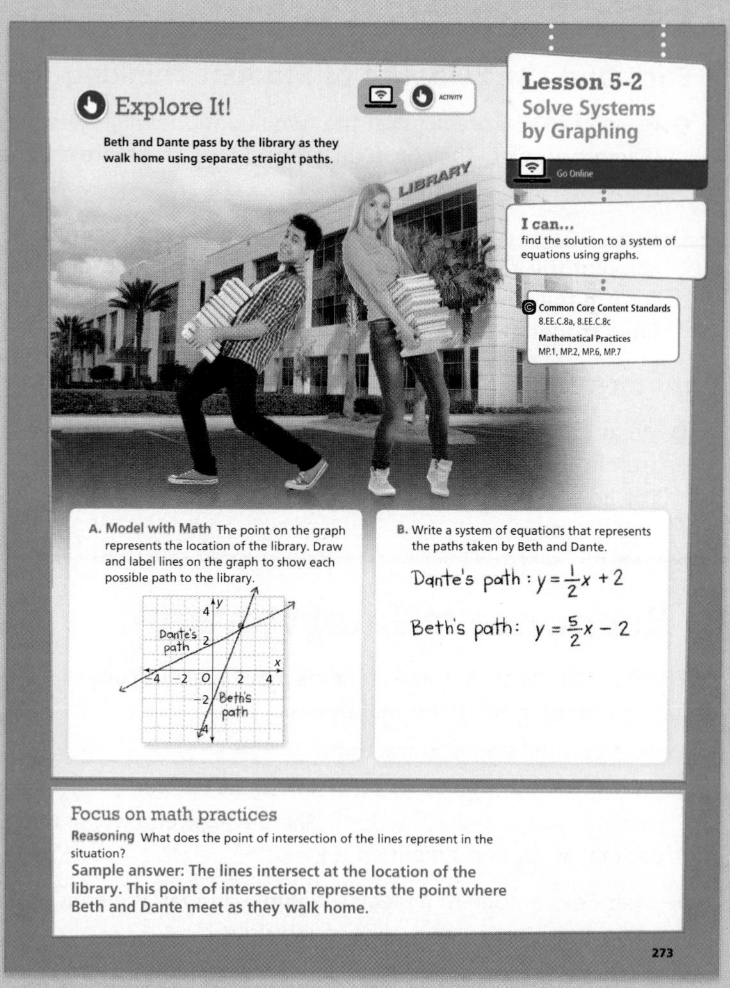


**Jarred** draws two slanted lines that intersect at the library, (2, 3).

# STEP 2 | Visual Learning

Go Online

 Visual Learning  Assess

## ETP Establish Mathematics Goals to Focus Learning

Engage students in a discussion about the ***Essential Question***. Make sure they understand that the point of intersection $(x, y)$ is the solution to the system, and that it means there is a single solution.

## EXAMPLE 1  Solve a System by Graphing

### ETP Use and Connect Mathematical Representations

**Q:** The point (100, 95) is the solution to the system. What does that mean? [Sample answer: It means that when $x = 100$ and $y = 95$, both equations are true.]

**Q:** How do the axis labels help to interpret the meaning of the point of intersection? [Sample answer: The horizontal label represents the $x$-value, 100, in minutes. The vertical label represents the $y$-value, 95, in dollars. So at 100 minutes both plans would cost $95.]

**Q:** Why are the slopes of the lines 0.20 and 0.25, respectively? [Sample answer: 0.20 and 0.25 are the coefficients of the $x$-variable because they are the cost in dollars per $x$ minutes for each plan.]

## Try It! 

### ETP Elicit and Use Evidence of Student Thinking

**Q:** How could you predict that the two equations will intersect? [Sample answer: They have different slopes; therefore they must intersect.]

**Q:** How can you graph each equation? [Sample answer: You can plot the $y$-intercept and then substitute a different value for $x$ in the equation, plot the resulting point, and draw a line through the two points.]

### Convince Me!

**Q:** What if one equation is true and the other equation is not true for the $x$- and $y$-values? [Sample answer: It is possible the lines were drawn incorrectly and do not match the equations.]

**Visual Learning Animation Plus** is available online.

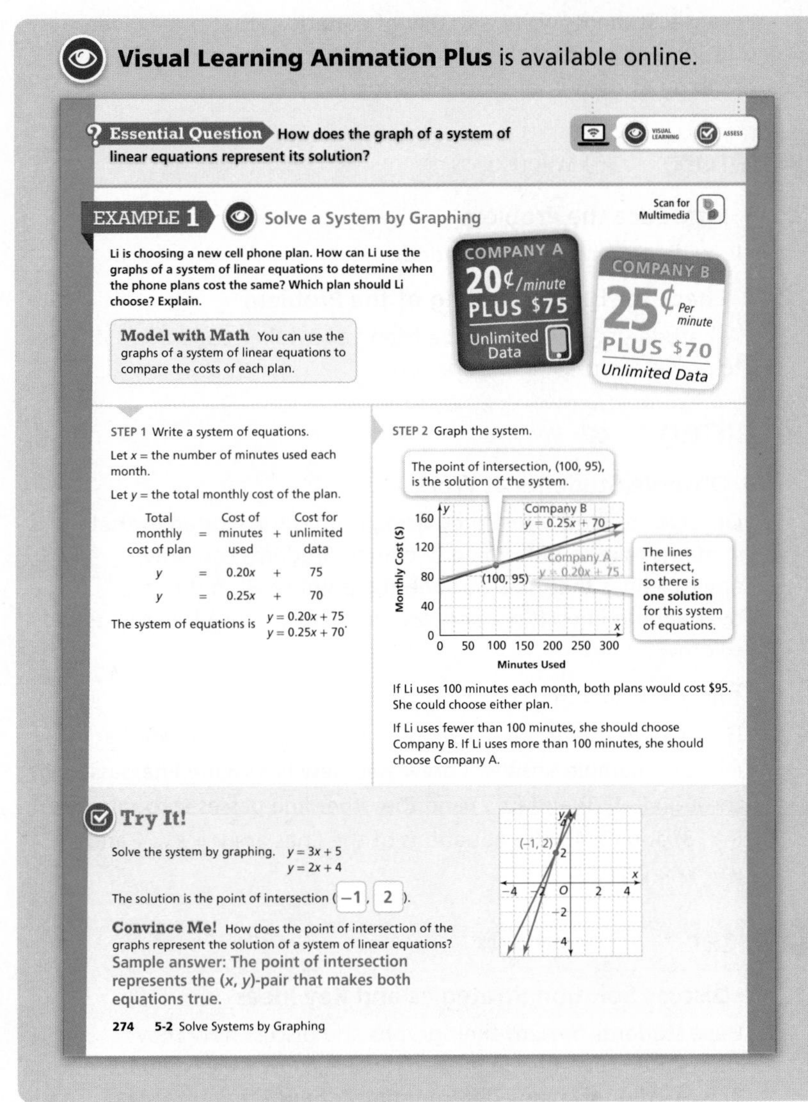

Essential Question How does the graph of a system of linear equations represent its solution?

EXAMPLE 1 Solve a System by Graphing

Scan for Multimedia

Li is choosing a new cell phone plan. How can Li use the graphs of a system of linear equations to determine when the phone plans cost the same? Which plan should Li choose? Explain.



**Model with Math** You can use the graphs of a system of linear equations to compare the costs of each plan.

STEP 1 Write a system of equations.

Let $x$ = the number of minutes used each month.

Let $y$ = the total monthly cost of the plan.

| Total monthly cost of plan | = | Cost of minutes used | + | Cost for unlimited data |
|---|---|---|---|---|
| $y$ | = | $0.20x$ | + | 75 |
| $y$ | = | $0.25x$ | + | 70 |

The system of equations is $y = 0.20x + 75$, $y = 0.25x + 70$.

STEP 2 Graph the system.



If Li uses 100 minutes each month, both plans would cost $95. She could choose either plan.

If Li uses fewer than 100 minutes, she should choose Company B. If Li uses more than 100 minutes, she should choose Company A.

Try It!

Solve the system by graphing. $y = 3x + 5$, $y = 2x + 4$

The solution is the point of intersection (−1, 2).



**Convince Me!** How does the point of intersection of the graphs represent the solution of a system of linear equations? Sample answer: The point of intersection represents the $(x, y)$-pair that makes both equations true.

274 5-2 Solve Systems by Graphing

Students can access the ***Visual Learning Animation Plus*** by using the **BouncePages app** to scan this page. Students can download the app for free in their mobile devices' app store.

## Response to Intervention

**USE WITH EXAMPLE 1** Some students may have difficulty graphing equations with decimal slopes.

- Convert decimal slopes to fractions.

**Q:** How do you write 0.20 as a fraction in lowest terms? [$\frac{1}{5}$] How did you find this fraction? [Sample answer: I wrote the decimal as $\frac{20}{100}$ and simplified it.]

**Q:** What does a slope of $\frac{1}{5}$ mean? [Sample answer: It means to go up 1 unit for every 5 units to the right.]

**Q:** How do you write 0.25 as a fraction in lowest terms? [$\frac{1}{4}$] How did you find this fraction? [Sample answer: I wrote the decimal as $\frac{25}{100}$ and simplified it.]

**Q:** What does a slope of $\frac{1}{4}$ mean? [Sample answer: It means to go up 1 unit for every 4 units to the right.]

## Enrichment

**USE WITH EXAMPLE 1** Challenge students to further explore graphing linear systems to find a solution.

- Analyze Example 1.

**Q:** How could you change the equations so that there would not be a solution? [Sample answer: Change the slopes to be the same, but have different $y$-intercepts.]

**Q:** Give two possible equations that would have infinitely many solutions. [Sample answer: $c = 0.20m + 75$ and $10c = 2m + 750$]

**Q:** Give an equation for a third plan that also costs $95 for 100 minutes. Then, explain what the equation means in context. [Sample answer: $c = 0.30m + 65$; the plan costs $65 plus 30 cents per minute.]

Go Online

Activity Assess

## EXAMPLE 2 Graph a System of Equations with No Solution

### ETP Pose Purposeful Questions

**Q:** Is the second equation in slope-intercept form? Explain. [No; Sample answer: The coefficient of $y$ is not 1. It is not in the form $y = mx + b$.]

**Q:** How can the second equation be written in slope-intercept form? What is the result? [Sample answer: Subtract $2x$ from both sides and divide all terms by $-2$ to get $y = x + 1$.]

**Q:** Do you expect the graphs of the two equations to intersect? Why or why not? [Sample answer: They will not intersect because they have the same slope, but different $y$-intercepts.]

## EXAMPLE 3 Graph a System of Equations with Infinitely Many Solutions

### ETP Pose Purposeful Questions

**Q:** What do you notice about the equations when they are written in slope-intercept form? [Sample answer: The equations are the same, so the line that corresponds to each is the same.]

**Q:** If two equations have the same slope, are their corresponding lines always the same when graphed? [No; Sample answer: If the $y$-intercepts are different, then the lines will be parallel.]

## Try It!

**Formative** Assessment

### ETP Elicit and Use Evidence of Student Thinking

**Q:** Does the fact that the equations in Part b have negative slopes affect the number of solutions? Explain. [No; Sample answer: What matters is the fact that the slopes are the same and the $y$-intercepts are different so the system has no solution.]

**Examples and Try Its!** are available online.

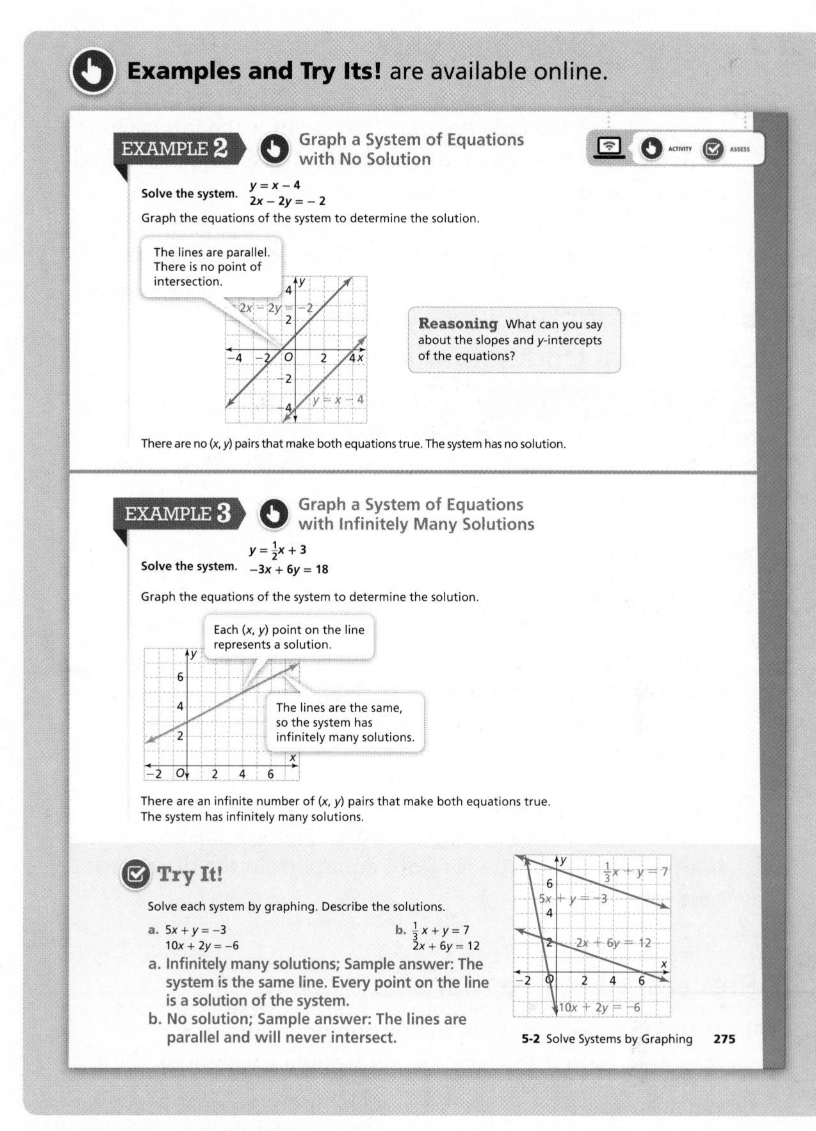

EXAMPLE 2 Graph a System of Equations with No Solution

Solve the system. $y = x - 4$, $2x - 2y = -2$

Graph the equations of the system to determine the solution.



There are no $(x, y)$ pairs that make both equations true. The system has no solution.

EXAMPLE 3 Graph a System of Equations with Infinitely Many Solutions

Solve the system. $y = \frac{1}{2}x + 3$, $-3x + 6y = 18$

Graph the equations of the system to determine the solution.



There are an infinite number of $(x, y)$ pairs that make both equations true. The system has infinitely many solutions.

Try It!

Solve each system by graphing. Describe the solutions.

a. $5x + y = -3$, $10x + 2y = -6$

b. $\frac{1}{3}x + y = 7$, $2x + 6y = 12$

a. Infinitely many solutions; Sample answer: The system is the same line. Every point on the line is a solution of the system.

b. No solution; Sample answer: The lines are parallel and will never intersect.



5-2 Solve Systems by Graphing 275

## ADDITIONAL EXAMPLES

**For additional examples go online.**

## ELL English Language Learners

**ENTERING** Complete Example 2.

Help English Language Learners identify different ways that lines can intersect.

Draw the following four pairs of lines: parallel, perpendicular, intersecting but not perpendicular, and overlapping. Provide students with four notecards and have them label each pair of lines.

**DEVELOPING** Complete Example 2.

Have students reread the problem and the solution.

**Q:** What does it mean for a system of equations to have no solution? [Sample answer: The lines do not intersect at any points.]

**EXPANDING** Complete Example 2.

Have students work with a partner to explain the meaning of the word parallel and how it relates to the fact that the lines do not intersect.

Go Online

## KEY CONCEPT

### ETP Pose Purposeful Questions

**Q:** What does it mean if a point $(x, y)$ is a solution to a system of equations? [Sample answer: That point is the intersection of the lines in the system of equations. Those values of $x$ and $y$ make both equations in the system true.]

## Do You Understand/Do You Know How?

Formative Assessment

### ETP Build Procedural Fluency from Conceptual Understanding

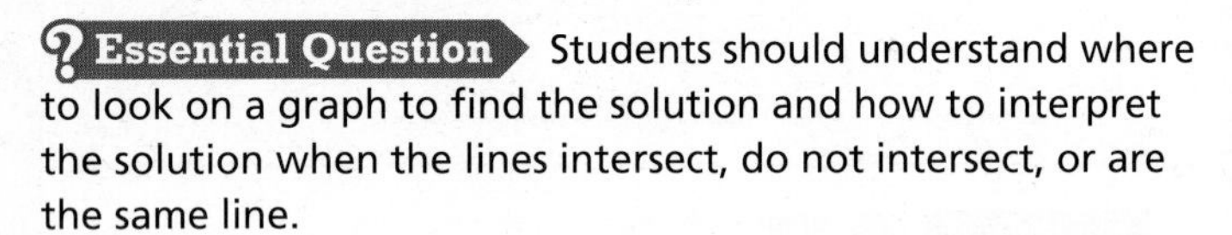

**Essential Question** Students should understand where to look on a graph to find the solution and how to interpret the solution when the lines intersect, do not intersect, or are the same line.

**ITEM 3**

**Q:** What does it mean if you substitute your solution into both equations and the results are not the same? [Sample answer: It could mean you made a mistake when substituting values and should check your work again, or it could mean you graphed the equations incorrectly and your solution is not correct.]

**Q:** Explain why you should substitute your solution into both equations when checking your work. [Sample answer: The solution has to be true for both equations in the system to be a solution.]

### Prevent Misconceptions

**ITEM 5** Have students rewrite the second equation in slope-intercept form if they are having trouble graphing it.

**Q:** How can you rewrite the second equation in slope-intercept form? [Subtract $6x$ from both sides, then divide all terms by 3.]

**Q:** What is the equation in slope-intercept form? [$y = -2x - 5$]

Available Online

KEY CONCEPT

The solution of a system of linear equations is the point of intersection of the lines defined by the equations.

One point of intersection: **one solution**

The solution is (−2, 1).

All points lie on the same line: **infinitely many solutions**

Parallel lines, no points of intersection: **no solution**

Do You Understand?

1. **Essential Question** How does the graph of a system of linear equations represent its solution?
Sample answer: A graph of a system of linear equations will show whether the lines intersect. If they intersect, the solution is the point of intersection. If the lines are parallel, there is no solution. If the lines are the same, there are infinitely many solutions, meaning that any point on the line is a solution to the system.
2. **Reasoning** If a system has no solution, what do you know about the lines being graphed?
Sample answer: The lines are parallel. They have the same slope, but different $y$-intercepts.
3. **Construct Arguments** In a system of linear equations, the lines described by each equation have the same slopes. What are the possible solutions of the system? Explain.
Sample answer: If the $y$-intercepts are the same, the system of linear equations has infinitely many solutions. If the $y$-intercepts are different, the system of linear equations has no solution.

Do You Know How?

**In 4–6, graph each system of equations and find the solution.**

4. $y = -3x - 5$
$y = 9x + 7$
$(-1, -2)$
5. $y = -2x - 5$
$6x + 3y = -15$
Infinitely many solutions
6. $y = -4x + 3$
$8x + 2y = 8$
No solution

276 5-2 Solve Systems by Graphing

## ADDITIONAL EXAMPLE 1

Help students transition to solving a system of equations with limitations on the values of $x$.

Make sure students understand how to use limitations on $x$ to solve the problem.

**Q:** How does knowing that Justin uses less than 300 minutes per month affect how you solve the problem? Explain. [Sample answer: The steps for solving the problem are the same. The limitation of 300 minutes per month helps determine which company's plan is cheaper.]

**Q:** How can you determine the greatest possible cost? Explain. [Sample answer: The point (300, 95) tells you that the cost of talking 300 minutes a month is \$95. Since Justin uses less than 300 minutes per month, he will pay something less than \$95.]

**Additional Examples** are available online.

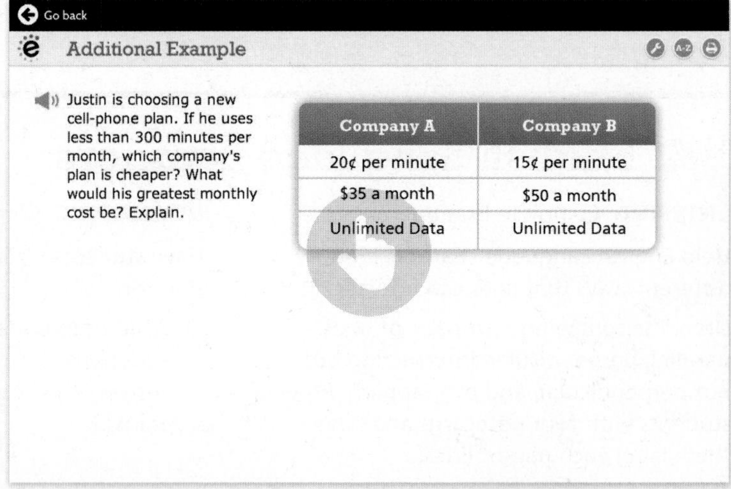
Go back

Additional Example

Justin is choosing a new cell-phone plan. If he uses less than 300 minutes per month, which company's plan is cheaper? What would his greatest monthly cost be? Explain.

| Company A | Company B |
|---|---|
| 20¢ per minute | 15¢ per minute |
| \$35 a month | \$50 a month |
| Unlimited Data | Unlimited Data |

**Answer:** Company A's plan is cheaper. Justin's greatest cost will be less than \$95.

Go Online

 Practice  Tutorials  Math Tools

# Practice & Problem Solving  

Interactive Practice and Virtual Nerd Tutorials are available online.

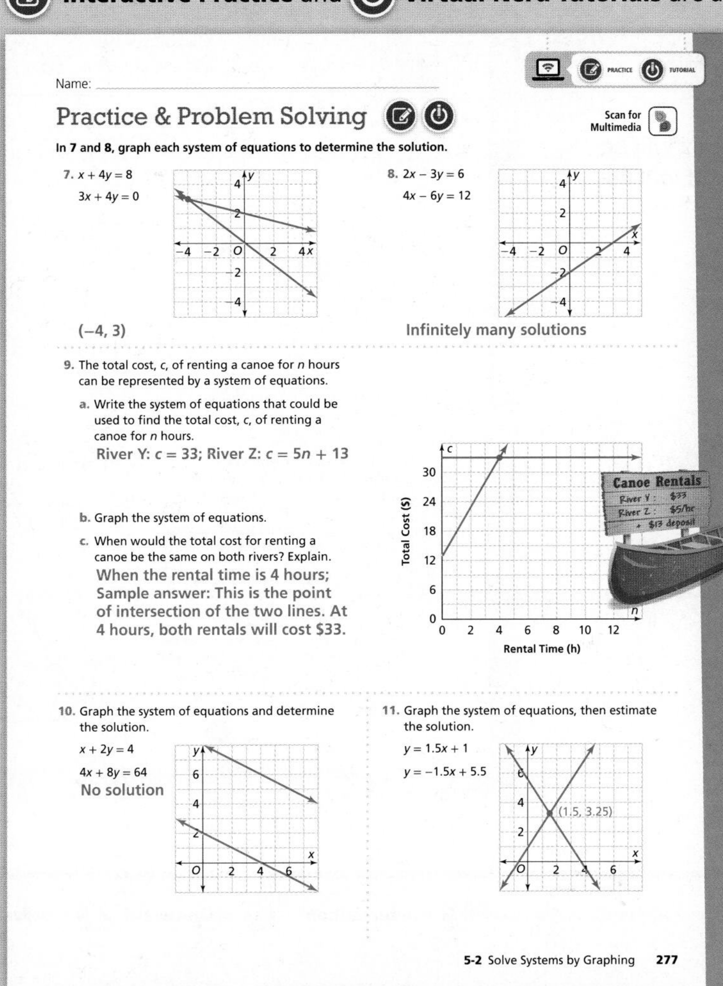
Name:

Practice & Problem Solving

Scan for Multimedia

In 7 and 8, graph each system of equations to determine the solution.

7. $x + 4y = 8$
$3x + 4y = 0$
(−4, 3)

8. $2x - 3y = 6$
$4x - 6y = 12$
Infinitely many solutions

9. The total cost, $c$, of renting a canoe for $n$ hours can be represented by a system of equations.

a. Write the system of equations that could be used to find the total cost, $c$, of renting a canoe for $n$ hours.
River Y: $c = 33$; River Z: $c = 5n + 13$

b. Graph the system of equations.

c. When would the total cost for renting a canoe be the same on both rivers? Explain.
When the rental time is 4 hours; Sample answer: This is the point of intersection of the two lines. At 4 hours, both rentals will cost $33.



10. Graph the system of equations and determine the solution.
$x + 2y = 4$
$4x + 8y = 64$
No solution

11. Graph the system of equations, then estimate the solution.
$y = 1.5x + 1$
$y = -1.5x + 5.5$
(1.5, 3.25)



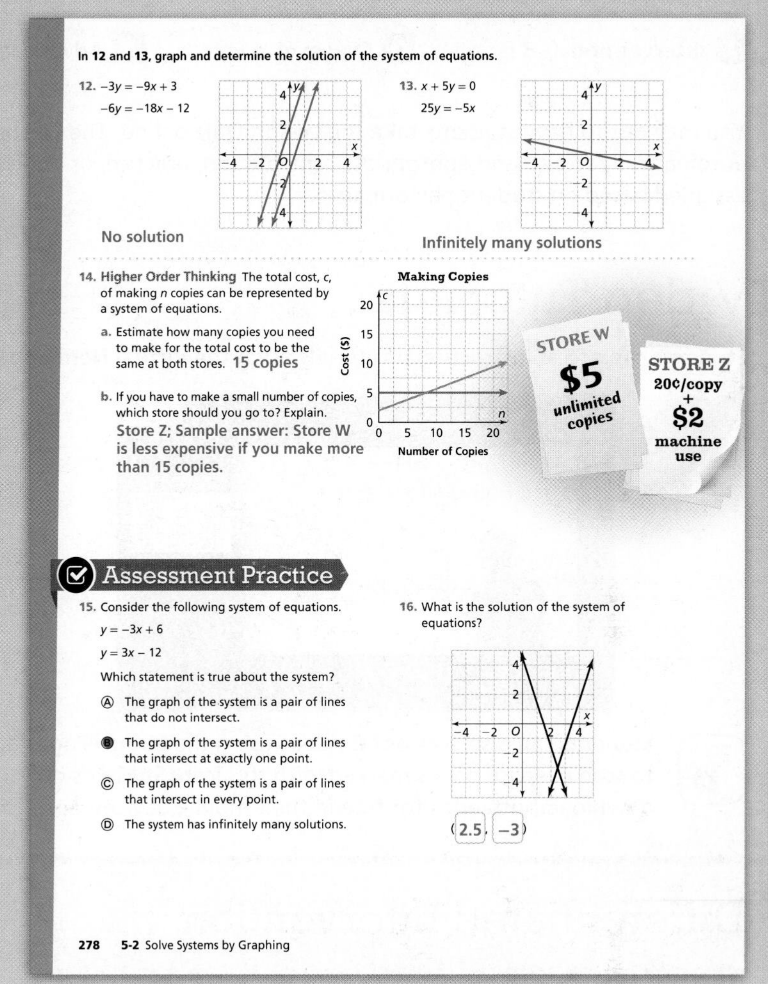
In 12 and 13, graph and determine the solution of the system of equations.

12. $-3y = -9x + 3$
$-6y = -18x - 12$
No solution

13. $x + 5y = 0$
$25y = -5x$
Infinitely many solutions

14. Higher Order Thinking The total cost, $c$, of making $n$ copies can be represented by a system of equations.

a. Estimate how many copies you need to make for the total cost to be the same at both stores. 15 copies

b. If you have to make a small number of copies, which store should you go to? Explain.
Store Z; Sample answer: Store W is less expensive if you make more than 15 copies.



Assessment Practice

15. Consider the following system of equations.
$y = -3x + 6$
$y = 3x - 12$
Which statement is true about the system?
Ⓐ The graph of the system is a pair of lines that do not intersect.
● The graph of the system is a pair of lines that intersect at exactly one point.
Ⓒ The graph of the system is a pair of lines that intersect in every point.
Ⓓ The system has infinitely many solutions.

16. What is the solution of the system of equations?
(2.5, −3)



## Error Intervention

**ITEM 9** Students may have difficulty writing the equation for River Y.

**Q:** How much will it cost to rent a canoe for 2 hours on River Y? For 4 hours? For any number of hours? [$33; $33; $33]

**Q:** If the cost is always $33, how can you express that as an equation? [$c = 33$]

## Challenge

**ITEM 9** Challenge students to interpret the graph.

**Q:** When would it be more beneficial to rent a canoe on River Y? How does the point of intersection help you answer this question? [Sample answer: If you plan to canoe for more than 4 hours, you would save money on River Y. Because the $x$-coordinate of the intersection is 4, the costs are equal for 4 hours, greater on River Z after 4 hours, and greater on River Y before 4 hours.]

You may opt to have students complete the automatically scored Practice & Problem Solving items online.

### Item Analysis

| Example | Items | DOK |
|---|---|---|
| 1 | 7, 11 | 1 |
| | 9, 15 | 2 |
| 2 | 10, 12 | 1 |
| | 14 | 3 |
| 3 | 8, 13 | 1 |

Go Online

Assess

Tutorials

Worksheets

# STEP 3 | Assess & Differentiate

## Lesson Quiz

Use the student scores on the Lesson Quiz to prescribe differentiated assignments.

**I** **Intervention** 0–3 Points **O** **On-Level** 4 Points **A** **Advanced** 5 Points

You may opt to have students take the Lesson Quiz online. The Lesson Quiz will be automatically scored and appropriate remediation, practice, or enrichment will be assigned based on student performance.

**Lesson Quiz** is available online.

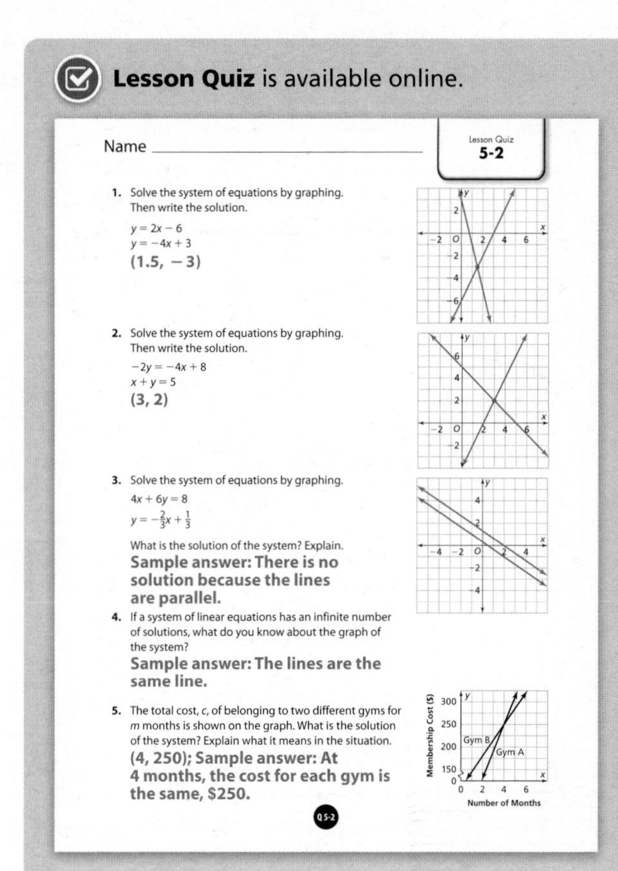

Name ______________________ Lesson Quiz 5-2

1. Solve the system of equations by graphing. Then write the solution.
   $y = 2x - 6$
   $y = -4x + 3$
   **(1.5, −3)**
2. Solve the system of equations by graphing. Then write the solution.
   $-2y = -4x + 8$
   $x + y = 5$
   **(3, 2)**
3. Solve the system of equations by graphing.
   $4x + 6y = 8$
   $y = -\frac{2}{3}x + \frac{1}{3}$
   What is the solution of the system? Explain.
   **Sample answer: There is no solution because the lines are parallel.**
4. If a system of linear equations has an infinite number of solutions, what do you know about the graph of the system?
   **Sample answer: The lines are the same line.**
5. The total cost, *c*, of belonging to two different gyms for *m* months is shown on the graph. What is the solution of the system? Explain what it means in the situation.
   **(4, 250); Sample answer: At 4 months, the cost for each gym is the same, $250.**

Q5-2

## Video Tutorials

Students can access instructional tutorials using the **Virtual Nerd app**.

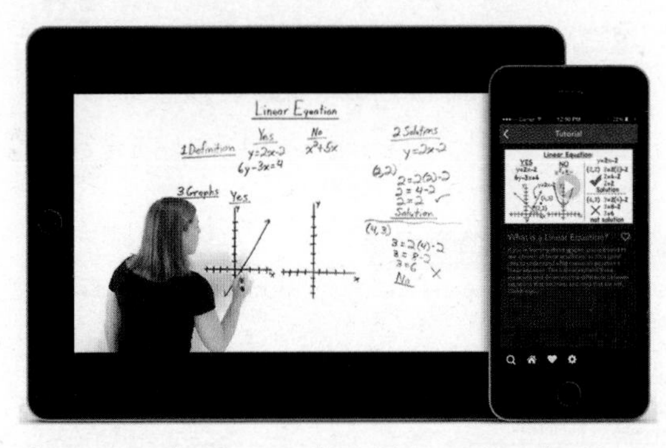

Students can also access the videos using the **BouncePages app** to scan exercise pages marked with this icon. Students can download both apps for free in their mobile devices' app store.

## Differentiated Intervention

**I** = Intervention **O** = On-Level **A** = Advanced

### Reteach to Build Understanding I

Provides scaffolded reteaching for the key lesson concepts.

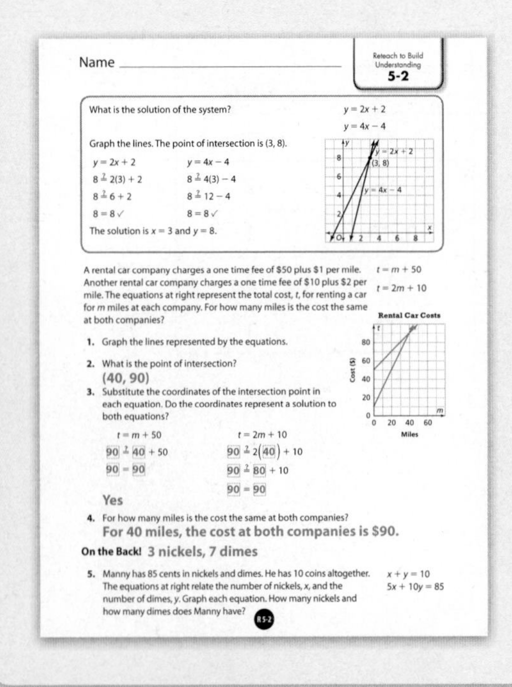

Name ______________________ Reteach to Build Understanding 5-2

What is the solution of the system? $y = 2x + 2$, $y = 4x - 4$

Graph the lines. The point of intersection is (3, 8).

| $y = 2x + 2$ | $y = 4x - 4$ |
|---|---|
| $8 \stackrel{?}{=} 2(3) + 2$ | $8 \stackrel{?}{=} 4(3) - 4$ |
| $8 \stackrel{?}{=} 6 + 2$ | $8 \stackrel{?}{=} 12 - 4$ |
| $8 = 8$ ✓ | $8 = 8$ ✓ |

The solution is $x = 3$ and $y = 8$.

A rental car company charges a one time fee of $50 plus $1 per mile. Another rental car company charges a one time fee of $10 plus $2 per mile. The equations at right represent the total cost, *t*, for renting a car for *m* miles at each company. For how many miles is the cost the same at both companies? $t = m + 50$, $t = 2m + 10$

Rental Car Costs

1. Graph the lines represented by the equations.
2. What is the point of intersection?
   **(40, 90)**
3. Substitute the coordinates of the intersection point in each equation. Do the coordinates represent a solution to both equations?

| $t = m + 50$ | $t = 2m + 10$ |
|---|---|
| $90 \stackrel{?}{=} 40 + 50$ | $90 \stackrel{?}{=} 2(40) + 10$ |
| $90 = 90$ | $90 \stackrel{?}{=} 80 + 10$ |
| | $90 = 90$ |

   **Yes**
4. For how many miles is the cost the same at both companies?
   **For 40 miles, the cost at both companies is $90.**

**On the Back!** **3 nickels, 7 dimes**

5. Manny has 85 cents in nickels and dimes. He has 10 coins altogether. The equations at right relate the number of nickels, *x*, and the number of dimes, *y*. Graph each equation. How many nickels and how many dimes does Manny have? $x + y = 10$, $5x + 10y = 85$

R5-2

### Additional Vocabulary Support I O

Helps students develop and reinforce understanding of key terms and concepts.

Name ______________________ Additional Vocabulary Support 5-2

**Complete the vocabulary chart.**

| Word or Phrase | Definition | Example |
|---|---|---|
| slope | The slope of a line is the ratio of the vertical change to the horizontal change between two points that lie on a line in the coordinate plane. | **Sample answers: For the equation $y = 5x + 1$, the slope is 5. For the equation $y = -2x + 4$, the slope is −2.** |
| *y*-intercept | **Sample answer: The *y*-intercept is the value of the *y*-coordinate at the point at which the graph of an equation intersects the *y*-axis.** | For the equation $y = x + 2$, the *y*-intercept is 2. For the equation $y = 4x - 1$, the *y*-intercept is −1. |
| linear equation | A linear equation is an equation in two variables whose graph is a line. | **Sample answers: $y = -8x - 2$; $y = 5x + 3$** |
| system of linear equations | **Sample answer: A system of linear equations is formed by two or more linear equations that use the same variables.** | $y = 0.5x + 4$, $y = -x - 2$; $2x - 3y = 6$, $x + 5y = -3$ |
| solution of a system of linear equations | The solution of a system of linear equations is any ordered pair that makes all equations in the system true. | **Sample answer: The solution to the system $y = x$, $y = -x$ is $x = 0$ and $y = 0$, or the point (0, 0).** |
| point of intersection | **Sample answer: The point of intersection of two lines is the point at which the two lines intersect, or cross, in the coordinate plane.** | The lines $y = 3x + 5$ and $y = 2x + 4$ intersect at the point (−1, 2). The lines $x + 4y = 8$ and $3x + 4y = 0$ intersect at the point (−4, 3). |

V5-2

### Build Mathematical Literacy I O

Provides support for struggling readers to build mathematical literacy.

Name ______________________ Build Mathematical Literacy 5-2

**Read the problem below. Then answer the questions to help you understand the problem.**

At Family Fun Park, admission is free, but ride tickets cost $6 each and parking costs $10. At Paradise Rides, the admission and parking is free, but the ride tickets cost $8 each. The total cost, *c*, to visit a theme park and go on *r* rides can be represented by a system of equations. Write and graph the system of equations. For how many rides will the cost at both parks be the same?

Theme Park Costs

1. Circle the important information about the cost of Family Fun Park.
   **Check students' work.**
2. Underline the important information about the cost of Paradise Rides.
   **Check students' work.**
3. What needs to be included in the answer to this problem?
   **The system of equations, a graph of the system of equations, and if applicable, the number of rides at each park that will cost the participant the same amount of money**
4. What will each equation in the system of equations represent?
   **One equation will represent the cost of attending Family Fun Park and the other will represent the cost of attending Paradise Rides.**
5. How is the cost of attending Family Fun Park similar to the cost of attending Paradise Rides?
   **The total cost of attending both theme parks depends on how many rides you go on.**
6. How is the cost of attending the theme parks different?
   **The total cost of only Family Fun Park includes parking.**

M5-2

Go Online

  Practice
 Worksheets
 Math Tools
 Math Games

# Additional Practice

You may opt to have students complete the automatically scored Additional Practice items online.

### Item Analysis

| Example | Items | DOK |
|---|---|---|
| 1 | 2 | 1 |
| | 3, 5, 9 | 2 |
| | 8 | 3 |
| 2 | 4, 7 | 2 |
| 3 | 1 | 1 |
| | 6 | 2 |

**Interactive Practice** is available online.

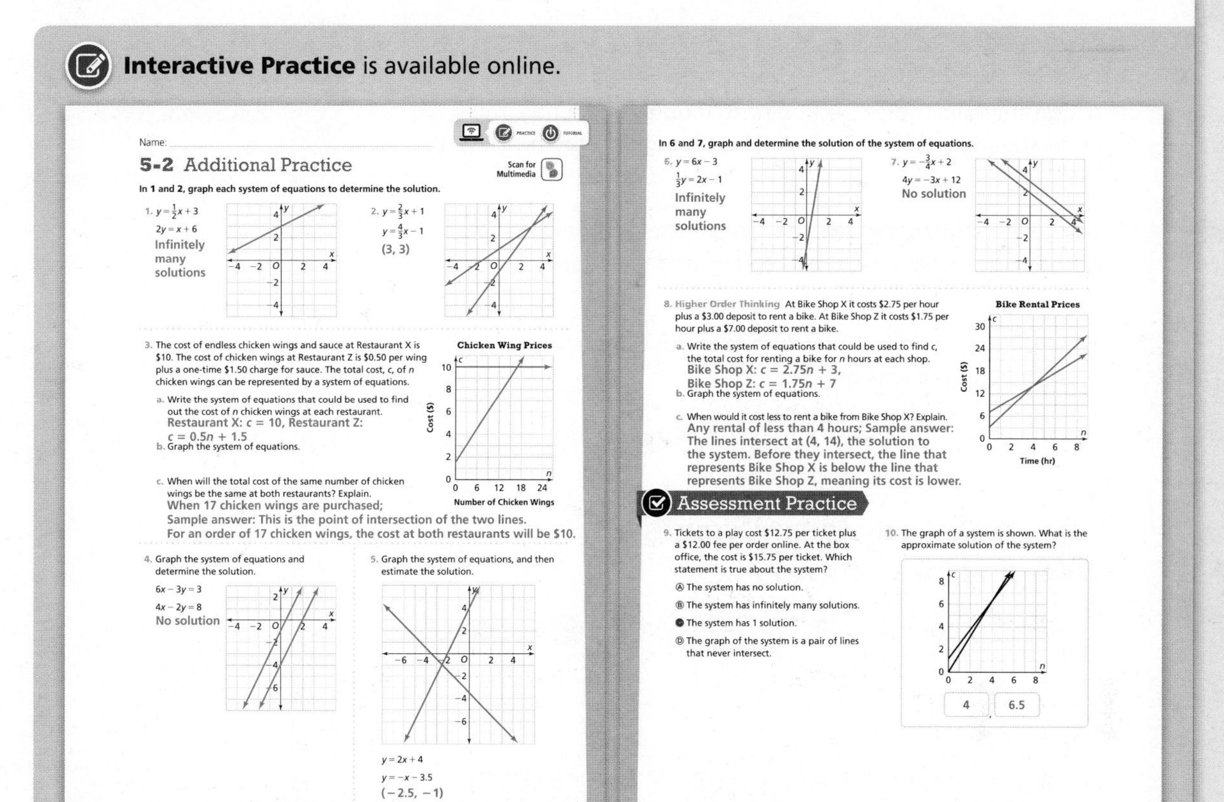

Name:

## 5-2 Additional Practice

Scan for Multimedia

In **1** and **2**, graph each system of equations to determine the solution.

1. $y = \frac{1}{2}x + 3$
   $2y = x + 6$
   Infinitely many solutions

2. $y = \frac{2}{3}x + 1$
   $y = \frac{4}{3}x - 1$
   (3, 3)

3. The cost of endless chicken wings and sauce at Restaurant X is \$10. The cost of chicken wings at Restaurant Z is \$0.50 per wing plus a one-time \$1.50 charge for sauce. The total cost, $c$, of $n$ chicken wings can be represented by a system of equations.
   a. Write the system of equations that could be used to find out the cost of $n$ chicken wings at each restaurant.
   Restaurant X: $c = 10$, Restaurant Z: $c = 0.5n + 1.5$
   b. Graph the system of equations.
   c. When will the total cost of the same number of chicken wings be the same at both restaurants? Explain.
   When 17 chicken wings are purchased; Sample answer: This is the point of intersection of the two lines. For an order of 17 chicken wings, the cost at both restaurants will be \$10.



4. Graph the system of equations and determine the solution.
   $6x - 3y = 3$
   $4x - 2y = 8$
   No solution

5. Graph the system of equations, and then estimate the solution.
   $y = 2x + 4$
   $y = -x - 3.5$
   $(-2.5, -1)$

5-2 Solve Systems by Graphing 63

In **6** and **7**, graph and determine the solution of the system of equations.

6. $y = 6x - 3$
   $\frac{1}{3}y = 2x - 1$
   Infinitely many solutions

7. $y = -\frac{3}{4}x + 2$
   $4y = -3x + 12$
   No solution

8. Higher Order Thinking At Bike Shop X it costs \$2.75 per hour plus a \$3.00 deposit to rent a bike. At Bike Shop Z it costs \$1.75 per hour plus a \$7.00 deposit to rent a bike.
   a. Write the system of equations that could be used to find $c$, the total cost for renting a bike for $n$ hours at each shop.
   Bike Shop X: $c = 2.75n + 3$,
   Bike Shop Z: $c = 1.75n + 7$
   b. Graph the system of equations.
   c. When would it cost less to rent a bike from Bike Shop X? Explain.
   Any rental of less than 4 hours; Sample answer: The lines intersect at (4, 14), the solution to the system. Before they intersect, the line that represents Bike Shop X is below the line that represents Bike Shop Z, meaning its cost is lower.



Assessment Practice

9. Tickets to a play cost \$12.75 per ticket plus a \$12.00 fee per order online. At the box office, the cost is \$15.75 per ticket. Which statement is true about the system?
   Ⓐ The system has no solution.
   Ⓑ The system has infinitely many solutions.
   ● The system has 1 solution.
   Ⓓ The graph of the system is a pair of lines that never intersect.

10. The graph of a system is shown. What is the approximate solution of the system?
    4, 6.5

64 5-2 Solve Systems by Graphing

# Differentiated Intervention

I = Intervention O = On-Level A = Advanced

## Enrichment O A

Presents engaging problems and activities that extend the lesson concepts.

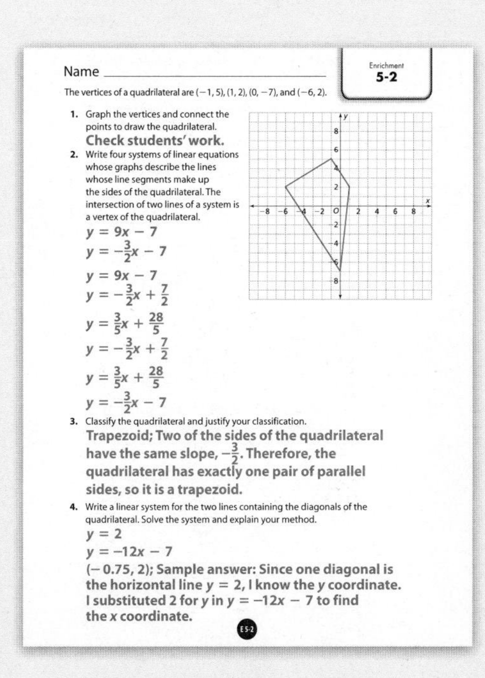

Name

Enrichment 5-2

The vertices of a quadrilateral are $(-1, 5)$, $(1, 2)$, $(0, -7)$, and $(-6, 2)$.

1. Graph the vertices and connect the points to draw the quadrilateral.
   Check students' work.
2. Write four systems of linear equations whose graphs describe the lines whose line segments make up the sides of the quadrilateral. The intersection of two lines of a system is a vertex of the quadrilateral.
   $y = 9x - 7$
   $y = -\frac{3}{2}x - 7$
   $y = 9x - 7$
   $y = -\frac{3}{2}x + \frac{7}{2}$
   $y = \frac{3}{5}x + \frac{28}{5}$
   $y = -\frac{3}{2}x + \frac{7}{2}$
   $y = \frac{3}{5}x + \frac{28}{5}$
   $y = -\frac{3}{2}x - 7$
3. Classify the quadrilateral and justify your classification.
   Trapezoid; Two of the sides of the quadrilateral have the same slope, $-\frac{3}{2}$. Therefore, the quadrilateral has exactly one pair of parallel sides, so it is a trapezoid.
4. Write a linear system for the two lines containing the diagonals of the quadrilateral. Solve the system and explain your method.
   $y = 2$
   $y = -12x - 7$
   $(-0.75, 2)$; Sample answer: Since one diagonal is the horizontal line $y = 2$, I know the $y$ coordinate. I substituted 2 for $y$ in $y = -12x - 7$ to find the $x$ coordinate.

E5-2

## Math Tools and Games I O A

Offers additional activities and games to build understanding and fluency.

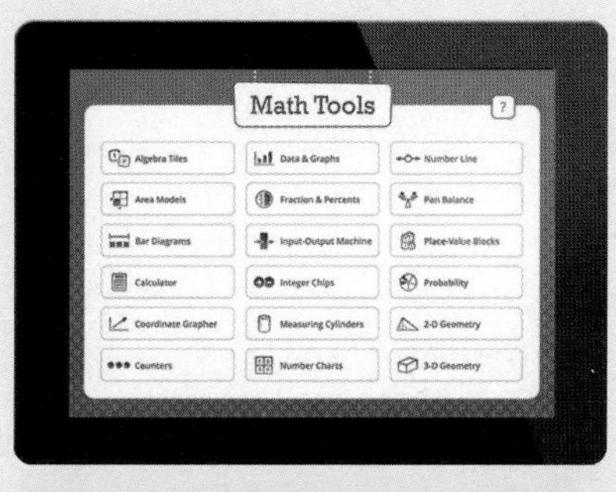


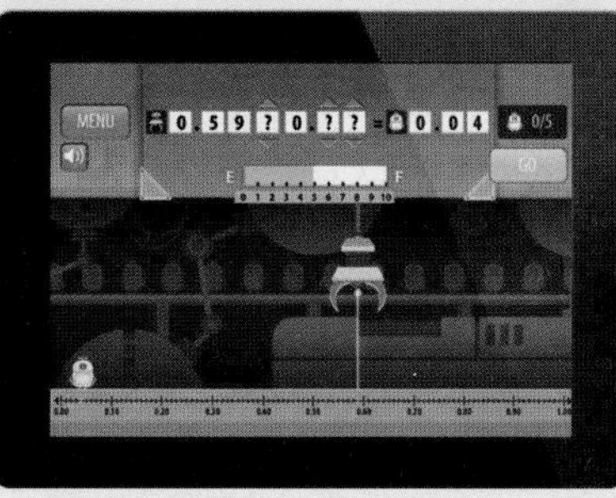


## Pick a Project and STEM Project I O A

Provides an additional opportunity for students to demonstrate understanding of key mathematical concepts.

# MID-TOPIC CHECKPOINT

Go Online

Assess

Assign the Mid-Topic Checkpoint to monitor students' understandings of concepts and skills taught in the first lessons in this topic.

Encourage students to use the self-assessment form at the bottom of the page to describe their level of understanding.

You may opt to have students take the automatically scored Mid-Topic Assessment online.

Use students' results to adjust instruction as needed.

## Item Analysis for Diagnosis and Intervention

| Item | DOK | MDIS | Lesson | Standard |
|---|---|---|---|---|
| 1 | 2 | K33 | 5-1 | 8.EE.C.8b |
| 2 | 1 | K33 | 5-1 | 8.EE.C.8b |
| 3 | 2 | K34 | 5-2 | 8.EE.C.8a |
| 4 | 2 | K33 | 5-1 | 8.EE.C.8a |
| 5 | 2 | K34 | 5-2 | 8.EE.C.8a, 8.EE.C.8c |
| 6 | 2 | K33 | 5-1 | 8.EE.C.8b |

## Scoring Guide

| Score | Recommendations |
|---|---|
| Greater Than 85% | Assign the corresponding MDIS for items answered incorrectly. Use Enrichment activities with the student. |
| 70%–85% | Assign the corresponding MDIS for items answered incorrectly. You may also assign Reteach to Build Understanding and Virtual Nerd Video assets for the lessons correlated to the items the student answered incorrectly. |
| Less Than 70% | Assign the corresponding MDIS for items answered incorrectly. Assign appropriate intervention lessons available online. You may also assign Reteach to Build Understanding, Additional Vocabulary Support, Build Mathematical Literacy, and Virtual Nerd Video assets for the lessons correlated to the items the student answered incorrectly. |

Available Online

Name:

MID-TOPIC CHECKPOINT — TOPIC 5

1. **Vocabulary** How can you determine the number of solutions of a system by looking at the equations? *Lesson 5-1*
   Sample answer: Identify the slope and $y$-intercept of each equation in the system. If the slopes are different, the system has one solution. If the slopes are the same and the $y$-intercepts are different, the system has no solution. If the slopes are the same and the $y$-intercepts are the same, the system has infinitely many solutions.
2. How many solutions does the system of equations have? Explain. *Lesson 5-1*
   $2x - 9y = -5$
   $4x - 6y = 2$
   One solution; Sample answer: The equations have different slopes, so there is one solution.
3. Graph the system of equations and find the solution. *Lesson 5-2*
   $y = 2x - 1$
   $y = \frac{1}{2}x + 2$
   (2, 3)

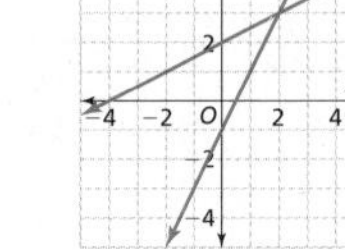

4. One equation in a system is $y = -3x + 7$. Which equation gives the system no solution? *Lesson 5-1*
   Ⓐ $y = -3x + 7$
   Ⓑ $y = 3x + 5$
   ● $y = -3x + 5$
   Ⓓ $y = \frac{1}{3}x - 7$
5. Finn bought 12 movie tickets. Student tickets cost \$4, and adult tickets cost \$8. Finn spent a total of \$60. Write and graph a system of equations to find the number of student and adult tickets Finn bought. *Lesson 5-2*
   $x + y = 12$, or $y = -x + 12$, and $4x + 8y = 60$, or $y = -0.5x + 7.5$, student tickets: 9; adult tickets: 3

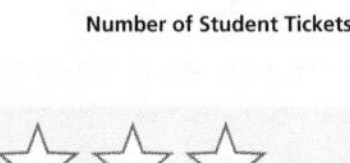

Types of Movie Tickets



6. What value of $m$ gives the system infinitely many solutions? *Lesson 5-1*
   $-x + 4y = 32$
   $y = mx + 8$
   $m = \frac{1}{4}$

How well did you do on the mid-topic checkpoint? Fill in the stars.

Topic 5 Analyze and Solve Systems of Linear Equations 279

### Mid-Topic Assessment Master

Name

Topic 5 Mid-Topic Assessment

1. Vocabulary How can you tell there is no solution of a system of equations by looking at the equations or the graph? Explain.
   **Sample answer: The equations would have the same slope but different $y$-intercepts. The graph of the system would show parallel lines.**
2. How many solutions does this system of equations have? Explain.
   $y = -2x + 2$
   $2y + 4x = 4$
   **Infinitely many solutions; Sample answer: The lines have the same slope, −2, and $y$-intercept, 2. They are the same line.**
3. Graph the system of equations and write the solution.
   $y = -3 + \frac{1}{2}x$
   $3x + 2y = 2$
   **(2, −2)**

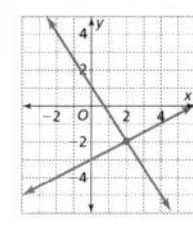

4. The first equation in a system is $5x + 2y = -4$. Which equation gives a system with no solution?
   Ⓐ $y = 2x + 6$
   Ⓑ $y = \frac{1}{2}x - 2$
   Ⓒ $y = 2x + 7$
   ● $y = -\frac{5}{2}x - 3$
5. Mrs. Hernandez bought 18 pens for her class. Highlighters cost \$3 each, and gel pens cost \$2.50 each. She spent a total of \$50. Write and graph a system of equations to find the number of highlighters and gel pens Mrs. Hernandez bought.
   **$x + y = 18$ and $3x + 2.5y = 50$; 10 highlighters and 8 gel pens**

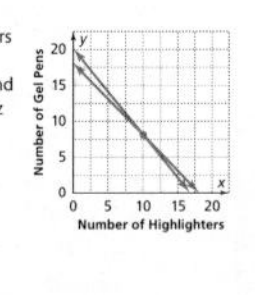



6. What value of $m$ gives the system infinitely many solutions?
   $-x + 2y = 16$
   $y = mx + 8$
   $m = \frac{1}{2}$

Mid-Topic Assessment 1 of 1

# MID-TOPIC PERFORMANCE TASK

Go Online

Assess

Assess students' ability to apply the concepts and skills in the first part of the topic using the Mid-Topic Performance Task, found in the Student's Edition or online.

## Item Analysis for Diagnosis and Intervention

| Part | DOK | MDIS | Lesson | Standard |
|---|---|---|---|---|
| A | 2 | K33, K34 | 5-2 | 8.EE.C.8a |
| B | 2 | K50, K52 | 5-1 | 8.EE.C.8b |
| C | 2 | K50, K52 | 5-2 | 8.EE.C.8a |

## Scoring Rubric

| Part | Points | Mid-Topic Performance Task |
|---|---|---|
| A | 2 | Correct solution and explanation. |
| | 1 | Correct solution. |
| B | 2 | Correct solution and explanation. |
| | 1 | Correct solution. |
| C | 2 | Correct solution and explanation. |
| | 1 | Correct solution. |

## Scoring Guide

| Score | Recommendations |
|---|---|
| Greater Than 85% | Assign the corresponding MDIS for items answered incorrectly. Use Enrichment activities with the student. |
| 70%–85% | Assign the corresponding MDIS for items answered incorrectly. You may also assign Reteach to Build Understanding and Virtual Nerd Video assets for the lessons correlated to the items the student answered incorrectly. |
| Less Than 70% | Assign the corresponding MDIS for items answered incorrectly. Assign appropriate intervention lessons available online. You may also assign Reteach to Build Understanding, Additional Vocabulary Support, Build Mathematical Literacy, and Virtual Nerd Video assets for the lessons correlated to the items the student answered incorrectly. |

Available Online

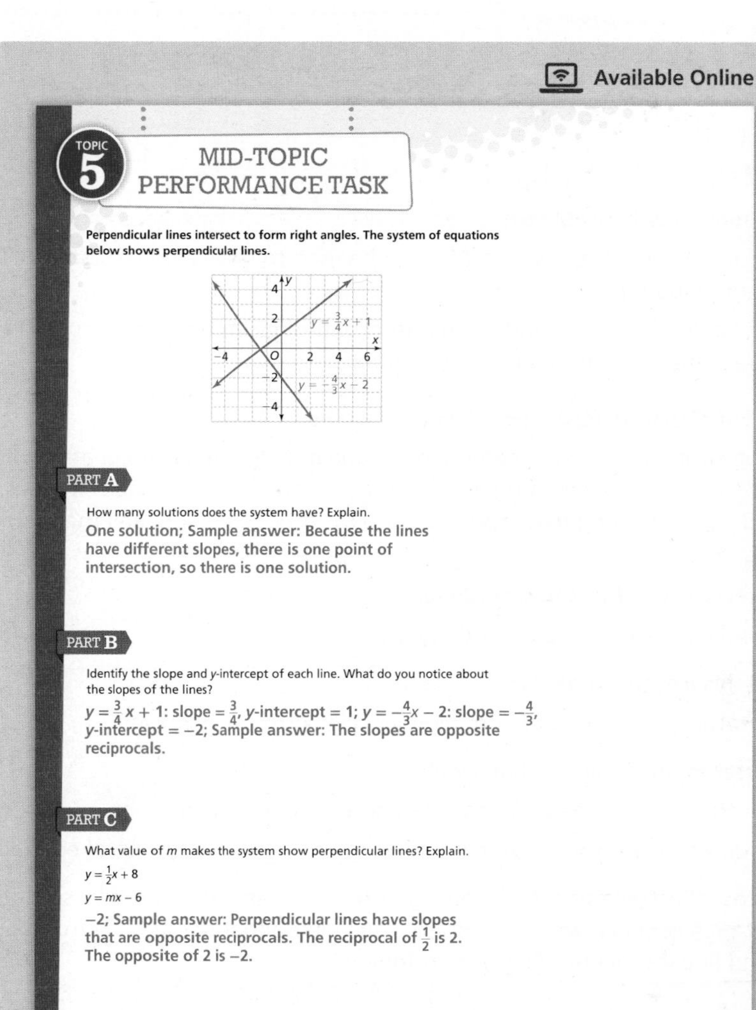

TOPIC 5 MID-TOPIC PERFORMANCE TASK

Perpendicular lines intersect to form right angles. The system of equations below shows perpendicular lines.



PART A

How many solutions does the system have? Explain.

One solution; Sample answer: Because the lines have different slopes, there is one point of intersection, so there is one solution.

PART B

Identify the slope and y-intercept of each line. What do you notice about the slopes of the lines?

$y = \frac{3}{4}x + 1$: slope $= \frac{3}{4}$, y-intercept $= 1$; $y = -\frac{4}{3}x - 2$: slope $= -\frac{4}{3}$, y-intercept $= -2$; Sample answer: The slopes are opposite reciprocals.

PART C

What value of $m$ makes the system show perpendicular lines? Explain.

$y = \frac{1}{2}x + 8$

$y = mx - 6$

$-2$; Sample answer: Perpendicular lines have slopes that are opposite reciprocals. The reciprocal of $\frac{1}{2}$ is 2. The opposite of 2 is $-2$.

280 Topic 5 Analyze and Solve Systems of Linear Equations

Go Online

Activity

Lesson
# 5-3 Solving Systems by Substitution

## Lesson Overview

FOCUS

### Mathematics Objective

**Students will be able to:**

✔ understand how substitution can be used to solve a linear system of equations.

✔ apply this understanding to interpret the results with one solution, no solutions, or infinitely many solutions.

### Essential Understanding

Substitution is a useful method for solving a system of linear equations. It is accomplished by rewriting one of the equations for one variable in terms of the other, substituting that expression into the other equation, and then solving.

COHERENCE

**Previously in this topic, students:**

- solved systems of equations by graphing.

**In this lesson, students:**

- solve systems of equations algebraically, using substitution.

**Later in this topic, students will:**

- solve systems of equations algebraically, using elimination.
- determine which method is easiest to use to solve a system of equations.

**Cross-Cluster Connection** Solving systems of linear equations by substitution (8.EE.3) connects to work with solving linear equations (8.EE.2) from Topic 2 and linear functions (8.F.2) from Topic 3.

RIGOR

This lesson emphasizes a blend of **conceptual understanding** and **procedural skill**.

- Students extend their prior understanding of solving systems of equations by graphing to solve them algebraically by substitution.
- Students practice solving systems of equations by substitution. They isolate a variable, substitute for each occurrence of the variable, then check the solution in both equations.

## Language Support

### Lesson Language Objective

Explain how to solve systems of equations by using substitution.

Additional resources are available in the **Language Support Handbook**.

## Math Anytime

### Today's Challenge

Use the Topic 5 problems any time during this topic.

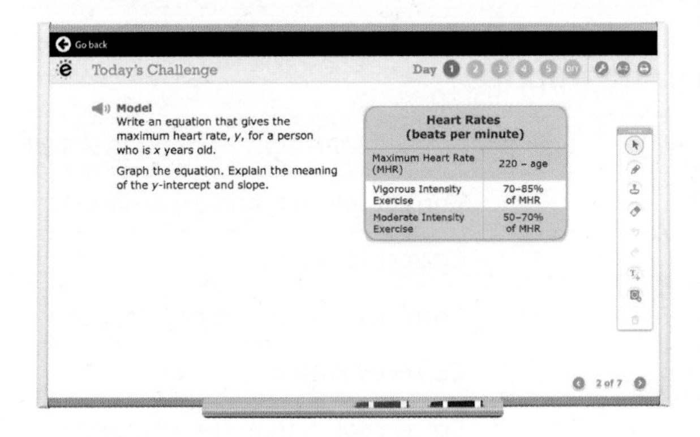


## Mathematics Overview | Common Core Standards

### Content Standards

In this lesson, you will focus on **8.EE.C.8b** and **8.EE.C.8c**.

- **8.EE.C.8b** Solve systems of two linear equations in two variables algebraically, and estimate solutions by graphing the equations. Solve simple cases by inspection.
- **8.EE.C.8c** Solve real-world and mathematical problems leading to two linear equations in two variables.

### Mathematical Practice Standards

**MP.2 Reason Abstractly and Quantitatively**
Students use algebra to solve for a variable, substitute for that variable, and then simplify the resulting equation to find a solution. When a numerical statement results, they show whether the system has no solution or infinitely many solutions.

**MP.6 Attend to Precision**
Students follow and communicate the specific steps needed to solve a system of equations by substitution. They will recognize that solving by substitution yields an exact solution, while solving by graphing may yield an approximate solution in some cases.

# STEP 1 | Problem-Based Learning

15-20 min

Go Online

Activity

## Explain It! Formative Assessment

**Purpose** Students interpret a point of intersection in a given context and connect it to solving a system of equations in the Visual Learning Bridge.

### ETP Before — WHOLE CLASS

**1 Introduce the Problem**

Provide graph paper, as needed.

**2 Check for Understanding of the Problem**

Engage students with the problem by asking: Have you ever taken a taxi ride? How do taxi fares work?

### ETP During — SMALL GROUP

**3 Observe Students at Work**

Observe students while they work, noting the strategies that students use to approach the problem.

- **How do students evaluate Jackson's choice?** Students consider the lines representing each cab company and identify intervals where a given cab company is the best choice.
- **How do students relate the point of intersection to the context?** Students identify that the lines intersect at a point representing about 4 miles traveled, which means that either company could be chosen for the same price for a trip of that distance. If needed, ask What does the point of intersection mean in the context of the problem?

**Early Finishers**

How would the problem change if the initial cost for On Time Cabs was increased and the point of intersection was (5, 12)? [Sample answer: Speedy Cab Co. would be the best choice for a 4-mile trip.]

### ETP After — WHOLE CLASS

**4 Discuss Solution Strategies and Key Ideas**

Have students analyze and discuss Jackson's statement. They may note that while the line representing On Time Cabs has a lesser slope, the line representing Speedy Cab Co. has a lesser $y$-intercept (a lower initial cost for riding). Because of this, Speedy Cab Co. will be less expensive for certain distances. Have students discuss where they estimate the point of intersection is and what it means; the point of intersection is at about (4, 10) and it means that a roughly 4-mile ride will cost Jackson about $10 using either company.

**5 Consider Instructional Implications**

When presenting Example 1, discuss with students how they could use the graph to estimate the solution to the system in the Explain It, but could not find the exact solution using the graph. Discuss how algebraic methods can be used to find solutions to systems of equations with non-integer solutions.

## Analyze Student Work

**Explain It!** Activity is available online.

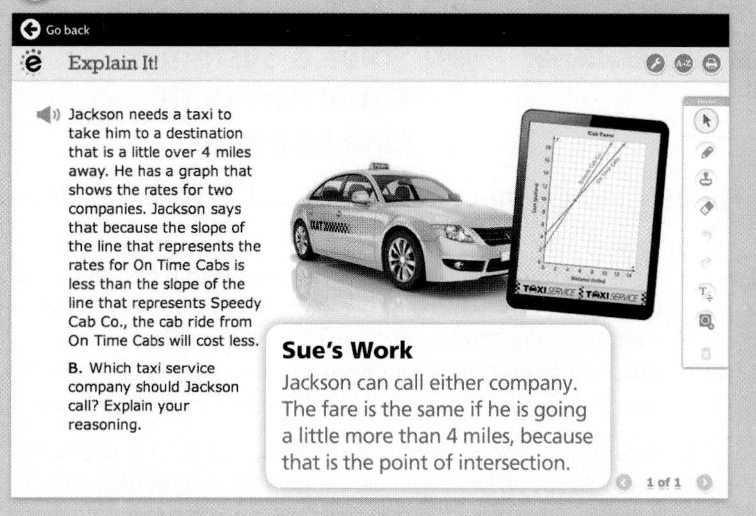


**Sue** bases her recommendation only on the point of intersection.

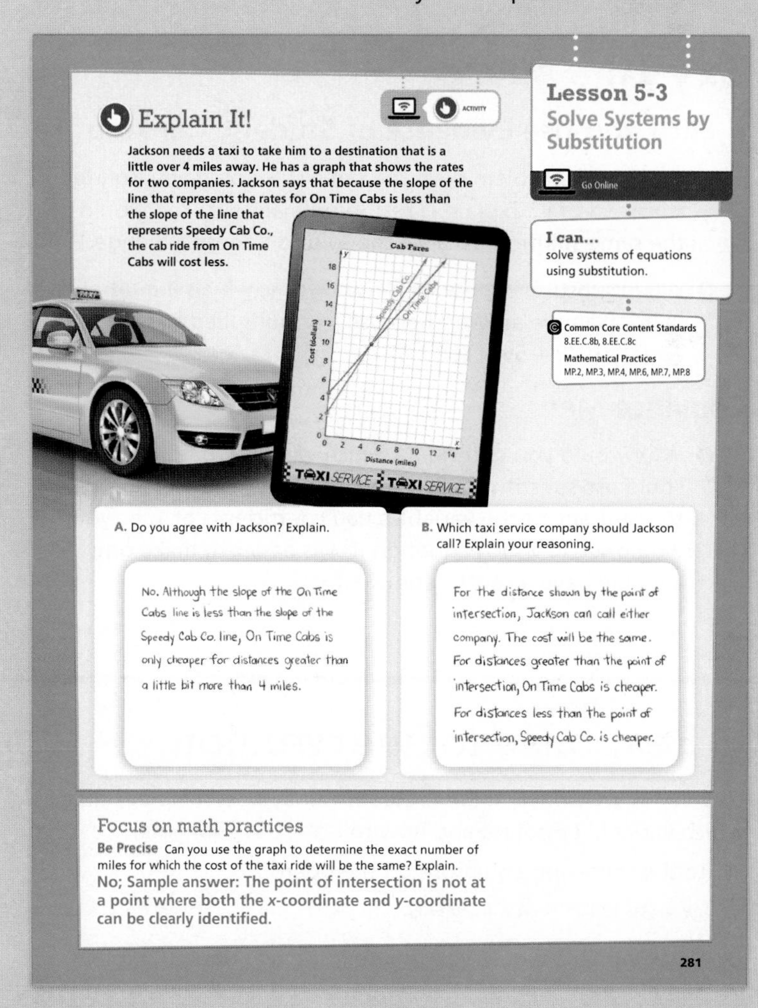


**Jimmy** gives different recommendations based on the number of miles Jackson wants to go.

EXPLAIN

Go Online

Visual Learning

Assess

# STEP 2 | Visual Learning

## ETP Establish Mathematics Goals to Focus Learning

Engage students in a discussion about the ***Essential Question***. Make sure they understand that using substitution to solve a system of equations is a useful method when it is easy to isolate one variable in one or both of the equations.

## EXAMPLE 1  Use Substitution to Solve a System of Equations with One Solution

### ETP Use and Connect Mathematical Representations

**Q:** Look at Step 1. Explain where each equation comes from. [Sample answer: The first equation shows that Gemma sold 800 tickets, which consisted of $c$ children's tickets and $a$ adult tickets. The second equation shows that Gemma collected a total of \$7,680 from $c$ children's tickets, which cost \$7.50 each, and $a$ adult tickets, which cost \$13.50 each.]

**Q:** What if you wanted to substitute the value for $a$ in terms of $c$ in the equation? What value for $a$ would you use? Explain. [Sample answer: You would solve $c + a = 800$ to get $a = 800 - c$.]

##  Try It!  Formative Assessment

### ETP Elicit and Use Evidence of Student Thinking

**Q:** Would the problem have the same solution if you isolated $x$ instead of $y$? Explain. [Yes; Sample answer: You would get the same solution because the solution doesn't change.]

**Q:** When substituting the expression for $y$, why is it multiplied by 5? [Sample answer: Because $y$ is multiplied by 5 in the equation $2x + 5y = 160$.]

### Convince Me!

**Q:** How would you determine which variable to isolate so you could use substitution? [Sample answer: You would look to see if any of the variables had coefficients of 1, or you would see in which equation it was easier to make one variable have a coefficient of 1.]

**Visual Learning Animation Plus** is available online.

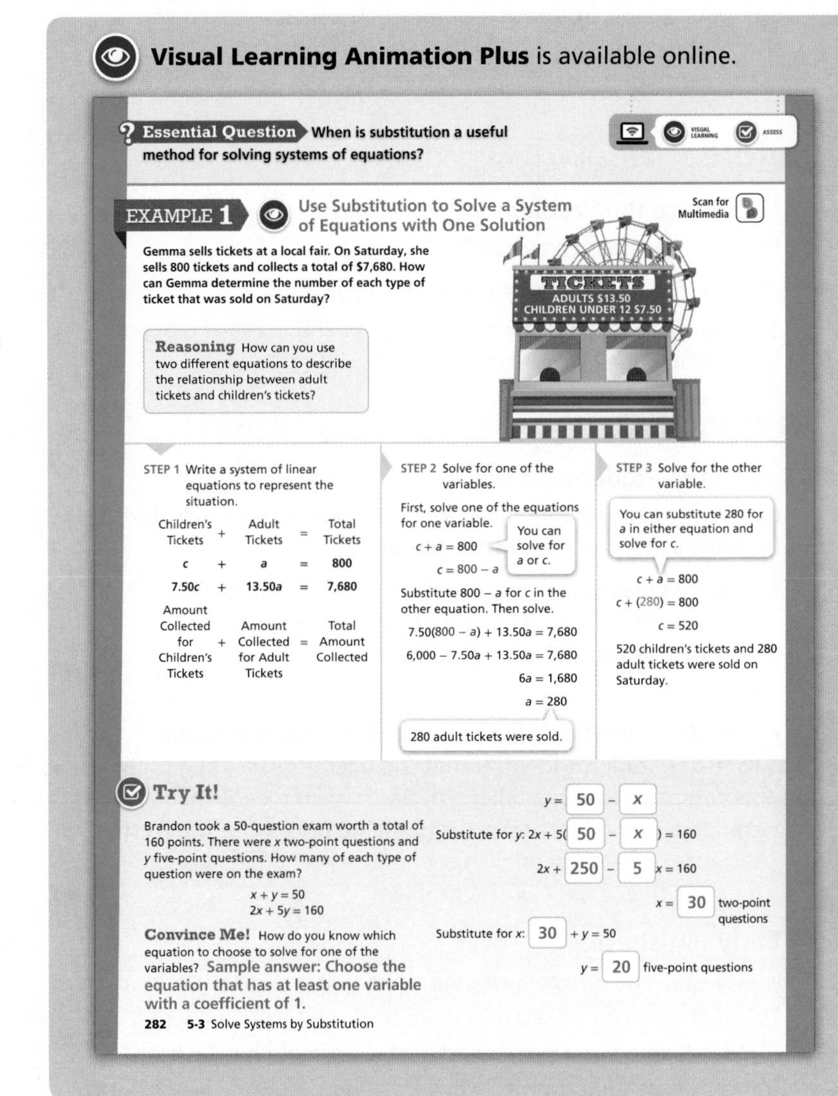

Essential Question When is substitution a useful method for solving systems of equations?

EXAMPLE 1 Use Substitution to Solve a System of Equations with One Solution

Scan for Multimedia

Gemma sells tickets at a local fair. On Saturday, she sells 800 tickets and collects a total of \$7,680. How can Gemma determine the number of each type of ticket that was sold on Saturday?



**Reasoning** How can you use two different equations to describe the relationship between adult tickets and children's tickets?

STEP 1 Write a system of linear equations to represent the situation.

| Children's Tickets | + | Adult Tickets | = | Total Tickets |
|---|---|---|---|---|
| $c$ | + | $a$ | = | 800 |
| $7.50c$ | + | $13.50a$ | = | 7,680 |
| Amount Collected for Children's Tickets | + | Amount Collected for Adult Tickets | = | Total Amount Collected |

STEP 2 Solve for one of the variables.

First, solve one of the equations for one variable.

$c + a = 800$

$c = 800 - a$

You can solve for $a$ or $c$.

Substitute $800 - a$ for $c$ in the other equation. Then solve.

$7.50(800 - a) + 13.50a = 7,680$

$6,000 - 7.50a + 13.50a = 7,680$

$6a = 1,680$

$a = 280$

280 adult tickets were sold.

STEP 3 Solve for the other variable.

You can substitute 280 for $a$ in either equation and solve for $c$.

$c + a = 800$

$c + (280) = 800$

$c = 520$

520 children's tickets and 280 adult tickets were sold on Saturday.

**Try It!**

Brandon took a 50-question exam worth a total of 160 points. There were $x$ two-point questions and $y$ five-point questions. How many of each type of question were on the exam?

$x + y = 50$

$2x + 5y = 160$

$y =$ 50 $-$ $x$

Substitute for $y$: $2x + 5($ 50 $-$ $x$ $) = 160$

$2x +$ 250 $-$ 5 $x = 160$

$x =$ 30 two-point questions

Substitute for $x$: 30 $+ y = 50$

$y =$ 20 five-point questions

**Convince Me!** How do you know which equation to choose to solve for one of the variables? Sample answer: Choose the equation that has at least one variable with a coefficient of 1.

282 5-3 Solve Systems by Substitution

Students can access the ***Visual Learning Animation Plus*** by using the **BouncePages app** to scan this page. Students can download the app for free in their mobile devices' app store.

## Response to Intervention

**USE WITH EXAMPLE 1** Some students may need help deciding which variable to isolate and how to isolate the variable.

Write the following equations on the board:

$x + 3y = 11 \quad 4x - 2y = 6$

**Q:** Which variable would you isolate in each equation? Explain. [Sample answer: In the first, you would isolate $x$ because it already has a coefficient of 1. In the second equation, you would isolate $y$ because then you would not have to work with fractions.]

**Q:** Solve each equation for that variable. [$x = -3y + 11$, $y = 2x - 3$]

##  Enrichment

**USE WITH EXAMPLE 1** Challenge advanced students to solve this problem: Mario has \$7.50 in dimes and quarters. The total number of coins is 48. How many dimes and quarters does he have?

**Q:** What information do you need to solve this problem that is not given in the question? [Sample answer: the values of dimes and quarters]

**Q:** Write a system of equations to model the situation. [$0.10d + 0.25q = 7.50$ or $10d + 25q = 750$; $d + q = 48$]

**Q:** Use substitution to solve. How many dimes and quarters does Mario have? [Mario has 30 dimes and 18 quarters.]

Go Online

Activity

Assess

# EXAMPLE 2  Use Substitution to Solve a System with No Solution

## ETP Pose Purposeful Questions

**Q:** Since both equations are set equal to *y*, what would you do first? [Sample answer: You would set up an equation using the two expressions that are equal to *y*.]

**Q:** What clues do you have that this will be a false statement? [Sample answer: The slopes are the same but the *y*-intercepts are different.]

**Q:** What is the relationship of the two lines made from the equations? [Sample answer: They are parallel.]

# EXAMPLE 3  Use Substitution to Solve a System with Infinitely Many Solutions

## ETP Pose Purposeful Questions

**Q:** What happened as a result of the substitution in Step 2? [Sample answer: The result was a true numerical statement with no variables.]

**Q:** A system with an infinite number of solutions is made up of equivalent equations. Show that this is true in Example 3. [Sample answer: If you multiply the first equation by −3, both equations are $3x + 6y = 254.73$]

#  Try It!  Formative Assessment

##  Elicit and Use Evidence of Student Thinking

**Q:** For Part a, if you solve both equations for the same variable, what does the result tell you? [Sample answer: If you solve for *y*, the slopes are the same but the *y*-intercepts are different, so the system has no solution.]

**Q:** For Part b, what statement do you end up with? Is it a true or false statement? [Sample answer: You end up with two numbers that are equal. It is a true statement.]

**Examples and Try Its!** are available online.

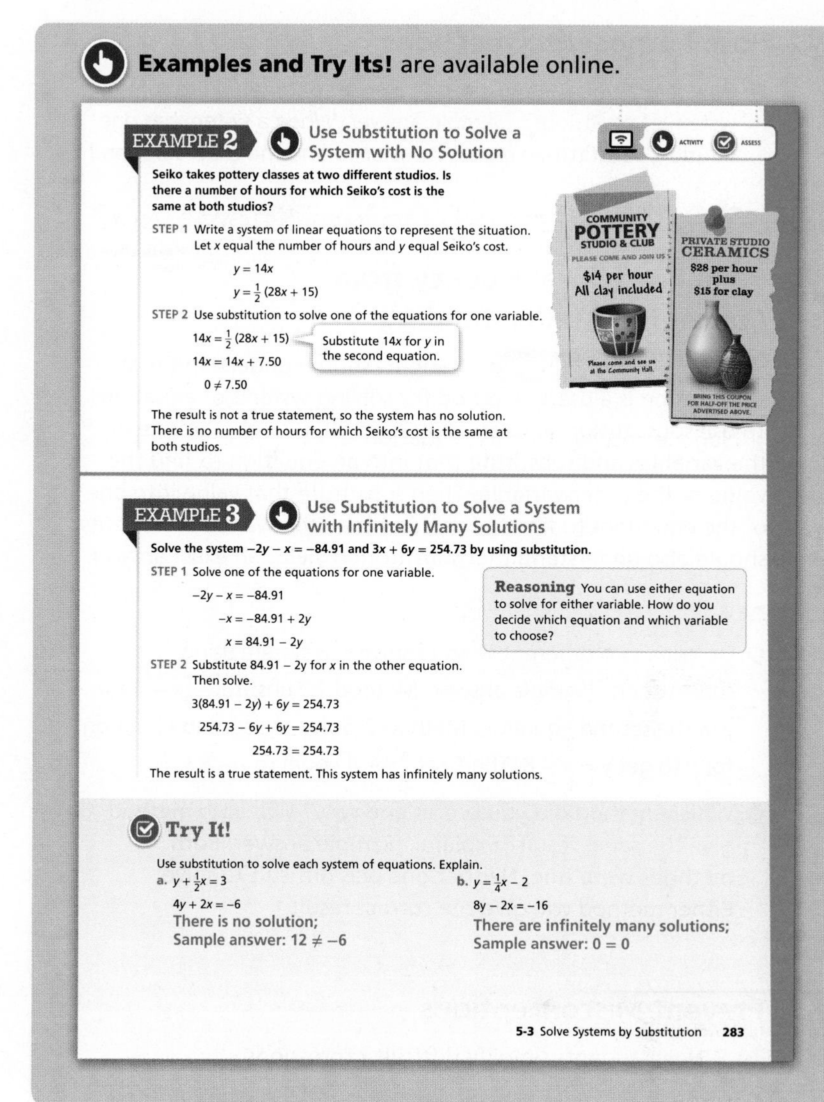

EXAMPLE 2 Use Substitution to Solve a System with No Solution

Seiko takes pottery classes at two different studios. Is there a number of hours for which Seiko's cost is the same at both studios?

STEP 1 Write a system of linear equations to represent the situation. Let *x* equal the number of hours and *y* equal Seiko's cost.

$y = 14x$

$y = \frac{1}{2}(28x + 15)$

STEP 2 Use substitution to solve one of the equations for one variable.

$14x = \frac{1}{2}(28x + 15)$

$14x = 14x + 7.50$

$0 \neq 7.50$

Substitute 14*x* for *y* in the second equation.

The result is not a true statement, so the system has no solution. There is no number of hours for which Seiko's cost is the same at both studios.



EXAMPLE 3 Use Substitution to Solve a System with Infinitely Many Solutions

Solve the system $-2y - x = -84.91$ and $3x + 6y = 254.73$ by using substitution.

STEP 1 Solve one of the equations for one variable.

$-2y - x = -84.91$

$-x = -84.91 + 2y$

$x = 84.91 - 2y$

**Reasoning** You can use either equation to solve for either variable. How do you decide which equation and which variable to choose?

STEP 2 Substitute $84.91 - 2y$ for *x* in the other equation. Then solve.

$3(84.91 - 2y) + 6y = 254.73$

$254.73 - 6y + 6y = 254.73$

$254.73 = 254.73$

The result is a true statement. This system has infinitely many solutions.

Try It!

Use substitution to solve each system of equations. Explain.

a. $y + \frac{1}{2}x = 3$
$4y + 2x = -6$
There is no solution;
Sample answer: $12 \neq -6$

b. $y = \frac{1}{4}x - 2$
$8y - 2x = -16$
There are infinitely many solutions;
Sample answer: $0 = 0$

5-3 Solve Systems by Substitution 283

ADDITIONAL EXAMPLES 

**For additional examples go online.**

# English Language Learners

**ENTERING** Complete Example 1.

Make sure students are familiar with the term substitution.

**Q:** What does the word substitution or substitute mean? Use it in a sentence. [Sample answer: It means to replace one thing with another. I will substitute honey for sugar on my oatmeal.]

**Q:** How is the word substitution or substituted used in Example 1? [Sample answer: An expression is substituted for a variable.]

**EMERGING** Complete Example 2.

Students may not be familiar with phrases like *throws pottery*, *community studio*, and *private studio*. Explain these terms, and make sure students know what it means when they pay a certain amount per hour. Then, have students summarize the problem in their own words.

**Q:** What is the same and what is different about the cost at each studio? [The hourly rate is the same. In one studio you pay for clay, and in the other you do not.]

**BRIDGING** Complete Example 1.

Give students the opportunity to explain how the system is solved using substitution. Listen for mathematically correct language.

**Q:** What does the word *substitution* mean? [Sample answer: Using one thing in place of another.]

**Q:** How does that relate to solving a system by substitution? [Sample answer: You substitute an expression in one variable for the other variable.]

# STEP 2 | Visual Learning *continued*

Go Online

Key Concept Assess Activity

## KEY CONCEPT

### ETP Pose Purposeful Questions

**Q:** Why might you use substitution instead of graphing to solve a system of equations? [Sample answer: When a system has one solution, substitution makes it easier to find the exact solution.]

## Do You Understand/Do You Know How?

### ETP Build Procedural Fluency from Conceptual Understanding

**Formative** Assessment

**Essential Question** Students should understand that substitution is a useful method for solving systems of equations. To use substitution, find an expression that is equal to one of the variables and substitute that into an equation to find the value of the other variable. Then substitute that value into one of the equations to find the value of the other variable. Students should also understand that substitution yields an exact answer.

**ITEM 4**

**Q:** Describe two different ways to solve this system using substitution. [Sample answer: Method 1: Substitute $\frac{1}{2}x + 4$ for $y$ in the second equation. Method 2: Solve the second equation for $y$ to get $y = x - 8$. Then, set $\frac{1}{2}x + 4$ equal to $x - 8$.]

**Q:** Which method did you prefer and why? Will each method give the same result? Explain. [Sample answer: Both methods were fine. Neither one was difficult to solve; Either method will give the correct result.]

Available Online

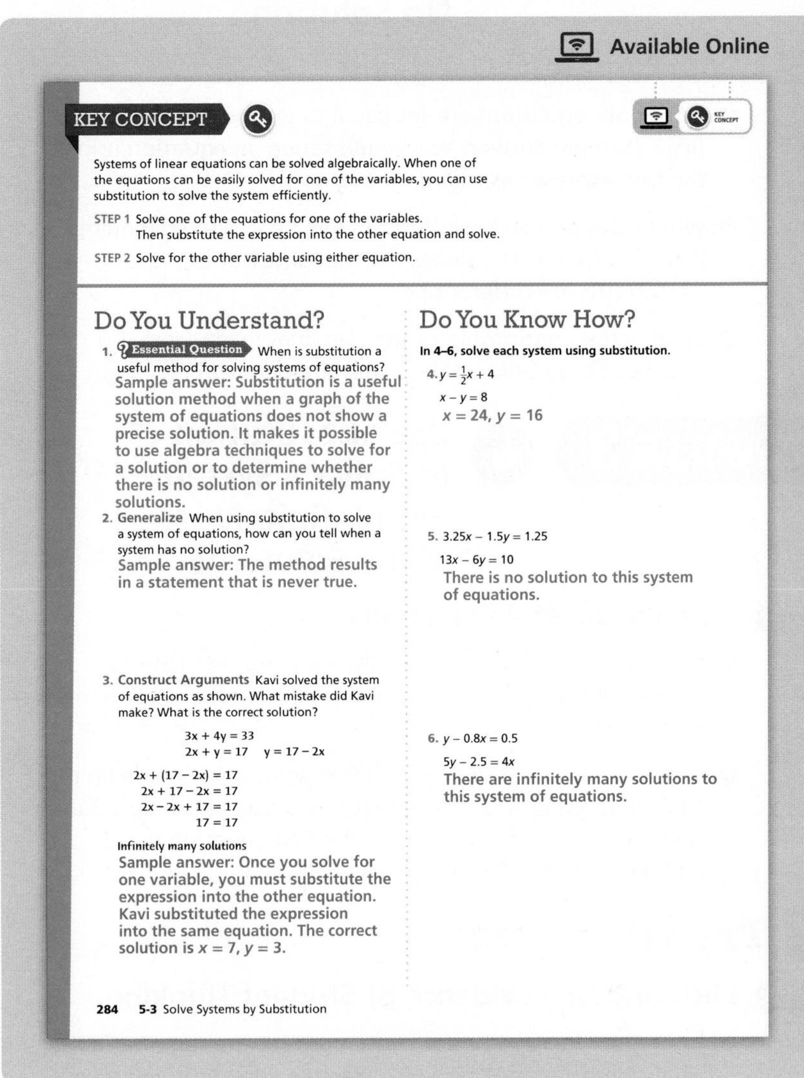

KEY CONCEPT

Systems of linear equations can be solved algebraically. When one of the equations can be easily solved for one of the variables, you can use substitution to solve the system efficiently.

STEP 1 Solve one of the equations for one of the variables. Then substitute the expression into the other equation and solve.

STEP 2 Solve for the other variable using either equation.

Do You Understand?

1. Essential Question When is substitution a useful method for solving systems of equations? Sample answer: Substitution is a useful solution method when a graph of the system of equations does not show a precise solution. It makes it possible to use algebra techniques to solve for a solution or to determine whether there is no solution or infinitely many solutions.
2. Generalize When using substitution to solve a system of equations, how can you tell when a system has no solution? Sample answer: The method results in a statement that is never true.
3. Construct Arguments Kavi solved the system of equations as shown. What mistake did Kavi make? What is the correct solution?

$3x + 4y = 33$
$2x + y = 17 \quad y = 17 - 2x$
$2x + (17 - 2x) = 17$
$2x + 17 - 2x = 17$
$2x - 2x + 17 = 17$
$17 = 17$
Infinitely many solutions

Sample answer: Once you solve for one variable, you must substitute the expression into the other equation. Kavi substituted the expression into the same equation. The correct solution is $x = 7$, $y = 3$.

Do You Know How?

In 4–6, solve each system using substitution.

4. $y = \frac{1}{2}x + 4$
$x - y = 8$
$x = 24$, $y = 16$

5. $3.25x - 1.5y = 1.25$
$13x - 6y = 10$
There is no solution to this system of equations.

6. $y - 0.8x = 0.5$
$5y - 2.5 = 4x$
There are infinitely many solutions to this system of equations.

284 5-3 Solve Systems by Substitution

### Prevent Misconceptions

**ITEM 5** Help students simplify difficult expressions.

**Q:** Sometimes students have difficulty working with decimals. All three of the numbers are decimals. What can you multiply the equation by to eliminate the decimals? What is the result? [4; $13x - 6y = 5$]

## ADDITIONAL EXAMPLE 2

Make sure students understand how to convert the information in the table into equations.

**Q:** What equation would you write for parking at each garage with a discounted ticket? [Sample answer: First Street: $y = 4(x - 1)$; AAA: $y = 4x - 3$]

**Q:** How would you use substitution to solve? [Sample answer: I would set $4(x - 1) = 4x - 3$. I would see there is no solution.]

**Additional Examples** are available online.

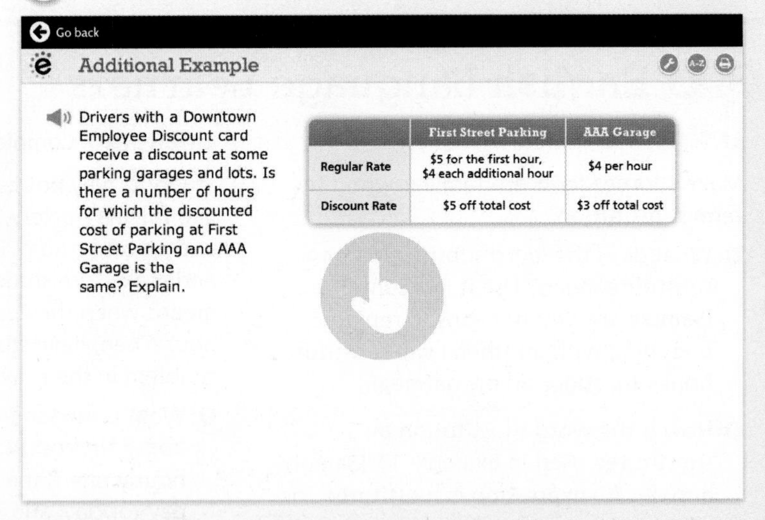

Go back

Additional Example

Drivers with a Downtown Employee Discount card receive a discount at some parking garages and lots. Is there a number of hours for which the discounted cost of parking at First Street Parking and AAA Garage is the same? Explain.

| | First Street Parking | AAA Garage |
|---|---|---|
| Regular Rate | $5 for the first hour, $4 each additional hour | $4 per hour |
| Discount Rate | $5 off total cost | $3 off total cost |

**Answer:** No, the system of equations has no solution.

Go Online

# Practice & Problem Solving

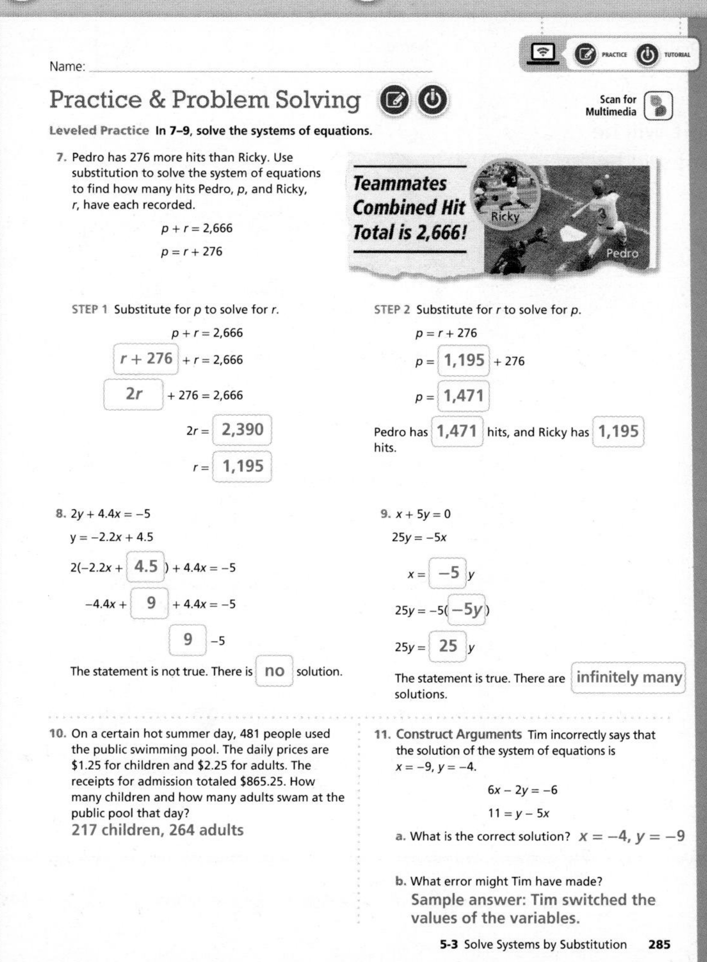

Name: ____________

## Practice & Problem Solving

Scan for Multimedia

**Leveled Practice** In 7–9, solve the systems of equations.

7. Pedro has 276 more hits than Ricky. Use substitution to solve the system of equations to find how many hits Pedro, $p$, and Ricky, $r$, have each recorded.

$p + r = 2,666$
$p = r + 276$



STEP 1 Substitute for $p$ to solve for $r$.

$p + r = 2,666$
$\boxed{r + 276} + r = 2,666$
$\boxed{2r} + 276 = 2,666$
$2r = \boxed{2,390}$
$r = \boxed{1,195}$

STEP 2 Substitute for $r$ to solve for $p$.

$p = r + 276$
$p = \boxed{1,195} + 276$
$p = \boxed{1,471}$

Pedro has $\boxed{1,471}$ hits, and Ricky has $\boxed{1,195}$ hits.

8. $2y + 4.4x = -5$
$y = -2.2x + 4.5$

$2(-2.2x + \boxed{4.5}) + 4.4x = -5$
$-4.4x + \boxed{9} + 4.4x = -5$
$\boxed{9} - 5$

The statement is not true. There is $\boxed{\text{no}}$ solution.

9. $x + 5y = 0$
$25y = -5x$

$x = \boxed{-5}y$
$25y = -5(\boxed{-5y})$
$25y = \boxed{25}y$

The statement is true. There are $\boxed{\text{infinitely many}}$ solutions.

10. On a certain hot summer day, 481 people used the public swimming pool. The daily prices are \$1.25 for children and \$2.25 for adults. The receipts for admission totaled \$865.25. How many children and how many adults swam at the public pool that day?
217 children, 264 adults

11. **Construct Arguments** Tim incorrectly says that the solution of the system of equations is $x = -9$, $y = -4$.

$6x - 2y = -6$
$11 = y - 5x$

a. What is the correct solution? $x = -4, y = -9$

b. What error might Tim have made?
Sample answer: Tim switched the values of the variables.

5-3 Solve Systems by Substitution 285

12. The number of water bottles, $y$, filled in $x$ minutes by each of two machines is given by the equations below. Use substitution to determine if there is a point at which the machines will have filled the same number of bottles.

$160x + 2y = 50$
$y + 80x = 50$

No; Sample answer: There is no solution to the system.

13. a. Use substitution to solve the system below.

$x = 8y - 4$
$x + 8y = 6$
$x = 1, y = \frac{5}{8}$

b. **Reasoning** Which expression would be easier to substitute into the other equation in order to solve the problem? Explain.
Sample answer: It would be easier to substitute the expression $8y - 4$ from the first equation into the second equation because the first equation already shows $x$ in terms of $y$.

14. The perimeter of a frame is 36 inches. The length is 2 inches greater than the width. What are the dimensions of the frame?

$W = 8$ in., $L = 10$ in.

15. **Higher Order Thinking** The members of the city cultural center have decided to put on a play once a night for a week. Their auditorium holds 500 people. By selling tickets, the members would like to raise \$2,050 every night to cover all expenses. Let $d$ represent the number of adult tickets sold at \$6.50. Let $s$ represent the number of student tickets sold at \$3.50 each.

a. If all 500 seats are filled for a performance, how many of each type of ticket must have been sold for the members to raise exactly \$2,050?
100 adult tickets, 400 student tickets

b. At one performance there were three times as many student tickets sold as adult tickets. If there were 480 tickets sold at that performance, how much below the goal of \$2,050 did ticket sales fall?
\$10

### Assessment Practice

16. What statements are true about the solution of the system?

$y = 145 - 5x$
$0.1y + 0.5x = 14.5$

- [x] There are infinitely many solutions.
- [ ] (20, 45) is a solution.
- [ ] (10, 95) is a solution.
- [ ] There is no solution.
- [x] There is more than one solution.

17. At an animal shelter, the number of dog adoptions one weekend was 10 less than 3 times the number of cat adoptions. The number of cat adoptions plus twice the number of dog adoptions was 8. How many cats and how many dogs were adopted that weekend?

4 cats; 2 dogs

286 5-3 Solve Systems by Substitution

## Error Intervention

**ITEM 11** Students may have trouble using substitution with negative integers.

**Q:** Solve the second equation for $y$. [$y = 5x + 11$]

**Q:** Substitute $5x + 11$ into the second equation. Rewrite the subtraction as addition of the opposite.
[$6x + (-2)(5x + 11) = -6$]

**Q:** Distribute and simplify.
[$6x + (-2)(5x) + (-2)(11) = -6$; $6x + (-10x) + (-22) = -6$
$- 4x = 16$; $x = -4$]

## English Language Learners

**ITEM 14** Students may need to be reminded about the meaning of the word *perimeter*.

**Q:** What is the perimeter of a figure? [Sample answer: Perimeter is the distance around the outside of the figure.]

**Q:** How do you find the perimeter of a rectangle? [Sample answer: Add the length twice and the width twice.]

You may opt to have students complete the automatically scored Practice & Problem Solving items online.

### Item Analysis

| Example | Items | DOK |
|---|---|---|
| 1 | 7 | 1 |
| | 10, 14, 17 | 2 |
| | 11, 13, 15 | 3 |
| 2 | 8 | 1 |
| | 12 | 2 |
| 3 | 9 | 1 |
| | 16 | 2 |

Go Online

Assess Tutorials Worksheets

STEP 3 | Assess & Differentiate

# Lesson Quiz

Formative Assessment

Use the student scores on the Lesson Quiz to prescribe differentiated assignments.

**I Intervention** 0–3 Points **O On-Level** 4 Points **A Advanced** 5 Points

You may opt to have students take the Lesson Quiz online. The Lesson Quiz will be automatically scored and appropriate remediation, practice, or enrichment will be assigned based on student performance.

# Video Tutorials

Students can access instructional tutorials using the **Virtual Nerd app**.

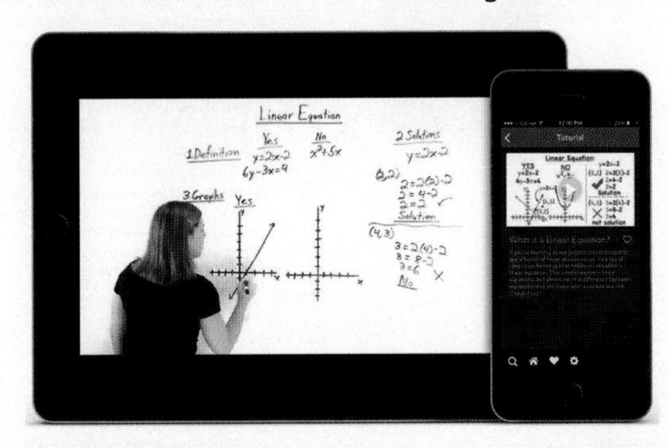

Students can also access the videos using the **BouncePages app** to scan exercise pages marked with this icon. Students can download both apps for free in their mobile devices' app store.

**Lesson Quiz** is available online.

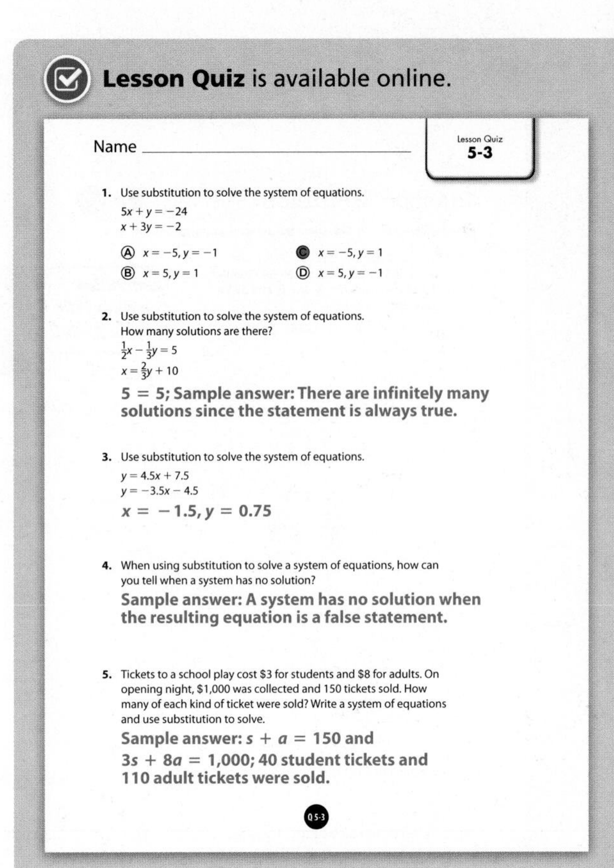

Name ______________ Lesson Quiz 5-3

1. Use substitution to solve the system of equations.
   $5x + y = -24$
   $x + 3y = -2$
   Ⓐ $x = -5, y = -1$ Ⓑ $x = 5, y = 1$ Ⓒ $x = -5, y = 1$ Ⓓ $x = 5, y = -1$
2. Use substitution to solve the system of equations. How many solutions are there?
   $\frac{1}{2}x - \frac{1}{3}y = 5$
   $x = \frac{2}{3}y + 10$
   **$5 = 5$; Sample answer: There are infinitely many solutions since the statement is always true.**
3. Use substitution to solve the system of equations.
   $y = 4.5x + 7.5$
   $y = -3.5x - 4.5$
   **$x = -1.5, y = 0.75$**
4. When using substitution to solve a system of equations, how can you tell when a system has no solution?
   **Sample answer: A system has no solution when the resulting equation is a false statement.**
5. Tickets to a school play cost $3 for students and $8 for adults. On opening night, $1,000 was collected and 150 tickets sold. How many of each kind of ticket were sold? Write a system of equations and use substitution to solve.
   **Sample answer: $s + a = 150$ and $3s + 8a = 1{,}000$; 40 student tickets and 110 adult tickets were sold.**

Q5-3

# Differentiated Intervention

I = Intervention O = On-Level A = Advanced

## Reteach to Build Understanding I

Provides scaffolded reteaching for the key lesson concepts.

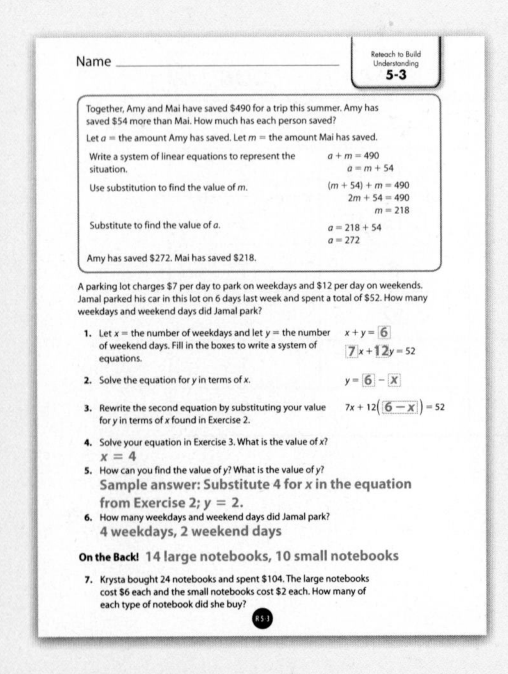

Name ______________ Reteach to Build Understanding 5-3

Together, Amy and Mai have saved $490 for a trip this summer. Amy has saved $54 more than Mai. How much has each person saved?

Let $a$ = the amount Amy has saved. Let $m$ = the amount Mai has saved.

Write a system of linear equations to represent the situation. $a + m = 490$, $a = m + 54$

Use substitution to find the value of $m$. $(m + 54) + m = 490$; $2m + 54 = 490$; $m = 218$

Substitute to find the value of $a$. $a = 218 + 54$; $a = 272$

Amy has saved $272. Mai has saved $218.

A parking lot charges $7 per day to park on weekdays and $12 per day on weekends. Jamal parked his car in this lot on 6 days last week and spent a total of $52. How many weekdays and weekend days did Jamal park?

1. Let $x$ = the number of weekdays and let $y$ = the number of weekend days. Fill in the boxes to write a system of equations. $x + y = \boxed{6}$; $\boxed{7}x + \boxed{12}y = 52$
2. Solve the equation for $y$ in terms of $x$. $y = \boxed{6} - \boxed{x}$
3. Rewrite the second equation by substituting your value for $y$ in terms of $x$ found in Exercise 2. $7x + 12(\boxed{6 - x}) = 52$
4. Solve your equation in Exercise 3. What is the value of $x$? **$x = 4$**
5. How can you find the value of $y$? What is the value of $y$? **Sample answer: Substitute 4 for $x$ in the equation from Exercise 2; $y = 2$.**
6. How many weekdays and weekend days did Jamal park? **4 weekdays, 2 weekend days**

On the Back! **14 large notebooks, 10 small notebooks**

7. Krysta bought 24 notebooks and spent $104. The large notebooks cost $6 each and the small notebooks cost $2 each. How many of each type of notebook did she buy?

R5-3

## Additional Vocabulary Support I O

Helps students develop and reinforce understanding of key terms and concepts.

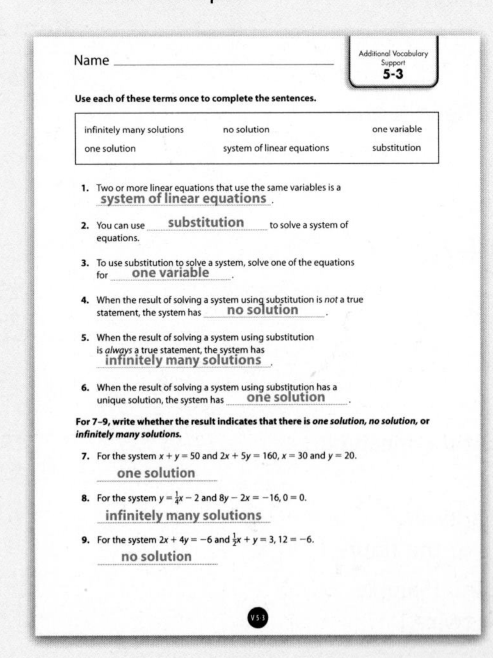

Name ______________ Additional Vocabulary Support 5-3

**Use each of these terms once to complete the sentences.**

| infinitely many solutions | no solution | one variable |
|---|---|---|
| one solution | system of linear equations | substitution |

1. Two or more linear equations that use the same variables is a **system of linear equations**.
2. You can use **substitution** to solve a system of equations.
3. To use substitution to solve a system, solve one of the equations for **one variable**.
4. When the result of solving a system using substitution is *not* a true statement, the system has **no solution**.
5. When the result of solving a system using substitution is *always* a true statement, the system has **infinitely many solutions**.
6. When the result of solving a system using substitution has a unique solution, the system has **one solution**.

**For 7–9, write whether the result indicates that there is *one solution, no solution,* or *infinitely many solutions.***

7. For the system $x + y = 50$ and $2x + 5y = 160$, $x = 30$ and $y = 20$. **one solution**
8. For the system $y = \frac{1}{4}x - 2$ and $8y - 2x = -16$, $0 = 0$. **infinitely many solutions**
9. For the system $2x + 4y = -6$ and $\frac{1}{2}x + y = 3$, $12 = -6$. **no solution**

V5-3

## Build Mathematical Literacy I O

Provides support for struggling readers to build mathematical literacy.

Name ______________ Build Mathematical Literacy 5-3

**Read the problem below. Then answer the questions to help you understand the problem.**

Members of the school band are selling pencils and erasers to raise money for a trip. On the first day, Misha sold a total of 30 items and collected $6.40. How many of each type of item did he sell?

Help us march at the Playoff Parade!
Pencils: 25¢ each
Erasers: 80¢ each

1. Underline the question you need to answer. **Check students' work.**
2. How many quantities is the problem asking you to find? Explain. **Two; The problem asks for the number of pencils and the number of erasers Misha sold.**
3. Highlight the information you can use to write a system of equations. Is all of the necessary information given in the text of the problem? Explain. **Check students' work; No; The prices of each item are given in the sign.**
4. To solve this problem, you can write a system of equations that contains the equation $x + y = 30$, where $x$ represents the number of pencils Misha sold and $y$ represents the number of erasers. Circle the information in the problem that is represented by this equation. **Check students' work.**
5. Explain how the equation $0.25x + 0.80y = 6.40$ represents the situation. **$0.25x$ is the amount earned from selling $x$ pencils and $0.80y$ is the amount earned by selling $y$ erasers. The sum is the total amount Misha collected, $6.40.**
6. Of the equations in Exercises 3 and 4, which equation would you solve for one of the variables in terms of the other variable? Explain. **$x + y = 30$; Sample answer: Neither $x$ nor $y$ has a coefficient, so you can easily solve for either variable.**

M5-3

# Additional Practice

You may opt to have students complete the automatically scored Additional Practice items online.

### Item Analysis

| Example | Items | DOK |
|---|---|---|
| 1 | 1 | 1 |
| | 4, 5, 6, 10 | 2 |
| | 8 | 3 |
| 2 | 2, 9 | 2 |
| 3 | 3 | 2 |
| | 7 | 3 |

**Interactive Practice** is available online.

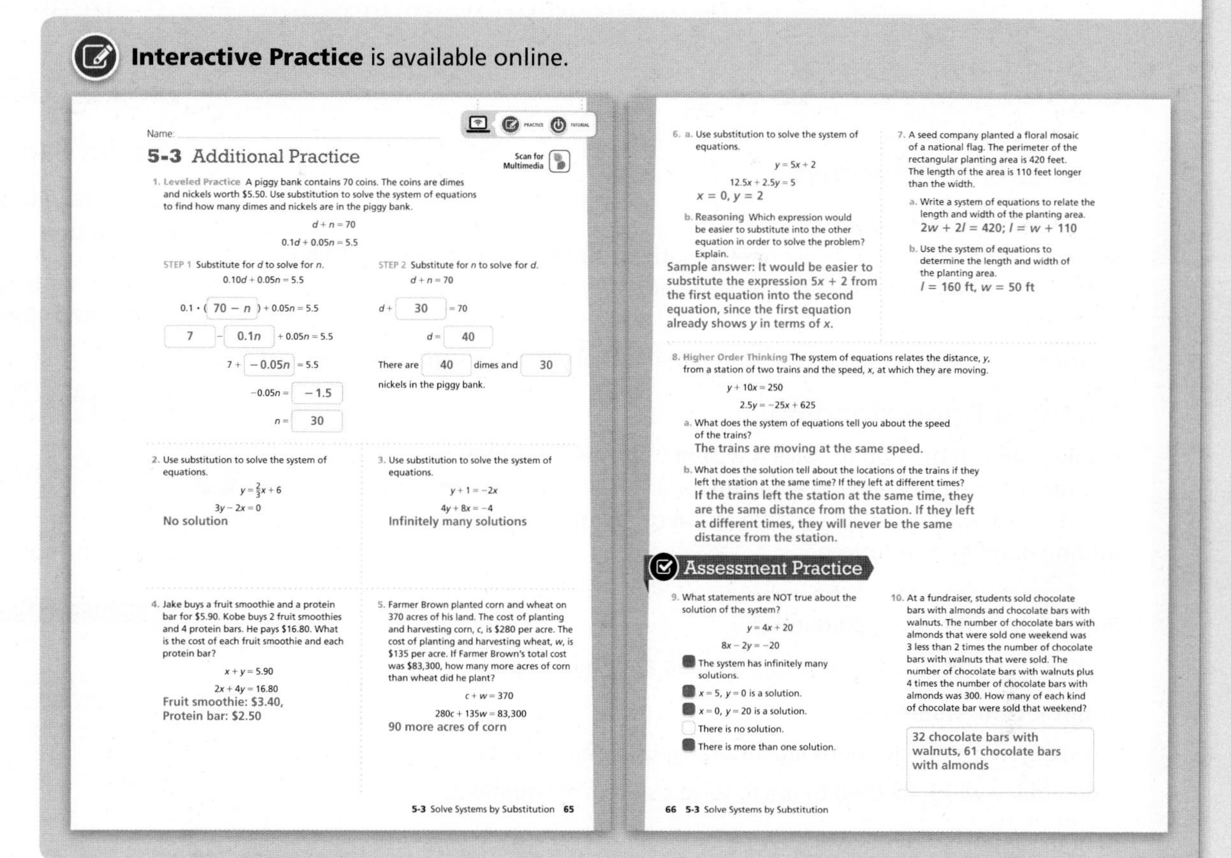

Name:

**5-3 Additional Practice**

Scan for Multimedia

1. Leveled Practice A piggy bank contains 70 coins. The coins are dimes and nickels worth $5.50. Use substitution to solve the system of equations to find how many dimes and nickels are in the piggy bank.

$d + n = 70$

$0.1d + 0.05n = 5.5$

STEP 1 Substitute for $d$ to solve for $n$.

$0.10d + 0.05n = 5.5$

$0.1 \cdot (70 - n) + 0.05n = 5.5$

$7 - 0.1n + 0.05n = 5.5$

$7 + -0.05n = 5.5$

$-0.05n = -1.5$

$n = 30$

STEP 2 Substitute for $n$ to solve for $d$.

$d + n = 70$

$d + 30 = 70$

$d = 40$

There are 40 dimes and 30 nickels in the piggy bank.

2. Use substitution to solve the system of equations.

$y = \frac{2}{3}x + 6$

$3y - 2x = 0$

No solution

3. Use substitution to solve the system of equations.

$y + 1 = -2x$

$4y + 8x = -4$

Infinitely many solutions

4. Jake buys a fruit smoothie and a protein bar for $5.90. Kobe buys 2 fruit smoothies and 4 protein bars. He pays $16.80. What is the cost of each fruit smoothie and each protein bar?

$x + y = 5.90$

$2x + 4y = 16.80$

Fruit smoothie: $3.40, Protein bar: $2.50

5. Farmer Brown planted corn and wheat on 370 acres of his land. The cost of planting and harvesting corn, $c$, is $280 per acre. The cost of planting and harvesting wheat, $w$, is $135 per acre. If Farmer Brown's total cost was $83,300, how many more acres of corn than wheat did he plant?

$c + w = 370$

$280c + 135w = 83,300$

90 more acres of corn

5-3 Solve Systems by Substitution 65

6. a. Use substitution to solve the system of equations.

$y = 5x + 2$

$12.5x + 2.5y = 5$

$x = 0, y = 2$

b. Reasoning Which expression would be easier to substitute into the other equation in order to solve the problem? Explain.

Sample answer: It would be easier to substitute the expression $5x + 2$ from the first equation into the second equation, since the first equation already shows $y$ in terms of $x$.

7. A seed company planted a floral mosaic of a national flag. The perimeter of the rectangular planting area is 420 feet. The length of the area is 110 feet longer than the width.

a. Write a system of equations to relate the length and width of the planting area.

$2w + 2l = 420; l = w + 110$

b. Use the system of equations to determine the length and width of the planting area.

$l = 160$ ft, $w = 50$ ft

8. Higher Order Thinking The system of equations relates the distance, $y$, from a station of two trains and the speed, $x$, at which they are moving.

$y + 10x = 250$

$2.5y = -25x + 625$

a. What does the system of equations tell you about the speed of the trains?

The trains are moving at the same speed.

b. What does the solution tell about the locations of the trains if they left the station at the same time? If they left at different times?

If the trains left the station at the same time, they are the same distance from the station. If they left at different times, they will never be the same distance from the station.

Assessment Practice

9. What statements are NOT true about the solution of the system?

$y = 4x + 20$

$8x - 2y = -20$

■ The system has infinitely many solutions.

■ $x = 5, y = 0$ is a solution.

■ $x = 0, y = 20$ is a solution.

□ There is no solution.

■ There is more than one solution.

10. At a fundraiser, students sold chocolate bars with almonds and chocolate bars with walnuts. The number of chocolate bars with almonds that were sold one weekend was 3 less than 2 times the number of chocolate bars with walnuts that were sold. The number of chocolate bars with walnuts plus 4 times the number of chocolate bars with almonds was 300. How many of each kind of chocolate bar were sold that weekend?

32 chocolate bars with walnuts, 61 chocolate bars with almonds

66 5-3 Solve Systems by Substitution

# Differentiated Intervention

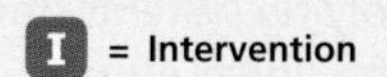 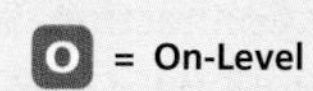 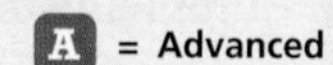

I = Intervention O = On-Level A = Advanced

## Enrichment O A

Presents engaging problems and activities that extend the lesson concepts.

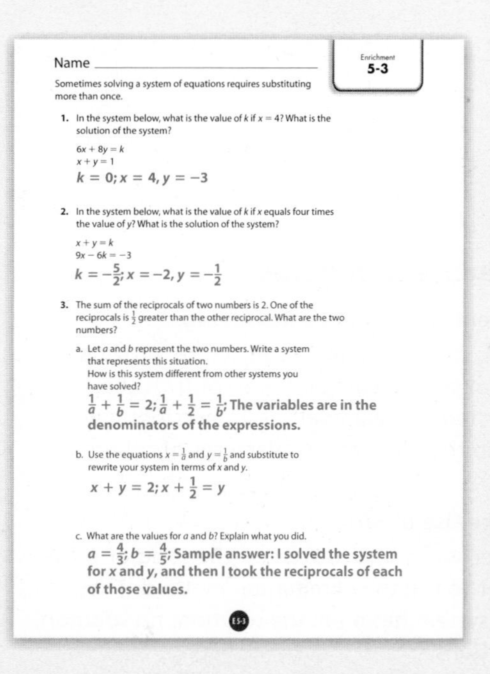

Name

Enrichment 5-3

Sometimes solving a system of equations requires substituting more than once.

1. In the system below, what is the value of $k$ if $x = 4$? What is the solution of the system?

$6x + 8y = k$

$x + y = 1$

$k = 0; x = 4, y = -3$

2. In the system below, what is the value of $k$ if $x$ equals four times the value of $y$? What is the solution of the system?

$x + y = k$

$9x - 6k = -3$

$k = -\frac{5}{2}; x = -2, y = -\frac{1}{2}$

3. The sum of the reciprocals of two numbers is 2. One of the reciprocals is $\frac{1}{2}$ greater than the other reciprocal. What are the two numbers?

a. Let $a$ and $b$ represent the two numbers. Write a system that represents this situation. How is this system different from other systems you have solved?

$\frac{1}{a} + \frac{1}{b} = 2; \frac{1}{a} + \frac{1}{2} = \frac{1}{b}$; The variables are in the denominators of the expressions.

b. Use the equations $x = \frac{1}{a}$ and $y = \frac{1}{b}$ and substitute to rewrite your system in terms of $x$ and $y$.

$x + y = 2; x + \frac{1}{2} = y$

c. What are the values for $a$ and $b$? Explain what you did.

$a = \frac{4}{3}; b = \frac{4}{5}$; Sample answer: I solved the system for $x$ and $y$, and then I took the reciprocals of each of those values.

## Math Tools and Games I O A

Offers additional activities and games to build understanding and fluency.

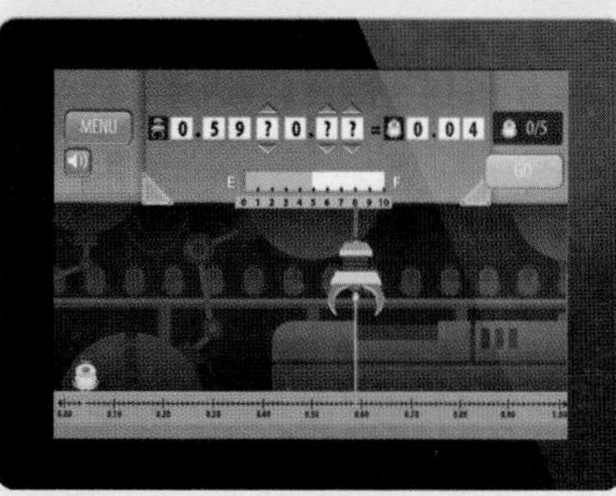


## Pick a Project and STEM Project I O A

Provides an additional opportunity for students to demonstrate understanding of key mathematical concepts.

Go Online

Video Activity

# Lesson 5-4 Solve Systems by Elimination

## Lesson Overview

FOCUS

### Mathematics Objective

**Students will be able to:**

✔ understand how the process of elimination can be used to solve a system of linear equations with no solution, one solution, or infinitely many solutions.

✔ apply this understanding to solve mathematical and real-world problems.

### Essential Understanding

Elimination can be used to solve a system of linear equations by adding or subtracting the equations to eliminate one variable, and use the resulting equation to find the other variable, or identify if there is no solution or an infinite number of solutions.

COHERENCE

**Previously in the topic, students:**

- solved systems of equations by graphing and using substitution.

**In this lesson, students:**

- solve systems of equations algebraically, using elimination.
- determine which method to use to solve a system of equations.

**In high school, students will:**

- solve nonlinear systems of equations using graphing, substitution, and elimination.

**Cross-Cluster Connection** Solving systems of linear equations (8.EE.3) connects to work with solving linear equations (8.EE.2) from Topic 2 and linear functions (8.F.2) from Topic 3.

RIGOR

This lesson emphasizes a blend of **conceptual understanding** and **procedural skill**.

- Students extend their learning of solving systems of equations by learning the algebraic process of elimination and relating this to the processes of solving using graphing and substitution.

## Language Support

### Lesson Language Objective

Explain how to solve systems of equations using elimination.

Additional resources are available in the **Language Support Handbook**.

## Math Anytime

### Today's Challenge

Use the Topic 5 problems any time during this topic.

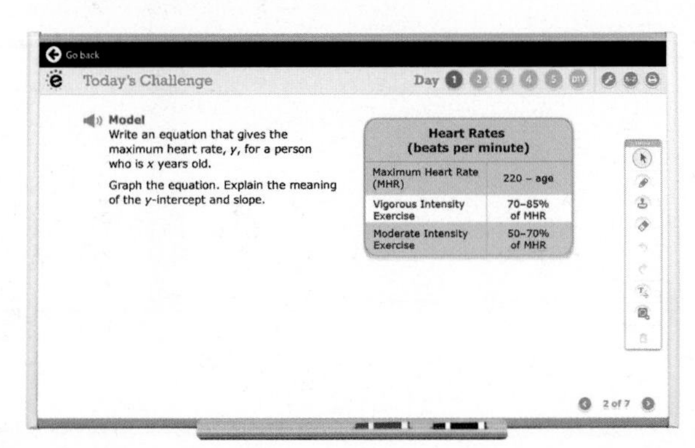


Watch the **Listen and Look For Video** for strategies and habits of mind to look for as students complete work on this lesson.

## Mathematics Overview | Common Core Standards

### Content Standards

In this lesson, you will focus on **8.EE.C.8b** and **8.EE.C.8c**.

- **8.EE.C.8b** Solve systems of two linear equations in two variables algebraically, and estimate solutions by graphing the equations. Solve simple cases by inspection.
- **8.EE.C.8c** Solve real-world and mathematical problems leading to two linear equations in two variables.

### Mathematical Practice Standards

**MP.3 Construct Arguments and Critique Reasoning**
Throughout this lesson, students make a conjecture, provide evidence, identify mistakes, and compare and contrast their solutions for solving systems by elimination. They critique not only their ideas but also the ideas and conjectures of others.

**MP.7 Look for and Make Use of Structure**
Students look for patterns and structures to either find or make opposite terms in order to use the elimination method. They interpret whether the system has a unique solution, no solution, or infinitely many solutions.

STEP 1 | Problem-Based Learning

15-20 min

Go Online
Activity

# Solve & Discuss It!

Formative Assessment

**Purpose** Students group and combine terms, connecting this to adding equations to solve systems in the Visual Learning Bridge.

## ETP Before — WHOLE CLASS

**1 Introduce the Problem**

**2 Check for Understanding of the Problem**

Ask students: How do you know if you can combine expressions?

## ETP During — SMALL GROUP

**3 Observe Students at Work**

Observe students while they work, noting the different solution paths they take to approach the problem. Students may identify like terms and combine them to form a simplified expression. Students may also group terms that have a common factor and then factor those terms to create an equivalent expression. If needed, ask What is the sum of opposite integers?

### Early Finishers

How would the problem change if the $2y$ was $3y$ instead? [Sample answer: $3y$ and $-3y$ are opposites, so the new expression could be $x + 2$.]

## ETP After — WHOLE CLASS

**4 Discuss Solution Strategies and Key Ideas**

Have students who combined like terms present first. Have them discuss how they found groups of like terms in the list and how they combined them; like terms have exactly the same variables and can be combined by adding the coefficients. Have students who used other strategies explain why their new expressions are equivalent to the original expressions; they used the properties of algebra.

Have students identify any opposite terms and discuss how finding opposite terms could make adding expressions easier; the sum of opposite terms is always 0.

**5 Consider Instructional Implications**

When presenting Example 1, ask students what happened when they added terms with opposite coefficients in the Solve and Discuss It; opposite terms have a sum of 0. Discuss with students how this process results in the removal of a variable in Example 1. Have students discuss how they could modify the initial expressions in the Solve & Discuss It to remove the variable $x$ when the expressions are added; they could change $3x$ to $2x$ or change $-2x$ to $-3x$.

## Analyze Student Work

**Solve and Discuss It!** Activity is available online.

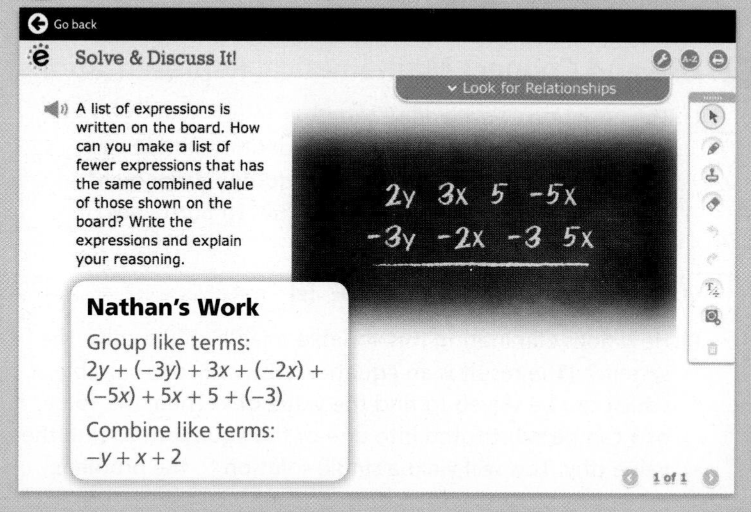


**Nathan** combines all the terms into one expression and combines like terms.

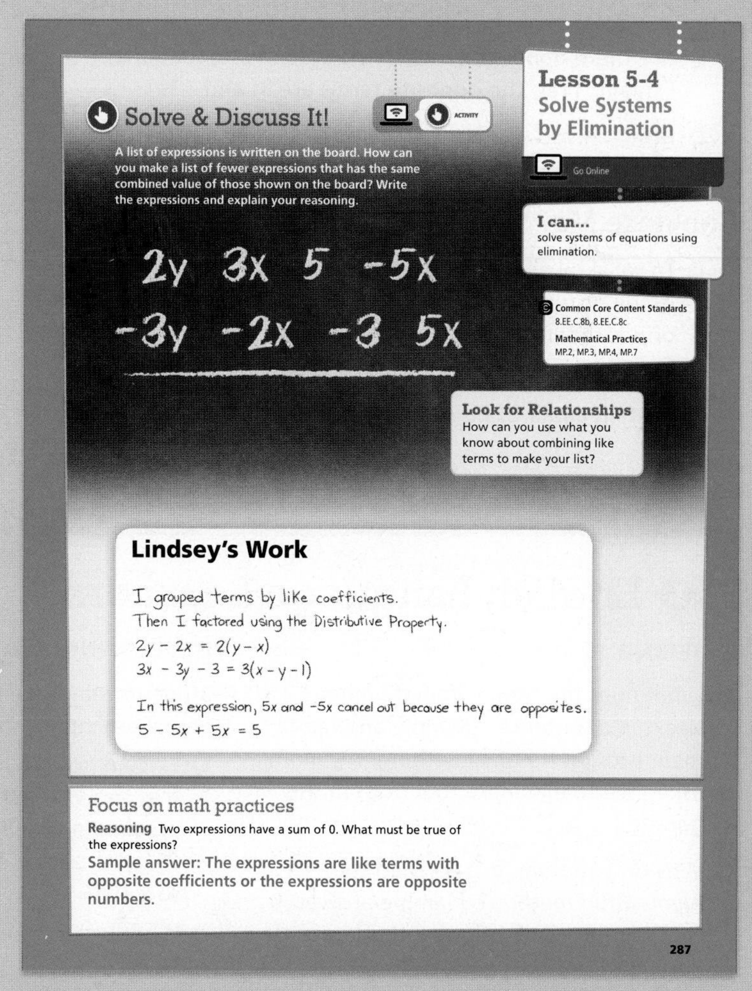


**Lindsey** uses the Distributive Property to combine terms with common factors.

# STEP 2 | Visual Learning

Go Online

Visual Learning

Assess

## Establish Mathematics Goals to Focus Learning

Engage students in a discussion about the ***Essential Question***. Make sure they can use properties of equality to add and subtract equations to eliminate a variable.

## EXAMPLE 1  Solve a System of Equations by Adding

### ETP Use and Connect Mathematical Representations

**Q:** The equations were added together to get a new equation. How do you know that the new equation is a true statement? [Sample answer: The Addition Property of Equality allows me to add equal values to both sides of an equation.]

**Q:** Which variable was eliminated? [$y$]

**Q:** How does eliminating this variable enable you to solve the system? [The result is an equation with only one variable, $x$, which can be solved to find the value of $x$. Then, the value of $x$ can be substituted into one of the equations to find the value of $y$. This will yield a single solution to the problem.]

##  Try It! 

**Formative** Assessment

### Elicit and Use Evidence of Student Thinking

**Q:** Are there opposite terms in the system of equations? Explain. [Yes, the opposite terms are $3s$ and $-3s$.]

**Q:** How can you check the solution? [Sample answer: Substitute $r = 2.5$ and $s = 3$ into the second equation.]

### Convince Me!

**Q:** To solve by elimination, when would you add the equations in the system? [Sample answer: When they contain a pair of opposite terms.]

**Q:** When would you subtract? [Sample answer: When they contain a pair of equivalent terms.]

**Visual Learning Animation Plus** is available online.

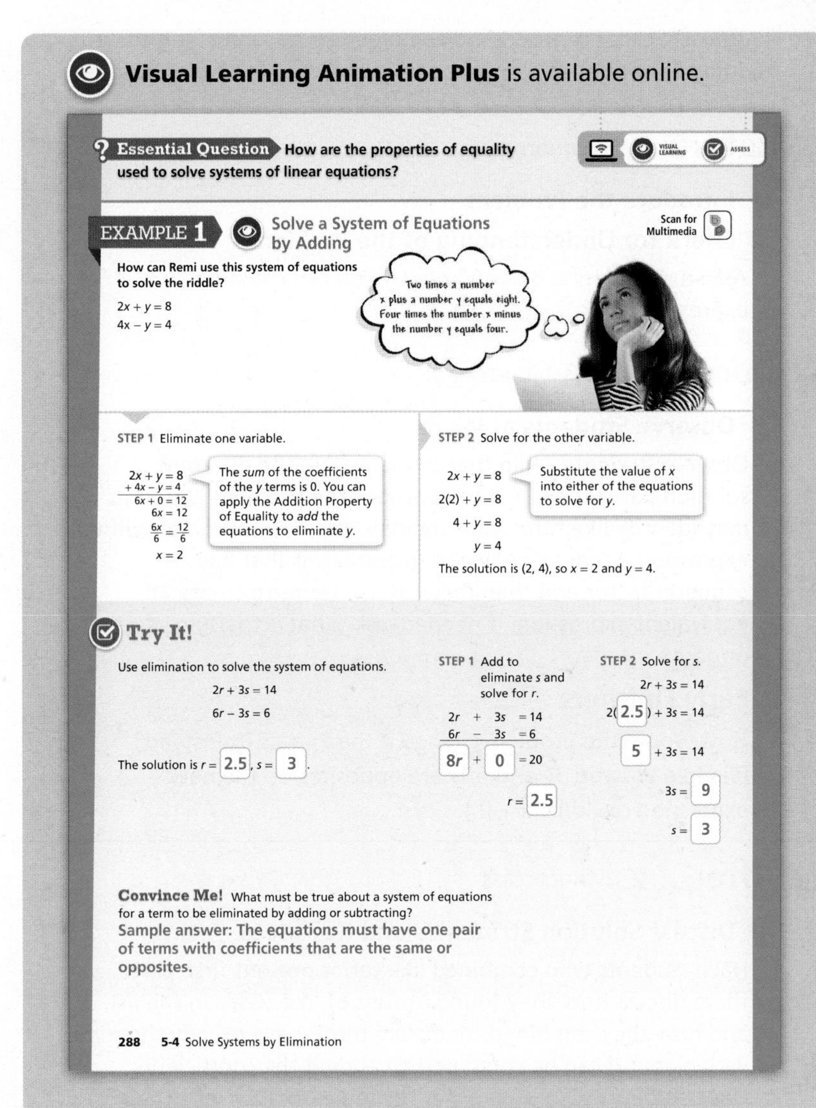

Essential Question How are the properties of equality used to solve systems of linear equations?

EXAMPLE 1 Solve a System of Equations by Adding

Scan for Multimedia

How can Remi use this system of equations to solve the riddle?

$2x + y = 8$

$4x - y = 4$



STEP 1 Eliminate one variable.

$$\begin{array}{r} 2x + y = 8 \\ +\ 4x - y = 4 \\ \hline 6x + 0 = 12 \\ 6x = 12 \\ \frac{6x}{6} = \frac{12}{6} \\ x = 2 \end{array}$$

The *sum* of the coefficients of the $y$ terms is 0. You can apply the Addition Property of Equality to *add* the equations to eliminate $y$.

STEP 2 Solve for the other variable.

$2x + y = 8$

$2(2) + y = 8$

$4 + y = 8$

$y = 4$

Substitute the value of $x$ into either of the equations to solve for $y$.

The solution is (2, 4), so $x = 2$ and $y = 4$.

Try It!

Use elimination to solve the system of equations.

$2r + 3s = 14$

$6r - 3s = 6$

The solution is $r =$ 2.5, $s =$ 3.

STEP 1 Add to eliminate $s$ and solve for $r$.

$2r + 3s = 14$

$6r - 3s = 6$

$8r + 0 = 20$

$r = 2.5$

STEP 2 Solve for $s$.

$2r + 3s = 14$

$2(2.5) + 3s = 14$

$5 + 3s = 14$

$3s = 9$

$s = 3$

**Convince Me!** What must be true about a system of equations for a term to be eliminated by adding or subtracting?
Sample answer: The equations must have one pair of terms with coefficients that are the same or opposites.

288 5-4 Solve Systems by Elimination

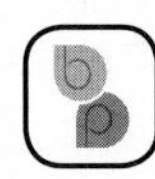

Students can access the ***Visual Learning Animation Plus*** by using the **BouncePages app** to scan this page. Students can download the app for free in their mobile devices' app store.

## ELL English Language Learners

**ENTERING** Example 1.

**Q:** What does the term eliminate mean? Use it in a sentence. [Sample answer: It means to get rid of something. My mom asked me to eliminate that mess in the garage.]

**Q:** Why do you think this is called the *elimination method*? [Sample answer: It is called the elimination method because you get rid of one variable.]

**DEVELOPING** Example 2.

Students may have trouble translating verbal descriptions into equations.

**Q:** Explain how you can write an equation that shows that there are 20 nickels and pennies in all. [Sample answer: There are 20 coins, all are either nickels or pennies, so $x + y = 20$.]

**Q:** What is the value of a penny? Of a nickel? [1 cent; 5 cents]

**Q:** Explain how you can write an equation for the total value of the coins. [Sample answer: Multiply the number of nickels by 5 and add to the number of pennies to get the total amount of money in cents.]

**EXPANDING** Example 1.

Students will benefit from articulating how the elimination method compares with the substitution method. Write this system on the board:

$$3x + 2y = 3$$

$$x + y = 2$$

Divide students into two groups. Have one group solve the system by substitution and the other by elimination. Then, have the groups share their work. Have students describe their solution processes and compare their descriptions.

Go Online

Activity

Assess

## EXAMPLE 2 Solve a System of Equations by Subtracting

**ETP** **Pose Purposeful Questions**

**Q:** What is the relationship in the equations between the terms with the variable $x$? [Sample answer: Both terms are equal.]

**Q:** Why is the second equation subtracted from the first equation? [Sample answer: So that the $x$-terms can be eliminated.]

**Q:** What would the solution be if you subtracted the first equation from the second equation? Explain. [Sample answer: The solution is the same, because changing the position of the equations when you use elimination does not change the solution.]

## EXAMPLE 3  Solve a System of Equations by Multiplying

**ETP** **Pose Purposeful Questions**

**Q:** After multiplying, how do you know that these equations will have the same solution? [Sample answer: Using the Multiplication Property of Equality to multiply all terms within an equation by the same number creates an equivalent equation, so the solution to the system will be the same.]

**Q:** What number instead of 2 could you have multiplied the second equation by and still used elimination to solve the system of equations? [Sample answer: You could have multiplied it by negative 2 and added or subtracted the equations.]

##  Try It!  Formative Assessment

 **Elicit and Use Evidence of Student Thinking**

**Q:** How would you eliminate a variable? [Sample answer: You would multiply the second equation by 3 and subtract it from the first equation.]

**Examples and Try Its!** are available online.

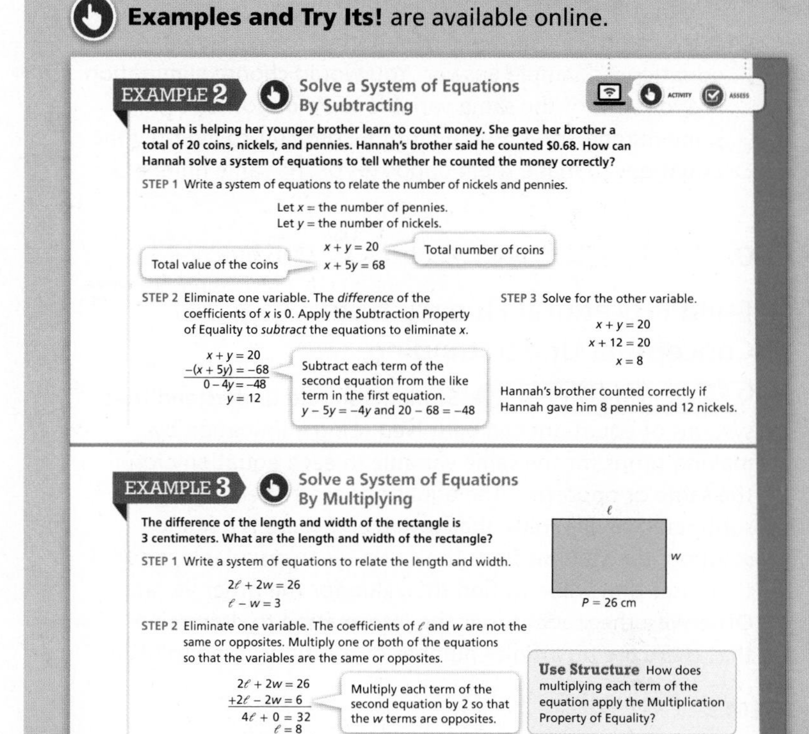

EXAMPLE 2 Solve a System of Equations By Subtracting

ACTIVITY ASSESS

**Hannah is helping her younger brother learn to count money. She gave her brother a total of 20 coins, nickels, and pennies. Hannah's brother said he counted $0.68. How can Hannah solve a system of equations to tell whether he counted the money correctly?**

STEP 1 Write a system of equations to relate the number of nickels and pennies.

Let $x$ = the number of pennies.
Let $y$ = the number of nickels.

$x + y = 20$ (Total number of coins)
$x + 5y = 68$ (Total value of the coins)

STEP 2 Eliminate one variable. The *difference* of the coefficients of $x$ is 0. Apply the Subtraction Property of Equality to *subtract* the equations to eliminate $x$.

$$\begin{aligned} x + y &= 20 \\ -(x + 5y) &= -68 \\ \hline 0 - 4y &= -48 \\ y &= 12 \end{aligned}$$

Subtract each term of the second equation from the like term in the first equation. $y - 5y = -4y$ and $20 - 68 = -48$

STEP 3 Solve for the other variable.

$$\begin{aligned} x + y &= 20 \\ x + 12 &= 20 \\ x &= 8 \end{aligned}$$

Hannah's brother counted correctly if Hannah gave him 8 pennies and 12 nickels.

EXAMPLE 3 Solve a System of Equations By Multiplying

**The difference of the length and width of the rectangle is 3 centimeters. What are the length and width of the rectangle?**

$\ell$, $w$, $P = 26$ cm

STEP 1 Write a system of equations to relate the length and width.

$$\begin{aligned} 2\ell + 2w &= 26 \\ \ell - w &= 3 \end{aligned}$$

STEP 2 Eliminate one variable. The coefficients of $\ell$ and $w$ are not the same or opposites. Multiply one or both of the equations so that the variables are the same or opposites.

$$\begin{aligned} 2\ell + 2w &= 26 \\ +2\ell - 2w &= 6 \\ \hline 4\ell + 0 &= 32 \\ \ell &= 8 \end{aligned}$$

Multiply each term of the second equation by 2 so that the $w$ terms are opposites.

**Use Structure** How does multiplying each term of the equation apply the Multiplication Property of Equality?

STEP 3 Solve for the other variable.

$$\begin{aligned} \ell - w &= 3 \\ 8 - w &= 3 \\ w &= 5 \end{aligned}$$

The length of the rectangle is 8 centimeters and the width is 5 centimeters.

**Try It!**

Use elimination to solve the system of equations. $3x - 5y = -9$, $x + 2y = 8$

$x = 2, y = 3$

5-4 Solve Systems by Elimination 289

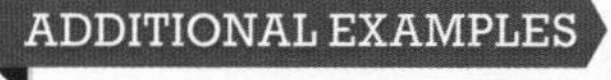 

ADDITIONAL EXAMPLES

**For additional examples go online.**

##  Response to Intervention

**USE WITH EXAMPLE 3** Students may need to review how to find the least common multiple. Review the following example to help them understand why this ability is helpful when using elimination to solve a system of equations. Write this system on the board:

$$5x + 6y = 42$$
$$8x + 8y = 59$$

**Q:** What is the least common multiple for 5 and 8? What is the least common multiple for 6 and 8? [40; 24]

**Q:** How can you use this information to help you use elimination to solve this system of equations? [Sample answer: To eliminate $y$, you want to get the terms equal to $24y$ and $-24y$. You can multiply the first equation by 4 and the second by $-3$ to accomplish this.]

##  Enrichment

**USE WITH EXAMPLE 2** Challenge students to write their own systems with different numbers of solutions.

**Q:** Write a system of equations that has one solution, one that has an infinite number of solutions, and one that has no solutions. Explain your strategy for determining each set of equations. Then show that each system fits the classification using elimination to solve them.

Go Online

 Key Concept  Assess  Activity

## KEY CONCEPT 

### ETP Pose Purposeful Questions

**Q:** Why would you choose elimination to solve a system of equations? [Sample answer: You would choose elimination if two terms of the same variable were opposites or the same number, or if it would not be difficult to multiply the equations to make them opposites or the same number.]

##  Do You Understand/Do You Know How?

Formative Assessment

### ETP Build Procedural Fluency from Conceptual Understanding

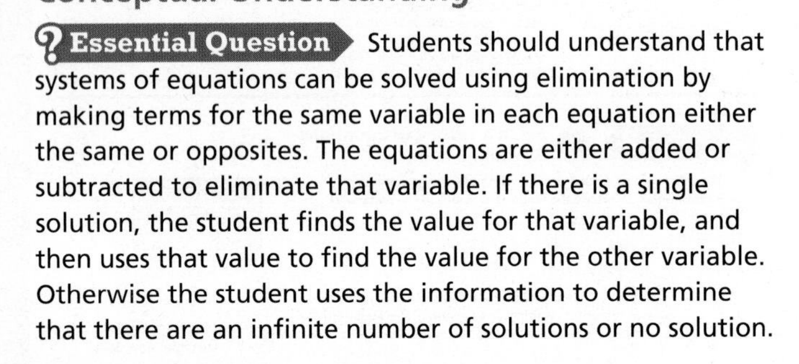

**Essential Question** Students should understand that systems of equations can be solved using elimination by making terms for the same variable in each equation either the same or opposites. The equations are either added or subtracted to eliminate that variable. If there is a single solution, the student finds the value for that variable, and then uses that value to find the value for the other variable. Otherwise the student uses the information to determine that there are an infinite number of solutions or no solution.

**ITEM 5**

**Q:** Which variable would you eliminate? Explain. [Sample answer: Multiply the second equation by 3 and eliminate *d*, because the *d*-terms have opposite signs and can be added.]

###  Prevent Misconceptions

**ITEM 6** Make sure students multiply each term in the equation by the same number. A common mistake is to multiply only the terms they want to eliminate.

**Q:** Why must you multiply the entire equation by the number you chose? [Sample answer: So the resulting equation is equivalent to the original equation.]

Available Online

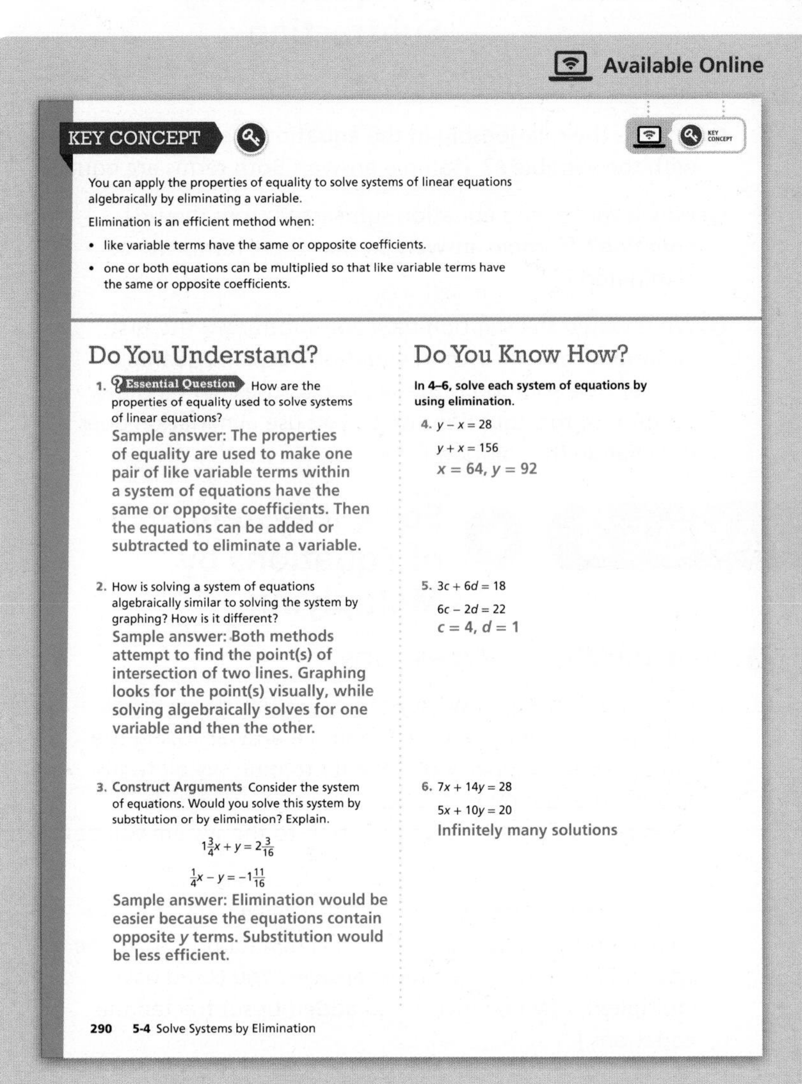

KEY CONCEPT

You can apply the properties of equality to solve systems of linear equations algebraically by eliminating a variable.

Elimination is an efficient method when:

- like variable terms have the same or opposite coefficients.
- one or both equations can be multiplied so that like variable terms have the same or opposite coefficients.

**Do You Understand?**

1. **Essential Question** How are the properties of equality used to solve systems of linear equations?
Sample answer: The properties of equality are used to make one pair of like variable terms within a system of equations have the same or opposite coefficients. Then the equations can be added or subtracted to eliminate a variable.

2. How is solving a system of equations algebraically similar to solving the system by graphing? How is it different?
Sample answer: Both methods attempt to find the point(s) of intersection of two lines. Graphing looks for the point(s) visually, while solving algebraically solves for one variable and then the other.

3. **Construct Arguments** Consider the system of equations. Would you solve this system by substitution or by elimination? Explain.
$1\frac{3}{4}x + y = 2\frac{3}{16}$
$\frac{1}{4}x - y = -1\frac{11}{16}$
Sample answer: Elimination would be easier because the equations contain opposite *y* terms. Substitution would be less efficient.

**Do You Know How?**

**In 4–6, solve each system of equations by using elimination.**

4. $y - x = 28$
$y + x = 156$
$x = 64, y = 92$

5. $3c + 6d = 18$
$6c - 2d = 22$
$c = 4, d = 1$

6. $7x + 14y = 28$
$5x + 10y = 20$
Infinitely many solutions

290 5-4 Solve Systems by Elimination

## ADDITIONAL EXAMPLE 3 

Help students solve a system of linear equations containing a decimal coefficient of a variable.

Use the questions below to help students solve.

**Q:** How could you use elimination to solve this problem? [Sample answer: You would multiply the equation for Happy Trails by 4 and the equation for Morning Break by 3. Then, subtract the equation for Morning Break from the equation for Happy Trails.]

**Q:** If you multiplied the equation for Happy Trails by 4 what would happen to the decimal coefficient for the number of pounds of dried fruit? [Sample answer: It would become the whole number 10.]

 **Additional Examples** are available online.

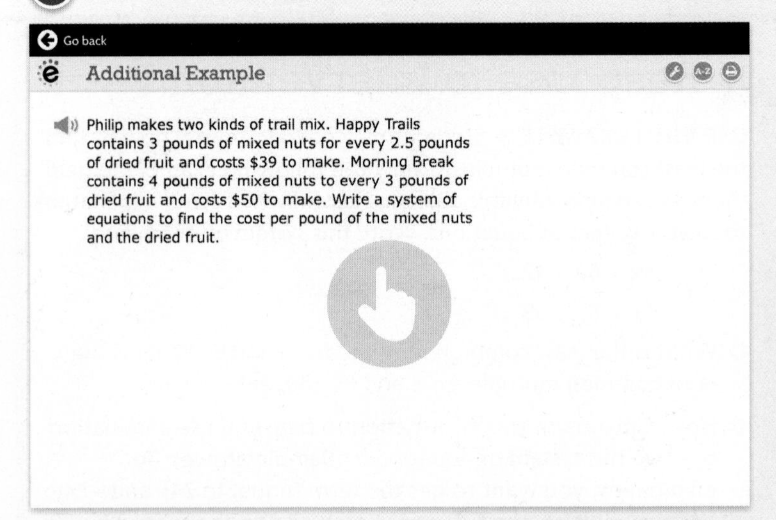


**Answer:** The mixed nuts cost $8 per pound. The dried fruit costs $6 per pound.

Go Online

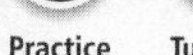

Practice Tutorials Math Tools

# Practice & Problem Solving

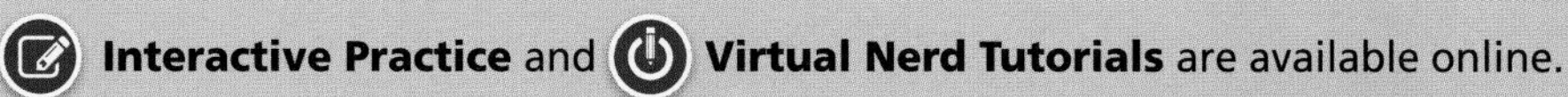

**Interactive Practice** and **Virtual Nerd Tutorials** are available online.

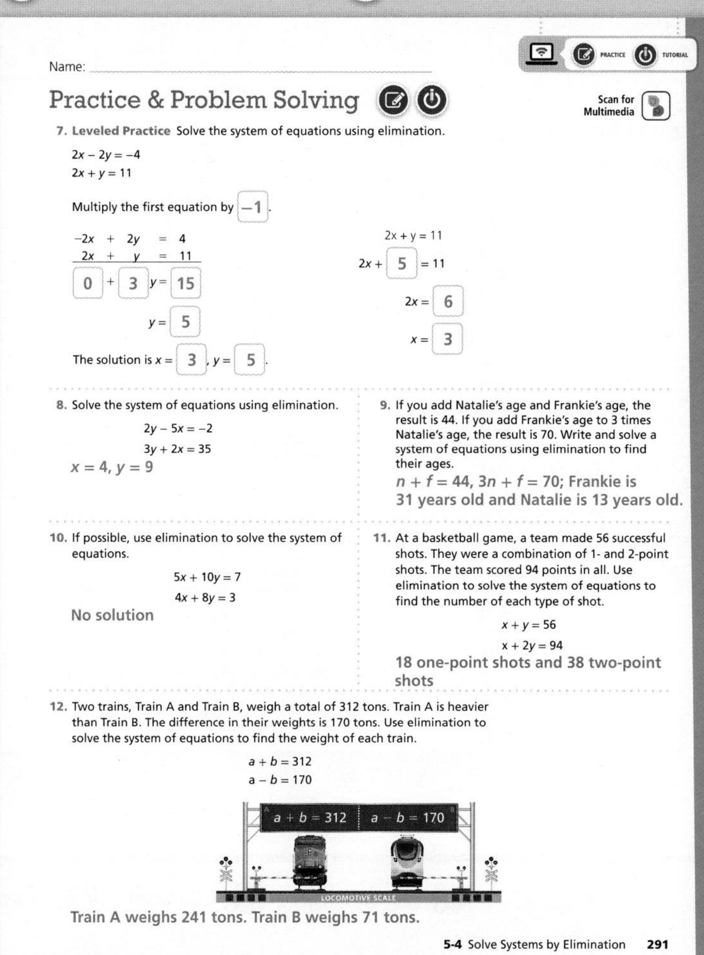

Name: ______________

Practice & Problem Solving

Scan for Multimedia

7. **Leveled Practice** Solve the system of equations using elimination.

$2x - 2y = -4$
$2x + y = 11$

Multiply the first equation by $\boxed{-1}$.

$-2x + 2y = 4$
$2x + y = 11$
$\boxed{0} + \boxed{3}y = \boxed{15}$
$y = \boxed{5}$

$2x + y = 11$
$2x + \boxed{5} = 11$
$2x = \boxed{6}$
$x = \boxed{3}$

The solution is $x = \boxed{3}$, $y = \boxed{5}$.

8. Solve the system of equations using elimination.

$2y - 5x = -2$
$3y + 2x = 35$

$x = 4, y = 9$

9. If you add Natalie's age and Frankie's age, the result is 44. If you add Frankie's age to 3 times Natalie's age, the result is 70. Write and solve a system of equations using elimination to find their ages.

$n + f = 44$, $3n + f = 70$; Frankie is 31 years old and Natalie is 13 years old.

10. If possible, use elimination to solve the system of equations.

$5x + 10y = 7$
$4x + 8y = 3$

No solution

11. At a basketball game, a team made 56 successful shots. They were a combination of 1- and 2-point shots. The team scored 94 points in all. Use elimination to solve the system of equations to find the number of each type of shot.

$x + y = 56$
$x + 2y = 94$

18 one-point shots and 38 two-point shots

12. Two trains, Train A and Train B, weigh a total of 312 tons. Train A is heavier than Train B. The difference in their weights is 170 tons. Use elimination to solve the system of equations to find the weight of each train.

$a + b = 312$
$a - b = 170$



Train A weighs 241 tons. Train B weighs 71 tons.



13. A deli offers two platters of sandwiches. Platter A has 2 roast beef sandwiches and 3 turkey sandwiches. Platter B has 3 roast beef sandwiches and 2 turkey sandwiches.

a. Model with Math Write a system of equations to represent the situation.

$2x + 3y = 31$, $3x + 2y = 29$

b. What is the cost of each sandwich?

Roast beef costs $5, and turkey costs $7.

Platter A $31.00
Platter B $29.00

14. Consider the system of equations.

$x - 3.1y = 11.5$
$-x + 3.5y = -13.5$

a. Solve the system by elimination.

$x = -4, y = -5$

b. If you solved this equation by substitution instead, what would the solution be? Explain.

$x = -4, y = -5$ Sample answer: The solution to a system of equations will always be the same no matter what solution method you choose.

15. **Higher Order Thinking** Determine the number of solutions for this system of equations by inspection only. Explain.

$3x + 4y = 17$
$21x + 28y = 109$

No solution; Sample answer: If the first equation is multiplied by 7, the variable terms will be equivalent to the variable terms in the second equation. The constant on the right of the equation will not be the same; it will be 119. So, the variable terms will be eliminated, but the constant will not. This will result in an untrue equation, so there is no solution.

## Assessment Practice

16. Four times a number $r$ plus half a number $s$ equals 12. Twice the number $r$ plus one fourth of the number $s$ equals 8. What are the two numbers?

Sample answer: There is no solution. There are no numbers $r$ and $s$ that meet these criteria.

17. Solve the system of equations.

$3m + 3n = 36$
$8m - 5n = 31$

$m = 7, n = 5$



## Error Intervention

**ITEM 13** Encourage students to define the variables they use to avoid confusion.

**Q:** What is your answer to Part a? Explain what each equation means. [Sample answer: The equation $2x + 3y = 31$ shows that 2 roast beef sandwiches, $2x$, and 3 turkey sandwiches, $3y$, cost a total of $31. The equation $3x + 2y = 29$ shows that 3 roast beef sandwiches, $3x$, and 2 turkey sandwiches, $2y$, cost a total of $29.]

## English Language Learners

**ITEM 11** Students may need help understanding the scoring in the basketball game. Ask students to tell what they know about the game of basketball. Make sure they understand that there are at least two ways to score in middle school basketball games. If a player makes a basket while the teams are guarding each other the score is worth two points. If a player makes a shot at the foul line when players are not allowed to guard each other the shot is worth only 1 point.

You may opt to have students complete the automatically scored Practice & Problem Solving items online.

### Item Analysis

| Example | Items | DOK |
|---|---|---|
| 1 | 12, 14 | 2 |
| 2 | 7 | 1 |
| | 9, 11, 12 | 2 |
| 3 | 7 | 1 |
| | 8, 10, 13, 15, 16, 17 | 2 |

# STEP 3 | Assess & Differentiate

Go Online

Assess Tutorials Worksheets

## Lesson Quiz

**Formative** Assessment

Use the student scores on the Lesson Quiz to prescribe differentiated assignments.

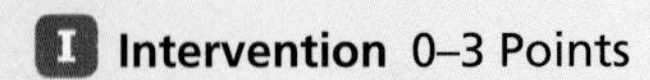
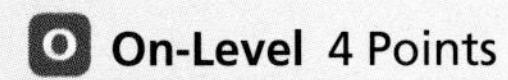

**I Intervention** 0–3 Points **O On-Level** 4 Points **A Advanced** 5 Points

You may opt to have students take the Lesson Quiz online. The Lesson Quiz will be automatically scored and appropriate remediation, practice, or enrichment will be assigned based on student performance.

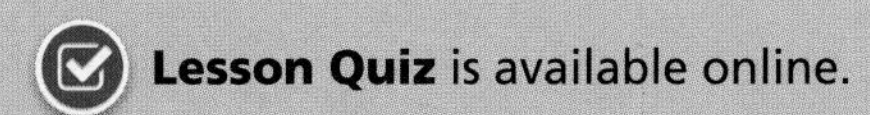

**Lesson Quiz** is available online.

Name ______________ Lesson Quiz **5-4**

1. Use elimination to solve the system of equations. Explain your method.
   $3x - 2y = 24$
   $x + 2y = 48$
   **$x = 18, y = 15$; Sample answer: I added the equations and then solved $4x = 72$.**
2. Use elimination to solve the system of equations. Explain your method.
   $2x - 2y = 24$
   $4x + 7y = -40$
   **$x = 4, y = -8$ Sample answer: I multiplied the first equation by $-2$ and added the second equation to get $11y = -88$.**
3. What is the solution of the system of equations?
   $2x + 3y = 26$
   $3x + 5y = 40$
   Ⓐ $x = 10, y = 2$ Ⓒ $x = -10, y = -2$
   Ⓑ $x = 10, y = -2$ Ⓓ $x = -10, y = 2$
4. Fill in the blanks to explain one way to solve this system of equations using elimination.
   $6x + 2y = 14$
   $5x - 2y = 8$
   First, add the two equations to get $11x =$ **22**. Then substitute **2** for $x$ in either equation to get $y =$ **1**.
5. Sylvester and Lin go to the amusement park. Sylvester plays 5 rounds of mini golf and takes 4 turns in the batting cages for $60. Lin plays 3 rounds of mini golf and takes 6 turns in the batting cages for $45. Write two equations to find the price for each activity. Then find the cost for each activity.
   **Sample answer: $5g + 4b = 60$; $3g + 6b = 45$. Mini golf costs $10 per round and batting cages cost $2.50 each turn.**

Q5-4

## Video Tutorials

Students can access instructional tutorials using the **Virtual Nerd app**.

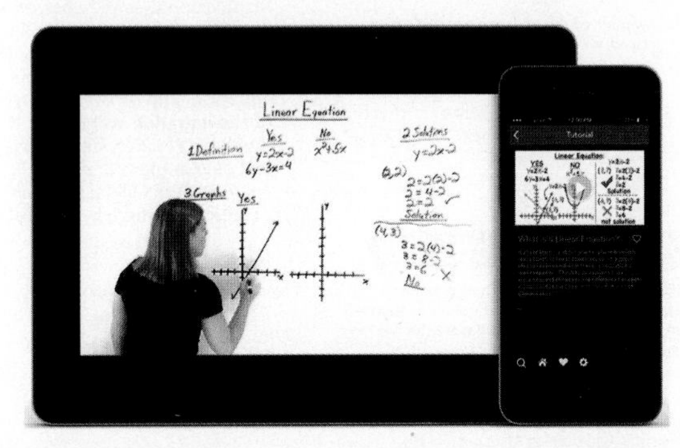

Students can also access the videos using the **BouncePages app** to scan exercise pages marked with this icon. Students can download both apps for free in their mobile devices' app store.

## Differentiated Intervention

**I** = Intervention **O** = On-Level **A** = Advanced

### Reteach to Build Understanding I

Provides scaffolded reteaching for the key lesson concepts.

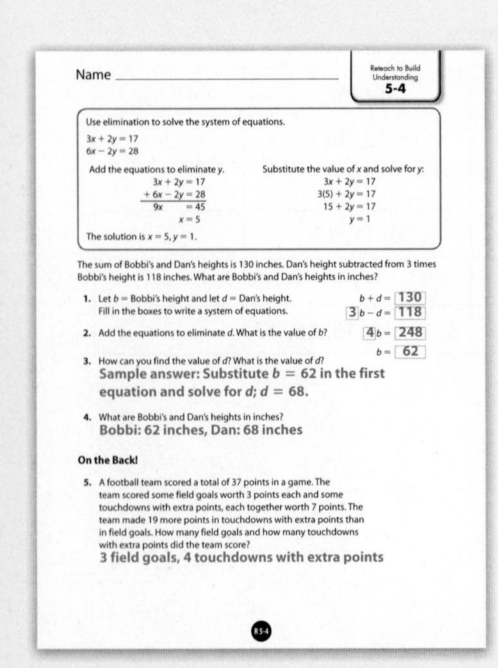

Name ______________ Reteach to Build Understanding **5-4**

Use elimination to solve the system of equations.
$3x + 2y = 17$
$6x - 2y = 28$

Add the equations to eliminate $y$.
$3x + 2y = 17$
$+ 6x - 2y = 28$
$9x = 45$
$x = 5$

Substitute the value of $x$ and solve for $y$:
$3x + 2y = 17$
$3(5) + 2y = 17$
$15 + 2y = 17$
$y = 1$

The solution is $x = 5, y = 1$.

The sum of Bobbi's and Dan's heights is 130 inches. Dan's height subtracted from 3 times Bobbi's height is 118 inches. What are Bobbi's and Dan's heights in inches?

1. Let $b$ = Bobbi's height and let $d$ = Dan's height. Fill in the boxes to write a system of equations. $b + d =$ **130**; **3**$b - d =$ **118**
2. Add the equations to eliminate $d$. What is the value of $b$? **4**$b =$ **248**; $b =$ **62**
3. How can you find the value of $d$? What is the value of $d$?
   **Sample answer: Substitute $b = 62$ in the first equation and solve for $d$; $d = 68$.**
4. What are Bobbi's and Dan's heights in inches?
   **Bobbi: 62 inches, Dan: 68 inches**

**On the Back!**

5. A football team scored a total of 37 points in a game. The team scored some field goals worth 3 points each and some touchdowns with extra points, each together worth 7 points. The team made 19 more points in touchdowns with extra points than in field goals. How many field goals and how many touchdowns with extra points did the team score?
   **3 field goals, 4 touchdowns with extra points**

R5-4

### Additional Vocabulary Support I O

Helps students develop and reinforce understanding of key terms and concepts.

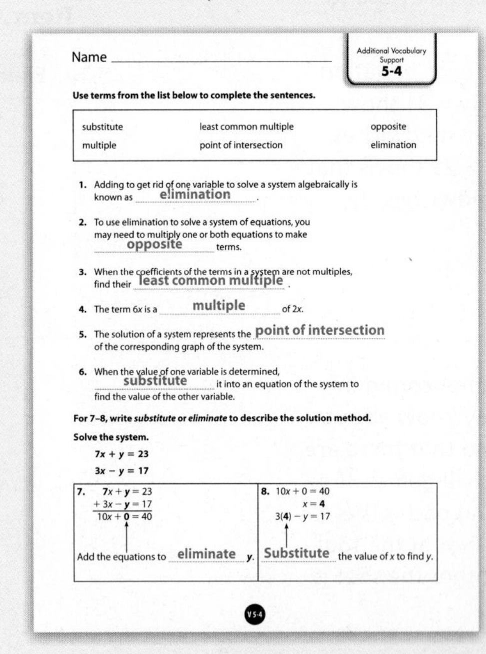

Name ______________ Additional Vocabulary Support **5-4**

**Use terms from the list below to complete the sentences.**

| substitute | least common multiple | opposite |
|---|---|---|
| multiple | point of intersection | elimination |

1. Adding to get rid of one variable to solve a system algebraically is known as **elimination**.
2. To use elimination to solve a system of equations, you may need to multiply one or both equations to make **opposite** terms.
3. When the coefficients of the terms in a system are not multiples, find their **least common multiple**.
4. The term $6x$ is a **multiple** of $2x$.
5. The solution of a system represents the **point of intersection** of the corresponding graph of the system.
6. When the value of one variable is determined, **substitute** it into an equation of the system to find the value of the other variable.

**For 7–8, write *substitute* or *eliminate* to describe the solution method.**

**Solve the system.**
$7x + y = 23$
$3x - y = 17$

| 7. $7x + y = 23$<br>$+ 3x - y = 17$<br>$10x + 0 = 40$<br>Add the equations to **eliminate** $y$. | 8. $10x + 0 = 40$<br>$x = 4$<br>$3(4) - y = 17$<br>**Substitute** the value of $x$ to find $y$. |
|---|---|

V5-4

### Build Mathematical Literacy I O

Provides support for struggling readers to build mathematical literacy.

Name ______________ Build Mathematical Literacy **5-4**

**Read the problem below. Then answer the questions to help you understand the problem.**

Lily exercises for a total of 150 minutes each week. She does weight training and cardio workouts. She spends more time doing cardio workouts. The difference between the time she spends on cardio workouts and the time she spends weight training is 72 minutes. How much time does Lily spend on each type of activity?

1. Highlight the question that you need to answer.
   **Check students' work.**
2. You can write a system of equations to represent this problem. What quantities should you represent with variables?
   **The number of minutes Lily spends on cardio workouts and the number of minutes Lily spends on weight training**
3. Circle the information in the problem that is represented by the equation $x + y = 150$ where $x$ represents cardio workouts and $y$ represents weight training.
   **Check students' work.**
4. Underline the information in the problem that you will use to write another equation.
   **Check students' work.**
5. Circle the equation that can represent the information you underlined in Exercise 4.
   $x + y = 72$ $y = 72x$ **($x - y = 72$)** $y = 72 - x$
6. Describe the correct answer to this problem, including the units.
   **Sample answer: The correct answer will be two lengths of time in minutes, the amount of time Lily spends on cardio workouts and the amount of time Lily spends weight training.**

M5-4

Go Online

Practice

Worksheets

Math Tools

Math Games

# Additional Practice

You may opt to have students complete the automatically scored Additional Practice items online.

### Item Analysis

| Example | Items | DOK |
|---|---|---|
| 1 | 1 | 1 |
| | 2, 4, 5 | 2 |
| 2 | 7, 8, 10 | 2 |
| 3 | 3, 6, 11 | 2 |
| | 9 | 3 |

**Interactive Practice** is available online.

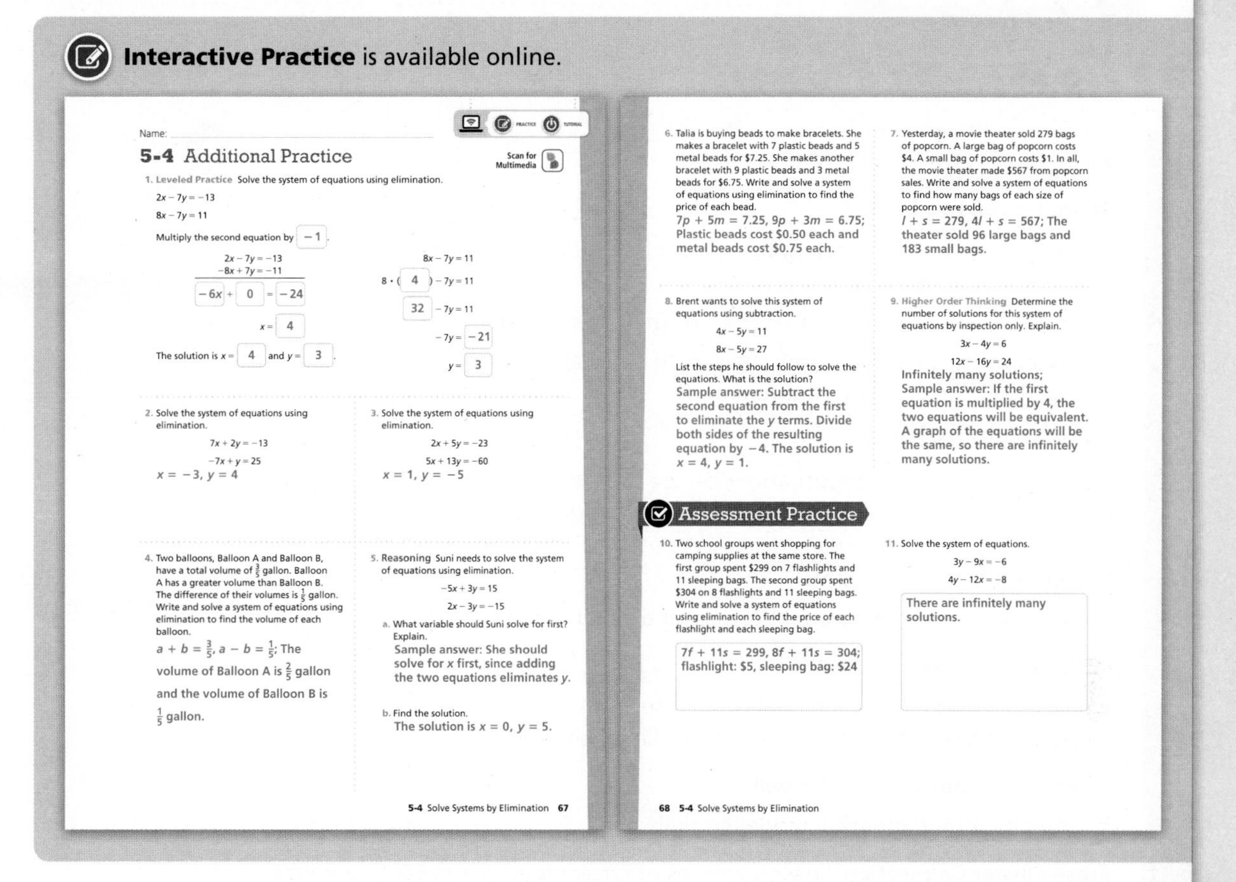

Name:

**5-4** Additional Practice

Scan for Multimedia

1. Leveled Practice Solve the system of equations using elimination.

$2x - 7y = -13$

$8x - 7y = 11$

Multiply the second equation by $-1$.

$2x - 7y = -13$
$-8x + 7y = -11$
$-6x + 0 = -24$
$x = 4$

$8x - 7y = 11$
$8 \cdot (4) - 7y = 11$
$32 - 7y = 11$
$-7y = -21$
$y = 3$

The solution is $x = 4$ and $y = 3$.

2. Solve the system of equations using elimination.
$7x + 2y = -13$
$-7x + y = 25$
$x = -3, y = 4$

3. Solve the system of equations using elimination.
$2x + 5y = -23$
$5x + 13y = -60$
$x = 1, y = -5$

4. Two balloons, Balloon A and Balloon B, have a total volume of $\frac{3}{5}$ gallon. Balloon A has a greater volume than Balloon B. The difference of their volumes is $\frac{1}{5}$ gallon. Write and solve a system of equations using elimination to find the volume of each balloon.
$a + b = \frac{3}{5}, a - b = \frac{1}{5}$; The volume of Balloon A is $\frac{2}{5}$ gallon and the volume of Balloon B is $\frac{1}{5}$ gallon.

5. Reasoning Suni needs to solve the system of equations using elimination.
$-5x + 3y = 15$
$2x - 3y = -15$
a. What variable should Suni solve for first? Explain.
Sample answer: She should solve for x first, since adding the two equations eliminates y.
b. Find the solution.
The solution is $x = 0, y = 5$.

5-4 Solve Systems by Elimination 67

6. Talia is buying beads to make bracelets. She makes a bracelet with 7 plastic beads and 5 metal beads for $7.25. She makes another bracelet with 9 plastic beads and 3 metal beads for $6.75. Write and solve a system of equations using elimination to find the price of each bead.
$7p + 5m = 7.25, 9p + 3m = 6.75$; Plastic beads cost $0.50 each and metal beads cost $0.75 each.

7. Yesterday, a movie theater sold 279 bags of popcorn. A large bag of popcorn costs $4. A small bag of popcorn costs $1. In all, the movie theater made $567 from popcorn sales. Write and solve a system of equations to find how many bags of each size of popcorn were sold.
$l + s = 279, 4l + s = 567$; The theater sold 96 large bags and 183 small bags.

8. Brent wants to solve this system of equations using subtraction.
$4x - 5y = 11$
$8x - 5y = 27$
List the steps he should follow to solve the equations. What is the solution?
Sample answer: Subtract the second equation from the first to eliminate the y terms. Divide both sides of the resulting equation by $-4$. The solution is $x = 4, y = 1$.

9. Higher Order Thinking Determine the number of solutions for this system of equations by inspection only. Explain.
$3x - 4y = 6$
$12x - 16y = 24$
Infinitely many solutions; Sample answer: If the first equation is multiplied by 4, the two equations will be equivalent. A graph of the equations will be the same, so there are infinitely many solutions.

Assessment Practice

10. Two school groups went shopping for camping supplies at the same store. The first group spent $299 on 7 flashlights and 11 sleeping bags. The second group spent $304 on 8 flashlights and 11 sleeping bags. Write and solve a system of equations using elimination to find the price of each flashlight and each sleeping bag.
$7f + 11s = 299, 8f + 11s = 304$; flashlight: $5, sleeping bag: $24

11. Solve the system of equations.
$3y - 9x = -6$
$4y - 12x = -8$
There are infinitely many solutions.

68 5-4 Solve Systems by Elimination

---

# Differentiated Intervention

I = Intervention   O = On-Level   A = Advanced

## Enrichment O A

Presents engaging problems and activities that extend the lesson concepts.

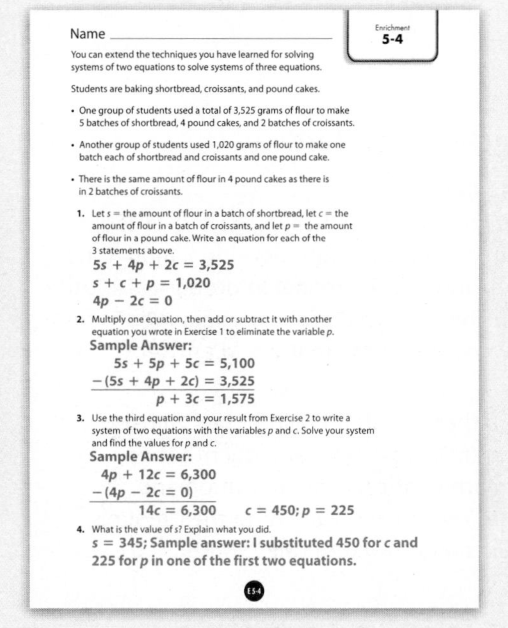

Name

Enrichment 5-4

You can extend the techniques you have learned for solving systems of two equations to solve systems of three equations.

Students are baking shortbread, croissants, and pound cakes.

- One group of students used a total of 3,525 grams of flour to make 5 batches of shortbread, 4 pound cakes, and 2 batches of croissants.
- Another group of students used 1,020 grams of flour to make one batch each of shortbread and croissants and one pound cake.
- There is the same amount of flour in 4 pound cakes as there is in 2 batches of croissants.

1. Let $s$ = the amount of flour in a batch of shortbread, let $c$ = the amount of flour in a batch of croissants, and let $p$ = the amount of flour in a pound cake. Write an equation for each of the 3 statements above.
$5s + 4p + 2c = 3,525$
$s + c + p = 1,020$
$4p - 2c = 0$

2. Multiply one equation, then add or subtract it with another equation you wrote in Exercise 1 to eliminate the variable $p$.
Sample Answer:
$5s + 5p + 5c = 5,100$
$-(5s + 4p + 2c) = 3,525$
$p + 3c = 1,575$

3. Use the third equation and your result from Exercise 2 to write a system of two equations with the variables $p$ and $c$. Solve your system and find the values for $p$ and $c$.
Sample Answer:
$4p + 12c = 6,300$
$-(4p - 2c = 0)$
$14c = 6,300$   $c = 450; p = 225$

4. What is the value of $s$? Explain what you did.
$s = 345$; Sample answer: I substituted 450 for $c$ and 225 for $p$ in one of the first two equations.

E54

## Math Tools and Games I O A

Offers additional activities and games to build understanding and fluency.

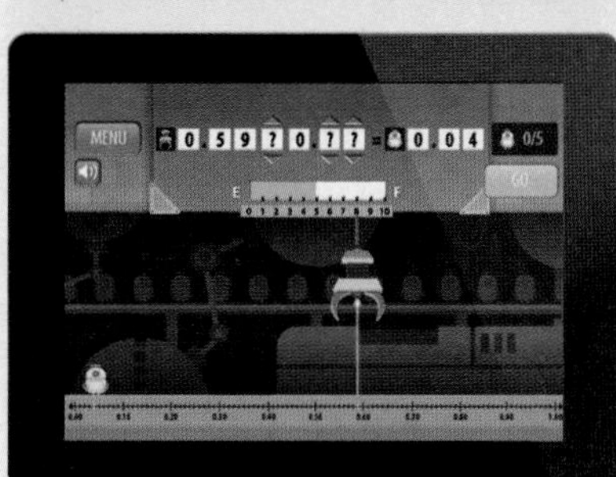


## Pick a Project and STEM Project I O A

Provides an additional opportunity for students to demonstrate understanding of key mathematical concepts.

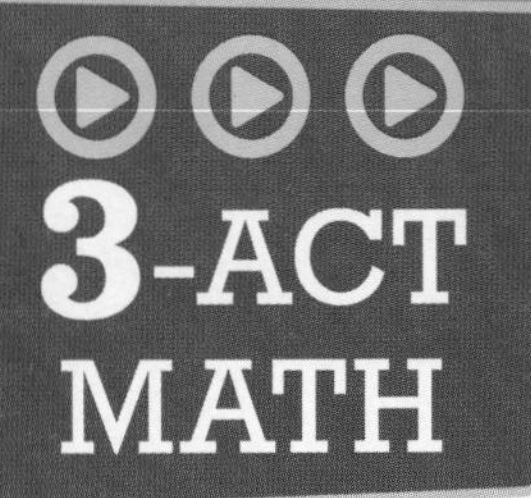


# 3-Act Mathematical Modeling: Ups and Downs

## Lesson Overview

### FOCUS

### Mathematics Objectives

**Students will be able to:**

- ✔ use mathematical modeling to represent a problem situation and to propose a solution.
- ✔ test and verify the appropriateness of their math models.
- ✔ explain why the results from their mathematical models may not align exactly to the problem situation.

### Essential Understanding

Many real-world problem situations can be represented with a mathematical model, but that model may not represent a real-world situation exactly.

### COHERENCE

**Earlier in this topic, students:**

- solved systems of linear equations using different methods.

**In this lesson, students:**

- develop a mathematical model to represent and propose a solution to a problem situation involving a system of linear equations.

**Later in this course, students will:**

- refine their mathematical modeling skills.

**Cross-Cluster Connection** Solving systems of linear equations (8.EE.3) connects to work with solving linear equations (8.EE.2) and linear functions (8.F.2).

### RIGOR

This mathematical modeling lesson focuses on **application** of both **math content** and **math practices** and **processes**.

- Students draw on their understanding of equality concepts to develop a representative model.
- Students apply their mathematical model to test and validate its applicability to similar problem situations.

## Math Anytime

### Today's Challenge

Use the Topic 5 problems any time during this topic.

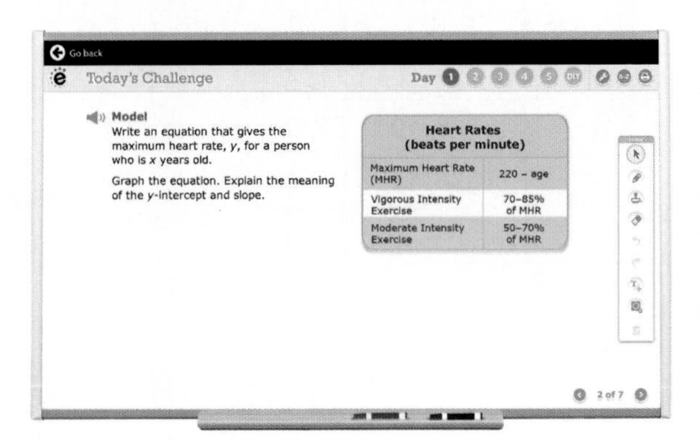


## Mathematics Overview | Common Core Standards

### Content Standards

In this lesson, students apply concepts and skills related to Common Core Standards **8.EE.C.8**, **8.SP.A.3**, and **8.F.B.4**.

**8.EE.C.8** Analyze and solve pairs of simultaneous linear equations.

- **8.SP.A.3** Use the equation of a linear model to solve problems in the context of bivariate measurement data, interpreting the slope and intercept.
- **8.F.B.4** Construct a function to model a linear relationship between two quantities. Determine the rate of change and initial value of the function from a description of a relationship or from two $(x, y)$ values, including reading these from a table or from a graph. Interpret the rate of change and initial value of a linear function in terms of the situation it models, and in terms of its graph or a table of values.

### Mathematical Practice Standards

**MP.4 Model with Mathematics**

The focus of this lesson is on mathematical modeling. Students identify the relationship among variables, develop a model that represents the situation, and use the model to propose a solution. Students interpret their solutions and propose explanations for why their answers may not match the real-world answer.

As students carry out mathematical modeling, they will also engage in sense-making (**MP.1**), abstract and quantitative reasoning (**MP.2**), and mathematical communication and argumentation (**MP.3**). In testing and validating their models, students look for patterns and structure (**MP.7**, **MP.8**).

# 3-Act Mathematical Modeling

Go Online

Video

## ACT 1 The Hook

Students will be tasked with determining whether taking the stairs or taking the elevator is faster.

### Play the Video and Brainstorm Questions

Have students complete **Question 1**. Encourage them to consider the situation and ask any questions that arise. Listen for interesting mathematical and non-mathematical questions. Ask students what makes each question interesting.

**Q:** What questions do you have? [Sample questions: Where are they going? Why did she take the stairs? How many floors are they traveling?]

### Pose the Main Question

After the question brainstorming, pose the Main Question students will be tasked with answering. Have students complete **Question 2**.

**Main Question**

**Q:** Which route is faster?

### Ask about Conjectures

Have students complete **Questions 3 and 4**. You can survey the class for the range of predictions.

**Q:** Why do you think your prediction is the answer to the Main Question?

**Q:** Who had a similar prediction?

**Q:** How many of you agree with that prediction?

**Q:** Who has a different prediction?

**3-Act Math Video** is available online.

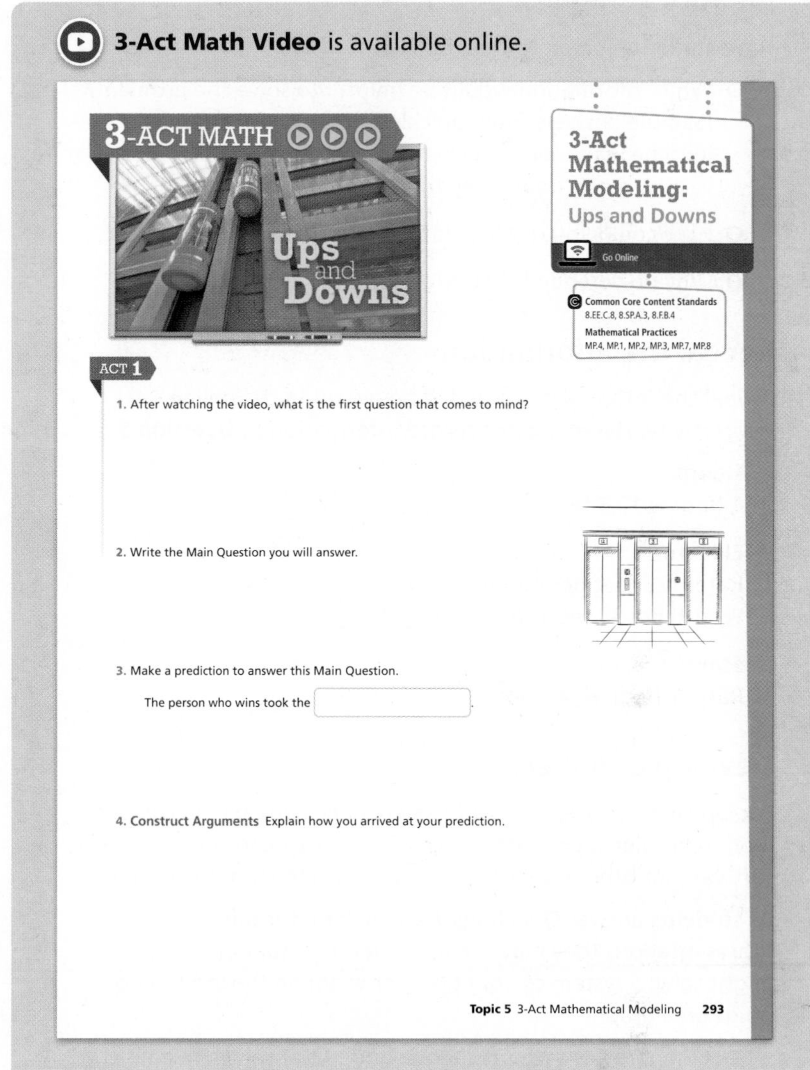
3-ACT MATH

Ups and Downs

3-Act Mathematical Modeling: Ups and Downs

Go Online

Common Core Content Standards
8.EE.C.8, 8.SP.A.3, 8.F.B.4

Mathematical Practices
MP.4, MP.1, MP.2, MP.3, MP.7, MP.8

ACT 1

1. After watching the video, what is the first question that comes to mind?

2. Write the Main Question you will answer.

3. Make a prediction to answer this Main Question.

The person who wins took the ______.

4. **Construct Arguments** Explain how you arrived at your prediction.

**Topic 5** 3-Act Mathematical Modeling **293**

# 3-Act Mathematical Modeling *continued*

## ACT 2 The Model 

### Identify Variables

Have students complete **Questions 5**.

**Q:** What information would be helpful to solve the problem? [Sample answers: How quickly she walks down stairs; how long he waits for the elevator; what the rate of the elevator is; how many floors they travel]

**Q:** How could you get that information?

**Q:** Why do you need that information?

### Reveal the Information

Reveal the information provided below using the online interactivity. Have students record information in **Question 5**.

Floors:
1 floor = 12.5 feet

**Elevator**
Rate: 125 feet per minute
Wait time: 38 seconds

**Stairs**
Rate: 1 floor, 8 seconds

### Develop a Model

For **Question 6,** students might select pencil and paper, concrete models, a ruler, a protractor, a calculator, a spreadsheet, digital software, or other grade-appropriate tools to solve the problem.

As students answer **Questions 7** and **8**, look for different representations they may use to model the situation. They might solve a system of equations, or examine the intersection point on a graph.

**Q:** Compare the rates of change and initial values. [Sample answer: The rate of change is greater for the stairs. The initial value for the stairs is 0, and the initial value for the elevator is 38.]

 **3-Act Math Activity** is available online.

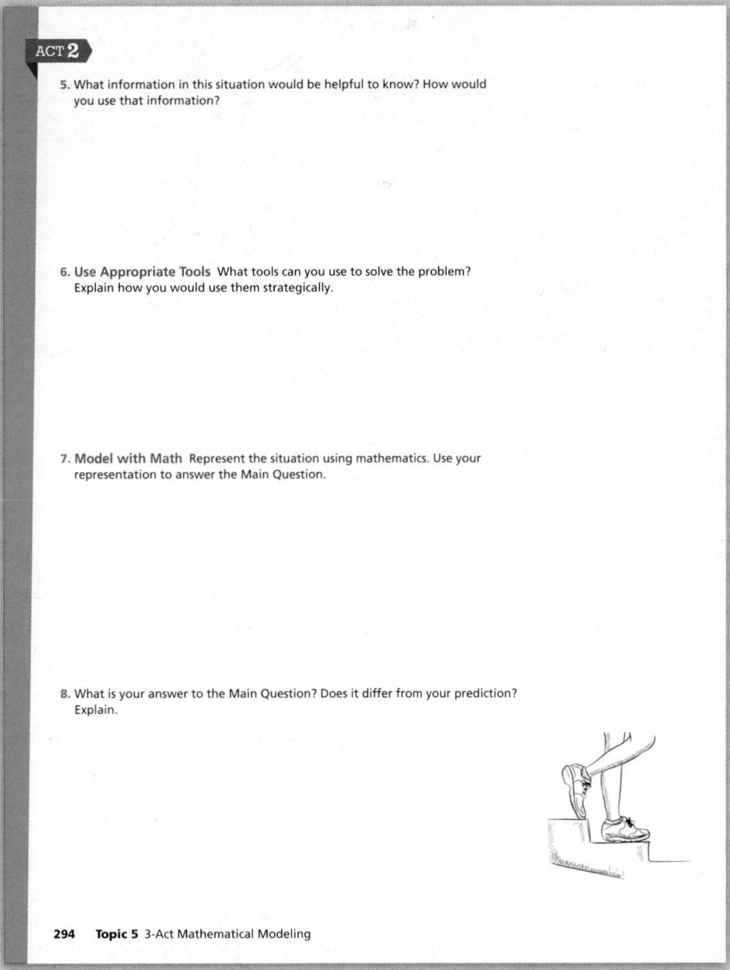

ACT 2

5. What information in this situation would be helpful to know? How would you use that information?

6. Use Appropriate Tools What tools can you use to solve the problem? Explain how you would use them strategically.

7. Model with Math Represent the situation using mathematics. Use your representation to answer the Main Question.

8. What is your answer to the Main Question? Does it differ from your prediction? Explain.

294 Topic 5 3-Act Mathematical Modeling

### Use the Model to Propose a Solution

After students answer **Questions 7 and 8**, facilitate a discussion about solution methods. If needed, project the possible student solutions (shown below).

### Possible Student Solutions

**Sasha's Work**

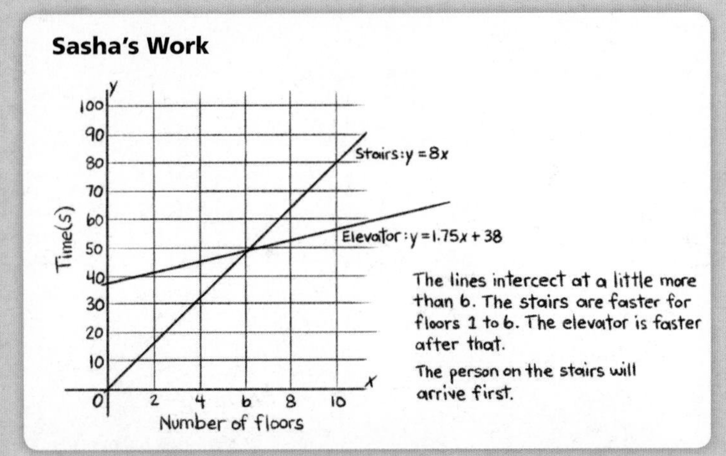


**Sasha** graphs both equations and estimates the solution. She uses the values of the equations on either side of the intersection point to answer the question.

**Hunter's Work**

$y = 1.75x + 38$
$y = 8x$
Substitute 8x for y.
$8x = 1.75x + 38$
$6.25x = 38$
$x = 6.08$

They take the same amount of time for 6.08 floors. The person in the elevator doesn't pass the person on the stairs until between the sixth and seventh floors.

**Hunter** also writes a system of equations and then uses the substitution method to solve for x. He interprets the meaning of the intersection point and uses rates to answer the question.

Go Online

Video

# ACT 3 The Solution and Sequel 

**3-Act Math Video** is available online.

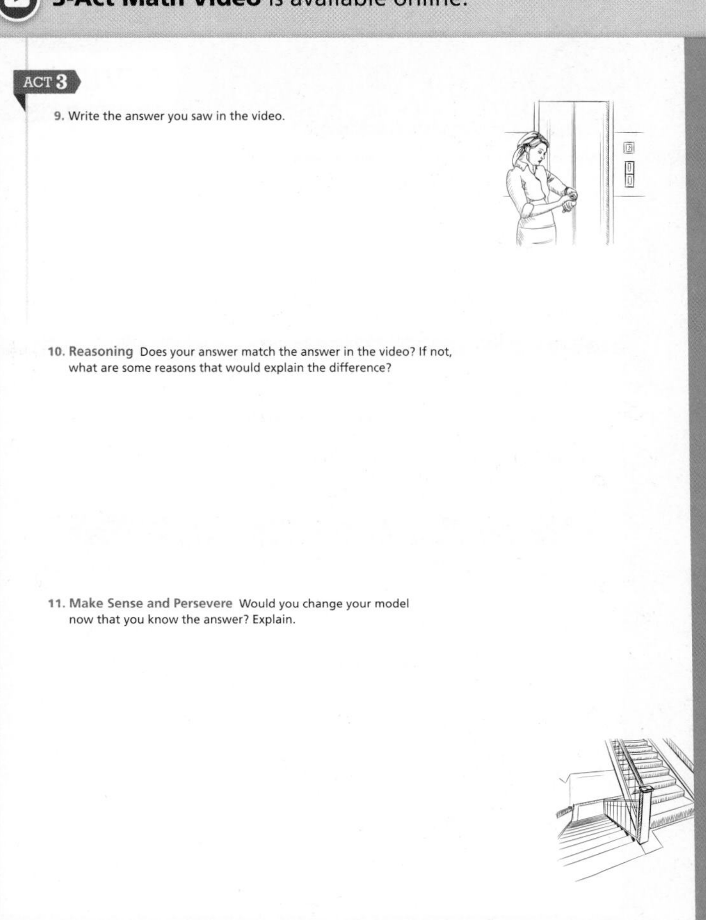

ACT 3

9. Write the answer you saw in the video.

10. **Reasoning** Does your answer match the answer in the video? If not, what are some reasons that would explain the difference?

11. **Make Sense and Persevere** Would you change your model now that you know the answer? Explain.

**Topic 5** 3-Act Mathematical Modeling **295**

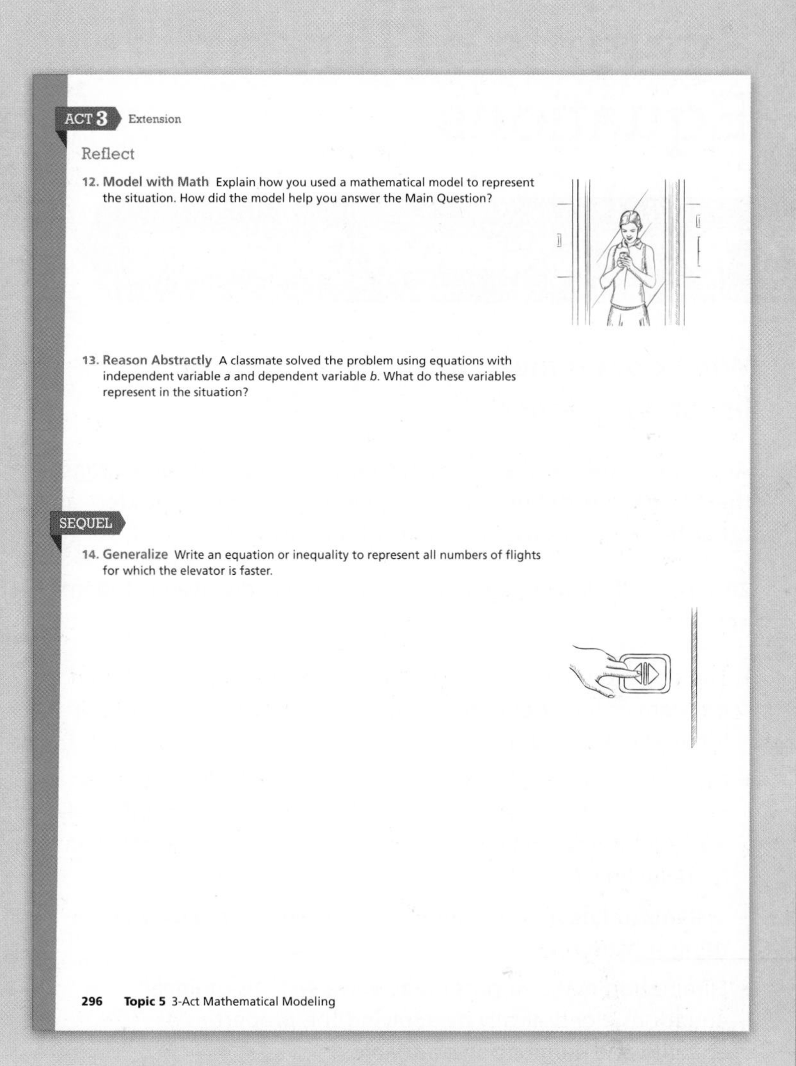

ACT 3 Extension

Reflect

12. **Model with Math** Explain how you used a mathematical model to represent the situation. How did the model help you answer the Main Question?

13. **Reason Abstractly** A classmate solved the problem using equations with independent variable *a* and dependent variable *b*. What do these variables represent in the situation?

SEQUEL

14. **Generalize** Write an equation or inequality to represent all numbers of flights for which the elevator is faster.

**296** **Topic 5** 3-Act Mathematical Modeling

## Use the Video to Reveal the Answer

The final part of the video shows the entire trip for both friends. Have students complete **Question 9**. Congratulate the students who were closest to the actual answer.

### Main Question Answer

**The person who arrives first took the stairs.**

## Validate Conclusions

After students complete **Questions 10 and 11**, encourage them to discuss possible sources of error inherent in using math to model real-world situations. Look for students to point out that their models are still useful even though they are not perfect.

**Q:** Why does your answer not match the answer in the video? [Sample answer: Neither rate is exactly constant. The elevator has to speed up and slow down, for example.]

**Q:** How useful was your model at predicting the answer?

**Q:** How could your model better represent the situation?

## Reflect on Thinking

**Reason Abstractly** If time allows, have students complete **Questions 12 and 13** as an extension. Use this opportunity to discuss how students incorporate mathematical processes during the task.

## Pose the Sequel

**Generalize** Use **Question 14** to present a similar problem situation involving solving systems of equations. You can assign to early finishers or as homework so students can test the usefulness of their models.

**Q:** Write an equation or inequality to represent all numbers of flights for which the elevator is faster.

Using their models and the answer in the video, look for students to use an inequality, such as $x > 6$ or $x \geq 7$.

**Q:** Would you expect the same answer if they both went up 6 floors? Explain. [Sample answer: No; it takes longer to walk up a flight of stairs than down one.]

Go Online

Glossary

# Analyze and Solve Systems of Linear Equations

## ? Topic Essential Question

**What does it mean to solve a system of linear equations?**

As students answer the Essential Question in writing, encourage them to include definitions, examples, non-examples, models, and other representations that support their answers.

Be sure the following are made explicit while discussing students' answers.

- The slope and *y*-intercept can help determine by inspection if a system of linear equations has no solution, one solution, or infinitely many solutions.
- Graphing systems of linear equations makes it possible to determine if the lines have one point of intersection, infinitely many solutions (all points lie on the same line), or no solution (parallel lines).
- Systems of linear equations can be solved algebraically by using substitution.
- Elimination makes it possible to solve systems of linear equations algebraically by applying the properties of equality and eliminating a variable.

Available Online

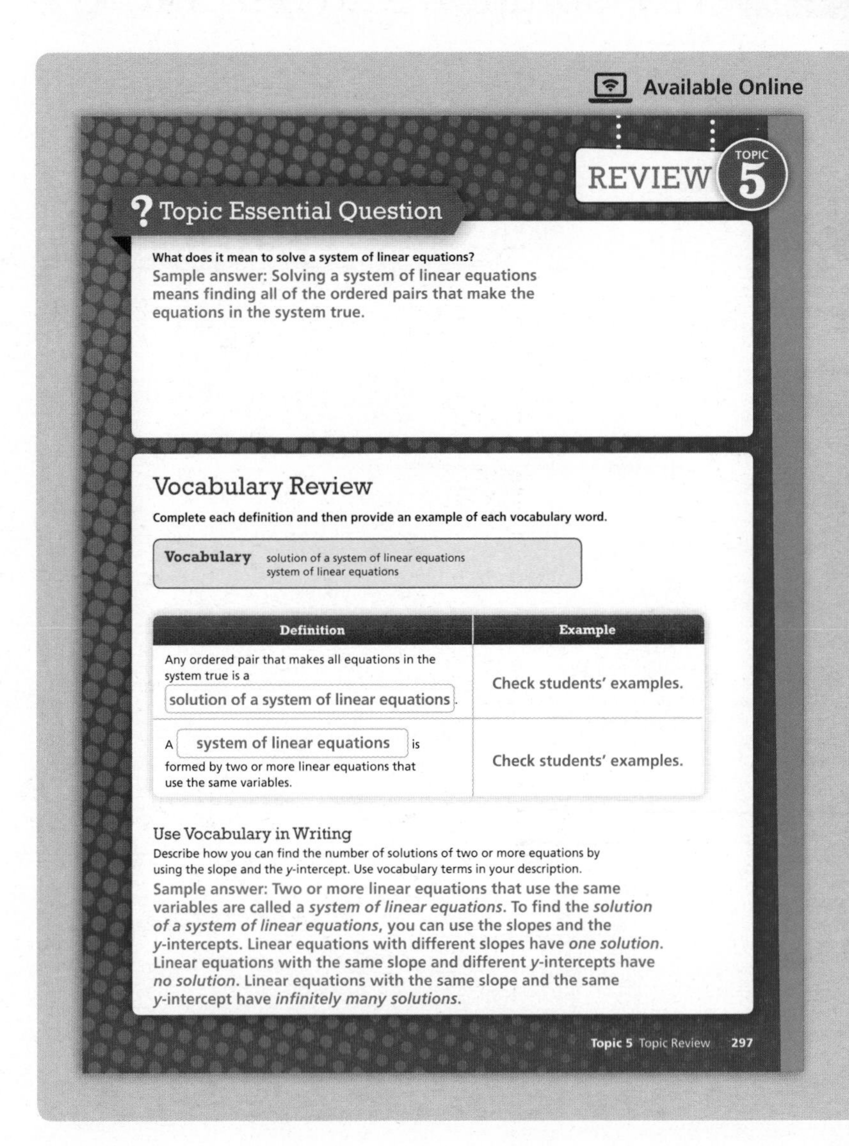

REVIEW TOPIC 5

? Topic Essential Question

What does it mean to solve a system of linear equations?

Sample answer: Solving a system of linear equations means finding all of the ordered pairs that make the equations in the system true.

Vocabulary Review

Complete each definition and then provide an example of each vocabulary word.

**Vocabulary** solution of a system of linear equations; system of linear equations

| Definition | Example |
|---|---|
| Any ordered pair that makes all equations in the system true is a solution of a system of linear equations. | Check students' examples. |
| A system of linear equations is formed by two or more linear equations that use the same variables. | Check students' examples. |

Use Vocabulary in Writing

Describe how you can find the number of solutions of two or more equations by using the slope and the *y*-intercept. Use vocabulary terms in your description.

Sample answer: Two or more linear equations that use the same variables are called a *system of linear equations*. To find the *solution of a system of linear equations*, you can use the slopes and the *y*-intercepts. Linear equations with different slopes have *one solution*. Linear equations with the same slope and different *y*-intercepts have *no solution*. Linear equations with the same slope and the same *y*-intercept have *infinitely many solutions*.

Topic 5 Topic Review 297

## Vocabulary Review

**ORAL LANGUAGE** Before students complete the page, reinforce oral language by using one or more of the following activities.

- Have students brainstorm synonyms of the words *system*, *solution*, *intersection*, *elimination*, and *substitution*, and share their findings with the class.
- Have students discuss the properties of equality and what they mean. Then have them work in groups to create a system of equations and discuss the steps needed to solve by elimination using these properties.

**WRITING IN MATH** After students complete the page, you can further reinforce writing in math by doing the following activity.

- Have students work in groups to create a real-world problem that involves a system of linear equations with no solution, one solution, or infinitely many solutions.

# Concepts and Skills Review

Available Online

## Concepts and Skills Review

### LESSON 5-1 Estimate Solutions by Inspection

**Quick Review**

**The slopes and $y$-intercepts of the linear equations in a system determine the relationship between the lines and the number of solutions.**

| | Same Slope? | Same y-intercept? |
|---|---|---|
| No Solution | Yes | No |
| One Solution | No | n/a |
| Infinitely Many Solutions | Yes | Yes |

**Example**

**How many solutions does the system of equations have? Explain.**

$y + 2x = 6$

$y - 8 = -2x$

Write each equation in slope-intercept form.

$y = -2x + 6$

$y = -2x + 8$

Identify the slope and $y$-intercept of each equation.

For the equation $y = -2x + 6$, the slope is $-2$ and the $y$-intercept is 6.

For the equation $y = -2x + 8$, the slope is $-2$ and the $y$-intercept is 8.

The equations have the same slope but different $y$-intercepts, so the system has no solution.

**Practice**

**Determine whether the system of equations has one solution, no solution, or infinitely many solutions.**

**1.** $y - 13 = 5x$
$y - 5x = 12$
**No solution**

**2.** $y = 2x + 10$
$3y - 6x = 30$
**Infinitely many solutions**

**3.** $-3x + \frac{1}{3}y = 12$
$2y = 18x + 72$
**Infinitely many solutions**

**4.** $y - \frac{1}{4}x = -1$
$y - 2 = 4x$
**One solution**

**5.** Michael and Ashley each buy $x$ pounds of turkey and $y$ pounds of ham. Turkey costs \$3 per pound at Store A and \$4.50 per pound at Store B. Ham costs \$4 per pound at Store A and \$6 per pound at Store B. Michael spends \$18 at Store A, and Ashley spends \$27 at Store B. Could Michael and Ashley have bought the same amount of turkey and ham? Explain.
**Yes; Sample answer: Use the equation $3x + 4y = 18$ for Michael and the equation $4.5x + 6y = 27$ for Ashley. Both equations can be written as $y = -0.75x + 4.5$. Since the lines have the same slope and same $y$-intercept, they are the same. There are infinitely many solutions for which $x$ and $y$ are the same for Michael and Ashley. They must have bought the same amount of turkey and ham.**



### LESSON 5-2 Solve Systems by Graphing

**Quick Review**

**Systems of equations can be solved by looking at their graphs. A system with one solution has one point of intersection. A system with infinitely many solutions has infinite points of intersection. A system with no solution has no points of intersection.**

**Example**

**Graph the system and determine its solution.**

$y = x + 4$

$y = -2x + 1$

Graph each equation in the system on the same coordinate plane.

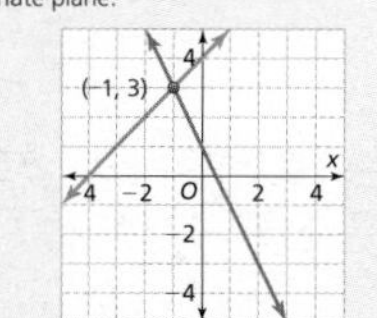


The point of intersection is $(-1, 3)$. This means the solution to the system is $(-1, 3)$.

**Practice**

**Graph each system and find the solution(s).**

**1.** $y = \frac{1}{2}x + 1$
$-2x + 4y = 4$

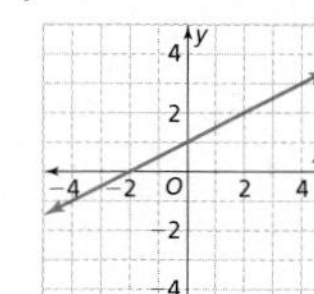


**Infinitely many solutions**

**2.** $y = -x - 3$
$y + x = 2$

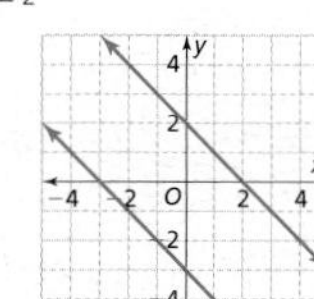


**No solution**

**3.** $2y = 6x + 4$
$y = -2x + 2$

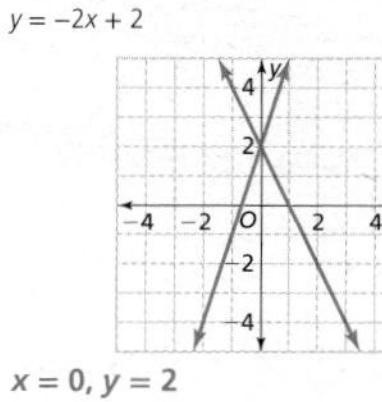


$x = 0, y = 2$

Available Online

LESSON 5-3 **Solve Systems by Substitution**

Quick Review

**To solve a system by substitution, write one equation for a variable in terms of the other. Substitute the expression into the other equation and solve. If the result is false, the system has no solution. If true, it has infinitely many solutions. If the result is a value, substitute to solve for the other variable.**

Example

**Use substitution to solve the system.**

$y = x + 1$
$y = 5x - 3$

Substitute $x + 1$ for $y$ in the second equation.

$(x + 1) = 5x - 3$
$4 = 4x$
$1 = x$

Substitute 1 for $x$ in the first equation.

$y = (1) + 1 = 2$

The solution is $x = 1$, $y = 2$.

Practice

**Use substitution to solve each system.**

1. $-3y = -2x - 1$
   $y = x - 1$
   **$x = 4$, $y = 3$**
2. $y = 5x + 2$
   $2y - 4 = 10x$
   **Infinitely many solutions**
3. $2y - 8 = 6x$
   $y = 3x + 2$
   **No solution**
4. $2y - 2 = 4x$
   $y = -x + 4$
   **$x = 1$, $y = 3$**

LESSON 5-4 **Solve Systems by Elimination**

Quick Review

**To solve a system by elimination, multiply one or both equations to make opposite terms. Add (or subtract) the equations to eliminate one variable. Substitute to solve for the other variable.**

Example

**Use elimination to solve the system.**

$2x - 9y = -5$
$4x - 6y = 2$

Multiply the first equation by −2. Then add.

$-4x + 18y = 10$
$4x - 6y = 2$
$12y = 12$
$y = 1$

Substitute 1 for $y$ in the first equation.

$2x - 9(1) = -5$
$2x - 9 = -5$
$2x = 4$
$x = 2$

The solution is $x = 2$, $y = 1$.

Practice

**Use elimination to solve each system.**

1. $-2x + 2y = 2$
   $4x - 4y = 4$
   **No solution**
2. $4x + 6y = 40$
   $-2x + y = 4$
   **$x = 1$, $y = 6$**
3. A customer at a concession stand bought 2 boxes of popcorn and 3 drinks for $12. Another customer bought 3 boxes of popcorn and 5 drinks for $19. How much does a box of popcorn cost? How much does a drink cost?
   **Box of popcorn: $3; drink: $2**

# Fluency Practice

Go Online

Games

## Pathfinder

Students maintain fluency with solving multi-step equations using the distributive property as they complete a game activity that reinforces mathematical practices.

**Getting Started** Students may work independently or with a partner. Go over the directions. Point out that each equation must be solved using the distributive property.

Students should solve each problem and compete their own puzzle. Encourage students to record their work on a separate sheet of paper.

**As Students Do the Activity** Remind students that they must follow the path of the solutions from least to greatest.

Some students may find all of the answers first and then shade in the path to follow. Allow this strategy as it provides the same fluency practice.

**Another Activity** Have students work together to write a new set of equations that involve the distributive property that result in a different path in the puzzle. Ask them to record the new clues on a separate sheet of paper.

Extra Challenge Create your own Pathfinder puzzle activity. Write a new problem for each clue and use paper to create the puzzle. Then trade your activity with a partner and complete your partner's Pathfinder activity.

Available Online

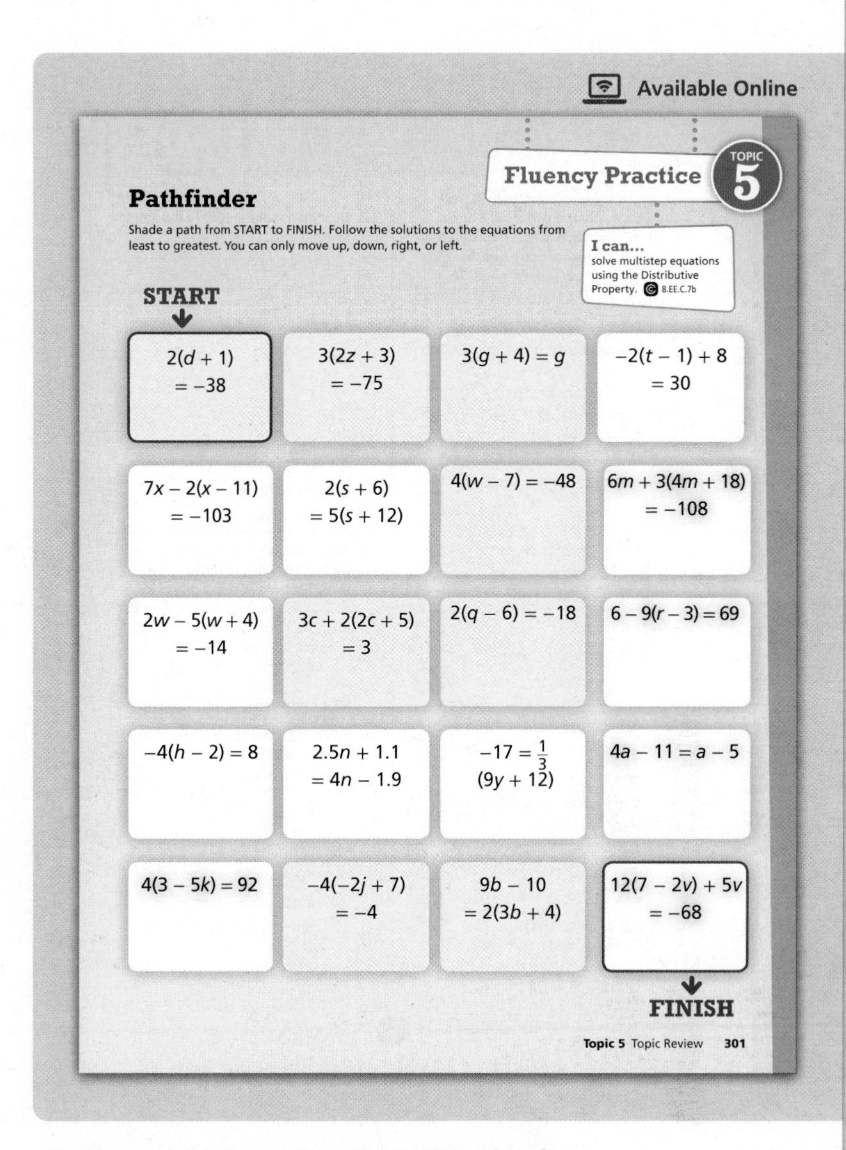

Fluency Practice TOPIC 5

**Pathfinder**

Shade a path from START to FINISH. Follow the solutions to the equations from least to greatest. You can only move up, down, right, or left.

**I can...** solve multistep equations using the Distributive Property. 8.EE.C.7b

START

| | | | |
|---|---|---|---|
| $2(d+1) = -38$ | $3(2z+3) = -75$ | $3(g+4) = g$ | $-2(t-1)+8 = 30$ |
| $7x - 2(x-11) = -103$ | $2(s+6) = 5(s+12)$ | $4(w-7) = -48$ | $6m + 3(4m+18) = -108$ |
| $2w - 5(w+4) = -14$ | $3c + 2(2c+5) = 3$ | $2(q-6) = -18$ | $6 - 9(r-3) = 69$ |
| $-4(h-2) = 8$ | $2.5n + 1.1 = 4n - 1.9$ | $-17 = \frac{1}{3}(9y+12)$ | $4a - 11 = a - 5$ |
| $4(3-5k) = 92$ | $-4(-2j+7) = -4$ | $9b - 10 = 2(3b+4)$ | $12(7-2v) + 5v = -68$ |

FINISH

Topic 5 Topic Review 301

### Common Core Content Standards

**8.EE.C.7b** Solve linear equations with rational number coefficients, including equations whose solutions require expanding expressions using the distributive property and collecting like terms.

### Mathematical Practices

MP.1, MP.7, MP.8

# Assessment

Go Online

Assess

Available Online

Name ______________________

Topic 5
Assessment
Form A

1. Two students are reading a novel. Ashley reads 10 pages per day. Carly reads 8 pages per day, but she starts early and is already on page 40. **3 points**

**Part A**

Write a system of equations to represent the situation, using $d$ for days and $p$ for pages.

$p = 10d, p = 8d + 40$

**Part B**

Graph the system of equations.

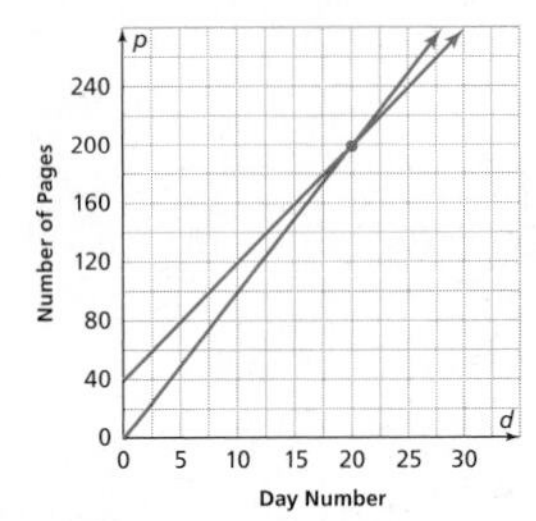


**Part C**

What does the point of intersection of the graph tell you?

**Sample answer: On day 20, both girls should be on page 200.**

2. How many solutions does the system of equations have? **1 point**

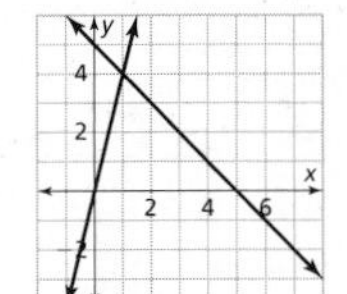


Ⓐ No solution
Ⓑ One solution: $x = 0, y = 5$
Ⓒ One solution: $x = 1, y = 4$
Ⓓ Infinitely many solutions

3. Adventure Play sells an mp3 player for $18.00 and charges $3.25 per song. King Music sells a player for $23.00 and charges $2.00 per song. For how many songs will the cost be the same? **1 point**

Ⓐ 3 songs
Ⓑ 4 songs
Ⓒ 5 songs
Ⓓ 6 songs

4. Solve the system of equations using elimination. How many solutions does the system have? **1 point**

$15j + 12k = 18$
$5j + 4k = 6$

Ⓐ No solution
Ⓑ One solution: $j = 3, k = 3$
Ⓒ One solution: $j = 10, k = 8$
Ⓓ Infinitely many solutions

Assessment, Form A 1 of 2

5. Solve the system of equations using elimination. **1 point**

$15q - 4r = 62$
$5q + 8r = 86$

Ⓐ $q = -7, r = -6$
Ⓑ $q = 6, r = 7$
Ⓒ $q = -7, r = -7$
Ⓓ $q = 6, r = 6$

6. What is the solution of the system of equations? Explain. **1 point**

$18x + 15 - y = 0$
$5y = 90x + 12$

**No solution; Sample answer: 75 = 12 is not a true statement.**

7. Use substitution. What is the solution of the system of equations? Explain. **1 point**

$y = \frac{1}{2}x + 2$
$2y = x + 4$

**Infinitely many solutions; Sample answer: The two equations represent the same line.**

8. Sia sells large candles for $3 each and small candles for $2 each. She sold 17 candles for $46.00. How many of each size candle did she sell? **1 point**

Ⓐ 4 small and 13 large candles
Ⓑ 5 small and 12 large candles
Ⓒ 12 small and 5 large candles
Ⓓ 13 small and 4 large candles

9. Bowler World charges $5.00 to rent shoes and $1.10 per game. Lucky Spares charges $3.00 for shoes and $1.50 per game. **2 points**

**Part A**

Write a system of equations to represent the situation, using $g$ for number of games and $c$ for cost.

$c = 1.1g + 5,$
$c = 1.5g + 3$

**Part B**

For how many games is the cost the same for both locations? What is that cost?

**5 games; $10.50**

10. A 40-question test has 108 possible points. There are $m$ 4-point questions and $n$ 2-point questions. How many of each type of questions are on the test? **1 point**

Ⓐ $m = 19, n = 21$
Ⓑ $m = 26, n = 14$
Ⓒ $m = 14, n = 26$
Ⓓ $m = 21, n = 19$

Assessment, Form A 2 of 2

Assess students' understanding of the topic concepts and skills using the Topic Assessments found online.

Use the Item Analysis Chart on the facing page to assign intervention to students based on their scores on the paper and pencil version of the Topic Assessments.

You may opt to have students take the Topic Assessment online. The online assessment is auto-scored, with differentiated intervention automatically assigned to students based on their scores.

You can use ExamView to generate additional Topic Assessments.

There are two versions of the Topic Assessment, Form A and Form B. These parallel versions assess the same content item for item. The Item Analysis chart on the next page can be used with both versions.

## Scoring Guide: Forms A and B

| Score | Recommendations |
|---|---|
| Greater Than 85% | Assign the corresponding MDIS for items answered incorrectly. Use Enrichment activities with the student. |
| 70%–85% | Assign the corresponding MDIS for items answered incorrectly. You may also assign Reteach to Build Understanding and Virtual Nerd Video assets for the lessons correlated to the items the student answered incorrectly. |
| Less Than 70% | Assign the corresponding MDIS for items answered incorrectly. Assign appropriate intervention lessons available online. You may also assign Reteach to Build Understanding, Additional Vocabulary Support, Build Mathematical Literacy, and Virtual Nerd Video assets for the lessons correlated to the items the student answered incorrectly. |

Go Online

Assess

Available Online

Name ______________________

Topic 5
Assessment
Form B

1. Two students are reading a book. Keith reads 6 pages a day. Tameka reads 5 pages a day, but he starts sooner and has already read 15 pages. **3 points**

**Part A**

Write a system of equations to represent the situation, using *d* for days and *p* for pages.

$p = 6d, p = 5d + 15$

**Part B**

Graph the system of equations.

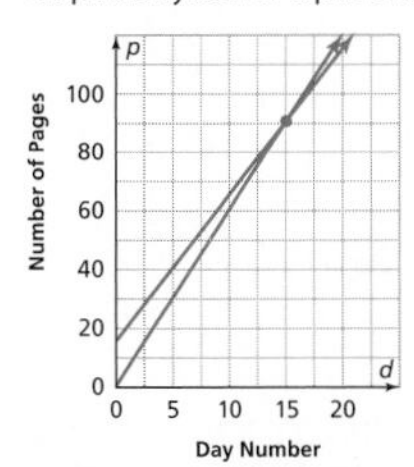

**Part C**

Will Keith and Tameka ever be on the same page on the same day? Explain.

**Yes; Sample answer: On Day 15, both students should be on page 90.**

2. How many solutions does the system of equations have? **1 point**

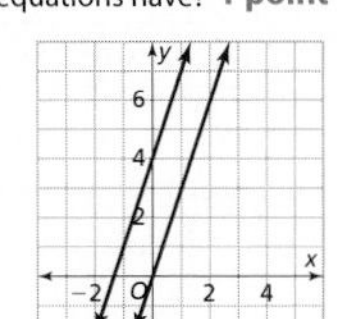

(A) No solution
(B) One solution: $x = 0, y = 0$
(C) One solution: $x = 0, y = 5$
(D) Infinitely many solutions

3. Taxi A charges a fee of \$3.50, plus \$1.75 per mile. Taxi B charges a fee of \$1.25, plus \$2.00 per mile. At what distance would the taxis cost the same? **1 point**

(A) 2 miles
(B) 5 miles
(C) 9 miles
(D) 15 miles

4. Solve the system of equations. How many solutions does the system have? **1 point**

$6x + 3y = 24$
$y = -2x + 8$

(A) No solution
(B) One solution: $x = 2, y = 4$
(C) One solution: $x = 3, y = 2$
(D) Infinitely many solutions



5. Solve the system of equations using elimination. **1 point**

$72f - 12g = 96$
$6f - 2g = 10$

(A) $f = -2, g = 1$
(B) $f = -1, g = 2$
(C) $f = 1, g = -2$
(D) $f = 2, g = -1$

6. What is the solution to the system of equations? Explain. **1 point**

$16x - 2 - 2y = 0$
$y = 8x + 4$

**No solution; Sample answer: $-10 = 0$ is not a true statement.**

7. Use substitution. What is the solution to the system of equations? Explain. **1 point**

$y = \frac{1}{4}x + 4$
$12y - 48 = 3x$

**Infinitely many solutions; Sample answer: The equations represent the same line.**

8. Nia sells pizzas. Large pizzas cost \$8 each, and small pizzas cost \$6 each. She sold 12 pizzas for \$84. How many of each size pizza did Nia sell? **1 point**

(A) 4 small and 8 large pizzas
(B) 5 small and 7 large pizzas
(C) 6 small and 6 large pizzas
(D) 10 small and 2 large pizzas

9. Ice Dream charges \$4 to rent ice skates, plus \$1.50 per hour to skate. Skating Paradise charges \$1 to rent ice skates, plus \$3 per hour to skate. **2 points**

**Part A**

Write a system of equations to represent the situation, using *h* for number of hours and *c* for cost.

$c = 1.5h + 4,$
$c = 3h + 1$

**Part B**

For how many hours is the cost for both locations equivalent? What is this cost?

**2 hours; \$7.00**

10. A 40-question test has 132 possible points. There are *m* 5-point questions and *n* 1-point questions. How many of each type of question is on the test? **1 point**

(A) $m = 23, n = 17$
(B) $m = 25, n = 25$
(C) $m = 30, n = 20$
(D) $m = 35, n = 15$

## Item Analysis for Diagnosis and Intervention: Forms A and B

| Item | Points | DOK | MDIS | Standard |
|---|---|---|---|---|
| 1A | 1 | 2 | K35 | 8.EE.C.8b, 8.EE.C.8c |
| 1B | 1 | 2 | K34 | 8.EE.C.8a, 8.EE.C.8b |
| 1C | 1 | 2 | K35 | 8.EE.C.8a |
| 2 | 1 | 1 | K33 | 8.EE.C.8a, 8.EE.C.8b |
| 3 | 1 | 2 | K34 | 8.EE.C.8b, 8.EE.C.8c |
| 4 | 1 | 2 | K35 | 8.EE.C.8b, 8.EE.C.8c |
| 5 | 1 | 2 | K36 | 8.EE.C.8b |

| Item | Points | DOK | MDIS | Standard |
|---|---|---|---|---|
| 6 | 1 | 3 | K34 | 8.EE.C.8b |
| 7 | 1 | 3 | K35 | 8.EE.C.8b, 8.EE.C.8c |
| 8 | 1 | 2 | K35 | 8.EE.C.8b, 8.EE.C.8c |
| 9A | 1 | 2 | K35 | 8.EE.C.8c |
| 9B | 1 | 2 | K35 | 8.EE.C.8a, 8.EE.C.8c |
| 10 | 1 | 2 | K34 | 8.EE.C.8b, 8.EE.C.8c |

# TOPIC 5 Performance Task

Go Online

Assess

Assess students' ability to apply the topic concepts and skills using the Topic Performance Tasks found online.

Available Online

Name ______________________

Topic 5
Performance Task
Form A

Jayden and Carson are selling T-shirts and sweatshirts with the school logo. Jayden sells 9 T-shirts and 3 sweatshirts for \$288. Carson sells 1 T-shirt and 6 sweatshirts for \$270. Find the selling prices of each item.

**1.** Write a system of equations to represent the situation. **2 points**

**Sample answer:** $9t + 3s = 288$
$t + 6s = 270$

**2.** Solve the system of equations.

**Part A**

Use elimination or substitution to solve. Show your work. **2 points**

**Sample answer:**

$2(9t + 3s) = 2(288)$
$18t + 6s = 576$
$-(t + 6s = 270)$
$17t = 306$
$t = 18$

$18 + 6s = 270$
$6s = 252$
$s = 42$

**Part B**

Which method of solving did you choose? Explain your reasoning. **2 points**

**Sample answer: Elimination; Since 6*s* is a multiple of 3*s*, I multiplied the first equation by 2 on both sides. I subtracted the second equation from the first to eliminate the variable, *s*. I thought elimination would be easier than substituting with large numbers.**

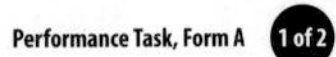
Performance Task, Form A

1 of 2

**3.** What does the solution of the system mean in this situation? **1 point**

**Sample answer: T-shirts sell for \$18 each and sweatshirts sell for \$42 each.**

**4.** Graph and label the system of equations. **2 points**

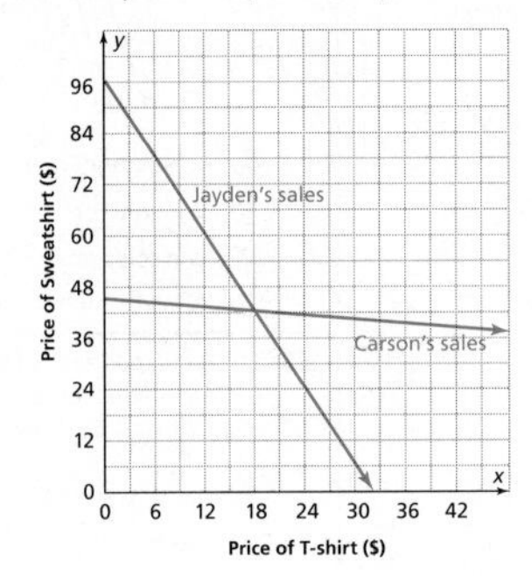


**Part A**

What is the point of intersection of the graph? **1 point**

**(18, 42)**

**Part B**

How does your answer in Part A relate to your answer in Question 3 above? Explain what this means in terms of a system of equations. **2 points**

**Sample answer: They are the same. The solution of a system of equations is shown by the intersection of the lines on the graph. In this situation, there is only one solution, \$18 for a T-shirt and \$42 for a sweatshirt, so the lines intersect at one point, (18, 42).**

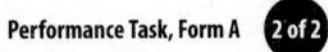
Performance Task, Form A

2 of 2

## Item Analysis for Diagnosis and Intervention: Form A

| Item | DOK | MDIS | Standard |
|---|---|---|---|
| 1 | 3 | K27, K28 | 8.EE.C.8c |
| 2A | 2 | K35, K36 | 8.EE.C.8b |
| 2B | 2 | K35, K36 | 8.EE.C.8b |
| 3 | 3 | K35, K36 | 8.EE.C.8a |
| 4 | 3 | K49 | 8.EE.C.8a |
| 4A | 3 | K34 | 8.EE.C.8a |
| 4B | 4 | K34–K36 | 8.EE.C.8a |

## Scoring Rubric: Forms A and B

| Item | Points (Form A) | Points (Form B) |
|---|---|---|
| 1 | 2: Two correct equations<br>1: One correct equation | 2: Two correct equations<br>1: One correct equation |
| 2 | A/B 2: Correct response<br>1: Partially correct response | 2: Both lines and intersection correct<br>1: One line correct |
| 3 | 1: Correct meaning | 2: Correct answer and explanation<br>1: Correct answer or explanation |
| 4 | 2: Two correct lines<br>1: One correct line<br>A 1: Correct point of intersection<br>B 2: Correct answer and explanation<br>1: Correct answer or explanation | 1: Correct answer |
| 5 | N/A | A/B 2: Correct response<br>1: Partially correct response |
| 6 | N/A | 2: Correct answer and explanation<br>1: Correct answer or explanation |

Go Online

Assess

Available Online

Name ______________________

Topic 5
Performance Task
Form B

Frankie is comparing the monthly costs of two cellphone plans. Talk-It-Up offers unlimited talk, text, and data for $95 each month. Talk-Is-Cheap offers unlimited talk and text for $35, plus $10 per gigabyte of data per month.

1. Write a system of equations to represent the situation using $g$ to represent the number of gigabytes. **2 points**

**Sample answer: $c = 95$; $c = 35 + 10g$**

2. Graph the system of equations. **2 points**

**Sample answer:**

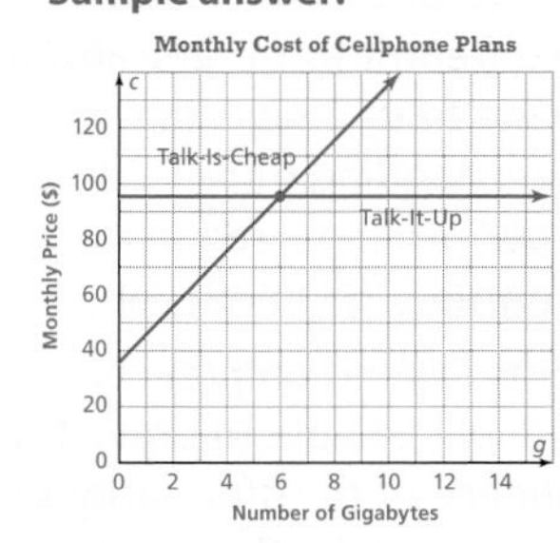


3. What is the solution of the system? Explain what it means in the situation. **1 point**

**(6, 95); Sample answer: When Talk-Is-Cheap uses 6 gigabytes of data, both plans cost $95.**

4. What cellphone plan would be the best value if Frankie uses 8 gigabytes of data per month? Explain. **1 point**

**Talk-It-Up; Sample answer: Frankie would pay $115 with Talk-Is-Cheap, $35 for the phone and $120 for the data. Talk-It-Up is only $95.**

Performance Task, Form B  1 of 2

5. Ana and Peter compare their cellphone plans.

**Part A**

Ana uses Talk-A-Lot and Peter uses Talk-to-Me. Each company charges the same amount per hour of talk time, however Ana and Peter will never be charged the same amount. Write a system of equations that could represent the situation. Explain. **2 points**

**Sample answer: $c = 10h + 5$; $c = 10h$; Talk-A-Lot could charge $10 per hour for talk with free data. Talk-to-Me could charge $10 per hour for talk and a flat fee of $5 per month for data. On a graph, the lines would be parallel but never intersect.**

**Part B**

Graph the system of equations from Part A. Label the graph. **2 points**

**Sample answer:**

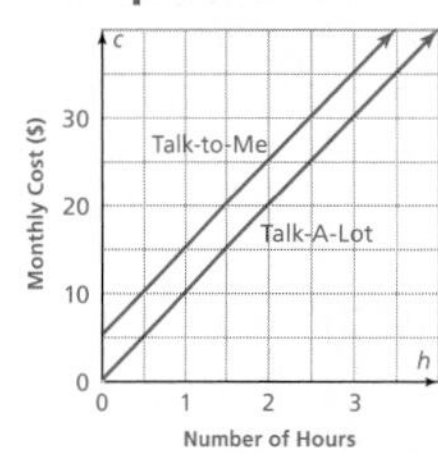


6. If a system of equations for two different cellphone plans had infinitely many solutions, what would the graph look like? Explain what it would mean in the problem situation. **2 points**

**Sample answer: The graph would be the same line. This would mean that the cellphone plans charge the same fees.**

Performance Task, Form B  2 of 2

## Item Analysis for Diagnosis and Intervention: Form B

| Item | DOK | MDIS | Standard |
|---|---|---|---|
| 1 | 3 | K27, K28 | 8.EE.C.8c |
| 2 | 2 | K49 | 8.EE.C.8b |
| 3 | 3 | K34 | 8.EE.C.8a |
| 4 | 3 | K34 | 8.EE.C.8c |
| 5A | 4 | K27, K28 | 8.EE.C.8 |
| 5B | 2 | K49 | 8.EE.C.8b |
| 6 | 3 | K34 | 8.EE.C.8c |

## Scoring Guide: Forms A and B

| Score | Recommendations |
|---|---|
| Greater Than 85% | Assign the corresponding MDIS for items answered incorrectly. Use Enrichment activities with the student. |
| 70%–85% | Assign the corresponding MDIS for items answered incorrectly. You may also assign Reteach to Build Understanding and Virtual Nerd Video assets for the lessons correlated to the items the student answered incorrectly. |
| Less Than 70% | Assign the corresponding MDIS for items answered incorrectly. Assign appropriate intervention lessons available online. You may also assign Reteach to Build Understanding, Additional Vocabulary Support, Build Mathematical Literacy, and Virtual Nerd Video assets for the lessons correlated to the items the student answered incorrectly. |

# 6 Congruence and Similarity

TOPIC

## Math Background Focus

### Transformations

- **Translation, Reflection, and Rotation** In Lesson 6-1, students utilize the properties of translations to perform and describe a translation of a two-dimensional figure. In Lesson 6-2, students use properties of reflection to create images that have the same size and shape but a different orientation. In Lesson 6-3, students identify and perform rotations of a two-dimensional figure. They describe the rotation in terms of the center of rotation and number of degrees the figure has been rotated.

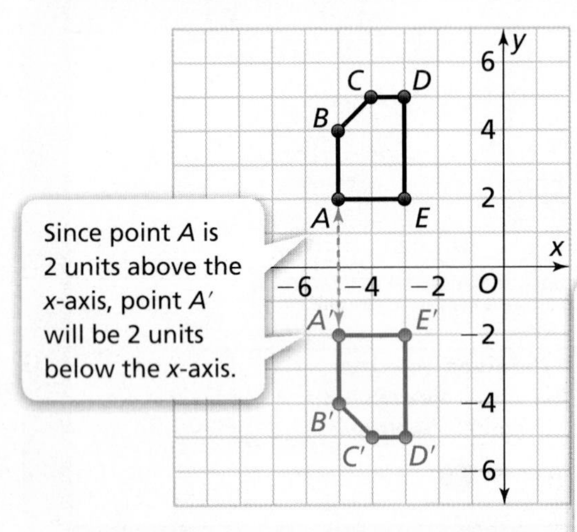


The corresponding side lengths and angle measures remain the same but the position and orientation are different.

- **Dilations** In Lesson 6-6, students understand that dilation is a transformation that changes the size of a figure but not its shape, angle measure, or proportional size. They make sense of the properties of dilations to dilate or enlarge a figure in a coordinate plane.

### Congruent and Similar Figures

- **Compose Transformations** In Lesson 6-4, students apply their knowledge to perform a sequence of transformations. They will describe and perform two different forms of transformation, one at a time, to map a preimage to its image. In Lesson 6-5, students develop a deeper understanding of reflections, rotations, and translations by performing a sequence of transformations to identify congruent geometric objects.
- **Similarity** In Lesson 6-7, students expand on previous lessons to recognize similar figures and will be able to prove the similarity by performing a sequence of transformations using rotations, reflections, translations, and dilations. In Lesson 6-10, they determine whether triangles are similar and solve similar triangle problems.

Describe a sequence of transformations that shows that quadrilateral *RSTU* is similar to quadrilateral *VXYZ*.

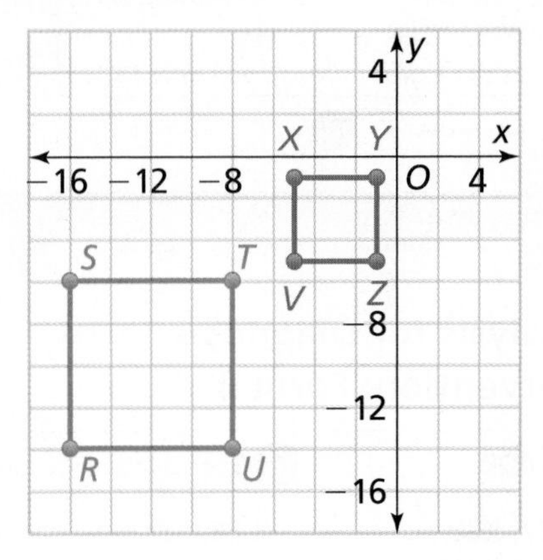

Go Online

Video

# Lines and Angles

- **Angles and Lines** In Lesson 6-8, students recognize the relationship of angles that are formed by parallel lines and a transversal. They understand which pairs of angles created by parallel lines and a transversal are congruent and which are supplementary. In Lesson 6-9, students find interior and exterior angle measures of triangles.

**What must *x* equal if lines *c* and *d* are parallel? Explain.**

The 60° angle and the angle with measure $2x + 10$ are corresponding angles. For lines *c* and *d* to be parallel, the corresponding angles must be congruent.

$$2x + 10 = 60$$
$$2x + 10 - 10 = 60 - 10$$
$$2x = 50$$
$$x = 25$$

If $x = 25$, then lines *c* and *d* are parallel lines.

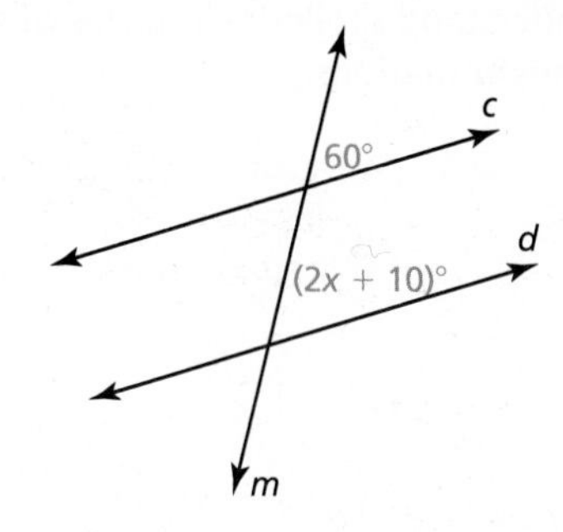


**Professional Development Videos** Topic Overview Videos and Listen and Look For Lesson Videos present additional important information about the content.

# Advanced Concepts for the Teacher

- **Dilations and Similar Figures** Consider $\triangle ABC$ with vertices $A(x_1, y_1)$, $B(x_2, y_2)$, and $C(x_3, y_3)$.

Dilate the figure with scale factor *k* and center of dilation (0, 0). $\triangle A'B'C'$ has vertices $A'(kx_1, ky_1)$, $B'(kx_2, ky_2)$, and $C'(kx_3, ky_3)$.

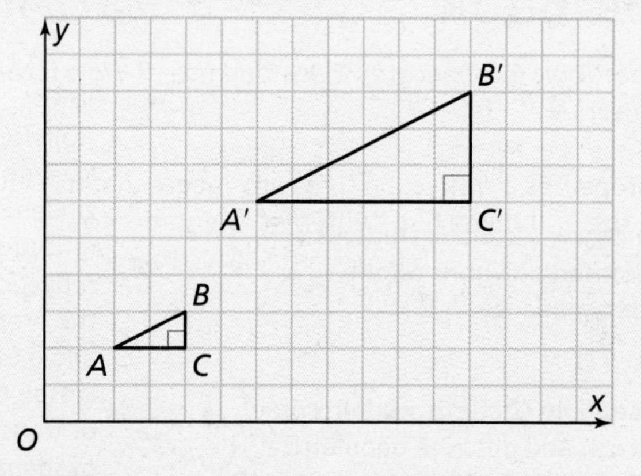


When two polygons are similar, the ratios of corresponding side lengths are equal. The length of a side can be calculated as the distance between the two points in the coordinate grid.

The distance between points *A* and *B* is

$$d(A, B) = \sqrt{(x_2 - x_1)^2 + (y_2 - y_1)^2}$$

The distance between points *A'* and *B'* is

$$d(A', B') = \sqrt{(kx_2 - kx_1)^2 + (ky_2 - ky_1)^2}$$
$$= \sqrt{(k(x_2 - x_1))^2 + (k(y_2 - y_1))^2}$$
$$= \sqrt{(k^2(x_2 - x_1)^2 + k^2(y_2 - y_1)^2}$$
$$= \sqrt{k^2((x_2 - x_1)^2 + (y_2 - y_1)^2)}$$
$$= k\sqrt{(x_2 - x_1)^2 + (y_2 - y_1)^2}$$
$$= k \cdot d(A, B)$$

The distance between points *A'* and *B'* is equal to *k* times the distance between points *A* and *B*. Therefore the ratio of the length of side *AB* to side *A'B'* is 1 : *k*.

Similar algebraic reasoning can be used to show that corresponding side lengths in the original polygon and its dilation are proportional. The ratios of the corresponding side length are 1 : *k* for all sides of the polygon. This reasoning can also be extended to comparing polygons that have been dilated when the center of dilation is not the origin.

# Math Background Coherence

Students learn best when concepts are connected throughout the curriculum. This coherence is achieved within clusters, across clusters, across domains, and across grade levels.

## Look Back

*How does Topic 6 connect to what students learned earlier?*

### Grade 6

- **Geometry** In Grade 6, students represented polygons on the coordinate plane.

### Grade 7

- **Geometry** In Grade 7, students draw, construct, and describe geometrical figures and the relationships between them. They solve real-life and mathematical problems involving angle measure, area, surface area, and volume.

## Topic 6

*How is content connected within Topic 6?*

- **Transformations** In Lesson 6-1, students learn to translate a figure. In Lesson 6-2, students verify the properties of a reflection while identifying and performing reflections. In Lesson 6-3, students apply the properties of center of rotation and angle of rotation to create images. In Lesson 6-4, students describe sequences of transformations applied to a variety of shapes. In Lesson 6-6, students review dilations and make sense of scale factors.

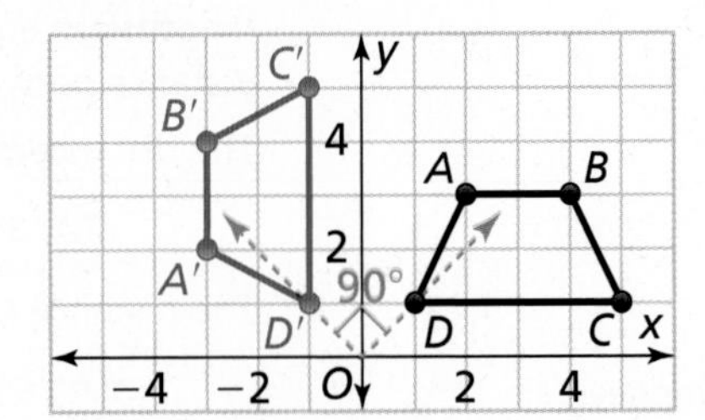


**Generalize** The *x*- and *y*-coordinates of a point change in a predictable way when rotated in a counterclockwise direction about the origin.

| Angle of Rotation | Rule |
|---|---|
| 90° | $(x, y) \rightarrow (-y, x)$ |
| 180° | $(x, y) \rightarrow (-x, -y)$ |
| 270° | $(x, y) \rightarrow (y, -x)$ |

- **Congruent and Similar Figures** In Lesson 6-5, students determine congruency by identifying the transformations that produced two figures. In Lesson 6-7, students understand and verify similarity of figures.
- **Angle Measurements** In Lesson 6-8, students learn about the relationships of angles that are formed by parallel lines and a transversal. In Lesson 6-9, students determine missing measurements of the interior and exterior angles of a triangle. In Lesson 6-10, students find angle measurements using triangle similarity.

## Look Ahead

*How does Topic 6 connect to what students will learn later?*

### High School Geometry

- In high school geometry, students build on Topic 6 concepts to experiment with transformations in the plane, understand congruence in terms of rigid motions, and understand similarity in terms of similarity transformations.

Go Online

# Math Background Rigor

A rigorous curriculum emphasizes conceptual understanding, procedural fluency, and applications.

## Conceptual Understanding

- **Understand Properties of Transformations** In Lesson 6-1, students understand the concept of translating figures and how the resulting images are related to the preimages. In Lesson 6-2, students understand the concept of reflecting figures and recognize how the image is a flip of the preimage and that the two figures are an equal distance away from the line of reflection. In Lesson 6-6, students develop their understanding of dilation to find and graph images.

  **What is a rule that describes the translation that maps trapezoid *PQRS* onto trapezoid *P′Q′R′S′*?**

  The translation maps every point of *PQRS* to its corresponding point of *P′Q′R′S′*.

  **Use Structure** How do you know which vertex of the trapezoid to use to determine the rule?

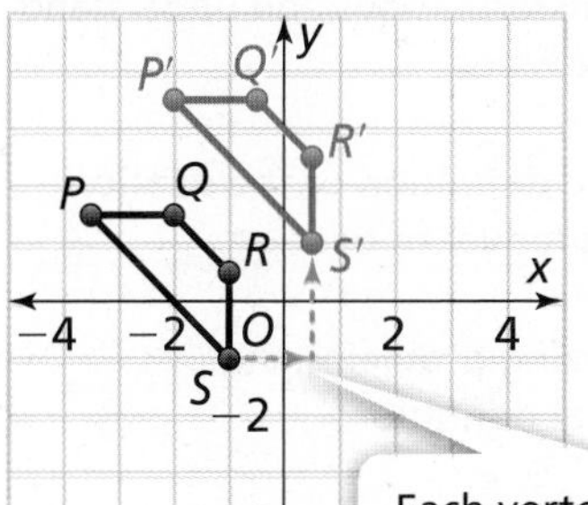


Each vertex of trapezoid *PQRS* is translated 3 units to the right and 4 units up.

- **Identify Congruent Figures** In Lesson 6-5, students will recognize that congruent figures have the same shape and size. They know that congruent images are created by a sequence of reflections, rotations, and translations.

- **Recognize Angle Relationships** In Lesson 6-8, students recognize that parallel lines and a transversal create sets of angles. They will learn that there are angle-based relationships that can be used to categorize and determine the measurements of unknown angles. In Lesson 6-9, students build on their understanding of angle-based relationships and determine the missing measurements of interior and exterior angles of triangles.

## Procedural Skill and Fluency

- **Transforming Images** In Lesson 6-1, students translate preimages into images and explore how their properties affect the image. In Lesson 6-2, they perform reflections and identify the changes made to the preimages. In Lesson 6-4, students develop fluency by sequentially transforming figures and determining whether the order of the transformations leads to different solutions.

You can map $\triangle ABC$ onto $\triangle A''B''C''$ by a translation 3 units right followed by a 90° clockwise rotation about the origin.

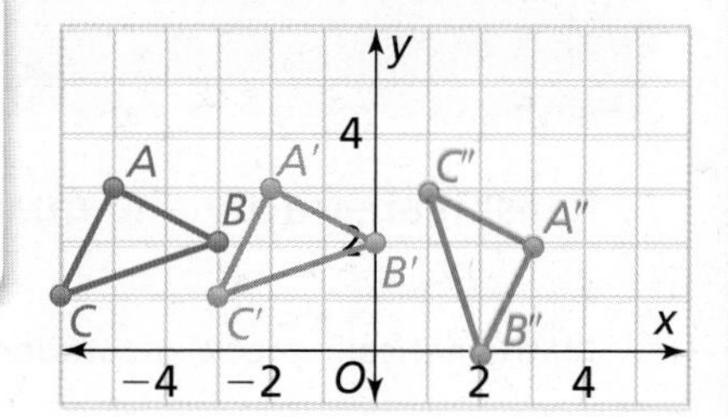


- **Congruency and Similarity** In Lesson 6-5, students apply their understanding of translations, reflections, and rotations to identify congruent figures. In Lesson 6-6, students reinforce their understanding of dilation using scale factors to expand and reduce the size of shapes. In Lesson 6-7, students perform multiple transformations on figures to identify and create similar figures. In Lesson 6-10, students develop fluency in comparing angle measures of two triangles to determine their similarity.

## Applications

- **Similar Figures** In Lesson 6-4, students use two transformations to map figures to one another. In Lesson 6-7, students use dilation, along with an additional transformation, to identify and compare similar figures. In Lesson 6-9, students use their knowledge of the sum of angles in a triangle to calculate the missing measurements of the interior and exterior angles.
- **Angles** In Lesson 6-8, students apply their understanding of the relationship between angles created by parallel lines and a transversal by finding the measurement of angles in different situations. In Lesson 6-10, students will apply Angle-Angle Criterion to find the measure of angles in similar triangles.

  Streets A and B run parallel to each other. The measure of $\angle 6$ is 155°. What is the measure of $\angle 4$?

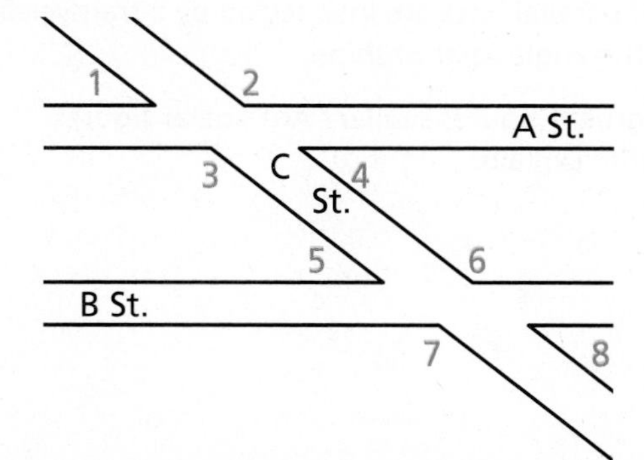

# Math Practices

The math practices and processes describe the behaviors and thinking habits that mathematically proficient students demonstrate when actively engaged in mathematics work. Opportunities for engagement in the practices and the development of expertise in these important behaviors and thinking habits exist throughout the topic and program. Here we focus on mathematical reasoning and explaining.

As students solve transformation problems, look for these behaviors to assess and identify students who demonstrate proficiency with mathematical reasoning and explaining.

**Math Practices Within Topic 6 Lessons**

| **Reason abstractly and quantitatively. (MP.2)** | **Construct viable arguments and critique the reasoning of others. (MP.3)** |
|---|---|
| Mathematically proficient students: | Mathematically proficient students: |
| • Recognize and understand the concept of rotations and how to perform them. | • Justify their conclusions about reflections with mathematical ideas. |
| • Represent and interpret congruence with or without a coordinate grid. | • Consider their reasoning about why they rotate figures a certain way or apply certain rules to the rotation of a figure. |
| • Construct and label representations that preserve angle measures and resize all lengths. | • Make sense of accuracy in transformations and understand angles and congruency relationships. |
| • Use their knowledge of dilation and transformation to recognize whether figures are similar. | • Use their understanding of the definition of the dilation to verify images that are the product of dilation. |
| • Make sense of the relationship between angles created by parallel lines and a transversal. | • Construct arguments by analyzing problems and using established mathematical definitions. |

Help students become more proficient with mathematical reasoning and explanation.

If students do not understand transformations and are unable to map preimages to images, then use these questioning strategies to help them develop reasoning and explaining skills as they solve problems throughout the topic.

**Q:** How does a dilation change the preimage?

**Q:** What comes to mind when you see the word *rotation* in a problem?

**Q:** A pair of parallel lines are intersected by a transversal. Explain the angle relationships.

**Q:** Are congruent figures similar? Are similar figures congruent? Explain.

**Q:** What evidence did you use to support your solution?

**Q:** Are there similarities between reflections and rotations? Explain.

**Q:** How could you prove that figures are similar?

**Q:** How did you check whether your approach worked?

# Topic Readiness Assessment

Go Online

Topic Readiness Assessment Masters

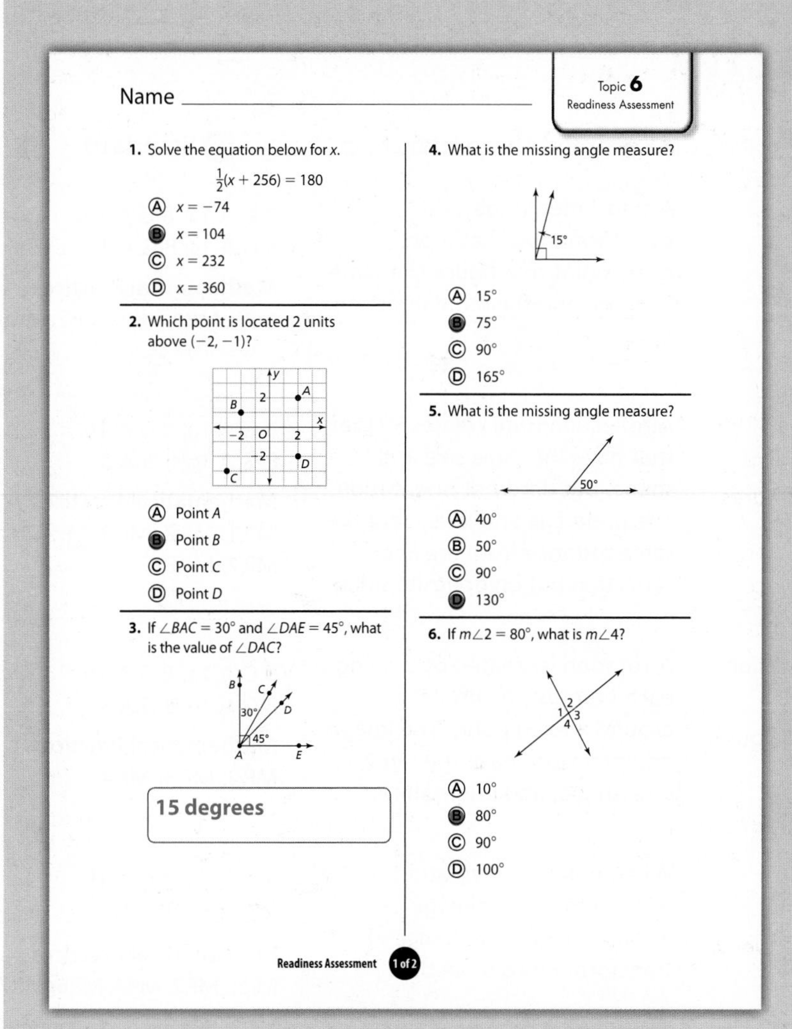

Name ____________________

Topic 6
Readiness Assessment

1. Solve the equation below for $x$.

$\frac{1}{2}(x + 256) = 180$

Ⓐ $x = -74$
Ⓑ $x = 104$
Ⓒ $x = 232$
Ⓓ $x = 360$

2. Which point is located 2 units above $(-2, -1)$?

Ⓐ Point $A$
Ⓑ Point $B$
Ⓒ Point $C$
Ⓓ Point $D$

3. If $\angle BAC = 30°$ and $\angle DAE = 45°$, what is the value of $\angle DAC$?

15 degrees

4. What is the missing angle measure?

Ⓐ 15°
Ⓑ 75°
Ⓒ 90°
Ⓓ 165°

5. What is the missing angle measure?

Ⓐ 40°
Ⓑ 50°
Ⓒ 90°
Ⓓ 130°

6. If $m\angle 2 = 80°$, what is $m\angle 4$?

Ⓐ 10°
Ⓑ 80°
Ⓒ 90°
Ⓓ 100°

Readiness Assessment 1 of 2

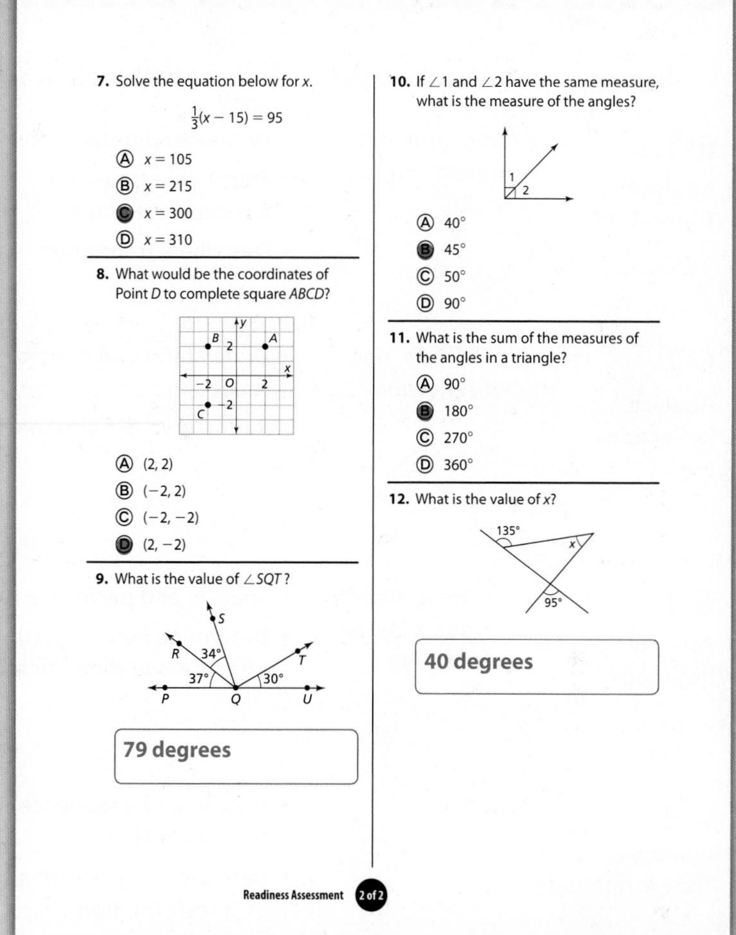

7. Solve the equation below for $x$.

$\frac{1}{3}(x - 15) = 95$

Ⓐ $x = 105$
Ⓑ $x = 215$
Ⓒ $x = 300$
Ⓓ $x = 310$

8. What would be the coordinates of Point $D$ to complete square $ABCD$?

Ⓐ $(2, 2)$
Ⓑ $(-2, 2)$
Ⓒ $(-2, -2)$
Ⓓ $(2, -2)$

9. What is the value of $\angle SQT$?

79 degrees

10. If $\angle 1$ and $\angle 2$ have the same measure, what is the measure of the angles?

Ⓐ 40°
Ⓑ 45°
Ⓒ 50°
Ⓓ 90°

11. What is the sum of the measures of the angles in a triangle?

Ⓐ 90°
Ⓑ 180°
Ⓒ 270°
Ⓓ 360°

12. What is the value of $x$?

40 degrees

Readiness Assessment 2 of 2

Assess students' understanding of prerequisite concepts and skills using the Topic Readiness Assessment.

You may opt to have students take the Topic Readiness Assessment online.

## Scoring Guide

| Score | Recommendations |
|---|---|
| Greater Than 85% | Assign the corresponding MDIS for items answered incorrectly. Use Enrichment activities with the student during the topic. |
| 70%–85% | Assign the corresponding MDIS for items answered incorrectly. Monitor the student during Step 1 and Try It! parts of the lessons for personalized remediation needs. |
| Less Than 70% | Assign the corresponding MDIS for items answered incorrectly. Assign appropriate intervention lessons available online. |

## Item Analysis for Diagnosis and Remediation

| Item | DOK | MDIS | Standard |
|---|---|---|---|
| 1 | 2 | L45 | 6.EE.A.3 |
| 2 | 2 | K46 | 6.NS.C.6b |
| 3 | 2 | N3 | 7.G.B.5 |
| 4 | 2 | N3 | 7.G.B.5 |
| 5 | 2 | N3 | 7.G.B.5 |
| 6 | 2 | N3 | 7.G.B.5 |
| 7 | 2 | L45 | 6.EE.A.3 |
| 8 | 2 | K46 | 6.G.A.3 |
| 9 | 2 | N3 | 7.G.B.5 |
| 10 | 2 | N3 | 7.G.B.5 |
| 11 | 1 | N3 | 7.G.B.5 |
| 12 | 2 | N3 | 7.G.B.5 |

TOPIC 6

# Topic Planner

## Congruence and Similarity

| Lesson | Vocabulary | Objective | Essential Understanding | Standard |
|---|---|---|---|---|
| **6-1** Analyze Translations | transformation, translation, image | • Understand translations.<br>• Translate a figure on a coordinate plane.<br>• Describe a translation. | A translation (slide) is a transformation that moves every point of a figure the same distance and the same direction. | 8.G.A.1a, 8.G.A.1b, 8.G.A.1c, 8.G.A.3<br>**Mathematical Practices**<br>MP.3, MP.4, MP.6, MP.7, MP.8 |
| **6-2** Analyze Reflections | reflection, line of reflection | • Understand and describe a reflection.<br>• Reflect two-dimensional figures. | A reflection (flip) creates images that have the same size and shape, but different orientation. The preimage and image are the same distance from the line of reflection but on opposite sides. | 8.G.A.1a, 8.G.A.1b, 8.G.A.1c, 8.G.A.3<br>**Mathematical Practices**<br>MP.1, MP.2, MP.3, MP.4, MP.7, MP.8 |
| **6-3** Analyze Rotations | rotation, angle of rotation, center of rotation | • Identify and perform a rotation.<br>• Determine how a rotation affects a two-dimensional figure. | A rotation is created by moving each point of the preimage around a fixed point. The image and preimage have the same size, shape, and orientation. | 8.G.A.1a, 8.G.A.1b, 8.G.A.1c, 8.G.A.3<br>**Mathematical Practices**<br>MP.2, MP.3, MP.4 |
| **6-4** Compose Transformations | none | • Understand a sequence of transformations.<br>• Describe and perform a sequence of transformations. | When one transformation will not map a preimage into its image, a sequence of transformations is needed. | 8.G.A.1a, 8.G.A.1b, 8.G.A.1c, 8.G.A.3<br>**Mathematical Practices**<br>MP.1, MP.2, MP.4, MP.6, MP.7 |
| 3-Act Mathematical Modeling: Tricks of the Trade | none | • Use mathematical modeling to represent a problem situation and to propose a solution. | Many real-world problem situations can be represented with a mathematical model, but that model may not represent a real-world situation exactly. | 8.G.A.1, 8.G.A.2<br>**Mathematical Practices**<br>MP.4 |
| **6-5** Understand Congruent Figures | congruent | • Understand congruence of figures using a series of transformations.<br>• Identify congruent figures. | A sequence of translations, reflections, and rotations can map one figure to another without changing its shape or size. | 8.G.A.2, 8.G.A.3<br>**Mathematical Practices**<br>MP.2, MP.3, MP.7 |

## Lesson Resources

Digital

Print

**Student's Edition**

**Additional Practice Workbook**

**Teaching Resources**
- Reteach to Build Understanding
- Additional Vocabulary Support
- Build Mathematical Literacy
- Enrichment

**Assessment Resources**
- Lesson Quiz

Digital

**Digital Lesson Courseware**
- Today's Challenge
- Visual Learning Animation Plus
- Key Concept
- Additional Examples
- 3-Act Mathematical Modeling
- Online Practice powered by MathXL for School
- Adaptive Practice
- Virtual Nerd Video Tutorials
- Animated Glossary
- Digital Math Tools
- Online Math Games

**Lesson Support for Teachers**
- Listen and Look For PD Lesson Video

The suggested pacing for each lesson is 2 days for a 45-minute math class and 1 day for a 90-minute class.

Go Online

Digital

| Lesson | Vocabulary | Objective | Essential Understanding | Standard |
|---|---|---|---|---|
| **6-6** Describe Dilations | dilation, scale factor, enlargement, reduction | • Understand dilations.<br>• Dilate to enlarge or reduce a figure in a coordinate plane. | A dilation is a transformation that changes the size of a figure. In a dilation, the preimage and image have the same shape, angle measures, and proportions. | 8.G.A.3, 8.G.A.4<br>**Mathematical Practices** MP.2, MP.3, MP.7, MP.8 |
| **6-7** Understand Similar Figures | similar | • Understand similarity.<br>• Complete a similarity transformation.<br>• Identify similar figures. | Two-dimensional figures are similar if there is a sequence of translations, reflections, rotations, and dilations that map one figure onto the other. | 8.G.A.3, 8.G.A.4<br>**Mathematical Practices** MP.2, MP.3, MP.6, MP.7, MP.8 |
| **6-8** Angles, Lines, and Transversals | transversal, corresponding angles, alternate interior angles, same-side interior angles | • Understand the relationships of angles formed by parallel lines and a transversal.<br>• Find unknown angle measures. | If parallel lines are intersected by a transversal, then corresponding and alternate interior angles are congruent, and same-side interior angles are supplementary. | 8.G.A.5<br>**Mathematical Practices** MP.2, MP.5, MP.7 |
| **6-9** Interior and Exterior Angles of Triangles | remote interior angles, exterior angle of a triangle | • Understand the relationship of the interior angles of a triangle.<br>• Find unknown angle measures. | The measure of an exterior angle of a triangle is equal to the sum of the measures of its remote interior angles. | 8.G.A.5<br>**Mathematical Practices** MP.2, MP.4, MP.7, MP.8 |
| **6-10** Angle-Angle Triangle Similarity | none | • Determine whether triangles are similar.<br>• Solve problems involving similar triangles. | If two angles in one triangle are congruent to two angles in another triangle, the triangles are similar triangles. | 8.G.A.5<br>**Mathematical Practices** MP.2, MP.3 |

# Topic Resources

Digital

Print

### Student's Edition
- Review What You Know
- Language Development Activity
- Mid-Topic Checkpoint and Performance Task
- Topic Review
- Fluency Practice Activity
- enVision® STEM Project
- Pick a Project

### Assessment Resources
- Topic Readiness Assessment
- Mid-Topic Assessment
- Topic Assessment
- Topic Performance Task

Digital

### Topic Support for Students
- Math Practice Animations
- enVision® STEM Project
- 3-Act Mathematical Modeling Lesson

### Topic Support for Teachers
- Topic Overview Video
- ExamView Test Generator

# Congruence and Similarity

Available Online

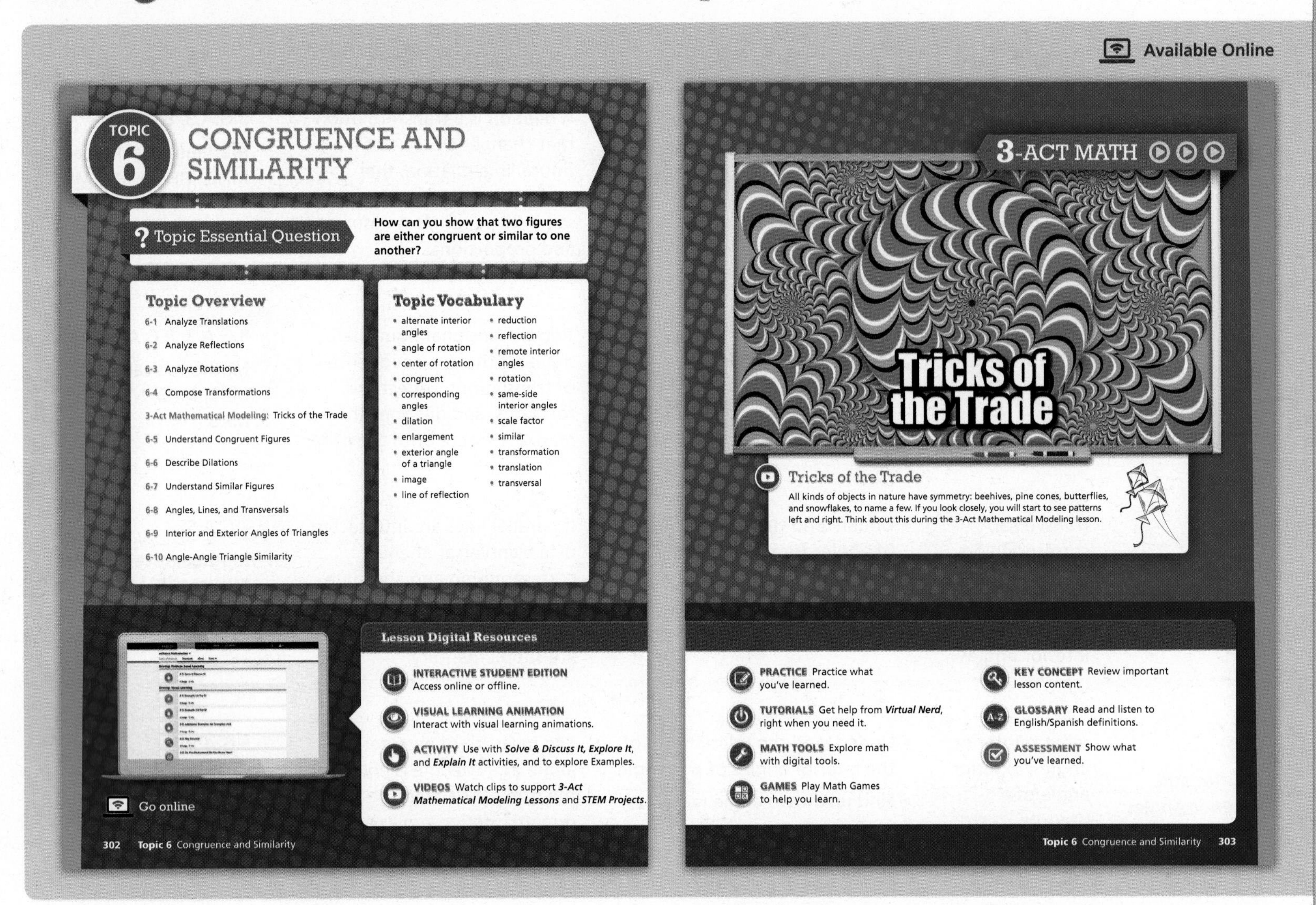

TOPIC 6 CONGRUENCE AND SIMILARITY

? Topic Essential Question

How can you show that two figures are either congruent or similar to one another?

**Topic Overview**



**Topic Vocabulary**

- alternate interior angles
- angle of rotation
- center of rotation
- congruent
- corresponding angles
- dilation
- enlargement
- exterior angle of a triangle
- image
- line of reflection
- reduction
- reflection
- remote interior angles
- rotation
- same-side interior angles
- scale factor
- similar
- transformation
- translation
- transversal

Go online

**Lesson Digital Resources**

- **INTERACTIVE STUDENT EDITION** Access online or offline.
- **VISUAL LEARNING ANIMATION** Interact with visual learning animations.
- **ACTIVITY** Use with *Solve & Discuss It, Explore It,* and *Explain It* activities, and to explore Examples.
- **VIDEOS** Watch clips to support *3-Act Mathematical Modeling Lessons* and *STEM Projects*.

302 Topic 6 Congruence and Similarity

3-ACT MATH

Tricks of the Trade

Tricks of the Trade

All kinds of objects in nature have symmetry: beehives, pine cones, butterflies, and snowflakes, to name a few. If you look closely, you will start to see patterns left and right. Think about this during the 3-Act Mathematical Modeling lesson.

- **PRACTICE** Practice what you've learned.
- **TUTORIALS** Get help from *Virtual Nerd*, right when you need it.
- **MATH TOOLS** Explore math with digital tools.
- **GAMES** Play Math Games to help you learn.
- **KEY CONCEPT** Review important lesson content.
- **GLOSSARY** Read and listen to English/Spanish definitions.
- **ASSESSMENT** Show what you've learned.

Topic 6 Congruence and Similarity 303

## Topic Essential Question

**How can you show that two figures are either congruent or similar to one another?**

Revisit the Topic Essential Question throughout the topic. See the Teacher's Edition for the Topic Review for notes about answering the question.

## 3-Act Mathematical Modeling

**Generate excitement about the upcoming 3-Act Mathematical Modeling lesson by having students read about the math modeling problem for this topic.**

See the Teacher's Edition lesson support for notes about how to use the lesson video in your classroom.

TOPIC 6

# enVision® STEM Project

Go Online

Video

## Forest Health

In this project, students will explore the science of forestry. They will explore plant, animal, human, and other indicators of forest health. Students will analyze how changes in these indicators affect the health of the forest and how forest health affects population growth of various forest species.

### What's the Math?

Students use ratios and similar triangles to measure the health of various forest elements. Using what they know about similar triangles will allow students to measure tree heights. Students can use equivalent ratios to help generalize data to larger sections of forests.

### What's the Science?

Students use mathematical representations to represent forest health indicators and to support their judgment of forest health. They will also analyze problems facing our forests and solutions that can improve forest health.

### What's the Engineering and Technology?

Students think like engineers as they gather, analyze, synthesize, and present data in clear and understandable ways. Students develop and use their own clinometer to help evaluate tree health.

### Introduce the Project

Present the project by having students discuss what they know about forest health. The questions below can be used to guide the discussion.

**Q:** What indicators can you examine to determine if a tree is healthy? [Sample answer: height, diameter of trunk, growth rate, and presence of lichen or fungus on the tree]

**Q:** Why is studying animal populations an important element of forest health? [Sample answer: Understanding the changes in populations allows for planning needed resources to keep the forest healthy. Sudden changes in animal population can indicate a problem in the forest.]

**Q:** What are some problems that impact our forests? [Sample answer: Natural disasters, diseases, and logging and other human interference]

**Q:** How can you improve the health of local forests? [Sample answer: Prevent littering, monitoring hunting and fishing activities to ensure healthy animal populations, and avoid introduction of new species of plants or animals that could disrupt the ecosystem.] You can launch this project any time after Topic 6.

Show the Topic 6 STEM video to generate interest in the project.

Teacher resources that provide students with project details and support are available online.

**enVision STEM Project Video** is available online.

TOPIC 6 enVision STEM Project

Did You Know?

Trees provide wood for cooking and heating for half of the world's population.

As trees grow, carbon dioxide is removed from the atmosphere for photosynthesis. Forests are called "carbon sinks" because one acre of forest absorbs six tons of carbon dioxide and puts out four tons of oxygen.

Carbon Dioxide

Oxygen

Sunlight

In addition to providing oxygen and improving air quality, trees conserve water and soil and preserve wildlife.

Trees provide lumber for buildings, tools, and furniture. Other products include rubber, sponges, cork, paper, chocolate, nuts, and fruit.

About 30% of land is covered by forests.

Forests are now being managed to preserve wildlife and old growth forests, protect biodiversity, safeguard watersheds, and develop recreation, as well as extract timber.

Forests also need managed to prevent raging wildfires, invasive species, overgrazing, and disease.

Your Task: Forest Health

The proper management of forests is a growing science. You and your classmates will learn about forest health indicators and use what you know about similar triangles and ratios to gather and interpret data in order to assess the health of a forest.

304 Topic 6 enVision STEM Project

### Common Core Content Standards

8.G.A.4, 8.G.A.3

### Mathematical Practices Standards

MP.1, MP.2, MP.3, MP.5

### Next Generation Science Standards

MS-LS2-1, MS-LS2-4, MS-ESS3-3, MS-ESS3-4

# Get Ready!

Go Online

Glossary

## Review What You Know!

Assign the Review What You Know to activate prior knowledge and practice the prerequisite skills needed for success in this topic.

Encourage students to work independently or with a partner. Use these questioning strategies to help them get started.

### Multiplying Real Numbers

**Q:** How do you multiply a whole number and a fraction? [Sample answer: Convert the whole number into a fraction by placing a 1 in the denominator and then multiplying the two fractions.]

### Identifying Points on a Coordinate Plane

**Q:** Suppose point $A$ is located at (10, 6). What do the two digits in the parentheses represent? [Sample answer: The first digit is the $x$-coordinate of the point and the second is the $y$-coordinate.]

**Q:** Describe a strategy used to identify a point's location on the coordinate plane. [Sample answer: The $x$-coordinate represents where the point is in the $x$-direction. The $y$-coordinate represents the point's location in the $y$-direction.]

### Supplementary Angles

**Q:** Complete this statement: *Supplementary angles add up to ______ degrees*. Explain. [180; Sample answer: They form a straight angle.]

Available Online

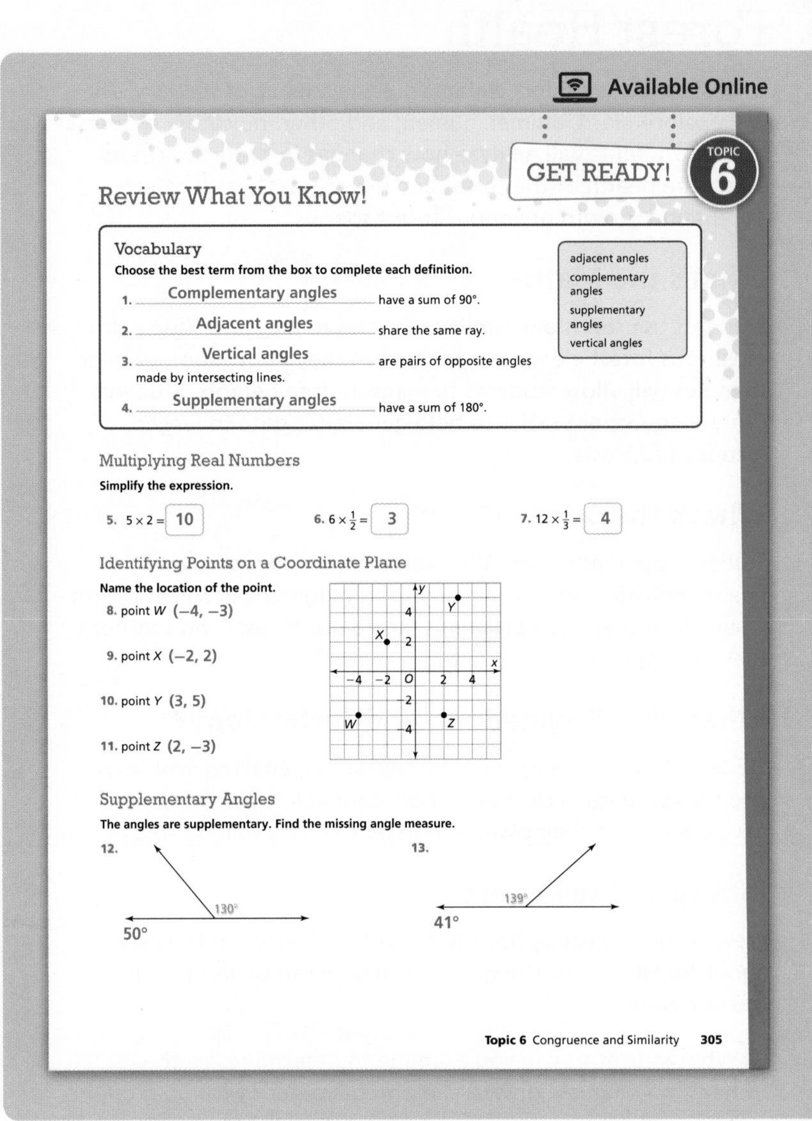

GET READY! TOPIC 6

Review What You Know!

Vocabulary

Choose the best term from the box to complete each definition.

adjacent angles
complementary angles
supplementary angles
vertical angles

1. Complementary angles have a sum of 90°.
2. Adjacent angles share the same ray.
3. Vertical angles are pairs of opposite angles made by intersecting lines.
4. Supplementary angles have a sum of 180°.

Multiplying Real Numbers

Simplify the expression.

5. $5 \times 2 =$ 10
6. $6 \times \frac{1}{2} =$ 3
7. $12 \times \frac{1}{3} =$ 4

Identifying Points on a Coordinate Plane

Name the location of the point.

8. point $W$ (−4, −3)
9. point $X$ (−2, 2)
10. point $Y$ (3, 5)
11. point $Z$ (2, −3)

Supplementary Angles

The angles are supplementary. Find the missing angle measure.

12. 130° — 50°
13. 139° — 41°

Topic 6 Congruence and Similarity 305

### Item Analysis for Diagnosis and Intervention

| Item | MDIS | Standard |
|---|---|---|
| 1 | N4 | 7.G.B.5 |
| 2 | N4 | 7.G.B.5 |
| 3 | N4 | 7.G.B.5 |
| 4 | N4 | 7.G.B.5 |
| 5–7 | K5 | 7.EE.B.3 |
| 8–11 | K46 | 6.G.A.3 |
| 12–13 | N4 | 7.G.B.5 |

## Vocabulary Review

You may choose to strengthen vocabulary with the following activity.

- **Assign students one of the numbered sentence completions or a vocabulary word. Then have students find someone who has the match to his or her definition or word.**

Go Online

Glossary

# Language Development

As students complete each lesson, have them fill in the graphic organizer with an illustration of the indicated transformation. Fill in the sentence to indicate whether the *image* is congruent or similar to the *preimage*. This will help to build their understanding of transformations performed on figures.

Help students distinguish key differences when comparing preimages to images.

**Q:** What is a preimage? An image? [Sample answer: A preimage is the original figure. The image is the figure after the preimage has been transformed.]

**Q:** Which transformations do not alter the size of the preimages? [Reflection, translation, and rotation]

**Q:** How are congruent and similar figures the same? How are they different? [Sample answer: Congruent figures have the same shape and size. If you place one on top of the other, the angles and side lengths match. Similar figures have congruent angles, but can be different sizes.]

## Extension for Language Development

Challenge students to use their graphic organizers to summarize the transformations learned in this topic. Encourage them to provide an example of each type of transformation.

## Word Wall

To help students comprehend the meaning of *congruent*, assist them in making a word wall. Invite students to draw two-dimensional figures that are congruent on a coordinate grid to show this, and display them under the word *Congruent*. Remind students that two-dimensional figures are congruent if there is a series of translations, reflections, and rotations that map one figure onto the other. Instructions on how to design a word wall are included in the Language Support Handbook.

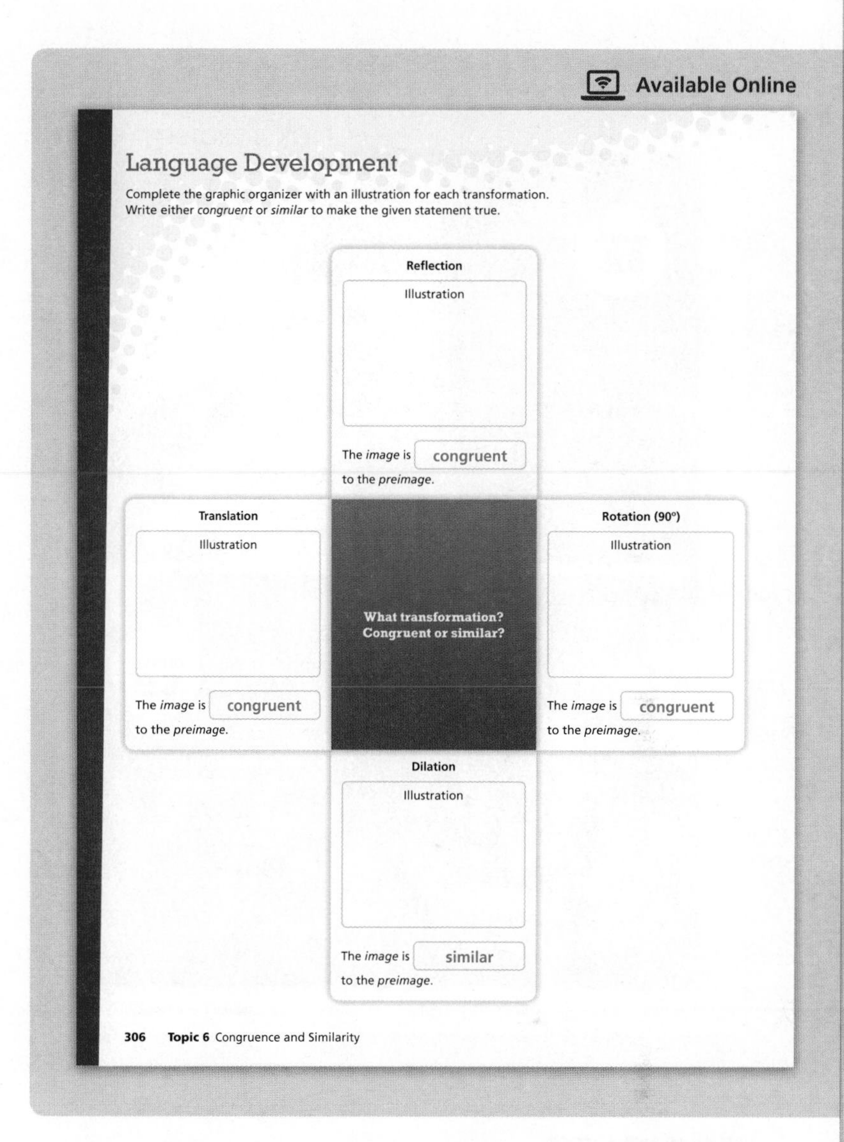
Available Online

Language Development

Complete the graphic organizer with an illustration for each transformation.
Write either *congruent* or *similar* to make the given statement true.

Reflection
Illustration
The *image* is congruent to the *preimage*.

Translation
Illustration
The *image* is congruent to the *preimage*.

What transformation? Congruent or similar?

Rotation (90°)
Illustration
The *image* is congruent to the *preimage*.

Dilation
Illustration
The *image* is similar to the *preimage*.

306 **Topic 6** Congruence and Similarity

For additional resources, see the **Language Support Handbook.**

TOPIC 6

# Pick a Project

Available Online

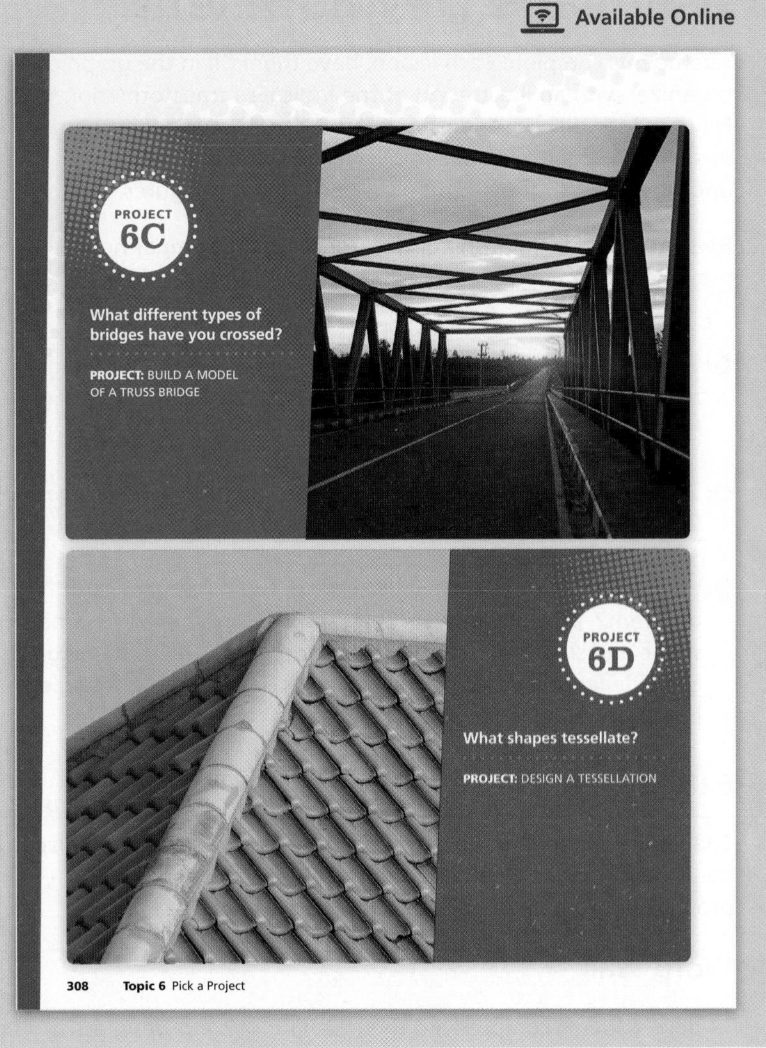


## Overview

A variety of rich projects is provided for each topic. Students may select the project that is most interesting to them.

| Project | Different Engaging Contexts | Different Activity Modalities | Different Final Products |
|---|---|---|---|
| 6A | Mathematicians | Write | Biography |
| 6B | Similar shapes | Record | Video |
| 6C | Truss bridges | Build | Model |
| 6D | Tessellations | Design | Tessellation |

## Selecting a Project

Introduce each project option with the students. Sharing the resource masters with students might help them choose.

## During the Project

**Pacing** Projects will be completed over a number of lessons. The amount of time students spend on each project will vary. You may wish to let early finishers choose an additional project.

**Grouping** You might have students work independently, with a partner, or in small groups.

**Content** Projects are related to the content of this topic. As students continue their work on projects throughout the topic, new math ideas should be incorporated.

**Project Sharing** Invite students to share their completed projects with a partner, a small group, or with the whole class. Encourage students to discuss how they demonstrated math practices during the project. Provide students an opportunity for reflection by asking what interesting information they learned and what math they used in the project.

**Extensions** Extension suggestions are included for each project.

**Look For** Did students achieve the goal of the project? Did they apply math correctly in the project?

Go Online

Worksheets

## Project 6A 8.G.A.2, 8.G.A.4

**Materials** no special materials needed

**Guidelines** Students will be able to update their biographies after each lesson.

**Extension** Ask students to review and evaluate another student's biography. Have them analyze the content of the biography, its style, and its presentation.

## Project 6B 8.G.A.4

**Materials** video recorder

**Guidelines** Students should wait until after learning about similar figures to describe the figures in detail and film their videos.

**Extension** Ask students to find at least two items in the real world that are the same shape but *not* similar. Have them describe in detail how these items are not similar.

## Project 6C 8.G.A.5

**Materials** straws, pins, craft sticks, glue

**Guidelines** Students can update their projects after learning about triangles and Angle-Angle Triangle similarity.

**Extension** Ask students to test their bridges and determine which bridge supports more load. Have them write a paragraph including whether the bridge they thought would support more load actually did. Ask them to come up with a plan to rebuild the weaker bridge so that it is stronger.

## Project 6D 8.G.A.2

**Materials** arts and crafts supplies

**Guidelines** Students will be able to make tiles and update their projects after each lesson.

**Extension** Ask students to describe the symmetry of their tessellation tiles. Can a tile without a line of symmetry tessellate? Explain.

Available Online

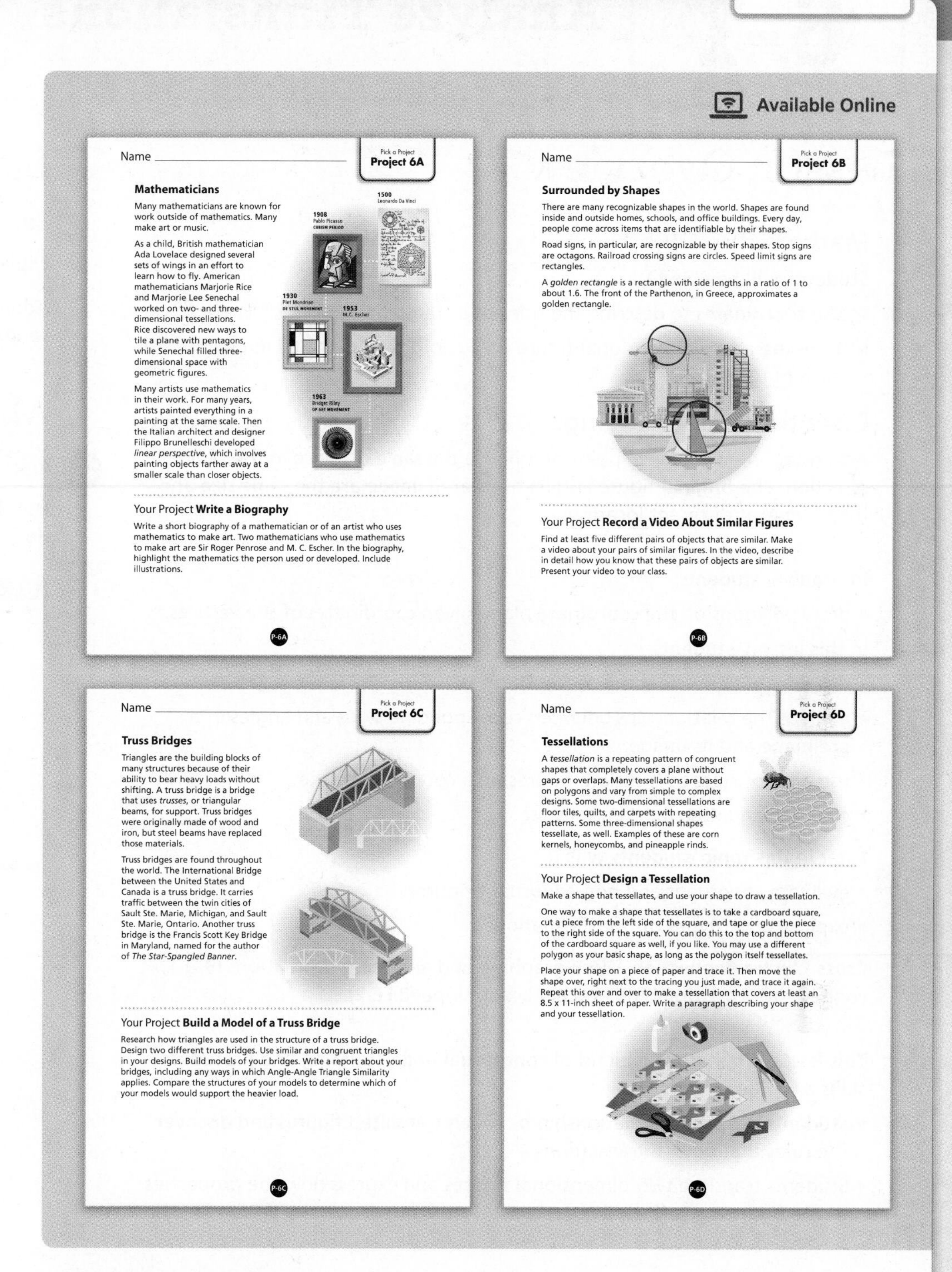

Name ______ Pick a Project **Project 6A**

**Mathematicians**

Many mathematicians are known for work outside of mathematics. Many make art or music.

As a child, British mathematician Ada Lovelace designed several sets of wings in an effort to learn how to fly. American mathematicians Marjorie Rice and Marjorie Lee Senechal worked on two- and three-dimensional tessellations. Rice discovered new ways to tile a plane with pentagons, while Senechal filled three-dimensional space with geometric figures.

Many artists use mathematics in their work. For many years, artists painted everything in a painting at the same scale. Then the Italian architect and designer Filippo Brunelleschi developed *linear perspective*, which involves painting objects farther away at a smaller scale than closer objects.



Your Project **Write a Biography**

Write a short biography of a mathematician or of an artist who uses mathematics to make art. Two mathematicians who use mathematics to make art are Sir Roger Penrose and M. C. Escher. In the biography, highlight the mathematics the person used or developed. Include illustrations.

P-6A

Name ______ Pick a Project **Project 6B**

**Surrounded by Shapes**

There are many recognizable shapes in the world. Shapes are found inside and outside homes, schools, and office buildings. Every day, people come across items that are identifiable by their shapes.

Road signs, in particular, are recognizable by their shapes. Stop signs are octagons. Railroad crossing signs are circles. Speed limit signs are rectangles.

A *golden rectangle* is a rectangle with side lengths in a ratio of 1 to about 1.6. The front of the Parthenon, in Greece, approximates a golden rectangle.

Your Project **Record a Video About Similar Figures**

Find at least five different pairs of objects that are similar. Make a video about your pairs of similar figures. In the video, describe in detail how you know that these pairs of objects are similar. Present your video to your class.

P-6B

Name ______ Pick a Project **Project 6C**

**Truss Bridges**

Triangles are the building blocks of many structures because of their ability to bear heavy loads without shifting. A truss bridge is a bridge that uses *trusses*, or triangular beams, for support. Truss bridges were originally made of wood and iron, but steel beams have replaced those materials.

Truss bridges are found throughout the world. The International Bridge between the United States and Canada is a truss bridge. It carries traffic between the twin cities of Sault Ste. Marie, Michigan, and Sault Ste. Marie, Ontario. Another truss bridge is the Francis Scott Key Bridge in Maryland, named for the author of *The Star-Spangled Banner*.

Your Project **Build a Model of a Truss Bridge**

Research how triangles are used in the structure of a truss bridge. Design two different truss bridges. Use similar and congruent triangles in your designs. Build models of your bridges. Write a report about your bridges, including any ways in which Angle-Angle Triangle Similarity applies. Compare the structures of your models to determine which of your models would support the heavier load.

P-6C

Name ______ Pick a Project **Project 6D**

**Tessellations**

A *tessellation* is a repeating pattern of congruent shapes that completely covers a plane without gaps or overlaps. Many tessellations are based on polygons and vary from simple to complex designs. Some two-dimensional tessellations are floor tiles, quilts, and carpets with repeating patterns. Some three-dimensional shapes tessellate, as well. Examples of these are corn kernels, honeycombs, and pineapple rinds.

Your Project **Design a Tessellation**

Make a shape that tessellates, and use your shape to draw a tessellation.

One way to make a shape that tessellates is to take a cardboard square, cut a piece from the left side of the square, and tape or glue the piece to the right side of the square. You can do this to the top and bottom of the cardboard square as well, if you like. You may use a different polygon as your basic shape, as long as the polygon itself tessellates.

Place your shape on a piece of paper and trace it. Then move the shape over, right next to the tracing you just made, and trace it again. Repeat this over and over to make a tessellation that covers at least an 8.5 x 11-inch sheet of paper. Write a paragraph describing your shape and your tessellation.

P-6D

## Scoring Guide

Provide a scoring rubric to students as they begin work on the project.

For students who score Below Expectations on any goal, review the rubric score with them in detail. Encourage them to update their project, or select a different project, to demonstrate their understanding of the mathematics in this topic.

**Sample Scoring Rubric**

| Below Expectations (0–1 point: Explain.) | Meets Goal (2 points) | Above Expectations (3–4 points: Explain.) |
|---|---|---|
| | **Mathematics:** The project accurately demonstrates understanding of a key mathematical concept from the topic. | |
| | **Context:** The mathematics from the topic connects to the project context in a logical and natural way. | |
| | **Presentation:** The directions and guidelines were accurately followed. | |

Go Online

Activity

# Lesson 6-1 Analyze Translations

## Lesson Overview

FOCUS

### Mathematics Objective

**Students will be able to:**

- ✔ use coordinates to describe the rules of a translation.
- ✔ translate a two-dimensional figure on a coordinate plane by mapping each of its vertices.

### Essential Understanding

A translation moves every point of a figure the same distance in the same direction. The original figure and its translated image are the same size and shape, only at different locations.

COHERENCE

**In Grade 6, students:**

- drew polygons on the coordinate plane given coordinates of the vertices.

**In this lesson, students:**

- develop an understanding of translations.
- analyze the relationships between corresponding sides and angles of a preimage and its image.
- use a set of rules to translate figures on a coordinate plane.
- evaluate and describe translations.

**Later in this topic, students will:**

- evaluate congruent and non-congruent figures.
- explore other types of transformations.

**Cross-Cluster Connection** Work graphing and analyzing translations (8.G.1) connects to work graphing and analyzing slope (8.EE.2).

RIGOR

This lesson emphasizes a blend of **conceptual understanding** and **procedural skills and fluency**.

- Students explore the relationship between translated figures and discover the rules that govern translations.
- Students translate two-dimensional figures and express how the properties of the figures are affected.

## Language Support

### Lesson Language Objective

Explain how to translate two-dimensional figures.

Additional resources are available in the **Language Support Handbook**.

## Math Anytime

### Today's Challenge

Use the Topic 6 problems any time during this topic.

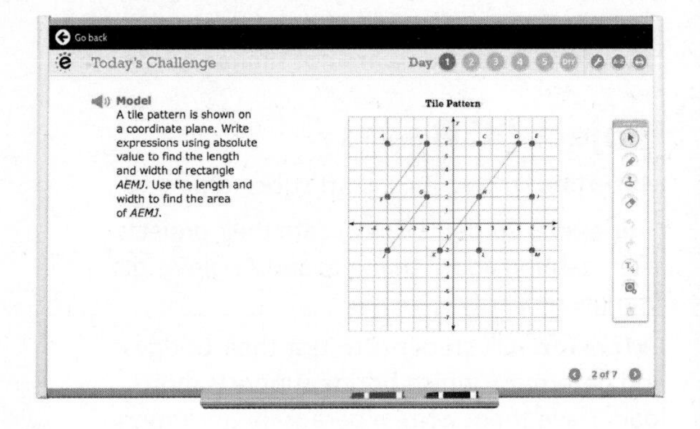


## Mathematics Overview — Common Core Standards

### Content Standards

In this lesson, you will focus on Common Core Standards **8.G.A.1a, 8.G.A.1b, 8.G.A.1c,** and **8.G.A.3**.

- **8.G.A.1a** Lines are taken to lines, and line segments to line segments of the same length.
- **8.G.A.1b** Angles are taken to angles of the same measure.
- **8.G.A.1c** Parallel lines are taken to parallel lines.
- **8.G.A.3** Describe the effect of dilations, translations, rotations, and reflections on two-dimensional figures using coordinates.

### Mathematical Practice Standards

**MP.6 Attend to Precision**
In order to accurately translate a two-dimensional figure, the students must be precise regarding the size, shape, and location of the preimage and the image.

**MP.7 Look for and Make Use of Structure**
Students will find and analyze the patterns between a preimage and its image. They will compare the properties of the preimage and image to ensure structural integrity.

# STEP 1 | Problem-Based Learning

15-20 min

Go Online

Activity

## Solve & Discuss It!

Formative Assessment

**Purpose** Students determine whether two figures have the same side lengths and the same angle measures and connect it to translating a figure on a coordinate plane in Example 2.

### ETP Before — WHOLE CLASS

**1 Introduce the Problem**

Provide graph paper, rulers, and protractors, as needed.

**2 Check for Understanding of the Problem**

Activate prior knowledge by asking: What are the properties of a trapezoid?

### ETP During — SMALL GROUP

**3 Observe Students at Work**

Students might use a ruler to measure each side length and a protractor to measure each angle, and then compare measurements. Students may use a subset of angle and side measurements to compose the shapes. Other students may trace the shapes and overlap them to study the side lengths and angles. If needed, provide students with graph paper, rulers, and protractors to help solve the problem.

**Early Finishers**

How would the problem change if the height of each trapezoid is doubled? [Sample answer: The figures would still have the same side lengths and angle measures.]

### ETP After — WHOLE CLASS

**4 Discuss Solution Strategies and Key Ideas**

Consider having groups who measured each side and each angle share first, followed by those who used other strategies. Have students discuss whether two quadrilaterals can have the same side lengths and different angle measures; two quadrilaterals can have the same side lengths and different angle measures. A rhombus and square can meet these conditions.

Have students discuss how they could determine if the side lengths and angle measures of the figures are the same if one of the figures was cut out with scissors or traced; you could place the cut out figure on top of the other figure to see if they are the same size and shape.

**5 Consider Instructional Implications**

After presenting Example 2, refer students back to the figures in the Solve & Discuss It and have them discuss whether Figure 2 is a translation of Figure 1; yes, if you slide Figure 1 to the right the figures would line up because they are the same size and shape and are facing the same direction. Then have students draw Figure 1 on graph paper and translate it 6 units up and 3 units right.

## Analyze Student Work

**Solve and Discuss It!** Activity is available online.

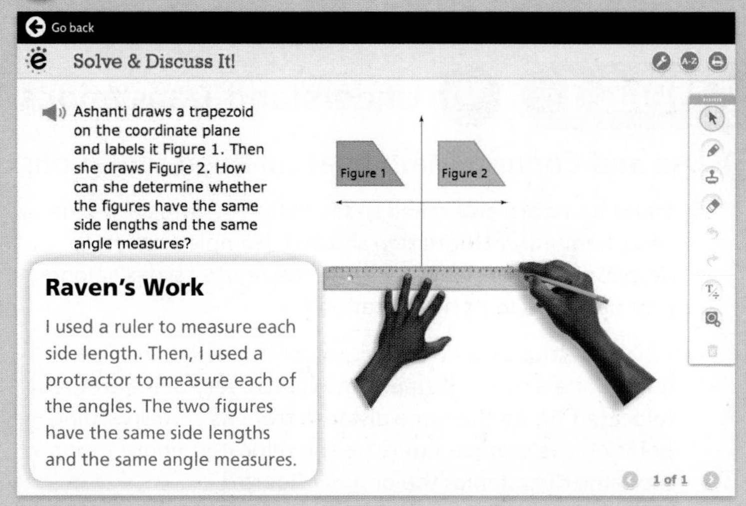


**Raven** used the appropriate tools to determine the length of each side and the measure of each angle. Then, she compared the measurements.

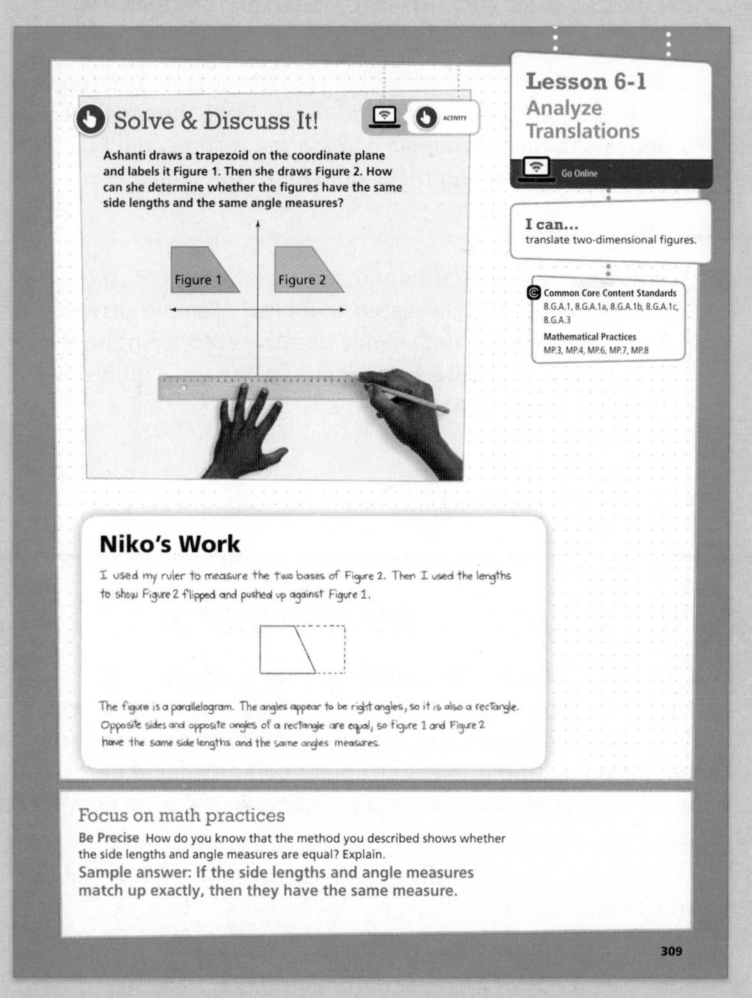


**Niko** flips Figure 2 and pushes it against Figure 1 to form a rectangle. If the sides of the figures are the same, then the angles have to be the same.

# STEP 2 | Visual Learning

Go Online

## Establish Mathematics Goals to Focus Learning

Engage students in a discussion about the ***Essential Question***. Make sure they understand that a translation is one type of transformation. In a translation, all points of the preimage move the same distance in the same direction. The resulting image and the preimage have the same size, shape, and orientation.

## EXAMPLE 1  Understand Translations

ETP **Use and Connect Mathematical Representations**

**Q:** Translations are also called slides. Why does the term *slide* describe the transformation shown? [Sample answer: It describes the translation because the figure "slides" along a straight line to its new location.]

**Q:** What questions could you ask to determine if a figure has undergone a slide? [Sample answer: Is every point on the relocated figure the same distance from its corresponding point on the original figure? Is the relocated figure facing the same direction as the original figure?]

## Try It!

**Elicit and Use Evidence of Student Thinking**

**Q:** What tools and processes could help you draw the new location of the table correctly? [Sample answer: Use tools such as a pencil, ruler, and grid paper. Since the small table appears to be rectangular, naming the vertices could be useful in maintaining the alignment of the table.]

### Convince Me!

**Q:** Why are the side lengths and angle measurements the same in the original and translated triangles? [Sample answer: The dimensions do not change because every point on the translated triangle is located 2 units right and 3 units down from the original triangle.]

**Visual Learning Animation Plus** is available online.

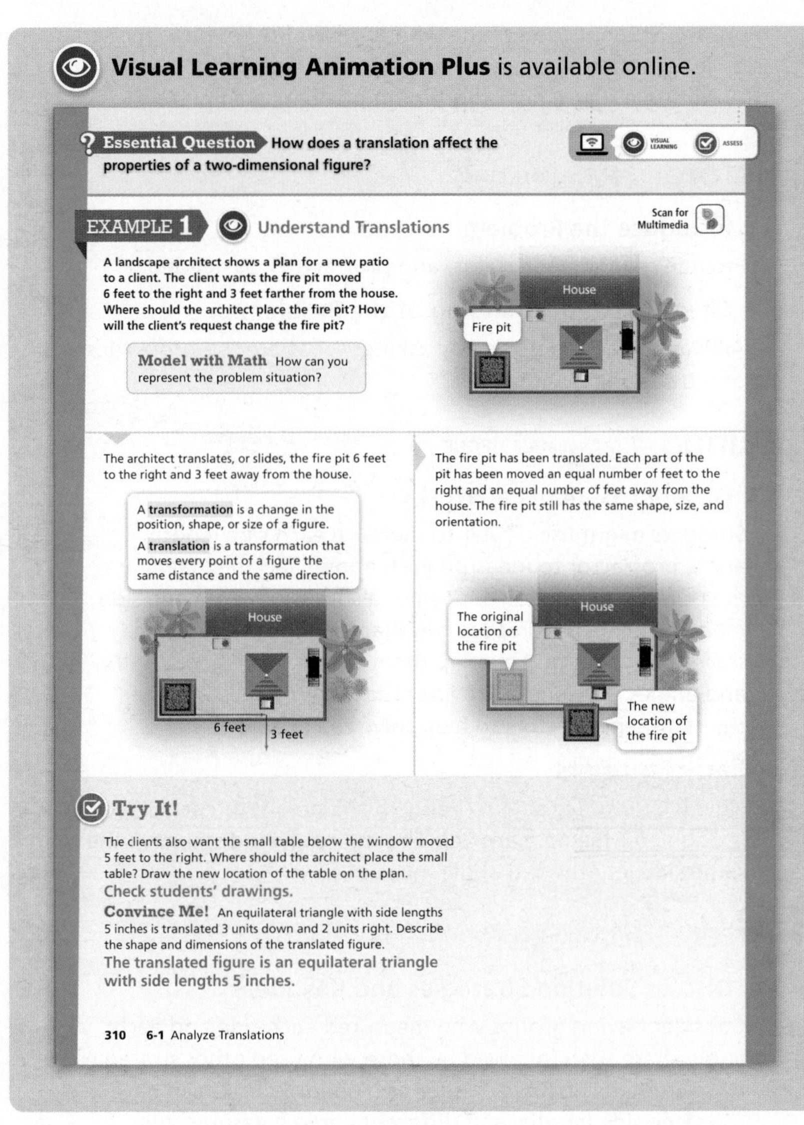

Essential Question How does a translation affect the properties of a two-dimensional figure?

EXAMPLE 1 Understand Translations

Scan for Multimedia

A landscape architect shows a plan for a new patio to a client. The client wants the fire pit moved 6 feet to the right and 3 feet farther from the house. Where should the architect place the fire pit? How will the client's request change the fire pit?

Model with Math How can you represent the problem situation?

The architect translates, or slides, the fire pit 6 feet to the right and 3 feet away from the house.

A **transformation** is a change in the position, shape, or size of a figure.

A **translation** is a transformation that moves every point of a figure the same distance and the same direction.

The fire pit has been translated. Each part of the pit has been moved an equal number of feet to the right and an equal number of feet away from the house. The fire pit still has the same shape, size, and orientation.



Try It!

The clients also want the small table below the window moved 5 feet to the right. Where should the architect place the small table? Draw the new location of the table on the plan.

Check students' drawings.

Convince Me! An equilateral triangle with side lengths 5 inches is translated 3 units down and 2 units right. Describe the shape and dimensions of the translated figure.

The translated figure is an equilateral triangle with side lengths 5 inches.

310 6-1 Analyze Translations

Students can access the ***Visual Learning Animation Plus*** by using the **BouncePages app** to scan this page. Students can download the app for free in their mobile devices' app store.

## Response to Intervention

**USE WITH EXAMPLE 1** Students may have difficulty understanding the only change in a translation is the placement of the shape. The shape's size and orientation stay the same. Use the following questions to help students determine that each point on the figure moves the same distance in the same direction.

**Q:** How does each corner of the original fire pit move to form the new figure? [Sample answer: Each corner moves 6 feet right and 3 feet down.]

**Q:** Suppose the upper left corner moves 6 feet right but the upper right corner moves 8 feet right. Would this movement still be a translation? Explain. [No; Sample answer: In a translation, the original figure and translated figure are the exact same size and shape. This movement would result in a figure with a longer top.]

## Enrichment

**USE WITH EXAMPLE 2** Challenge students to use what they know about coordinates and adding or subtracting integers to verify that their image is correct.

- Subtract coordinates to verify the location of the image.

**Q:** If the figure is translated 8 units down, how would you determine what the $y$-coordinates of the image are? [Sample answer: You would subtract 8 from each $y$-coordinate. For example, $y = 6$ would become $y = -2$.]

**Q:** If the figure is translated 3 units left, how would you determine what the $x$-coordinates of the image are? [Sample answer: You would subtract 3 from each $x$-coordinate. For example, $x = -1$ would become $x = -4$.]

Go Online

Activity

Assess

## EXAMPLE 2  Translate a Figure on a Coordinate Plane

### ETP Pose Purposeful Questions

**Q:** Why is it helpful to label the vertices? [Sample answer: Labeling the vertices makes it much easier to show the image maintains the orientation of the preimage.]

**Q:** For any translated figure, what is true about the preimage and the image? [Sample answer: Their corresponding side lengths are equal and their corresponding angles have the same measure.]

## EXAMPLE 3  Describe a Translation

### ETP Pose Purposeful Questions

**Q:** Notice the word *maps* is being used as a verb. In your own words, what is the meaning of the term *maps*? [Sample answer: The movement of a figure so that every part of a figure is associated with every corresponding part of another figure]

**Q:** Suppose points *P*, *Q*, and *R* were translated 3 units right and 4 units up, but point *S* was not. Is this still a translation? Explain. [No; Sample answer: In order for an image to be the result of a translation every point of the preimage must move the same distance in the same direction.]

## Try It!  Formative Assessment

###  Elicit and Use Evidence of Student Thinking

**Q:** How did you find the $m\angle A'$? [Sample answer: Corresponding angles have the same measure. If $m\angle A = 30°$, then $m\angle A'$ is also $30°$.]

**Examples and Try Its!** are available online.

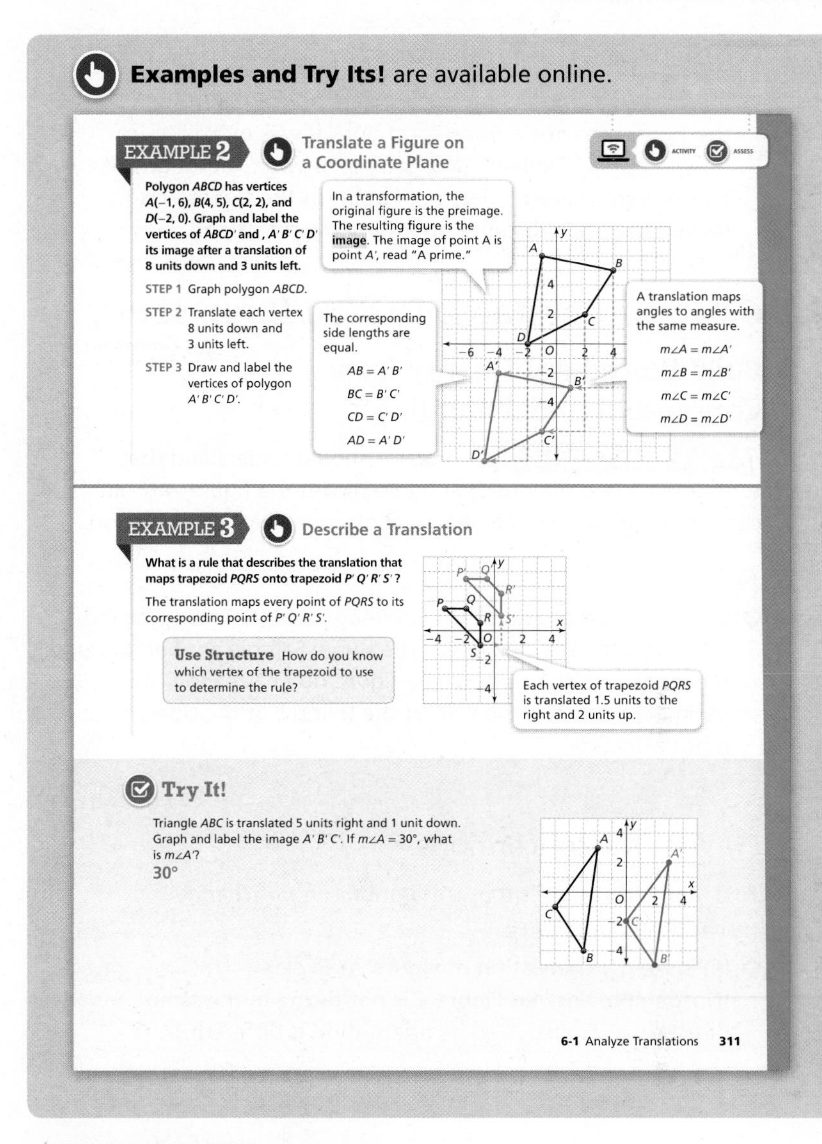
EXAMPLE 2 Translate a Figure on a Coordinate Plane

Polygon *ABCD* has vertices *A*(−1, 6), *B*(4, 5), *C*(2, 2), and *D*(−2, 0). Graph and label the vertices of *ABCD* and , *A′B′C′D′* its image after a translation of 8 units down and 3 units left.

STEP 1 Graph polygon *ABCD*.

STEP 2 Translate each vertex 8 units down and 3 units left.

STEP 3 Draw and label the vertices of polygon *A′B′C′D′*.

In a transformation, the original figure is the preimage. The resulting figure is the **image**. The image of point A is point A′, read "A prime."

The corresponding side lengths are equal.

AB = A′B′

BC = B′C′

CD = C′D′

AD = A′D′

A translation maps angles to angles with the same measure.

m∠A = m∠A′

m∠B = m∠B′

m∠C = m∠C′

m∠D = m∠D′

EXAMPLE 3 Describe a Translation

What is a rule that describes the translation that maps trapezoid *PQRS* onto trapezoid *P′Q′R′S′*?

The translation maps every point of *PQRS* to its corresponding point of *P′Q′R′S′*.

Use Structure How do you know which vertex of the trapezoid to use to determine the rule?

Each vertex of trapezoid *PQRS* is translated 1.5 units to the right and 2 units up.

Try It!

Triangle *ABC* is translated 5 units right and 1 unit down. Graph and label the image *A′B′C′*. If m∠A = 30°, what is m∠A′?

30°

6-1 Analyze Translations 311

## ADDITIONAL EXAMPLES 

**For additional examples go online.**

## English Language Learners

**BEGINNING** Use with Example 2.

Some of the terms and vocabulary can be confusing. Working in small groups can increase understanding.

**Q:** What does the prefix pre- mean? [Sample answer: before]

**Q:** Why is the original figure called the preimage? [Sample answer: The preimage is the figure before a transformation.]

**Q:** What does corresponding mean? [Sample answer: Parts of two figures that are in the same location within each figure.]

**INTERMEDIATE** Use with Example 2.

Writing the terms in sentences can reinforce skills and solidify vocabulary. Have students complete the sentences.

**Q:** A ________ is a change in position, shape, or size of a figure. [transformation]

**Q:** A ________ moves every point of a figure the same distance and the same direction. [translation]

**Q:** In a transformation, the original figure is the ________, and the resulting figure is the ________. [preimage, image]

**ADVANCED** Use with Example 2.

Some of the vocabulary can be confusing.

**Q:** How does the meaning of *translation* differ in geometry? [Sample answer: *Translation* often refers to changing from one language into another. In geometry, *translation* refers to moving every point of a figure the same distance in the same direction.]

# STEP 2 | Visual Learning *continued*

Go Online

 Key Concept  Assess  Activity

## KEY CONCEPT 

### ETP Pose Purposeful Questions

**Q:** Eric moved a figure 3 units right and 6 units up. He said the figure was *not* a translation since it was moved twice. Do you agree? Explain. [No; Sample answer: Although the points were moved twice, each point of the figure was moved the same distance and the same direction.]

##  Do You Understand/Do You Know How?

Formative Assessment

### ETP Build Procedural Fluency from Conceptual Understanding

**Essential Question** Students should understand that translating a two-dimensional figure moves the figure without changing the figure's size, shape, angle measure, or orientation.

**ITEM 2**

**Q:** Would the perimeter of the preimage and the image be the same or different? Explain. [The same; Sample answer: Since the lengths of the sides of the figure do not change, the perimeter, which is the sum of the lengths of the sides, is not affected.]

### Prevent Misconceptions

**ITEM 4** Remind students that translations do not change the orientation of a figure.

**Q:** Is Figure C a translation of Figure A? Explain. [No; Sample answer: Figure C is not facing in the same direction as Figure A, so its orientation is different.]

Available Online

KEY CONCEPT

A *translation*, or slide, is a *transformation* that moves every point of a figure the same distance and the same direction.

Preimage

Image

A translation maps angles to angles with the same measure.

$m\angle D = m\angle D'$

$m\angle E = m\angle E'$

$m\angle F = m\angle F'$

A translation maps line segments to line segments of the same length.

$DE = D'E'$

$DF = D'F'$

$EF = E'F'$

### Do You Understand?

1. **Essential Question** How does a translation affect the properties of a two-dimensional figure?
   Sample answer: Corresponding sides and angles have the same measures in a preimage and its image. Parallel lines are still parallel. Also the orientation is the same.

2. **Construct Arguments** Triangle *L'M'N'* is the image of triangle *LMN* after a translation. How are the side lengths and angle measures of the triangles related? Explain.
   Sample answer: A translation slides a preimage to an image. This means that the two figures will have the same size, shape, and orientation. So the side lengths of the triangles are equal and the angle measures are qual.

3. **Generalize** Sanjay determined that one vertex of a figure was mapped to its image by translating the point 2 units left and 7 units down. What is the rule that maps the other vertices of the figure to their images?
   Sample answer: Every point of the figure is mapped to its image the same distance and in the same direction, so the rule for mapping each point is the same; move 2 units left and 7 units down.

### Do You Know How?

**In 4–6, use the coordinate plane.**

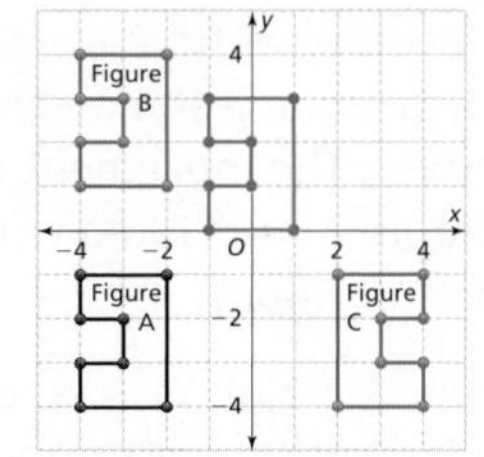


4. Which figure is a translation of Figure A? Explain.
   Figure B; Sample answer: Figure B is a translation of Figure A since it slides each coordinate 5 units up.

5. Graph the translation of Figure A 3 units right and 4 units up.
   Check students' graphs.

6. Describe the translation needed to move Figure B to the same position as the image from Item 5.
   Translate Figure B 3 units right and 1 unit down.

312 **6-1** Analyze Translations

## ADDITIONAL EXAMPLE 2 

This question requires students to graph coordinates with decimals and translate the figure a decimal value.

**Q:** When you graph each point, how is the procedure to graph points *M* and *O* different than when graphing points *N* and *P*? How is the procedure the same? [Sample answer: Points *M* and *O* will be graphed in between two grid lines. Points *N* and *P* will be graphed at the intersection of the grid lines. For all of the points, the first number tells how far to move along the *x*-axis and the second number tells how far to move along the *y*-axis.]

**Q:** How many grid lines will the figure move in each direction? [Sample answer: The figure will move four and one-half grid lines left and five and one-half grid lines up.]

**Additional Examples** are available online.

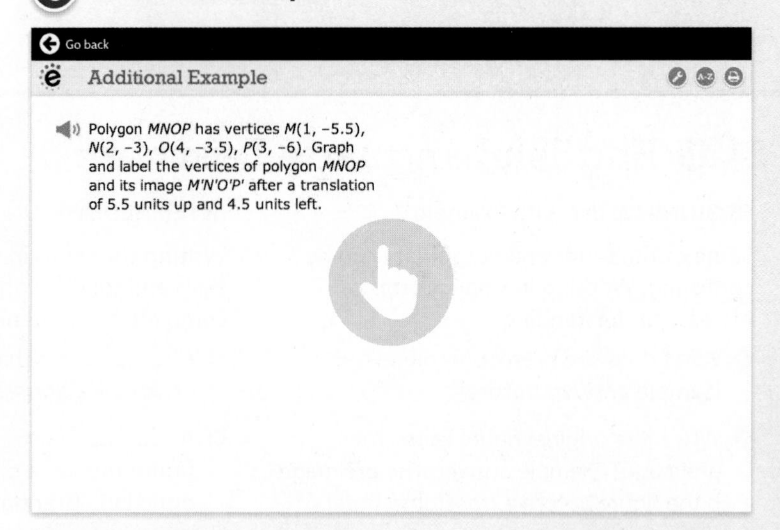


**Answer:** Check student's graphs.

Go Online

Practice

Tutorials

Math Tools

# Practice & Problem Solving

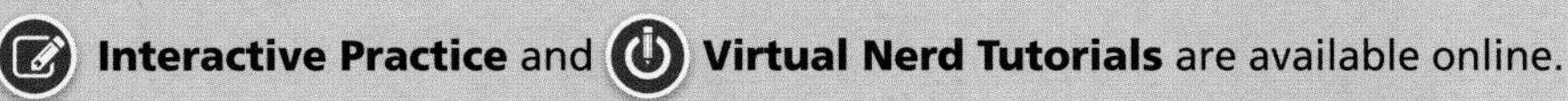
**Interactive Practice** and **Virtual Nerd Tutorials** are available online.

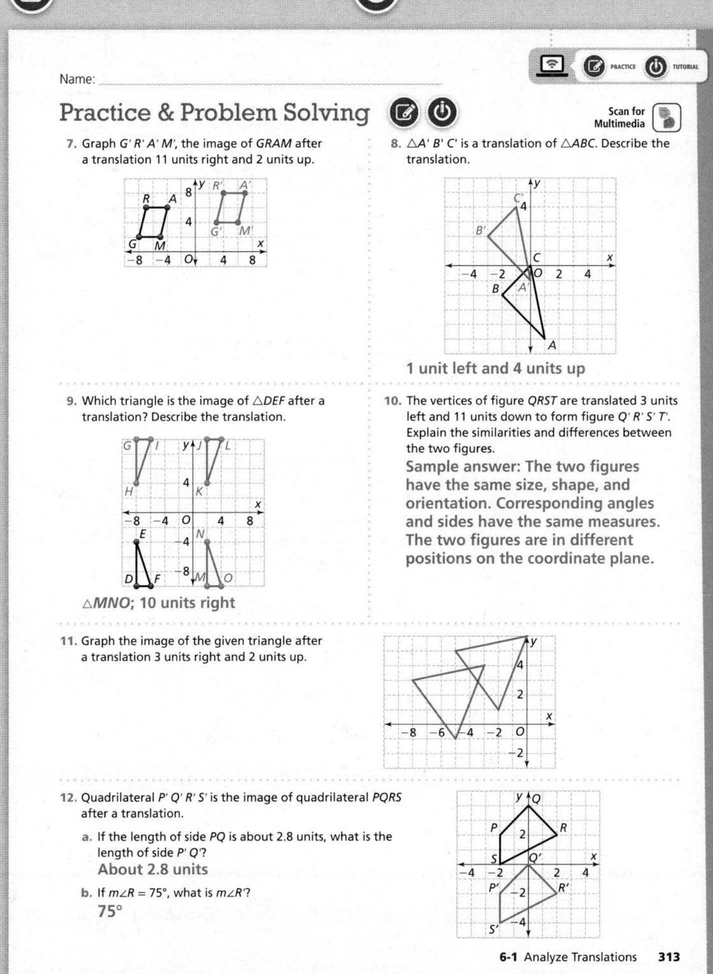
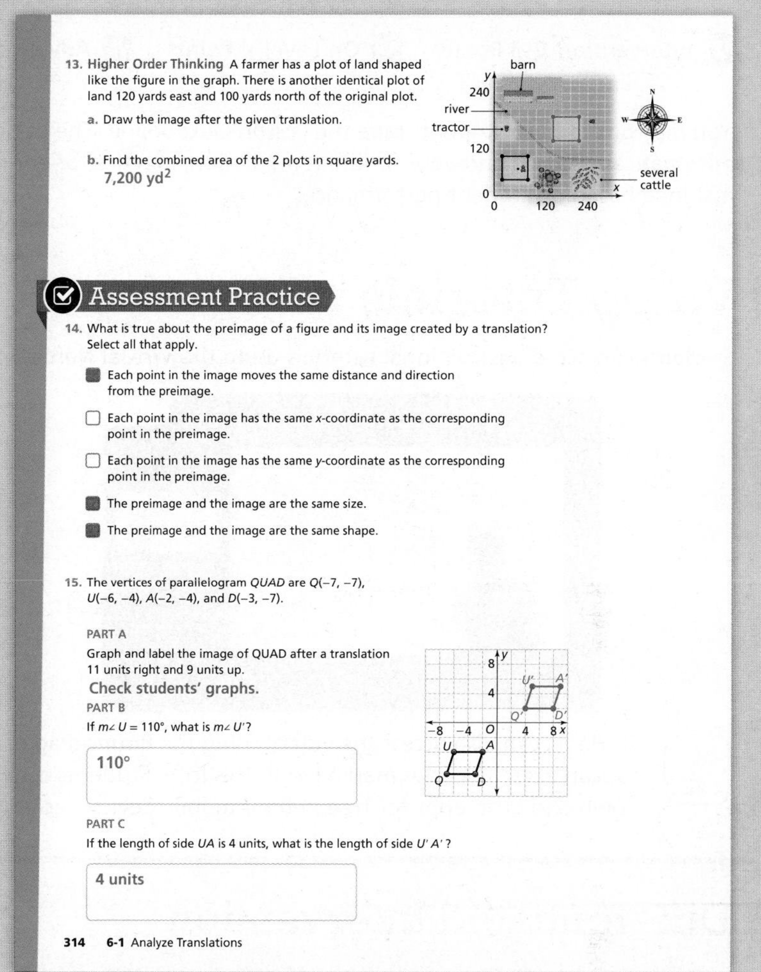

## Error Intervention

**ITEM 8** Some students may struggle with figures that are in two different quadrants on the coordinate plane. Help these students focus on moving the vertices the correct number of units in the correct direction.

**Q:** Describe the movement of $A$ to $A'$, $B$ to $B'$, and $C$ to $C'$. [1 unit left, 4 units up; 1 unit left, 4 units up; 1 unit left, 4 units up]

## English Language Learners

**ITEM 10** Students may struggle expressing how the figure changes since they are asked to focus on language to understand the problem. Review with them that they do not need to know where the preimage and the image are.

- Are the figures the same shape?
- Are the figures the same size?
- Are the figures facing in the same direction?
- Are the figures in the same location?

You may opt to have students complete the automatically scored Practice & Problem Solving items online.

### Item Analysis

| Example | Items | DOK |
|---|---|---|
| 1 | 10 | 2 |
| 2 | 7 | 1 |
| | 11, 12, 14, 15 | 2 |
| | 13 | 3 |
| 3 | 8 | 1 |
| | 9 | 2 |

# STEP 3 | Assess & Differentiate

Go Online

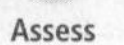

Assess Tutorials Worksheets

## Lesson Quiz

Formative Assessment

RtI Use the student scores on the Lesson Quiz to prescribe differentiated assignments.

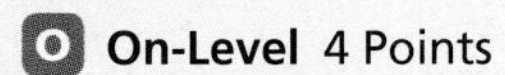

**I Intervention** 0–3 Points **O On-Level** 4 Points **A Advanced** 5 Points

You may opt to have students take the Lesson Quiz online. The Lesson Quiz will be automatically scored and appropriate remediation, practice, or enrichment will be assigned based on student performance.

**Lesson Quiz** is available online.

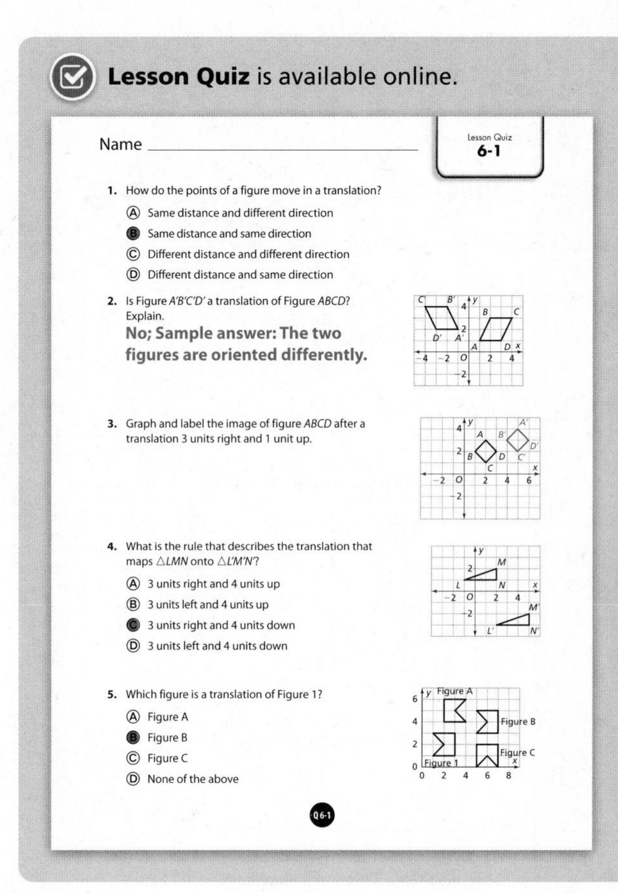
Name ____________ Lesson Quiz 6-1

1. How do the points of a figure move in a translation?
   Ⓐ Same distance and different direction
   Ⓑ Same distance and same direction
   Ⓒ Different distance and different direction
   Ⓓ Different distance and same direction
2. Is Figure $A'B'C'D'$ a translation of Figure $ABCD$? Explain.
   **No; Sample answer: The two figures are oriented differently.**
3. Graph and label the image of figure $ABCD$ after a translation 3 units right and 1 unit up.
4. What is the rule that describes the translation that maps $\triangle LMN$ onto $\triangle L'M'N'$?
   Ⓐ 3 units right and 4 units up
   Ⓑ 3 units left and 4 units up
   Ⓒ 3 units right and 4 units down
   Ⓓ 3 units left and 4 units down
5. Which figure is a translation of Figure 1?
   Ⓐ Figure A
   Ⓑ Figure B
   Ⓒ Figure C
   Ⓓ None of the above

Q6-1

## Video Tutorials

Students can access instructional tutorials using the **Virtual Nerd app**.

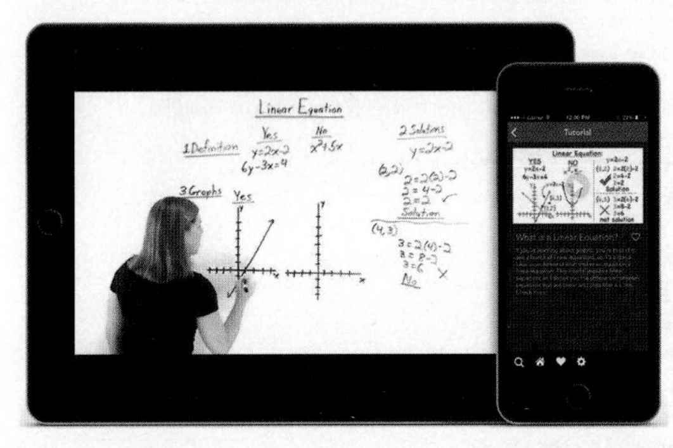

Students can also access the videos using the **BouncePages app** to scan exercise pages marked with this icon. Students can download both apps for free in their mobile devices' app store.

## Differentiated Intervention

**I** = Intervention **O** = On-Level **A** = Advanced

### Reteach to Build Understanding I

Provides scaffolded reteaching for the key lesson concepts.

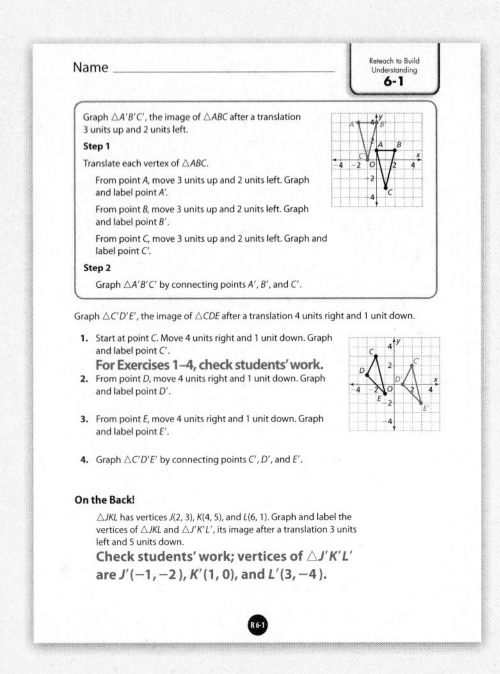
Name ____________ Reteach to Build Understanding 6-1

Graph $\triangle A'B'C'$, the image of $\triangle ABC$ after a translation 3 units up and 2 units left.

**Step 1**
Translate each vertex of $\triangle ABC$.
From point $A$, move 3 units up and 2 units left. Graph and label point $A'$.
From point $B$, move 3 units up and 2 units left. Graph and label point $B'$.
From point $C$, move 3 units up and 2 units left. Graph and label point $C'$.

**Step 2**
Graph $\triangle A'B'C'$ by connecting points $A'$, $B'$, and $C'$.

Graph $\triangle C'D'E'$, the image of $\triangle CDE$ after a translation 4 units right and 1 unit down.

1. Start at point $C$. Move 4 units right and 1 unit down. Graph and label point $C'$.
   **For Exercises 1–4, check students' work.**
2. From point $D$, move 4 units right and 1 unit down. Graph and label point $D'$.
3. From point $E$, move 4 units right and 1 unit down. Graph and label point $E'$.
4. Graph $\triangle C'D'E'$ by connecting points $C'$, $D'$, and $E'$.

**On the Back!**
$\triangle JKL$ has vertices $J(2, 3)$, $K(4, 5)$, and $L(6, 1)$. Graph and label the vertices of $\triangle JKL$ and $\triangle J'K'L'$, its image after a translation 3 units left and 5 units down.
**Check students' work; vertices of $\triangle J'K'L'$ are $J'(-1, -2)$, $K'(1, 0)$, and $L'(3, -4)$.**

R6-1

### Additional Vocabulary Support I O

Helps students develop and reinforce understanding of key terms and concepts.

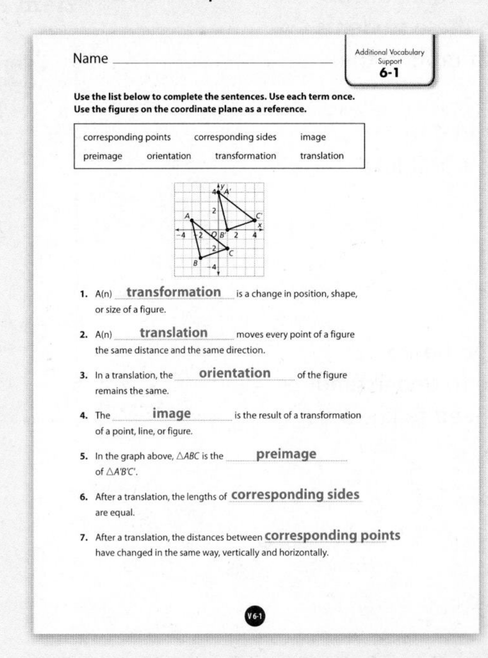
Name ____________ Additional Vocabulary Support 6-1

**Use the list below to complete the sentences. Use each term once. Use the figures on the coordinate plane as a reference.**

| corresponding points | corresponding sides | image |
|---|---|---|
| preimage | orientation | transformation | translation |

1. A(n) **transformation** is a change in position, shape, or size of a figure.
2. A(n) **translation** moves every point of a figure the same distance and the same direction.
3. In a translation, the **orientation** of the figure remains the same.
4. The **image** is the result of a transformation of a point, line, or figure.
5. In the graph above, $\triangle ABC$ is the **preimage** of $\triangle A'B'C'$.
6. After a translation, the lengths of **corresponding sides** are equal.
7. After a translation, the distances between **corresponding points** have changed in the same way, vertically and horizontally.

V6-1

### Build Mathematical Literacy I O

Provides support for struggling readers to build mathematical literacy.

Name ____________ Build Mathematical Literacy 6-1

**Read the problem below. Then answer the questions to identify the steps for solving the problem.**

$\triangle A'B'C'$ is a translation of $\triangle ABC$. Describe the translation.

1. Which figure is the preimage, and which figure is the image? How do you know?
   **Sample answer: Triangle $ABC$ is the preimage, because it is the figure that has been translated, or moved. Triangle $A'B'C'$ is the image, because it is the result of the translation.**
2. Why do you need to distinguish the image from the preimage to solve the problem?
   **Sample answer: I need to identify corresponding points and decide how the coordinates from a point on the preimage can be transformed into the coordinates of the corresponding point on the image.**
3. To describe a translation, what information must you include?
   **The horizontal and vertical distance that each point in the preimage moves to form the image**
4. What are the coordinates of points $A$ and $A'$?
   ***$A$*(2, 5) and *$A'$*(5, 3)**
5. For a point in the preimage and its corresponding image, which coordinate changes in a horizontal translation? A vertical translation?
   **The $x$-coordinate changes in a horizontal translation and the $y$-coordinate changes in a vertical translation.**

M6-1

Go Online

Practice

Worksheets

Math Tools

Math Games

# Additional Practice

You may opt to have students complete the automatically scored Additional Practice items online.

### Item Analysis

| Example | Items | DOK |
|---|---|---|
| 1 | 3, 5 | 2 |
| 2 | 1, 2, 8 | 2 |
| | 7 | 3 |
| 3 | 4, 6 | 2 |

**Interactive Practice** is available online.

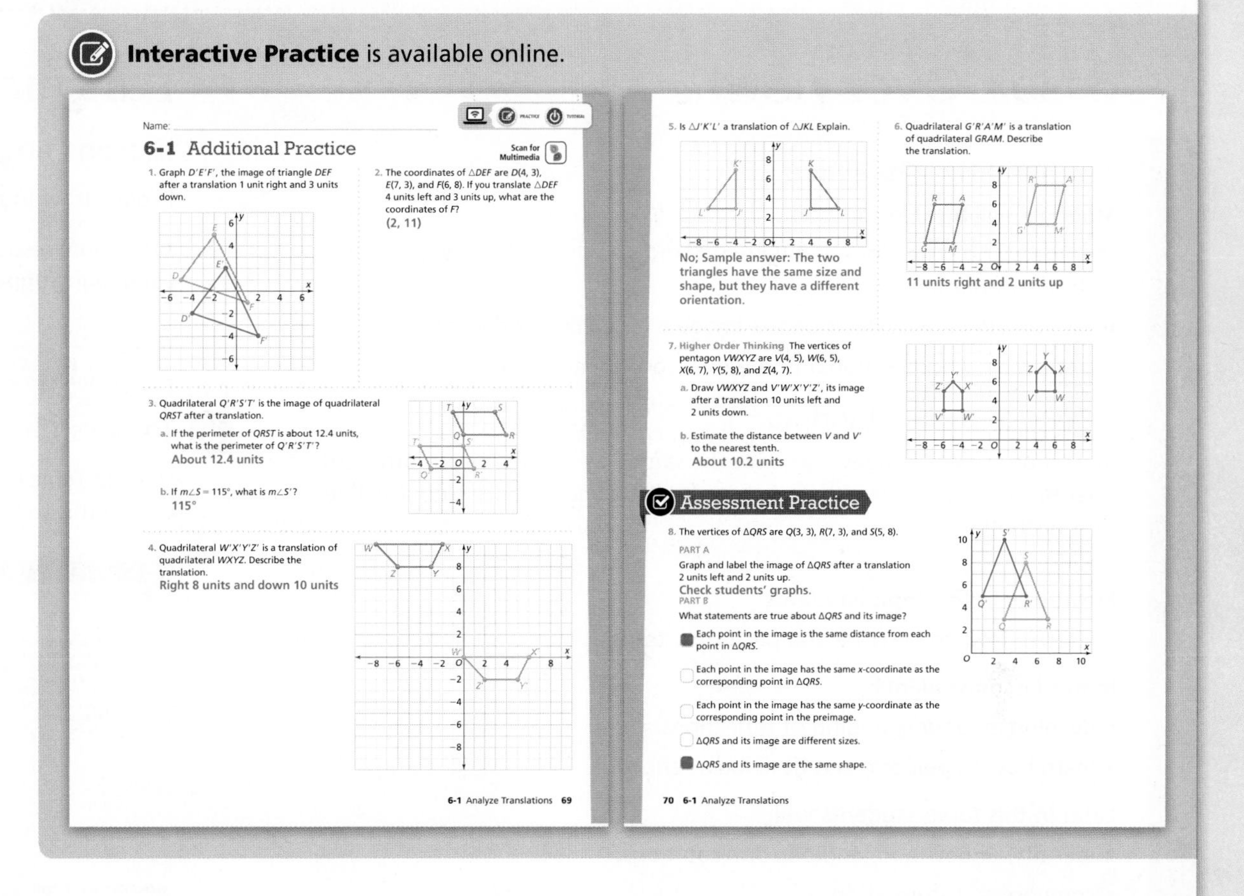
Name:

**6-1** Additional Practice

Scan for Multimedia

1. Graph $D'E'F'$, the image of triangle $DEF$ after a translation 1 unit right and 3 units down.

2. The coordinates of $\triangle DEF$ are $D(4, 3)$, $E(7, 3)$, and $F(6, 8)$. If you translate $\triangle DEF$ 4 units left and 3 units up, what are the coordinates of $F$?
(2, 11)

3. Quadrilateral $Q'R'S'T'$ is the image of quadrilateral $QRST$ after a translation.
a. If the perimeter of $QRST$ is about 12.4 units, what is the perimeter of $Q'R'S'T'$?
About 12.4 units
b. If $m\angle S = 115°$, what is $m\angle S'$?
115°

4. Quadrilateral $W'X'Y'Z'$ is a translation of quadrilateral $WXYZ$. Describe the translation.
Right 8 units and down 10 units

6-1 Analyze Translations 69

5. Is $\triangle J'K'L'$ a translation of $\triangle JKL$. Explain.
No; Sample answer: The two triangles have the same size and shape, but they have a different orientation.

6. Quadrilateral $G'R'A'M'$ is a translation of quadrilateral $GRAM$. Describe the translation.
11 units right and 2 units up

7. **Higher Order Thinking** The vertices of pentagon $VWXYZ$ are $V(4, 5)$, $W(6, 5)$, $X(6, 7)$, $Y(5, 8)$, and $Z(4, 7)$.
a. Draw $VWXYZ$ and $V'W'X'Y'Z'$, its image after a translation 10 units left and 2 units down.
b. Estimate the distance between $V$ and $V'$ to the nearest tenth.
About 10.2 units

Assessment Practice

8. The vertices of $\Delta QRS$ are $Q(3, 3)$, $R(7, 3)$, and $S(5, 8)$.
PART A
Graph and label the image of $\Delta QRS$ after a translation 2 units left and 2 units up.
Check students' graphs.
PART B
What statements are true about $\Delta QRS$ and its image?
- [x] Each point in the image is the same distance from each point in $\Delta QRS$.
- [ ] Each point in the image has the same $x$-coordinate as the corresponding point in $\Delta QRS$.
- [ ] Each point in the image has the same $y$-coordinate as the corresponding point in the preimage.
- [ ] $\Delta QRS$ and its image are different sizes.
- [x] $\Delta QRS$ and its image are the same shape.

70 6-1 Analyze Translations

# Differentiated Intervention

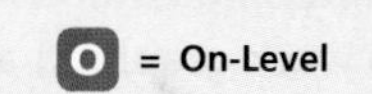
I = Intervention O = On-Level A = Advanced

## Enrichment O A

Presents engaging problems and activities that extend the lesson concepts.

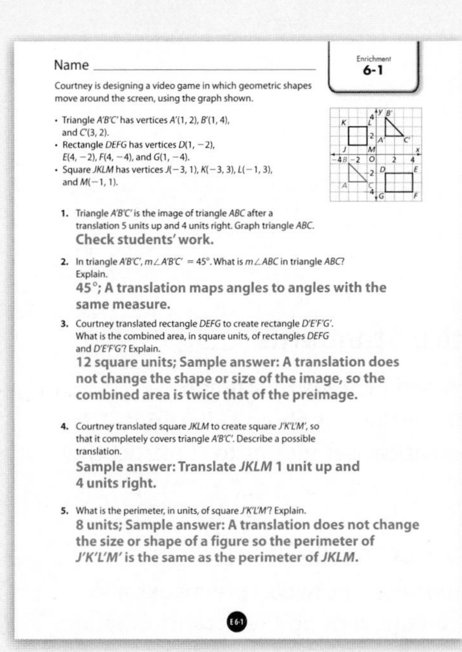
Name

Enrichment 6-1

Courtney is designing a video game in which geometric shapes move around the screen, using the graph shown.

- Triangle $A'B'C'$ has vertices $A'(1, 2)$, $B'(1, 4)$, and $C'(3, 2)$.
- Rectangle $DEFG$ has vertices $D(1, -2)$, $E(4, -2)$, $F(4, -4)$, and $G(1, -4)$.
- Square $JKLM$ has vertices $J(-3, 1)$, $K(-3, 3)$, $L(-1, 3)$, and $M(-1, 1)$.

1. Triangle $A'B'C'$ is the image of triangle $ABC$ after a translation 5 units up and 4 units right. Graph triangle $ABC$.
Check students' work.
2. In triangle $A'B'C'$, $m\angle A'B'C' = 45°$. What is $m\angle ABC$ in triangle $ABC$? Explain.
45°; A translation maps angles to angles with the same measure.
3. Courtney translated rectangle $DEFG$ to create rectangle $D'E'F'G'$. What is the combined area, in square units, of rectangles $DEFG$ and $D'E'F'G'$? Explain.
12 square units; Sample answer: A translation does not change the shape or size of the image, so the combined area is twice that of the preimage.
4. Courtney translated square $JKLM$ to create square $J'K'L'M'$, so that it completely covers triangle $A'B'C'$. Describe a possible translation.
Sample answer: Translate $JKLM$ 1 unit up and 4 units right.
5. What is the perimeter, in units, of square $J'K'L'M'$? Explain.
8 units; Sample answer: A translation does not change the size or shape of a figure so the perimeter of $J'K'L'M'$ is the same as the perimeter of $JKLM$.

E6-1

## Math Tools and Games I O A

Offers additional activities and games to build understanding and fluency.

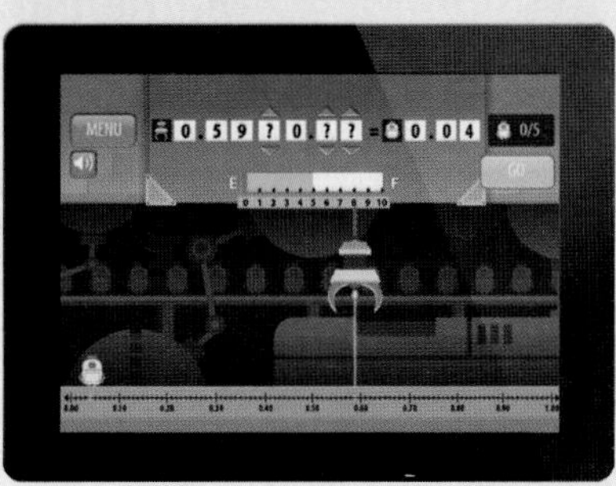


## Pick a Project and STEM Project I O A

Provides an additional opportunity for students to demonstrate understanding of key mathematical concepts.

Go Online

Activity

# Lesson 6-2 Analyze Reflections

## Lesson Overview

FOCUS

### Mathematics Objective

**Students will be able to:**

- ✔ understand reflections as a type of transformation and how they differ from translations.
- ✔ use coordinates to describe the image created by a reflection.
- ✔ reflect a two-dimensional figure on a coordinate plane.

### Essential Understanding

Reflections create images that have the same size and shape but different orientation. The image and preimage are the same distance from the line of reflection.

COHERENCE

**Previously in this topic, students:**

- learned how to describe and perform a translation.

**In this lesson students:**

- develop an understanding of reflections.
- learn how to perform and describe a reflection.

**Later in this topic, students will:**

- identify, understand, and perform rotations.
- compose transformations.

**Cross-Cluster Connection** Work graphing and analyzing reflections (8.G.1) connects to work graphing and analyzing slope (8.EE.2).

RIGOR

This lesson emphasizes a blend of **conceptual understanding** and **procedural skill and fluency**.

- Students will understand the concept of reflecting figures and how the resulting images are related to the preimages.
- Students will practice reflecting figures and explore the properties of reflections.

## Language Support

### Lesson Language Objective

Explain how to reflect two-dimensional figures.

Additional resources are available in the **Language Support Handbook**.

## Math Anytime

### Today's Challenge

Use the Topic 6 problems any time during this topic.

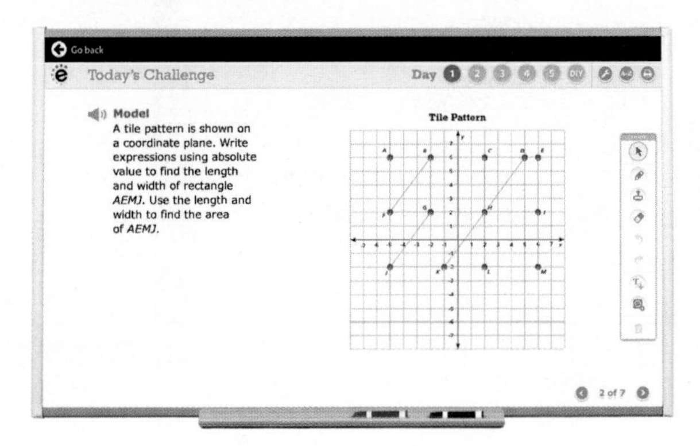


## Mathematics Overview — Common Core Standards

### Content Standards

In this lesson, you will focus on Common Core Standards **8.G.A.1a, 8.G.A.1b, 8.G.A.1c,** and **8.G.A.3**.

- **8.G.A.1a** Lines are taken to lines, and line segments to line segments of the same length.
- **8.G.A.1b** Angles are taken to angles of the same measure.
- **8.G.A.1c** Parallel lines are taken to parallel lines.
- **8.G.A.3** Describe the effect of dilations, translations, rotations, and reflections on two-dimensional figures using coordinates.

### Mathematical Practice Standards

**MP.3 Construct Arguments and Critique Reasoning**
Students will analyze their conclusions about reflections. They will use established mathematical definitions to construct their own arguments.

**MP.7 Look for and Make Use of Structure**
Students will identify relationships between preimages and images to determine the rules governing their transformation.

# STEP 1 | Problem-Based Learning

15-20 min

Go Online

Activity

## Solve & Discuss It!

Formative Assessment

**Purpose** Students analyze two figures for common properties and connect it to reflecting a figure on a coordinate plane in Example 2.

### ETP Before — WHOLE CLASS

**1 Introduce the Problem**

Provide graph paper, ruler, and protractor, as needed.

**2 Check for Understanding of the Problem**

Activate prior knowledge by asking: What are the properties of a triangle?

### ETP During — SMALL GROUP

**3 Observe Students at Work**

Students might count the grid squares or measure to find the triangles have the same dimensions and angles. They might fold the graph paper along the pencil to determine that the figures have the same size and shape but are mirror images of each other. If needed, provide graph paper for students to draw and explore the figures. Look for students to use other methods to establish that the triangles have the same shape and size, with Figure 2 being a reflection of Figure 1.

**Early Finishers**

How would the problem change if the pencil was horizontal and 3 units below Figure 1? [Sample answer: Figure 2 would be drawn 6 units below Figure 1. Figure 1 and Figure 2 would still be the same size and shape and but Figure 2 would be upside down.]

### ETP After — WHOLE CLASS

**4 Discuss Solution Strategies and Key Ideas**

Consider having groups who counted the grid squares or measured with rulers to determine that the figures are the same size and shape share first, followed by those who folded the paper along the pencil. Have students discuss the connections between the strategies; when folding a shape onto another shape, if the shapes match then the side lengths and angle measures of each shape are the same.

Have students discuss how the distance from each vertex on Figure 1 to the pencil relates to the distance from each vertex on Figure 2 to the pencil; the distance from the pencil to the vertices on each figure is the same.

**5 Consider Instructional Implications**

After presenting Example 2, refer students back to the problem in the Solve & Discuss It and have them describe the similarities between the triangles and the shapes in Example 2; for both sets of figures, each point in the original figure has a corresponding point in the reflected figure that is the same distance away from the line of reflection. Both sets of figures show a reflection. The shapes in Example 2 are reflected across the $x$-axis, and the triangles in the Solve & Discuss It are reflected across the pencil.

## Analyze Student Work

**Solve and Discuss It!** Activity is available online.

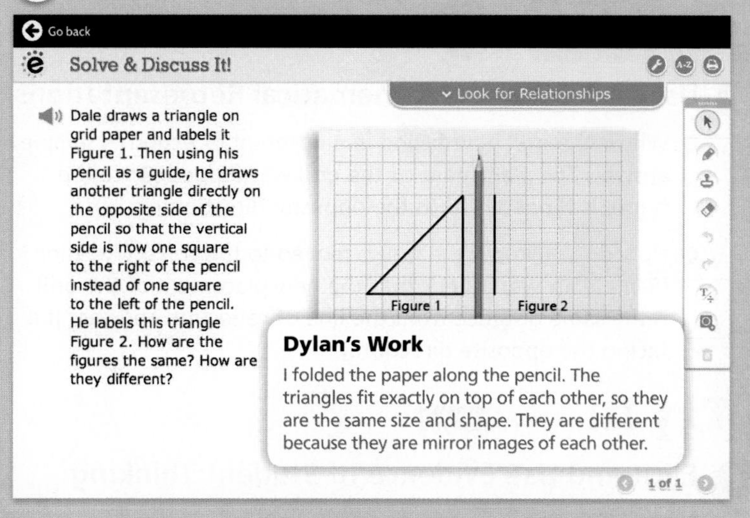


**Dylan** determines that the figures are the same by folding the paper so the figures fit on top of each other exactly.

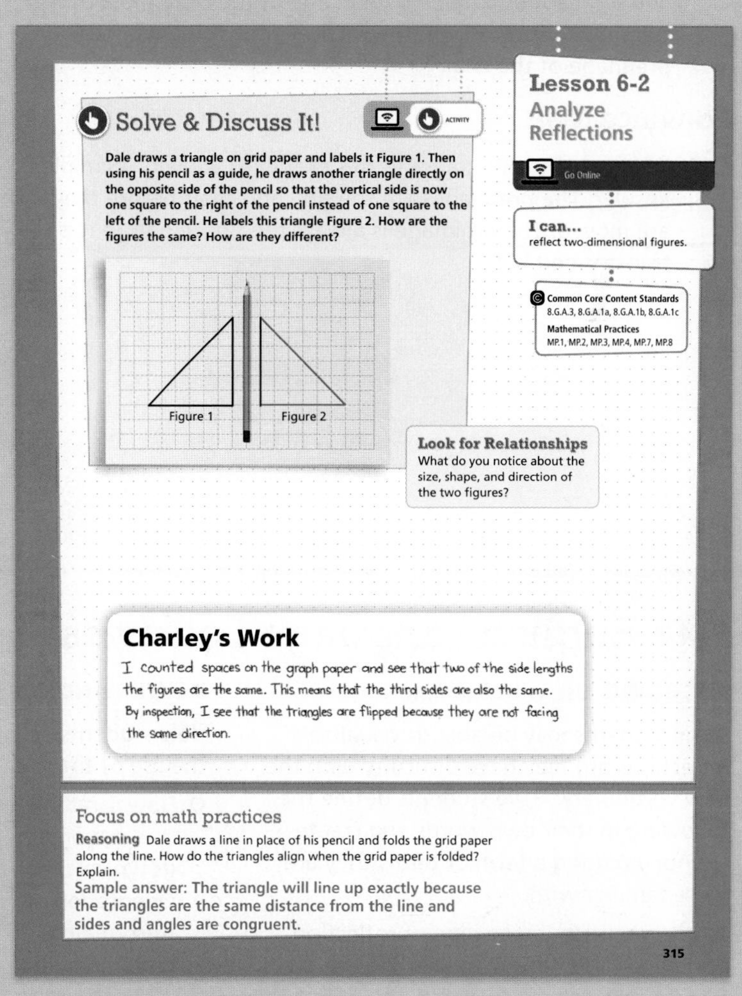


**Charley** analyzes the figures using the graph paper as a guide and determines that the triangles have the same dimensions but are not facing the same direction.

# STEP 2 | Visual Learning

Go Online

Visual Learning

Assess

## ETP Establish Mathematics Goals to Focus Learning

Engage students in a discussion about the ***Essential Question***. Make sure they understand the definition of transformation and how the term relates to a reflection, and remind them of the geometric properties of two-dimensional figures.

## EXAMPLE 1  Understand Reflections

### ETP Use and Connect Mathematical Representations

**Q:** Why is the grill now facing in a different direction? [Sample answer: The placement of the grill was flipped. Once the figure is flipped it faces the opposite direction.]

**Q:** How do you know the grill is moved to the correct location? [Sample answer: Check that the new placement of the grill is the same distance from the line of reflection and that it is facing the opposite direction.]

##  Try It!  Formative Assessment

### ETP Elicit and Use Evidence of Student Thinking

**Q:** How does the vertical line segment help you determine the location of the chair? [Sample answer: Use the vertical line segment as a guide. The image of the chair must be the same distance from the vertical line segment as the preimage of the chair.]

### Convince Me!

**Q:** What are the preimages in this example? Explain. [Sample answer: The preimages are the grill and chair before they are moved. The preimage is always the figure before it is transformed.]

**Visual Learning Animation Plus** is available online.

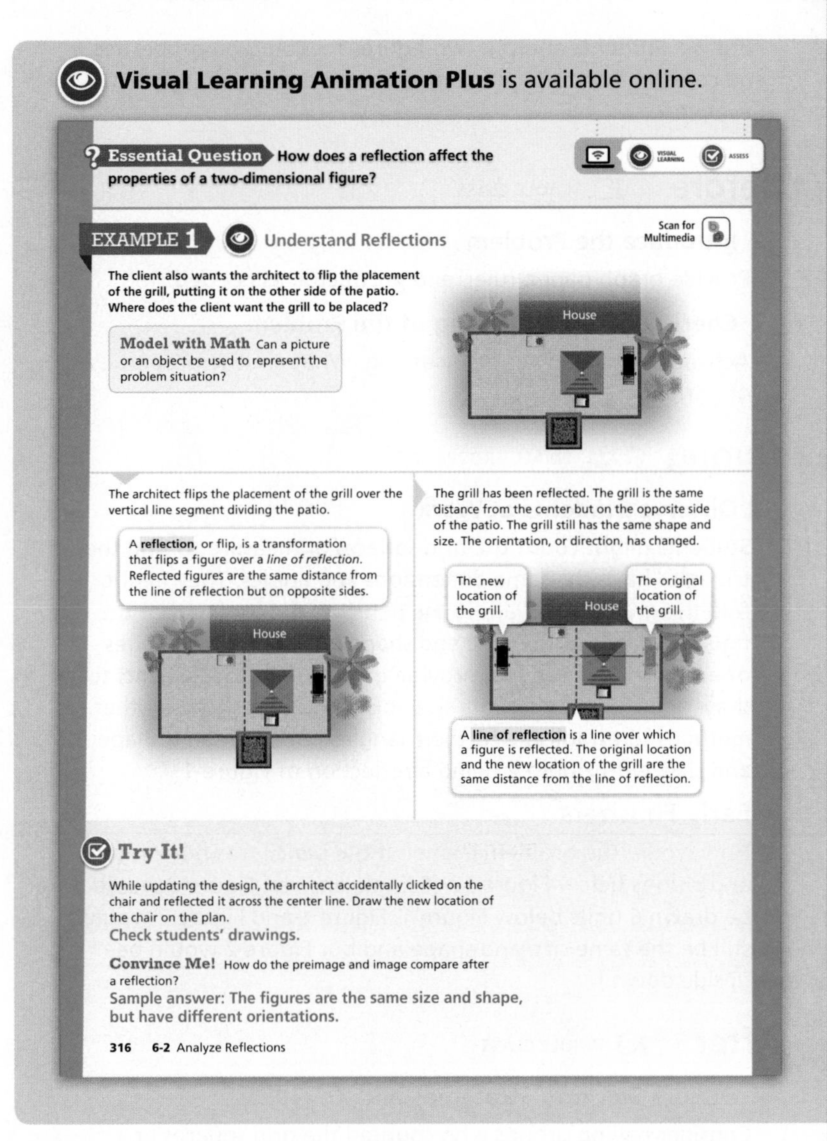
Essential Question How does a reflection affect the properties of a two-dimensional figure?

EXAMPLE 1 Understand Reflections

Scan for Multimedia

The client also wants the architect to flip the placement of the grill, putting it on the other side of the patio. Where does the client want the grill to be placed?

Model with Math Can a picture or an object be used to represent the problem situation?

House

The architect flips the placement of the grill over the vertical line segment dividing the patio.

A **reflection**, or flip, is a transformation that flips a figure over a *line of reflection*. Reflected figures are the same distance from the line of reflection but on opposite sides.

House

The grill has been reflected. The grill is the same distance from the center but on the opposite side of the patio. The grill still has the same shape and size. The orientation, or direction, has changed.

The new location of the grill.

House

The original location of the grill.

A **line of reflection** is a line over which a figure is reflected. The original location and the new location of the grill are the same distance from the line of reflection.

Try It!

While updating the design, the architect accidentally clicked on the chair and reflected it across the center line. Draw the new location of the chair on the plan.

Check students' drawings.

Convince Me! How do the preimage and image compare after a reflection?

Sample answer: The figures are the same size and shape, but have different orientations.

316 6-2 Analyze Reflections

Students can access the ***Visual Learning Animation Plus*** by using the **BouncePages app** to scan this page. Students can download the app for free in their mobile devices' app store.

## ELL English Language Learners

**EMERGING** Use with Example 1.

Some students may be able to visualize reflections but may have difficulty with the new vocabulary. Have students define the following in their own words and create a synonym using a term or terms they are more familiar with.

architect, client, image, line of reflection, preimage, orientation, reflection, transformation

**DEVELOPING** Use with Example 1.

Help students become more familiar with the use of the vocabulary in a math context.

**Q:** How can the meaning of the word *orientation* differ in geometry from its typical usage? [Sample answer: Orientation can refer to adjusting to new surroundings. In geometry, it refers to the placement and direction a figure faces.]

**Q:** How is a reflection in a mirror similar to a geometric reflection? [Sample answer: A reflection in a mirror and a geometric reflection are the same size and shape just backwards.]

**EXPANDING** Use with Example 1.

Have advanced students work in pairs or small groups to determine how the following pairs of words are related.

preimage and image

translation and reflection

reflection and transformation

reflection and line of reflection

Listen for students' use of academic language to help them develop fluency.

Go Online

Activity

Assess

# EXAMPLE 2  Reflect a Figure on a Coordinate Plane

## ETP Pose Purposeful Questions

**Q:** What do the red and green dashed lines show? Sample answer: The lines show the points *A* and *A′* are the same distance from the *x*-axis.]

**Q:** How can you check that *D′* is graphed correctly? [Sample answer: Count the distance *D′* is from the *x*-axis. Since *D* is 5 units from the *x*-axis, *D′* should also be 5 units from the *x*-axis.]

##  Try It! 

##  Elicit and Use Evidence of Student Thinking

**Q:** Compare the signs of the *x*- and *y*-coordinates of *N* and *N′*. What do you notice? [Sample answer: The sign of the *x*-coordinate changes. The sign of the *y*-coordinate stays the same.]

# EXAMPLE 3  Describe a Reflection

##  Pose Purposeful Questions

**Q:** How does $(x, y) \rightarrow (-x, y)$ describe a reflection across the *y*-axis? [Sample answer: The *x*-coordinate changes signs, the mapping uses a negative to show the *x*-coordinate changing signs. The *y*-coordinate stays the same, the *y* remains the same in the mapping.]

**Q:** A rule for a reflection across the *y*-axis is shown. Using math symbols, write a rule for a reflection across the *x*-axis. [$(x, y) \rightarrow (x, -y)$]

##  Try It! 

##  Elicit and Use Evidence of Student Thinking

**Q:** Does the rule $(x, y) \rightarrow (-x, y)$ still apply in this example? Explain. [No; Sample answer: That rule only applies when a figure is reflected over the *y*-axis. The coordinates of point *A* are (−4, 4), and the coordinates of *A′* are (0, 4), not (4, 4).]

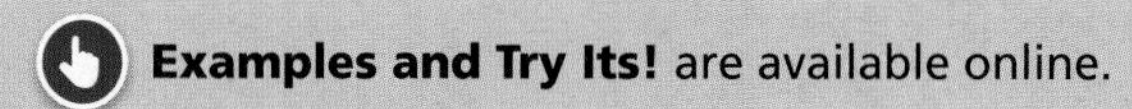
**Examples and Try Its!** are available online.

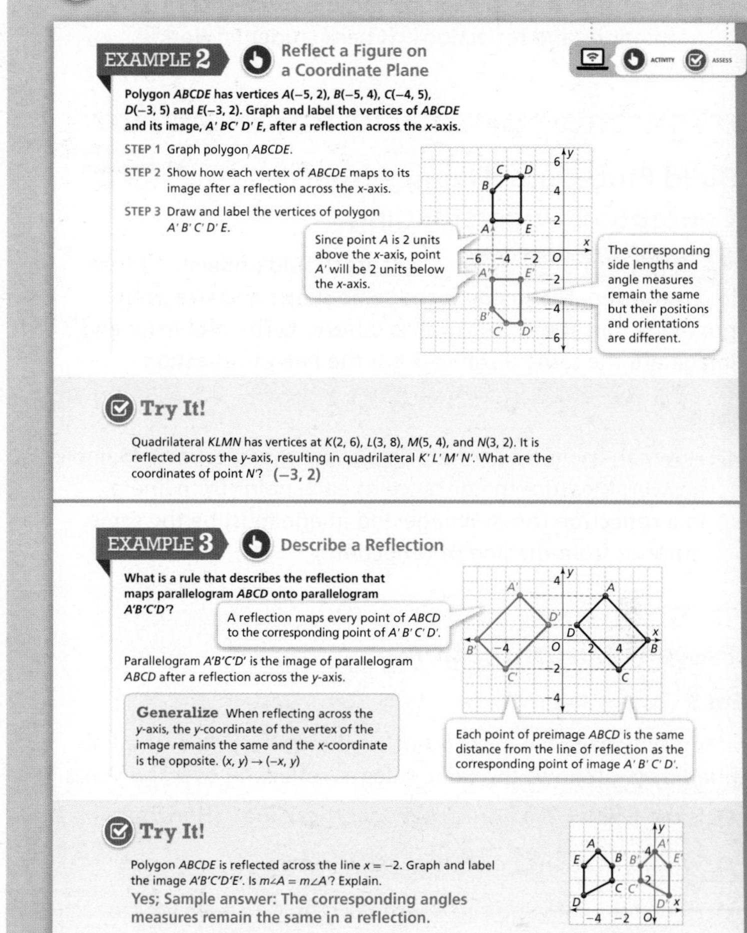
EXAMPLE 2 Reflect a Figure on a Coordinate Plane

**Polygon *ABCDE* has vertices *A*(−5, 2), *B*(−5, 4), *C*(−4, 5), *D*(−3, 5) and *E*(−3, 2). Graph and label the vertices of *ABCDE* and its image, *A′ B′ C′ D′ E*, after a reflection across the *x*-axis.**

STEP 1 Graph polygon *ABCDE*.

STEP 2 Show how each vertex of *ABCDE* maps to its image after a reflection across the *x*-axis.

STEP 3 Draw and label the vertices of polygon *A′ B′ C′ D′ E*.



Try It!

Quadrilateral *KLMN* has vertices at *K*(2, 6), *L*(3, 8), *M*(5, 4), and *N*(3, 2). It is reflected across the *y*-axis, resulting in quadrilateral *K′ L′ M′ N′*. What are the coordinates of point *N′*? (−3, 2)

EXAMPLE 3 Describe a Reflection

**What is a rule that describes the reflection that maps parallelogram *ABCD* onto parallelogram *A′B′C′D′*?**



Parallelogram *A′B′C′D′* is the image of parallelogram *ABCD* after a reflection across the *y*-axis.

**Generalize** When reflecting across the *y*-axis, the *y*-coordinate of the vertex of the image remains the same and the *x*-coordinate is the opposite. $(x, y) \rightarrow (-x, y)$



Try It!

Polygon *ABCDE* is reflected across the line $x = -2$. Graph and label the image *A′B′C′D′E′*. Is $m\angle A = m\angle A'$? Explain.
Yes; Sample answer: The corresponding angles measures remain the same in a reflection.

6-2 Analyze Reflections 317

ADDITIONAL EXAMPLES 

**For additional examples go online.**

#  Response to Intervention

**USE WITH EXAMPLE 3** Students may have difficulty determining which axis the figure reflected over. Have these students compare the coordinates of the preimage and image and then determine to which rule the points apply.

**Q:** How do the *x*-coordinates of the points in the preimage and image compare? [Sample answer: The signs are opposite.]

**Q:** How do the *y*-coordinates of the points in the preimage and image compare? [The signs stay the same.]

# Enrichment

**USE WITH EXAMPLE 3** Challenge students to try reflections across lines that are not one of the axes.

Have students plot the points (−1, −1), (0, 0), and (1, 1) and connect them to form a line.

**Q:** Reflect the triangle formed by the points *A*(−3, 2), *B*(−2, 5), and *C*(− 1, 1) over the line you drew. What are the coordinates of the image? [*A′* (2, −3), *B′* (5, −2), and *C′* (1, −1)]

**Q:** Examine how the coordinates change. What general rule can you write for this reflection? [Sample answer: The *x* and *y* coordinates exchange places. The general rule is $(x, y) \rightarrow (y, x)$.]

Go Online

Key Concept

Assess

Activity

# STEP 2 | Visual Learning *continued*

## KEY CONCEPT

### ETP Pose Purposeful Questions

**Q:** Draw a Venn diagram comparing the properties of translations and reflections. [Check students' work.]

## Do You Understand/Do You Know How?

Formative Assessment

### ETP Build Procedural Fluency from Conceptual Understanding

**Essential Question** Students should understand that in a reflection, the image is the same shape and size as the preimage, but the orientation is different. The preimage and image are the same distance from the line of reflection.

**ITEM 4**

**Q:** How can using a ruler help to answer the question? [Sample answer: Measure the distance of each point from line *g*. In a reflection the preimage and image must be the same distance from the line of reflection.]

Available Online

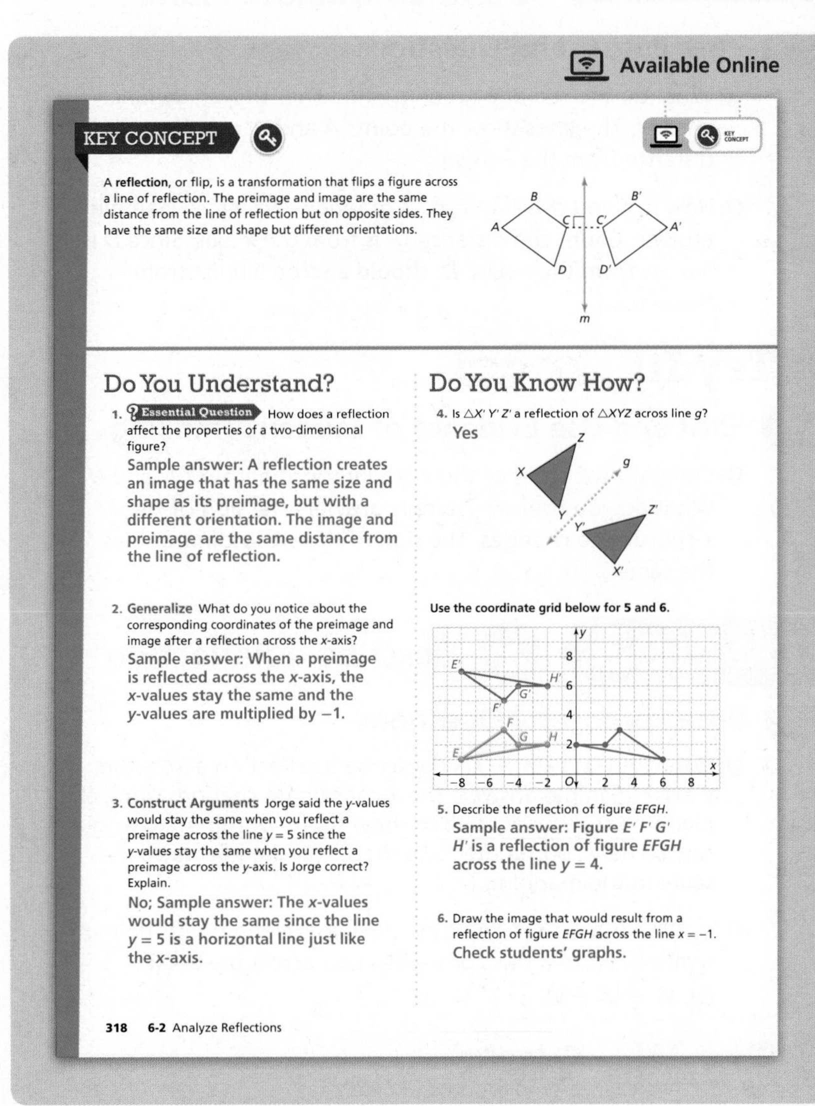

KEY CONCEPT

A **reflection**, or flip, is a transformation that flips a figure across a line of reflection. The preimage and image are the same distance from the line of reflection but on opposite sides. They have the same size and shape but different orientations.



**Do You Understand?**

1. **Essential Question** How does a reflection affect the properties of a two-dimensional figure?
Sample answer: A reflection creates an image that has the same size and shape as its preimage, but with a different orientation. The image and preimage are the same distance from the line of reflection.

2. **Generalize** What do you notice about the corresponding coordinates of the preimage and image after a reflection across the *x*-axis?
Sample answer: When a preimage is reflected across the *x*-axis, the *x*-values stay the same and the *y*-values are multiplied by $-1$.

3. **Construct Arguments** Jorge said the *y*-values would stay the same when you reflect a preimage across the line $y = 5$ since the *y*-values stay the same when you reflect a preimage across the *y*-axis. Is Jorge correct? Explain.
No; Sample answer: The *x*-values would stay the same since the line $y = 5$ is a horizontal line just like the *x*-axis.

**Do You Know How?**

4. Is $\triangle X'Y'Z'$ a reflection of $\triangle XYZ$ across line *g*?
Yes



Use the coordinate grid below for 5 and 6.



5. Describe the reflection of figure *EFGH*.
Sample answer: Figure *E′ F′ G′ H′* is a reflection of figure *EFGH* across the line $y = 4$.

6. Draw the image that would result from a reflection of figure *EFGH* across the line $x = -1$.
Check students' graphs.

318 6-2 Analyze Reflections

### Prevent Misconceptions

**ITEM 3**

Students may have the misconception that reflecting over a line defined by *y* = follows the same rules as reflecting over the *y*-axis.

**Q:** Is the line $y = 5$ a horizontal or vertical line? [Horizontal]

**Q:** Which axis is the horizontal axis? [*x*-axis]

**Q:** How does knowing the orientation of $y = 5$ help you to decide which general rule to use? [Sample answer: Since $y = 5$ and the *x*-axis are horizontal lines and the *x*-coordinates stay the same when a figure is reflected over the *x*-axis, the *x*-coordinates must stay the same when a figure is reflected over the line $y = 5$.]

## ADDITIONAL EXAMPLE 2

Have students reflect a figure over a vertical line with this additional example.

**Q:** Is the line $x = 3$ a horizontal or vertical line? [Vertical]

**Q:** Which axis is also a vertical line? [*y*-axis]

**Q:** How can you use the orientation of $x = 3$ to help you solve the problem? [Sample answer: When reflecting over the *y*-axis, the *y*-coordinate stays the same. Since $x = 3$ and the *y*-axis are both vertical lines, when reflecting over the line $x = 3$ the *y*-coordinates will also stay the same.]

**Additional Examples** are available online

Go back

Additional Example

Triangle *QRS* has vertices *Q*(5, 2), *R*(7, 5), and *S*(9, 1). Graph and label the vertices of triangle *QRS* and its image *Q′R′S′*, after a reflection across the line $x = 3$.

**Answer:** A triangle with points at *Q′*(1, 2), *R′*(−1, 5), and *S′*(−3, 1)

Go Online

 Practice  Tutorials  Math Tools

# Practice & Problem Solving  

 **Interactive Practice** and **Virtual Nerd Video Tutorials** are available online.

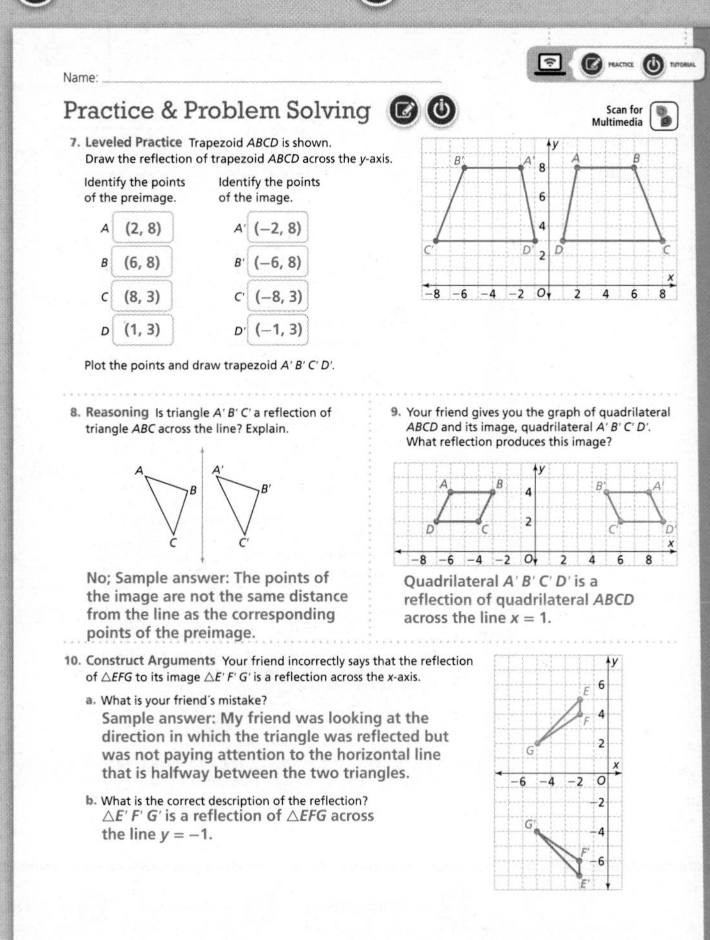

Name: ______

## Practice & Problem Solving

Scan for Multimedia

7. **Leveled Practice** Trapezoid $ABCD$ is shown. Draw the reflection of trapezoid $ABCD$ across the $y$-axis.

| Identify the points of the preimage. | Identify the points of the image. |
|---|---|
| $A$ (2, 8) | $A'$ (−2, 8) |
| $B$ (6, 8) | $B'$ (−6, 8) |
| $C$ (8, 3) | $C'$ (−8, 3) |
| $D$ (1, 3) | $D'$ (−1, 3) |

Plot the points and draw trapezoid $A'B'C'D'$.

8. **Reasoning** Is triangle $A'B'C'$ a reflection of triangle $ABC$ across the line? Explain.

No; Sample answer: The points of the image are not the same distance from the line as the corresponding points of the preimage.

9. Your friend gives you the graph of quadrilateral $ABCD$ and its image, quadrilateral $A'B'C'D'$. What reflection produces this image?

Quadrilateral $A'B'C'D'$ is a reflection of quadrilateral $ABCD$ across the line $x = 1$.

10. **Construct Arguments** Your friend incorrectly says that the reflection of $\triangle EFG$ to its image $\triangle E'F'G'$ is a reflection across the $x$-axis.

a. What is your friend's mistake?

Sample answer: My friend was looking at the direction in which the triangle was reflected but was not paying attention to the horizontal line that is halfway between the two triangles.

b. What is the correct description of the reflection?

$\triangle E'F'G'$ is a reflection of $\triangle EFG$ across the line $y = -1$.

6-2 Analyze Reflections 319

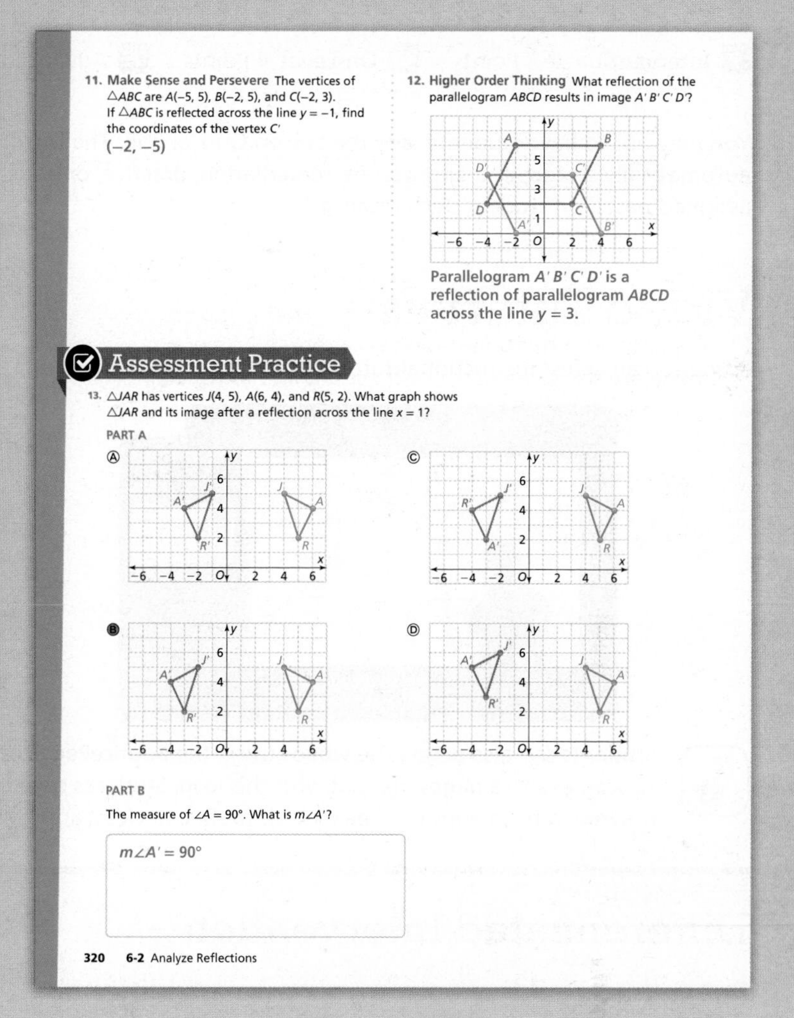

11. **Make Sense and Persevere** The vertices of $\triangle ABC$ are $A(-5, 5)$, $B(-2, 5)$, and $C(-2, 3)$. If $\triangle ABC$ is reflected across the line $y = -1$, find the coordinates of the vertex $C'$.

(−2, −5)

12. **Higher Order Thinking** What reflection of the parallelogram $ABCD$ results in image $A'B'C'D'$?

Parallelogram $A'B'C'D'$ is a reflection of parallelogram $ABCD$ across the line $y = 3$.

### Assessment Practice

13. $\triangle JAR$ has vertices $J(4, 5)$, $A(6, 4)$, and $R(5, 2)$. What graph shows $\triangle JAR$ and its image after a reflection across the line $x = 1$?

PART A

Ⓐ Ⓑ Ⓒ Ⓓ

PART B

The measure of $\angle A = 90°$. What is $m\angle A'$?

$m\angle A' = 90°$

320 6-2 Analyze Reflections

## Error Intervention

**ITEM 8** Students may have difficulty identifying reflections and translations. Encourage them to focus on the orientation of the preimage and image.

**Q:** Describe the orientation of the preimage and image. [Sample answer: The orientation of both figures is the same.]

**Q:** How does knowing the orientation of the figures help to determine the type of transformation? [Sample answer: In a translation, the orientation of the figures is the same. In a reflection, the orientation of the figures is different.]

## Challenge

**ITEM 10** Challenge students to reflect triangle $EFG$ over the line $y = x$.

Have students use grid paper and draw a coordinate plane. Then have them draw the figure and the line $y = x$. Have students compare the coordinates they find for triangle $E'F'G'$ and confirm the reflection is correct.

You may opt to have students complete the automatically scored Practice & Problem Solving items online.

### Item Analysis

| Example | Items | DOK |
|---|---|---|
| 1 | 8 | 2 |
| 2 | 7, 13 | 2 |
|  | 11 | 3 |
| 3 | 9 | 2 |
|  | 10, 12 | 3 |

STEP 3 | Assess & Differentiate

Go Online

 Assess  Tutorials  Worksheets

# Lesson Quiz

Use the student scores on the Lesson Quiz to prescribe differentiated assignments.

**I Intervention** 0–3 Points **O On-Level** 4 Points **A Advanced** 5 Points

You may opt to have students take the Lesson Quiz online. The Lesson Quiz will be automatically scored, and appropriate remediation, practice, or enrichment will be assigned based on student performance.

**Lesson Quiz** is available online.

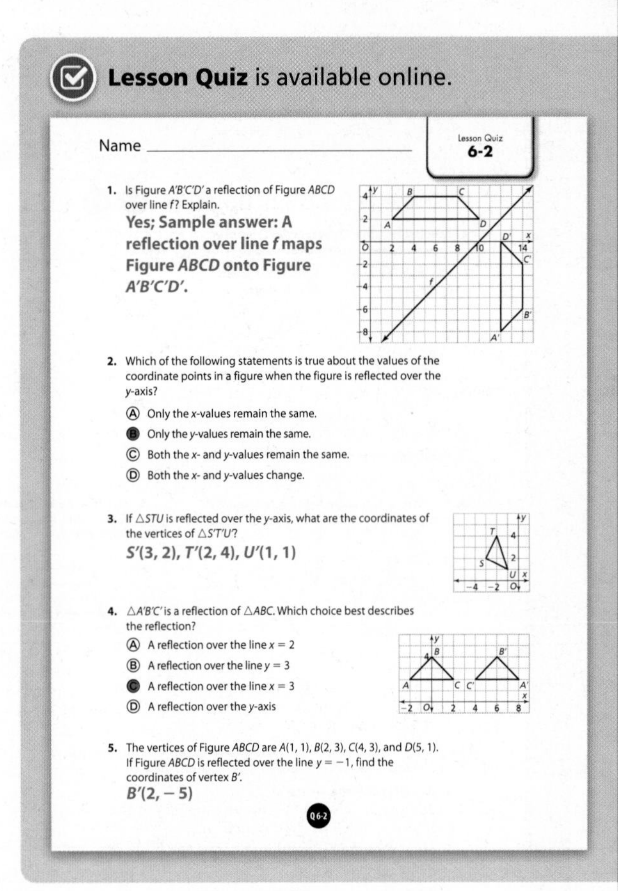

Name ______ Lesson Quiz 6-2

1. Is Figure $A'B'C'D'$ a reflection of Figure $ABCD$ over line $f$? Explain.
   **Yes; Sample answer: A reflection over line $f$ maps Figure $ABCD$ onto Figure $A'B'C'D'$.**
2. Which of the following statements is true about the values of the coordinate points in a figure when the figure is reflected over the $y$-axis?
   Ⓐ Only the $x$-values remain the same.
   Ⓑ Only the $y$-values remain the same.
   Ⓒ Both the $x$- and $y$-values remain the same.
   Ⓓ Both the $x$- and $y$-values change.
3. If $\triangle STU$ is reflected over the $y$-axis, what are the coordinates of the vertices of $\triangle S'T'U'$?
   **$S'(3, 2)$, $T'(2, 4)$, $U'(1, 1)$**
4. $\triangle A'B'C'$ is a reflection of $\triangle ABC$. Which choice best describes the reflection?
   Ⓐ A reflection over the line $x = 2$
   Ⓑ A reflection over the line $y = 3$
   Ⓒ A reflection over the line $x = 3$
   Ⓓ A reflection over the $y$-axis
5. The vertices of Figure $ABCD$ are $A(1, 1)$, $B(2, 3)$, $C(4, 3)$, and $D(5, 1)$. If Figure $ABCD$ is reflected over the line $y = -1$, find the coordinates of vertex $B'$.
   **$B'(2, -5)$**

Q6-2

# Video Tutorials

Students can access instructional tutorials using the **Virtual Nerd app**.

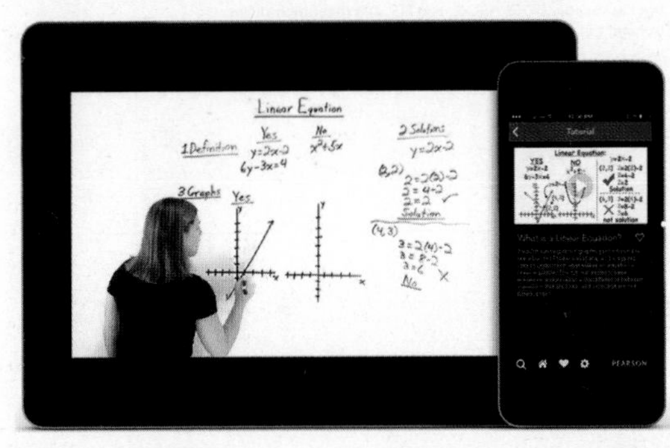

Students can also access the videos using the **BouncePages app** to scan exercise pages marked with this icon. Students can download both apps for free in their mobile devices' app store.

# Differentiated Intervention

**I** = Intervention **O** = On-Level **A** = Advanced

## Reteach to Build Understanding I

Provides scaffolded reteaching for the key lesson concepts.

## Additional Vocabulary Support I O

Helps students develop and reinforce understanding of key terms and concepts.

## Build Mathematical Literacy I O

Provides support for struggling readers to build mathematical literacy.

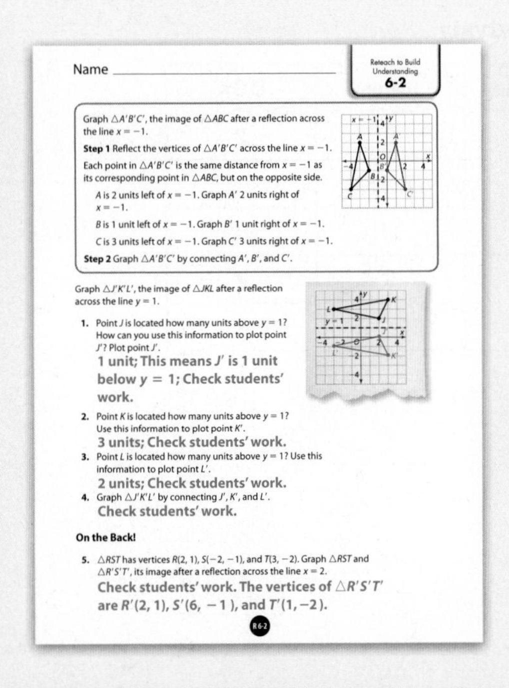

Name ______ Reteach to Build Understanding 6-2

Graph $\triangle A'B'C'$, the image of $\triangle ABC$ after a reflection across the line $x = -1$.

**Step 1** Reflect the vertices of $\triangle A'B'C'$ across the line $x = -1$.

Each point in $\triangle A'B'C'$ is the same distance from $x = -1$ as its corresponding point in $\triangle ABC$, but on the opposite side.

$A$ is 2 units left of $x = -1$. Graph $A'$ 2 units right of $x = -1$.

$B$ is 1 unit left of $x = -1$. Graph $B'$ 1 unit right of $x = -1$.

$C$ is 3 units left of $x = -1$. Graph $C'$ 3 units right of $x = -1$.

**Step 2** Graph $\triangle A'B'C'$ by connecting $A'$, $B'$, and $C'$.

Graph $\triangle J'K'L'$, the image of $\triangle JKL$ after a reflection across the line $y = 1$.

1. Point $J$ is located how many units above $y = 1$? How can you use this information to plot point $J'$? Plot point $J'$.
   **1 unit; This means $J'$ is 1 unit below $y = 1$; Check students' work.**
2. Point $K$ is located how many units above $y = 1$? Use this information to plot point $K'$.
   **3 units; Check students' work.**
3. Point $L$ is located how many units above $y = 1$? Use this information to plot point $L'$.
   **2 units; Check students' work.**
4. Graph $\triangle J'K'L'$ by connecting $J'$, $K'$, and $L'$.
   **Check students' work.**

On the Back!

5. $\triangle RST$ has vertices $R(2, 1)$, $S(-2, -1)$, and $T(3, -2)$. Graph $\triangle RST$ and $\triangle R'S'T'$, its image after a reflection across the line $x = 2$.
   **Check students' work. The vertices of $\triangle R'S'T'$ are $R'(2, 1)$, $S'(6, -1)$, and $T'(1, -2)$.**

R6-2

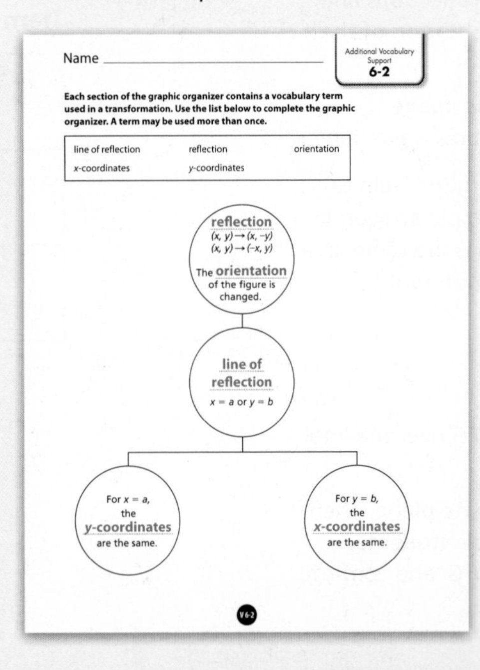

Name ______ Additional Vocabulary Support 6-2

Each section of the graphic organizer contains a vocabulary term used in a transformation. Use the list below to complete the graphic organizer. A term may be used more than once.

| line of reflection | reflection | orientation |
|---|---|---|
| x-coordinates | y-coordinates | |



V6-2

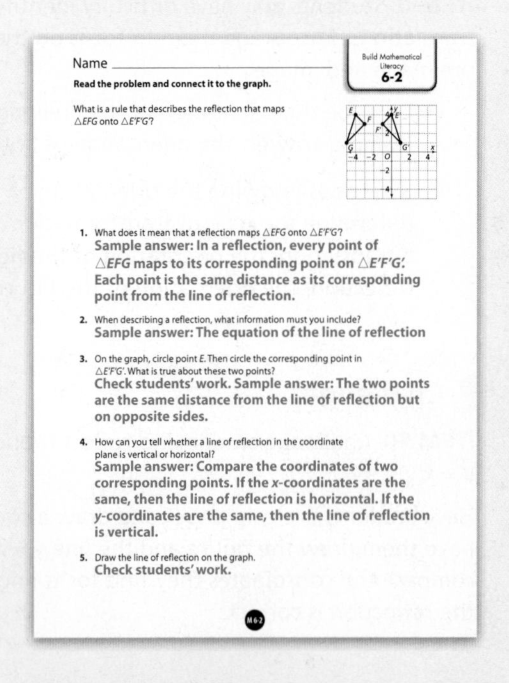

Name ______ Build Mathematical Literacy 6-2

Read the problem and connect it to the graph.

What is a rule that describes the reflection that maps $\triangle EFG$ onto $\triangle E'F'G'$?

1. What does it mean that a reflection maps $\triangle EFG$ onto $\triangle E'F'G'$?
   **Sample answer: In a reflection, every point of $\triangle EFG$ maps to its corresponding point on $\triangle E'F'G'$. Each point is the same distance as its corresponding point from the line of reflection.**
2. When describing a reflection, what information must you include?
   **Sample answer: The equation of the line of reflection**
3. On the graph, circle point $E$. Then circle the corresponding point in $\triangle E'F'G'$. What is true about these two points?
   **Check students' work. Sample answer: The two points are the same distance from the line of reflection but on opposite sides.**
4. How can you tell whether a line of reflection in the coordinate plane is vertical or horizontal?
   **Sample answer: Compare the coordinates of two corresponding points. If the $x$-coordinates are the same, then the line of reflection is horizontal. If the $y$-coordinates are the same, then the line of reflection is vertical.**
5. Draw the line of reflection on the graph.
   **Check students' work.**

M6-2

Go Online

Practice

Worksheets

Math Tools

Math Games

# Additional Practice

You may opt to have students complete the automatically scored Additional Practice items online.

### Item Analysis

| Example | Items | DOK |
|---|---|---|
| 1 | 2, 8 | 2 |
| 2 | 1, 5 | 2 |
| | 7 | 3 |
| 3 | 3, 4, 6 | 2 |

**Interactive Practice** is available online.

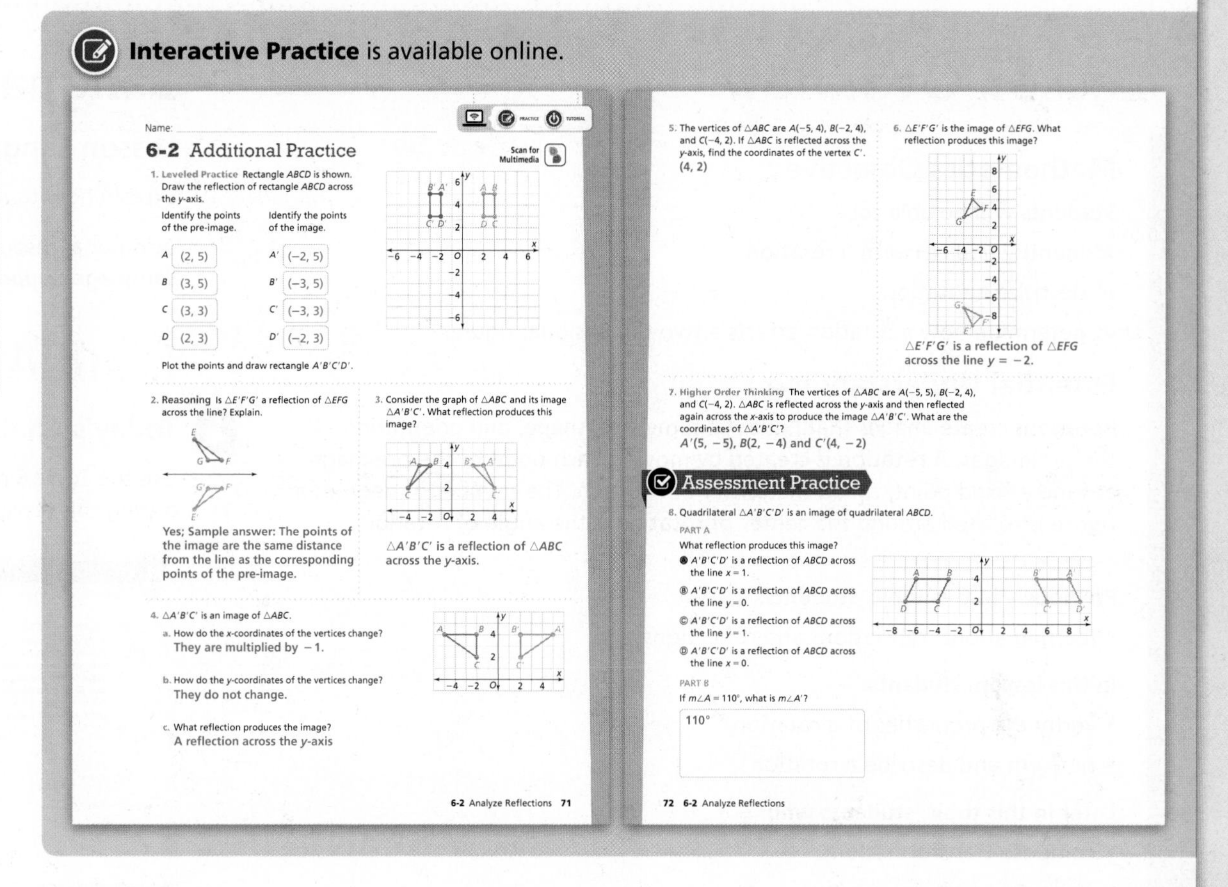

Name:

**6-2 Additional Practice**

Scan for Multimedia

1. **Leveled Practice** Rectangle $ABCD$ is shown. Draw the reflection of rectangle $ABCD$ across the $y$-axis.

| Identify the points of the pre-image. | Identify the points of the image. |
|---|---|
| $A$ (2, 5) | $A'$ (−2, 5) |
| $B$ (3, 5) | $B'$ (−3, 5) |
| $C$ (3, 3) | $C'$ (−3, 3) |
| $D$ (2, 3) | $D'$ (−2, 3) |

Plot the points and draw rectangle $A'B'C'D'$.

2. **Reasoning** Is $\triangle E'F'G'$ a reflection of $\triangle EFG$ across the line? Explain.

Yes; Sample answer: The points of the image are the same distance from the line as the corresponding points of the pre-image.

3. Consider the graph of $\triangle ABC$ and its image $\triangle A'B'C'$. What reflection produces this image?

$\triangle A'B'C'$ is a reflection of $\triangle ABC$ across the $y$-axis.

4. $\triangle A'B'C'$ is an image of $\triangle ABC$.

a. How do the $x$-coordinates of the vertices change?
They are multiplied by −1.

b. How do the $y$-coordinates of the vertices change?
They do not change.

c. What reflection produces the image?
A reflection across the $y$-axis

6-2 Analyze Reflections 71

5. The vertices of $\triangle ABC$ are $A(-5, 4)$, $B(-2, 4)$, and $C(-4, 2)$. If $\triangle ABC$ is reflected across the $y$-axis, find the coordinates of the vertex $C'$.
(4, 2)

6. $\triangle E'F'G'$ is the image of $\triangle EFG$. What reflection produces this image?

$\triangle E'F'G'$ is a reflection of $\triangle EFG$ across the line $y = -2$.

7. **Higher Order Thinking** The vertices of $\triangle ABC$ are $A(-5, 5)$, $B(-2, 4)$, and $C(-4, 2)$. $\triangle ABC$ is reflected across the $y$-axis and then reflected again across the $x$-axis to produce the image $\triangle A'B'C'$. What are the coordinates of $\triangle A'B'C'$?
$A'(5, -5)$, $B(2, -4)$ and $C'(4, -2)$

**Assessment Practice**

8. Quadrilateral $\triangle A'B'C'D'$ is an image of quadrilateral $ABCD$.

PART A
What reflection produces this image?
● $A'B'C'D'$ is a reflection of $ABCD$ across the line $x = 1$.
Ⓑ $A'B'C'D'$ is a reflection of $ABCD$ across the line $y = 0$.
Ⓒ $A'B'C'D'$ is a reflection of $ABCD$ across the line $y = 1$.
Ⓓ $A'B'C'D'$ is a reflection of $ABCD$ across the line $x = 0$.

PART B
If $m\angle A = 110°$, what is $m\angle A'$?
110°

72 6-2 Analyze Reflections

# Differentiated Intervention

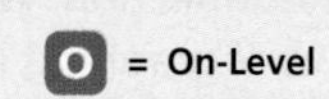
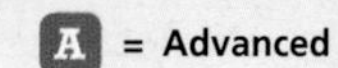
I = Intervention O = On-Level A = Advanced

## Enrichment O A

Presents engaging problems and activities that extend the lesson concepts.

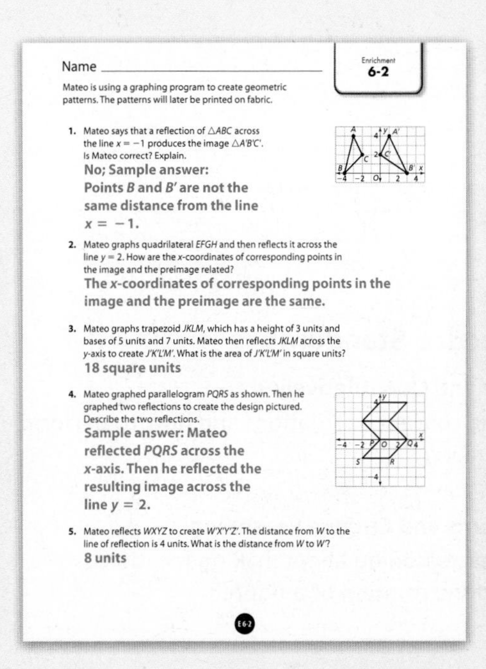

Name

Enrichment 6-2

Mateo is using a graphing program to create geometric patterns. The patterns will later be printed on fabric.

1. Mateo says that a reflection of $\triangle ABC$ across the line $x = -1$ produces the image $\triangle A'B'C'$. Is Mateo correct? Explain.
No; Sample answer: Points $B$ and $B'$ are not the same distance from the line $x = -1$.

2. Mateo graphs quadrilateral $EFGH$ and then reflects it across the line $y = 2$. How are the $x$-coordinates of corresponding points in the image and the preimage related?
The $x$-coordinates of corresponding points in the image and the preimage are the same.

3. Mateo graphs trapezoid $JKLM$, which has a height of 3 units and bases of 5 units and 7 units. Mateo then reflects $JKLM$ across the $y$-axis to create $J'K'L'M'$. What is the area of $J'K'L'M'$ in square units?
18 square units

4. Mateo graphed parallelogram $PQRS$ as shown. Then he graphed two reflections to create the design pictured. Describe the two reflections.
Sample answer: Mateo reflected $PQRS$ across the $x$-axis. Then he reflected the resulting image across the line $y = 2$.

5. Mateo reflects $WXYZ$ to create $W'X'Y'Z'$. The distance from $W$ to the line of reflection is 4 units. What is the distance from $W$ to $W'$?
8 units

## Math Tools and Games I O A

Offers additional activities and games to build understanding and fluency.

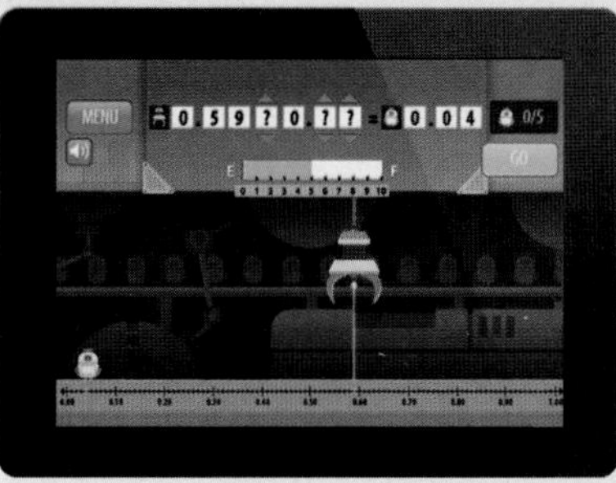

## Pick a Project and STEM Project I O A

Provides an additional opportunity for students to demonstrate understanding of key mathematical concepts.

Go Online

Activity

# Lesson 6-3 Analyze Rotations

## Lesson Overview

FOCUS

### Mathematics Objective

**Students will be able to:**

- ✔ identify and perform a rotation.
- ✔ describe a rotation.
- ✔ determine how a rotation affects a two-dimensional figure.

### Essential Understanding

Rotations create images that have the same size, shape, and orientation as the preimages. A rotation is created by moving each point of the preimage around a fixed point, called the center of rotation. The number of degrees a figure is rotated around the center of rotation is the angle of rotation.

COHERENCE

**Previously in this topic, students:**

- learned about translations and reflections.

**In this lesson, students:**

- verify the properties of a rotation.
- perform and describe a rotation.

**Later in this topic, students will:**

- compose transformations.
- understand congruent figures.

**Cross-Cluster Connection** Work graphing and analyzing rotations (8.G.1) connects to work graphing and analyzing slope (8.EE.2).

RIGOR

This lesson emphasizes a blend of **conceptual understanding** and **procedural skill and fluency**.

- Students will understand the concept of rotating figures and how the resulting images are related to the preimages.
- Students will practice rotating preimages into images, and consider and explore any changes in properties.

## Language Support

### Lesson Language Objective

Explain how to rotate a two-dimensional figure.

Additional resources are available in the **Language Support Handbook**.

## Math Anytime

### Today's Challenge

Use the Topic 6 problems any time during this topic.

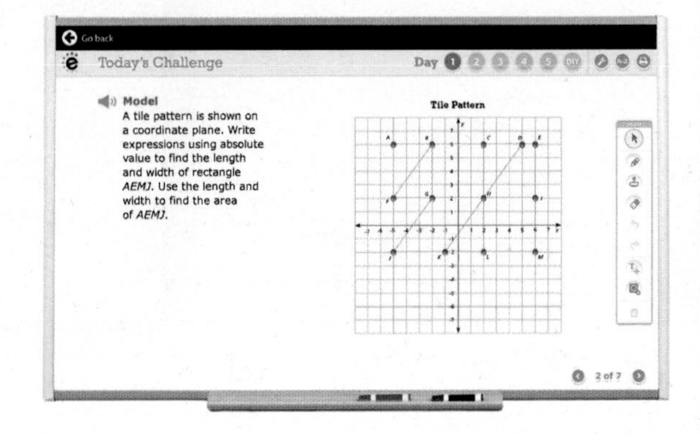


## Mathematics Overview | Common Core Standards

### Content Standards

In this lesson, you will focus on Common Core Standards **8.G.A.1a, 8.G.A.1b, 8.G.A.1c** and **8.G.A.3**.

- **8.G.A.1a** Lines are taken to lines, and line segments to line segments of the same length.
- **8.G.A.1b** Angles are taken to angles of the same measure.
- **8.G.A.1c** Parallel lines are taken to parallel lines.
- **8.G.A.3** Describe the effect of dilations, translations, rotations, and reflections on two-dimensional figures using coordinates.

### Mathematical Practice Standards

**MP.2 Reason Abstractly and Quantitatively**
Students understand the concept of rotations and how to perform them using abstract thinking.

**MP.3 Construct Arguments and Critique Reasoning**
Students will justify their reasoning about making rotations, or apply certain rules to the rotation of a figure.

# STEP 1 | Problem-Based Learning

15-20 min

Go Online

Activity

## Explain It!

Formative Assessment

**Purpose** Students explore the position of a point on a circle after a rotation about the center and connect it to completing a rotation in Example 2.

### ETP Before — WHOLE CLASS

**1 Introduce the Problem**

Provide grid paper, compass, and protractor, as needed.

**2 Check for Understanding of the Problem**

Engage students with the problem by asking: Have you ever ridden a Ferris wheel?

### ETP During — SMALL GROUP

**3 Observe Students at Work**

- **How do students explain whether they agree with Maria?** Students might draw a diagonal through the center the Ferris wheel to show that Maria completed half of a turn, or they might draw a quarter turn to determine that Maria did not complete a quarter turn. Students may also reference objects where they are familiar with quarter-turns, such as the quarter hours on a clock. Students may also use a compass to model the problem
- **How do students use angle measures to describe the change in position of the car?** Students may consider the half turn as the sum of two quarter turns (90° + 90°) or half of a full turn (360° ÷ 2). Students may also measure the change using a protractor. If needed, ask How many degrees are in one full rotation?

**Early Finishers**

How would the problem change if Maria said she completed $\frac{1}{2}$ turn before the car stopped? [Sample answer: Maria would be correct. One-half turn is 180°.]

### ETP After — WHOLE CLASS

**4 Discuss Solution Strategies and Key Ideas**

Consider having groups share their solutions to part (A) first, followed by part (B). Have students discuss whether the answer would change depending on which way the Ferris wheel rotates; since the Ferris wheel completes half a turn, Maria would be in the same position regardless of whether the rotation was clockwise or counterclockwise.

**5 Consider Instructional Implications**

After presenting Example 2, refer students back to the problem in the Explain It and have them draw the Ferris wheel on graph paper with the center at the origin and radius of 20. The start position is a point at (–20, 0). Have students discuss what this means. Ask students what coordinates represent Maria's position after a 270° rotation; (–20, 0).

## Analyze Student Work

**Explain It!** Activity is available online.

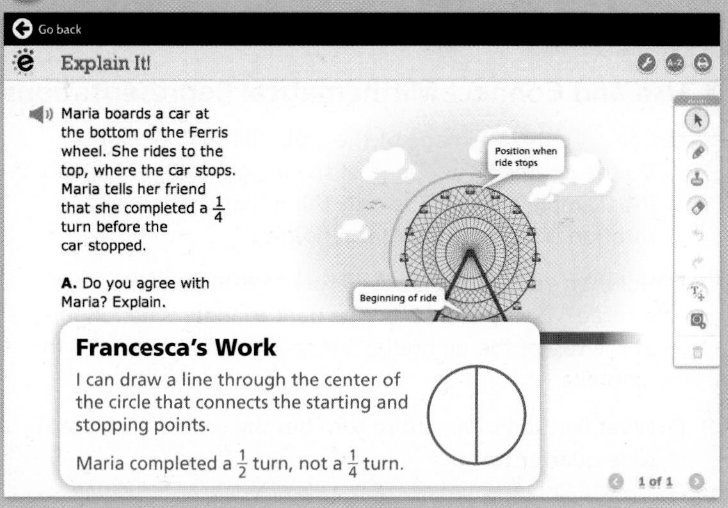


**Francesca** uses a diagonal across the Ferris wheel to show that Maria completed $\frac{1}{2}$ of a turn.

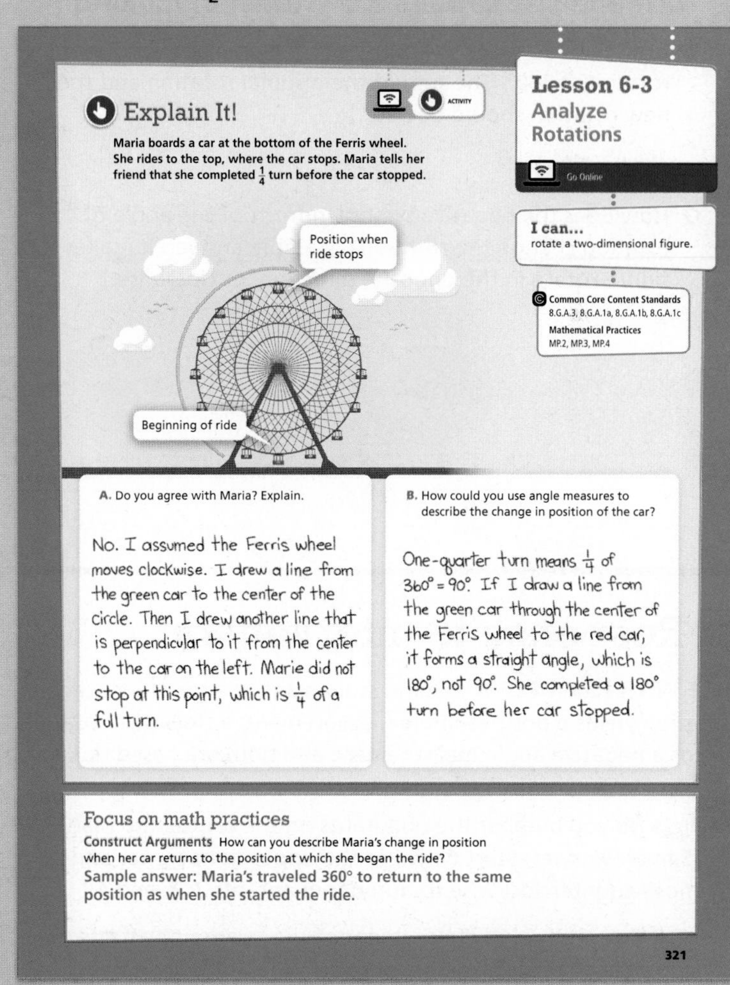
Explain It!

Maria boards a car at the bottom of the Ferris wheel. She rides to the top, where the car stops. Maria tells her friend that she completed $\frac{1}{4}$ turn before the car stopped.

Lesson 6-3
Analyze Rotations

Go Online

I can… rotate a two-dimensional figure.

Common Core Content Standards 8.G.A.3, 8.G.A.1a, 8.G.A.1b, 8.G.A.1c
Mathematical Practices MP.2, MP.3, MP.4

Position when ride stops

Beginning of ride

A. Do you agree with Maria? Explain.

No. I assumed the Ferris wheel moves clockwise. I drew a line from the green car to the center of the circle. Then I drew another line that is perpendicular to it from the center to the car on the left. Marie did not stop at this point, which is $\frac{1}{4}$ of a full turn.

B. How could you use angle measures to describe the change in position of the car?

One-quarter turn means $\frac{1}{4}$ of 360° = 90°. If I draw a line from the green car through the center of the Ferris wheel to the red car, it forms a straight angle, which is 180°, not 90°. She completed a 180° turn before her car stopped.

Focus on math practices

Construct Arguments How can you describe Maria's change in position when her car returns to the position at which she began the ride?

Sample answer: Maria's traveled 360° to return to the same position as when she started the ride.

321

**David** uses two radii that form a straight angle to show that Maria did not complete only $\frac{1}{4}$ of a turn.

# STEP 2 | Visual Learning

Go Online

Visual Learning

Assess

## ETP Establish Mathematics Goals to Focus Learning

Engage students in a discussion about the ***Essential Question***. Make sure they understand the definition of transformation and how it relates to a rotation, and remember the geometric properties of two-dimensional figures.

## EXAMPLE 1  Understand Rotations

### ETP Use and Connect Mathematical Representations

**Q:** Compare the preimage of the umbrella to the image. Do the perimeter and area of the image change? Explain. [No; Sample answer: The only thing that changes in a rotation is the position of the figure.]

**Q:** How can you tell from the picture that the umbrella has rotated? [Sample answer: The dark triangle is no longer at the top of the umbrella; it is now on the left side of the umbrella.]

**Q:** What fraction of an entire turn has the umbrella rotated? [one-quarter turn]

##  Try It!  Formative Assessment

### ETP Elicit and Use Evidence of Student Thinking

**Q:** How can you check your answer? [Sample answer: An entire rotation is 360°. The sum of the original rotation and the new rotation should be 360°.]

### Convince Me!

**Q:** How does the negative symbol in front of the angle of rotation change the rotation? [Sample answer: It makes the figure rotate in the opposite direction, or clockwise.]

**Visual Learning Animation Plus** is available online.

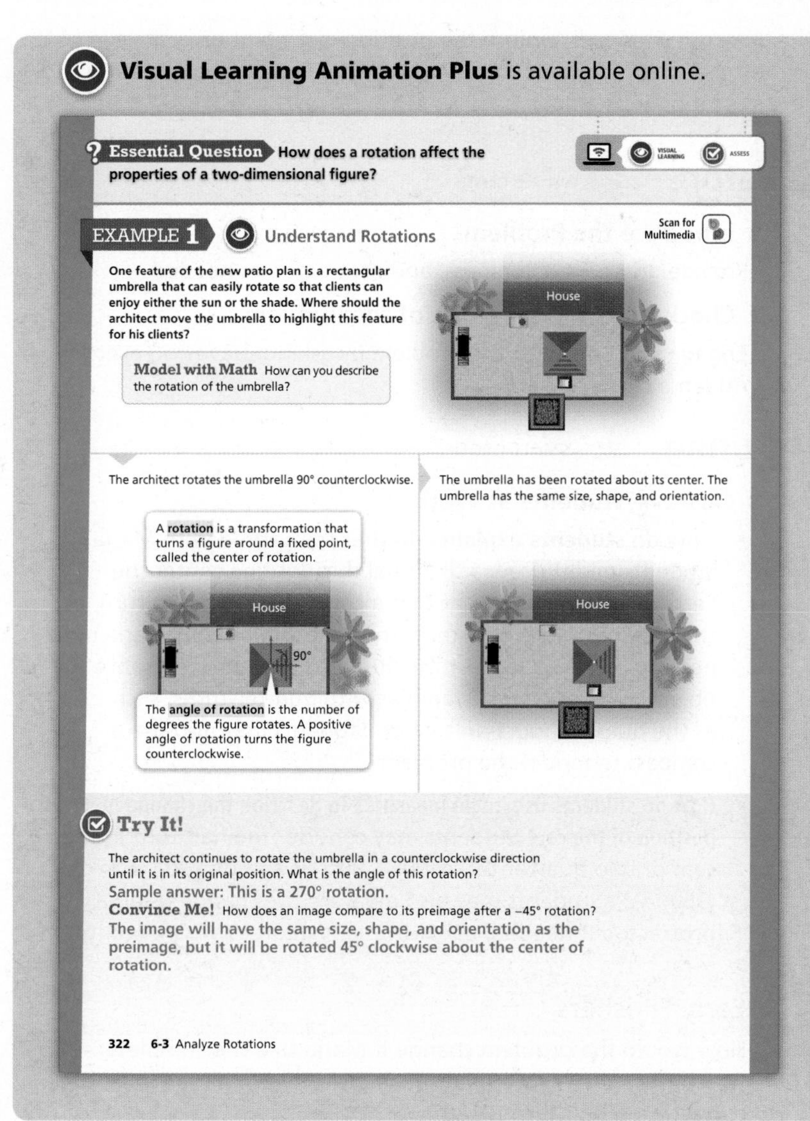

**Essential Question** How does a rotation affect the properties of a two-dimensional figure?

EXAMPLE 1 Understand Rotations

Scan for Multimedia

One feature of the new patio plan is a rectangular umbrella that can easily rotate so that clients can enjoy either the sun or the shade. Where should the architect move the umbrella to highlight this feature for his clients?

**Model with Math** How can you describe the rotation of the umbrella?



The architect rotates the umbrella 90° counterclockwise.

A **rotation** is a transformation that turns a figure around a fixed point, called the center of rotation.



The **angle of rotation** is the number of degrees the figure rotates. A positive angle of rotation turns the figure counterclockwise.

The umbrella has been rotated about its center. The umbrella has the same size, shape, and orientation.



**Try It!**

The architect continues to rotate the umbrella in a counterclockwise direction until it is in its original position. What is the angle of this rotation?
Sample answer: This is a 270° rotation.

**Convince Me!** How does an image compare to its preimage after a −45° rotation?
The image will have the same size, shape, and orientation as the preimage, but it will be rotated 45° clockwise about the center of rotation.

322 6-3 Analyze Rotations

Students can access the ***Visual Learning Animation Plus*** by using the **BouncePages app** to scan this page. Students can download the app for free in their mobile devices' app store.

##  Response to Intervention

**USE WITH EXAMPLE 3** Remind students that a counterclockwise rotation yields a positive angle measurement, a clockwise rotation yields a negative angle measurement and both are based upon the numbering of the quadrants.

**Q:** How do you number the quadrants on the coordinate plane? [Sample answer: Start with 1 in the upper right corner and move counterclockwise to number quadrants 2, 3, and 4.]

**Q:** How do you think the placement of the quadrants affects the sign of a rotation? [Sample answer: When a figure moves from a smaller numbered quadrant to a larger one, the sign of the rotation is positive. When a figure moves from a larger numbered quadrant to a smaller one, the sign of the rotation is negative.]

##  Enrichment

**USE WITH EXAMPLE 2** Challenge students to create another column in the table labeled "clockwise rotations." Have them determine the corresponding clockwise rotation for each rule. Ask students to confirm their rule using an example.

Go Online

Activity

Assess

## EXAMPLE 2  Complete a Rotation

### ETP Pose Purposeful Questions

**Q:** How do you know if you should turn the figure clockwise or counterclockwise? [Sample answer: The degree of rotation is a positive value, so the figure is turned counterclockwise.]

**Q:** How can you use the quadrant numbers to help describe the movement of the trapezoid? [Sample answer: The trapezoid moves from Quadrant I to Quadrant II.]

##  Try It! 

**Formative** Assessment

### ETP Elicit and Use Evidence of Student Thinking

**Q:** How do the coordinates of the points change for this rotation? [Sample answer: Multiply the *x*-coordinate by −1, then interchange the *x*- and *y*-coordinates.]

## EXAMPLE 3  Describe a Rotation

### ETP Pose Purposeful Questions

**Q:** Why can the rotation be described by a −90° rotation? [Sample answer: A rotation of 270° in a positive direction is the same as a rotation of 90° in a negative direction. This is true because the sum of both rotations is 360°.]

**Q:** How could you use the rules to determine the rotation? [Sample answer: List the coordinates of the preimage and image in a mapping diagram. Then find the rule the coordinates follow.]

##  Try It! 

**Formative** Assessment

###  Elicit and Use Evidence of Student Thinking

**Q:** Alice is listing the coordinates of the points to find the rule to answer the question. Should she list all of the corresponding points? Explain. [Sample answer: She only needs to list one set of corresponding points to find the rule. The other points can be used to check her answer.]

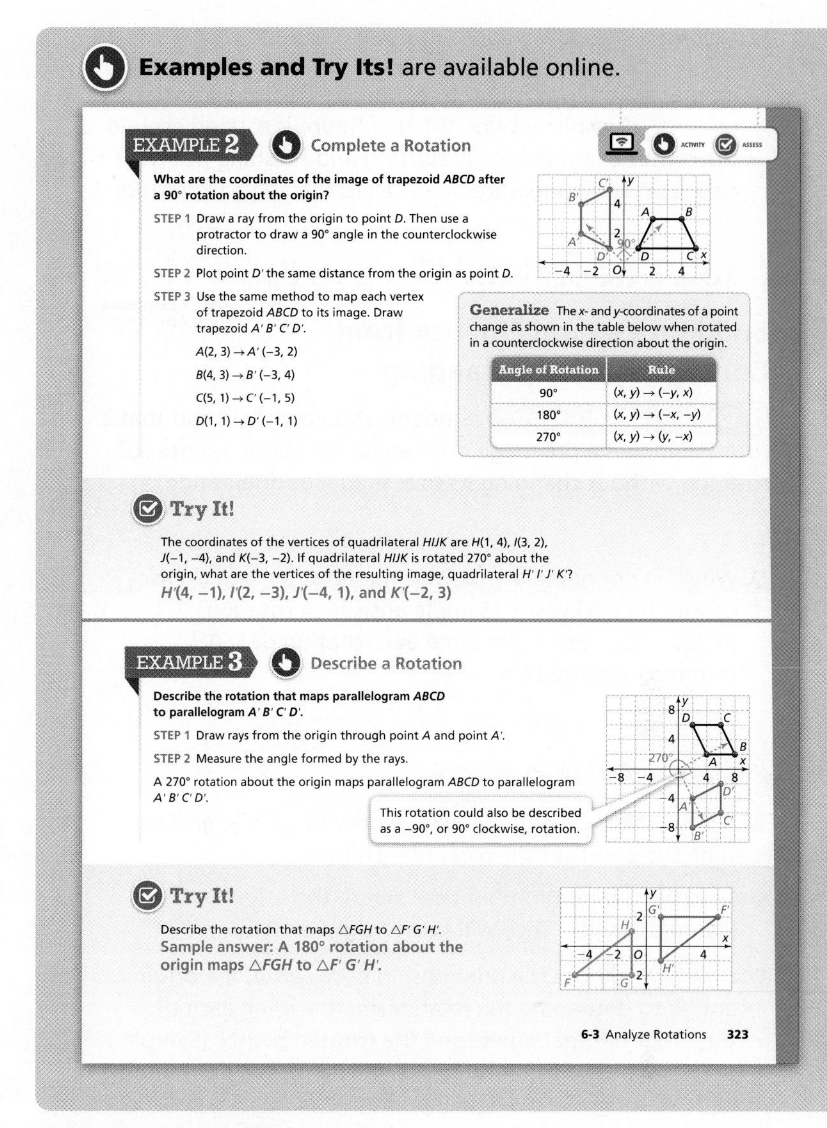

**Examples and Try Its!** are available online.

EXAMPLE 2 Complete a Rotation

**What are the coordinates of the image of trapezoid *ABCD* after a 90° rotation about the origin?**

STEP 1 Draw a ray from the origin to point *D*. Then use a protractor to draw a 90° angle in the counterclockwise direction.

STEP 2 Plot point *D′* the same distance from the origin as point *D*.

STEP 3 Use the same method to map each vertex of trapezoid *ABCD* to its image. Draw trapezoid *A′ B′ C′ D′*.

$A(2, 3) \rightarrow A'(-3, 2)$

$B(4, 3) \rightarrow B'(-3, 4)$

$C(5, 1) \rightarrow C'(-1, 5)$

$D(1, 1) \rightarrow D'(-1, 1)$



**Generalize** The *x*- and *y*-coordinates of a point change as shown in the table below when rotated in a counterclockwise direction about the origin.

| Angle of Rotation | Rule |
|---|---|
| 90° | $(x, y) \rightarrow (-y, x)$ |
| 180° | $(x, y) \rightarrow (-x, -y)$ |
| 270° | $(x, y) \rightarrow (y, -x)$ |

Try It!

The coordinates of the vertices of quadrilateral *HIJK* are *H*(1, 4), *I*(3, 2), *J*(−1, −4), and *K*(−3, −2). If quadrilateral *HIJK* is rotated 270° about the origin, what are the vertices of the resulting image, quadrilateral *H′ I′ J′ K′*?
*H′*(4, −1), *I′*(2, −3), *J′*(−4, 1), and *K′*(−2, 3)

EXAMPLE 3 Describe a Rotation

**Describe the rotation that maps parallelogram *ABCD* to parallelogram *A′ B′ C′ D′*.**

STEP 1 Draw rays from the origin through point *A* and point *A′*.

STEP 2 Measure the angle formed by the rays.

A 270° rotation about the origin maps parallelogram *ABCD* to parallelogram *A′ B′ C′ D′*.

This rotation could also be described as a −90°, or 90° clockwise, rotation.



Try It!

Describe the rotation that maps △*FGH* to △*F′ G′ H′*.
Sample answer: A 180° rotation about the origin maps △*FGH* to △*F′ G′ H′*.



6-3 Analyze Rotations 323

## ADDITIONAL EXAMPLES 

**For additional examples go online.**

# English Language Learners

**ENTERING** Have students read Example 1 and circle any words that they do not understand.

Working in small groups, have students discuss the words they circled and try to determine their meaning. You may wish to have students translate the words into their own language.

**DEVELOPING** Solve Example 2.

Have students list the definition of the following in their own words: angle of rotation, clockwise, resulting image.

Have them identify any other important terms from the lesson and discuss their meaning with a partner.

**EXPANDING** Solve Example 3.

Have students work with a partner. Ask them to take turns describing the process needed to find the angle of rotation. Then have students discuss how a protractor could be used to help them determine the angle of rotation. Encourage them to discuss how to use a protractor to measure an angle.

# STEP  Visual Learning *continued*

Go Online

Key Concept

Assess

Activity

## KEY CONCEPT

### ETP Pose Purposeful Questions

**Q:** How are the terms *center of rotation* and *angle of rotation* related? [Sample answer: When a figure is rotated around the center of rotation, the starting and finishing positions create an angle measurement, called the angle of rotation.]

## Do You Understand/Do You Know How?

**Formative** Assessment

### ETP Build Procedural Fluency from Conceptual Understanding

**Essential Question** Students should understand that a rotation moves a preimage onto an image about a center of rotation without changing its size, shape, or orientation.

**ITEM 2**

**Q:** Why is it not necessary to list if the rotation is clockwise or counterclockwise? [Sample answer: A rotation of 360° clockwise is the same as a rotation of 360° counterclockwise.]

### Prevent Misconceptions

**ITEM 4** Students may not understand how to use the grid to determine the points of the rotated rectangle.

**Q:** Describe the relationship between *A*, the origin, and *A′*. [Sample answer: They will form a right angle.]

**Q:** How can you use the relationship between *A*, the origin, and *A′* to determine the relationship between each of the other original points and the rotated point? [Sample answer: Each of the rotated points will form a right angle with the origin and original point.]

Available Online

KEY CONCEPT 

A rotation is a transformation that turns a figure about a fixed point called the center of rotation. The angle of rotation is the number of degrees the figure is rotated. The *x*- and *y*-coordinates change in predictable ways when rotated.

**Counterclockwise Rotations about the Origin**

| Angle of Rotation | Transformation |
|---|---|
| 90° | $(x, y) \rightarrow (-y, x)$ |
| 180° | $(x, y) \rightarrow (-x, -y)$ |
| 270° | $(x, y) \rightarrow (y, -x)$ |

**Do You Understand?**

1. **Essential Question** How does a rotation affect the properties of a two-dimensional figure?
   Sample answer: A rotation changes the position of the figure but it does not change the size, shape, or orientation of the figure.

2. **Reasoning** If a preimage is rotated 360 degrees about the origin how can you describe its image?
   Sample answer: It will not change the image, because 360° is a full rotation and the resulting image would be in the same place as the preimage.

3. **Construct Arguments** In Example 3, side *AB* is parallel to side *DC*. How are side *A′B′* and side *D′C′* related? Explain.
   Sample answer: Side *A′B′* and side *D′C′* are also parallel because the angle measures and side lengths are the same after a figure is rotated.

**Do You Know How?**

4. The coordinates of the vertices of rectangle *ABCD* are *A*(3, −2), *B*(3, 2), *C*(−3, 2), and *D*(−3, −2).
   a. Rectangle *ABCD* is rotated 90° about the origin. What are the coordinates of the vertices of rectangle *A′B′C′D′*?
   *A′*(2, 3), *B′*(−2, 3), *C′*(−2, −3), and *D′*(2, −3)
   b. What are the measures of the angles of *A′B′C′D′*?
   Sample answer: The preimage is a rectangle and the image is also a rectangle, so its angle measures are all 90°.

5. Describe the counterclockwise rotation that maps △*QRS* to △*Q′R′S′*.

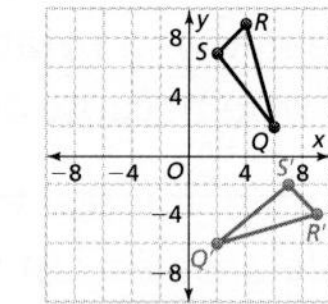


△*Q′R′S′* is a 270° rotation about the origin of △*QRS*.

324 6-3 Analyze Rotations

## ADDITIONAL EXAMPLE 3 

Help students transition from finding one rotation to finding two rotations for a given preimage and image.

Make sure students understand that for every rotation clockwise there is also a rotation counterclockwise.

**Q:** Why is rotating a figure 90° clockwise the same as rotating the figure 270° counterclockwise? [Sample answer: Rotating a figure 90° clockwise moves the figure one quadrant to the right. Rotating a figure 270° counterclockwise moves the figure three quadrants to the left. Both ways, the figure ends up in the same quadrant.]

**Additional Examples** are available online

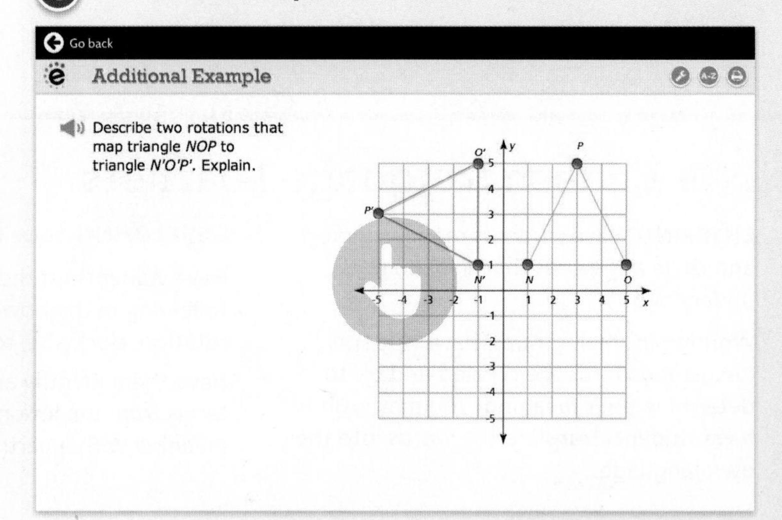


**Answer:** Rotation of 90° or −270°

Go Online

Practice Tutorials Math Tools

# Practice & Problem Solving

**Interactive Practice** and **Virtual Nerd Tutorials** are available online.

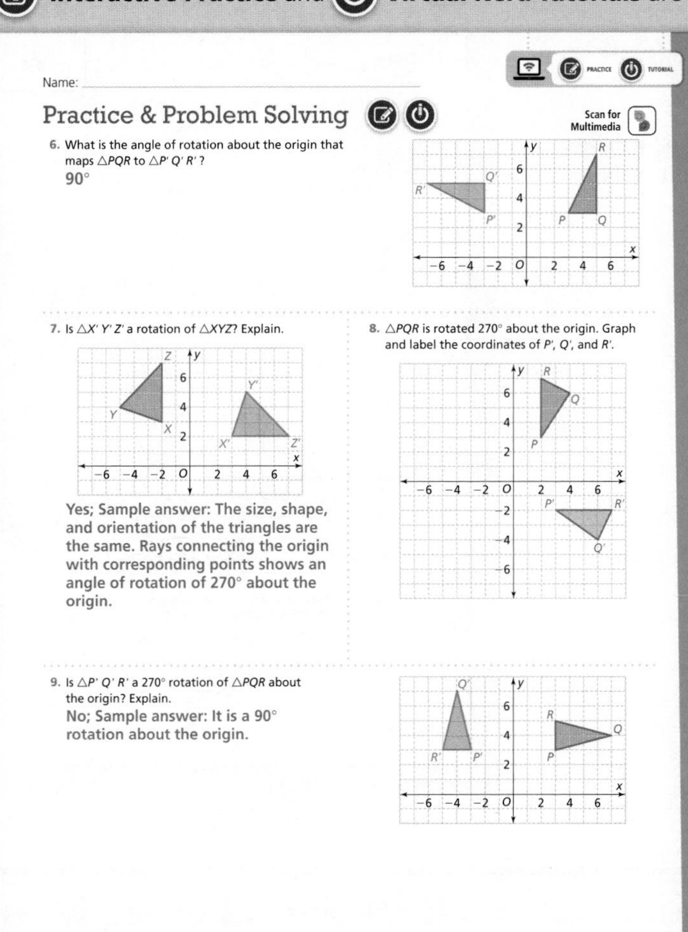

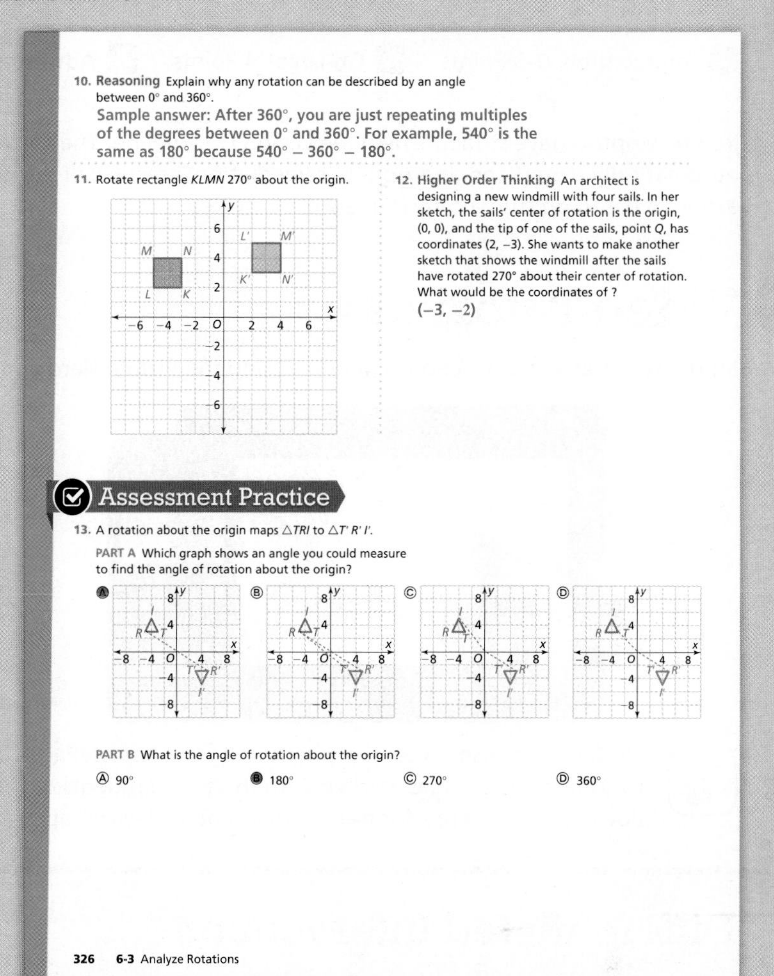

## Error Intervention

**ITEM 11** Since the figure is a square, students may have difficulty labeling the image and incorrectly keep the labels in the same spot.

**Q:** The vertex labeled *M* is in the upper left hand corner in the preimage. Where can you expect it to be in the image? Explain. [Sample answer: In the image, the vertex labeled M will be in the upper right hand corner. Since the figure is rotated 270° it is rotated three-quarters of a full turn.]

## Challenge

**ITEM 11** Challenge students to see patterns in different degrees of rotations that are equivalent.

**Q:** Suppose there is a point *Q* which is graphed at (1, 2) on this grid. What are three different rotations that will map the point onto Q′ (–2, 1)? [Sample answer: 90° counterclockwise, 270° clockwise, and 450° counterclockwise]

You may opt to have students complete the automatically scored Practice & Problem Solving items online.

### Item Analysis

| Example | Items | DOK |
|---|---|---|
| 1 | 7, 9 | 2 |
| | 10 | 3 |
| 2 | 8, 11 | 2 |
| | 12 | 3 |
| 3 | 6 | 2 |
| | 13 | 3 |

## STEP 3 | Assess & Differentiate

Go Online

Assess Tutorials Worksheets

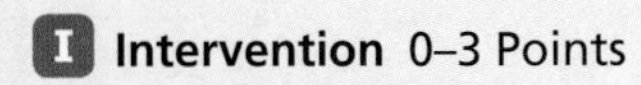

# Lesson Quiz

**Formative** Assessment

Use the student scores on the Lesson Quiz to prescribe differentiated assignments.

**I Intervention** 0–3 Points **O On-Level** 4 Points **A Advanced** 5 Points

You may opt to have students take the Lesson Quiz online. The Lesson Quiz will be automatically scored and appropriate remediation, practice, or enrichment will be assigned based on student performance.

**Lesson Quiz** is available online.

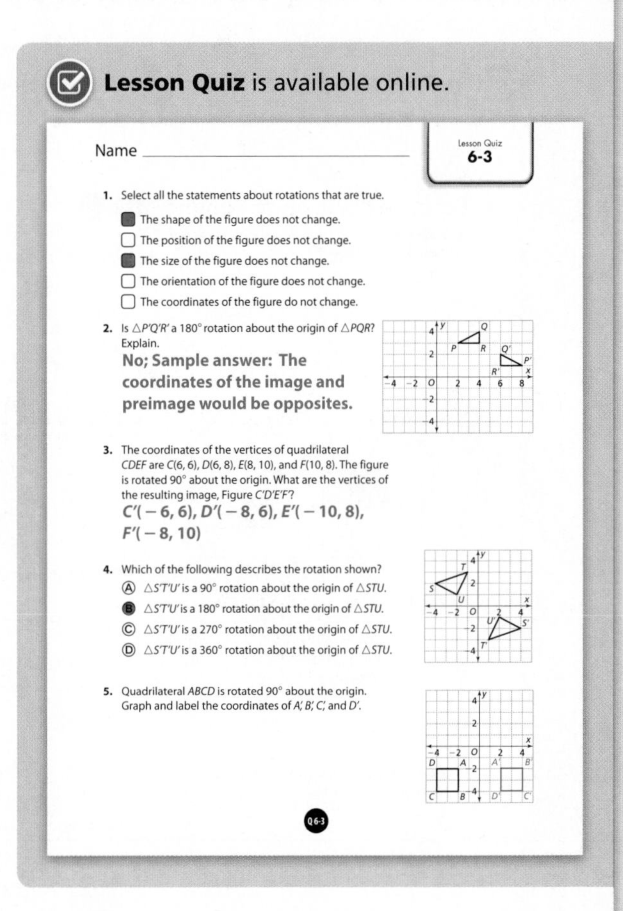

Name ______________ Lesson Quiz 6-3

1. Select all the statements about rotations that are true.
   - ■ The shape of the figure does not change.
   - □ The position of the figure does not change.
   - ■ The size of the figure does not change.
   - □ The orientation of the figure does not change.
   - □ The coordinates of the figure do not change.
2. Is $\triangle P'Q'R'$ a 180° rotation about the origin of $\triangle PQR$? Explain.
   **No; Sample answer: The coordinates of the image and preimage would be opposites.**
3. The coordinates of the vertices of quadrilateral *CDEF* are *C*(6, 6), *D*(6, 8), *E*(8, 10), and *F*(10, 8). The figure is rotated 90° about the origin. What are the vertices of the resulting image, Figure *C′D′E′F′*?
   **$C'(-6, 6)$, $D'(-8, 6)$, $E'(-10, 8)$, $F'(-8, 10)$**
4. Which of the following describes the rotation shown?
   - Ⓐ $\triangle S'T'U'$ is a 90° rotation about the origin of $\triangle STU$.
   - ● $\triangle S'T'U'$ is a 180° rotation about the origin of $\triangle STU$.
   - Ⓒ $\triangle S'T'U'$ is a 270° rotation about the origin of $\triangle STU$.
   - Ⓓ $\triangle S'T'U'$ is a 360° rotation about the origin of $\triangle STU$.
5. Quadrilateral *ABCD* is rotated 90° about the origin. Graph and label the coordinates of *A′*, *B′*, *C′*, and *D′*.

Q6-3

# Video Tutorials

Students can access instructional tutorials using the **Virtual Nerd app**.

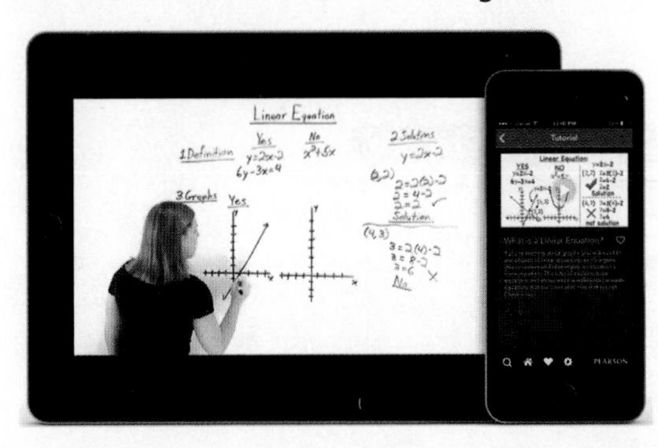

Students can also access the videos using the **BouncePages app** to scan exercise pages marked with this icon. Students can download both apps for free in their mobile devices' app store.

# Differentiated Intervention

**I** = Intervention **O** = On-Level **A** = Advanced

## Reteach to Build Understanding I

Provides scaffolded reteaching for the key lesson concepts.

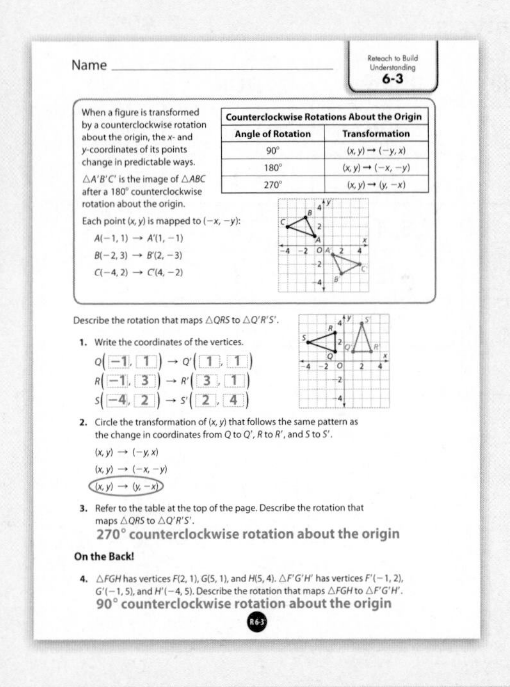

Name ______________ Reteach to Build Understanding 6-3

When a figure is transformed by a counterclockwise rotation about the origin, the *x*- and *y*-coordinates of its points change in predictable ways.

| Counterclockwise Rotations About the Origin | |
|---|---|
| Angle of Rotation | Transformation |
| 90° | $(x, y) \rightarrow (-y, x)$ |
| 180° | $(x, y) \rightarrow (-x, -y)$ |
| 270° | $(x, y) \rightarrow (y, -x)$ |

$\triangle A'B'C'$ is the image of $\triangle ABC$ after a 180° counterclockwise rotation about the origin.

Each point $(x, y)$ is mapped to $(-x, -y)$:

$A(-1, 1) \rightarrow A'(1, -1)$
$B(-2, 3) \rightarrow B'(2, -3)$
$C(-4, 2) \rightarrow C'(4, -2)$

Describe the rotation that maps $\triangle QRS$ to $\triangle Q'R'S'$.

1. Write the coordinates of the vertices.
   $Q(-1, 1) \rightarrow Q'(1, 1)$
   $R(-1, 3) \rightarrow R'(3, 1)$
   $S(-4, 2) \rightarrow S'(2, 4)$
2. Circle the transformation of $(x, y)$ that follows the same pattern as the change in coordinates from *Q* to *Q′*, *R* to *R′*, and *S* to *S′*.
   $(x, y) \rightarrow (-y, x)$
   $(x, y) \rightarrow (-x, -y)$
   **(circled)** $(x, y) \rightarrow (y, -x)$
3. Refer to the table at the top of the page. Describe the rotation that maps $\triangle QRS$ to $\triangle Q'R'S'$.
   **270° counterclockwise rotation about the origin**

**On the Back!**

4. $\triangle FGH$ has vertices *F*(2, 1), *G*(5, 1), and *H*(5, 4). $\triangle F'G'H'$ has vertices $F'(-1, 2)$, $G'(-1, 5)$, and $H'(-4, 5)$. Describe the rotation that maps $\triangle FGH$ to $\triangle F'G'H'$.
   **90° counterclockwise rotation about the origin**

R6-3

## Additional Vocabulary Support I O

Helps students develop and reinforce understanding of key terms and concepts.

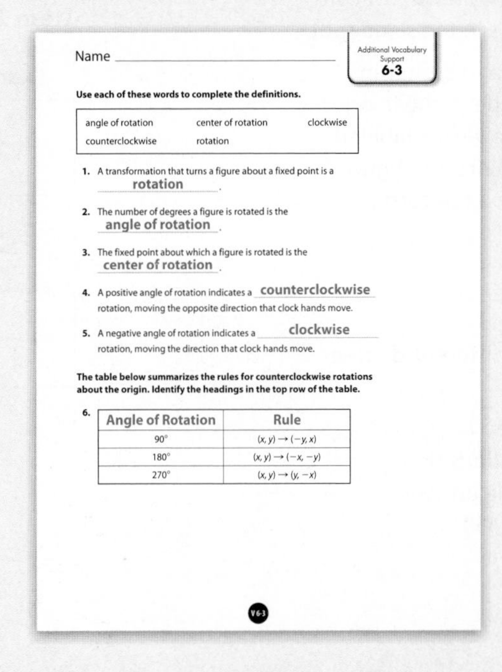

Name ______________ Additional Vocabulary Support 6-3

**Use each of these words to complete the definitions.**

| angle of rotation | center of rotation | clockwise |
|---|---|---|
| counterclockwise | rotation | |

1. A transformation that turns a figure about a fixed point is a **rotation**.
2. The number of degrees a figure is rotated is the **angle of rotation**.
3. The fixed point about which a figure is rotated is the **center of rotation**.
4. A positive angle of rotation indicates a **counterclockwise** rotation, moving the opposite direction that clock hands move.
5. A negative angle of rotation indicates a **clockwise** rotation, moving the direction that clock hands move.

**The table below summarizes the rules for counterclockwise rotations about the origin. Identify the headings in the top row of the table.**

6.

| Angle of Rotation | Rule |
|---|---|
| 90° | $(x, y) \rightarrow (-y, x)$ |
| 180° | $(x, y) \rightarrow (-x, -y)$ |
| 270° | $(x, y) \rightarrow (y, -x)$ |

V6-3

## Build Mathematical Literacy I O

Provides support for struggling readers to build mathematical literacy.

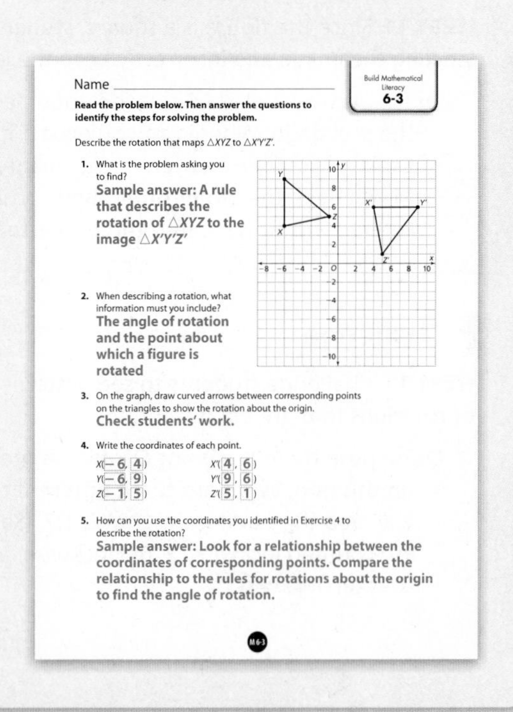

Name ______________ Build Mathematical Literacy 6-3

**Read the problem below. Then answer the questions to identify the steps for solving the problem.**

Describe the rotation that maps $\triangle XYZ$ to $\triangle X'Y'Z'$.

1. What is the problem asking you to find?
   **Sample answer: A rule that describes the rotation of $\triangle XYZ$ to the image $\triangle X'Y'Z'$**
2. When describing a rotation, what information must you include?
   **The angle of rotation and the point about which a figure is rotated**
3. On the graph, draw curved arrows between corresponding points on the triangles to show the rotation about the origin.
   **Check students' work.**
4. Write the coordinates of each point.
   $X(-6, 4)$ $X'(4, 6)$
   $Y(-6, 9)$ $Y'(9, 6)$
   $Z(-1, 5)$ $Z'(5, 1)$
5. How can you use the coordinates you identified in Exercise 4 to describe the rotation?
   **Sample answer: Look for a relationship between the coordinates of corresponding points. Compare the relationship to the rules for rotations about the origin to find the angle of rotation.**

M6-3

Practice

Worksheets

Math Tools

Math Games

# Additional Practice

You may opt to have students complete the automatically scored Additional Practice items online.

### Item Analysis

| Example | Items | DOK |
|---|---|---|
| 1 | 2, 5 | 2 |
| 2 | 4, 6 | 2 |
| | 7 | 3 |
| 3 | 1, 3, 8 | 2 |

**Interactive Practice** is available online.

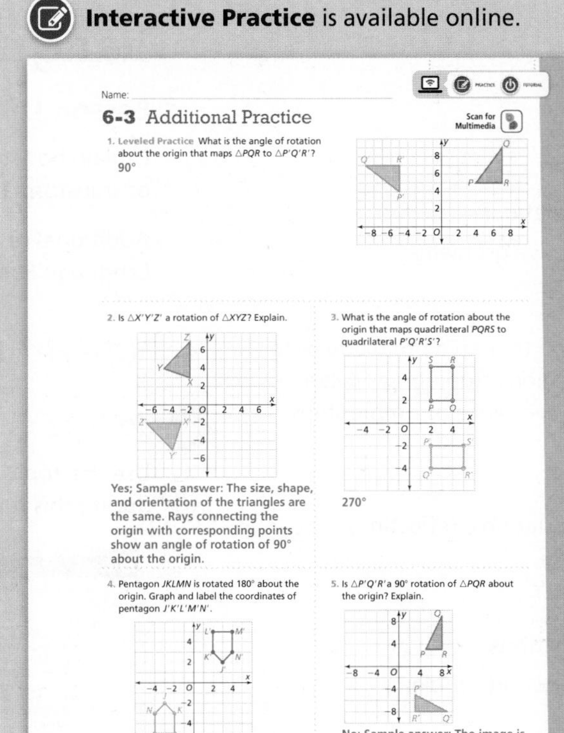
Name

6-3 Additional Practice

Scan for Multimedia

1. Leveled Practice What is the angle of rotation about the origin that maps $\triangle PQR$ to $\triangle P'Q'R'$?
90°

2. Is $\triangle X'Y'Z'$ a rotation of $\triangle XYZ$? Explain.
Yes; Sample answer: The size, shape, and orientation of the triangles are the same. Rays connecting the origin with corresponding points show an angle of rotation of 90° about the origin.

3. What is the angle of rotation about the origin that maps quadrilateral $PQRS$ to quadrilateral $P'Q'R'S'$?
270°

4. Pentagon $JKLMN$ is rotated 180° about the origin. Graph and label the coordinates of pentagon $J'K'L'M'N'$.

5. Is $\triangle P'Q'R'$ a 90° rotation of $\triangle PQR$ about the origin? Explain.
No; Sample answer: The image is a 270° rotation about the origin.

6-3 Analyze Rotations 73

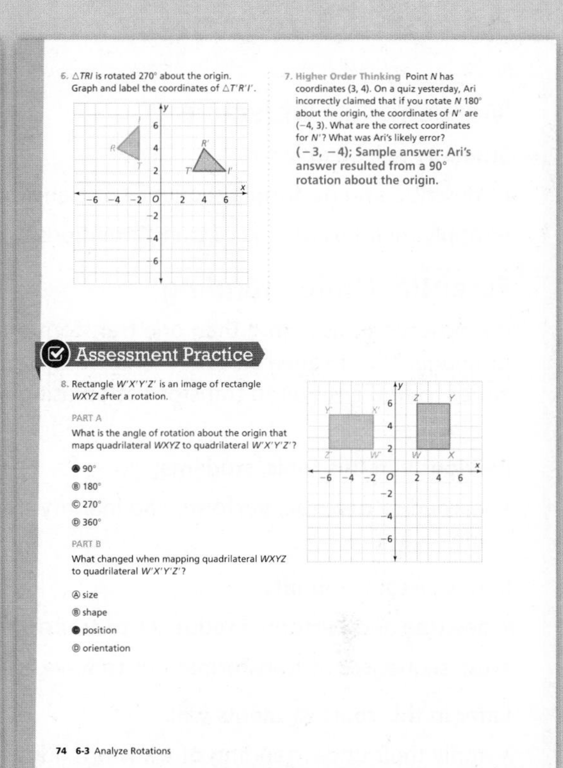
6. $\triangle TRI$ is rotated 270° about the origin. Graph and label the coordinates of $\triangle T'R'I'$.

7. Higher Order Thinking Point $N$ has coordinates (3, 4). On a quiz yesterday, Ari incorrectly claimed that if you rotate $N$ 180° about the origin, the coordinates of $N'$ are (−4, 3). What are the correct coordinates for $N'$? What was Ari's likely error?
(−3, −4); Sample answer: Ari's answer resulted from a 90° rotation about the origin.

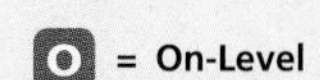
Assessment Practice

8. Rectangle $W'X'Y'Z'$ is an image of rectangle $WXYZ$ after a rotation.

PART A
What is the angle of rotation about the origin that maps quadrilateral $WXYZ$ to quadrilateral $W'X'Y'Z'$?
● 90°
Ⓑ 180°
Ⓒ 270°
Ⓓ 360°

PART B
What changed when mapping quadrilateral $WXYZ$ to quadrilateral $W'X'Y'Z'$?
Ⓐ size
Ⓑ shape
● position
Ⓓ orientation

74 6-3 Analyze Rotations

# Differentiated Intervention

I = Intervention O = On-Level A = Advanced

## Enrichment 

Presents engaging problems and activities that extend the lesson concepts.

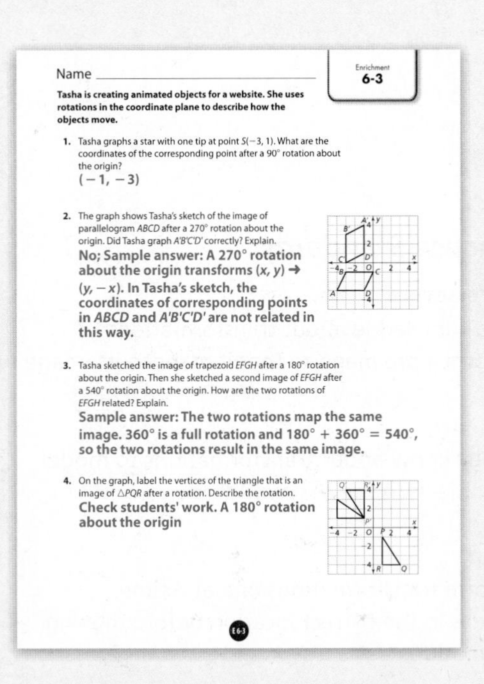
Name

Enrichment 6-3

Tasha is creating animated objects for a website. She uses rotations in the coordinate plane to describe how the objects move.

1. Tasha graphs a star with one tip at point $S(-3, 1)$. What are the coordinates of the corresponding point after a 90° rotation about the origin?
(−1, −3)

2. The graph shows Tasha's sketch of the image of parallelogram $ABCD$ after a 270° rotation about the origin. Did Tasha graph $A'B'C'D'$ correctly? Explain.
No; Sample answer: A 270° rotation about the origin transforms $(x, y) \rightarrow (y, -x)$. In Tasha's sketch, the coordinates of corresponding points in $ABCD$ and $A'B'C'D'$ are not related in this way.

3. Tasha sketched the image of trapezoid $EFGH$ after a 180° rotation about the origin. Then she sketched a second image of $EFGH$ after a 540° rotation about the origin. How are the two rotations of $EFGH$ related? Explain.
Sample answer: The two rotations map the same image. 360° is a full rotation and 180° + 360° = 540°, so the two rotations result in the same image.

4. On the graph, label the vertices of the triangle that is an image of $\triangle PQR$ after a rotation. Describe the rotation.
Check students' work. A 180° rotation about the origin

## Math Tools and Games I O A

Offers additional activities and games to build understanding and fluency.

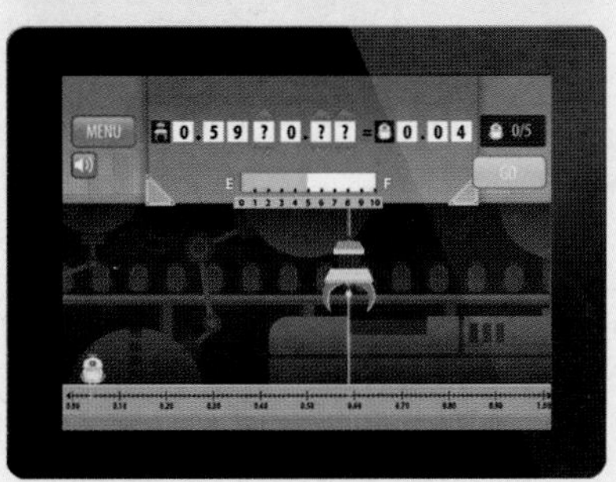


## Pick a Project and STEM Project I O A

Provides an additional opportunity for students to demonstrate understanding of key mathematical concepts.

Lesson 6-4

# Compose Transformations

Go Online

Video Activity

## Lesson Overview

FOCUS

### Mathematics Objective

**Students will be able to:**

✔ describe and perform a sequence of transformations.

✔ apply their knowledge of transformations to solve problems.

### Essential Understanding

It is possible to use more than one transformation to map a preimage onto its image. This is called a sequence of transformations. Sometimes it can be easier to find a required transformation using a sequence of simple steps.

COHERENCE

**Previously in this topic, students:**

- learned to describe, perform, and identify translations, reflections, and rotations.

**In this lesson, students:**

- describe and perform a sequence of transformations.
- use sequences of transformations to solve real-world problems.

**Later in this topic, students will:**

- apply their understanding of transformations to the concepts of dilations and similarity.

**Cross-Cluster Connection** Coordinate mapping of transformations (8.G.1) connects to work defining functions (8.F.1).

RIGOR

This lesson emphasizes a blend of **procedural skills and fluency** and **application**.

- Students will practice transforming a preimage into its image through a sequence of steps and explore whether the order of the transformations leads to different answers.
- Students will apply their understanding of transformations and how to use them in sequence to solve problems involving floor plans.

## Language Support

### Lesson Language Objective

Explain how to describe and perform a sequence of transformations.

Additional resources are available in the **Language Support Handbook**.

## Math Anytime

### Today's Challenge

Use the Topic 6 problems any time during this topic.

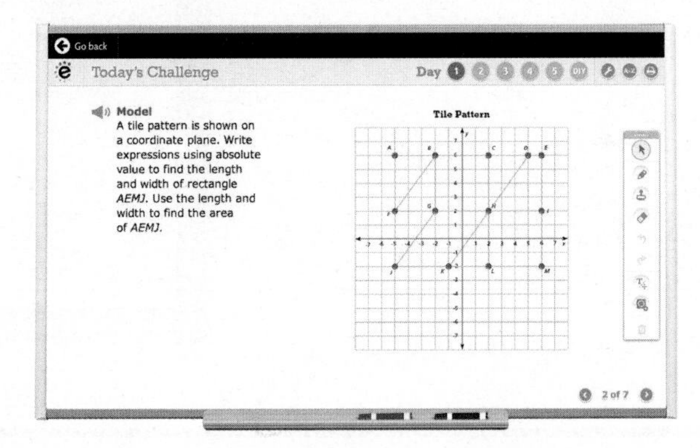


Watch the **Listen and Look For Video** for strategies and habits of mind to look for as students complete work on this lesson.

## Mathematics Overview — Common Core Standards

### Content Standards

In this lesson, you will focus on **8.G.A.1a, 8.G.A.1b, 8.G.A.1c,** and **8.G.A.3**.

- **8.G.A.1a** Lines are taken to lines, and line segments to line segments of the same length.
- **8.G.A.1b** Angles are taken to angles of the same measure.
- **8.G.A.1c** Parallel lines are taken to parallel lines.
- **8.G.A.3** Describe the effect of dilations, translations, rotations, and reflections on two-dimensional figures using coordinates.

### Mathematical Practice Standards

**MP.1 Make Sense and Persevere**
Students apply previous knowledge about transformations to decipher how to transform a preimage so that it maps to its image.

**MP.4 Model with Math**
Students apply what they know about transformations to model how they would move objects in the real world.

**MP.6 Attend to Precision**
Students carefully perform transformations one at a time, ensuring that the figure is in the correct location before moving on to the next transformation.

STEP 1 | Problem-Based Learning

15-20 min

Go Online

Activity

# Solve & Discuss It!

Formative Assessment

**Purpose** Students determine the transformation(s) required to map one figure onto another and connect it to completing a sequence of transformations on a coordinate plane in Example 2.

## ETP Before

WHOLE CLASS

**1 Introduce the Problem**

Provide graph paper, ruler, and scissors, as needed.

**2 Check for Understanding of the Problem**

Ensure students understand the problem by asking: What does it mean to map one figure onto another?

## ETP During

SMALL GROUP

**3 Observe Students at Work**

Students will apply known transformation types to map Figure A onto Figure B. Students might rotate Figure A 180° about the origin to map it onto Figure B, or they might reflect either figure across both axes, in any order. If needed, provide students with graph paper and scissors to model the problem.

### Early Finishers

How would the problem change if you map Figure B onto Figure A? [Sample answer: The solutions would not change because the same transformations that map Figure A onto Figure B also map Figure B onto Figure A.]

## ETP After

WHOLE CLASS

**4 Discuss Solution Strategies and Key Ideas**

Consider having groups who used a rotation share first, followed by those who used two reflections. Have students discuss the similarities between Figure A and Figure B; they are the same size and shape. Have them discuss the differences between Figure A and Figure B; Figure B is upside down and pointing in the opposite direction compared to Figure A, and it is in a different location.

**5 Consider Instructional Implications**

After presenting Example 2, refer students back to the problem in the Solve & Discuss It and have them translate Figure A 3 units right, and then reflect it across the line $y = 2$.

## Analyze Student Work

**Solve and Discuss It!** Activity is available online.

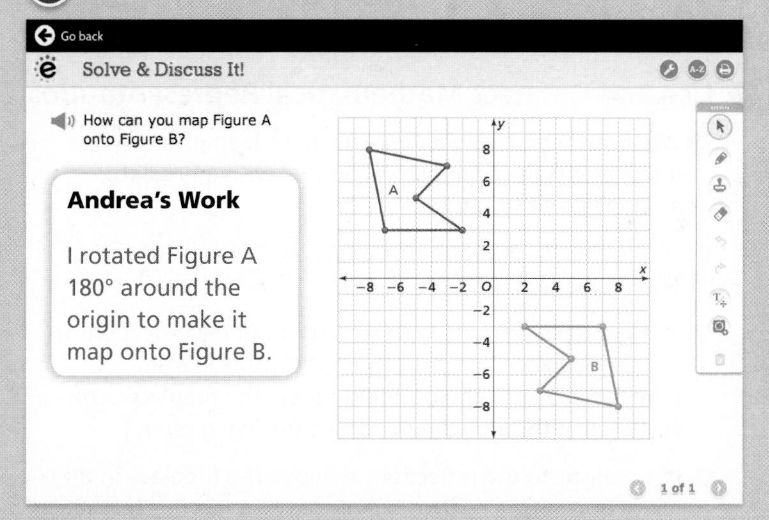


**Andrea** rotates Figure A 180° about the origin. She uses one transformation to map Figure A onto Figure B.

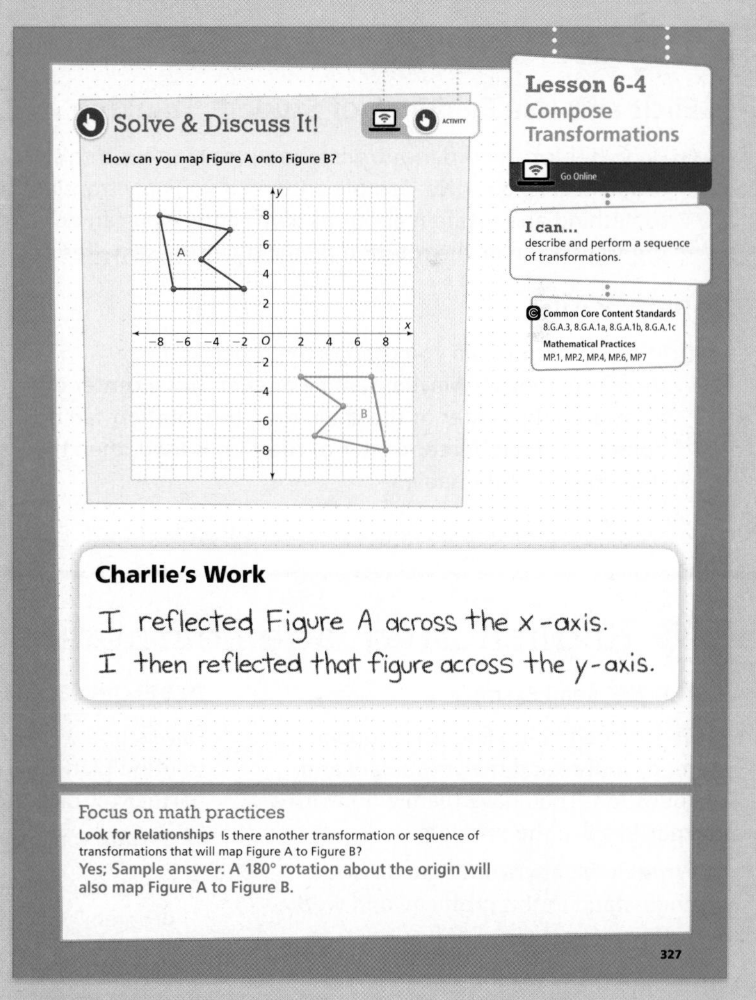


**Charlie** reflects Figure A across the $x$-axis and then across the $y$-axis. He uses two transformations to map Figure A onto Figure B.

# STEP 2 | Visual Learning

Go Online

Visual Learning

Assess

## Establish Mathematics Goals to Focus Learning

Engage students in a discussion about the ***Essential Question***. Make sure they understand how to translate, reflect, and rotate a two-dimensional figure.

## EXAMPLE 1  Understand a Sequence of Transformations

### Use and Connect Mathematical Representations

**Q:** What does the scale model represent? [Sample answer: It represents the floor plan of a room with a fireplace, a cabinet, and furniture.]

**Q:** Which transformations are being used? [Sample answer: Translation and rotation]

**Q:** In the model, can you use a sequence of only reflections to get the fireplace into the top right corner? Explain. [Yes; Sample answer: You could reflect the fireplace across a vertical line through the middle of the living room.]

**Q:** Is it realistic to use reflections to move the fireplace in the real world? Explain. [No; Sample answer: It is not realistic to flip a fireplace upside down in the real world. It wouldn't work if it is upside down.]

##  Try It!  Formative Assessment

### Elicit and Use Evidence of Student Thinking

**Q:** Do you think the order of transformations matters in this problem? Explain. [No; Sample answer: If you only translate something and rotate it about its own center, you can do the translation or the rotation first and get the same result.]

### Convince Me!

**Q:** In this situation, can you change the order of the transformations? [Maybe; Sample answer: If the center of rotation is the center of the chair, then the rotation can be done first. If a different center of rotation is used, then the chair might hit the table.]

**Visual Learning Animation Plus** is available online.

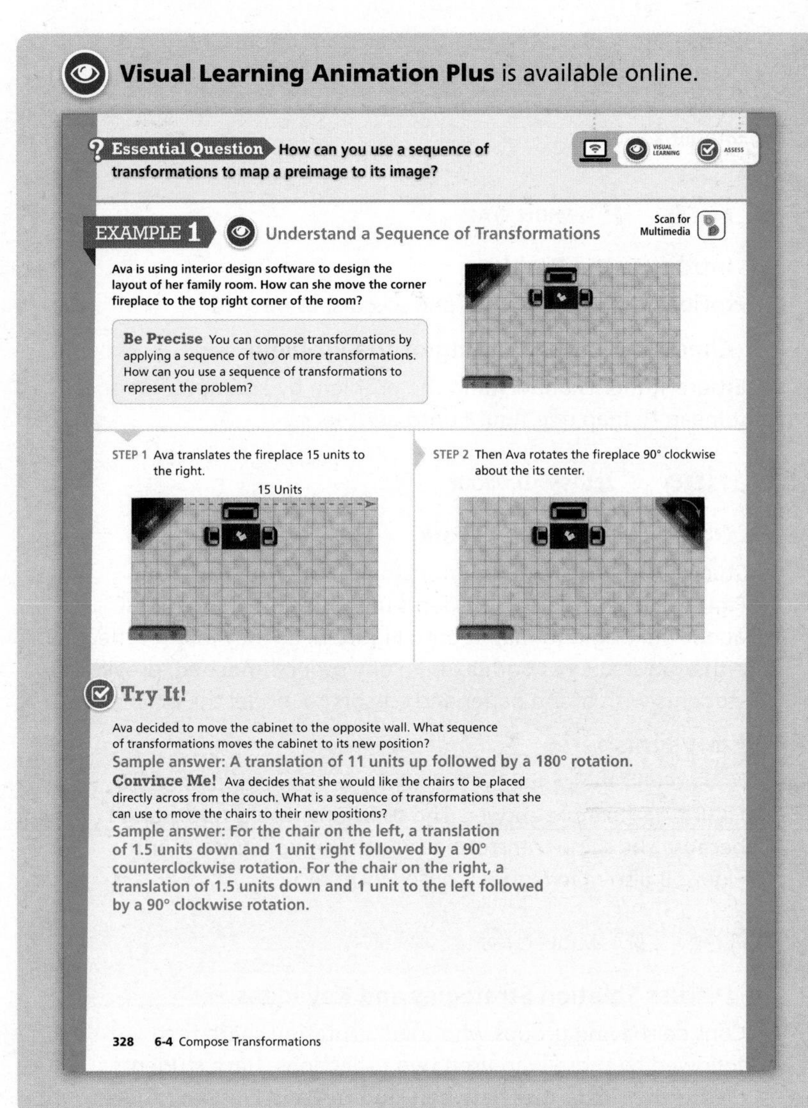
Essential Question How can you use a sequence of transformations to map a preimage to its image?

EXAMPLE 1 Understand a Sequence of Transformations

Scan for Multimedia

Ava is using interior design software to design the layout of her family room. How can she move the corner fireplace to the top right corner of the room?

**Be Precise** You can compose transformations by applying a sequence of two or more transformations. How can you use a sequence of transformations to represent the problem?

STEP 1 Ava translates the fireplace 15 units to the right.

15 Units

STEP 2 Then Ava rotates the fireplace 90° clockwise about the its center.

**Try It!**

Ava decided to move the cabinet to the opposite wall. What sequence of transformations moves the cabinet to its new position?

Sample answer: A translation of 11 units up followed by a 180° rotation.

**Convince Me!** Ava decides that she would like the chairs to be placed directly across from the couch. What is a sequence of transformations that she can use to move the chairs to their new positions?

Sample answer: For the chair on the left, a translation of 1.5 units down and 1 unit right followed by a 90° counterclockwise rotation. For the chair on the right, a translation of 1.5 units down and 1 unit to the left followed by a 90° clockwise rotation.

328 6-4 Compose Transformations

Students can access the ***Visual Learning Animation Plus*** by using the **BouncePages app** to scan this page. Students can download the app for free in their mobile devices' app store.

## English Language Learners

**ENTERING** Read Example 1.

Make sure beginning English language learners understand the vocabulary and the question. Then have them work with a partner to solve the problem.

**Q:** Write down any words you do not understand in this problem, and work with your partner to define them.

**Q:** Restate the problem.

Listen for students who are struggling to find the right words and help them develop academic fluency.

**DEVELOPING** Read Example 1.

Have students rewrite the problem and a solution plan. Then, have them work with a partner to solve the problem.

**Q:** Restate the problem.

**Q:** What steps will you use to solve the problem?

Look for students who are trying to use academic vocabulary and help them internalize it so they can develop fluency.

**BRIDGING** Solve Example 1.

Have students draw their own model and write their own questions, following the structure of Example 1. Then trade with a partner and solve each other's problem. In the end, the students should discuss their approaches and results out loud.

**Q:** Write a problem like the one in Example 1.

**Q:** Trade with a partner and solve each other's problem.

**Q:** Compare your approaches.

Go Online

Activity

Assess

## EXAMPLE 2  Complete a Sequence of Transformations on a Coordinate Plane

### Pose Purposeful Questions

**Q:** Where is the line of reflection located relative to the preimage after it has been translated? Why does this matter? [Sample answer: The line of reflection is inside the preimage. This means the image will have vertices on both sides of the line of reflection.]

**Q:** If you had reflected first and then translated the figure, would the image be the same? [No; Sample answer: If you reflect over the line $x = -3$ first, you would then need to translate it 7 units right to have it be the same image.]

## EXAMPLE 3  Describe a Sequence of Transformations

### Pose Purposeful Questions

**Q:** How do the coordinates of the vertices of $\triangle ABC$ change after the translation? [Sample answer: 8 is added to each $x$-coordinate, and 6 is subtracted from each $y$-coordinate.]

**Q:** If you reflect $\triangle ABC$ over the $y$-axis first, would the same translation map it onto $\triangle A''B''C''$? Explain. [No; Sample answer: If you reflect $\triangle ABC$ over the $y$-axis, the image will be in Quadrant I. Then, the translation would need to be 8 units left and 6 units down to map to $\triangle A''B''C''$.]

##  Try It!  Formative Assessment

### Elicit and Use Evidence of Student Thinking

**Q:** Could you map $\triangle ABC$ onto $\triangle A''B''C''$ without using a reflection? Explain. [No; Sample answer: The two triangles have opposite orientations. From $A$ to $B$ to $C$ is clockwise, but from $A''$ to $B''$ to $C''$ is counterclockwise. Only a reflection changes orientation.]

**Examples and Try Its!** are available online.

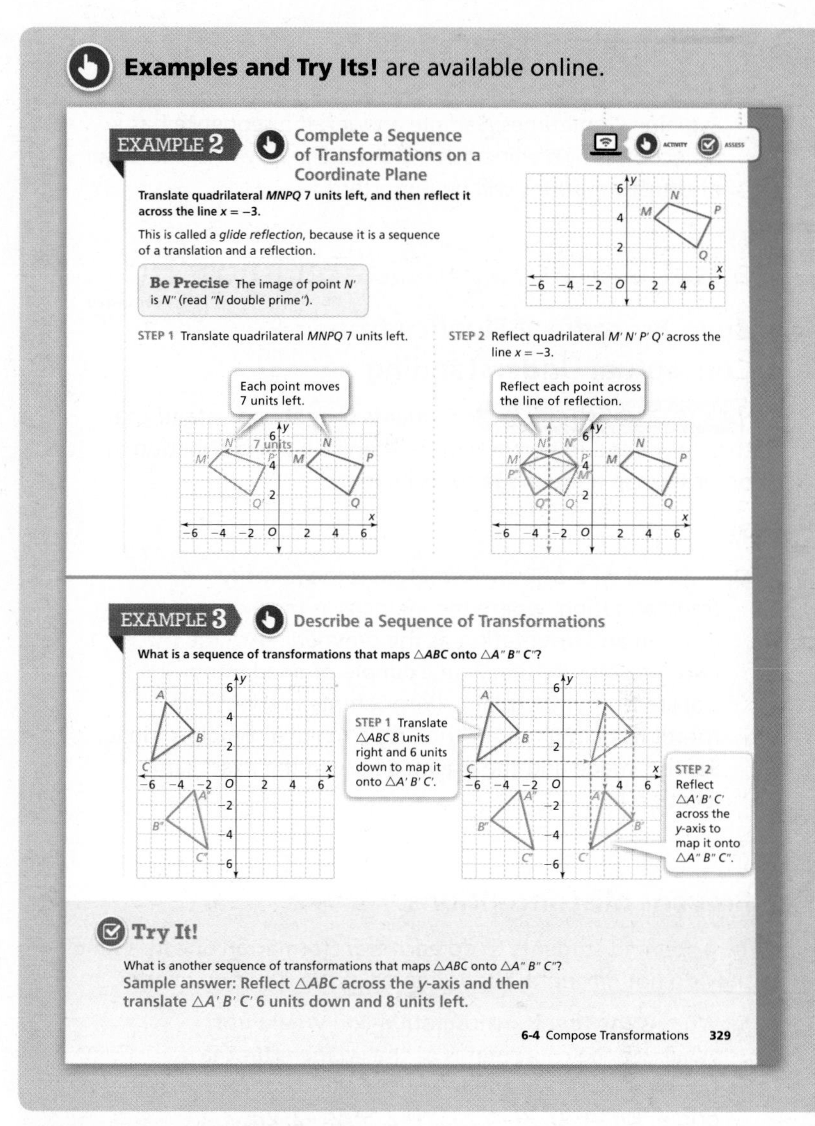

EXAMPLE 2 Complete a Sequence of Transformations on a Coordinate Plane

Translate quadrilateral $MNPQ$ 7 units left, and then reflect it across the line $x = -3$.

This is called a *glide reflection*, because it is a sequence of a translation and a reflection.

**Be Precise** The image of point $N'$ is $N''$ (read "$N$ double prime").

STEP 1 Translate quadrilateral $MNPQ$ 7 units left.

STEP 2 Reflect quadrilateral $M'N'P'Q'$ across the line $x = -3$.



EXAMPLE 3 Describe a Sequence of Transformations

What is a sequence of transformations that maps $\triangle ABC$ onto $\triangle A''B''C''$?



Try It!

What is another sequence of transformations that maps $\triangle ABC$ onto $\triangle A''B''C''$?

Sample answer: Reflect $\triangle ABC$ across the $y$-axis and then translate $\triangle A'B'C'$ 6 units down and 8 units left.

6-4 Compose Transformations 329

## ADDITIONAL EXAMPLES 

**For additional examples go online.**

##  Response to Intervention

**USE WITH EXAMPLE 1** Remind students about the properties of each type of transformation.

- Have students work with a partner and review the three transformations they have learned.

  **Q:** Describe in your own words what it means to translate a two-dimensional figure. [Sample answer: It means to slide a figure without changing its size, shape, or orientation.]

  **Q:** Describe in your own words what it means to rotate a two-dimensional figure. [Sample answer: It means to turn a figure without changing its size, shape, or orientation.]

  **Q:** Describe in your own words what it means to reflect a two-dimensional figure. [Sample answer: It means to flip a figure without changing its size or shape. The orientation of the image is opposite the orientation of the preimage.]

##  Enrichment

**USE WITH EXAMPLE 2** Challenge advanced students to understand what an identity transformation is.

- Read the three examples below. For each transformation sequence, determine where the final image is located.

  **Q:** A figure is reflected across the $y$-axis twice. [Same location as the preimage]

  **Q:** A 90° rotation about the origin is performed four times in sequence. [Same location as the preimage]

  **Q:** A figure is translated two units right, two units down, two units left, and two units up. [Same location as the preimage]

  **Q:** These are all identity transformations. What do you think an identity transformation is? [A transformation, or sequence of transformations, that results in the image being in the same exact location as the preimage.]

Go Online

 Key Concept  Assess  Activity

## KEY CONCEPT 

### ETP Pose Purposeful Questions

**Q:** Is the order of transformations in a sequence important? Explain. [Sometimes; Sample answer: If a sequence has a reflection across a line other than the *x*- or *y*-axis, the order of transformations will be important.]

##  Do You Understand/Do You Know How?

**Formative** Assessment

###  Build Procedural Fluency from Conceptual Understanding

**Essential Question** Students should understand that they may need to perform more than one transformation in order to map a preimage to its image.

**ITEM 2**

**Q:** A special type of transformation is the *identity transformation*, where the image is in the exact same location and orientation as the preimage. Are the two rotations in Item 2 an example of an identity transformation? Explain. [Yes; Sample answer: Two rotations of 180° about the origin make a complete circle. So, the image and the preimage are in the exact same location.]

###  Prevent Misconceptions

**ITEM 4** Remind students to do each transformation one at a time so they do not mix up the coordinates of the resulting images.

**Q:** What is the first transformation you would use? What are the coordinates of the image after that transformation? [Sample answer: 90° rotation about the origin; *W*(−4, 2), *X*(−4, 5), *Y*(−2, 5), *Z*(−2, 2)]

Available Online

KEY CONCEPT

You can use a sequence of two or more transformations to map a preimage to its image.

You can map △*ABC* onto △*A*″*B*″*C*″ by a translation 3 units right followed by a 90° clockwise rotation about the origin.

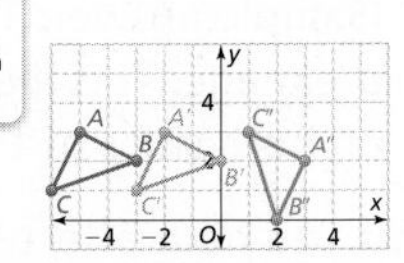


**Do You Understand?**

1. **Essential Question** How can you use a sequence of transformations to map a preimage to its image?
Sample answer: You can compose a transformation of the preimage to its image by applying a sequence of two or more transformations to the preimage until it becomes the image.

2. **Make Sense and Persevere** A preimage is rotated 180° about the origin and then rotated 180° about the origin again. Compare the preimage and image.
Sample answer: The preimage and the image are the same figure in the same location with the same orientation.

3. **Reasoning** A figure *ABC*, with vertices *A*(2, 1), *B*(7, 4), and *C*(2, 7), is rotated 90° clockwise about the origin, and then reflected across the *y*-axis. Describe another sequence that would result in the same image.
Sample answer: A 90° counterclockwise rotation about the origin, followed by a reflection across the *x*-axis.

**Do You Know How?**

In 4–6, use the diagram below.

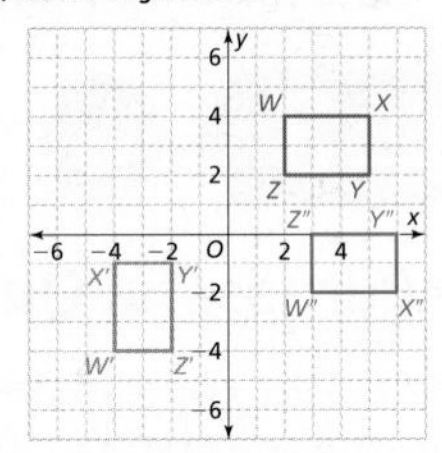


4. Describe a sequence of transformations that maps rectangle *WXYZ* onto rectangle *W′X′Y′Z′*.
Sample answer: A 90° counterclockwise rotation about the origin followed by a translation 6 units down.

5. Describe another way that you could map rectangle *WXYZ* onto *W′X′Y′Z′*.
Sample answer: Rotate the figure 90 degrees about the point *Z* and then translate it down 6 units and then 4 units to the left.

6. Draw the image of rectangle *WXYZ* after a reflection across the line $y = 1$ and a translation 1 unit right. Label the image *W*″*X*″*Y*″*Z*″.
Check students' graphs.

330 6-4 Compose Transformations

## ADDITIONAL EXAMPLE 3 

Help students determine which transformations will be needed to map △*DEF* to △*D′E′F′*.

**Q:** What could be one of the transformations in the sequence? Explain. [A reflection; Sample answer: The orientation of the points has changed, and a reflection changes orientation.]

**Q:** Is there only one line that could be the line of reflection? Explain. [No; Sample answer: A vertical line would make the most sense in this situation, but you could use any vertical line. Depending on the line you choose, the transformation that follows it will change.]

**Additional Examples** are available online.

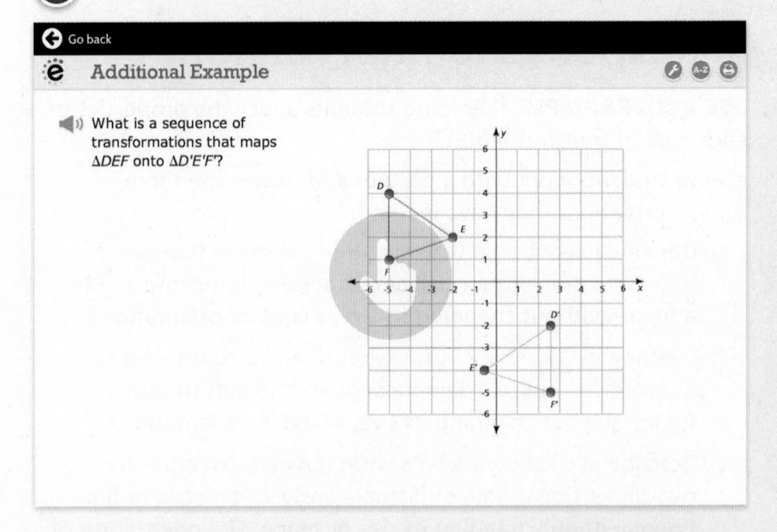


**Sample answer:** A reflection across the line $x = -2$ followed by a translation 2.5 units right and 6 units down

Go Online

Practice

Tutorials

Math Tools

# Practice & Problem Solving

**Interactive Practice** and **Virtual Nerd Video Tutorials** are available online.

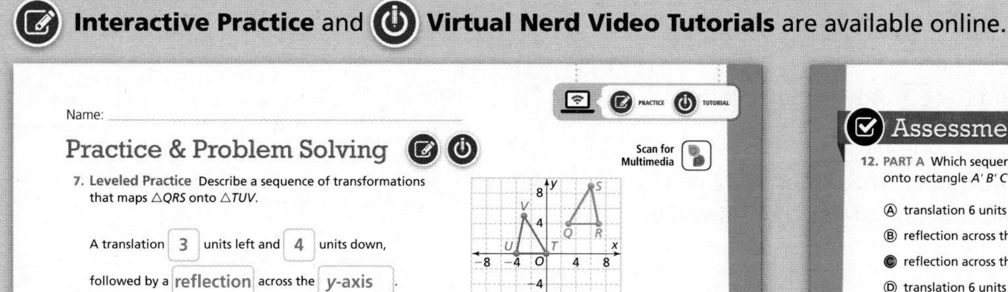

Name: ____________________

## Practice & Problem Solving

Scan for Multimedia

7. **Leveled Practice** Describe a sequence of transformations that maps $\triangle QRS$ onto $\triangle TUV$.

A translation [3] units left and [4] units down, followed by a [reflection] across the [y-axis].

8. **Model with Math** A family moves a table, shown as rectangle *EFGH*, by translating it 3 units left and 3 units down followed by a 90° rotation about the origin. Graph *E′ F′ G′ H′* to show the new location of the table.

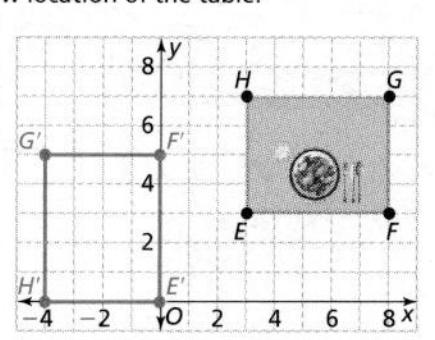

9. Describe a sequence of transformations that maps quadrilateral *ABCD* to quadrilateral *HIJK*.

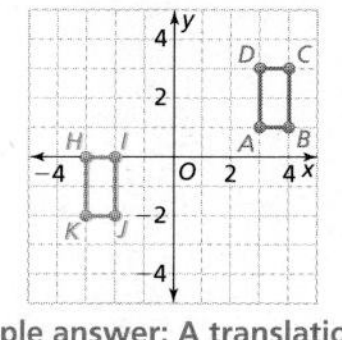

Sample answer: A translation 6 units left and 1 unit down, followed by a reflection across the *x*-axis.

10. Map $\triangle QRS$ to $\triangle Q'R'S'$ with a reflection across the *y*-axis followed by a translation 6 units down.

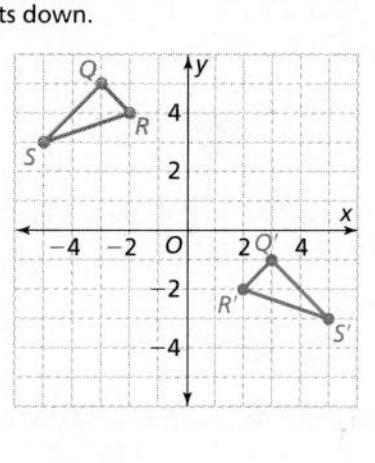

11. **Higher Order Thinking** A student says that he was rearranging furniture at home and he used a glide reflection to move a table with legs from one side of the room to the other. Will a glide reflection result in a functioning table? Explain.

No; Sample answer: You cannot do a glide reflection with a table, because that requires a reflection, which would flip the table upside down.

6-4 Compose Transformations 331

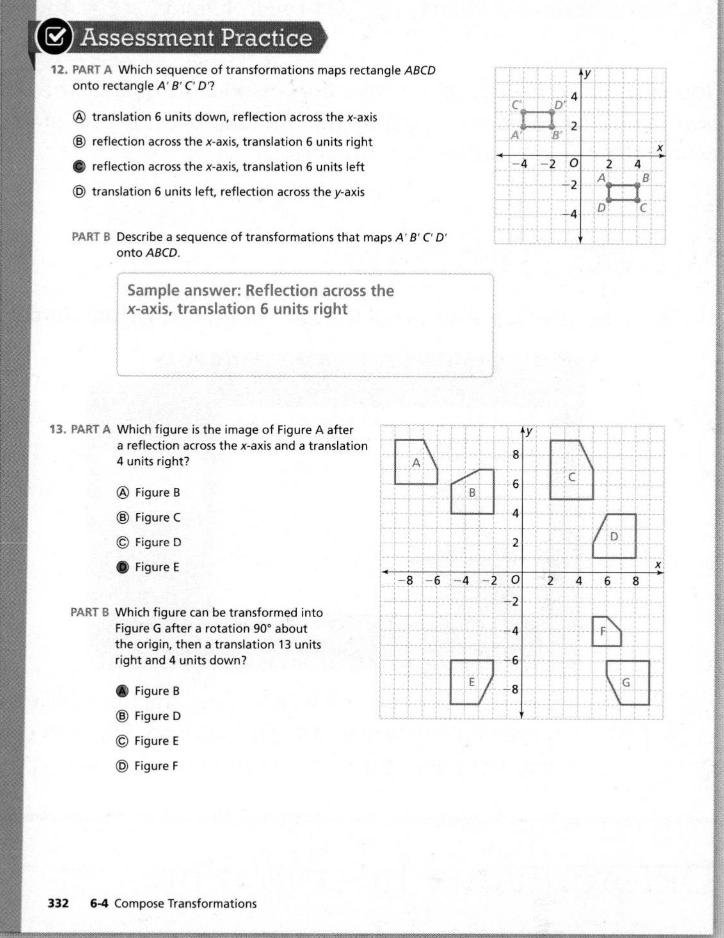

## Assessment Practice

12. PART A Which sequence of transformations maps rectangle *ABCD* onto rectangle *A′ B′ C′ D′*?

Ⓐ translation 6 units down, reflection across the *x*-axis
Ⓑ reflection across the *x*-axis, translation 6 units right
● reflection across the *x*-axis, translation 6 units left
Ⓓ translation 6 units left, reflection across the *y*-axis

PART B Describe a sequence of transformations that maps *A′ B′ C′ D′* onto *ABCD*.

Sample answer: Reflection across the *x*-axis, translation 6 units right

13. PART A Which figure is the image of Figure A after a reflection across the *x*-axis and a translation 4 units right?

Ⓐ Figure B
Ⓑ Figure C
Ⓒ Figure D
● Figure E

PART B Which figure can be transformed into Figure G after a rotation 90° about the origin, then a translation 13 units right and 4 units down?

● Figure B
Ⓑ Figure D
Ⓒ Figure E
Ⓓ Figure F

332 6-4 Compose Transformations

## English Language Learners

**ITEM 11** Have students work through this problem with a partner to develop fluency and internalize academic language.

**Q:** What does it mean to rearrange furniture? [Sample answer: To change the location of furniture in a room]

**Q:** What would a functioning table be? [Sample answer: A table that is able to be used]

## Challenge

**ITEM 9** Challenge students to find five different sequences that will map quadrilateral *ABCD* to quadrilateral *HIJK*.

**Q:** What transformation is part of every sequence you found? [A reflection]

You may opt to have students complete the automatically scored Practice & Problem Solving items online.

### Item Analysis

| Example | Items | DOK |
|---|---|---|
| 1 | 7, 9 | 1 |
| 2 | 10 | 1 |
|  | 8 | 2 |
|  | 13 | 3 |
| 3 | 11, 12 | 2 |

STEP 3 | Assess & Differentiate

Go Online

 Assess  Tutorials  Worksheets

# Lesson Quiz

RtI Use the student scores on the Lesson Quiz to prescribe differentiated assignments.

**I Intervention** 0–3 Points **O On-Level** 4 Points **A Advanced** 5 Points

You may opt to have students take the Lesson Quiz online. The Lesson Quiz will be automatically scored and appropriate remediation, practice, or enrichment will be assigned based on student performance.

**Lesson Quiz** is available online.

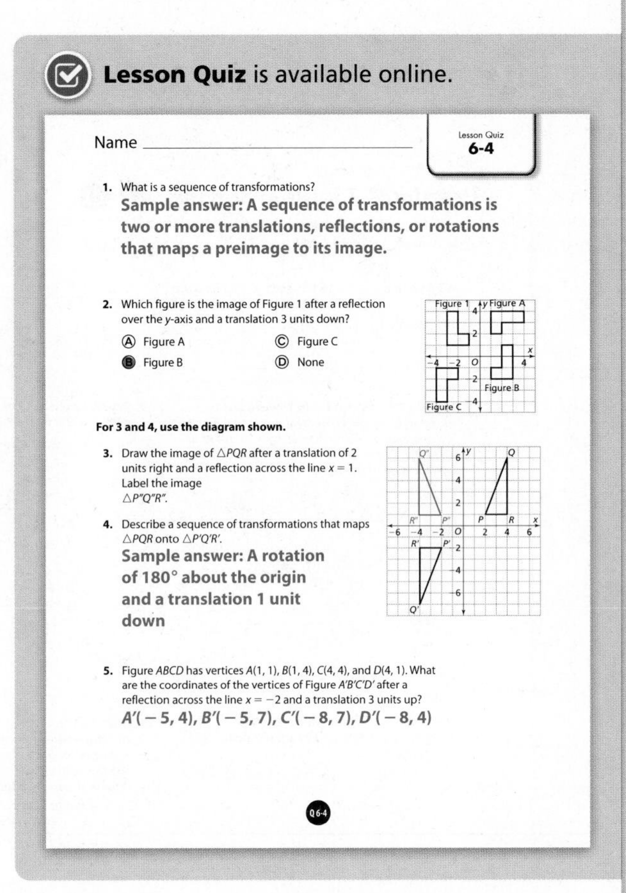

Name ____________ Lesson Quiz 6-4

1. What is a sequence of transformations?
   **Sample answer: A sequence of transformations is two or more translations, reflections, or rotations that maps a preimage to its image.**

2. Which figure is the image of Figure 1 after a reflection over the $y$-axis and a translation 3 units down?
   Ⓐ Figure A Ⓒ Figure C
   Ⓑ Figure B Ⓓ None

For 3 and 4, use the diagram shown.

3. Draw the image of $\triangle PQR$ after a translation of 2 units right and a reflection across the line $x = 1$. Label the image $\triangle P''Q''R''$.

4. Describe a sequence of transformations that maps $\triangle PQR$ onto $\triangle P'Q'R'$.
   **Sample answer: A rotation of 180° about the origin and a translation 1 unit down**

5. Figure $ABCD$ has vertices $A(1, 1)$, $B(1, 4)$, $C(4, 4)$, and $D(4, 1)$. What are the coordinates of the vertices of Figure $A'B'C'D'$ after a reflection across the line $x = -2$ and a translation 3 units up?
   **$A'(-5, 4), B'(-5, 7), C'(-8, 7), D'(-8, 4)$**

Q6-4

# Video Tutorials

Students can access instructional tutorials using the **Virtual Nerd app**.

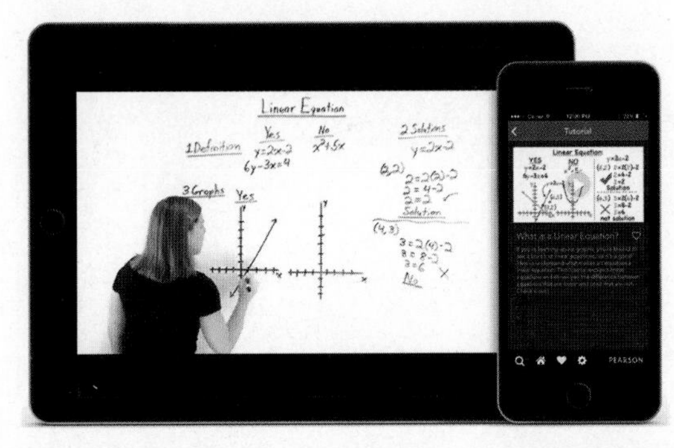

Students can also access the videos using the **BouncePages app** to scan exercise pages marked with this icon. Students can download both apps for free in their mobile devices' app store.

# Differentiated Intervention

**I** = Intervention **O** = On-Level **A** = Advanced

## Reteach to Build Understanding I

Provides scaffolded reteaching for the key lesson concepts.

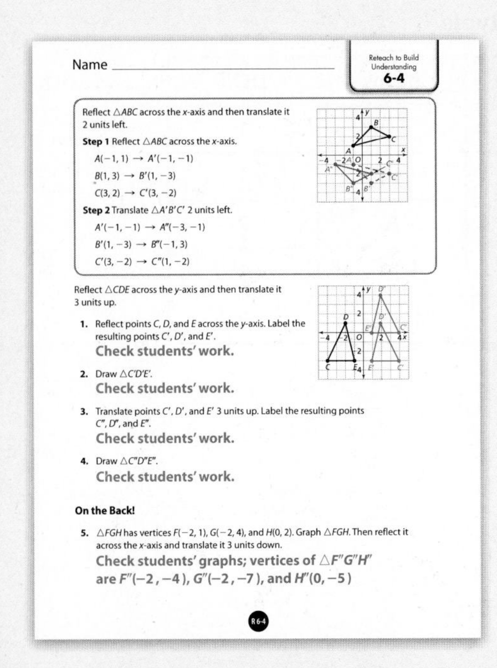

Name ____________ Reteach to Build Understanding 6-4

Reflect $\triangle ABC$ across the $x$-axis and then translate it 2 units left.

**Step 1** Reflect $\triangle ABC$ across the $x$-axis.

$A(-1, 1) \rightarrow A'(-1, -1)$
$B(1, 3) \rightarrow B'(1, -3)$
$C(3, 2) \rightarrow C'(3, -2)$

**Step 2** Translate $\triangle A'B'C'$ 2 units left.

$A'(-1, -1) \rightarrow A''(-3, -1)$
$B'(1, -3) \rightarrow B''(-1, 3)$
$C'(3, -2) \rightarrow C''(1, -2)$

Reflect $\triangle CDE$ across the $y$-axis and then translate it 3 units up.

1. Reflect points $C$, $D$, and $E$ across the $y$-axis. Label the resulting points $C'$, $D'$, and $E'$.
   **Check students' work.**
2. Draw $\triangle C'D'E'$.
   **Check students' work.**
3. Translate points $C'$, $D'$, and $E'$ 3 units up. Label the resulting points $C''$, $D''$, and $E''$.
   **Check students' work.**
4. Draw $\triangle C''D''E''$.
   **Check students' work.**

**On the Back!**

5. $\triangle FGH$ has vertices $F(-2, 1)$, $G(-2, 4)$, and $H(0, 2)$. Graph $\triangle FGH$. Then reflect it across the $x$-axis and translate it 3 units down.
   **Check students' graphs; vertices of $\triangle F''G''H''$ are $F''(-2, -4)$, $G''(-2, -7)$, and $H''(0, -5)$**

R6-4

## Additional Vocabulary Support I O

Helps students develop and reinforce understanding of key terms and concepts.

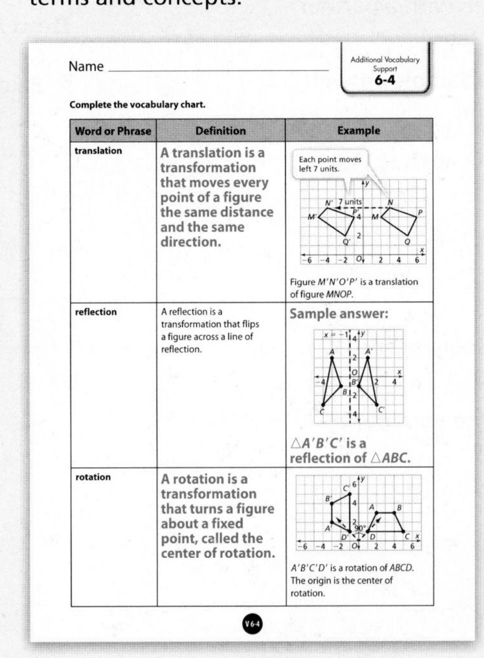

Name ____________ Additional Vocabulary Support 6-4

**Complete the vocabulary chart.**

| Word or Phrase | Definition | Example |
|---|---|---|
| translation | **A translation is a transformation that moves every point of a figure the same distance and the same direction.** | Each point moves left 7 units. Figure $M'N'O'P'$ is a translation of figure $MNOP$. |
| reflection | A reflection is a transformation that flips a figure across a line of reflection. | **Sample answer:** **$\triangle A'B'C'$ is a reflection of $\triangle ABC$.** |
| rotation | **A rotation is a transformation that turns a figure about a fixed point, called the center of rotation.** | $A'B'C'D'$ is a rotation of $ABCD$. The origin is the center of rotation. |

V6-4

## Build Mathematical Literacy I O

Provides support for struggling readers to build mathematical literacy.

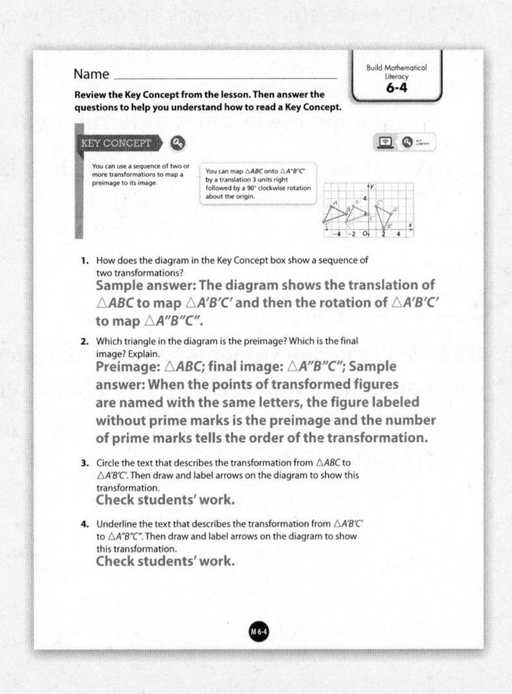

Name ____________ Build Mathematical Literacy 6-4

**Review the Key Concept from the lesson. Then answer the questions to help you understand how to read a Key Concept.**

KEY CONCEPT

You can use a sequence of two or more transformations to map a preimage to its image.

You can map $\triangle ABC$ onto $\triangle A''B''C''$ by a translation 3 units right followed by a 90° clockwise rotation about the origin.

1. How does the diagram in the Key Concept box show a sequence of two transformations?
   **Sample answer: The diagram shows the translation of $\triangle ABC$ to map $\triangle A'B'C'$ and then the rotation of $\triangle A'B'C'$ to map $\triangle A''B''C''$.**
2. Which triangle in the diagram is the preimage? Which is the final image? Explain.
   **Preimage: $\triangle ABC$; final image: $\triangle A''B''C''$; Sample answer: When the points of transformed figures are named with the same letters, the figure labeled without prime marks is the preimage and the number of prime marks tells the order of the transformation.**
3. Circle the text that describes the transformation from $\triangle ABC$ to $\triangle A'B'C'$. Then draw and label arrows on the diagram to show this transformation.
   **Check students' work.**
4. Underline the text that describes the transformation from $\triangle A'B'C'$ to $\triangle A''B''C''$. Then draw and label arrows on the diagram to show this transformation.
   **Check students' work.**

M6-4

Go Online

Practice | Worksheets | Math Tools | Math Games

# Additional Practice

You may opt to have students complete the automatically scored Additional Practice items online.

### Item Analysis

| Example | Items | DOK |
|---|---|---|
| 1 | 5 | 3 |
| 2 | 3, 6 | 2 |
| 3 | 1 | 1 |
|  | 2, 4, 7 | 2 |

**Interactive Practice** is available online.

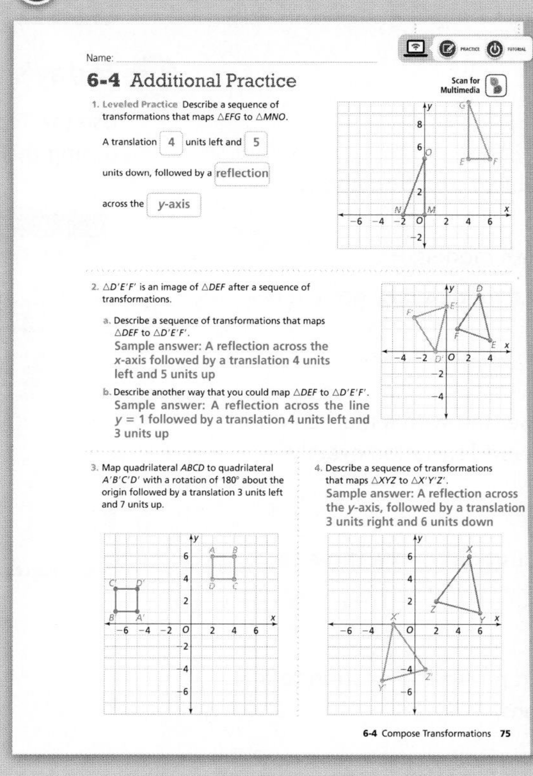

Name:

**6-4** Additional Practice

Scan for Multimedia

1. Leveled Practice Describe a sequence of transformations that maps △EFG to △MNO.

A translation 4 units left and 5 units down, followed by a reflection across the y-axis

2. △D′E′F′ is an image of △DEF after a sequence of transformations.

a. Describe a sequence of transformations that maps △DEF to △D′E′F′.
Sample answer: A reflection across the x-axis followed by a translation 4 units left and 5 units up

b. Describe another way that you could map △DEF to △D′E′F′.
Sample answer: A reflection across the line $y = 1$ followed by a translation 4 units left and 3 units up

3. Map quadrilateral ABCD to quadrilateral A′B′C′D′ with a rotation of 180° about the origin followed by a translation 3 units left and 7 units up.

4. Describe a sequence of transformations that maps △XYZ to △X′Y′Z′.
Sample answer: A reflection across the y-axis, followed by a translation 3 units right and 6 units down

6-4 Compose Transformations 75

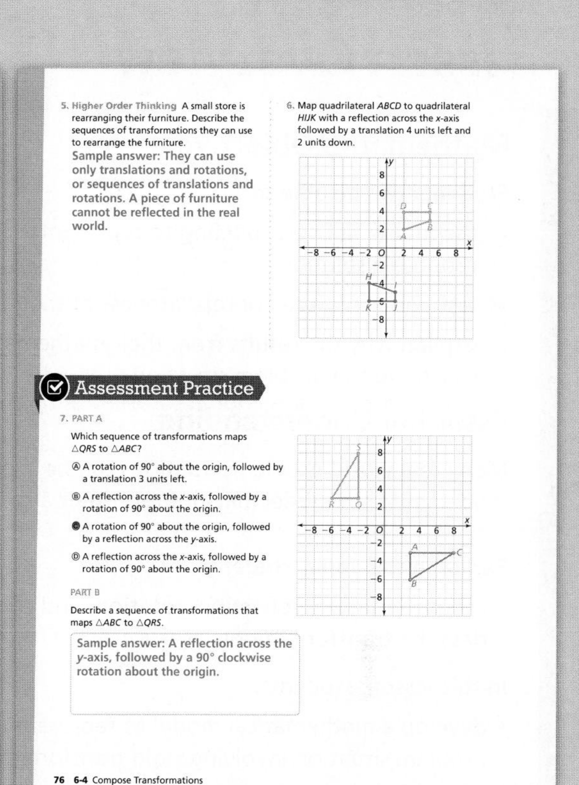

5. Higher Order Thinking A small store is rearranging their furniture. Describe the sequences of transformations they can use to rearrange the furniture.
Sample answer: They can use only translations and rotations, or sequences of translations and rotations. A piece of furniture cannot be reflected in the real world.

6. Map quadrilateral ABCD to quadrilateral HIJK with a reflection across the x-axis followed by a translation 4 units left and 2 units down.

Assessment Practice

7. PART A

Which sequence of transformations maps △QRS to △ABC?

Ⓐ A rotation of 90° about the origin, followed by a translation 3 units left.

Ⓑ A reflection across the x-axis, followed by a rotation of 90° about the origin.

● A rotation of 90° about the origin, followed by a reflection across the y-axis.

Ⓓ A reflection across the x-axis, followed by a rotation of 90° about the origin.

PART B

Describe a sequence of transformations that maps △ABC to △QRS.

Sample answer: A reflection across the y-axis, followed by a 90° clockwise rotation about the origin.

76 6-4 Compose Transformations

# Differentiated Intervention

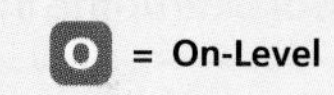 I = Intervention O = On-Level 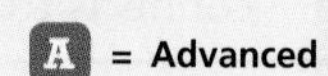 A = Advanced

## Enrichment O A

Presents engaging problems and activities that extend the lesson concepts.

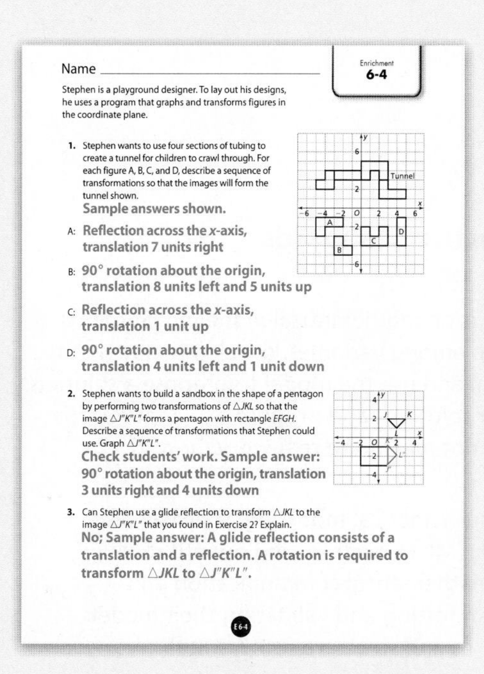

Name

Enrichment 6-4

Stephen is a playground designer. To lay out his designs, he uses a program that graphs and transforms figures in the coordinate plane.

1. Stephen wants to use four sections of tubing to create a tunnel for children to crawl through. For each figure A, B, C, and D, describe a sequence of transformations so that the images will form the tunnel shown.
Sample answers shown.

A: Reflection across the x-axis, translation 7 units right

B: 90° rotation about the origin, translation 8 units left and 5 units up

C: Reflection across the x-axis, translation 1 unit up

D: 90° rotation about the origin, translation 4 units left and 1 unit down

2. Stephen wants to build a sandbox in the shape of a pentagon by performing two transformations of △JKL so that the image △J″K″L″ forms a pentagon with rectangle EFGH. Describe a sequence of transformations that Stephen could use. Graph △J″K″L″.
Check students' work. Sample answer: 90° rotation about the origin, translation 3 units right and 4 units down

3. Can Stephen use a glide reflection to transform △JKL to the image △J″K″L″ that you found in Exercise 2? Explain.
No; Sample answer: A glide reflection consists of a translation and a reflection. A rotation is required to transform △JKL to △J″K″L″.

## Math Tools and Games I O A

Offers additional activities and games to build understanding and fluency.

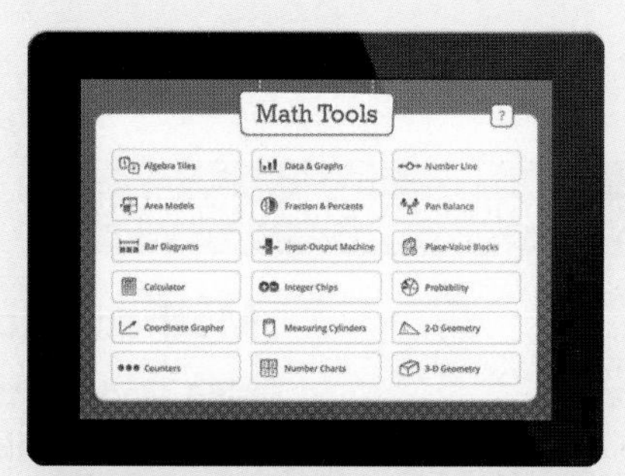


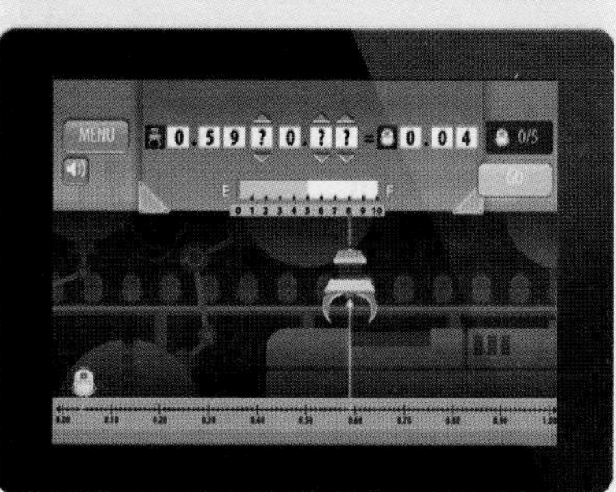


## Pick a Project and STEM Project I O A

Provides an additional opportunity for students to demonstrate understanding of key mathematical concepts.

3-ACT MATH

# 3-Act Mathematical Modeling: Tricks of the Trade

## Lesson Overview

FOCUS

### Mathematics Objective

**Students will be able to:**

- ✔ use mathematical modeling to represent a problem situation and to propose a solution.
- ✔ test and verify the appropriateness of their math models.
- ✔ explain why the results from their mathematical models may not align exactly to the problem situation.

### Essential Understanding

Many real-world problem situations can be represented with a mathematical model, but that model may not represent a real-world situation exactly.

COHERENCE

**Earlier in this topic, students:**

- used translation, reflection, rotation, and compositions of the three to describe transformations.

**In this lesson, students:**

- develop a mathematical model to represent and propose a solution to a problem situation involving rigid transformations.

**Later in this course, students will:**

- refine their mathematical modeling skills.

**Cross-Cluster Connection** Coordinate mapping of transformations (8.G.1) connects to work defining functions (8.F.1).

RIGOR

This mathematical modeling lesson focuses on **application** of both **math content** and **math practices and processes**.

- Students draw on their understanding of geometry concepts to develop a representative model.
- Students apply their mathematical model to test and validate its applicability to similar problem situations.

## Math Anytime

### Today's Challenge

Use the Topic 6 problems any time during this topic.

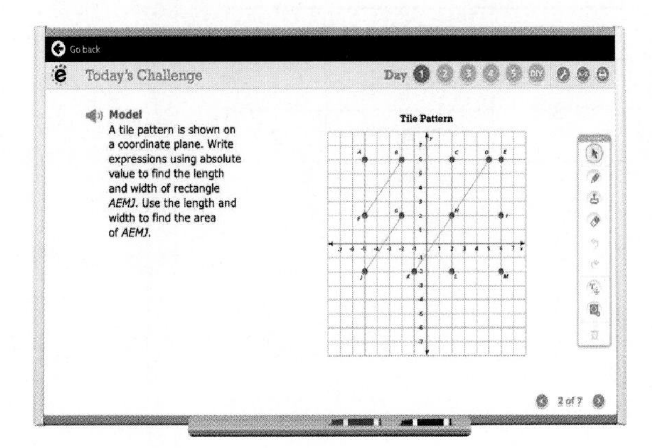


## Mathematics Overview — Common Core Standards

### Content Standards

In this lesson, students apply concepts and skills related to Common Core Standards **8.G.A.1** and **8.G.A.2.**

- **8.G.A.1** Verify experimentally the properties of rotations, reflections, and translations.
- **8.G.A.2** Understand that a two-dimensional figure is congruent to another if the second can be obtained from the first by a sequence of rotations, reflections, and translations; given two congruent figures, describe a sequence that exhibits the congruence between them.

### Mathematical Practice Standards

**MP.4 Model with Math**

The focus of this lesson is on mathematical modeling. Students identify the relationship among variables, develop a model that represents the situation, and use the model to propose a solution. Students interpret their solutions and propose explanations for why their answers may not match the real-world answer.

As students carry out mathematical modeling, they will also engage in sense-making **(MP.1)**, abstract and quantitative reasoning **(MP.2)**, and mathematical communication and argumentation **(MP.3)**. In testing and validating their models, students look for patterns and structure **(MP.7, MP.8)**.

Go Online

Video

# ACT 1 The Hook

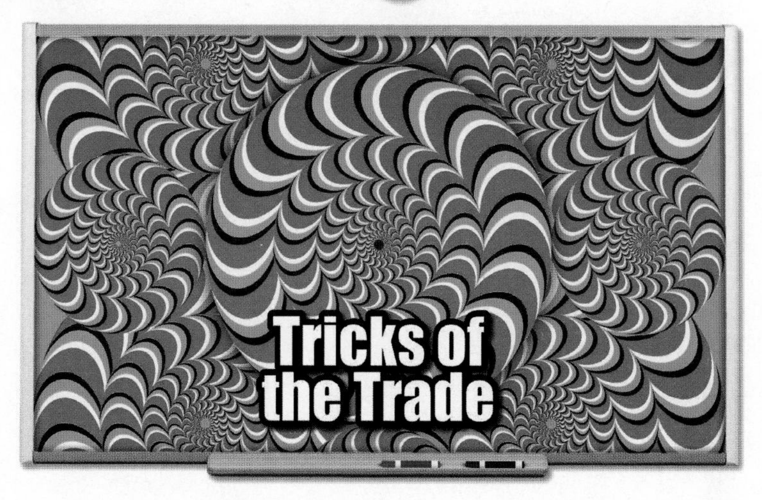


Students will be tasked with determining which shapes in each image are the same and what sameness means.

## Play the Video and Brainstorm Questions

Have students complete Question 1. Encourage them to consider the situation and ask any questions that arise. Listen for interesting mathematical and non-mathematical questions. Ask students what makes each question interesting.

**Q:** What questions do you have? [Sample questions: How were these images made? What kind of pattern is that? Which shape is bigger/darker/longer?]

## Pose the Main Question

After the question brainstorming, pose the Main Question students will be tasked with answering. Have students complete **Question 2**.

**Main Question**

**Q:** In each image, which shapes are the same?

## Ask about Predictions

Have students complete **Questions 3 and 4**. You can survey the class for the range of predictions.

**Q:** Why do you think your prediction is the answer to the Main Question?

**Q:** Who had a similar prediction?

**Q:** How many of you agree with that prediction?

**Q:** Who has a different prediction?

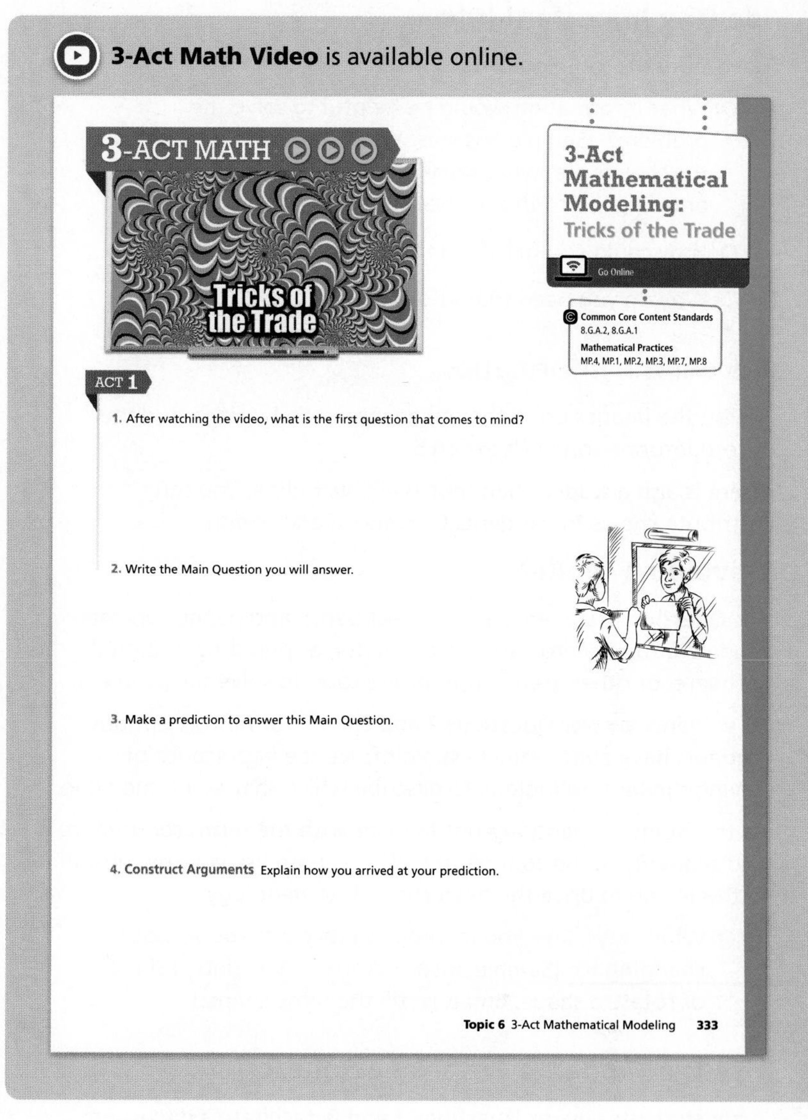

**3-Act Math Video** is available online.

3-ACT MATH

Tricks of the Trade

3-Act Mathematical Modeling: Tricks of the Trade

Go Online

Common Core Content Standards 8.G.A.2, 8.G.A.1
Mathematical Practices MP.4, MP.1, MP.2, MP.3, MP.7, MP.8

ACT 1

1. After watching the video, what is the first question that comes to mind?

2. Write the Main Question you will answer.

3. Make a prediction to answer this Main Question.

4. Construct Arguments Explain how you arrived at your prediction.

Topic 6 3-Act Mathematical Modeling 333

# 3-Act Mathematical Modeling *continued*

## ACT 2 The Model

### Identify Important Info

Have students complete **Questions 5**

**Q:** What information would be helpful to solve the problem? [Sample answers: What the dimensions of the shapes are; what *same* means; whether rotation or reflection counts as the same]

**Q:** How could you get that information?

**Q:** Why do you need that information?

### Reveal the information

Revisit the images using the online interactivity. Have students record information in **Question 5.**

There is also a student handout available online. You can distribute copies for students to draw on and measure.

### Develop a Model

For **Question 6**, students might select pencil and paper, concrete models, a ruler, a protractor, a calculator, a spreadsheet, digital software, or other grade-appropriate tools to solve the problem.

As students answer **Questions 7 and 8**, look for misconceptions students have about sameness. Reinforce the importance of having similar terminology to describe which shapes are the same.

At this point, students are not familiar with the terms *congruence* and *similarity* in the context of math. You can use your discussion in this lesson to drive the need for such terminology.

**Q:** What ways have you learned to move a shape without changing it? [Sample answer: You can translate, reflect, or rotate a shape, and it is still the same shape.]

### Use the Model to Propose a Solution

After students answer **Questions 7 and 8,** facilitate a discussion about solution methods. If needed, project the possible student solutions (shown below).

**3-Act Math Activity** is available online.

ACT 2

5. What information in this situation would be helpful to know? How would you use that information?

6. Use Appropriate Tools What tools can you use to solve the problem? Explain how you would use them strategically.

7. Model with Math Represent the situation using mathematics. Use your representation to answer the Main Question.

8. What is your answer to the Main Question? Does it differ from your prediction? Explain.

334 Topic 6 3-Act Mathematical Modeling

### Possible Student Solutions

**Penny's Work**

Image 1: The two circles in the middle both have the same diameter.

Image 2: The pieces are the same size. I measured the top and bottom arc of each piece.

Image 3: The angles in each shape are 90°, and they all have the same side length. They are all the same square.

Image 4: The squares are all the same size, though some are white and some are gray.

**Penny** uses measurement to decide which shapes are the same size. She explains her reasoning for each image.

**Evan's Work**

Image 1: The large circles on the left are all the same. The small circles on the right are all the same.

Image 2: The roads are the same shape, but the bottom road looks longer.

Image 3: Each row slants to either the left or right. Some shapes are the same size, and some are reflections of others.

Image 4: I covered up all the squares except for A and B, and they are the same.

**Evan** relies on perception for some images and measurement for others. He explains his reasoning for each image.

## ACT 3 The Solution and Sequel

**3-Act Math Video** is available online.

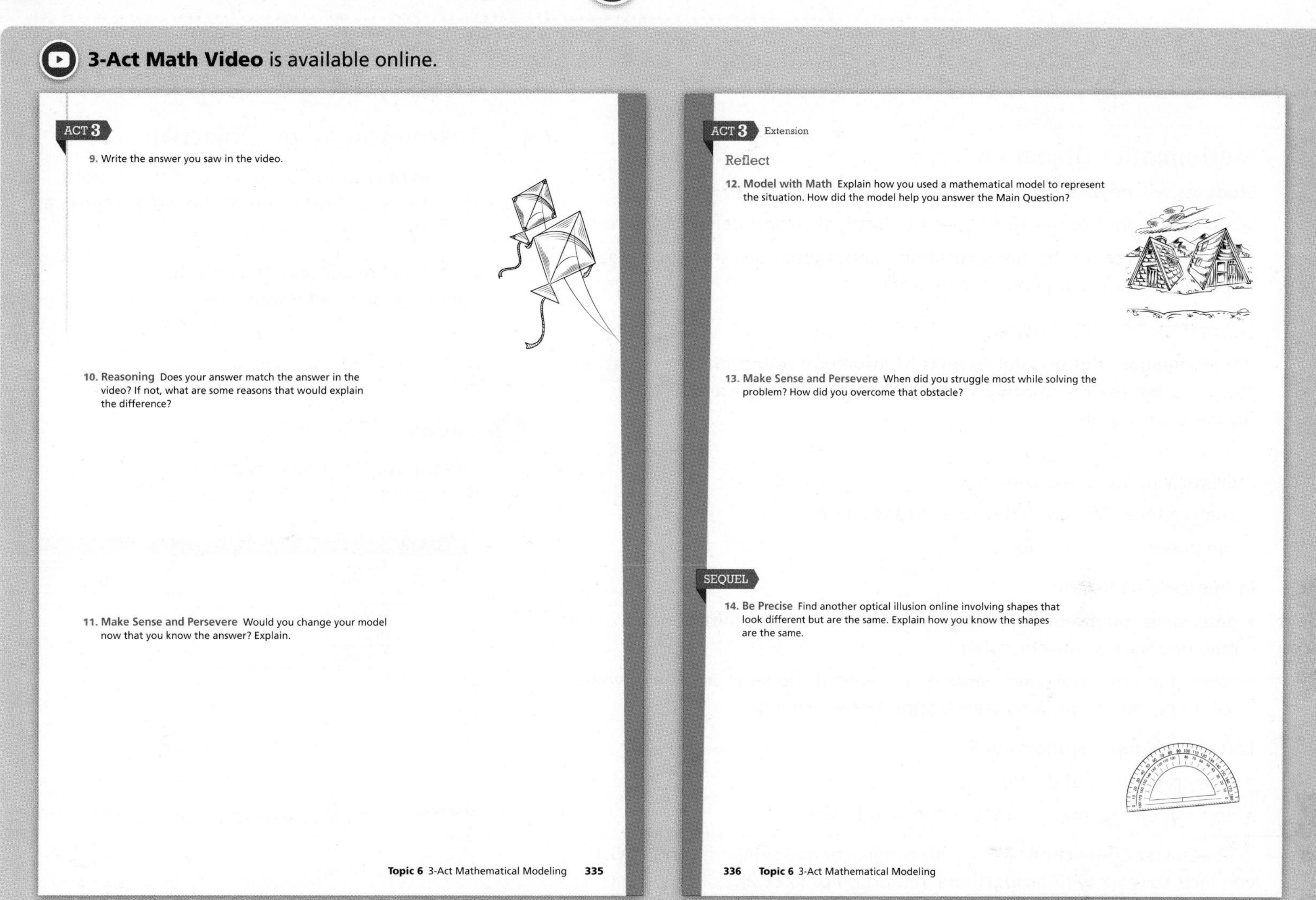

ACT 3

9. Write the answer you saw in the video.

10. Reasoning Does your answer match the answer in the video? If not, what are some reasons that would explain the difference?

11. Make Sense and Persevere Would you change your model now that you know the answer? Explain.

Topic 6 3-Act Mathematical Modeling 335

ACT 3 Extension

Reflect

12. Model with Math Explain how you used a mathematical model to represent the situation. How did the model help you answer the Main Question?

13. Make Sense and Persevere When did you struggle most while solving the problem? How did you overcome that obstacle?

SEQUEL

14. Be Precise Find another optical illusion online involving shapes that look different but are the same. Explain how you know the shapes are the same.

336 Topic 6 3-Act Mathematical Modeling

### Use the Video to Reveal the Answer

The final part of the video shows which images are the same. Have students complete **Question 9**. Congratulate the students who were closest to the actual answer.

#### Main Question Answer

**Image 1: The orange circles are the same.**
**Image 2: The first and third roads are the same.**
**Image 3: All shapes are the same sized square, either white or black.**
**Image 4: Squares A and B are the same color.**

### Validate Conclusions

After students complete **Questions 10 and 11**, discuss possible sources of error. Look for students to point out that their models are still useful even though they are not perfect.

**Q:** Why does your answer not match the answer in the video? [Sample answer: The other objects in the image make the shapes look different. This was true for Images 1 and 4.]

**Q:** How useful was your model at predicting the answer?

**Q:** How could your model better represent the situation?

### Reflect on Thinking

**Make Sense and Persevere** If time allows, have students complete **Questions 12 and 13** as an extension. Use this opportunity to discuss how students incorporate mathematical processes during the task.

### Pose the Sequel

**Be Precise** Use **Question 15** to present a similar problem situation involving transformations. You can assign to early finishers or as homework so students can test the usefulness of their models.

**Q:** Find another optical illusion online involving shapes that look different but are the same. Explain how you know the shapes are the same.

Look for students to choose from a number of optical illusions available online. In most cases, students should use a rigid transformation (or composition of transformations) to describe how they are the same.

Go Online

Activity

Lesson
6-5

# Understand Congruent Figures

## Lesson Overview

FOCUS

### Mathematics Objective

**Students will be able to:**

✔ use a sequence of transformations to justify the congruence of figures.

✔ understand that reflections, rotations, and translations are actions that produce congruent geometric figures.

### Essential Understanding

When a sequence of transformations (translations, reflections, and rotations) maps one figure onto another figure with the same shape and size, the figures are congruent.

COHERENCE

**Previously in this topic, students:**

- analyzed translations, reflections, and rotations.
- composed transformations.

**In this lesson, students:**

- determine congruency by identifying the sequence of transformations that map one figure onto the other.
- understand that the congruence of a geometric figure is preserved when rotations, reflections, and translations are performed.

**Later in this topic, students will:**

- verify properties of dilations.
- perform enlargements and reductions of figures.

**Cross-Cluster Connection** Work with congruent and similar figures (8.G.1) connects to work with proportional relationships (8.EE.2).

RIGOR

This lesson emphasizes a blend of **conceptual understanding** and **procedural skill and fluency**.

- Students extend their understanding of congruent figures.
- Students apply their understanding of translations, reflections, rotations, and sequences of transformations to identify congruent figures.

## Language Support

### Lesson Language Objective

Explain how to use a sequence of translations, reflections, and rotations to show that figures are congruent.

Additional resources are available in the **Language Support Handbook**.

## Math Anytime

### Today's Challenge

Use the Topic 6 problems any time during this topic.

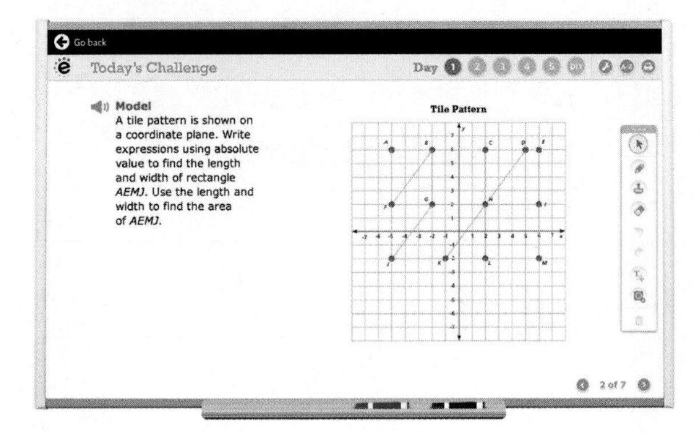


## Mathematics Overview | Common Core Standards

### Content Standards

In this lesson, you will focus on Common Core Standards **8.G.A.2** and **8.G.A.3**.

- **8.G.A.2** Understand that a two-dimensional figure is congruent to another if the second can be obtained from the first by a sequence of rotations, reflections, and translations; given two congruent figures, describe a sequence that exhibits the congruence between them.
- **8.G.A.3** Describe the effect of dilations, translations, rotations, and reflections on two-dimensional figures using coordinates.

### Mathematical Practice Standards

**MP.2 Reason Abstractly and Quantitatively**
Students will use reasoning to determine which transformations are used to map one figure onto a congruent figure.

**MP.7 Look for and Make Use of Structure**
Students will identify rotations, translations, and reflections on a coordinate grid to prove congruency.

Go Online

Activity

15-20 min

STEP 1 | Problem-Based Learning

# Solve & Discuss It!

Formative Assessment

**Purpose** Students describe the transformations required to map one shape onto another and connect it to identifying congruent figures in Example 2.

## ETP Before — WHOLE CLASS

### 1 Introduce the Problem

Provide graph paper, as needed.

### 2 Check for Understanding of the Problem

Engage students with the problem by asking: Have you ever played a game similar to the one shown?

## ETP During — SMALL GROUP

### 3 Observe Students at Work

Students will rotate and translate the blue shape until it maps to the given position. Students need to rotate the shape 180° about its center translate it 2 units left and 4 units down in total, but they could do these steps in different orders. If needed ask, What is the different about the outlined shape compared to the blue shape?

### Early Finishers

How would the problem change if you wanted to fit the blue shape into the whole in the green section, with the top of the blue shape flat? [Sample answer: I could rotate the shape 90° counter-clockwise around the center, then translate to right 2 units and down 4 units.]

## ETP After — WHOLE CLASS

### 4 Discuss Solution Strategies and Key Ideas

Consider having groups who used a reflection and a translation share first, followed by those who used a rotation and a translation, and then groups who used other methods. Have students discuss how a figure might change after undergoing a sequence of transformations; the location of the figure will change unless the sequence returns it to its original position. If the sequence includes a rotation or reflection, the orientation of the figure will change. The size and shape of the figure will not change.

Have students discuss why different sequences of transformations can have the same result; for the blue shape, a rotation of 180° results in the same orientation for the shape as a reflection across a vertical line, and a reflection across a horizontal line has the same result as a vertical translation. Have students discuss whether the blue shape can map onto the dashed shape using just translations; no, because the blue shape and the dashed shape have different orientations, and a translation maintains the orientation of a shape.

### 5 Consider Instructional Implications

After presenting Example 2, refer students back to the problem in the Solve & Discuss It and have them discuss whether the blue shape is congruent to the dashed shape; the shapes are congruent since a sequence of transformations maps one figure onto the other.

## Analyze Student Work

**Solve and Discuss It!** Activity is available online.

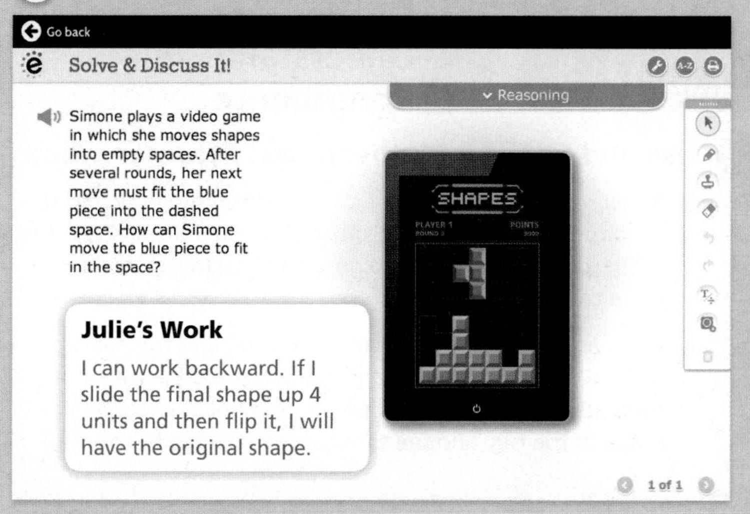


**Julie** uses a visual method and works backward to map the transformations.

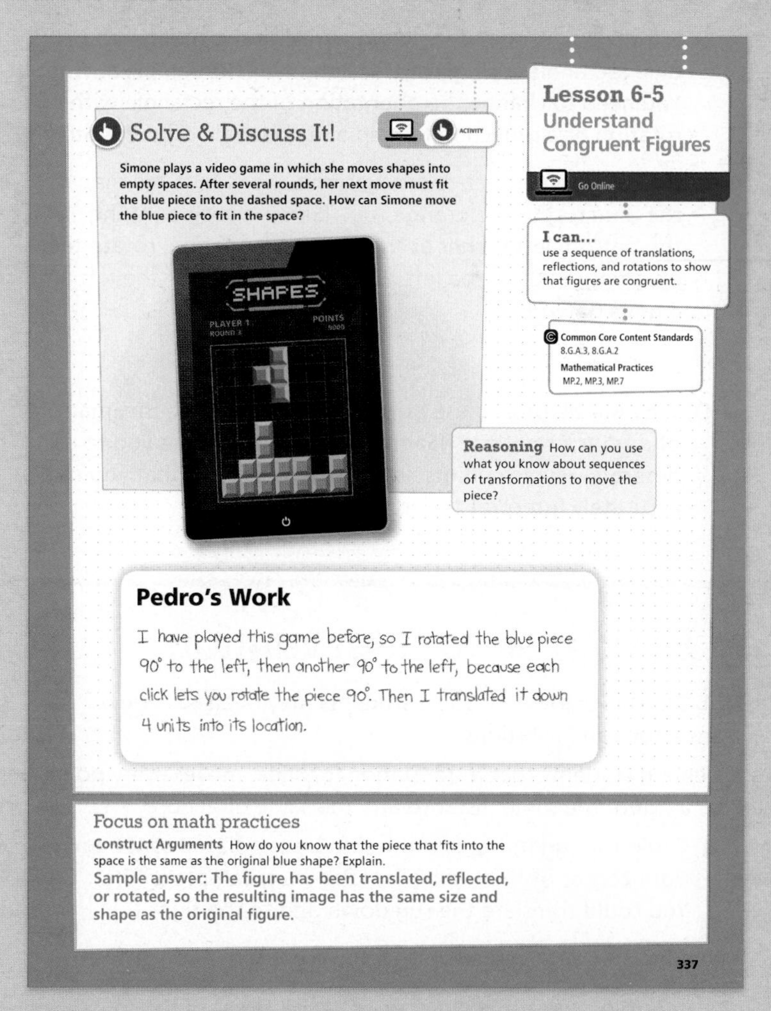


**Pedro** uses prior knowledge of the game and makes a series of rotations and a translation down.

EXPLAIN

## STEP 2 | Visual Learning

Go Online

Visual Learning
Assess

### ETP Establish Mathematics Goals to Focus Learning

Engage students in a discussion about the ***Essential Question***. Make sure they understand that when a rotation, reflection, or translation maps one figure to another, its shape or size do not change. Reflections and rotations can change the orientation of the figure, but translations do not.

## EXAMPLE 1  Understand Congruence

###  Use and Connect Mathematical Representations

**Q:** If Ava reversed the order of the transformations, would the result prove congruence? Explain. [Yes; Sample answer: The living room rug would map onto the hearth rug, making them congruent.]

**Q:** Why can we say that the living room rug and the hearth rug are congruent figures? [Sample answer: Because a translation followed by a rotation does not change the size or shape of the rug, and the sofa rug maps to the hearth rug]

##  Try It!  Formative Assessment

###  Elicit and Use Evidence of Student Thinking

**Q:** Is it possible to show the congruence of the orange and blue rectangles using just translations? [No; Sample answer: You need to change the orientation of the rectangle with a rotation or a reflection to map one rectangle onto the other.]

**Q:** Describe one sequence of transformations that will map the blue rug to the orange rug. [Sample answer: Using the bottom left corner as the center of rotation, rotate the blue figure 90° to the left. Translate it 2 units to the left and 5 units down.]

### Convince Me!

**Q:** Why is it helpful to use prime notation to name the image of a transformation? [Sample answer: It enables you to determine which points are corresponding, so that you can accurately interpret the transformation.]

**Visual Learning Animation Plus** is available online.

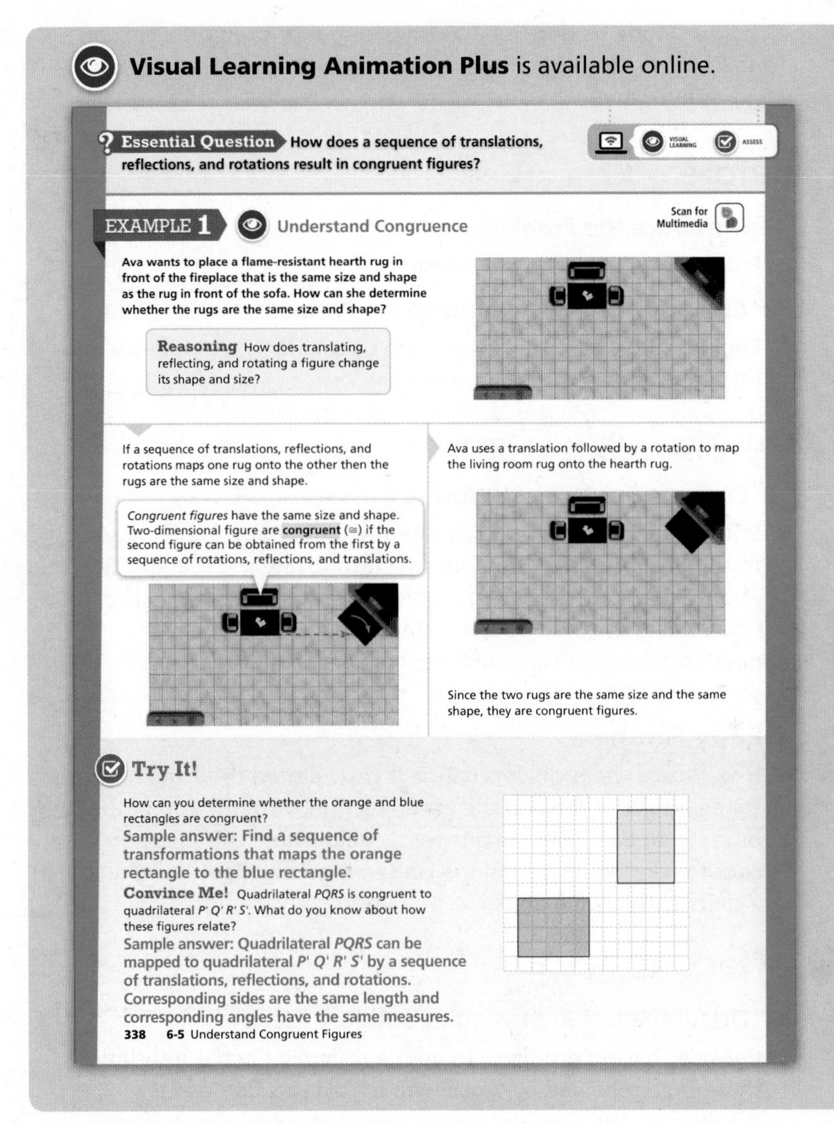

**Essential Question** How does a sequence of translations, reflections, and rotations result in congruent figures?

EXAMPLE 1 Understand Congruence

Scan for Multimedia

Ava wants to place a flame-resistant hearth rug in front of the fireplace that is the same size and shape as the rug in front of the sofa. How can she determine whether the rugs are the same size and shape?

**Reasoning** How does translating, reflecting, and rotating a figure change its shape and size?

If a sequence of translations, reflections, and rotations maps one rug onto the other then the rugs are the same size and shape.

*Congruent figures* have the same size and shape. Two-dimensional figure are **congruent** (≅) if the second figure can be obtained from the first by a sequence of rotations, reflections, and translations.

Ava uses a translation followed by a rotation to map the living room rug onto the hearth rug.

Since the two rugs are the same size and the same shape, they are congruent figures.

**Try It!**

How can you determine whether the orange and blue rectangles are congruent?
Sample answer: Find a sequence of transformations that maps the orange rectangle to the blue rectangle.

**Convince Me!** Quadrilateral *PQRS* is congruent to quadrilateral *P' Q' R' S'*. What do you know about how these figures relate?
Sample answer: Quadrilateral *PQRS* can be mapped to quadrilateral *P' Q' R' S'* by a sequence of translations, reflections, and rotations. Corresponding sides are the same length and corresponding angles have the same measures.

338 6-5 Understand Congruent Figures

 Students can access the ***Visual Learning Animation Plus*** by using the **BouncePages app** to scan this page. Students can download the app for free in their mobile devices' app store.

##  Response to Intervention

**USE WITH EXAMPLE 1** Some students may need to review translations and rotations.

- Remind students that a translation, or slide, moves every point of a figure the same distance and the same direction.

  **Q:** Could the rug in front of the sofa be translated to the lower right corner of the room? Explain. [Yes; Sample answer: You could translate the rug down and to the right.]

- Remind students that a rotation turns a figure about a fixed point.

  **Q:** If you rotate the rug in front of the sofa 90° clockwise, how would its orientation change? [Sample answer: The rug top and bottom edges would be 2 units long and the sides would be 3 units long.]

##  Enrichment

**USE WITH EXAMPLE 1** Reinforce students' use of transformations to determine if the two figures are congruent.

Suppose Ava wants to move the two chairs so that they face the sofa and are on the opposite sides of the rug from the sofa.

**Q:** What sequence of transformations is needed for this move? [Sample answer: Translate both chairs down and then rotate them 90°. Rotate the left chair counterclockwise and the right chair clockwise. Translate the two chairs so they touch.]

**Q:** Are the sofa and the pushed-together chairs congruent figures? Explain. [No; Sample answer: Reflect the pushed-together chairs across a line of reflection halfway between them and the sofa. They will not map exactly, so they are not congruent.]

Go Online

Activity Assess

## EXAMPLE 2  Identify Congruent Figures

### ETP Pose Purposeful Questions

**Q:** In part A, what is the function of the line $x = -1$? [Sample answer: It is the line of reflection.]

**Q:** What is the advantage of using $x = -1$ rather than $x = 0$ as the line of reflection? [Sample answer: If you use $x = 0$, the reflected figure *ABCD* overlaps figure *QRST* making it difficult to see exactly how to translate it.]

**Q:** In part B, how is $\triangle JKL$ transformed from the first step to the second? [Sample answer: $\triangle JKL$ moves 1 unit left and 1 unit up.]

**Q:** How does this sequence of transformations show that the triangles are not congruent? [Sample answer: The sides do not have the same lengths, so the triangles are not congruent.]

##  Try It!  Formative Assessment

###  Elicit and Use Evidence of Student Thinking

**Q:** Before you can map Figure 1 onto Figure 2, what do you need to decide? Explain. [Sample answer: You need to decide which vertices correspond. You can match up the 2-unit sides of the figures and then look at the adjacent sides and angles to identify the remaining corresponding sides.]

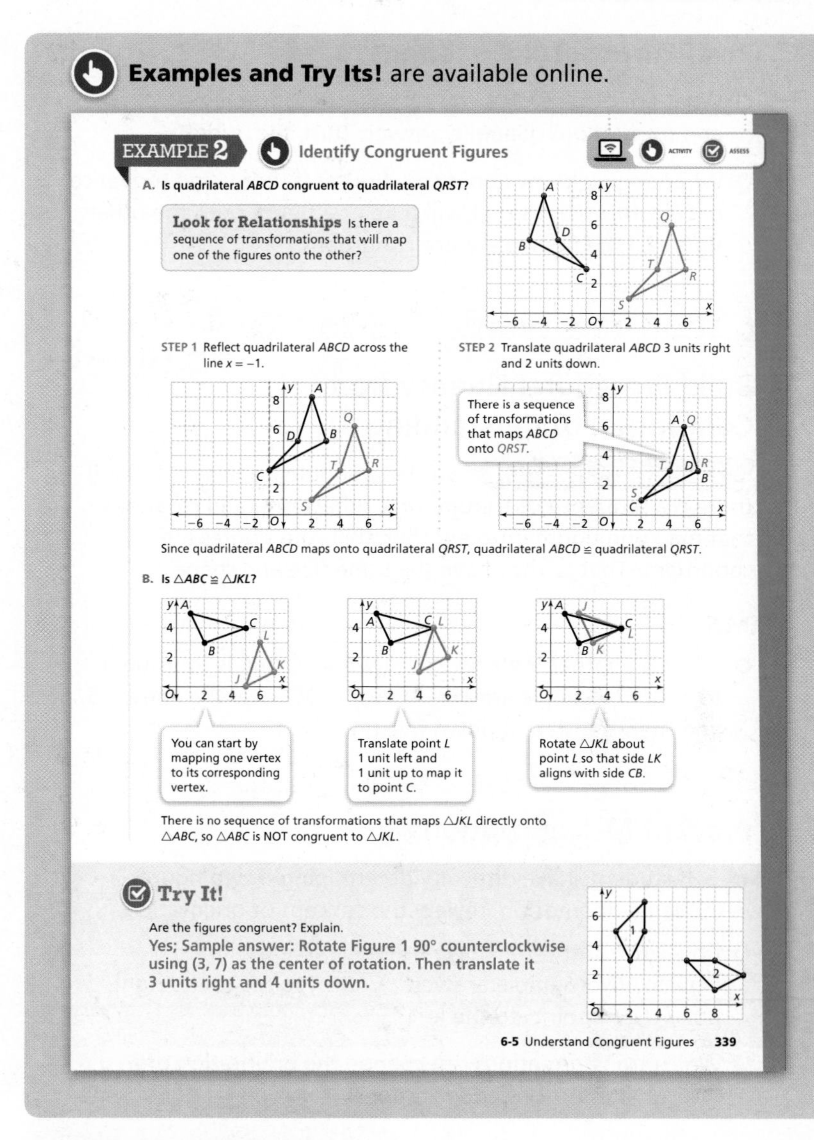

**Examples and Try Its!** are available online.

EXAMPLE 2 Identify Congruent Figures

ACTIVITY ASSESS

A. Is quadrilateral *ABCD* congruent to quadrilateral *QRST*?

**Look for Relationships** Is there a sequence of transformations that will map one of the figures onto the other?

STEP 1 Reflect quadrilateral *ABCD* across the line $x = -1$.

STEP 2 Translate quadrilateral *ABCD* 3 units right and 2 units down.

There is a sequence of transformations that maps *ABCD* onto *QRST*.

Since quadrilateral *ABCD* maps onto quadrilateral *QRST*, quadrilateral $ABCD \cong$ quadrilateral *QRST*.

B. Is $\triangle ABC \cong \triangle JKL$?

You can start by mapping one vertex to its corresponding vertex.

Translate point *L* 1 unit left and 1 unit up to map it to point *C*.

Rotate $\triangle JKL$ about point *L* so that side *LK* aligns with side *CB*.

There is no sequence of transformations that maps $\triangle JKL$ directly onto $\triangle ABC$, so $\triangle ABC$ is NOT congruent to $\triangle JKL$.

Try It!

Are the figures congruent? Explain.

Yes; Sample answer: Rotate Figure 1 90° counterclockwise using (3, 7) as the center of rotation. Then translate it 3 units right and 4 units down.

6-5 Understand Congruent Figures 339

## ADDITIONAL EXAMPLES 

**For additional examples go online.**

## ELL English Language Learners

**ENTERING** Use with Example 1.

Display the term *congruent*. Have students look at the two rectangles in the Example 1 Try It! Count the side lengths to show that they are the same.

**Q:** Are the rectangles the same *size*? Why? [Yes. The side lengths are the same.]

**Q:** Are the rectangles the same *shape*? Explain. [Yes. The figures are rectangles.]

**Q:** Are the rectangles *congruent*? Explain. [Yes. The figures are the same size and the same shape.]

**DEVELOPING** Use with Example 2.

Direct students' attention to the last figure in Example 2, part A.

**Q:** Are quadrilaterals *ABCD* and *QRST* *congruent*? Explain. [Yes. The figures are the same size and the same shape. They *map* so one figure is on top of the other figure.]

Direct students' attention to the last figure in Example 2, part B.

**Q:** Are $\triangle ABC$ and $\triangle JKL$ *congruent*? Explain. [No; Only one side length is the same.]

**EXPANDING** Use with Example 1.

Have students work with a partner or in small groups to make a list of words in the example that they might not know, and write their definitions. The list might include: *fireplace*, *flame-resistant*, *hearth*, *sofa*, and *obtained*.

Ask each student to choose three of the words and use them in a written sentence. The student's partner or group members will evaluate whether the words are used correctly. Students should edit their sentences as needed, and volunteers can share their sentences with the whole group.

Go Online

Key Concept

Assess

Activity

# KEY CONCEPT

## ETP Pose Purposeful Questions

**Q:** What are other words you can use for *rotation*, *reflection*, and *translation*? [Sample answer: Turn, flip, slide]

**Q:** What do you know about two figures if there is no sequence of transformations that will map one figure onto the other figure? [The figures are not congruent.]

Available Online

KEY CONCEPT

Two-dimensional figures are congruent if there is a sequence of translations, reflections, and rotations that maps one figure onto the other.

The rectangles are congruent. They have the same size and shape.

When comparing two-dimensional figures, the order of the corresponding points in the name of each figure must be the same. Quadrilateral *ABCD* is congruent to quadrilateral *EFGH*.

**Do You Understand?**

1. **Essential Question** How does a sequence of translations, reflections, and rotations result in congruent figures?
Sample answer: A sequence of translations, reflections, and rotations maps one figure onto another without changing its shape or size.

2. **Reasoning** Does a sequence of transformations have to include a translation, a reflection, and a rotation to result in congruent figures? Explain.
No; Sample answer: The sequence of transformations just needs to include one or more of these transformations.

3. **Construct Arguments** Is there a sequence of reflections, rotations, and translations that makes the preimage and image not only congruent, but identical in orientation? Explain.
Yes; Sample answer: If you use only rotations and translations, the orientation will be maintained. Only a reflection would change the orientation.

**Do You Know How?**

4. A rectangle with an area of 25 square centimeters is rotated and reflected in the coordinate plane. What will be the area of the resulting image? Explain.
25 $cm^2$; Sample answer: The resulting image will have the same area because rotations and reflections do not change the size or shape of a figure.

In 5 and 6, use the coordinate grid below.

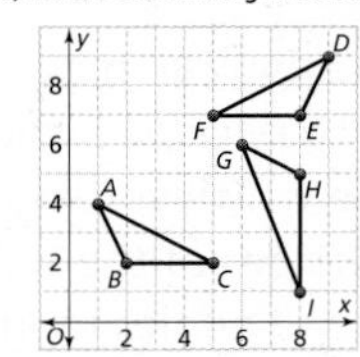

5. Is $\triangle ABC \cong \triangle DEF$? Explain.
Yes; Sample answer: You can map $\triangle ABC$ onto $\triangle DEF$ by reflecting $\triangle ABC$ across the line $x = 5$ and then translating 5 units up.

6. Is $\triangle ABC \cong \triangle GHI$? Explain.
No; Sample answer: You cannot map $\triangle ABC$ onto $\triangle GHI$ by a sequence of translations, reflections, and rotations.

340 6-5 Understand Congruent Figures

# Do You Understand/Do You Know How?

Formative Assessment

## ETP Build Procedural Fluency from Conceptual Understanding

**Essential Question** Students should understand that if there is a sequence of translations, reflections, and rotations that map one figure onto another, then the figures are congruent. That is, they have the same size and shape.

**ITEM 5**

**Q:** What is another method to show that $\triangle ABC$ is congruent to $\triangle DEF$? [Sample answer: Reflect $\triangle DEF$ over the line $x = 5$, and then translate it down five units.]

## Prevent Misconceptions

**ITEM 5** If students have difficulty determining if two figures have the same orientation, review the concept of orientation.

**Q:** Do $\triangle ABC$ and $\triangle DEF$ have the same orientation? Explain. [No; Sample answer: $\triangle ABC$ "points to the right," but $\triangle DEF$ "points to the left."]

**Q:** Which transformations can change the orientation of a figure? [Reflections and rotations]

# ADDITIONAL EXAMPLE 2

Help students understand that often there is more than one sequence of translations that will map one figure onto another to prove congruency.

**Q:** Is there a sequence of rotations that includes a reflection that will prove that the two triangles are congruent? Explain. [Yes; Sample answer: Translate $\triangle ABC$ 7 units left. Rotate it 90 degrees clockwise so that side *AB* is parallel to side *KJ* of $\triangle JKL$. Reflect $\triangle ABC$ across the line $y = -2$.]

**Q:** Suppose $\triangle JKL$ is reflected across the line $y = -3.5$. What one transformation could prove that the triangles are congruent? [Sample answer: A 90° counterclockwise rotation]

**Additional Examples** are available online.

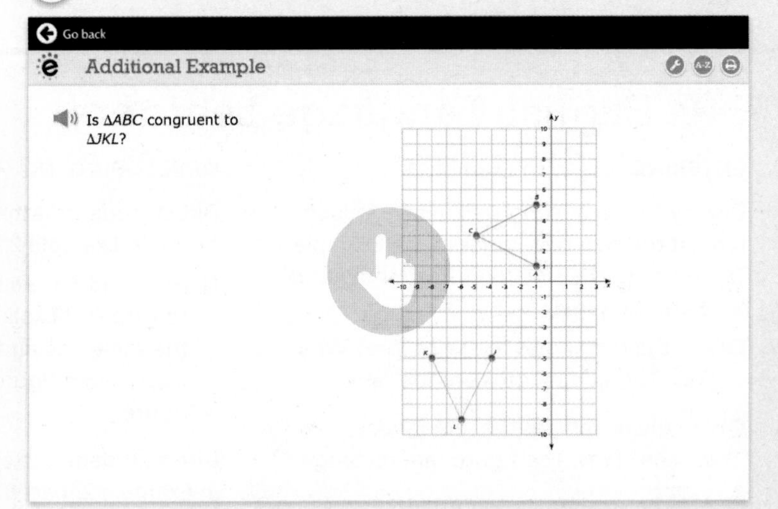


**Answer:** Yes; The figures are the same size and the same shape.

Go Online

Practice Tutorials Math Tools

# Practice & Problem Solving  

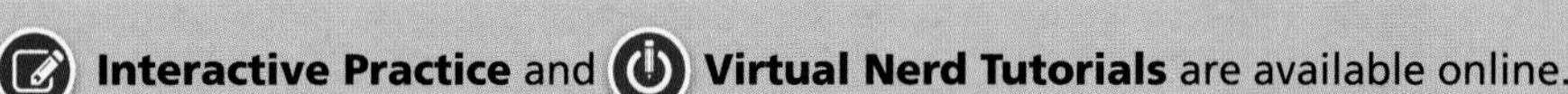

**Interactive Practice** and **Virtual Nerd Tutorials** are available online.

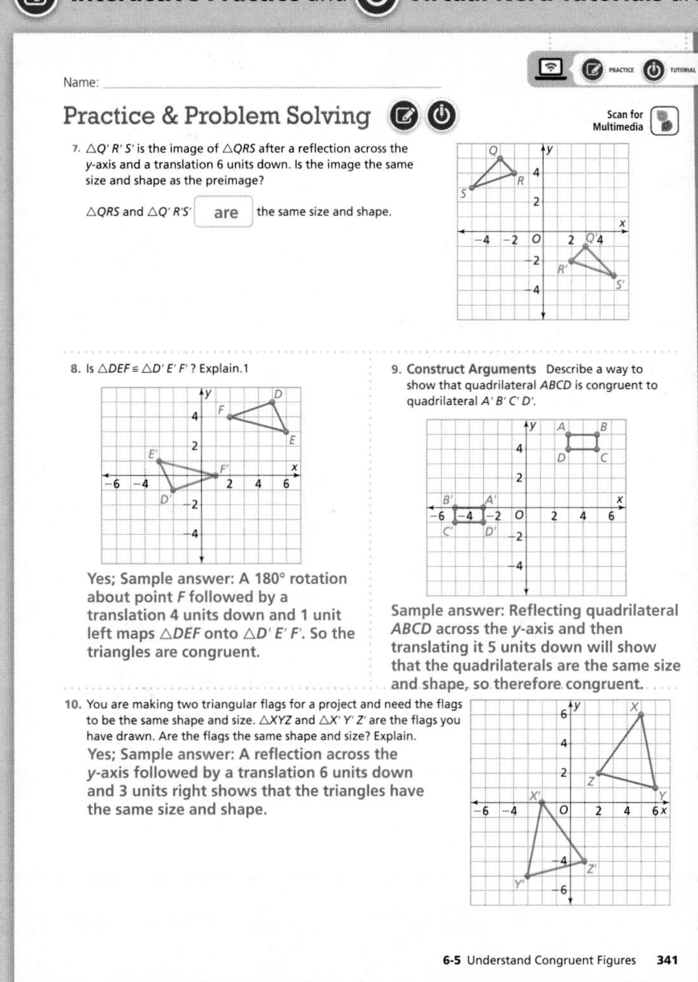

Name:

Practice & Problem Solving

Scan for Multimedia

7. △Q′R′S′ is the image of △QRS after a reflection across the y-axis and a translation 6 units down. Is the image the same size and shape as the preimage?

△QRS and △Q′R′S′ **are** the same size and shape.

8. Is △DEF ≅ △D′E′F′? Explain.

**Yes; Sample answer: A 180° rotation about point F followed by a translation 4 units down and 1 unit left maps △DEF onto △D′E′F′. So the triangles are congruent.**

9. **Construct Arguments** Describe a way to show that quadrilateral ABCD is congruent to quadrilateral A′B′C′D′.

**Sample answer: Reflecting quadrilateral ABCD across the y-axis and then translating it 5 units down will show that the quadrilaterals are the same size and shape, so therefore congruent.**

10. You are making two triangular flags for a project and need the flags to be the same shape and size. △XYZ and △X′Y′Z′ are the flags you have drawn. Are the flags the same shape and size? Explain.

**Yes; Sample answer: A reflection across the y-axis followed by a translation 6 units down and 3 units right shows that the triangles have the same size and shape.**

6-5 Understand Congruent Figures 341

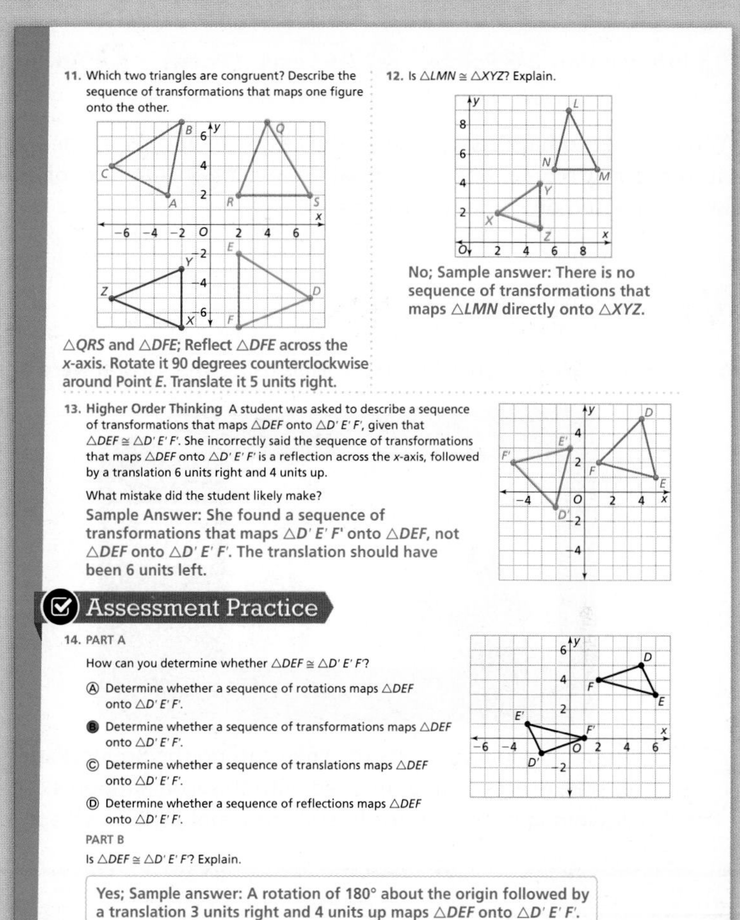

11. Which two triangles are congruent? Describe the sequence of transformations that maps one figure onto the other.

**△QRS and △DFE; Reflect △DFE across the x-axis. Rotate it 90 degrees counterclockwise around Point E. Translate it 5 units right.**

12. Is △LMN ≅ △XYZ? Explain.

**No; Sample answer: There is no sequence of transformations that maps △LMN directly onto △XYZ.**

13. **Higher Order Thinking** A student was asked to describe a sequence of transformations that maps △DEF onto △D′E′F′, given that △DEF ≅ △D′E′F′. She incorrectly said the sequence of transformations that maps △DEF onto △D′E′F′ is a reflection across the x-axis, followed by a translation 6 units right and 4 units up.

What mistake did the student likely make?

**Sample Answer: She found a sequence of transformations that maps △D′E′F′ onto △DEF, not △DEF onto △D′E′F′. The translation should have been 6 units left.**

Assessment Practice

14. PART A

How can you determine whether △DEF ≅ △D′E′F′?

Ⓐ Determine whether a sequence of rotations maps △DEF onto △D′E′F′.

● Determine whether a sequence of transformations maps △DEF onto △D′E′F′.

Ⓒ Determine whether a sequence of translations maps △DEF onto △D′E′F′.

Ⓓ Determine whether a sequence of reflections maps △DEF onto △D′E′F′.

PART B

Is △DEF ≅ △D′E′F′? Explain.

**Yes; Sample answer: A rotation of 180° about the origin followed by a translation 3 units right and 4 units up maps △DEF onto △D′E′F′.**

342 6-5 Understand Congruent Figures

## Error Intervention

**ITEM 12** Some students may see that side *MN* is equal to side *YZ* and think that the figures are congruent. Help them remember that to prove congruency they must map one figure onto the other.

**Q:** If △*XYZ* is rotated so side *YZ* is parallel to side *MN*, what do you notice about the sides of the two triangles? [Sample answer: The parallel sides both measure 3 units. The other corresponding sides do not appear to be equal.]

## Challenge

**ITEM 13 Higher Order Thinking** Reinforce students' understanding of transformations.

Instruct students to draw a figure with a different orientation that is congruent to △*DEF* and its image. List the coordinates of the vertices of the triangle and describe how you can map it to both of the other figures. [Check students' work.]

You may opt to have students complete the automatically scored Practice & Problem Solving items online.

### Item Analysis

| Example | Items | DOK |
|---|---|---|
| 1 | 7 | 1 |
| | 9, 10, 14 | 2 |
| 2 | 8, 12 | 2 |
| | 11, 13 | 3 |

## STEP 3 | Assess & Differentiate

Go Online

Assess

Tutorials

Worksheets

# Lesson Quiz

Formative Assessment

Use the student scores on the Lesson Quiz to prescribe differentiated assignments.

**I Intervention** 0–3 Points   **O On-Level** 4 Points   **A Advanced** 5 Points

You may opt to have students take the Lesson Quiz online. The Lesson Quiz will be automatically scored, and appropriate remediation, practice, or enrichment will be assigned based on student performance.

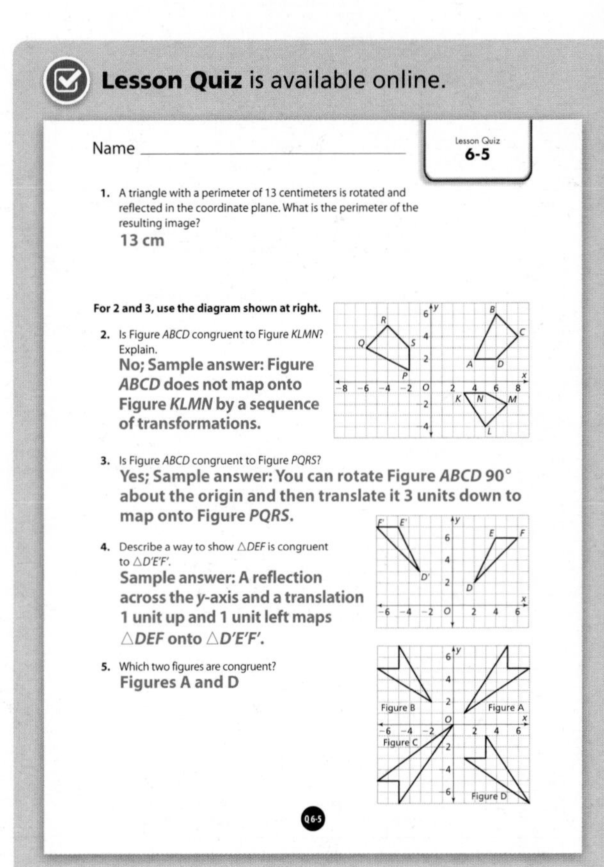

**Lesson Quiz** is available online.

Name ____________  Lesson Quiz 6-5

1. A triangle with a perimeter of 13 centimeters is rotated and reflected in the coordinate plane. What is the perimeter of the resulting image?
   **13 cm**

**For 2 and 3, use the diagram shown at right.**

2. Is Figure *ABCD* congruent to Figure *KLMN*? Explain.
   **No; Sample answer: Figure *ABCD* does not map onto Figure *KLMN* by a sequence of transformations.**
3. Is Figure *ABCD* congruent to Figure *PQRS*?
   **Yes; Sample answer: You can rotate Figure *ABCD* 90° about the origin and then translate it 3 units down to map onto Figure *PQRS*.**
4. Describe a way to show $\triangle DEF$ is congruent to $\triangle D'E'F'$.
   **Sample answer: A reflection across the *y*-axis and a translation 1 unit up and 1 unit left maps $\triangle DEF$ onto $\triangle D'E'F'$.**
5. Which two figures are congruent?
   **Figures A and D**

Q6-5

# Video Tutorials

Students can access instructional tutorials using the **Virtual Nerd app**.

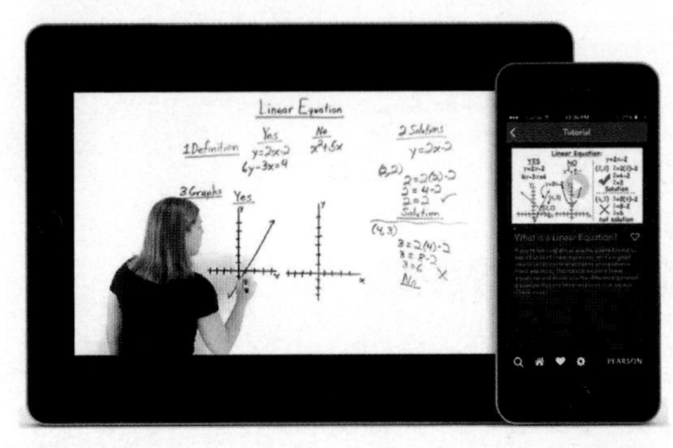

Students can also access the videos using the **BouncePages app** to scan exercise pages marked with this icon. Students can download both apps for free in their mobile devices' app store.

# Differentiated Intervention

**I** = Intervention   **O** = On-Level   **A** = Advanced

### Reteach to Build Understanding I

Provides scaffolded reteaching for the key lesson concepts.

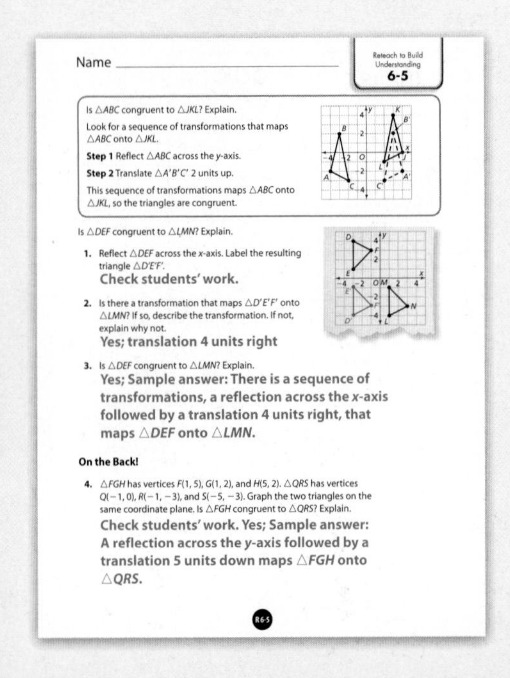

Name ____________  Reteach to Build Understanding 6-5

Is $\triangle ABC$ congruent to $\triangle JKL$? Explain.

Look for a sequence of transformations that maps $\triangle ABC$ onto $\triangle JKL$.

**Step 1** Reflect $\triangle ABC$ across the *y*-axis.

**Step 2** Translate $\triangle A'B'C'$ 2 units up.

This sequence of transformations maps $\triangle ABC$ onto $\triangle JKL$, so the triangles are congruent.

Is $\triangle DEF$ congruent to $\triangle LMN$? Explain.

1. Reflect $\triangle DEF$ across the *x*-axis. Label the resulting triangle $\triangle D'E'F'$.
   **Check students' work.**
2. Is there a transformation that maps $\triangle D'E'F'$ onto $\triangle LMN$? If so, describe the transformation. If not, explain why not.
   **Yes; translation 4 units right**
3. Is $\triangle DEF$ congruent to $\triangle LMN$? Explain.
   **Yes; Sample answer: There is a sequence of transformations, a reflection across the *x*-axis followed by a translation 4 units right, that maps $\triangle DEF$ onto $\triangle LMN$.**

**On the Back!**

4. $\triangle FGH$ has vertices $F(1, 5)$, $G(1, 2)$, and $H(5, 2)$. $\triangle QRS$ has vertices $Q(-1, 0)$, $R(-1, -3)$, and $S(-5, -3)$. Graph the two triangles on the same coordinate plane. Is $\triangle FGH$ congruent to $\triangle QRS$? Explain.
   **Check students' work. Yes; Sample answer: A reflection across the *y*-axis followed by a translation 5 units down maps $\triangle FGH$ onto $\triangle QRS$.**

R6-5

### Additional Vocabulary Support I O

Helps students develop and reinforce understanding of key terms and concepts.

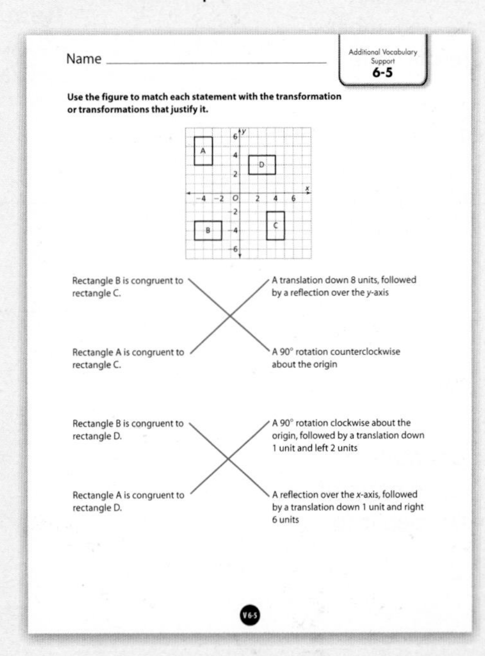

Name ____________  Additional Vocabulary Support 6-5

**Use the figure to match each statement with the transformation or transformations that justify it.**

Rectangle B is congruent to rectangle C. — A 90° rotation counterclockwise about the origin

Rectangle A is congruent to rectangle C. — A translation down 8 units, followed by a reflection over the *y*-axis

Rectangle B is congruent to rectangle D. — A reflection over the *x*-axis, followed by a translation down 1 unit and right 6 units

Rectangle A is congruent to rectangle D. — A 90° rotation clockwise about the origin, followed by a translation down 1 unit and left 2 units

V6-5

### Build Mathematical Literacy I O

Provides support for struggling readers to build mathematical literacy.

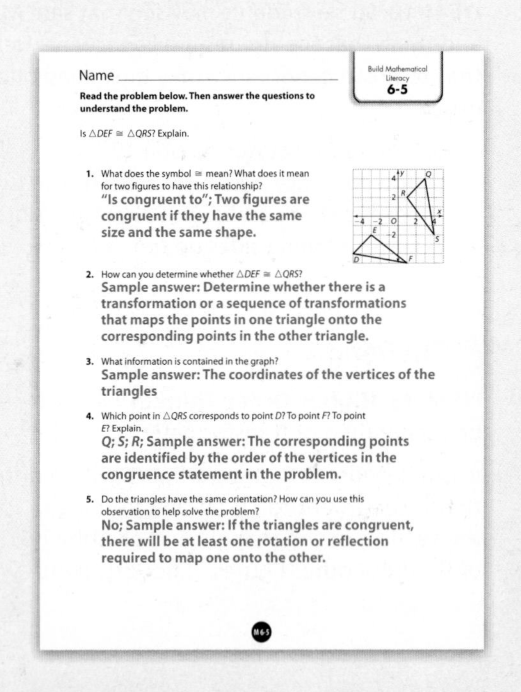

Name ____________  Build Mathematical Literacy 6-5

**Read the problem below. Then answer the questions to understand the problem.**

Is $\triangle DEF \cong \triangle QRS$? Explain.

1. What does the symbol $\cong$ mean? What does it mean for two figures to have this relationship?
   **"Is congruent to"; Two figures are congruent if they have the same size and the same shape.**
2. How can you determine whether $\triangle DEF \cong \triangle QRS$?
   **Sample answer: Determine whether there is a transformation or a sequence of transformations that maps the points in one triangle onto the corresponding points in the other triangle.**
3. What information is contained in the graph?
   **Sample answer: The coordinates of the vertices of the triangles**
4. Which point in $\triangle QRS$ corresponds to point *D*? To point *F*? To point *E*? Explain.
   ***Q*; *S*; *R*; Sample answer: The corresponding points are identified by the order of the vertices in the congruence statement in the problem.**
5. Do the triangles have the same orientation? How can you use this observation to help solve the problem?
   **No; Sample answer: If the triangles are congruent, there will be at least one rotation or reflection required to map one onto the other.**

M6-5

Go Online

Practice

Worksheets

Math Tools

Math Games

# Additional Practice

You may opt to have students complete the automatically scored Additional Practice items online.

### Item Analysis

| Example | Items | DOK |
|---|---|---|
| 1 | 1 | 1 |
| | 4, 5, 8A | 2 |
| 2 | 3, 6, 8B | 2 |
| | 2, 7 | 3 |

**Interactive Practice** is available online.

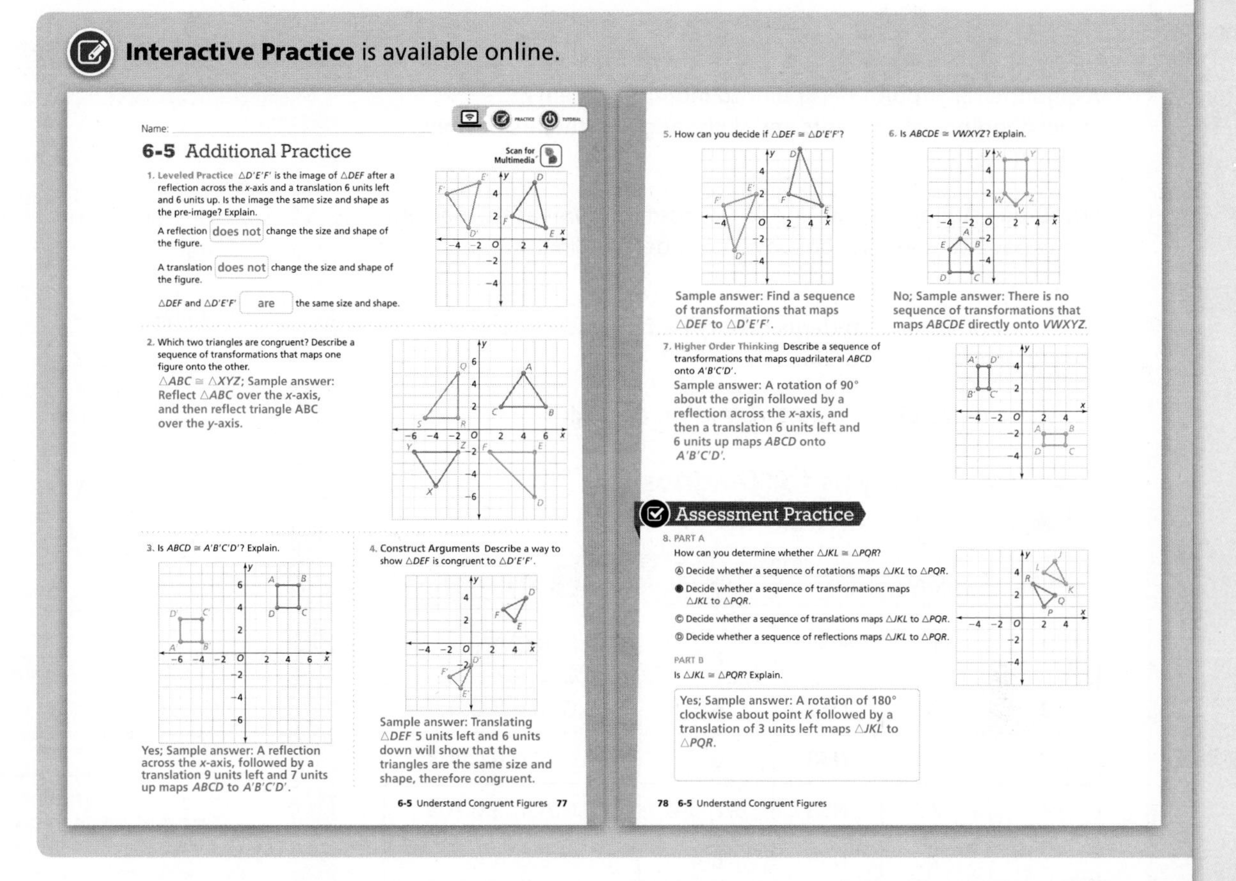

Name:

6-5 Additional Practice

Scan for Multimedia

1. Leveled Practice $\triangle D'E'F'$ is the image of $\triangle DEF$ after a reflection across the $x$-axis and a translation 6 units left and 6 units up. Is the image the same size and shape as the pre-image? Explain.

A reflection does not change the size and shape of the figure.

A translation does not change the size and shape of the figure.

$\triangle DEF$ and $\triangle D'E'F'$ are the same size and shape.

2. Which two triangles are congruent? Describe a sequence of transformations that maps one figure onto the other.

$\triangle ABC \cong \triangle XYZ$; Sample answer: Reflect $\triangle ABC$ over the $x$-axis, and then reflect triangle ABC over the $y$-axis.

3. Is $ABCD \cong A'B'C'D'$? Explain.

Yes; Sample answer: A reflection across the $x$-axis, followed by a translation 9 units left and 7 units up maps $ABCD$ to $A'B'C'D'$.

4. Construct Arguments Describe a way to show $\triangle DEF$ is congruent to $\triangle D'E'F'$.

Sample answer: Translating $\triangle DEF$ 5 units left and 6 units down will show that the triangles are the same size and shape, therefore congruent.

6-5 Understand Congruent Figures 77

5. How can you decide if $\triangle DEF \cong \triangle D'E'F'$?

Sample answer: Find a sequence of transformations that maps $\triangle DEF$ to $\triangle D'E'F'$.

6. Is $ABCDE \cong VWXYZ$? Explain.

No; Sample answer: There is no sequence of transformations that maps $ABCDE$ directly onto $VWXYZ$.

7. Higher Order Thinking Describe a sequence of transformations that maps quadrilateral $ABCD$ onto $A'B'C'D'$.

Sample answer: A rotation of 90° about the origin followed by a reflection across the $x$-axis, and then a translation 6 units left and 6 units up maps $ABCD$ onto $A'B'C'D'$.

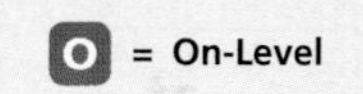
Assessment Practice

8. PART A

How can you determine whether $\triangle JKL \cong \triangle PQR$?

Ⓐ Decide whether a sequence of rotations maps $\triangle JKL$ to $\triangle PQR$.

● Decide whether a sequence of transformations maps $\triangle JKL$ to $\triangle PQR$.

Ⓒ Decide whether a sequence of translations maps $\triangle JKL$ to $\triangle PQR$.

Ⓓ Decide whether a sequence of reflections maps $\triangle JKL$ to $\triangle PQR$.

PART B

Is $\triangle JKL \cong \triangle PQR$? Explain.

Yes; Sample answer: A rotation of 180° clockwise about point $K$ followed by a translation of 3 units left maps $\triangle JKL$ to $\triangle PQR$.

78 6-5 Understand Congruent Figures

# Differentiated Intervention

I = Intervention   O = On-Level   A = Advanced

## Enrichment O A

Presents engaging problems and activities that extend the lesson concepts.

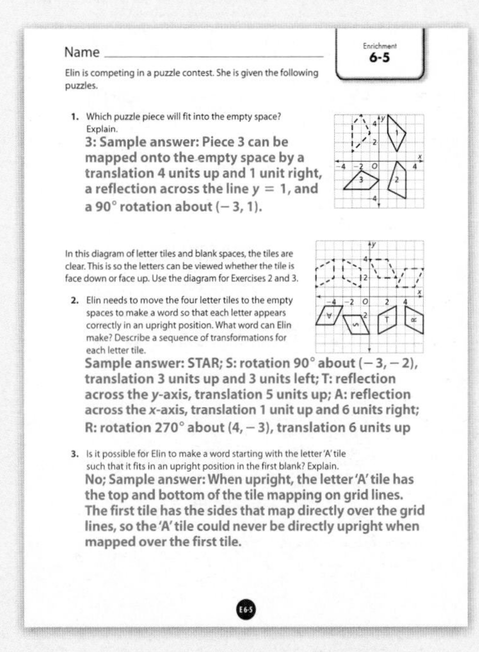

Name

Enrichment 6-5

Elin is competing in a puzzle contest. She is given the following puzzles.

1. Which puzzle piece will fit into the empty space? Explain.

3: Sample answer: Piece 3 can be mapped onto the empty space by a translation 4 units up and 1 unit right, a reflection across the line $y = 1$, and a 90° rotation about $(-3, 1)$.

In this diagram of letter tiles and blank spaces, the tiles are clear. This is so the letters can be viewed whether the tile is face down or face up. Use the diagram for Exercises 2 and 3.

2. Elin needs to move the four letter tiles to the empty spaces to make a word so that each letter appears correctly in an upright position. What word can Elin make? Describe a sequence of transformations for each letter tile.

Sample answer: STAR; S: rotation 90° about $(-3, -2)$, translation 3 units up and 3 units left; T: reflection across the $y$-axis, translation 5 units up; A: reflection across the $x$-axis, translation 1 unit up and 6 units right; R: rotation 270° about $(4, -3)$, translation 6 units up

3. Is it possible for Elin to make a word starting with the letter 'A' tile such that it fits in an upright position in the first blank? Explain.

No; Sample answer: When upright, the letter 'A' tile has the top and bottom of the tile mapping on grid lines. The first tile has the sides that map directly over the grid lines, so the 'A' tile could never be directly upright when mapped over the first tile.

E6-5

## Math Tools and Games I O A

Offers additional activities and games to build understanding and fluency.

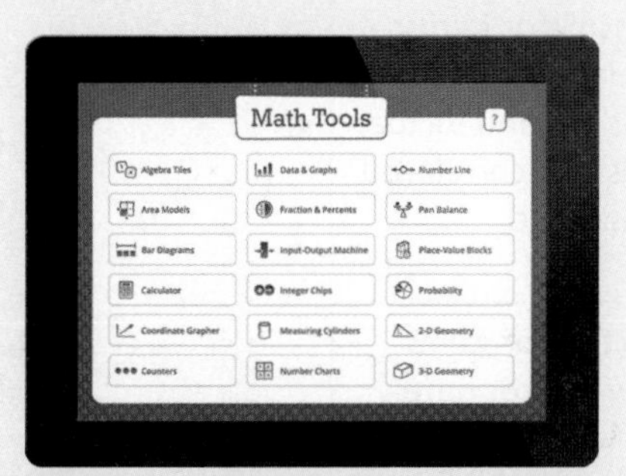


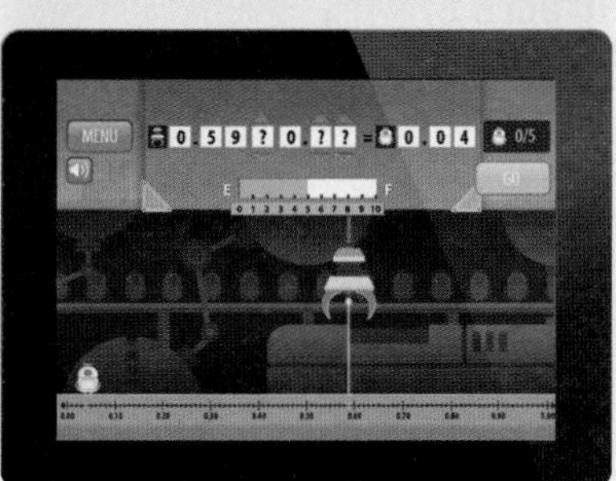


## Pick a Project and STEM Project I O A

Provides an additional opportunity for students to demonstrate understanding of key mathematical concepts.

# MID-TOPIC CHECKPOINT

Go Online

Assess

Assign the Mid-Topic Checkpoint to monitor students' understandings of concepts and skills taught in the first lessons in this topic.

Encourage students to use the self-assessment form at the bottom of the page to describe their level of understanding.

You may opt to have students take the automatically-scored Mid-Topic Assessment online.

Use students' results to adjust instruction as needed.

## Item Analysis for Diagnosis and Intervention

| Item | DOK | MDIS | Lesson | Standard |
|---|---|---|---|---|
| 1 | 1 | N58 | 6-1, 6-2, 6-3 | 8.G.A.1 |
| 2 | 2 | N58 | 6-3 | 8.G.A.1, 8.G.A.3 |
| 3 | 2 | N58 | 6-1 | 8.G.A.1, 8.G.A.3 |
| 4 | 2 | N58 | 6-2, 6-4 | 8.G.A.1, 8.G.A.3 |
| 5 | 2 | N59 | 6-4 | 8.G.A.2 |
| 6 | 3 | N59, N60 | 6-5 | 8.G.A.2, 8.G.A.3 |

## Scoring Guide

| Score | Recommendations |
|---|---|
| Greater Than 85% | Assign the corresponding MDIS for items answered incorrectly. Use Enrichment activities with the student. |
| 70%–85% | Assign the corresponding MDIS for items answered incorrectly. You may also assign Reteach to Build Understanding and Virtual Nerd Video assets for the lessons correlated to the items the student answered incorrectly. |
| Less Than 70% | Assign the corresponding MDIS for items answered incorrectly. Assign appropriate intervention lessons available online. You may also assign Reteach to Build Understanding, Additional Vocabulary Support, Build Mathematical Literacy, and Virtual Nerd Video assets for the lessons correlated to the items the student answered incorrectly. |

**Available Online**

Name:

TOPIC 6 MID-TOPIC CHECKPOINT

1. **Vocabulary** Describe three transformations where the image and preimage have the same size and shape. *Lesson 6-1, Lesson 6-2, and Lesson 6-3*
   Sample answer: A translation, or slide, is a transformation that moves every point of a figure the same distance in the same direction. A reflection is a transformation that flips a figure across a line of reflection. A rotation turns a figure about a fixed point.

**For 2–6, use the figures below.**

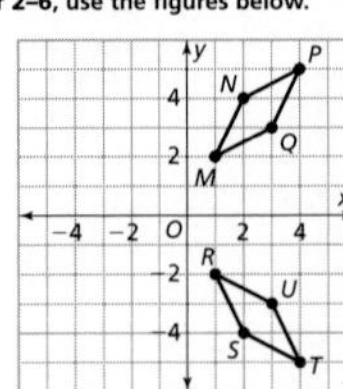


2. What are the coordinates of each point after quadrilateral *RSTU* is rotated 90° about the origin? *Lesson 6-3*
   $R'(2, 1)$, $S'(4, 2)$, $T'(5, 4)$, $U'(3, 3)$
3. What are the coordinates of each point after quadrilateral *MNPQ* is translated 2 units right and 5 units down? *Lesson 6-1*
   $M'(3, -3)$, $N'(4, -1)$, $P'(6, 0)$, $Q'(5, -2)$
4. What are the coordinates of each point after quadrilateral *MNPQ* is reflected across the *x*-axis and then translated 3 units left? *Lessons 6-2 and 6-4*
   $M'(-2, -2)$, $N'(-1, -4)$, $P'(1, -5)$, $Q'(0, -3)$
5. Which series of transformations maps quadrilateral *MNPQ* onto quadrilateral *RSTU*? *Lesson 6-4*
   Ⓐ reflection across the *x*-axis, translation 4 units down
   Ⓑ reflection across the *y*-axis, translation 4 units down
   Ⓒ rotation 180° about the origin, and then reflection across the *x*-axis
   ● rotation 180° about the origin, and then reflection across the *y*-axis
6. Is quadrilateral *MNPQ* congruent to quadrilateral *RSTU*? Explain. *Lesson 6-5*
   Yes; Sample answer: Quadrilateral *MNPQ* can be mapped onto quadrilateral *RSTU* after a rotation of 180° about the origin, and then a reflection across the *y*-axis, so quadrilateral *MNPQ* is congruent to quadrilateral *RSTU*.

**How well did you do on the mid-topic checkpoint? Fill in the stars.** ☆☆☆

**Topic 6** Congruence and Similarity **343**

**Mid-Topic Assessment Master**

Name

1. **Vocabulary** What type of transformation is a translation?
   **Sample answer: A translation is a transformation that moves every point in a figure the same distance and the same direction.**

**For 2–6, use the figures shown at right.**

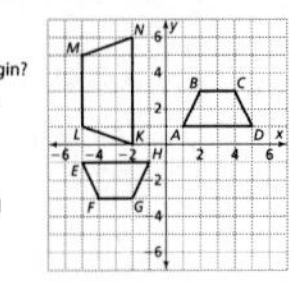


2. What are the coordinates of each point after quadrilateral *ABCD* is rotated 270° about the origin?
   $A'(1, -1)$, $B'(3, -2)$, $C'(3, -4)$, $D'(1, -5)$
3. What are the coordinates of each point after quadrilateral *EFGH* is translated 3 units right and 2 units down?
   $E'(-2, -3)$, $F'(-1, -5)$, $G'(1, -5)$, $H'(2, -3)$
4. What are the coordinates of each point after quadrilateral *ABCD* is reflected across the *y*-axis and then translated 2 units down?
   $A'(-1, -1)$, $B'(-2, 1)$, $C'(-4, 1)$, $D'(-5, -1)$
5. Which sequence of transformations maps quadrilateral *ABCD* onto quadrilateral *EFGH*?
   Ⓐ Rotation of 180° about the origin, translation 6 units left
   Ⓑ Reflection across the *y*-axis, translation 6 units left
   ● Reflection across the *x*-axis, translation 6 units left
   Ⓓ Translation 6 units left, reflection across the *y*-axis
6. Is quadrilateral *ABCD* congruent to quadrilateral *KLMN*? Fill in the blanks to explain your answer.
   Quadrilateral *ABCD* <u>is not</u> congruent to quadrilateral *KLMN*.
   Quadrilateral *ABCD* <u>cannot</u> be mapped onto quadrilateral *KLMN* through a series of rotations, reflections, or translations.

Mid-Topic Assessment 

# MID-TOPIC PERFORMANCE TASK

Go Online

Assess students' ability to apply the concepts and skills in the first part of the topic using the Mid-Topic Performance Task, found in the Student's Edition or online.

## Item Analysis for Diagnosis and Intervention

| Part | DOK | MDIS | Lesson | Standard |
|---|---|---|---|---|
| A | 3 | N58 | 6-2 | 8.G.A.1, 8.G.A.3 |
| B | 3 | N58 | 6-3 | 8.G.A.1, 8.G.A.3 |
| C | 1 | N59 | 6-4 | 8.G.A.2 |

## Scoring Rubric

| Part | Points | Mid-Topic Performance Task |
|---|---|---|
| A | 1 | Correct explanation |
| B | 1 | Correct explanation |
| C | 1 | Correct answer |

## Scoring Guide

| Score | Recommendations |
|---|---|
| Greater Than 85% | Assign the corresponding MDIS for items answered incorrectly. Use Enrichment activities with the student. |
| 70%–85% | Assign the corresponding MDIS for items answered incorrectly. You may also assign Reteach to Build Understanding and Virtual Nerd Video assets for the lessons correlated to the items the student answered incorrectly. |
| Less Than 70% | Assign the corresponding MDIS for items answered incorrectly. Assign appropriate intervention lessons available online. You may also assign Reteach to Build Understanding, Additional Vocabulary Support, Build Mathematical Literacy, and Virtual Nerd Video assets for the lessons correlated to the items the student answered incorrectly. |

Available Online

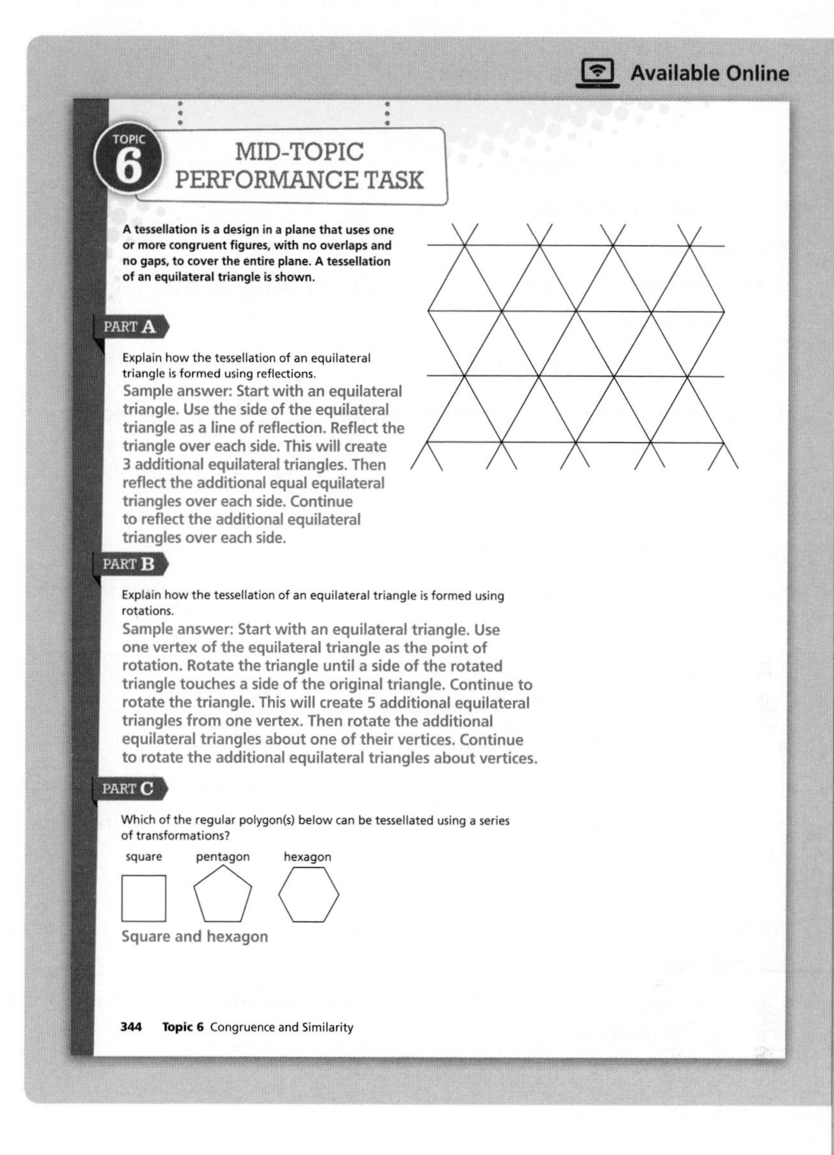

TOPIC 6

MID-TOPIC PERFORMANCE TASK

A tessellation is a design in a plane that uses one or more congruent figures, with no overlaps and no gaps, to cover the entire plane. A tessellation of an equilateral triangle is shown.

PART A

Explain how the tessellation of an equilateral triangle is formed using reflections.

Sample answer: Start with an equilateral triangle. Use the side of the equilateral triangle as a line of reflection. Reflect the triangle over each side. This will create 3 additional equilateral triangles. Then reflect the additional equal equilateral triangles over each side. Continue to reflect the additional equilateral triangles over each side.

PART B

Explain how the tessellation of an equilateral triangle is formed using rotations.

Sample answer: Start with an equilateral triangle. Use one vertex of the equilateral triangle as the point of rotation. Rotate the triangle until a side of the rotated triangle touches a side of the original triangle. Continue to rotate the triangle. This will create 5 additional equilateral triangles from one vertex. Then rotate the additional equilateral triangles about one of their vertices. Continue to rotate the additional equilateral triangles about vertices.

PART C

Which of the regular polygon(s) below can be tessellated using a series of transformations?

square pentagon hexagon

Square and hexagon

344 Topic 6 Congruence and Similarity

Go Online

Video Activity

Lesson 6-6

# Describe Dilations

## Lesson Overview

FOCUS

### Mathematics Objective

**Students will be able to:**

✔ verify the properties of a dilation.

✔ graph the image of a dilation given a fixed center and a common scale factor.

### Essential Understanding

After the dilation of a figure, the preimage and its image are the same shape and orientation, but different sizes. A scale factor greater than 1 produces an enlargement. A scale factor between 0 and 1 produces a reduction.

COHERENCE

**Previously in this topic, students:**

- analyzed and identified transformations of geometric figures including translations, reflections, and rotations.

**In this lesson, students:**

- understand and perform dilations.

**Later in this topic, students will:**

- use a sequence of transformations to show that geometric figures are similar.

**Cross-Cluster Connection** Work with congruent and similar figures (8.G.1) connects to work with proportional relationships (8.EE.2).

RIGOR

This lesson emphasizes a blend of **conceptual understanding** and **procedural skill and fluency**.

- Students apply their understanding of preimage and image to learn the concept of dilation.
- Students find the scale factor of a dilation.

## Language Support

### Lesson Language Objective

Describe how to dilate two-dimensional figures.

Additional resources are available in the **Language Support Handbook**.

## Math Anytime

### Today's Challenge

Use the Topic 6 problems any time during this topic.

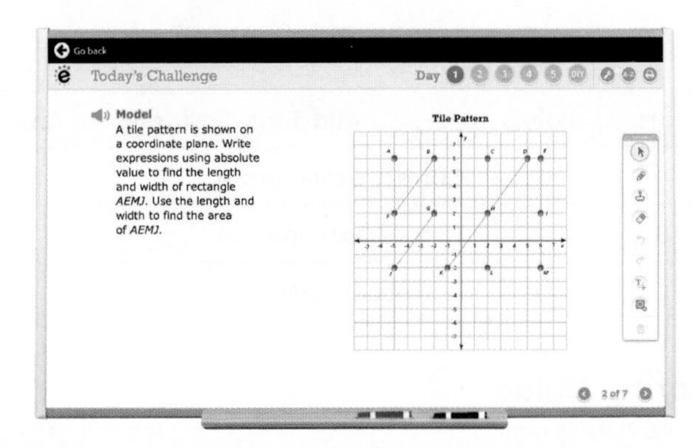


Watch the **Listen and Look For Video** for strategies and habits of mind to look for as students complete work on this lesson.

## Mathematics Overview | Common Core Standards

### Content Standards

In this lesson, you will focus on Common Core Standards **8.G.A.3** and **8.G.A.4**.

- **8. G.A.3.** Describe the effects of dilations, translations, rotations, and reflections on two-dimensional figures using coordinates.
- **8. G.A.4.** Understand that a two-dimensional figure is similar to another if the second can be obtained from the first by a sequence of rotations, reflections, translations, and dilations; given two similar, two-dimensional figures, describe a sequence that exhibits the similarity between them.

### Mathematical Practice Standards

**MP.7 Look for and Make Use of Structure**
Students analyze and describe the relationship between the preimage and the image after a dilation.

**MP.8 Generalize**
Students explain patterns, discuss methods and solution strategies, and evaluate the result of a dilation given a scale factor and a fixed center.

# STEP 1 Problem-Based Learning

15-20 min

Go Online

Activity

## Solve & Discuss It!

Formative Assessment

**Purpose** Students engage in productive struggle, analyzing two related shapes and connecting it to dilating a figure on a coordinate plane in Example 2.

### ETP Before

WHOLE CLASS

**1 Introduce the Problem**

Provide graph paper, rulers, and protractors, as needed.

**2 Check for Understanding of the Problem**

Engage students with the problem by asking: What is a splash pad?

### ETP During

SMALL GROUP

**3 Observe Students at Work**

Students might notice that the triangles are the same shape but not the same size, or that they are both right triangles but are different sizes. Student might show that the side lengths of $\triangle ABC$ are proportional to the side lengths of $\triangle ADE$, or they might notice that the side lengths of $\triangle ADE$ are two and a half times the side lengths of $\triangle ABC$. If needed, provide students with graph paper to sketch the triangles and the tools to measure them.

**Early Finishers**

How would the problem change if point $D$ is located at (0, 6) and point $E$ is at (6, 0)? [Sample answer: The triangles are still the same shape, but the side lengths of $\triangle ADE$ are now three times the side lengths of $\triangle ABC$.]

### ETP After

WHOLE CLASS

**4 Discuss Solution Strategies and Key Ideas**

Consider having groups who identified that the side lengths of the original triangle are $\frac{2}{5}$ the size of the side lengths of the new triangle share first, followed by those who identified that the new triangle has side lengths that are two and a half times the length of the original triangle. Have students discuss the connections between the two results; the results reflect same proportional relationship, since multiplying the side lengths of $\triangle ABC$ by 2.5 gives the side lengths of $\triangle ADE$, and multiplying the side lengths of $\triangle ADE$ by $\frac{2}{5}$ gives the side lengths of $\triangle ABC$.

Have students discuss how the angles of the triangles compare; the measures of the angles in $\triangle ABC$ are equal to the measures of the angles in $\triangle ADE$.

**5 Consider Instructional Implications**

After presenting Example 2, refer students back to the problem in the Solve & Discuss It and have them identify the scale factor of the dilation; $\frac{5}{2}$.

## Analyze Student Work

**Solve and Discuss It!** Activity is available online.

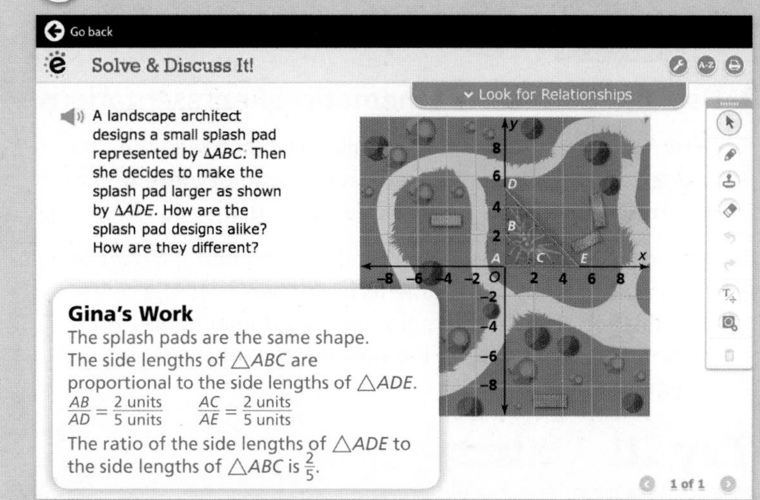


**Gina** observes that the splash pads share the same shape, and she correctly concludes that the side lengths of $\triangle ABC$ are proportional to the side lengths of $\triangle ADE$.

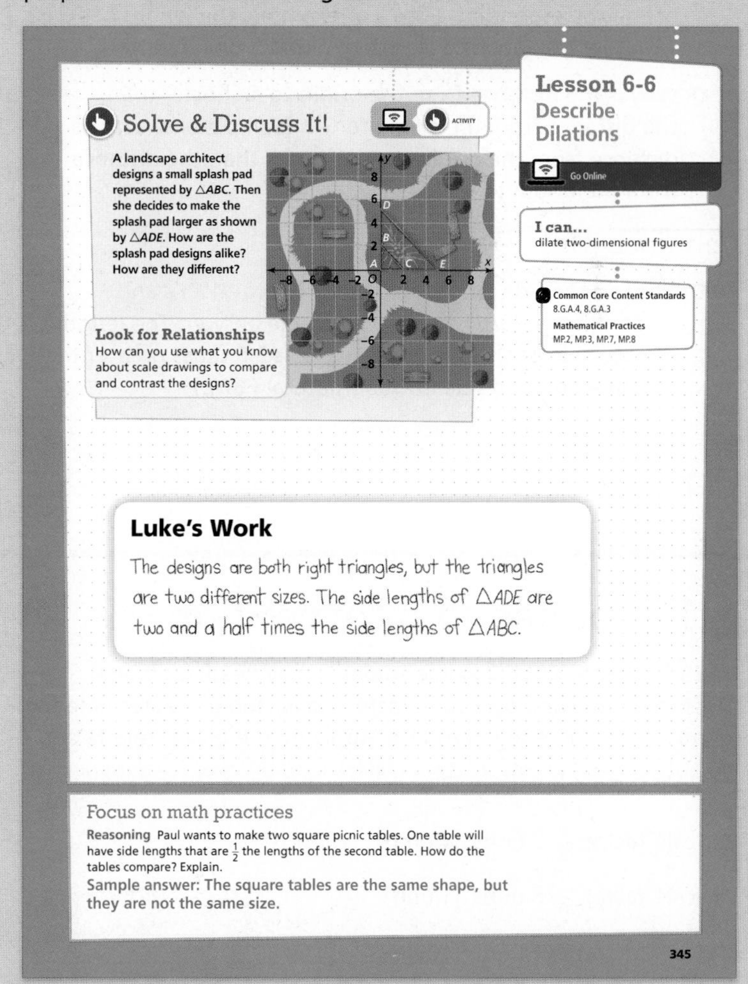


**Luke** uses $\triangle ABC$ as the preimage and $\triangle ADE$ as the image. Therefore, he correctly concludes that the side lengths of $\triangle ADE$ are two and a half times the side lengths of $\triangle ABC$.

Go Online

# STEP 2 | Visual Learning

## ETP Establish Mathematics Goals to Focus Learning

Engage students in a discussion about the ***Essential Question***. Make sure they have an understanding of the relationship between the preimage and image of a transformation and the concept of a dilation.

## EXAMPLE 1  Understand Dilations

###  ETP Use and Connect Mathematical Representations

**Q:** How can you determine the scale factor between the two open spaces? [The scale factor is the ratio of the length of corresponding sides, so the scale factor is 3.]

**Q:** How do the dotted segments help you to find the dilation? [Sample answer: The segments are drawn from the center of dilation through the point on the original figure. The corresponding point on the new figure is also on the segment.]

##  Try It!  Formative Assessment

### ETP Elicit and Use Evidence of Student Thinking

**Q:** How can you show that the scale factor is 5? [Sample answer: To show the scale factor is 5, determine the length of the corresponding sides. For example, the length of *FG* is 1 unit length, and the length of *F′G′* is 5 unit lengths.]

**Q:** Why is the distance from the origin to *F′* shorter than the distance from the origin to *G′*? [Sample answer: The distance from the origin to *F* is shorter than the distance from the origin to *G*.]

### Convince Me!

**Q:** How do the side lengths of Quadrilateral *WXYZ* and Quadrilateral *FGHI* compare? [Sample answer: The length of each side of Quadrilateral *WXYZ* is 3.5 times greater than its corresponding side in Quadrilateral *FGHI*.]

**Visual Learning Animation Plus** is available online.

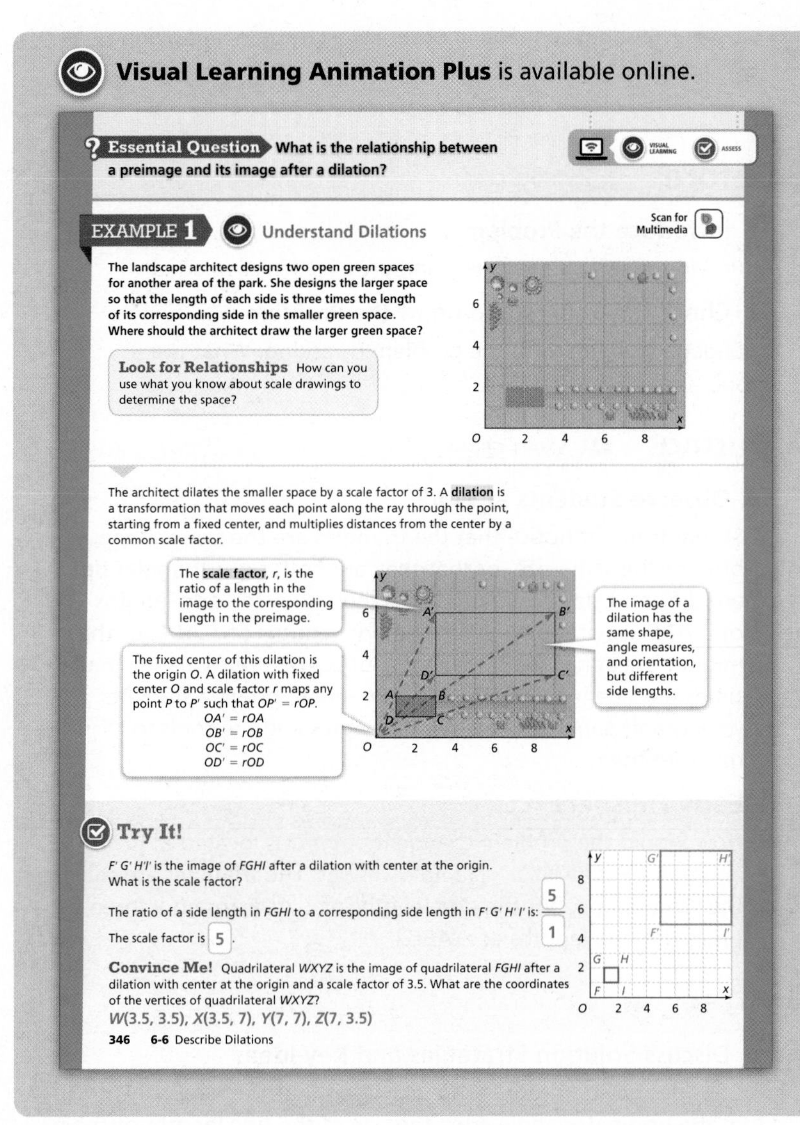

**Essential Question** What is the relationship between a preimage and its image after a dilation?

**EXAMPLE 1** Understand Dilations

Scan for Multimedia

The landscape architect designs two open green spaces for another area of the park. She designs the larger space so that the length of each side is three times the length of its corresponding side in the smaller green space. Where should the architect draw the larger green space?

**Look for Relationships** How can you use what you know about scale drawings to determine the space?

The architect dilates the smaller space by a scale factor of 3. A **dilation** is a transformation that moves each point along the ray through the point, starting from a fixed center, and multiplies distances from the center by a common scale factor.

The **scale factor**, *r*, is the ratio of a length in the image to the corresponding length in the preimage.

The fixed center of this dilation is the origin *O*. A dilation with fixed center *O* and scale factor *r* maps any point *P* to *P′* such that $OP' = rOP$.
$OA' = rOA$
$OB' = rOB$
$OC' = rOC$
$OD' = rOD$

The image of a dilation has the same shape, angle measures, and orientation, but different side lengths.

**Try It!**

*F′G′H′I′* is the image of *FGHI* after a dilation with center at the origin. What is the scale factor?

The ratio of a side length in *FGHI* to a corresponding side length in *F′G′H′I′* is: $\frac{5}{1}$

The scale factor is 5.

**Convince Me!** Quadrilateral *WXYZ* is the image of quadrilateral *FGHI* after a dilation with center at the origin and a scale factor of 3.5. What are the coordinates of the vertices of quadrilateral *WXYZ*?

*W*(3.5, 3.5), *X*(3.5, 7), *Y*(7, 7), *Z*(7, 3.5)

346 6-6 Describe Dilations

Students can access the ***Visual Learning Animation Plus*** by using the **BouncePages app** to scan this page. Students can download the app for free in their mobile devices' app store.

##  Response to Intervention

**USE WITH EXAMPLE 3** Some students may need additional practice multiplying by a scale factor. Have students determine the length of each line segment after applying the given scale factor.

**Q:** Scale factor: $\frac{1}{2}$; 4 units [2 units]

**Q:** Scale factor: $\frac{4}{5}$; 5 units [4 units]

**Q:** Scale factor: $\frac{1}{6}$; 6 units [1 unit]

**Q:** Scale factor: $\frac{5}{2}$; 4 units [10 units]

**Q:** Scale factor: $\frac{3}{5}$; 15 units [9 units]

**Q:** Scale factor: 12; $\frac{1}{2}$ unit [6 units]

##  Enrichment

**USE WITH EXAMPLE 1** Challenge students by asking them to create their own open space plan. Ask them to create the original open space plan on grid paper. Then have them dilate the plan three different times. Have them determine the scale factor for each dilation.

Go Online

Activity

Assess

## EXAMPLE 2  Dilate to Enlarge a Figure on a Coordinate Plane

### ETP Pose Purposeful Questions

**Q:** What do the dashed lines show in the figure? [Sample answer: The dashed lines show the distance from the center of dilation to the original point and to the corresponding point of the image.]

**Q:** How can you compare the distance from point *A* to the origin to the distance from point *A′* to the origin? [The distance from point *A′* to the origin is twice as long as the distance from point *A* to the origin.]

**Q:** Why must you first determine the coordinates of each vertex of the preimage? [Sample answer: You will need to multiply these coordinates by the scale factor to find the vertices of the image.]

## EXAMPLE 3  Dilate to Reduce a Figure

###  ETP Pose Purposeful Questions

**Q:** Why is the image closer to the center of dilation than the preimage? [Sample answer: The scale factor's value is between 0 and 1, so the distance from the center of dilation to the image must be less than the distance from the center of dilation to the preimage.]

##  Try It!  Formative Assessment

###  ETP Elicit and Use Evidence of Student Thinking

**Q:** Will the scale factor be greater than 1 or between 0 and 1? Explain. [Sample answer: Point *L′* is closer to the center of dilation than *L*. Therefore the scale factor must be between 0 and 1.]

**Examples and Try Its!** are available online.

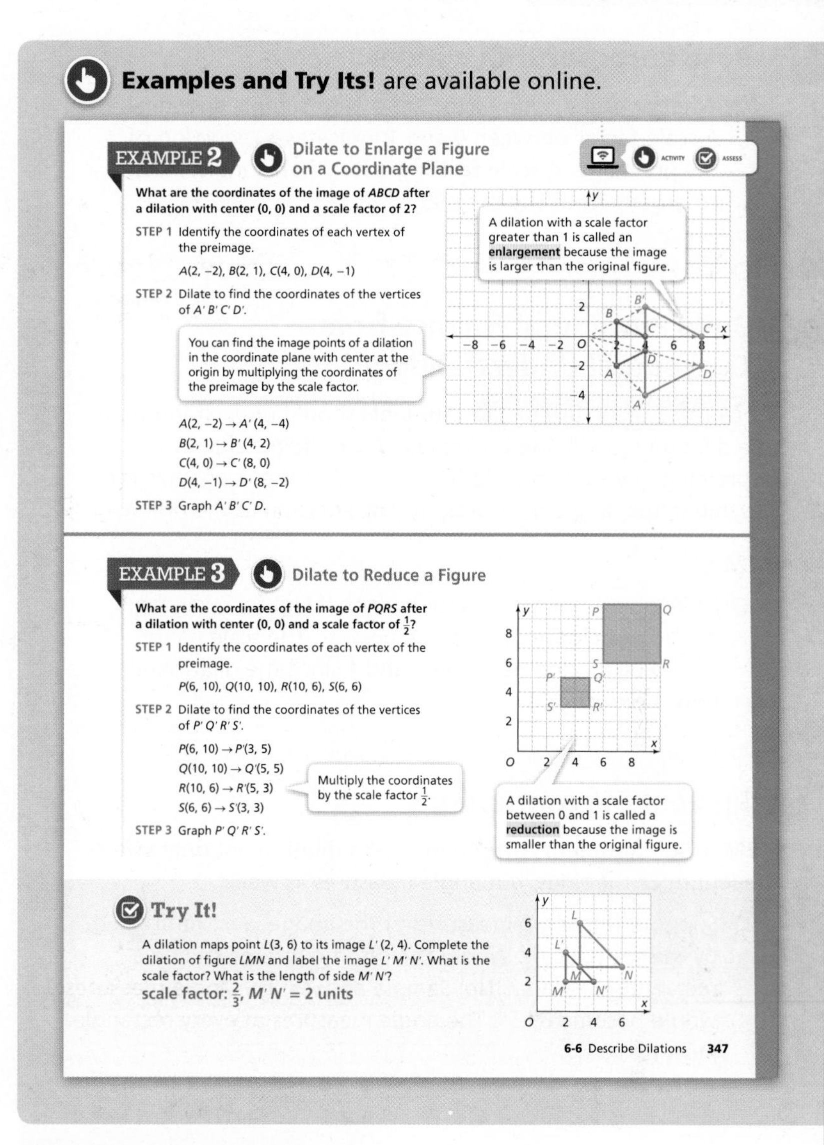
EXAMPLE 2 Dilate to Enlarge a Figure on a Coordinate Plane

**What are the coordinates of the image of *ABCD* after a dilation with center (0, 0) and a scale factor of 2?**

STEP 1 Identify the coordinates of each vertex of the preimage.

*A*(2, −2), *B*(2, 1), *C*(4, 0), *D*(4, −1)

STEP 2 Dilate to find the coordinates of the vertices of *A′B′C′D′*.

You can find the image points of a dilation in the coordinate plane with center at the origin by multiplying the coordinates of the preimage by the scale factor.

*A*(2, −2) → *A′*(4, −4)
*B*(2, 1) → *B′*(4, 2)
*C*(4, 0) → *C′*(8, 0)
*D*(4, −1) → *D′*(8, −2)

STEP 3 Graph *A′B′C′D′*.

A dilation with a scale factor greater than 1 is called an **enlargement** because the image is larger than the original figure.

EXAMPLE 3 Dilate to Reduce a Figure

**What are the coordinates of the image of *PQRS* after a dilation with center (0, 0) and a scale factor of $\frac{1}{2}$?**

STEP 1 Identify the coordinates of each vertex of the preimage.

*P*(6, 10), *Q*(10, 10), *R*(10, 6), *S*(6, 6)

STEP 2 Dilate to find the coordinates of the vertices of *P′Q′R′S′*.

*P*(6, 10) → *P′*(3, 5)
*Q*(10, 10) → *Q′*(5, 5)
*R*(10, 6) → *R′*(5, 3)
*S*(6, 6) → *S′*(3, 3)

Multiply the coordinates by the scale factor $\frac{1}{2}$.

STEP 3 Graph *P′Q′R′S′*.

A dilation with a scale factor between 0 and 1 is called a **reduction** because the image is smaller than the original figure.

Try It!

A dilation maps point *L*(3, 6) to its image *L′*(2, 4). Complete the dilation of figure *LMN* and label the image *L′M′N′*. What is the scale factor? What is the length of side *M′N′*?

scale factor: $\frac{2}{3}$, *M′N′* = 2 units

6-6 Describe Dilations 347

## ADDITIONAL EXAMPLES 

**For additional examples go online.**

## ELL English Language Learners

**ENTERING** Complete Examples 2 and 3.

Write *enlargement* and *reduction* on the board. Help students read each word.

**Q:** Do you see another word in the word *enlargement*? [Large]

If students struggle, underline the word *large* in *enlargement*. Then ask:

**Q:** Do you think *enlargement* means bigger or smaller? Why? [Sample answer: It means bigger. Since it has *large* within the word, it probably means larger.]

Repeat the process for *reduction*. Write the word *reduce* on the board. Have students compare this word to *reduction*.

**EMERGING** Complete Examples 2 and 3.

Define for students the meaning of *synonym*. Have students brainstorm synonyms for the following words. Write the words on the board as students think of synonyms.

**Q:** Give a synonym for *enlargement*. [Sample answer: Larger, magnification, or expansion]

**Q:** Give a synonym for *reduction*. [Sample answer: Smaller, shrunk]

**EXPANDING** Complete Examples 2 and 3.

Have students write the definitions for *enlargement*, *reduction*, *scale*, *scale model*, and *scale factor* in their own words. Then organize students into pairs and have each student share their definitions with each other. Finally, have students edit each other's work so that each partner has a definition for each word they can share with the class.

Go Online

Key Concept

Assess

Activity

# STEP 2 | Visual Learning *continued*

## KEY CONCEPT

### ETP Pose Purposeful Questions

**Q:** What does the scale factor indicate? [Sample answer: A scale factor between 0 and 1 indicates a reduction of the preimage. A scale factor greater than 1 indicates an enlargement of the preimage.]

## Do You Understand/Do You Know How?

**Formative** Assessment

### Build Procedural Fluency from Conceptual Understanding

**Essential Question** Students should understand that a dilation is an image that results from the resizing of a preimage by a given scale factor and that the image has the same shape, angle measures, and orientation as the preimage.

**ITEM 4**

**Q:** How would the scale factor change if Figure 1 was the dilation of Figure 3? [Sample answer: The scale factor would be a value between 0 and 1 since the dilation is now a reduction.]

### Prevent Misconceptions

**ITEM 3** Some students may think that a dilation not only affects the length of the sides, but angle measures as well.

**Q:** Suppose the angle measures of the image were multiplied by the scale factor. Would the resulting shape still be a rectangle? Explain. [No; Sample answer: The angle measures would become 67.5°. The angle measures of every rectangle must be 90°.]

Available Online

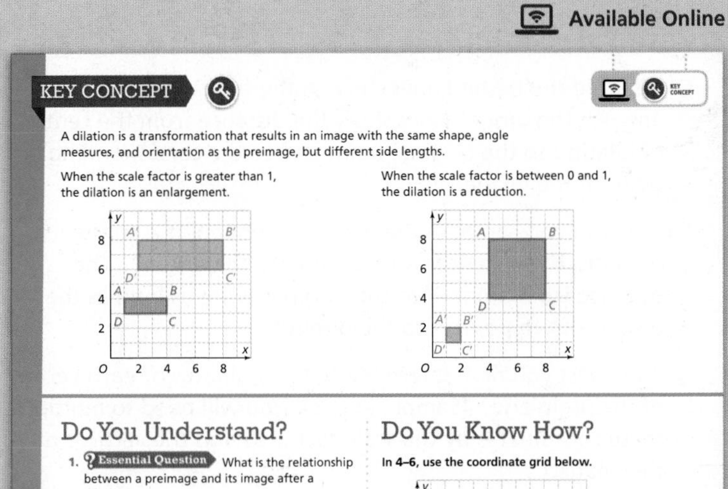
KEY CONCEPT

A dilation is a transformation that results in an image with the same shape, angle measures, and orientation as the preimage, but different side lengths.

When the scale factor is greater than 1, the dilation is an enlargement.

When the scale factor is between 0 and 1, the dilation is a reduction.

**Do You Understand?**

1. **Essential Question** What is the relationship between a preimage and its image after a dilation?
Sample answer: The image and preimage are the same shape and orientation, but not the same size. An enlargement makes the image larger than the preimage. A reduction makes the image smaller than the preimage.

2. **Generalize** When will a dilation be a reduction? When will it be an enlargement?
Sample answer: A reduction will occur when the scale factor of the dilation is between 0 and 1. An enlargement will occur when the scale factor is greater than 1.

3. **Reasoning** Flora draws a rectangle with points at (12, 12), (15, 12), (15, 9) and (12, 9). She dilates the figure with center at the origin and a scale factor of $\frac{3}{4}$. What is the measure of each angle in the image? Explain.
90°; Sample answer: A dilation keeps the same shape, and a rectangle has four 90-degree angles.

**Do You Know How?**

**In 4–6, use the coordinate grid below.**

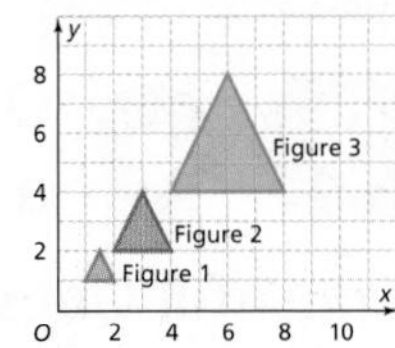


4. Figure 3 is the image of Figure 1 after a dilation with center at the origin. What is the scale factor? Explain.
4; Sample answer: The ratio of the base length of Figure 3 to the base length of Figure 1 is 4 to 1, so the scale factor is 4.

5. What are the coordinates of the image of Figure 2 after a dilation with center at the origin and a scale factor of 3?
(6, 6), (12, 6), and (9, 12)

6. Which figures represent a dilation with a scale factor of $\frac{1}{2}$?
Figure 2 to Figure 1 and Figure 3 to Figure 2

348 6-6 Describe Dilations

## ADDITIONAL EXAMPLE 2

Help students transition to finding the image of a figure graphed in more than one quadrant using this additional example.

Make sure students understand the procedure for finding the points of the image remains the same.

**Q:** What is the procedure for finding the points of any image after a dilation? [Sample answer: Identify the coordinates of each vertex. Multiply the coordinates of the preimage by the scale factor. Graph the new vertices.]

**Additional Examples** are available online.

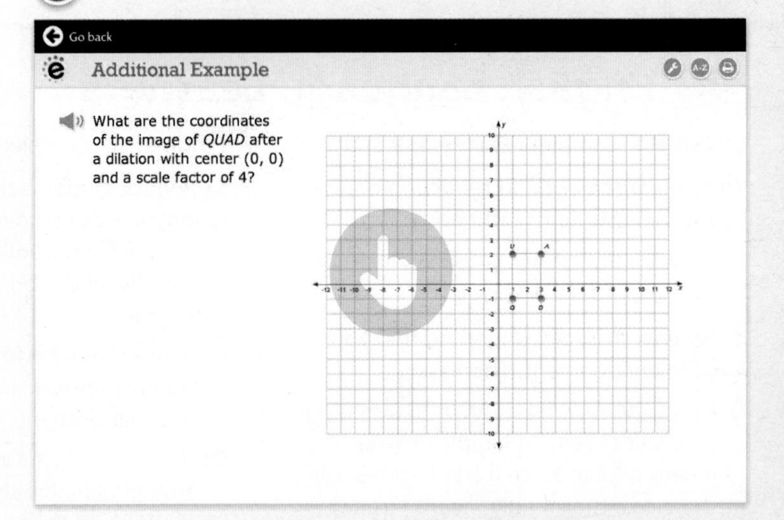


**Answer:** $Q'(4, -4)$, $U'(4, 8)$, $A'(12, 8)$, $D'(12, -4)$

# Practice & Problem Solving  

Interactive Practice and Virtual Nerd Tutorials are available online.

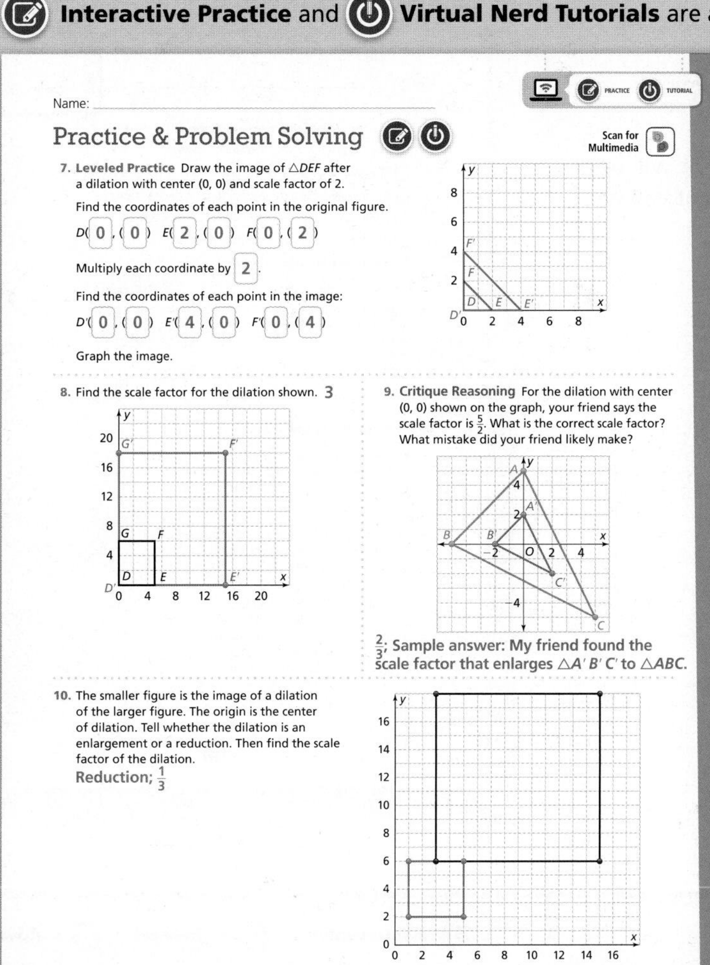

Name:

## Practice & Problem Solving

Scan for Multimedia

7. **Leveled Practice** Draw the image of $\triangle DEF$ after a dilation with center (0, 0) and scale factor of 2.

   Find the coordinates of each point in the original figure.

   $D$(0, 0) $E$(2, 0) $F$(0, 2)

   Multiply each coordinate by 2.

   Find the coordinates of each point in the image:

   $D'$(0, 0) $E'$(4, 0) $F'$(0, 4)

   Graph the image.

8. Find the scale factor for the dilation shown. 3

9. **Critique Reasoning** For the dilation with center (0, 0) shown on the graph, your friend says the scale factor is $\frac{5}{2}$. What is the correct scale factor? What mistake did your friend likely make?

   $\frac{2}{5}$; Sample answer: My friend found the scale factor that enlarges $\triangle A'B'C'$ to $\triangle ABC$.

10. The smaller figure is the image of a dilation of the larger figure. The origin is the center of dilation. Tell whether the dilation is an enlargement or a reduction. Then find the scale factor of the dilation.

    Reduction; $\frac{1}{3}$



11. **Higher Order Thinking** $Q'R'S'T'$ is the image of $QRST$ after a dilation with center at the origin.

    a. Find the scale factor. $\frac{1}{4}$

    b. Find the area of each parallelogram. What is the relationship between the areas?

    Area of $Q'R'S'T' = 9$,
    Area of $QRST = 144$;
    Sample answer: Since the length of each side of $QRST$ is 4 times the length of each side of $Q'R'S'T'$, the area of $QRST$ is $4 \times 4$, or 16 times greater, than the area of $Q'R'S'T'$.

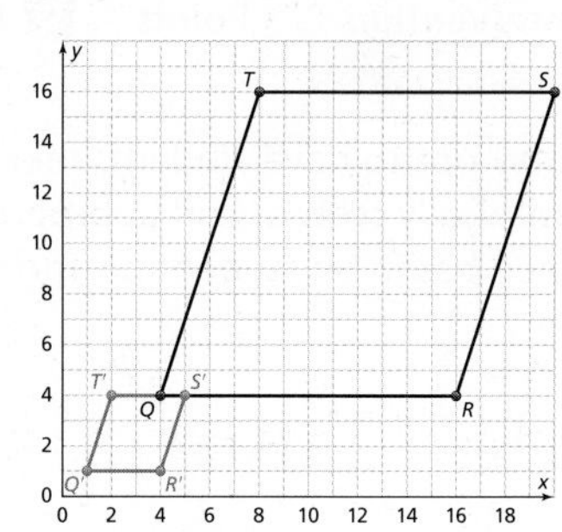

## Assessment Practice

12. Triangle $PQR$ is the image of $\triangle JKL$ after a dilation. Is the dilation an enlargement or a reduction? Explain.

    Ⓐ An enlargement, because the image is larger than the original figure

    Ⓑ An enlargement, because the image is smaller than the original figure

    Ⓒ A reduction, because the image is smaller than the original figure

    Ⓓ A reduction, because the image is larger than the original figure

13. Rectangle $QUAD$ has coordinates $Q(0, 0)$, $U(0, 3)$, $A(6, 3)$, and $D(6, 0)$. $Q'U'A'D'$ is the image of $QUAD$ after a dilation with center (0, 0) and a scale factor of 6. What are the coordinates of point $D'$? Explain.

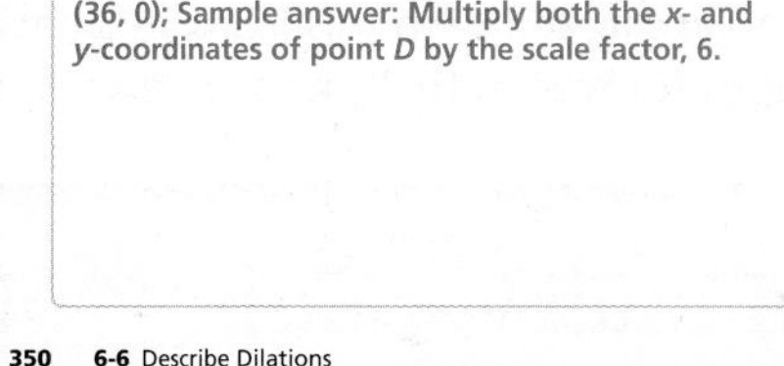

(36, 0); Sample answer: Multiply both the x- and y-coordinates of point D by the scale factor, 6.



## Error Intervention

**ITEM 9 Critique Reasoning** Some students may think the given scale factor is correct since it is a fraction.

**Q:** Is the value of $\frac{5}{2}$ between 0 and 1 or greater than 1? Explain. [Greater than 1; Sample answer: The fraction represents 2.5 which has a value greater than 1.]

**Q:** Will this scale factor create an enlargement or reduction? [Enlargement]

## Challenge

**ITEM 8** Ask students to write a general rule for this transformation using variables. Then have them test their rule using the coordinates in the figures.

You may opt to have students complete the automatically scored Practice & Problem Solving items online.

### Item Analysis

| Example | Items | DOK |
|---|---|---|
| 1 | 9, 10 | 2 |
| 2 | 7, 8 | 1 |
|  | 12, 13 | 2 |
| 3 | 11 | 2 |

EVALUATE

STEP 3 Assess & Differentiate

Go Online

Assess Tutorials Worksheets

# Lesson Quiz

**Formative** Assessment

Use the student scores on the Lesson Quiz to prescribe differentiated assignments.

**I Intervention** 0–3 Points **O On-Level** 4 Points **A Advanced** 5 Points

You may opt to have students take the Lesson Quiz online. The Lesson Quiz will be automatically scored, and appropriate remediation, practice, or enrichment will be assigned based on student performance.

**Lesson Quiz** is available online.

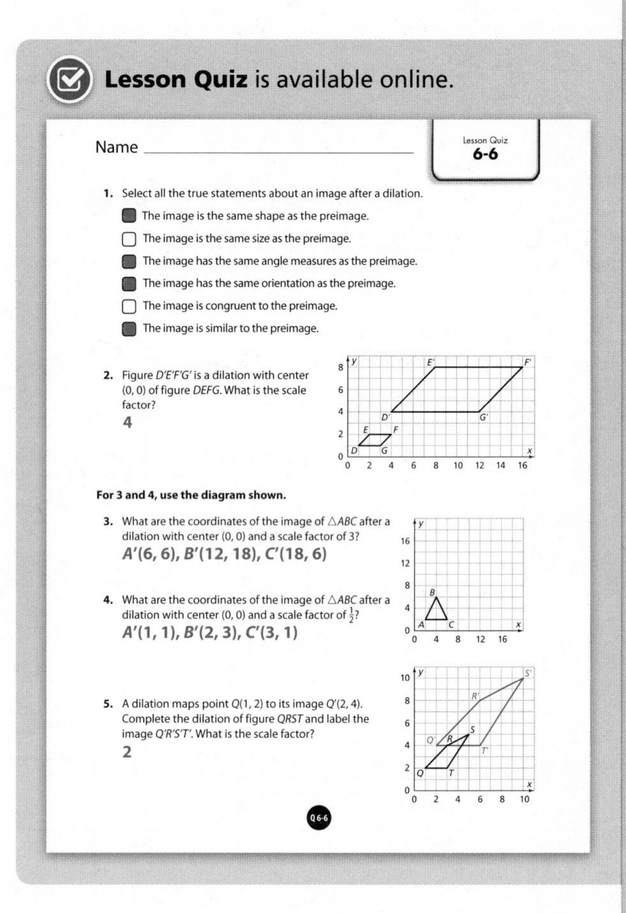

Name ______________ Lesson Quiz 6-6

1. Select all the true statements about an image after a dilation.
   - [x] The image is the same shape as the preimage.
   - [ ] The image is the same size as the preimage.
   - [x] The image has the same angle measures as the preimage.
   - [x] The image has the same orientation as the preimage.
   - [ ] The image is congruent to the preimage.
   - [x] The image is similar to the preimage.

2. Figure $D'E'F'G'$ is a dilation with center (0, 0) of figure $DEFG$. What is the scale factor?
   4

For 3 and 4, use the diagram shown.

3. What are the coordinates of the image of $\triangle ABC$ after a dilation with center (0, 0) and a scale factor of 3?
   $A'(6, 6), B'(12, 18), C'(18, 6)$

4. What are the coordinates of the image of $\triangle ABC$ after a dilation with center (0, 0) and a scale factor of $\frac{1}{2}$?
   $A'(1, 1), B'(2, 3), C'(3, 1)$

5. A dilation maps point $Q(1, 2)$ to its image $Q'(2, 4)$. Complete the dilation of figure $QRST$ and label the image $Q'R'S'T'$. What is the scale factor?
   2

Q6-6

# Video Tutorials

Students can access instructional tutorials using the **Virtual Nerd app**.

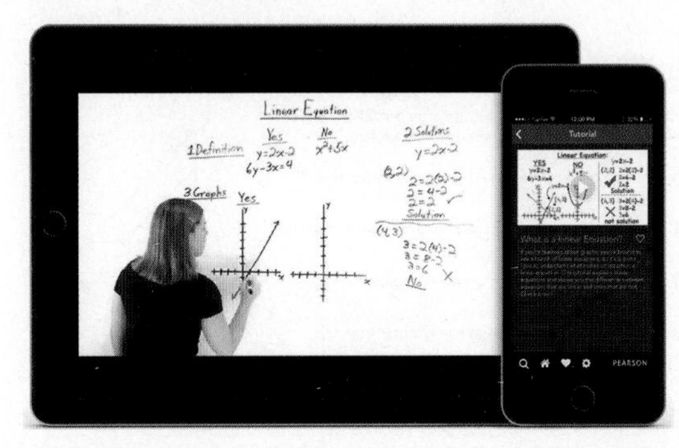

Students can also access the videos using the **BouncePages app** to scan exercise pages marked with this icon. Students can download both apps for free in their mobile devices' app store.

# Differentiated Intervention

I = Intervention O = On-Level A = Advanced

## Reteach to Build Understanding I

Provides scaffolded reteaching for the key lesson concepts.

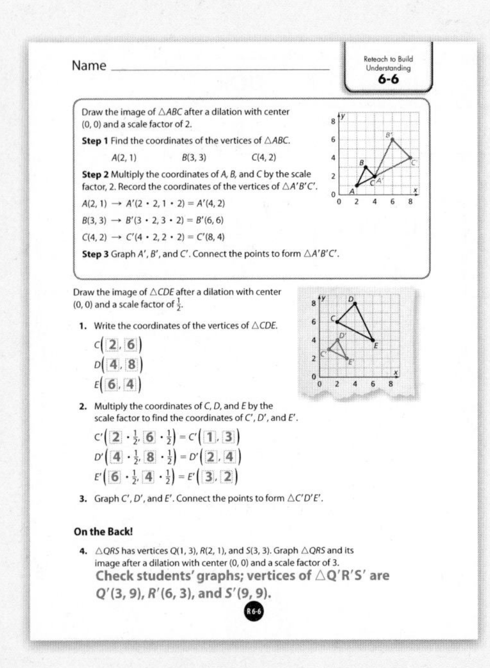

Name ______________ Reteach to Build Understanding 6-6

Draw the image of $\triangle ABC$ after a dilation with center (0, 0) and a scale factor of 2.

**Step 1** Find the coordinates of the vertices of $\triangle ABC$.
$A(2, 1)$ $B(3, 3)$ $C(4, 2)$

**Step 2** Multiply the coordinates of $A$, $B$, and $C$ by the scale factor, 2. Record the coordinates of the vertices of $\triangle A'B'C'$.
$A(2, 1) \rightarrow A'(2 \cdot 2, 1 \cdot 2) = A'(4, 2)$
$B(3, 3) \rightarrow B'(3 \cdot 2, 3 \cdot 2) = B'(6, 6)$
$C(4, 2) \rightarrow C'(4 \cdot 2, 2 \cdot 2) = C'(8, 4)$

**Step 3** Graph $A'$, $B'$, and $C'$. Connect the points to form $\triangle A'B'C'$.

Draw the image of $\triangle CDE$ after a dilation with center (0, 0) and a scale factor of $\frac{1}{2}$.

1. Write the coordinates of the vertices of $\triangle CDE$.
   $C(2, 6)$
   $D(4, 8)$
   $E(6, 4)$
2. Multiply the coordinates of $C$, $D$, and $E$ by the scale factor to find the coordinates of $C'$, $D'$, and $E'$.
   $C'(2 \cdot \frac{1}{2}, 6 \cdot \frac{1}{2}) = C'(1, 3)$
   $D'(4 \cdot \frac{1}{2}, 8 \cdot \frac{1}{2}) = D'(2, 4)$
   $E'(6 \cdot \frac{1}{2}, 4 \cdot \frac{1}{2}) = E'(3, 2)$
3. Graph $C'$, $D'$, and $E'$. Connect the points to form $\triangle C'D'E'$.

**On the Back!**

4. $\triangle QRS$ has vertices $Q(1, 3)$, $R(2, 1)$, and $S(3, 3)$. Graph $\triangle QRS$ and its image after a dilation with center (0, 0) and a scale factor of 3.
   Check students' graphs; vertices of $\triangle Q'R'S'$ are $Q'(3, 9)$, $R'(6, 3)$, and $S'(9, 9)$.

R6-6

## Additional Vocabulary Support I O

Helps students develop and reinforce understanding of key terms and concepts.

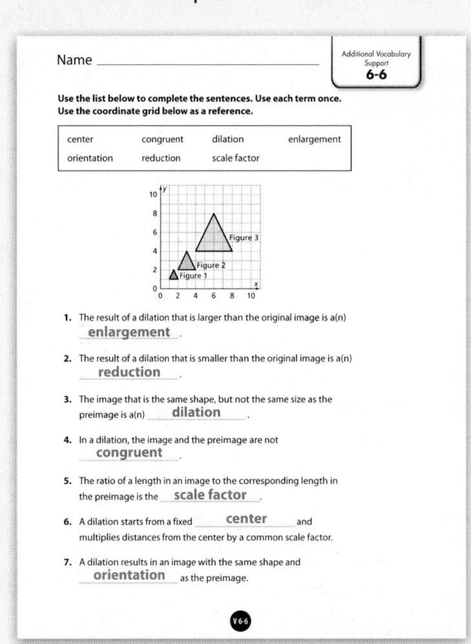

Name ______________ Additional Vocabulary Support 6-6

**Use the list below to complete the sentences. Use each term once. Use the coordinate grid below as a reference.**

| center | congruent | dilation | enlargement |
| --- | --- | --- | --- |
| orientation | reduction | scale factor | |

1. The result of a dilation that is larger than the original image is a(n) enlargement.
2. The result of a dilation that is smaller than the original image is a(n) reduction.
3. The image that is the same shape, but not the same size as the preimage is a(n) dilation.
4. In a dilation, the image and the preimage are not congruent.
5. The ratio of a length in an image to the corresponding length in the preimage is the scale factor.
6. A dilation starts from a fixed center and multiplies distances from the center by a common scale factor.
7. A dilation results in an image with the same shape and orientation as the preimage.

V6-6

## Build Mathematical Literacy I O

Provides support for struggling readers to build mathematical literacy.

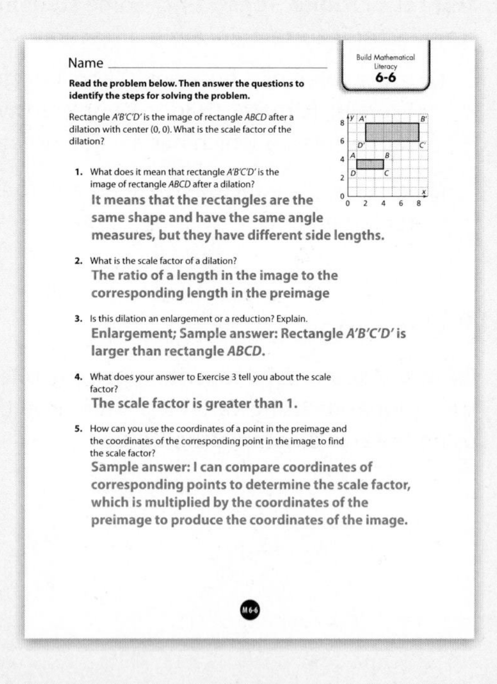

Name ______________ Build Mathematical Literacy 6-6

**Read the problem below. Then answer the questions to identify the steps for solving the problem.**

Rectangle $A'B'C'D'$ is the image of rectangle $ABCD$ after a dilation with center (0, 0). What is the scale factor of the dilation?

1. What does it mean that rectangle $A'B'C'D'$ is the image of rectangle $ABCD$ after a dilation?
   It means that the rectangles are the same shape and have the same angle measures, but they have different side lengths.
2. What is the scale factor of a dilation?
   The ratio of a length in the image to the corresponding length in the preimage
3. Is this dilation an enlargement or a reduction? Explain.
   Enlargement; Sample answer: Rectangle $A'B'C'D'$ is larger than rectangle $ABCD$.
4. What does your answer to Exercise 3 tell you about the scale factor?
   The scale factor is greater than 1.
5. How can you use the coordinates of a point in the preimage and the coordinates of the corresponding point in the image to find the scale factor?
   Sample answer: I can compare coordinates of corresponding points to determine the scale factor, which is multiplied by the coordinates of the preimage to produce the coordinates of the image.

M6-6

Go Online

Practice

Worksheets

Math Tools

Math Games

# Additional Practice

You may opt to have students complete the automatically scored Additional Practice items online.

**Item Analysis**

| Example | Items | DOK |
|---|---|---|
| 1 | 8 | 2 |
| | 3 | 3 |
| 2 | 4, 5 | 2 |
| | 6 | 3 |
| 3 | 1, 2, 7 | 2 |

**Interactive Practice** is available online.

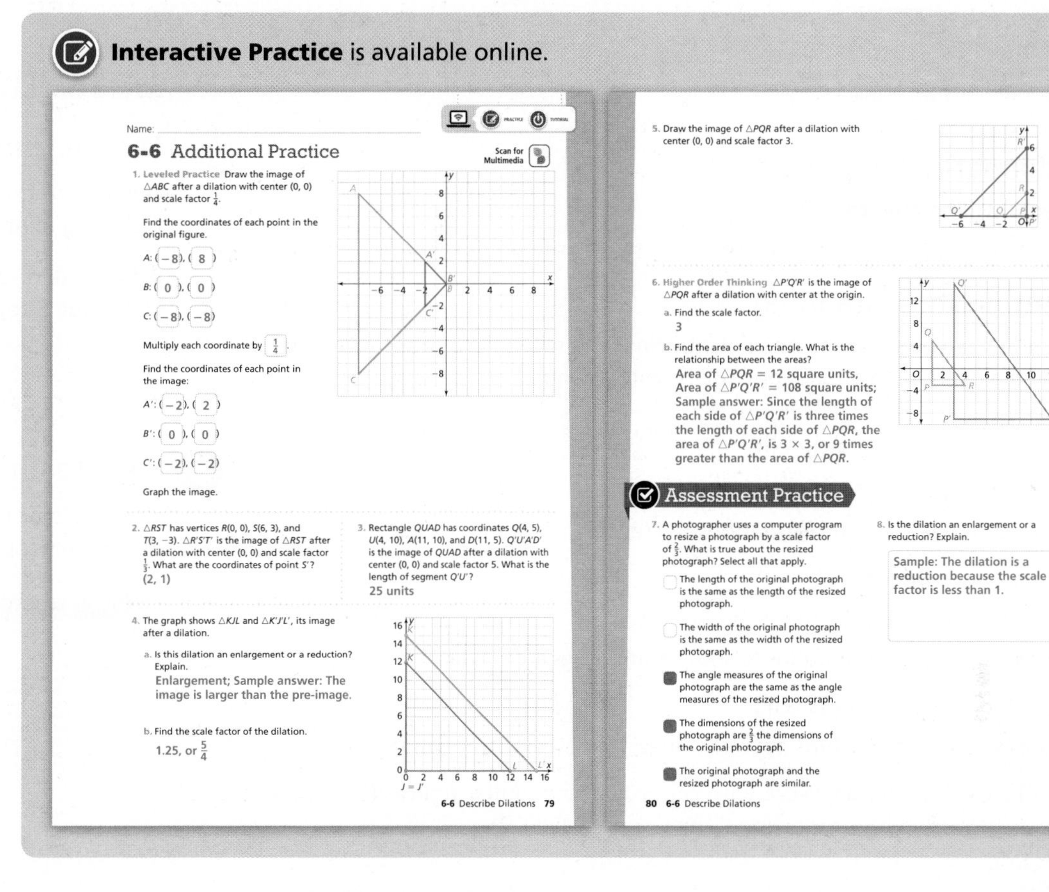
Name:

## 6-6 Additional Practice

Scan for Multimedia

1. Leveled Practice Draw the image of $\triangle ABC$ after a dilation with center (0, 0) and scale factor $\frac{1}{4}$.

Find the coordinates of each point in the original figure.

A: (−8), (8)

B: (0), (0)

C: (−8), (−8)

Multiply each coordinate by $\frac{1}{4}$.

Find the coordinates of each point in the image:

A′: (−2), (2)

B′: (0), (0)

C′: (−2), (−2)

Graph the image.

2. $\triangle RST$ has vertices R(0, 0), S(6, 3), and T(3, −3). $\triangle R'S'T'$ is the image of $\triangle RST$ after a dilation with center (0, 0) and scale factor $\frac{1}{3}$. What are the coordinates of point S′?
(2, 1)

3. Rectangle QUAD has coordinates Q(4, 5), U(4, 10), A(11, 10), and D(11, 5). Q′U′A′D′ is the image of QUAD after a dilation with center (0, 0) and scale factor 5. What is the length of segment Q′U′?
25 units

4. The graph shows $\triangle KJL$ and $\triangle K'J'L'$, its image after a dilation.

a. Is this dilation an enlargement or a reduction? Explain.
Enlargement; Sample answer: The image is larger than the pre-image.

b. Find the scale factor of the dilation.
1.25, or $\frac{5}{4}$

6-6 Describe Dilations 79

5. Draw the image of $\triangle PQR$ after a dilation with center (0, 0) and scale factor 3.

6. Higher Order Thinking $\triangle P'Q'R'$ is the image of $\triangle PQR$ after a dilation with center at the origin.

a. Find the scale factor.
3

b. Find the area of each triangle. What is the relationship between the areas?
Area of $\triangle PQR$ = 12 square units, Area of $\triangle P'Q'R'$ = 108 square units; Sample answer: Since the length of each side of $\triangle P'Q'R'$ is three times the length of each side of $\triangle PQR$, the area of $\triangle P'Q'R'$, is 3 × 3, or 9 times greater than the area of $\triangle PQR$.

Assessment Practice

7. A photographer uses a computer program to resize a photograph by a scale factor of $\frac{3}{5}$. What is true about the resized photograph? Select all that apply.

- ☐ The length of the original photograph is the same as the length of the resized photograph.
- ☐ The width of the original photograph is the same as the width of the resized photograph.
- ■ The angle measures of the original photograph are the same as the angle measures of the resized photograph.
- ■ The dimensions of the resized photograph are $\frac{3}{5}$ the dimensions of the original photograph.
- ■ The original photograph and the resized photograph are similar.

8. Is the dilation an enlargement or a reduction? Explain.
Sample: The dilation is a reduction because the scale factor is less than 1.

80 6-6 Describe Dilations

# Differentiated Intervention

I = Intervention  O = On-Level  A = Advanced

## Enrichment O A

Presents engaging problems and activities that extend the lesson concepts.

## Math Tools and Games I O A

Offers additional activities and games to build understanding and fluency.

## Pick a Project and STEM Project I O A

Provides an additional opportunity for students to demonstrate understanding of key mathematical concepts.

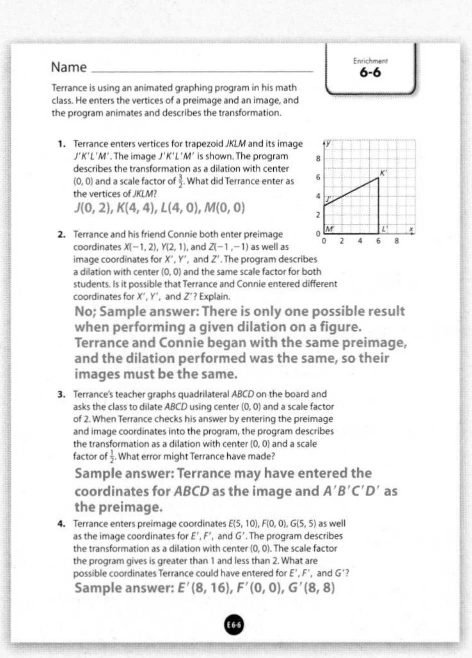
Name

Enrichment 6-6

Terrance is using an animated graphing program in his math class. He enters the vertices of a preimage and an image, and the program animates and describes the transformation.

1. Terrance enters vertices for trapezoid JKLM and its image J′K′L′M′. The image J′K′L′M′ is shown. The program describes the transformation as a dilation with center (0, 0) and a scale factor of $\frac{1}{2}$. What did Terrance enter as the vertices of JKLM?
J(0, 2), K(4, 4), L(4, 0), M(0, 0)

2. Terrance and his friend Connie both enter preimage coordinates X(−1, 2), Y(2, 1), and Z(−1, −1) as well as image coordinates for X′, Y′, and Z′. The program describes a dilation with center (0, 0) and the same scale factor for both students. Is it possible that Terrance and Connie entered different coordinates for X′, Y′, and Z′? Explain.
No; Sample answer: There is only one possible result when performing a given dilation on a figure. Terrance and Connie began with the same preimage, and the dilation performed was the same, so their images must be the same.

3. Terrance's teacher graphs quadrilateral ABCD on the board and asks the class to dilate ABCD using center (0, 0) and a scale factor of 2. When Terrance checks his answer by entering the preimage and image coordinates into the program, the program describes the transformation as a dilation with center (0, 0) and a scale factor of $\frac{1}{2}$. What error might Terrance have made?
Sample answer: Terrance may have entered the coordinates for ABCD as the image and A′B′C′D′ as the preimage.

4. Terrance enters preimage coordinates E(5, 10), F(0, 0), G(5, 5) as well as the image coordinates for E′, F′, and G′. The program describes the transformation as a dilation with center (0, 0). The scale factor the program gives is greater than 1 and less than 2. What are possible coordinates Terrance could have entered for E′, F′, and G′?
Sample answer: E′(8, 16), F′(0, 0), G′(8, 8)

E66

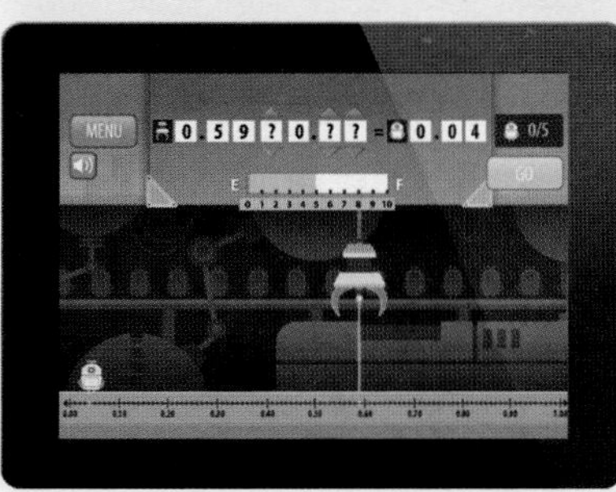


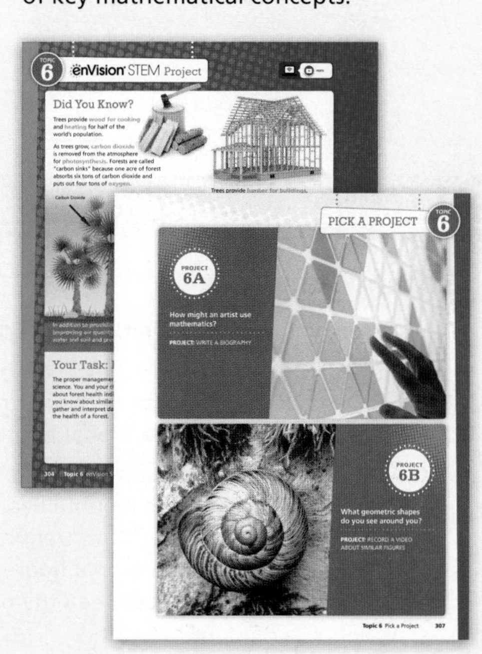

Go Online

Lesson 6-7

# Understand Similar Figures

## Lesson Overview

FOCUS

### Mathematics Objective

**Students will be able to:**

✔ perform a sequence of transformations to identify similar figures.

### Essential Understanding

Two figures can be shown to be similar by finding a sequence of transformations, including a dilation, that maps one figure onto the other.

COHERENCE

**Previously in this topic, students:**

- learned to describe dilations.
- used a sequence of transformations to create an image from a preimage.

**In this lesson, students:**

- understand the concept of similar figures.
- use a series of transformations to show that figures are similar.

**Later in this topic, students will:**

- reason about relationships between lines, angles, and transversals.

**Cross-Cluster Connection** Work with congruent and similar figures (8.G.1) connects to work with proportional relationships (8.EE.2).

RIGOR

This lesson emphasizes a blend of **procedural skill and fluency** and **application**.

- Students examine graphs of transformations to identify information to accurately solve problems.
- Students apply their understanding of graphs and coordinates to find required transformations.

## Language Support

### Lesson Language Objective

Tell how to use a sequence of transformations including dilations to show that figures are similar.

Additional resources are available in the **Language Support Handbook**.

## Math Anytime

### Today's Challenge

Use the Topic 6 problems any time during this topic.

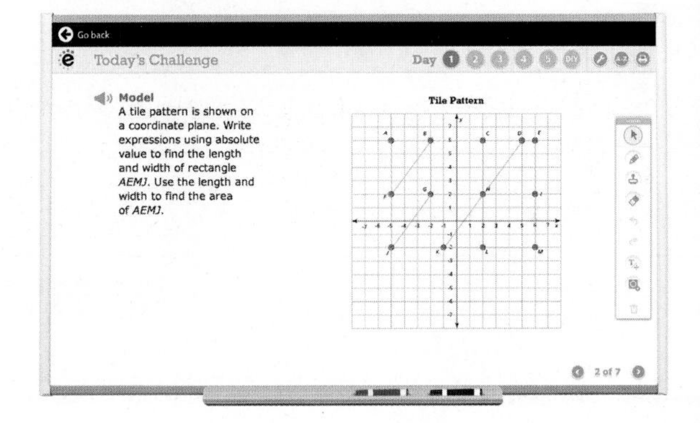


## Mathematics Overview | Common Core Standards

### Content Standards

In this lesson, you will focus on Common Core Standards **8.G.A.3** and **8.G.A.4**.

- **8.G.A.3** Describe the effect of dilations, translations, rotations, and reflections on two-dimensional figures using coordinates.
- **8.G.A.4** Understand that a two-dimensional figure is similar to another if the second can be obtained from the first by a sequence of rotations, reflections, translations, and dilations; given two similar two-dimensional figures, describe a sequence that exhibits the similarity between them.

### Mathematical Practice Standards

**MP.2 Reason Abstractly and Quantitatively**
Students will use their knowledge of transformations to decide if figures are similar. Students will be able to verify similarity through sequences of transformations.

**MP.8 Generalize**
Students will repeatedly apply the mapping formula $(x, y) \rightarrow (kx, ky)$ to sequences of transformations and dilations, working algebraically with coordinates and visually with graphs to solve problems.

STEP 1 | Problem-Based Learning

15-20 min

Go Online

Activity

# Solve & Discuss It!

**Purpose** Students compare two figures on a coordinate plane and connect it to understanding similarity in the Visual Learning Bridge.

## ETP Before — WHOLE CLASS

### 1 Introduce the Problem

Provide graph paper, rulers, and protractors, as needed.

### 2 Check for Understanding of the Problem

Ensure students understand the problem by drawing two squares on the board, one larger than the other, and asking students how the figures are alike and how they are different.

## ETP During — SMALL GROUP

### 3 Observe Students at Work

Students will describe how the shapes are alike and different. They might say the figures are alike because both figures are right triangles, they have the same shape, and they also have the same orientation. Students may observe that the triangles have the same shape by referencing angles or ratios of side lengths. Students might say the figures are different because they have different side lengths and $\triangle A'B'C'$ is smaller than $\triangle ABC$. needed, ask Is there anything you learned in the previous lesson that can help you solve this problem?

### Early Finishers

How would the problem change if point $C'$ was located at (0, 1)? [Sample answer: Both figures remain right triangles, but they would have different shapes.]

## ETP After — WHOLE CLASS

### 4 Discuss Solution Strategies and Key Ideas

Consider having groups share how the two figures are alike first, followed by how they are different. Have students discuss the characteristics they can use to compare the two triangles; side lengths, angle measures, and orientation.

Have students discuss the "clues" in the drawing that let them know the two triangles are related; the triangles are labeled with the same letters except the smaller triangle has prime marks next to its letters.

### 5 Consider Instructional Implications

After presenting Example 1, refer students back to the problem in the Solve & Discuss It and have them determine whether the triangles are similar; yes, the triangles are similar since you can map $\triangle ABC$ onto $\triangle A'B'C'$ by translating $\triangle ABC$ down 1 unit then dilating by a scale factor of $\frac{1}{2}$ with the center at the origin.

## Analyze Student Work

**Solve and Discuss It!** Activity is available online.

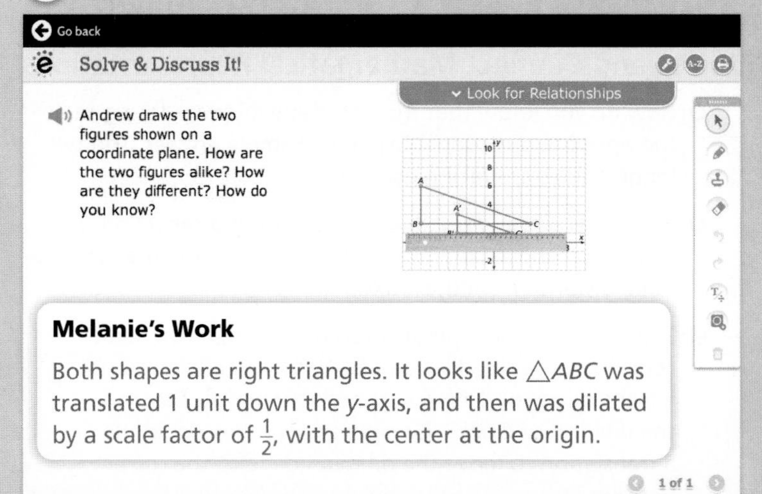


**Melanie** makes use of the coordinate plane to distinguish facts about the two figures.

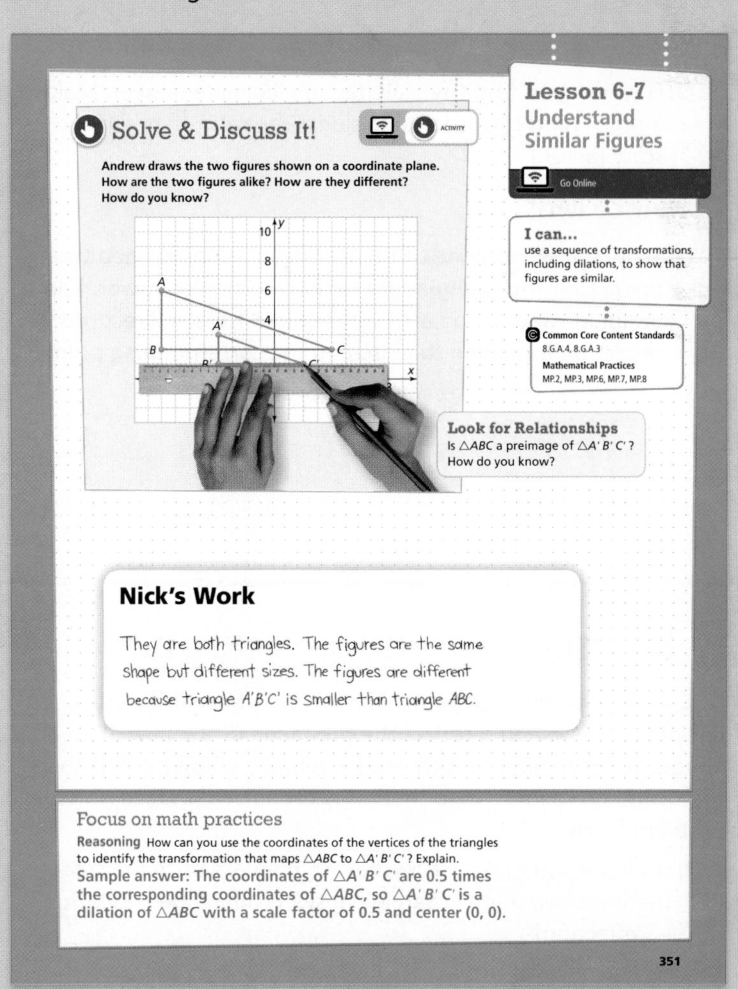

Lesson 6-7 Understand Similar Figures

Solve & Discuss It!

Andrew draws the two figures shown on a coordinate plane. How are the two figures alike? How are they different? How do you know?

I can… use a sequence of transformations, including dilations, to show that figures are similar.

Common Core Content Standards 8.G.A.4, 8.G.A.3
Mathematical Practices MP.2, MP.3, MP.6, MP.7, MP.8

Look for Relationships Is $\triangle ABC$ a preimage of $\triangle A'B'C'$? How do you know?

Nick's Work

They are both triangles. The figures are the same shape but different sizes. The figures are different because triangle A'B'C' is smaller than triangle ABC.

Focus on math practices

Reasoning How can you use the coordinates of the vertices of the triangles to identify the transformation that maps $\triangle ABC$ to $\triangle A'B'C'$? Explain.
Sample answer: The coordinates of $\triangle A'B'C'$ are 0.5 times the corresponding coordinates of $\triangle ABC$, so $\triangle A'B'C'$ is a dilation of $\triangle ABC$ with a scale factor of 0.5 and center (0, 0).

351

**Nick** uses his observation of the figures themselves to state how they are alike and different.

Go Online

Visual Learning

Assess

# STEP 2 | Visual Learning

##  Establish Mathematics Goals to Focus Learning

Engage students in a discussion about the ***Essential Question***. Make sure they understand how to perform different transformations on a given figure.

## EXAMPLE 1  Understand Similarity

### ETP Use and Connect Mathematical Representations

**Q:** How do you know that the two trapezoids are facing in the opposite directions? Explain. [Sample answer: The two longest sides are facing each other.]

**Q:** How do you know the dilation of *GHJK* is a reflection of *ABCD* over the *x*-axis? [Sample answer: Both figures are the same distance from the *x*-axis.]

**Q:** Suppose the reflection of *ABCD* did not have the same coordinates as the dilation of *GHJK*. How could you use a transformation to map the reflection of *ABCD* onto the dilation of *GHJK*? [Sample answer: You could use a translation to move the dilated image to the correct position.]

##  Try It!  Formative Assessment

###  Elicit and Use Evidence of Student Thinking

**Q:** How can you find the scale factor? [Sample answer: Make a ratio using corresponding sides. The ratio $\frac{18}{8}$ or $\frac{9}{4}$ is the scale factor.]

### Convince Me!

**Q:** Why is reflection one of the transformations needed to prove that the triangles are similar? [Sample answer: The preimage and image are pointing in different directions. A reflection is needed to match up the corresponding points.]

**Visual Learning Animation Plus** is available online.

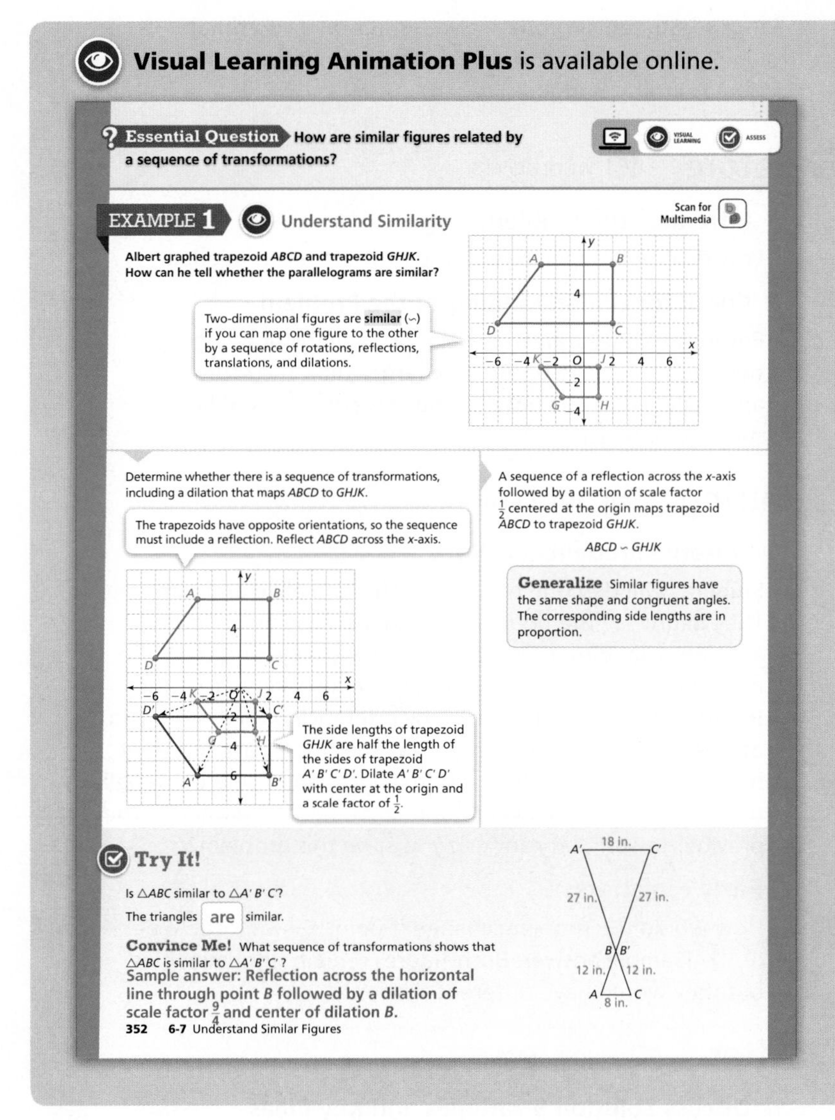
? Essential Question How are similar figures related by a sequence of transformations?

EXAMPLE 1 Understand Similarity

Scan for Multimedia

Albert graphed trapezoid *ABCD* and trapezoid *GHJK*. How can he tell whether the parallelograms are similar?

Two-dimensional figures are **similar** (~) if you can map one figure to the other by a sequence of rotations, reflections, translations, and dilations.

Determine whether there is a sequence of transformations, including a dilation that maps *ABCD* to *GHJK*.

The trapezoids have opposite orientations, so the sequence must include a reflection. Reflect *ABCD* across the *x*-axis.

The side lengths of trapezoid *GHJK* are half the length of the sides of trapezoid *A′B′C′D′*. Dilate *A′B′C′D′* with center at the origin and a scale factor of $\frac{1}{2}$.

A sequence of a reflection across the *x*-axis followed by a dilation of scale factor $\frac{1}{2}$ centered at the origin maps trapezoid *ABCD* to trapezoid *GHJK*.

*ABCD* ~ *GHJK*

**Generalize** Similar figures have the same shape and congruent angles. The corresponding side lengths are in proportion.

Try It!

Is △*ABC* similar to △*A′B′C′*?

The triangles are similar.

**Convince Me!** What sequence of transformations shows that △*ABC* is similar to △*A′B′C′*?

Sample answer: Reflection across the horizontal line through point *B* followed by a dilation of scale factor $\frac{9}{4}$ and center of dilation *B*.

352 6-7 Understand Similar Figures

Students can access the ***Visual Learning Animation Plus*** by using the **BouncePages app** to scan this page. Students can download the app for free in their mobile devices' app store.

##  Response to Intervention

**USE WITH EXAMPLE 2** Some students may have difficulty deciding if they should reflect the preimage or the new dilated image. You may wish to have students make a flowchart at the top of the problem to help them stay organized and see how the problem flows.

**Q:** How can you make a flowchart to help organize the steps of the transformation? [Sample answer: preimage → dilation → reflection]

##  Enrichment

**USE WITH EXAMPLE 2** Challenge advanced students to determine if the order of the transformations affects the placement of the final image. First have students create and record a formal prediction. Then have students prove or disprove their prediction by creating their own preimage and list of two transformations. Have them complete the transformations in both orders and investigate whether the answer is the same. Finally have them write a concluding sentence to state whether their prediction was true or false and explain the results.

Go Online

 Activity  Assess

## EXAMPLE 2  Complete a Similarity Transformation

### ETP Pose Purposeful Questions

**Q:** In Step 2, why do each of the letters have two marks? [Sample answer: They indicate an image of the image.]

**Q:** Why is the figure $J'K'L'M'$ created? [Sample answer: The problem contains more than one transformation. This is the middle step.]

**Q:** Do you think there is a dilation that would map *JKLM* directly on to $J''K''L''M''$? Explain. [No; Sample answer: The dilation does not change the orientation, and *JKLM* and $J''K''L''M''$ have opposite orientations.]

## EXAMPLE 3  Identify Similar Figures

### ETP Pose Purposeful Questions

**Q:** What are the coordinates of the vertices of $A'B'C'D'$ after the 180° rotation? [Sample answer: $A'(-4, -4)$, $B'(-8, -4)$, $C'(-6, 2)$, $(-2, 2)$]

**Q:** How do you know that corresponding angles are equal in Figures *ABCD* and *EFGH*? [Sample answer: None of the transformations changes the angle measure. Since a series of transformations can map *ABCD* directly onto *EFGH*, they have congruent corresponding angles.]

##  Try It!  Formative Assessment

### ETP Elicit and Use Evidence of Student Thinking

**Q:** What are the coordinates *JKL* after the reflection? [$J'(4, -4)$, $K'(6, 0)$, $L'(4, 1)$]

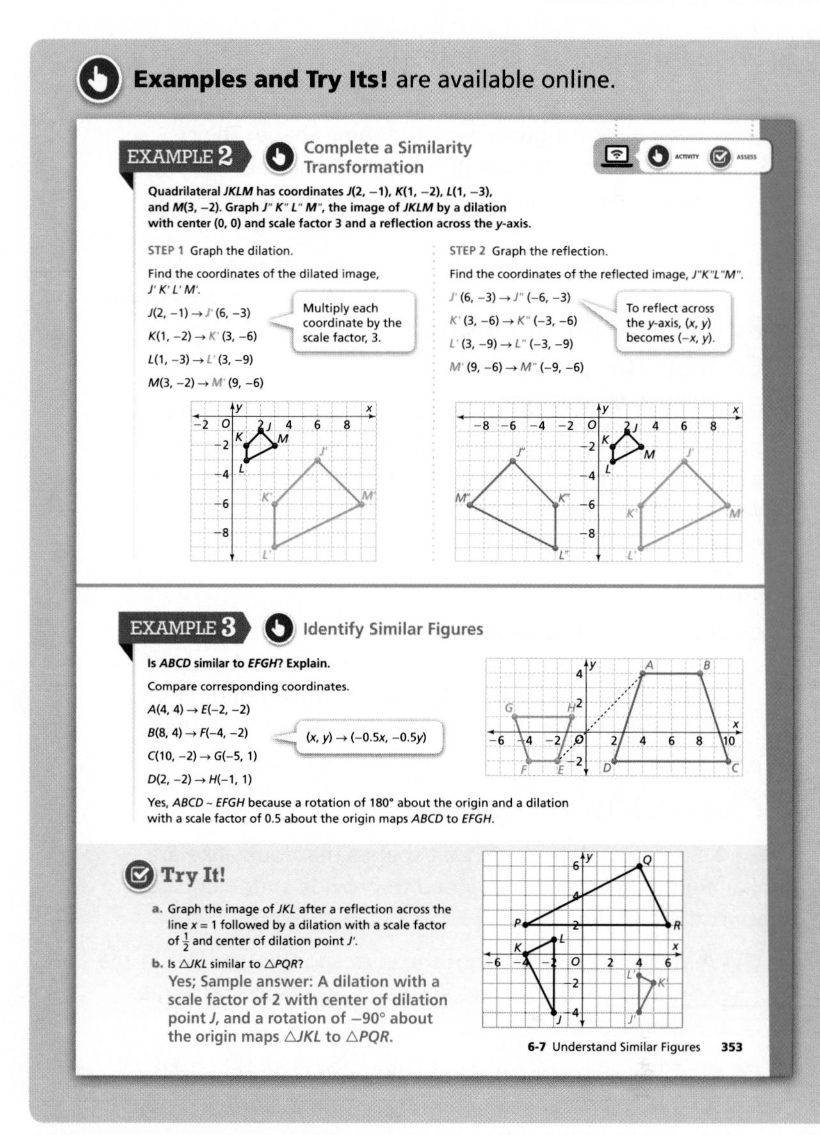

**Examples and Try Its!** are available online.

EXAMPLE 2 Complete a Similarity Transformation

ACTIVITY ASSESS

**Quadrilateral *JKLM* has coordinates $J(2, -1)$, $K(1, -2)$, $L(1, -3)$, and $M(3, -2)$. Graph $J''K''L''M''$, the image of *JKLM* by a dilation with center (0, 0) and scale factor 3 and a reflection across the *y*-axis.**

STEP 1 Graph the dilation.

Find the coordinates of the dilated image, $J'K'L'M'$.

$J(2, -1) \rightarrow J'(6, -3)$

$K(1, -2) \rightarrow K'(3, -6)$

$L(1, -3) \rightarrow L'(3, -9)$

$M(3, -2) \rightarrow M'(9, -6)$

Multiply each coordinate by the scale factor, 3.

STEP 2 Graph the reflection.

Find the coordinates of the reflected image, $J''K''L''M''$.

$J'(6, -3) \rightarrow J''(-6, -3)$

$K'(3, -6) \rightarrow K''(-3, -6)$

$L'(3, -9) \rightarrow L''(-3, -9)$

$M'(9, -6) \rightarrow M''(-9, -6)$

To reflect across the *y*-axis, $(x, y)$ becomes $(-x, y)$.

EXAMPLE 3 Identify Similar Figures

**Is *ABCD* similar to *EFGH*? Explain.**

Compare corresponding coordinates.

$A(4, 4) \rightarrow E(-2, -2)$

$B(8, 4) \rightarrow F(-4, -2)$

$C(10, -2) \rightarrow G(-5, 1)$

$D(2, -2) \rightarrow H(-1, 1)$

$(x, y) \rightarrow (-0.5x, -0.5y)$

Yes, $ABCD \sim EFGH$ because a rotation of 180° about the origin and a dilation with a scale factor of 0.5 about the origin maps *ABCD* to *EFGH*.

Try It!

a. Graph the image of *JKL* after a reflection across the line $x = 1$ followed by a dilation with a scale factor of $\frac{1}{2}$ and center of dilation point $J'$.

b. Is $\triangle JKL$ similar to $\triangle PQR$?

Yes; Sample answer: A dilation with a scale factor of 2 with center of dilation point *J*, and a rotation of −90° about the origin maps $\triangle JKL$ to $\triangle PQR$.

6-7 Understand Similar Figures 353

## ADDITIONAL EXAMPLES 

**For additional examples go online.**

## ELL English Language Learners

**EMERGING** Ask students to read Example 1.

Help students review their knowledge of transformations. Have students describe how each figure would move.

**Q:** Translation 1 left, 2 up and reflection over the *x*-axis.

**Q:** Rotation of 90° around the origin and dilation with a scale factor of 3 centered at the origin.

**Q:** Reflection across the *x*-axis and reflection across the *y*-axis.

**Q:** Dilation with scale factor 2 centered at the origin and a reflection over the line $x = 2$.

**DEVELOPING** Ask students to read Example 3.

Have students write a summary of the overall process in their own words.

**Q:** What are some ways to transform a figure on a coordinate plane? [Rotation, reflection, translation, dilation]

**Q:** What does it mean that one figure is mapped to another figure? [Sample answer: It means that a figure is moved onto another figure.]

**EXPANDING** Ask students to read Example 3.

Have students work with a partner. Read the problem aloud, and use mental math to explain their reasoning and/or suggestion. Have pairs of students focus on words they may not be familiar with, such as *corresponding*. Have them discuss why these words are important to the problem.

Go Online

 Key Concept  Assess  Activity

## KEY CONCEPT

### ETP Pose Purposeful Questions

**Q:** What characteristics do similar figures share? [Sample answer: Similar figures have the same shape. Their corresponding sides are proportional and their corresponding angles are congruent.]

## Do You Understand/Do You Know How?

**Formative** Assessment

### ETP Build Procedural Fluency from Conceptual Understanding

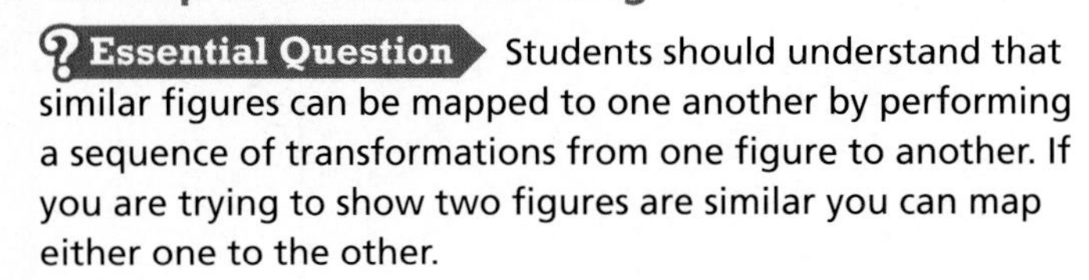

**Essential Question** Students should understand that similar figures can be mapped to one another by performing a sequence of transformations from one figure to another. If you are trying to show two figures are similar you can map either one to the other.

**ITEM 2**

**Q:** What is meant by a ratio of similar figures? Does this ratio affect the angle measures? [Sample answer: A ratio of similar figures is the ratio formed by corresponding side lengths. This ratio does not affect the angle measures.]

### Prevent Misconceptions

**ITEM 4** Students often think that shapes that look alike are similar. Remind students they need to provide statements to support their answer.

**Q:** What do you notice about the corresponding angles in the two trapezoids? [Sample answer: Corresponding angles are congruent.]

**Q:** What transformations would map *ABCD* onto *EFGH*? [Sample answer: A reduction by a scale factor of $\frac{1}{2}$ and a translation to the right and up.]

Available Online

KEY CONCEPT 

Two-dimensional figures are similar if there is a sequence of rotations, reflections, translations, and dilations that maps one figure onto the other.

**Do You Understand?**

1. **Essential Question** How are similar figures related by a sequence of transformations? Sample answer: Two figures are similar if you can map one figure to the other by a sequence of transformations including dilations.

2. Be Precise How do the angle measures and side lengths compare in similar figures? Sample answer: Corresponding angles are congruent and corresponding side lengths are related by the same ratio.

3. Generalize Does a given translation, reflection, or rotation, followed by a given dilation, always map a figure to the same image as that same dilation followed by that same translation, reflection, or rotation? Explain. No; Sample answer: A given translation, reflection, or rotation followed by a given dilation does not always map a figure to the same image as the same dilation followed by the same translation, reflection, or rotation. Check students' work.

**Do You Know How?**

4. Is trapezoid *ABCD* ~ trapezoid *EFGH*? Explain.

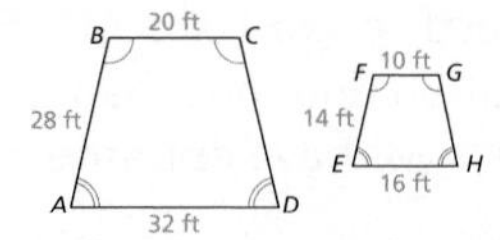


Yes; Sample answer: The figures have the same shape. Corresponding angles have the same angle measure, and corresponding sides have a ratio of $\frac{1}{2}$.

Use the graph for 5 and 6.

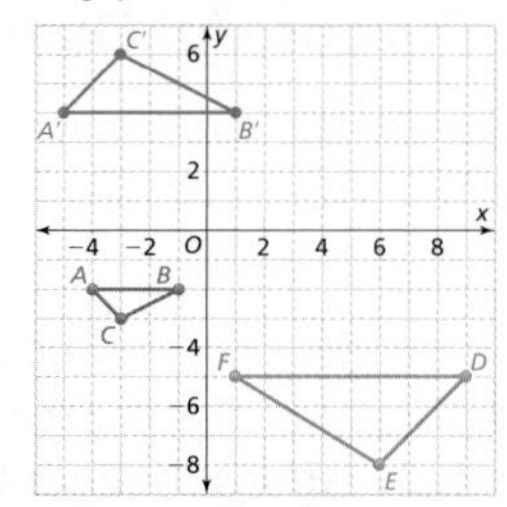


5. $\triangle ABC$ is dilated by a factor of 2 with a center of dilation at point C, reflected across the x-axis, and translated 3 units up. Graph the resulting similar figure. Check students' graphs.

6. Is $\triangle ABC$ similar to $\triangle DEF$? Explain. No; Sample answer: There is no sequence of transformations, including a dilation, that maps $\triangle ABC$ to $\triangle DEF$.

354 6-7 Understand Similar Figures

## ADDITIONAL EXAMPLE 1

Help students transition to solving problems with composite figures.

Make sure students understand that the ratio of side lengths must be the same for all sides in order for the figures to be similar.

**Q:** What is the ratio of side lengths of sides *AD* and *WZ*? [$\frac{3}{8}$]

**Q:** What is the ratio of side lengths of sides *CD* and *YZ*? [$\frac{1}{3}$]

**Additional Examples** are available online.

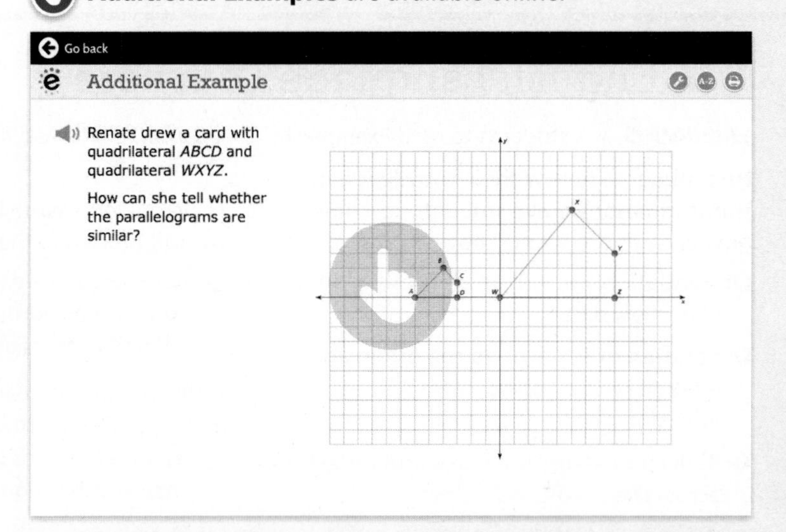


**Answer:** Shapes are not similar; There are different ratios for side lengths between the quadrilaterals. *YZ* is 3 times *CD*, but *WZ* is less than 3 times *AD*.

Go Online

Practice

Tutorials

Math Tools

# Practice & Problem Solving  

**Interactive Practice** and **Virtual Nerd Tutorials** are available online.

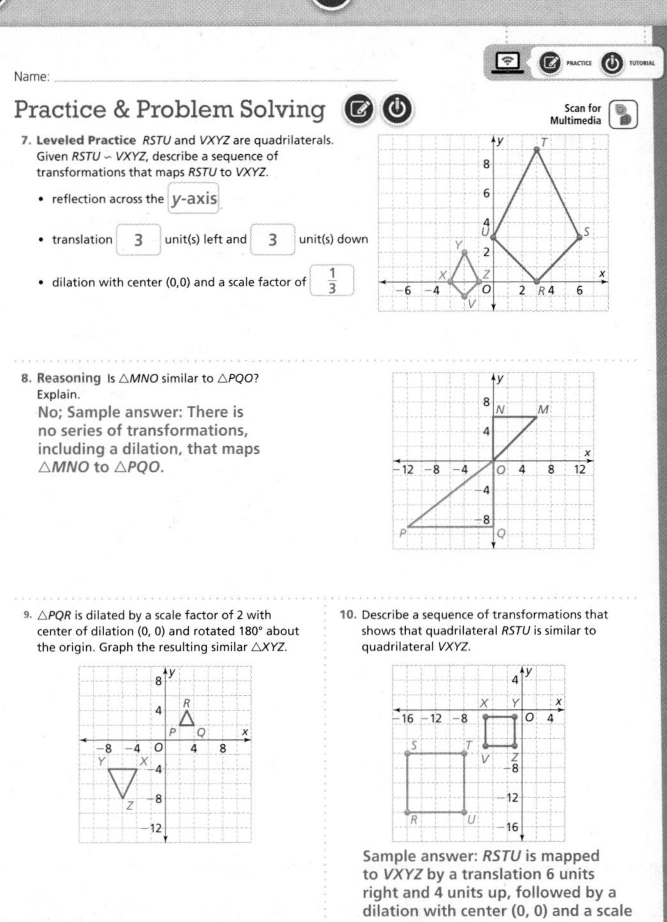

Name:

Practice & Problem Solving

Scan for Multimedia

7. **Leveled Practice** *RSTU* and *VXYZ* are quadrilaterals. Given *RSTU* ~ *VXYZ*, describe a sequence of transformations that maps *RSTU* to *VXYZ*.
   - reflection across the *y*-axis
   - translation 3 unit(s) left and 3 unit(s) down
   - dilation with center (0,0) and a scale factor of $\frac{1}{3}$

8. **Reasoning** Is $\triangle MNO$ similar to $\triangle PQO$? Explain.
   No; Sample answer: There is no series of transformations, including a dilation, that maps $\triangle MNO$ to $\triangle PQO$.

9. $\triangle PQR$ is dilated by a scale factor of 2 with center of dilation (0, 0) and rotated 180° about the origin. Graph the resulting similar $\triangle XYZ$.

10. Describe a sequence of transformations that shows that quadrilateral *RSTU* is similar to quadrilateral *VXYZ*.
    Sample answer: *RSTU* is mapped to *VXYZ* by a translation 6 units right and 4 units up, followed by a dilation with center (0, 0) and a scale factor of 0.5.

6-7 Understand Similar Figures 355

11. **Construct Arguments** Is $\triangle PQR$ similar to $\triangle XYZ$? Explain.
    Yes; Sample answer: Rotation 90° about the origin followed by a dilation with center at the origin and a scale factor of 2 maps $\triangle PQR$ to $\triangle XYZ$.

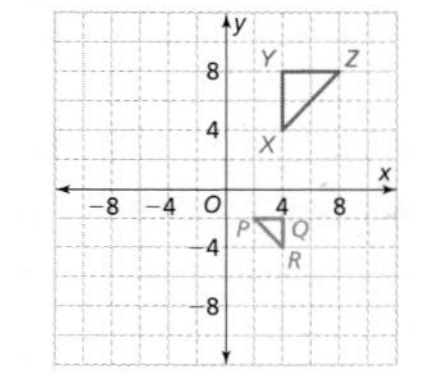

12. **Higher Order Thinking** Given $\triangle JKL \sim \triangle XYZ$, find two possible coordinates for missing point *Y*. For each coordinate chosen, describe a sequence of transformations, including a dilation, that will map $\triangle JKL$ to $\triangle XYZ$.
    Sample answer: Coordinate 1: (0, 2): translation 4 units left and dilation with center point *Z* and a scale factor of 0.5; Coordinate 2: (−4, 2): reflection across *y*-axis, and dilation with center point *Z* and a scale factor of 0.5

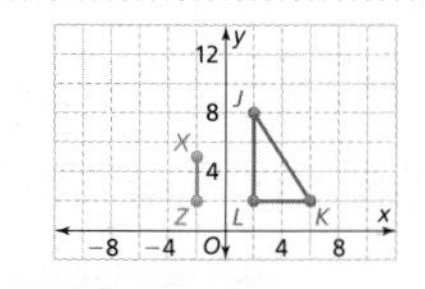

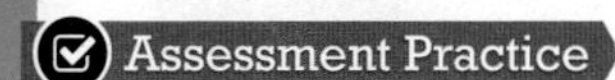

## Assessment Practice

13. Rajesh is making pennants in preparation for a school soccer game. He wants the pennants to be similar triangles. Which of these triangles could he use for the pennants?
    Ⓐ $\triangle QRS$ and $\triangle TVW$
    ● $\triangle QRS$ and $\triangle XYZ$
    Ⓒ $\triangle TVW$ and $\triangle JKL$
    Ⓓ $\triangle TVW$ and $\triangle XYZ$

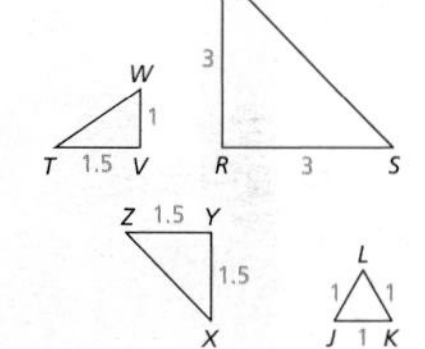

14. Determine whether the following pairs of triangles are similar or not similar.

| | Similar | Not Similar |
|---|---|---|
| $\triangle ABC$ and $\triangle DEF$ | ■ | □ |
| $\triangle ABC$ and $\triangle LMN$ | □ | ■ |
| $\triangle LMN$ and $\triangle DEF$ | □ | ■ |

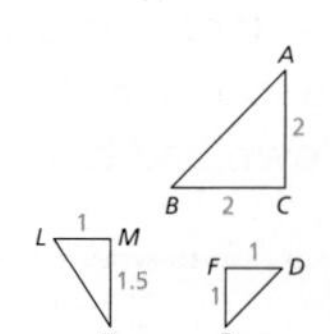

356 6-7 Understand Similar Figures

## Error Intervention

**ITEM 9** Students may correctly change the side lengths of the triangle, but may dilate it about point *P* rather than the origin.

**Q:** How can you use the coordinates of each vertex and the scale factor to dilate a figure? [Sample answer: Multiply each value in the coordinate by the scale factor.]

**Q:** Where will the coordinate of *P*′ be? [(2, 2)]

## Challenge

**ITEM 8** You can use this item to extend students' understanding of similar objects.

**Q:** How could you change the coordinate of point *M* so that the figures are similar? [Sample answer: Change point *M* to be graphed at (8, 6).]

You may opt to have students complete the automatically scored Practice & Problem Solving items online.

### Item Analysis

| Example | Items | DOK |
|---|---|---|
| 1 | 7, 10 | 2 |
| 2 | 9, 11, 12 | 2 |
| 3 | 8, 13, 14 | 2 |

# STEP 3 | Assess & Differentiate

Go Online

Assess Tutorials Worksheets

## Lesson Quiz

**Formative** Assessment

Use the student scores on the Lesson Quiz to prescribe differentiated assignments.

**I Intervention** 0–3 Points **O On-Level** 4 Points **A Advanced** 5 Points

You may opt to have students take the Lesson Quiz online. The Lesson Quiz will be automatically scored, and appropriate remediation, practice, or enrichment will be assigned based on student performance.

**Lesson Quiz** is available online.

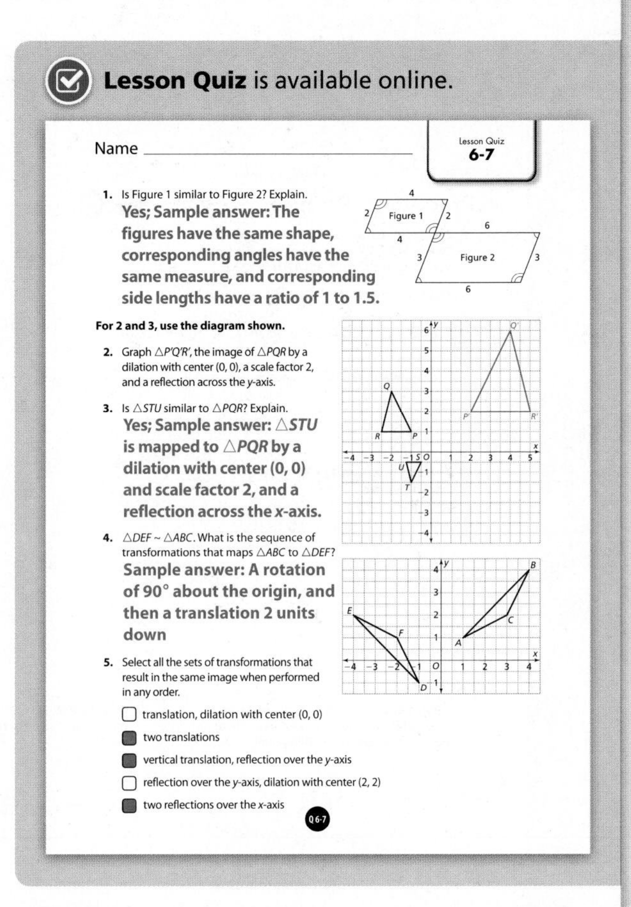

Name ______________ Lesson Quiz 6-7

1. Is Figure 1 similar to Figure 2? Explain.
Yes; Sample answer: The figures have the same shape, corresponding angles have the same measure, and corresponding side lengths have a ratio of 1 to 1.5.

For 2 and 3, use the diagram shown.

2. Graph $\triangle P'Q'R'$, the image of $\triangle PQR$ by a dilation with center (0, 0), a scale factor 2, and a reflection across the y-axis.

3. Is $\triangle STU$ similar to $\triangle PQR$? Explain.
Yes; Sample answer: $\triangle STU$ is mapped to $\triangle PQR$ by a dilation with center (0, 0) and scale factor 2, and a reflection across the x-axis.

4. $\triangle DEF \sim \triangle ABC$. What is the sequence of transformations that maps $\triangle ABC$ to $\triangle DEF$?
Sample answer: A rotation of 90° about the origin, and then a translation 2 units down

5. Select all the sets of transformations that result in the same image when performed in any order.
- ☐ translation, dilation with center (0, 0)
- ■ two translations
- ■ vertical translation, reflection over the y-axis
- ☐ reflection over the y-axis, dilation with center (2, 2)
- ■ two reflections over the x-axis

## Video Tutorials

Students can access instructional tutorials using the **Virtual Nerd app**.

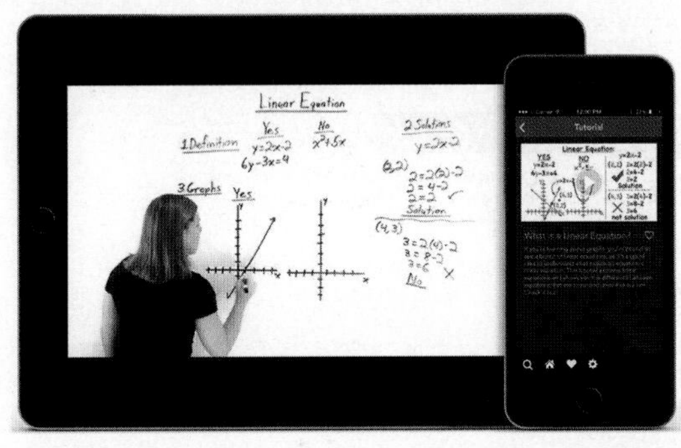

Students can also access the videos using the **BouncePages app** to scan exercise pages marked with this icon. Students can download both apps for free in their mobile devices' app store.

## Differentiated Intervention

**I** = Intervention **O** = On-Level **A** = Advanced

### Reteach to Build Understanding I

Provides scaffolded reteaching for the key lesson concepts.

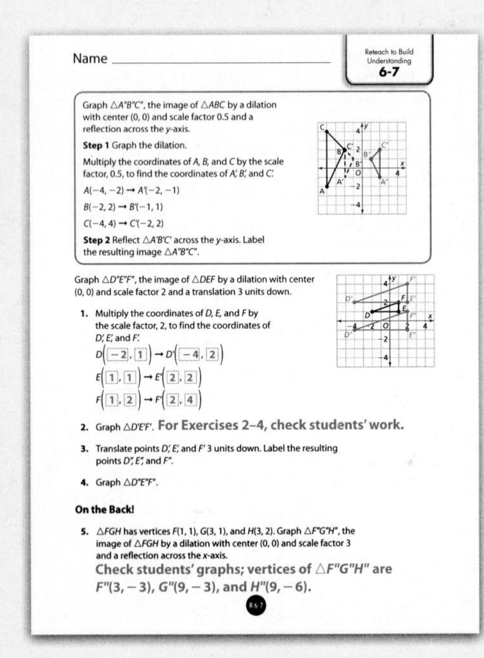

Name ______________ Reteach to Build Understanding 6-7

Graph $\triangle A''B''C''$, the image of $\triangle ABC$ by a dilation with center (0, 0) and scale factor 0.5 and a reflection across the y-axis.

**Step 1** Graph the dilation.
Multiply the coordinates of A, B, and C by the scale factor, 0.5, to find the coordinates of A′, B′, and C′.
$A(-4, -2) \rightarrow A'(-2, -1)$
$B(-2, 2) \rightarrow B'(-1, 1)$
$C(-4, 4) \rightarrow C'(-2, 2)$

**Step 2** Reflect $\triangle A'B'C'$ across the y-axis. Label the resulting image $\triangle A''B''C''$.

Graph $\triangle D''E''F''$, the image of $\triangle DEF$ by a dilation with center (0, 0) and scale factor 2 and a translation 3 units down.

1. Multiply the coordinates of D, E, and F by the scale factor, 2, to find the coordinates of D′, E′, and F′.
$D(-2, 1) \rightarrow D'(-4, 2)$
$E(1, 1) \rightarrow E'(2, 2)$
$F(1, 2) \rightarrow F'(2, 4)$
2. Graph $\triangle D'E'F'$. For Exercises 2–4, check students' work.
3. Translate points D′, E′, and F′ 3 units down. Label the resulting points D″, E″, and F″.
4. Graph $\triangle D''E''F''$.

**On the Back!**

5. $\triangle FGH$ has vertices F(1, 1), G(3, 1), and H(3, 2). Graph $\triangle F''G''H''$, the image of $\triangle FGH$ by a dilation with center (0, 0) and scale factor 3 and a reflection across the x-axis.
Check students' graphs; vertices of $\triangle F''G''H''$ are $F''(3, -3)$, $G''(9, -3)$, and $H''(9, -6)$.

### Additional Vocabulary Support I O

Helps students develop and reinforce understanding of key terms and concepts.

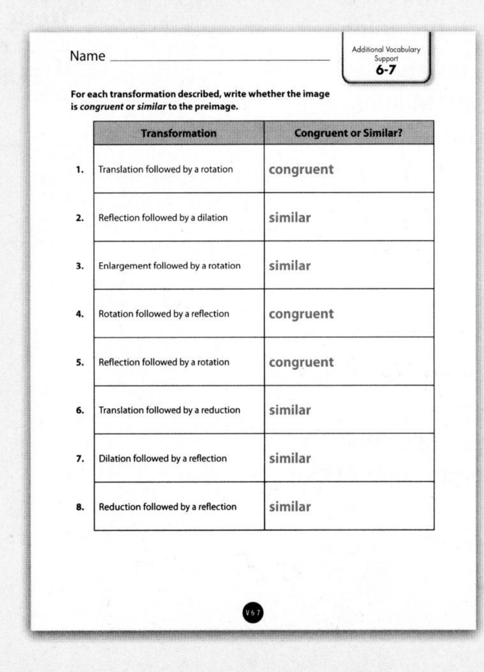

Name ______________ Additional Vocabulary Support 6-7

For each transformation described, write whether the image is *congruent* or *similar* to the preimage.

| | Transformation | Congruent or Similar? |
|---|---|---|
| 1. | Translation followed by a rotation | congruent |
| 2. | Reflection followed by a dilation | similar |
| 3. | Enlargement followed by a rotation | similar |
| 4. | Rotation followed by a reflection | congruent |
| 5. | Reflection followed by a rotation | congruent |
| 6. | Translation followed by a reduction | similar |
| 7. | Dilation followed by a reflection | similar |
| 8. | Reduction followed by a reflection | similar |

### Build Mathematical Literacy I O

Provides support for struggling readers to build mathematical literacy.

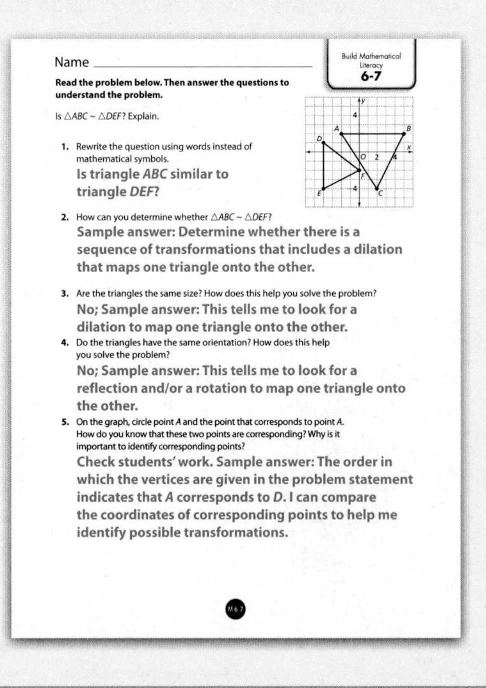

Name ______________ Build Mathematical Literacy 6-7

Read the problem below. Then answer the questions to understand the problem.

Is $\triangle ABC \sim \triangle DEF$? Explain.

1. Rewrite the question using words instead of mathematical symbols.
Is triangle ABC similar to triangle DEF?
2. How can you determine whether $\triangle ABC \sim \triangle DEF$?
Sample answer: Determine whether there is a sequence of transformations that includes a dilation that maps one triangle onto the other.
3. Are the triangles the same size? How does this help you solve the problem?
No; Sample answer: This tells me to look for a dilation to map one triangle onto the other.
4. Do the triangles have the same orientation? How does this help you solve the problem?
No; Sample answer: This tells me to look for a reflection and/or a rotation to map one triangle onto the other.
5. On the graph, circle point A and the point that corresponds to point A. How do you know that these two points are corresponding? Why is it important to identify corresponding points?
Check students' work. Sample answer: The order in which the vertices are given in the problem statement indicates that A corresponds to D. I can compare the coordinates of corresponding points to help me identify possible transformations.

Go Online

Practice | Worksheets | Math Tools | Math Games

# Additional Practice

You may opt to have students complete the automatically scored Additional Practice items online.

### Item Analysis

| Example | Items | DOK |
|---|---|---|
| 1 | 1 | 1 |
| | 4, 6 | 2 |
| 2 | 3 | 2 |
| | 7 | 3 |
| 3 | 2, 5 | 2 |

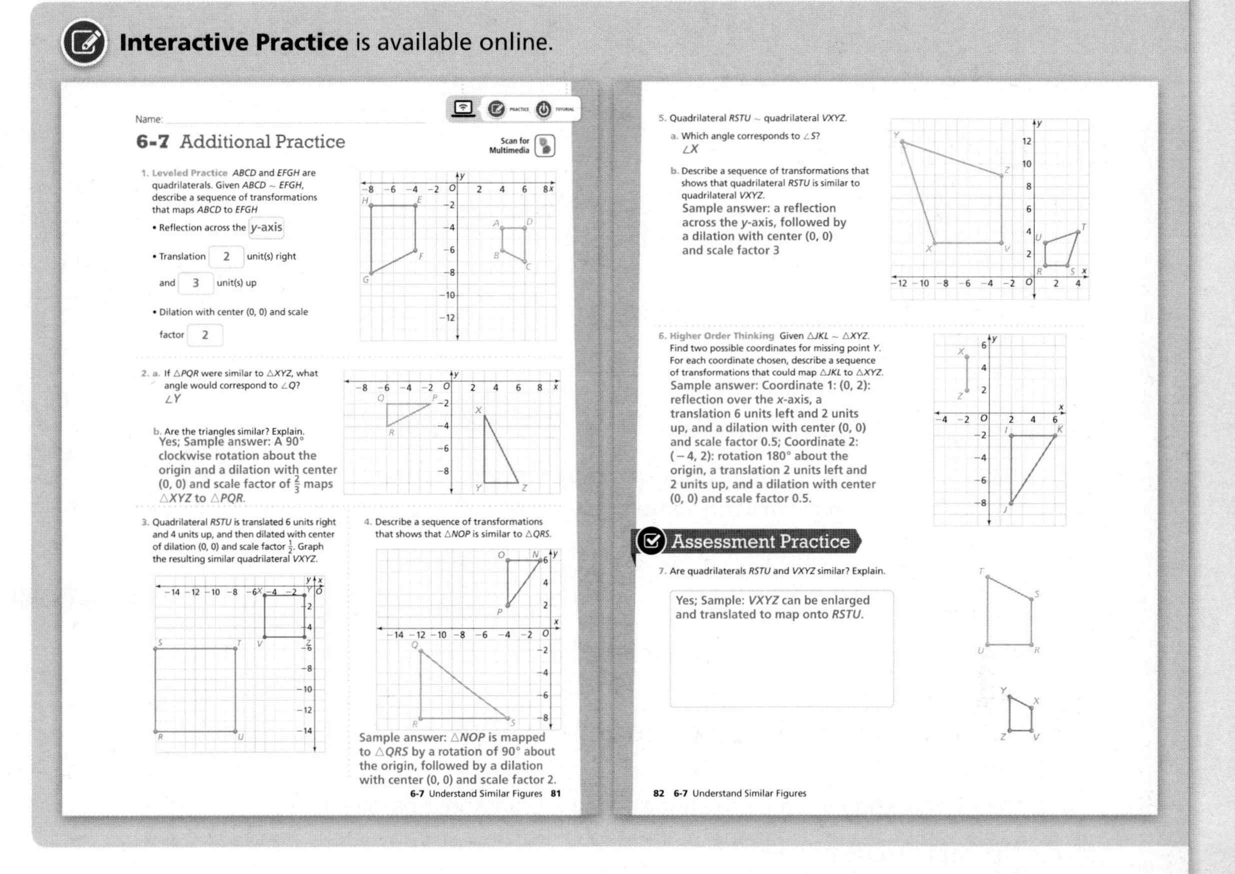

**Interactive Practice** is available online.

Name:

## 6-7 Additional Practice

Scan for Multimedia

1. Leveled Practice *ABCD* and *EFGH* are quadrilaterals. Given *ABCD* ~ *EFGH*, describe a sequence of transformations that maps *ABCD* to *EFGH*
   - Reflection across the *y*-axis
   - Translation 2 unit(s) right and 3 unit(s) up
   - Dilation with center (0, 0) and scale factor 2

2. a. If △*PQR* were similar to △*XYZ*, what angle would correspond to ∠*Q*?
   ∠*Y*

   b. Are the triangles similar? Explain.
   Yes; Sample answer: A 90° clockwise rotation about the origin and a dilation with center (0, 0) and scale factor of $\frac{2}{3}$ maps △*XYZ* to △*PQR*.

3. Quadrilateral *RSTU* is translated 6 units right and 4 units up, and then dilated with center of dilation (0, 0) and scale factor $\frac{1}{2}$. Graph the resulting similar quadrilateral *VXYZ*.

4. Describe a sequence of transformations that shows that △*NOP* is similar to △*QRS*.
   Sample answer: △*NOP* is mapped to △*QRS* by a rotation of 90° about the origin, followed by a dilation with center (0, 0) and scale factor 2.

6-7 Understand Similar Figures 81

5. Quadrilateral *RSTU* ~ quadrilateral *VXYZ*.
   a. Which angle corresponds to ∠*S*?
   ∠*X*

   b. Describe a sequence of transformations that shows that quadrilateral *RSTU* is similar to quadrilateral *VXYZ*.
   Sample answer: a reflection across the *y*-axis, followed by a dilation with center (0, 0) and scale factor 3

6. Higher Order Thinking Given △*JKL* ~ △*XYZ*. Find two possible coordinates for missing point *Y*. For each coordinate chosen, describe a sequence of transformations that could map △*JKL* to △*XYZ*.
   Sample answer: Coordinate 1: (0, 2): reflection over the *x*-axis, a translation 6 units left and 2 units up, and a dilation with center (0, 0) and scale factor 0.5; Coordinate 2: (−4, 2): rotation 180° about the origin, a translation 2 units left and 2 units up, and a dilation with center (0, 0) and scale factor 0.5.

Assessment Practice

7. Are quadrilaterals *RSTU* and *VXYZ* similar? Explain.
   Yes; Sample: *VXYZ* can be enlarged and translated to map onto *RSTU*.

82 6-7 Understand Similar Figures

## Differentiated Intervention

I = Intervention  O = On-Level  A = Advanced

### Enrichment O A

Presents engaging problems and activities that extend the lesson concepts.

### Math Tools and Games I O A

Offers additional activities and games to build understanding and fluency.

### Pick a Project and STEM Project I O A

Provides an additional opportunity for students to demonstrate understanding of key mathematical concepts.

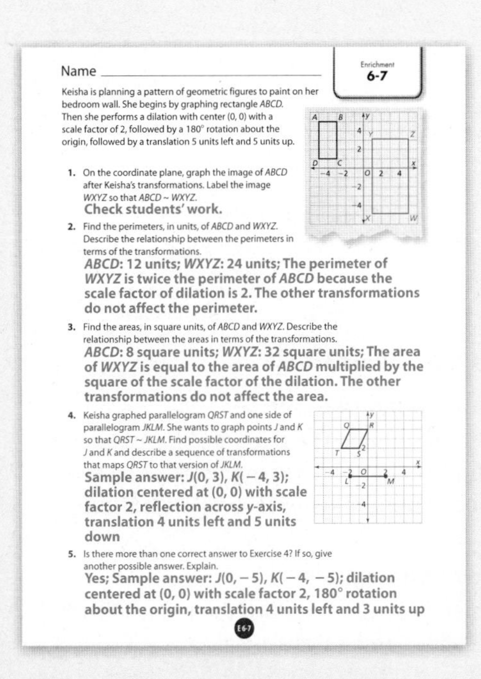

Name

Enrichment 6-7

Keisha is planning a pattern of geometric figures to paint on her bedroom wall. She begins by graphing rectangle *ABCD*. Then she performs a dilation with center (0, 0) with a scale factor of 2, followed by a 180° rotation about the origin, followed by a translation 5 units left and 5 units up.

1. On the coordinate plane, graph the image of *ABCD* after Keisha's transformations. Label the image *WXYZ* so that *ABCD* ~ *WXYZ*.
   Check students' work.
2. Find the perimeters, in units, of *ABCD* and *WXYZ*. Describe the relationship between the perimeters in terms of the transformations.
   *ABCD*: 12 units; *WXYZ*: 24 units; The perimeter of *WXYZ* is twice the perimeter of *ABCD* because the scale factor of dilation is 2. The other transformations do not affect the perimeter.
3. Find the areas, in square units, of *ABCD* and *WXYZ*. Describe the relationship between the areas in terms of the transformations.
   *ABCD*: 8 square units; *WXYZ*: 32 square units; The area of *WXYZ* is equal to the area of *ABCD* multiplied by the square of the scale factor of the dilation. The other transformations do not affect the area.
4. Keisha graphed parallelogram *QRST* and one side of parallelogram *JKLM*. She wants to graph points *J* and *K* so that *QRST* ~ *JKLM*. Find possible coordinates for *J* and *K* and describe a sequence of transformations that maps *QRST* to that version of *JKLM*.
   Sample answer: *J*(0, 3), *K*(−4, 3); dilation centered at (0, 0) with scale factor 2, reflection across *y*-axis, translation 4 units left and 5 units down
5. Is there more than one correct answer to Exercise 4? If so, give another possible answer. Explain.
   Yes; Sample answer: *J*(0, −5), *K*(−4, −5); dilation centered at (0, 0) with scale factor 2, 180° rotation about the origin, translation 4 units left and 3 units up

E 6-7

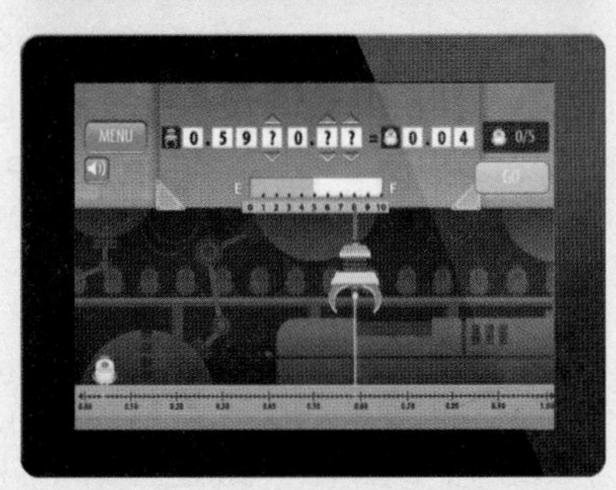

Go Online

Activity

# Lesson 6-8 Angles, Lines, and Transversals

## Lesson Overview

FOCUS

### Mathematics Objective

**Students will be able to:**

- ✔ identify relationships between angles formed by parallel lines and a transversal.
- ✔ determine the measures of angles formed by parallel lines and a transversal.
- ✔ reason about parallel lines.

### Essential Understanding

Corresponding angles and alternate interior angles formed by parallel lines and a transversal are congruent. Same-side interior angles are supplementary.

COHERENCE

**Previously in this topic, students:**

- worked with congruent figures and similar figures.

**In this lesson, students:**

- learn the special relationships of angles formed by parallel lines and a transversal.
- apply their knowledge of angle relationships to reason about parallel lines.

**Later in this topic, students will:**

- find the measures of angles in the interior and exterior of a triangle.
- show that triangles are similar.

RIGOR

This lesson emphasizes a blend of **conceptual understanding** and **procedural skill and fluency**.

- Students understand that the intersection of parallel lines and a transversal creates sets of angles whose measures have a relationship.
- Students draw conclusions about angles formed when parallel lines are cut by a transversal.

## Language Support

### Lesson Language Objective

Explain how to identify and find the measures of angles formed by parallel lines and a transversal.

Additional resources are available in the **Language Support Handbook**.

## Math Anytime

### Today's Challenge

Use the Topic 6 problems any time during this topic.

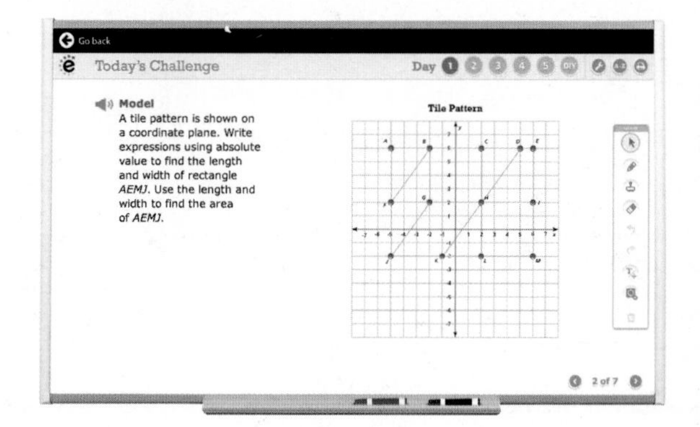


## Mathematics Overview | Common Core Standards

### Content Standards

In this lesson, you will focus on Common Core Standard **8.G.A.5**.

- **8.G.A.5** Use informal arguments to establish facts about the angle sum and exterior angle of triangles, about the angles created when parallel lines are cut by a transversal, and the angle-angle criterion for similarity of triangles.

### Mathematical Practice Standards

**MP.2 Reason Abstractly and Quantitatively**
Students use reasoning to determine the relationships between the angles formed by parallel lines and a transversal. They also write and solve equations to determine exact angle measures.

**MP.5 Use Appropriate Tools Strategically**
Students use protractors and rulers to explore the measures of angles formed by parallel lines and a transversal.

15-20 min

Go Online

Activity

# Solve & Discuss It!

Formative Assessment

**Purpose** Students analyze the relationships among angles formed by a line intersecting two parallel lines and connect it to the Visual Learning Bridge.

## ETP Before — WHOLE CLASS

**1 Introduce the Problem**

Provide rulers and protractors as needed.

**2 Check for Understanding of the Problem**

Activate prior knowledge by asking: What are the properties of parallel lines?

## ETP During — SMALL GROUP

**3 Observe Students at Work**

Student may measure all possible angles or use angle properties that they already know, such as supplementary and vertical angles in order to find angle measures. If needed, ask Are there any tools you can use to solve the problem?

**Early Finishers**

How would the problem change if the intersecting line is perpendicular to the parallel lines? [Sample answer: The angles formed are all congruent because they are all right angles.]

## ETP After — WHOLE CLASS

**4 Discuss Solution Strategies and Key Ideas**

Have students share the number of different angles they found. Any pair of parallel lines intersected by a single line forms eight angles which have either one of two possible measures.

Have them compare and discuss the connections they see; angles that occupy the same relative position at each intersection where the single line crosses the two parallel lines (corresponding angles) have the same measure. Angles on opposite sides of the single line between the two parallel lines have the same measure. Angles on the same side of the single line between the two parallel lines are supplementary.

**5 Consider Instructional Implications**

After presenting Example 1, refer students back to the diagram they drew for the problem in the Solve & Discuss It and have them identify the transversal, corresponding angles, alternate interior angles, and same-side interior angles.

## Analyze Student Work

**Solve and Discuss It!** Activity is available online.

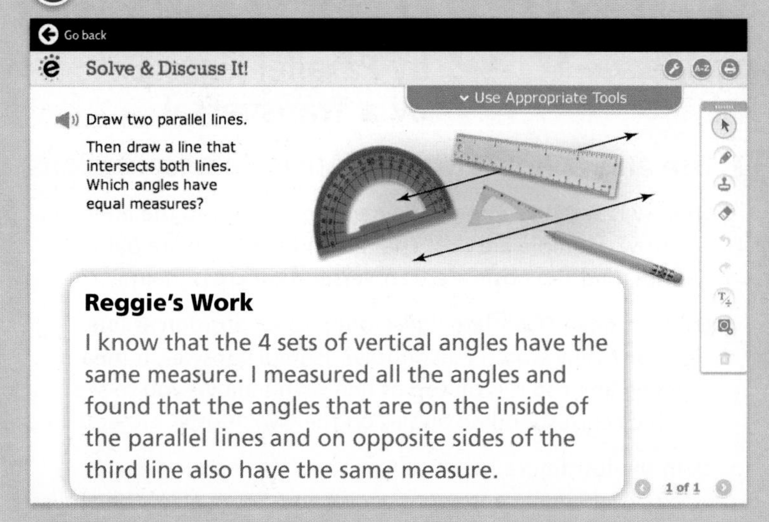


**Reggie** answers the question by identifying vertical angles and using his protractor to find other congruent angles.

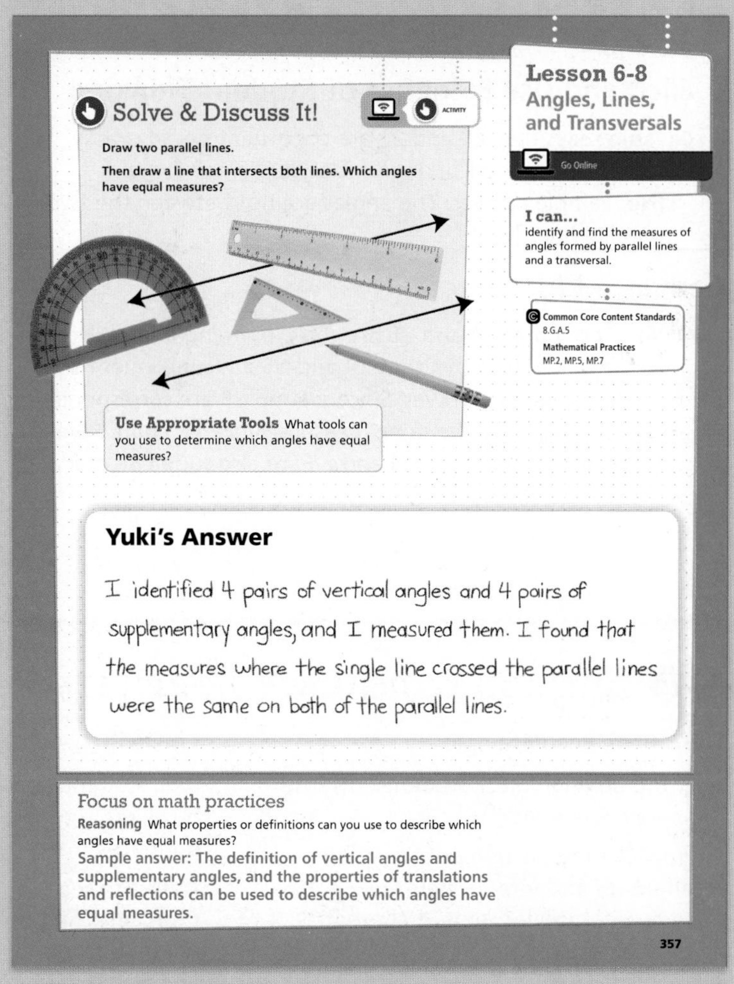


**Yuki** answers the question using what she knows about vertical and supplementary angles, and by using her protractor. She also observes that the angle measures where the single line crosses the parallel lines are the same.

# STEP 2 | Visual Learning

Go Online

Visual Learning

Assess

## ETP Establish Mathematics Goals to Focus Learning

Engage students in a discussion about the ***Essential Question***. Make sure students understand the concepts of congruent angles, vertical angles, supplementary angles, and parallel lines.

## EXAMPLE 1  Identify Angles Created by Parallel Lines Cut by a Transversal

### ETP Use and Connect Mathematical Representations

**Q:** How is Sarah's ramp with a handrail related to the lines you drew? [Sample answer: The rail and the ramp are parallel lines, and the posts are transversals that cross them.]

**Q:** What does "Translate line *r* to the same position as line *s*" mean? Why would you do this? [Sample answer: It means move line *r* so it is on top of line *s*. This allows you to see which corresponding angles on the two "posts" are equal.]

**Q:** In the last figure, why are line *r* and line *s* pulled apart again? [Sample answer: It allows you to see all of the angles around each of the parallel lines, and to observe that the angles inside of the parallel lines fall into two categories.]

##  Try It!  Formative Assessment

### ETP Elicit and Use Evidence of Student Thinking

**Q:** Janine says that ∠8 and ∠2 are congruent because they are alternate interior angles. Do you agree? Explain. [No; Sample answer: The angles are not between the two parallel lines.]

### Convince Me!

**Q:** You know that ∠4 and ∠8 are corresponding angles. How can this help to prove that ∠4 and ∠5 are supplementary angles? [Sample answer: Since ∠4 and ∠8 are corresponding angles, they have the same measure. Since ∠8 and ∠5 are supplementary angles, ∠4 and ∠5 are also supplementary.]

**Visual Learning Animation Plus** is available online.

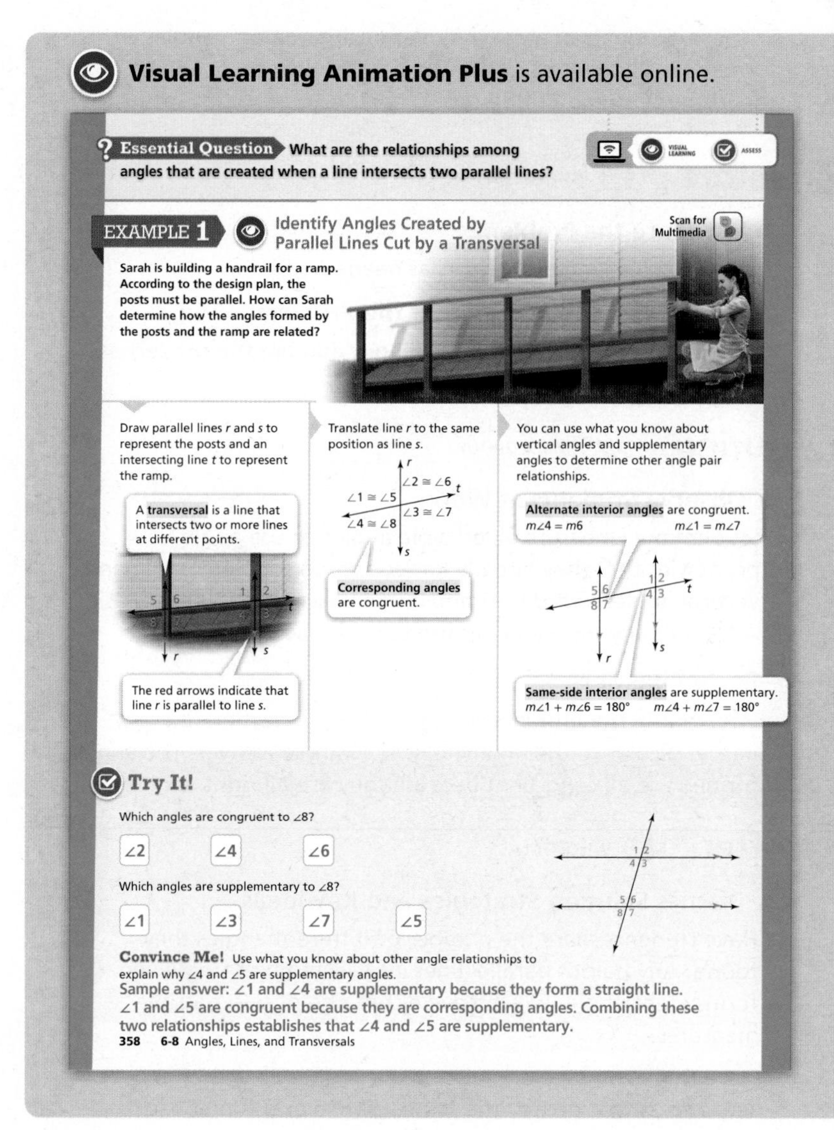

Essential Question What are the relationships among angles that are created when a line intersects two parallel lines?

EXAMPLE 1 Identify Angles Created by Parallel Lines Cut by a Transversal

Scan for Multimedia

Sarah is building a handrail for a ramp. According to the design plan, the posts must be parallel. How can Sarah determine how the angles formed by the posts and the ramp are related?

Draw parallel lines *r* and *s* to represent the posts and an intersecting line *t* to represent the ramp.

A **transversal** is a line that intersects two or more lines at different points.

The red arrows indicate that line *r* is parallel to line *s*.

Translate line *r* to the same position as line *s*.

∠1 ≅ ∠5 ∠2 ≅ ∠6 ∠3 ≅ ∠7 ∠4 ≅ ∠8

**Corresponding angles** are congruent.

You can use what you know about vertical angles and supplementary angles to determine other angle pair relationships.

**Alternate interior angles** are congruent. $m\angle 4 = m6$ $m\angle 1 = m\angle 7$

**Same-side interior angles** are supplementary. $m\angle 1 + m\angle 6 = 180°$ $m\angle 4 + m\angle 7 = 180°$

Try It!

Which angles are congruent to ∠8?

∠2 ∠4 ∠6

Which angles are supplementary to ∠8?

∠1 ∠3 ∠7 ∠5

Convince Me! Use what you know about other angle relationships to explain why ∠4 and ∠5 are supplementary angles.

Sample answer: ∠1 and ∠4 are supplementary because they form a straight line. ∠1 and ∠5 are congruent because they are corresponding angles. Combining these two relationships establishes that ∠4 and ∠5 are supplementary.

358 6-8 Angles, Lines, and Transversals

Students can access the ***Visual Learning Animation Plus*** by using the **Bounce Pages app** to scan this page. Students can download the app for free in their mobile devices' app store.

## ELL English Language Learners

**ENTERING** Read Example 1.

Help the beginning ELL students increase their vocabulary. Ask:

**Q:** How can the meaning of the words *alternate* and *interior* help you remember the location of alternate interior angles?

**Q:** How can the meanings of the words *same-side* and *interior* help you remember the location of same-side interior angles?

**EMERGING** Complete Example 1.

Help students practice their language skills by filling in the blanks to complete the sentences.

Angles that are on the same side of the transversal and between the two parallel lines are called _______ [same-side interior angles]. Angles that are on opposite sides of the transversal and between the two parallel lines are called _______ [alternate interior angles].

**EXPANDING** Complete Example 2.

Help advanced ELL students practice their language skills. Have pairs of students create a list of steps to describe how to find the measure of each angle in the figure.

Have one student change one measure in the figure. Have the other student describe how the change affects the other angle measures in the picture. Have students switch places and repeat.

Go Online

 Activity  Assess

## EXAMPLE 2  Find Unknown Angle Measures

###  Pose Purposeful Questions

**Q:** How do you know $\angle 4$ and $\angle 5$ are supplementary angles? [Sample answer: The angles are adjacent and form a straight line.]

**Q:** What is another way you could find the measures of $\angle 4$ and $\angle 5$? [Sample answer: $\angle 1$ and the 99° angle are supplementary, so the measure of $\angle 1$ is 81°. $\angle 1$ and $\angle 5$ are corresponding angles, so the measure of $\angle 5$ is also 81°. Since $\angle 4$ and $\angle 5$ are supplementary, the measure of $\angle 4$ is 99°.]

##  Try It!  Formative Assessment

###  Elicit and Use Evidence of Student Thinking

**Q:** How do you know that $\angle 7$ and $\angle 2$ are not congruent? [Sample answer: $\angle 2$ and $\angle 6$ are congruent corresponding angles. $\angle 6$ and $\angle 7$ are supplementary angles, so $\angle 2$ and $\angle 7$ are supplementary, not congruent.]

## EXAMPLE 3  Use Algebra to Find Unknown Angle Measures

### ETP Pose Purposeful Questions

**Q:** How do you know that $\angle 10$ and the angle marked 75° are corresponding angles? [Sample answer: If you use lines *a* and *c* as the pair of parallel lines, and line *t* as the transversal, then $\angle 10$ and the 75° angle are in corresponding positions.]

##  Try It!  Formative Assessment

###  Elicit and Use Evidence of Student Thinking

**Q:** What is the measure of $\angle 3$? How does knowing this measure help you solve the problem? [121°; Sample answer: $\angle 3$ and the angle marked $(x + 12)°$ are corresponding angles and congruent; therefore, $x + 12 = 121$.]

**Examples and Try Its!** are available online.

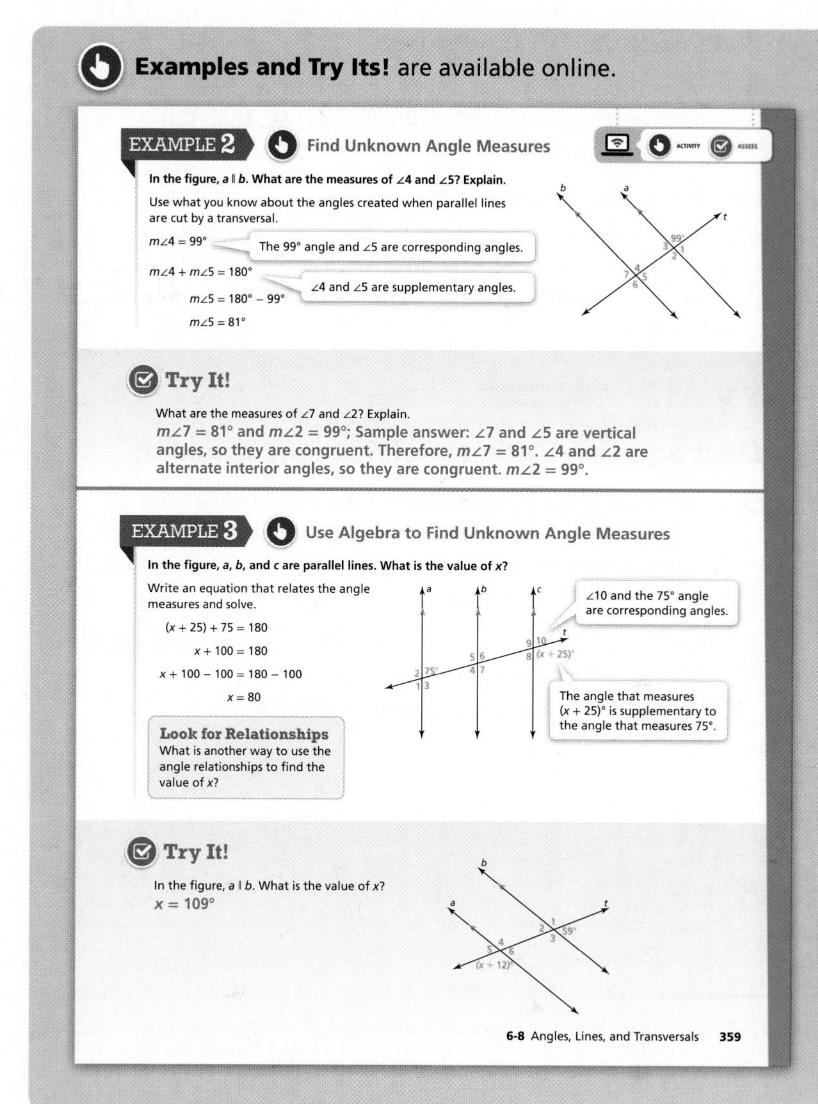

EXAMPLE 2 Find Unknown Angle Measures

ACTIVITY ASSESS

**In the figure, $a \parallel b$. What are the measures of $\angle 4$ and $\angle 5$? Explain.**

Use what you know about the angles created when parallel lines are cut by a transversal.

$m\angle 4 = 99°$ — The 99° angle and $\angle 5$ are corresponding angles.

$m\angle 4 + m\angle 5 = 180°$ — $\angle 4$ and $\angle 5$ are supplementary angles.

$m\angle 5 = 180° - 99°$

$m\angle 5 = 81°$



Try It!

What are the measures of $\angle 7$ and $\angle 2$? Explain.

$m\angle 7 = 81°$ and $m\angle 2 = 99°$; Sample answer: $\angle 7$ and $\angle 5$ are vertical angles, so they are congruent. Therefore, $m\angle 7 = 81°$. $\angle 4$ and $\angle 2$ are alternate interior angles, so they are congruent. $m\angle 2 = 99°$.

EXAMPLE 3 Use Algebra to Find Unknown Angle Measures

**In the figure, *a*, *b*, and *c* are parallel lines. What is the value of *x*?**

Write an equation that relates the angle measures and solve.

$(x + 25) + 75 = 180$

$x + 100 = 180$

$x + 100 - 100 = 180 - 100$

$x = 80$

$\angle 10$ and the 75° angle are corresponding angles.

The angle that measures $(x + 25)°$ is supplementary to the angle that measures 75°.



**Look for Relationships**
What is another way to use the angle relationships to find the value of *x*?

Try It!

In the figure, $a \parallel b$. What is the value of *x*?

$x = 109°$





## ADDITIONAL EXAMPLES 

**For additional examples go online.**

##  Response to Intervention

**USE WITH EXAMPLE 1** Some students may have difficulty identifying the angle pairs. Have these students trace parallel lines *m* and *n* and the transversal. Have them shade between the two parallel lines. Tell them these are the interior angles.

Have the students draw a circle around the angles formed by the line *m* and the transversal and a second circle around the angles formed by line *n* and the transversal. Have them point to the upper left corner of each circle. Point out that this angle pair forms corresponding angles. Repeat for other corresponding angles.

##  Enrichment

**USE WITH EXAMPLE 2** Challenge students to reach a conclusion about alternate exterior angles, which lie outside the parallel lines and on opposite sides of the transversal.

**Q:** Which angles are alternate exterior angles? [$\angle 7$ and $\angle 1$; $\angle 6$ and the angle marked 99°]

**Q:** What are the measures of the alternate exterior angles? [The measure of $\angle 7$ and $\angle 1$ is 81°. The measure of $\angle 6$ is 99°.]

**Q:** What seems to be true about alternate exterior angles? [Sample answer: Alternate exterior angles are congruent.]

Go Online

Activity

Assess

## EXAMPLE 4 Reason about Parallel Lines

### ETP Pose Purposeful Questions

**Q:** How can you check your answer? [Sample answer: Substitute 25 into $2x + 10$. If the value is 60, then the answer is correct.]

**Q:** Will any other values of $x$ make the equation true? Explain. [No; Sample answer: In order for the lines to be parallel, $2x + 10$ must equal 60. The only value of $x$ that makes this true is 25. Any other value will mean that the lines are not parallel.]

## Try It!

**Formative** Assessment

### ETP Elicit and Use Evidence of Student Thinking

**Q:** What is the relationship between the two given angles in part (a)? What does this tell you? Explain. [Sample answer: The two angles are alternate interior angles, which means that they are congruent.]

**Q:** What must the relationship between the two marked angles in Part b be for lines $g$ and $h$ to be parallel? [Sample answer: They must be supplementary.]

Available Online

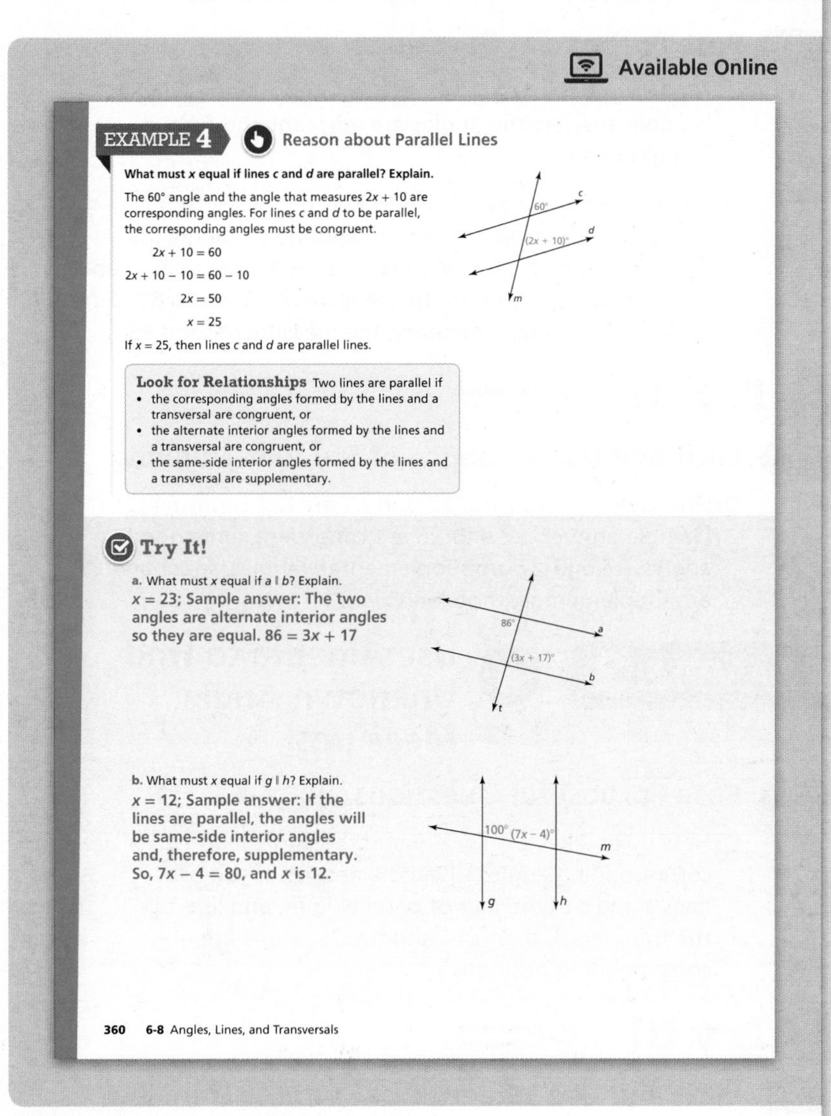

EXAMPLE 4 Reason about Parallel Lines

**What must $x$ equal if lines $c$ and $d$ are parallel? Explain.**

The 60° angle and the angle that measures $2x + 10$ are corresponding angles. For lines $c$ and $d$ to be parallel, the corresponding angles must be congruent.

$2x + 10 = 60$

$2x + 10 - 10 = 60 - 10$

$2x = 50$

$x = 25$

If $x = 25$, then lines $c$ and $d$ are parallel lines.

**Look for Relationships** Two lines are parallel if
- the corresponding angles formed by the lines and a transversal are congruent, or
- the alternate interior angles formed by the lines and a transversal are congruent, or
- the same-side interior angles formed by the lines and a transversal are supplementary.

Try It!

a. What must $x$ equal if $a \parallel b$? Explain.
$x = 23$; Sample answer: The two angles are alternate interior angles so they are equal. $86 = 3x + 17$

b. What must $x$ equal if $g \parallel h$? Explain.
$x = 12$; Sample answer: If the lines are parallel, the angles will be same-side interior angles and, therefore, supplementary. So, $7x - 4 = 80$, and $x$ is 12.

360 6-8 Angles, Lines, and Transversals

ADDITIONAL EXAMPLES

**For additional examples go online.**

## Response to Intervention

**USE WITH EXAMPLE 3** Some students may have difficulty identifying the angle pairs when there is more than one pair of parallel lines. Encourage these students to focus only on lines $a$ and $b$. Have them identify the angle pairs as a list on a separate sheet of paper. Then focus the students on lines $b$ and $c$ and identify angle pairs on the same sheet of paper. Have them compare the two lists and look for angles that show up in both lists. Ask:

**Q:** Which angles are corresponding and appear in the lists for both lines $a$ and $b$ and lines $b$ and $c$?

**Q:** Which angles are alternate interior and appear in the lists for both lines $a$ and $b$ and lines $b$ and $c$?

## Enrichment

**USE WITH EXAMPLE 2** Challenge advanced students with this activity.

Draw two parallel lines cut by a transversal. Then draw a second transversal so that a triangle is formed between the two parallel lines. Have students estimate the measure of one of the angles on each transversal. Then have them use what they know about parallel lines and traversals to find the measure of the other angles.

Go Online

Key Concept

Activity

# KEY CONCEPT

## ETP Pose Purposeful Questions

**Q:** How does identifying the relationship between the angle pairs when a pair of parallel lines is cut by a transversal help to determine all of the missing angle measures? [Sample answer: You can tell which angles are congruent angles and which are supplementary angles. This can help you find unknown angle measures.]

# Do You Understand/Do You Know How?

**Formative** Assessment

## ETP Build Procedural Fluency from Conceptual Understanding

**Essential Question** Students should know that when a transversal crosses two parallel lines, alternate interior angles and corresponding angles are congruent, and same-side interior angles are supplementary.

**ITEM 7**

**Q:** How can the relationship between ∠5 and ∠8 help you write an equation? [Sample answer: The angles are supplementary, so their measures have a sum of 180°.]

**Q:** What is $m\angle 5$? Explain. [95°; Sample answer: ∠1 and ∠5 are corresponding angles, so they are congruent.]

## Prevent Misconceptions

**ITEM 8** Students may have difficulty determining if they need to set the expressions equal to each other or set the sum equal to 180°.

**Q:** How would you show that line *a* is parallel to line *b*? [Sample answer: You would find the value of *x* that makes the equation $2x + 35 = 103$ true.]

Available Online

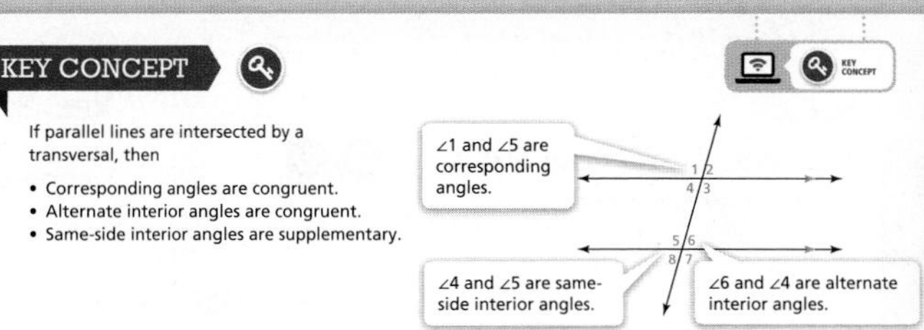


### Do You Understand?

1. **Essential Question** What are the relationships among angles that are created when a line intersects two parallel lines?
   Sample answer: Alternate interior angles are congruent. Corresponding angles are congruent. Same-side interior angles are supplementary.
2. When parallel lines are cut by a transversal, how can you use a translation to describe how angles are related?
   Sample answer: You can translate one of the parallel lines to the same position as the other parallel line to show that the angles are the same. Then you can use what you know about vertical angles and supplementary angles to describe other angle relationships.
3. How many angles are created when two parallel lines are cut by a transversal? How many different angle measures are there?
   There are 8 angles created and there are two different angle measures.
4. Use Structure How can you use angle measures to tell whether two lines are parallel?
   Sample answer: Two lines are parallel if the corresponding angles formed by the lines and a transversal are congruent, or if the alternate interior angles formed by the lines and a transversal are congruent, or if same side interior angles are supplementary.

### Do You Know How?

In 5–7, use the figure below.

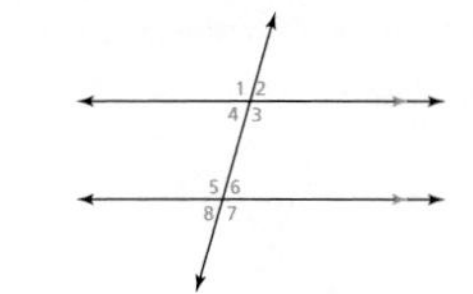


5. Which angles are congruent to ∠8?
   ∠2, ∠4 and ∠6
6. If $m\angle 4 = 70°$, what is $m\angle 6$? Explain.
   70°; Sample answer: The angles are alternate interior angles so their measures are congruent.
7. If $m\angle 1 = 95°$, write an equation that could be used to find the measure of ∠8. Find $m\angle 8$.
   $m\angle 8 + 95 = 180$; $m\angle 8 = 85°$
8. What must *x* equal if line *a* is parallel to line *b*?

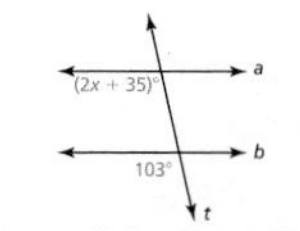


Line *a* is parallel to line *b* if $x = 34$.

6-8 Angles, Lines, and Transversals 361

# ADDITIONAL EXAMPLE 4

Help students transition to solving problems that reason about parallel lines using Algebra. Make sure students understand they can use what they already know to solve this problem.

**Q:** What is the relationship between the angle marked 75° and the angle marked $(3x + 15)°$? [Sample answer: They are corresponding angles.]

**Q:** In order for the lines to be parallel what must be true about the angle measures of the two given angles? [Sample answer: They must be congruent.]

**Additional Examples** are available online.

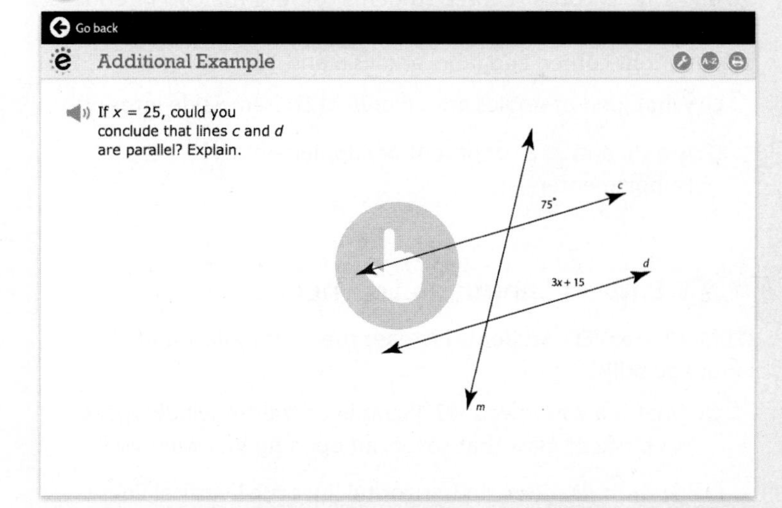


**Answer:** No; Sample answer: If lines *c* and *d* are parallel, then the marked angles are corresponding angles and must be congruent. If $3x \times 15 = 75°$, then $x = 20$, not 25.

Go Online

# Practice & Problem Solving  

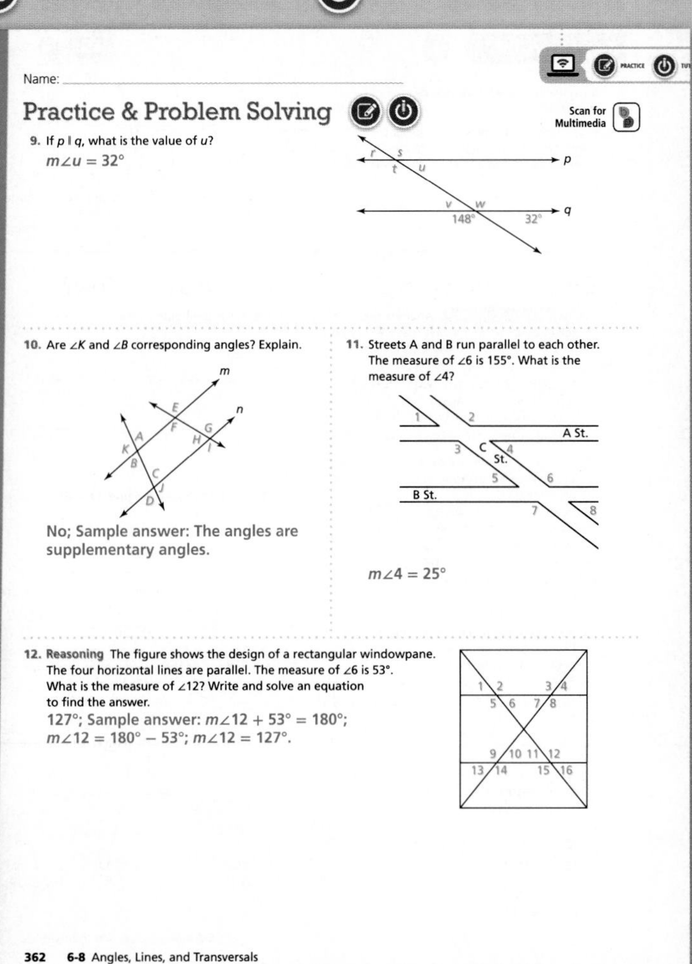

Name:

Practice & Problem Solving

Scan for Multimedia

9. If $p \parallel q$, what is the value of $u$?
$m\angle u = 32°$

10. Are $\angle K$ and $\angle B$ corresponding angles? Explain.
No; Sample answer: The angles are supplementary angles.

11. Streets A and B run parallel to each other. The measure of $\angle 6$ is 155°. What is the measure of $\angle 4$?
$m\angle 4 = 25°$

12. **Reasoning** The figure shows the design of a rectangular windowpane. The four horizontal lines are parallel. The measure of $\angle 6$ is 53°. What is the measure of $\angle 12$? Write and solve an equation to find the answer.
127°; Sample answer: $m\angle 12 + 53° = 180°$; $m\angle 12 = 180° - 53°$; $m\angle 12 = 127°$.

362 6-8 Angles, Lines, and Transversals

13. In the figure, $m \parallel n$. If $m\angle 8$ is $(4x + 7)°$ and $m\angle 2$ is 107°, what is the value of $x$? Explain.
$x = 16.5$; Sample answer: Because $\angle 2$ and $\angle 4$ are corresponding angles, $\angle 2$ and $\angle 8$ are supplementary. So, $(4x + 7) + 107 = 180$. $4x + 114 = 180$, so $4x = 66$. $x = 16.5$.

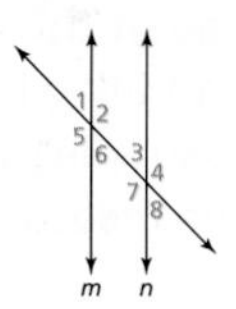

14. For the given figure, can you conclude $m \parallel n$? Explain.

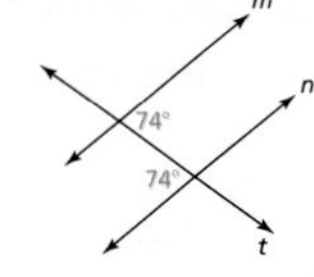

Yes; Sample answer: $m \parallel n$ because the labeled angles are congruent alternate interior angles that are equal.

15. Line $m$ is parallel to line $n$. Find the value of $x$ and each missing angle measure.

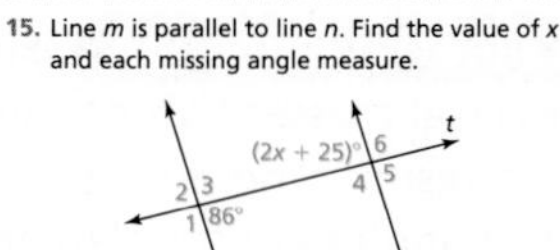

$x = 30.5$; $m\angle 2 = m\angle 5 = 86°$, $m\angle 1 = m\angle 3 = m\angle 4 = m\angle 6 = 94°$

16. **Higher Order Thinking**

a. Find the value of $x$ given that $r \parallel s$.

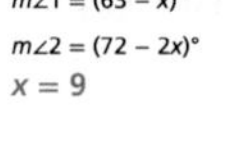

$m\angle 1 = (63 - x)°$
$m\angle 2 = (72 - 2x)°$
$x = 9$

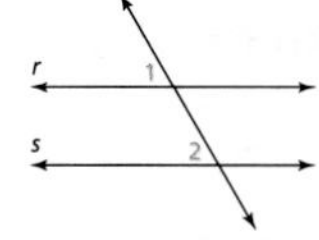

b. Find $m\angle 1$ and $m\angle 2$.
$m\angle 1 = 54°$; $m\angle 2 = 54°$

6-8 Angles, Lines, and Transversals 363

## Error Intervention

**ITEM 12 Reasoning** Students may have difficulty focusing in on $\angle 6$ and $\angle 12$. Encourage these students to trace the two interior parallel lines and the slanted line from the top left corner to the bottom right corner, and label angles 6 and 12.

**Q:** What kind of angles are $\angle 6$ and $\angle 12$? [same-side interior]

**Q:** Are $\angle 6$ and $\angle 12$ congruent or supplementary? [supplementary]

## English Language Learners

**ITEM 12** Help ELL Students increase their vocabulary and language skills.

**Q:** What is a windowpane? [Sample answer: A windowpane is a piece of glass that covers an opening in a window.]

**Q:** In which direction do horizontal lines run? vertical lines? [Sample answer: Horizontal lines run left to right. Vertical lines run up and down.]

**Q:** Are the vertical lines in the figure parallel? [Yes]

You may opt to have students complete the automatically scored Practice & Problem Solving items online.

### Item Analysis

| Example | Items | DOK |
|---|---|---|
| 1 | 10, 18 | 2 |
| 2 | 9 | 1 |
| | 11, 12, 17, 19 | 2 |
| 3 | 13, 15 | 2 |
| | 16 | 3 |
| 4 | 14 | 1 |

Go Online

Practice

Tutorials

Math Tools

## Challenge

**ITEM 17** Challenge advanced students to draw a figure similar to the one shown. Have them choose two angles that have a relationship and create an algebraic expression for each angle. Have students trade questions with another student and have the student determine the value of the variable and the measure of each angle. A sample is shown below.

**Q:** If $m\angle c = (2x + 7)^\circ$ and $m\angle d = (3x + 3)^\circ$, what is the value of $x$ and the measure of each angle? [$x = 34$; $m\angle c = 75^\circ$ and $m\angle d = 105^\circ$]

## Error Intervention

**ITEM 17** Students may incorrectly think there is a relationship between the measures of $\angle b$ and $\angle d$. Have them use their finger to trace the lines that form the two angles.

**Q:** Which transversal creates $\angle b$? $\angle d$? [Sample answer: The transversal on the left creates $\angle b$. The transversal on the right creates $\angle d$.]

**Q:** The lines that form $\angle b$ and $\angle d$ are not parallel. What does this tell you about their angle measures? Explain. [The angles do not have to be supplementary; Sample answer: The angles are same-side interior angles, but they are formed by non-parallel lines. Therefore, their measures are not necessarily supplementary.]

Available Online

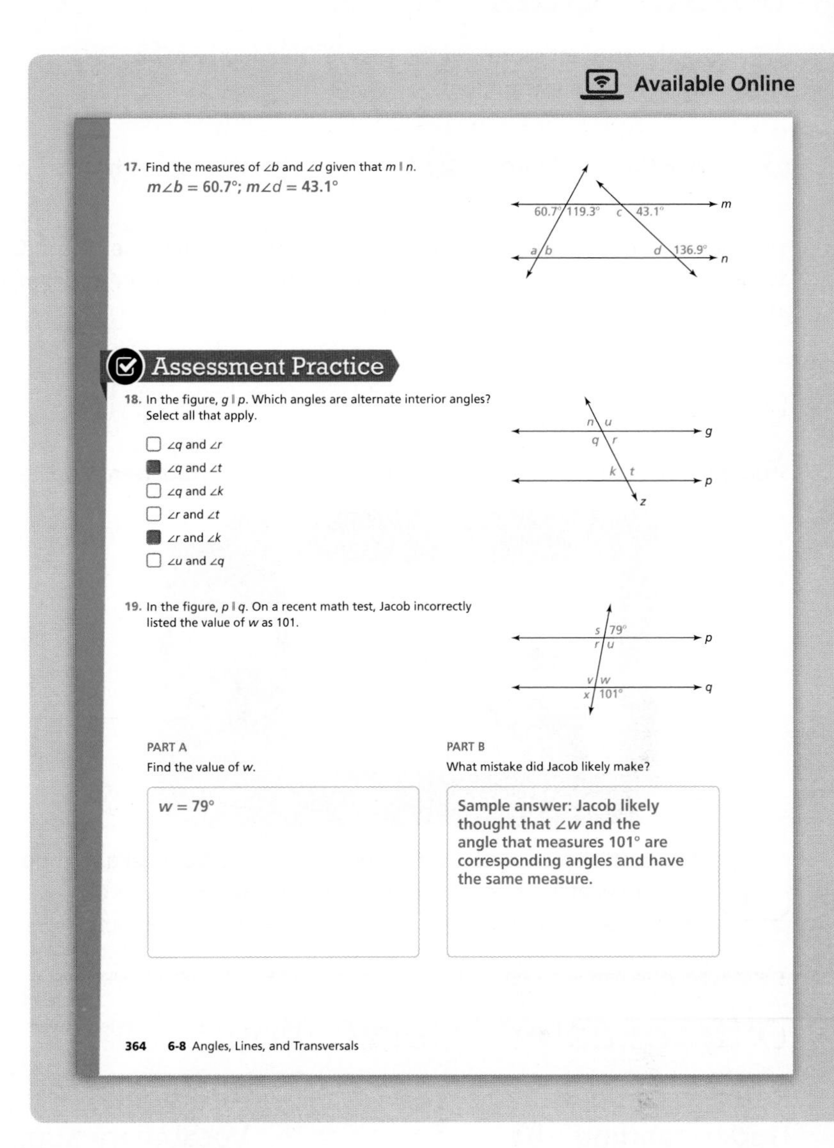

17. Find the measures of $\angle b$ and $\angle d$ given that $m \parallel n$.
$m\angle b = 60.7^\circ$; $m\angle d = 43.1^\circ$



**Assessment Practice**

18. In the figure, $g \parallel p$. Which angles are alternate interior angles? Select all that apply.

- ☐ $\angle q$ and $\angle r$
- ■ $\angle q$ and $\angle t$
- ☐ $\angle q$ and $\angle k$
- ☐ $\angle r$ and $\angle t$
- ■ $\angle r$ and $\angle k$
- ☐ $\angle u$ and $\angle q$



19. In the figure, $p \parallel q$. On a recent math test, Jacob incorrectly listed the value of $w$ as 101.



PART A
Find the value of $w$.

$w = 79^\circ$

PART B
What mistake did Jacob likely make?

Sample answer: Jacob likely thought that $\angle w$ and the angle that measures 101° are corresponding angles and have the same measure.

364 6-8 Angles, Lines, and Transversals

# STEP 3 Assess & Differentiate

Go Online

## Lesson Quiz

**Formative** Assessment

RtI Use the student scores on the Lesson Quiz to prescribe differentiated assignments.

**I** **Intervention** 0–3 Points **O** **On-Level** 4 Points **A** **Advanced** 5 Points

You may opt to have students take the Lesson Quiz online. The Lesson Quiz will be automatically scored and appropriate remediation, practice, or enrichment will be assigned based on student performance.

**Lesson Quiz** is available online.

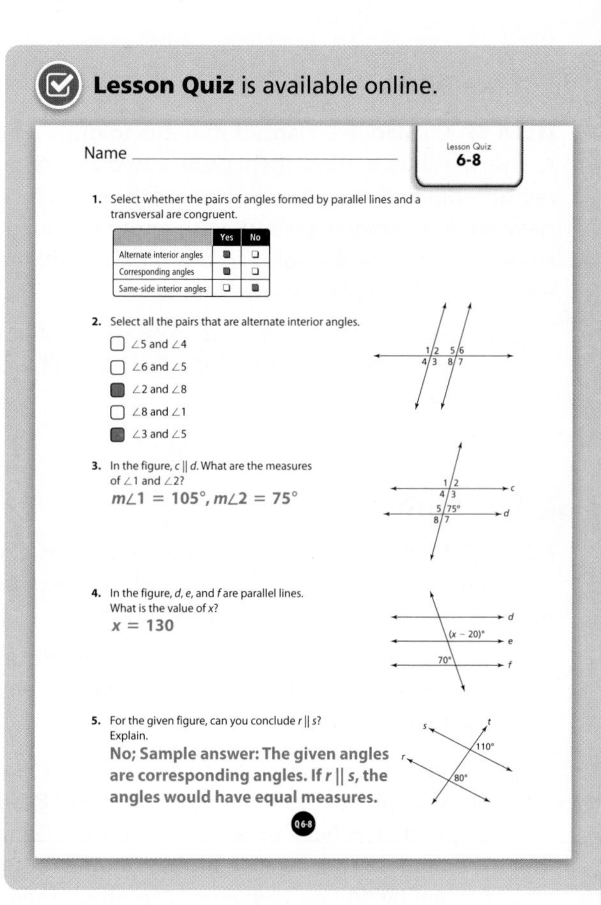

Name ______________ Lesson Quiz **6-8**

1. Select whether the pairs of angles formed by parallel lines and a transversal are congruent.

| | Yes | No |
|---|---|---|
| Alternate interior angles | ■ | ☐ |
| Corresponding angles | ■ | ☐ |
| Same-side interior angles | ☐ | ■ |

2. Select all the pairs that are alternate interior angles.

☐ $\angle 5$ and $\angle 4$
☐ $\angle 6$ and $\angle 5$
■ $\angle 2$ and $\angle 8$
☐ $\angle 8$ and $\angle 1$
■ $\angle 3$ and $\angle 5$

3. In the figure, $c \parallel d$. What are the measures of $\angle 1$ and $\angle 2$?
**$m\angle 1 = 105°, m\angle 2 = 75°$**

4. In the figure, $d$, $e$, and $f$ are parallel lines. What is the value of $x$?
**$x = 130$**

5. For the given figure, can you conclude $r \parallel s$? Explain.
**No; Sample answer: The given angles are corresponding angles. If $r \parallel s$, the angles would have equal measures.**

Q 6-8

## Video Tutorials

Students can access instructional tutorials using the **Virtual Nerd app**.

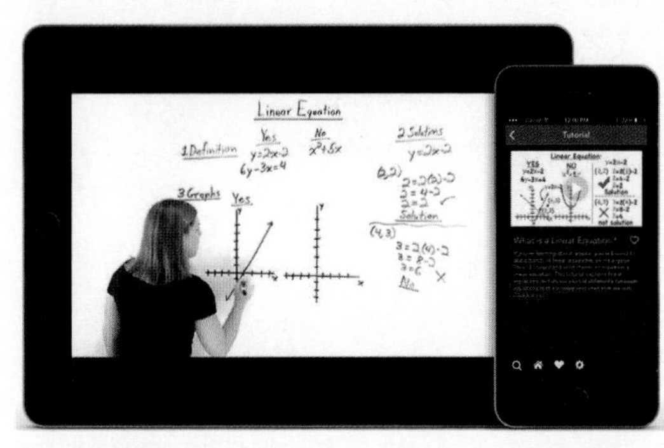

Students can also access the videos using the **BouncePages app** to scan exercise pages marked with this icon. Students can download both apps for free in their mobile devices' app store.

## Differentiated Intervention

**I** = Intervention **O** = On-Level **A** = Advanced

### Reteach to Build Understanding I

Provides scaffolded reteaching for the key lesson concepts.

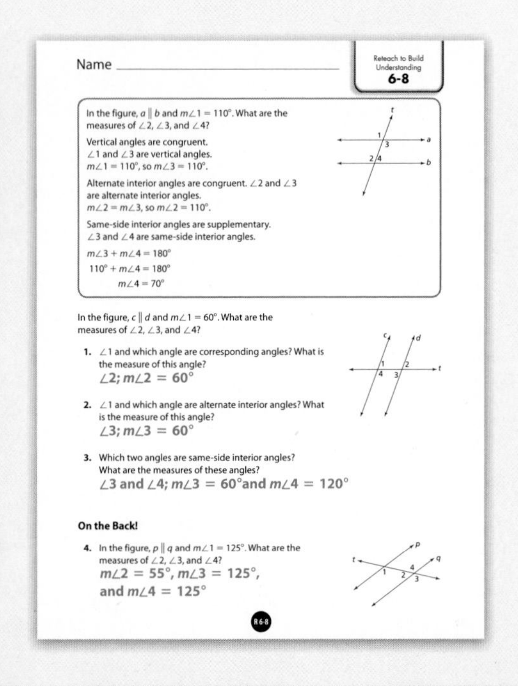

Name ______________ Reteach to Build Understanding **6-8**

In the figure, $a \parallel b$ and $m\angle 1 = 110°$. What are the measures of $\angle 2$, $\angle 3$, and $\angle 4$?

Vertical angles are congruent.
$\angle 1$ and $\angle 3$ are vertical angles.
$m\angle 1 = 110°$, so $m\angle 3 = 110°$.

Alternate interior angles are congruent. $\angle 2$ and $\angle 3$ are alternate interior angles.
$m\angle 2 = m\angle 3$, so $m\angle 2 = 110°$.

Same-side interior angles are supplementary.
$\angle 3$ and $\angle 4$ are same-side interior angles.

$m\angle 3 + m\angle 4 = 180°$
$110° + m\angle 4 = 180°$
$m\angle 4 = 70°$

In the figure, $c \parallel d$ and $m\angle 1 = 60°$. What are the measures of $\angle 2$, $\angle 3$, and $\angle 4$?

1. $\angle 1$ and which angle are corresponding angles? What is the measure of this angle?
**$\angle 2; m\angle 2 = 60°$**

2. $\angle 1$ and which angle are alternate interior angles? What is the measure of this angle?
**$\angle 3; m\angle 3 = 60°$**

3. Which two angles are same-side interior angles? What are the measures of these angles?
**$\angle 3$ and $\angle 4$; $m\angle 3 = 60°$ and $m\angle 4 = 120°$**

**On the Back!**

4. In the figure, $p \parallel q$ and $m\angle 1 = 125°$. What are the measures of $\angle 2$, $\angle 3$, and $\angle 4$?
**$m\angle 2 = 55°$, $m\angle 3 = 125°$, and $m\angle 4 = 125°$**

R 6-8

### Additional Vocabulary Support I O

Helps students develop and reinforce understanding of key terms and concepts.

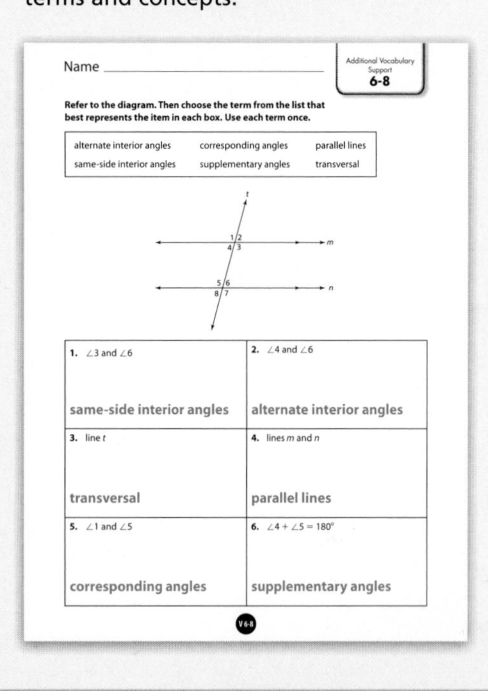

Name ______________ Additional Vocabulary Support **6-8**

**Refer to the diagram. Then choose the term from the list that best represents the item in each box. Use each term once.**

| | | |
|---|---|---|
| alternate interior angles | corresponding angles | parallel lines |
| same-side interior angles | supplementary angles | transversal |

| | |
|---|---|
| 1. $\angle 3$ and $\angle 6$<br>**same-side interior angles** | 2. $\angle 4$ and $\angle 6$<br>**alternate interior angles** |
| 3. line $t$<br>**transversal** | 4. lines $m$ and $n$<br>**parallel lines** |
| 5. $\angle 1$ and $\angle 5$<br>**corresponding angles** | 6. $\angle 4 + \angle 5 = 180°$<br>**supplementary angles** |

V 6-8

### Build Mathematical Literacy I O

Provides support for struggling readers to build mathematical literacy.

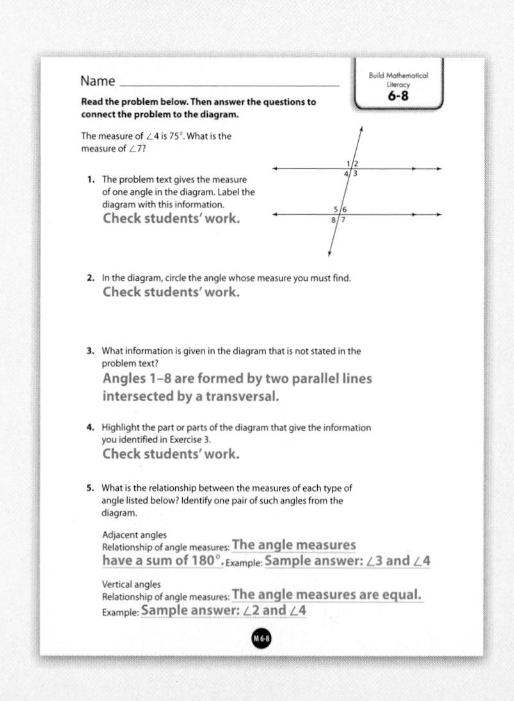

Name ______________ Build Mathematical Literacy **6-8**

**Read the problem below. Then answer the questions to connect the problem to the diagram.**

The measure of $\angle 4$ is 75°. What is the measure of $\angle 7$?

1. The problem text gives the measure of one angle in the diagram. Label the diagram with this information.
**Check students' work.**

2. In the diagram, circle the angle whose measure you must find.
**Check students' work.**

3. What information is given in the diagram that is not stated in the problem text?
**Angles 1–8 are formed by two parallel lines intersected by a transversal.**

4. Highlight the part or parts of the diagram that give the information you identified in Exercise 3.
**Check students' work.**

5. What is the relationship between the measures of each type of angle listed below? Identify one pair of such angles from the diagram.

Adjacent angles
Relationship of angle measures: **The angle measures have a sum of 180°.** Example: **Sample answer: $\angle 3$ and $\angle 4$**

Vertical angles
Relationship of angle measures: **The angle measures are equal.** Example: **Sample answer: $\angle 2$ and $\angle 4$**

M 6-8

Go Online

Practice

Worksheets

Math Tools

Math Games

# Additional Practice

You may opt to have students complete the automatically scored Additional Practice items online.

### Item Analysis

| Example | Items | DOK |
|---|---|---|
| 1 | 1 | 1 |
| | 2 | 2 |
| 2 | 3, 9 | 2 |
| 3 | 4, 7 | 2 |
| 4 | 5 | 2 |
| | 6, 8 | 3 |

**Interactive Practice** is available online.

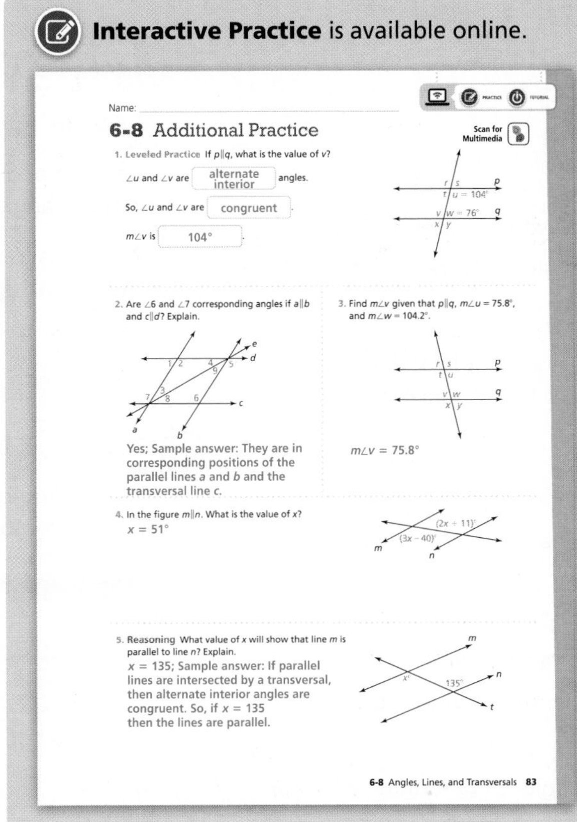

Name:

6-8 Additional Practice

Scan for Multimedia

1. Leveled Practice If $p \parallel q$, what is the value of $v$?

$\angle u$ and $\angle v$ are alternate interior angles.

So, $\angle u$ and $\angle v$ are congruent.

$m\angle v$ is 104°.

2. Are $\angle 6$ and $\angle 7$ corresponding angles if $a \parallel b$ and $c \parallel d$? Explain.

Yes; Sample answer: They are in corresponding positions of the parallel lines $a$ and $b$ and the transversal line $c$.

3. Find $m\angle v$ given that $p \parallel q$, $m\angle u = 75.8°$, and $m\angle w = 104.2°$.

$m\angle v = 75.8°$

4. In the figure $m \parallel n$. What is the value of $x$?

$x = 51°$

5. Reasoning What value of $x$ will show that line $m$ is parallel to line $n$? Explain.

$x = 135$; Sample answer: If parallel lines are intersected by a transversal, then alternate interior angles are congruent. So, if $x = 135$ then the lines are parallel.

6-8 Angles, Lines, and Transversals 83

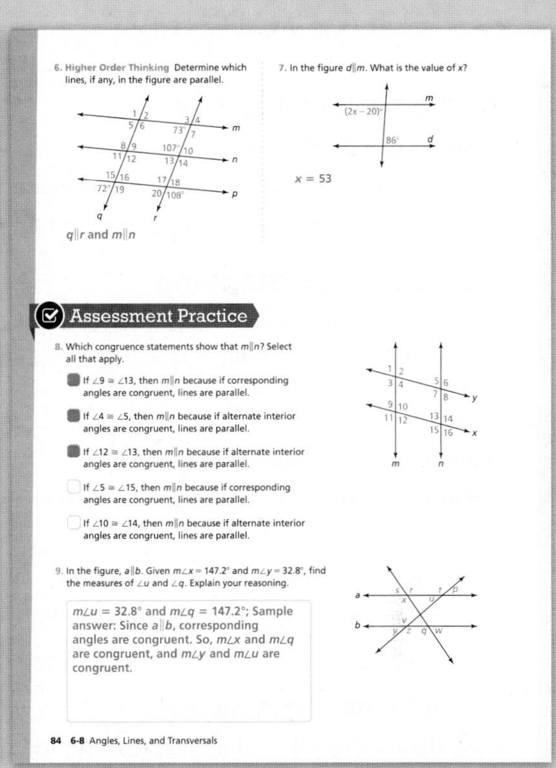

6. Higher Order Thinking Determine which lines, if any, in the figure are parallel.

$q \parallel r$ and $m \parallel n$

7. In the figure $d \parallel m$. What is the value of $x$?

$x = 53$

Assessment Practice

8. Which congruence statements show that $m \parallel n$? Select all that apply.

- [x] If $\angle 9 \cong \angle 13$, then $m \parallel n$ because if corresponding angles are congruent, lines are parallel.
- [x] If $\angle 4 \cong \angle 5$, then $m \parallel n$ because if alternate interior angles are congruent, lines are parallel.
- [x] If $\angle 12 \cong \angle 13$, then $m \parallel n$ because if alternate interior angles are congruent, lines are parallel.
- [ ] If $\angle 5 \cong \angle 15$, then $m \parallel n$ because if corresponding angles are congruent, lines are parallel.
- [ ] If $\angle 10 \cong \angle 14$, then $m \parallel n$ because if alternate interior angles are congruent, lines are parallel.

9. In the figure, $a \parallel b$. Given $m\angle x = 147.2°$ and $m\angle y = 32.8°$, find the measures of $\angle u$ and $\angle q$. Explain your reasoning.

$m\angle u = 32.8°$ and $m\angle q = 147.2°$; Sample answer: Since $a \parallel b$, corresponding angles are congruent. So, $m\angle x$ and $m\angle q$ are congruent, and $m\angle y$ and $m\angle u$ are congruent.

84 6-8 Angles, Lines, and Transversals

# Differentiated Intervention

I = Intervention O = On-Level A = Advanced

## Enrichment

Presents engaging problems and activities that extend the lesson concepts.

## Math Tools and Games

Offers additional activities and games to build understanding and fluency.

## Pick a Project and STEM Project

Provides an additional opportunity for students to demonstrate understanding of key mathematical concepts.

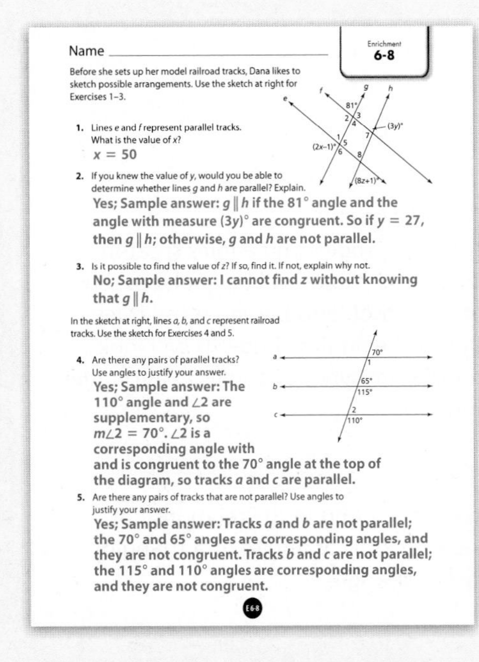

Name

Enrichment 6-8

Before she sets up her model railroad tracks, Dana likes to sketch possible arrangements. Use the sketch at right for Exercises 1–3.

1. Lines $e$ and $f$ represent parallel tracks. What is the value of $x$?
$x = 50$

2. If you knew the value of $y$, would you be able to determine whether lines $g$ and $h$ are parallel? Explain.
**Yes; Sample answer: $g \parallel h$ if the 81° angle and the angle with measure $(3y)°$ are congruent. So if $y = 27$, then $g \parallel h$; otherwise, $g$ and $h$ are not parallel.**

3. Is it possible to find the value of $z$? If so, find it. If not, explain why not.
**No; Sample answer: I cannot find $z$ without knowing that $g \parallel h$.**

In the sketch at right, lines $a$, $b$, and $c$ represent railroad tracks. Use the sketch for Exercises 4 and 5.

4. Are there any pairs of parallel tracks? Use angles to justify your answer.
**Yes; Sample answer: The 110° angle and $\angle 2$ are supplementary, so $m\angle 2 = 70°$. $\angle 2$ is a corresponding angle with and is congruent to the 70° angle at the top of the diagram, so tracks $a$ and $c$ are parallel.**

5. Are there any pairs of tracks that are not parallel? Use angles to justify your answer.
**Yes; Sample answer: Tracks $a$ and $b$ are not parallel; the 70° and 65° angles are corresponding angles, and they are not congruent. Tracks $b$ and $c$ are not parallel; the 115° and 110° angles are corresponding angles, and they are not congruent.**

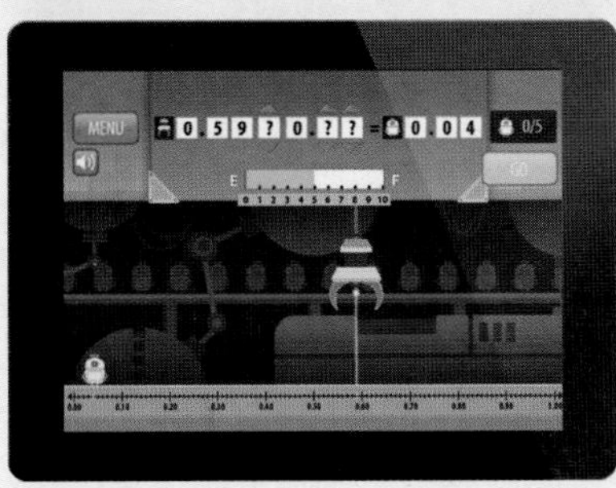

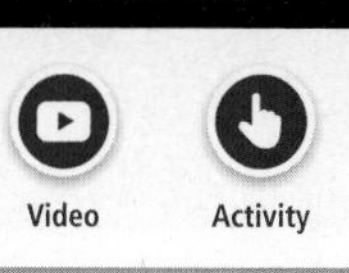


# Lesson 6-9 Interior and Exterior Angles of Triangles

## Lesson Overview

**FOCUS**

### Mathematics Objective

**Students will be able to:**

✔ determine unknown measures of interior and exterior angles of triangles.

✔ write and solve algebraic equations to find angle measures.

### Essential Understanding

The sum of the measures of the interior angles of a triangle is 180°. The measure of an exterior angle of a triangle is equal to the sum of the measures of the remote interior angles.

**COHERENCE**

**Previously in this topic, students:**

- learned the relationships of angles formed by parallel lines cut by a transversal.

**In this lesson, students:**

- learn to identify interior and exterior angles of a triangle.
- find unknown measures of interior and exterior angles of triangles.

**Later in this topic, students will:**

- use their knowledge of angle measures in triangles to determine whether two triangles are similar.

**Cross-Cluster Connection** Finding measures of angles of triangles (8.G.1) connects to solving equations (8.EE.3).

**RIGOR**

This lesson emphasizes a blend of **conceptual understanding** and **application**.

- Students learn how the interior angle measures and exterior angle measures of triangles are related.
- Students apply the concept of triangle-angle relationships to solve problems.

## Language Support

### Lesson Language Objective

Describe and show how to find the interior and exterior angle measures of a triangle.

Additional resources are available in the **Language Support Handbook**.

## Math Anytime

### Today's Challenge

Use the Topic 6 problems any time during this topic.

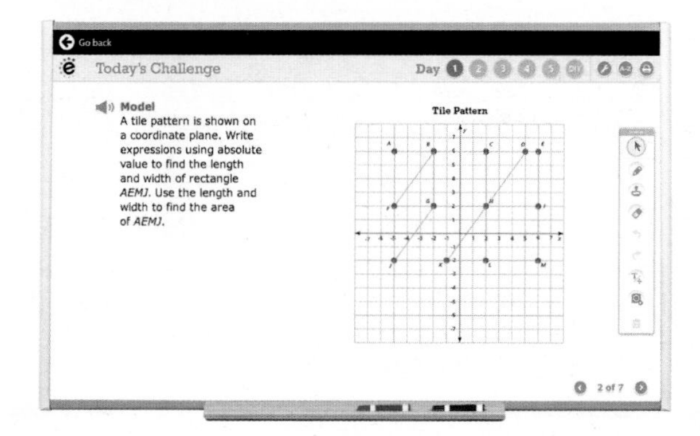


Watch the **Listen and Look For Video** for strategies and habits of mind to look for as students complete work on this lesson.

## Mathematics Overview | Common Core Standards

### Content Standards

In this lesson, you will focus on Common Core Standard **8.G.A.5**.

- **8.G.A.5** Use informal arguments to establish facts about the angle sum and exterior angle of triangles, about the angles created when parallel lines are cut by a transversal, and the angle-angle criterion for similarity of triangles.

### Mathematical Practice Standards

**MP.2 Reason Abstractly and Quantitatively**

The students will utilize angle-based relationships and algebraic knowledge to determine unknown measures of interior and exterior angles of triangles.

**MP.7 Look for and Make Use of Structure**

The properties and structure of triangles and angles created by a transversal intersecting parallel lines will be analyzed. The students will evaluate and solve problems based on the rules created by the relationships of the angles. Students will look for relationships between different types of angles in a triangle to write and solve equations.

**MP.8 Generalize**

Students will generalize patterns found in the relationship between the sum of the remote interior angles of a triangle and their corresponding exterior angle.

# STEP 1 | Problem-Based Learning

15-20 min

Go Online

Activity

##  Solve & Discuss It!

Formative Assessment

**Purpose** Students find the measure of an angle inside a triangle and connect it to finding interior angle measures in triangles in the Visual Learning Bridge.

### ETP Before — WHOLE CLASS

**1 Introduce the Problem**

Provide graph paper, rulers, and protractors, as needed.

**2 Check for Understanding of the Problem**

Ensure students understand the problem by asking: What is a kitchen backsplash? What is molding?

###  During — SMALL GROUP

**3 Observe Students at Work**

Students will find the missing angle measurements in the triangle. To find $m\angle 1$, students might use the fact that the sum of the measures of the angles in a triangle is 180°, or they might model the problem by modelling the top and bottom of the backsplash as parallel lines and the edges of the triangular tiles as transversals. If needed, ask Is there anything that you learned in the previous lesson that can help you solve the problem?

**Early Finishers**

How would the problem change if both of the labeled angles in the triangle measure 75°?
[Sample answer: $m\angle 1 = 180 - 75 - 75 = 30°$]

###  After — WHOLE CLASS

**4 Discuss Solution Strategies and Key Ideas**

Consider having groups who used parallel lines and a transversal share first, followed by those who used straight angles and the fact that the triangles are congruent, and then groups who used the formula for the sum of the angles in a triangle.

Have students discuss the connections between the strategies; all strategies result in equations equivalent to $65 + m\angle 1 + 65 = 180°$. Have students articulate how they could use transformations to show the tiles are congruent; if one tile was rotated 180° around its center and translated left or right, one tile could be mapped onto another.

**5 Consider Instructional Implications**

After presenting Example 1, refer students back to the problem in the Solve & Discuss It and have them discuss how their solutions are similar to the work in Example 1; the work in Example 1 shows the same reasoning used to solve the problem in the Solve & Discuss It.

## Analyze Student Work

**Solve and Discuss It!** Activity is available online.

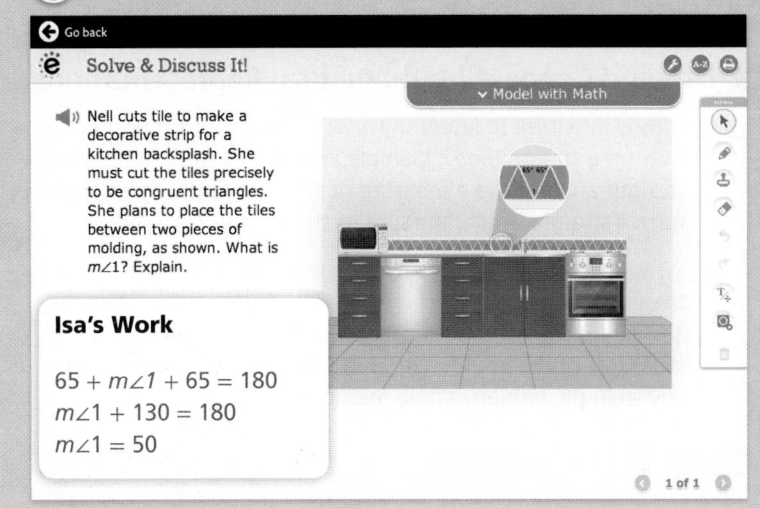


**Isa** finds the measure of <1 using the sum of the angles in a triangle.

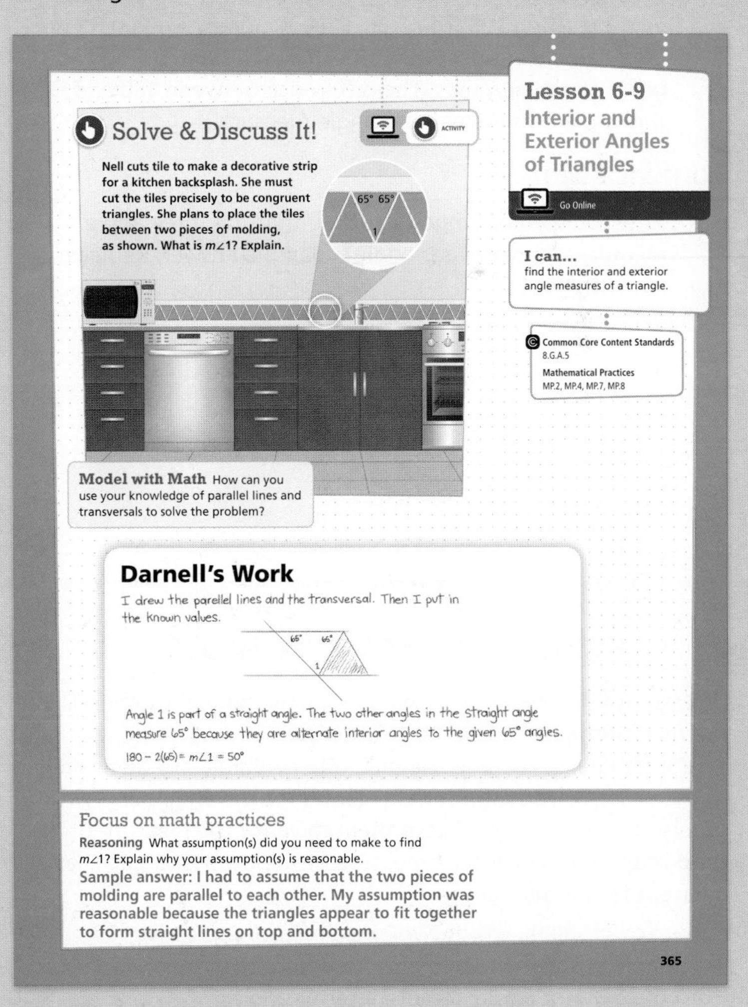
Lesson 6-9
Interior and Exterior Angles of Triangles

Go Online

Solve & Discuss It!

Nell cuts tile to make a decorative strip for a kitchen backsplash. She must cut the tiles precisely to be congruent triangles. She plans to place the tiles between two pieces of molding, as shown. What is $m\angle 1$? Explain.

I can... find the interior and exterior angle measures of a triangle.

Common Core Content Standards 8.G.A.5
Mathematical Practices MP.2, MP.4, MP.7, MP.8

Model with Math How can you use your knowledge of parallel lines and transversals to solve the problem?

**Darnell's Work**

I drew the parallel lines and the transversal. Then I put in the known values.

Angle 1 is part of a straight angle. The two other angles in the straight angle measure 65° because they are alternate interior angles to the given 65° angles.

180 − 2(65) = m∠1 = 50°

Focus on math practices

Reasoning What assumption(s) did you need to make to find $m\angle 1$? Explain why your assumption(s) is reasonable.
Sample answer: I had to assume that the two pieces of molding are parallel to each other. My assumption was reasonable because the triangles appear to fit together to form straight lines on top and bottom.

365

**Darnell** answers the question by focusing on the same-side interior angles and his knowledge of supplementary angles to set up and solve an equation.

# STEP 2 | Visual Learning

Go Online

 Visual Learning  Assess

## ETP Establish Mathematics Goals to Focus Learning

Engage students in a discussion about the ***Essential Question***. Make sure they remember the angle relationships formed by parallel lines intersected by a transversal.

## EXAMPLE 1  Relate Interior Angle Measures in Triangles

### ETP Use and Connect Mathematical Representations

**Q:** Why is it helpful to know that ∠1, ∠2, and ∠3 fit together to form a straight line? [Sample answer: All straight lines and straight angles have a measure of 180°. Since the three angles form a straight angle, the sum of their measures is 180°.]

**Q:** Why can you use the result about the sum of the measures of the interior angles of this triangle for any triangle? [Sample answer: Example 1 does not use numerical values for the measures of the angles. The representation can be used for any triangle with any angle measures.]

## Try It! Formative Assessment

### ETP Elicit and Use Evidence of Student Thinking

**Q:** Carmen says she can find the measure of the third angle by subtracting 108 from 180. Do you agree? Explain. [Yes; Sample answer: The value 108 is the sum of the two given angle measures. The difference between 180 and this value is the remaining angle measure.]

### Convince Me!

**Q:** How could you change the 96° so that the three angle measures can form a triangle? [Sample answer: Replace 96° with 86°.]

**Visual Learning Animation Plus** is available online.

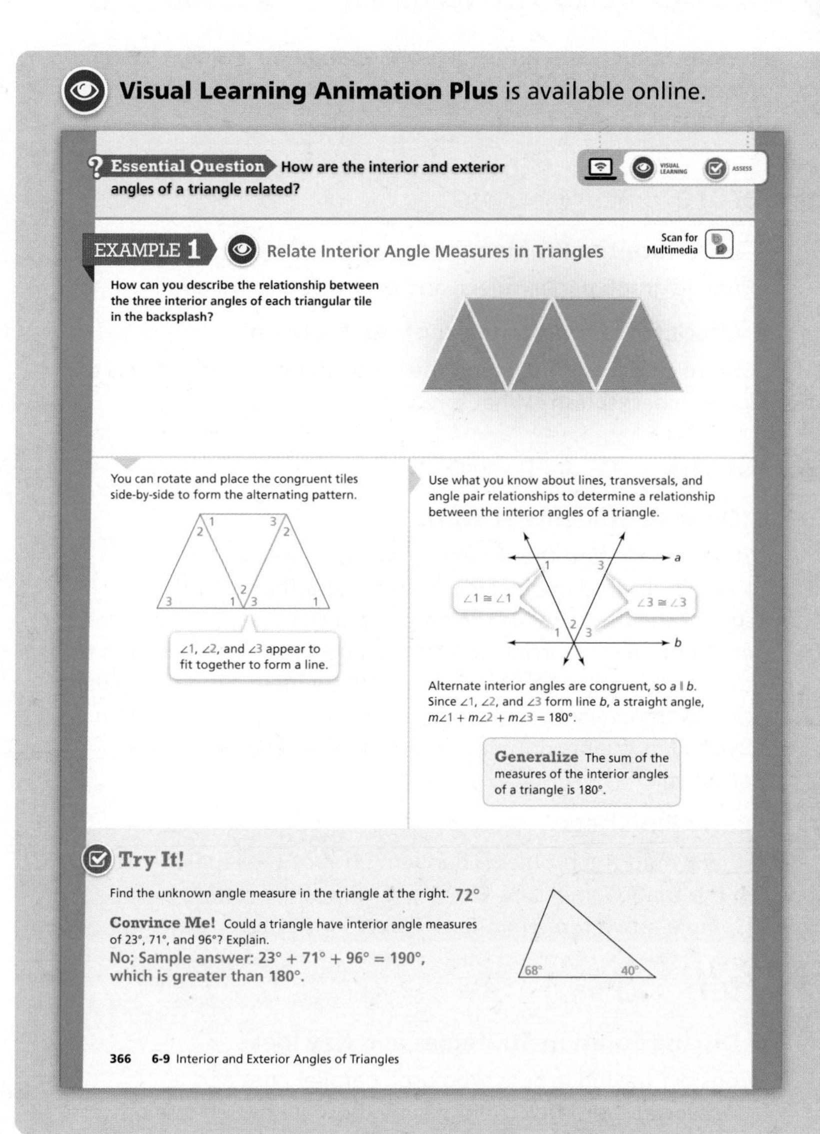

**Essential Question** How are the interior and exterior angles of a triangle related?

EXAMPLE 1 Relate Interior Angle Measures in Triangles

Scan for Multimedia

How can you describe the relationship between the three interior angles of each triangular tile in the backsplash?

You can rotate and place the congruent tiles side-by-side to form the alternating pattern.

∠1, ∠2, and ∠3 appear to fit together to form a line.

Use what you know about lines, transversals, and angle pair relationships to determine a relationship between the interior angles of a triangle.

∠1 ≅ ∠1

∠3 ≅ ∠3

Alternate interior angles are congruent, so *a* ∥ *b*. Since ∠1, ∠2, and ∠3 form line *b*, a straight angle, $m\angle 1 + m\angle 2 + m\angle 3 = 180°$.

**Generalize** The sum of the measures of the interior angles of a triangle is 180°.

**Try It!**

Find the unknown angle measure in the triangle at the right. 72°

**Convince Me!** Could a triangle have interior angle measures of 23°, 71°, and 96°? Explain.

No; Sample answer: 23° + 71° + 96° = 190°, which is greater than 180°.

68° 40°

366 6-9 Interior and Exterior Angles of Triangles

Students can access the ***Visual Learning Animation Plus*** by using the **BouncePages app** to scan this page. Students can download the app for free in their mobile devices' app store.

## Response to Intervention

**USE WITH EXAMPLE 2** Students may have difficulty generalizing the relationship between the remote interior angles and the exterior angle. Give these students other triangle problems similar to the example with different measures for the angles and with different exterior angles. Have them solve for the measure of the third interior angle and the measure of the exterior angle that is adjacent to the third angle.

**Q:** In each problem, which two angle measures are given? [Sample answer: The two interior angles that are not adjacent to the exterior angle; remote interior angles]

**Q:** In each problem, what do you notice about the sum of the measures of the remote interior angles and the measure of the exterior angle? [Sample answer: They are always equal.]

## Enrichment

**USE WITH EXAMPLE 1** Challenge advanced students to solve using algebra to determine unknown angle measures of a triangle. Give students the angle measures below, and ask them to find the numerical measure of each angle.

- $m\angle 1 = (2x + 4)°$, $m\angle 2 = (2x + 3)°$, $m\angle 3 = (2x - 1)°$ [$x = 29$, $m\angle 1 = 62°$, $m\angle 2 = 61°$, $m\angle 3 = 57°$]
- $m\angle 1 = (2x - 1)°$, $m\angle 2 = (3x + 5)°$, $m\angle 3 = (3x + 10)°$ [$x = 20.75$, $m\angle 1 = 40.5°$, $m\angle 2 = 67.25°$, $m\angle 3 = 72.25°$]

## EXAMPLE 2  Find Exterior Angle Measures

### ETP Pose Purposeful Questions

**Q:** Why do you think $\angle 4$ is called an exterior angle? [Sample answer: The angle is outside of (exterior to) the triangle.]

**Q:** How can you use the first two equations in the example to show that $m\angle 4$ is equal to the sum of $m\angle 2$ and $m\angle 3$? [Sample answer: The expressions $m\angle 1 + m\angle 4$ and the expression $m\angle 1 + m\angle 2 + m\angle 3$ are both equal to 180°, so they are equal to each other. When you subtract $m\angle 1$ from both expressions, you are left with $m\angle 4 = m\angle 2 + m\angle 3$.]

## EXAMPLE 3  Use Algebra to Find Unknown Angle Measures

###  Pose Purposeful Questions

**Q:** Why is it necessary to solve for $x$ first to find the angle measurements? [Sample answer: The angle measures are based upon the value of $x$.]

**Q:** Why does $m\angle 4 = m\angle 2 + m\angle 3$? [Sample answer: $\angle 4$ is an exterior angle of the triangle, and its measure is equal to the sum of the measures of its remote interior angles, $\angle 2$ and $\angle 3$.]

**Q:** How can you find $m\angle 4$ without substituting for $x$ in $(7x - 7)°$? [Sample answer: Use the value of $x$ to find $m\angle 2$ and $m\angle 3$. Their sum is $m\angle 4$.]

##  Try It!  Formative Assessment

###  Elicit and Use Evidence of Student Thinking

**Q:** How can you write the value of the other interior angle of the triangle in terms of $x$? [Sample answer: $(180 - 16x)°$]

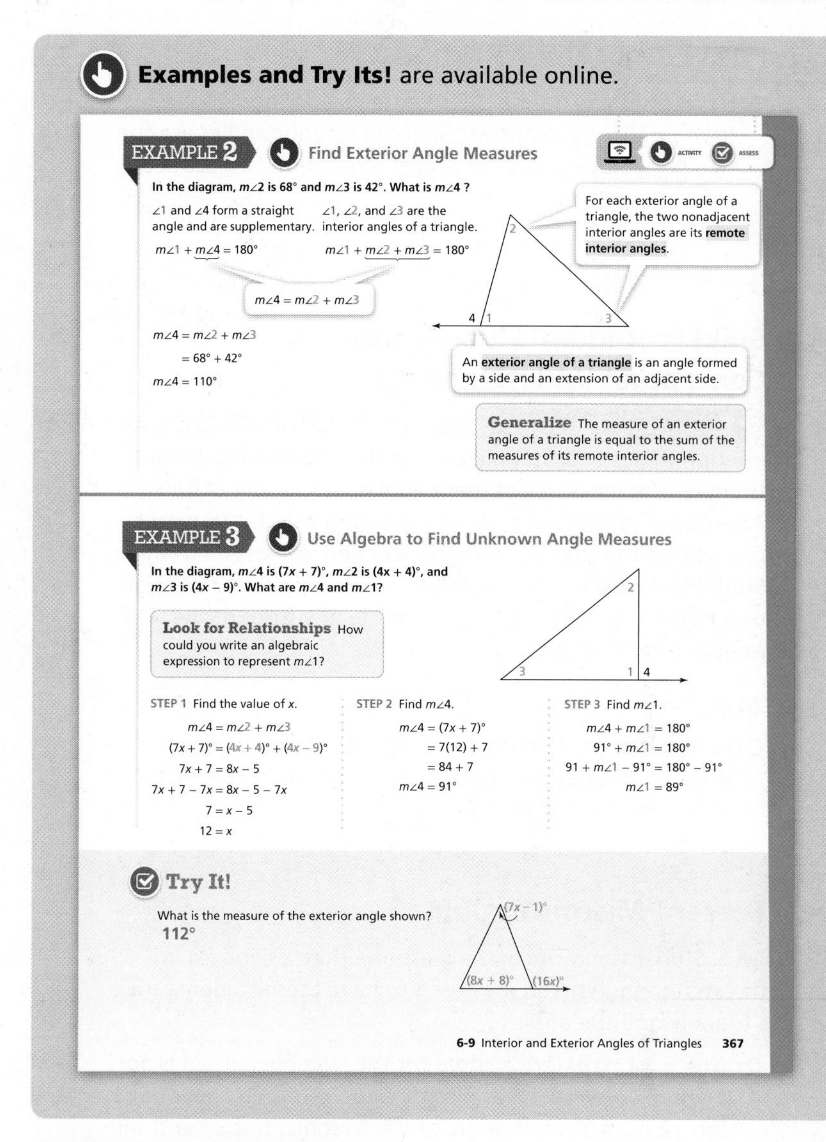
**Examples and Try Its!** are available online.

EXAMPLE 2 Find Exterior Angle Measures

**In the diagram, $m\angle 2$ is 68° and $m\angle 3$ is 42°. What is $m\angle 4$ ?**

$\angle 1$ and $\angle 4$ form a straight angle and are supplementary.

$m\angle 1 + m\angle 4 = 180°$

$\angle 1$, $\angle 2$, and $\angle 3$ are the interior angles of a triangle.

$m\angle 1 + m\angle 2 + m\angle 3 = 180°$

$m\angle 4 = m\angle 2 + m\angle 3$

$m\angle 4 = m\angle 2 + m\angle 3$
$= 68° + 42°$
$m\angle 4 = 110°$

For each exterior angle of a triangle, the two nonadjacent interior angles are its **remote interior angles**.

An **exterior angle of a triangle** is an angle formed by a side and an extension of an adjacent side.

**Generalize** The measure of an exterior angle of a triangle is equal to the sum of the measures of its remote interior angles.

EXAMPLE 3 Use Algebra to Find Unknown Angle Measures

**In the diagram, $m\angle 4$ is $(7x + 7)°$, $m\angle 2$ is $(4x + 4)°$, and $m\angle 3$ is $(4x - 9)°$. What are $m\angle 4$ and $m\angle 1$?**

**Look for Relationships** How could you write an algebraic expression to represent $m\angle 1$?

STEP 1 Find the value of $x$.

$m\angle 4 = m\angle 2 + m\angle 3$
$(7x + 7)° = (4x + 4)° + (4x - 9)°$
$7x + 7 = 8x - 5$
$7x + 7 - 7x = 8x - 5 - 7x$
$7 = x - 5$
$12 = x$

STEP 2 Find $m\angle 4$.

$m\angle 4 = (7x + 7)°$
$= 7(12) + 7$
$= 84 + 7$
$m\angle 4 = 91°$

STEP 3 Find $m\angle 1$.

$m\angle 4 + m\angle 1 = 180°$
$91° + m\angle 1 = 180°$
$91 + m\angle 1 - 91° = 180° - 91°$
$m\angle 1 = 89°$

Try It!

What is the measure of the exterior angle shown?
112°



6-9 Interior and Exterior Angles of Triangles 367

## ADDITIONAL EXAMPLES 

**For additional examples go online.**

## English Language Learners

**ENTERING** Use with Example 1.

Help students increase their vocabulary by reading the example and circling any words they are not familiar with, such as *tile*, *interior*, and *backsplash*.

**Q:** What words do you not know? Circle them.

Write the words students have circled on the board. Have students work together to come up with simple definitions or more familiar synonyms for these words. As you work through the example with students, refer to the synonyms and definitions you have written.

**EMERGING** Use with Example 3.

Help students practice their language skills by filling in the blanks to describe the steps to solve the problem.

**Q:** Step 1: First write the _______ [equation]. Combine _______ [like terms] and solve for the _______ [variable].

Step 2: Substitute the value of the variable and _______ [solve] to find the _______ [measure] of angle 4.

Step 3: _______ [Substitute] the value of the variable and solve to find the _______ [measure] of angle 1.

**EXPANDING** Ask students to review Example 3.

Have students work in groups of 3. Have one student explain the steps used to solve Step 1, a second student explain the steps used to solve Step 2, and the third to explain the steps used to solve Step 3. Encourage students to explain the mathematics that occurs in each line of each step. Help students clarify any steps that they do not understand.

Listen for students using appropriate math vocabulary in their explanations.

# STEP 2 | Visual Learning *continued*

Go Online

Key Concept | Assess | Activity

## KEY CONCEPT

### Pose Purposeful Questions

**Q:** How could you define the remote interior angles of a triangle? [Sample answer: Remote interior angles are the two nonadjacent interior angles in relation to a particular exterior angle.]

## Do You Understand/Do You Know How?

Formative Assessment

### Build Procedural Fluency from Conceptual Understanding

**Essential Question** Students should understand that interior angles of a triangle are the three angles inside the triangle. The measures of these angles have a sum of 180°. An exterior angle is outside of the triangle and is formed by one side of the triangle and an extended side of the triangle. Students should know that the measure of an exterior angle of a triangle is equal to the sum of the measures of the two remote interior angles.

**ITEM 4**

**Q:** How could you find $m\angle 2$ using $m\angle 4$? [Sample answer; Since $\angle 4$ is supplementary to the 37.3° angle, it is 142.7°. Therefore, $m\angle 2$ is 37.3°.]

### Prevent Misconceptions

**ITEM 5** Students may incorrectly assume that $\angle 3$ and $\angle 4$ are both exterior angles. You may wish to have these students trace the triangle and the angles.

**Q:** Why is $\angle 4$ an exterior angle for the triangle and $\angle 3$ is not? [Sample answer: The angles $\angle 2$ and $\angle 4$ form a linear pair, and $\angle 2$ is an interior angle of the triangle, but $\angle 3$ and the angle marked 79.4° do not form a linear pair.]

Available Online

KEY CONCEPT

The sum of the measures of the interior angles of a triangle is 180°.

$m\angle 1 + m\angle 2 + m\angle 3 = 180°$

The measure of an exterior angle of a triangle is equal to the sum of the measures of its remote interior angles.

$m\angle 2 + m\angle 3 = m\angle 4$

Remote interior angles

Exterior angle

**Do You Understand?**

1. **Essential Question** How are the interior and exterior angles of a triangle related?
Sample answer: An exterior angle is equal to the sum of its remote interior angles.

2. **Reasoning** Maggie draws a triangle with a right angle. The other two angles have equal measures. What are the possible values of the exterior angles for Maggie's triangle? Explain.
135° or 90°; Sample answer: Each exterior angle is supplementary to its adjacent interior angle. The interior angles are 45°, 45°, and 90° so the exterior angles are 135°, 135°, and 90°.

3. Brian draws a triangle with interior angles of 32° and 87°, and one exterior angle of 93°. Draw the triangle. Label all of the interior angles and the exterior angle.
Student's triangle should show angles of 32°, 87°, and 61° and an exterior angle adjacent to the 87° angle with a measure of 93°.

**Do You Know How?**

Use the diagram below for 4 and 5. Assume that $a \parallel b$.

3 37.3° 79.4° a 1 2 4 b

4. What are the measures of $\angle 1$ and $\angle 2$? Explain.
$m\angle 1 = 63.3°$, $m\angle 2 = 37.3°$; Sample answer: I know that $m\angle 2$ is 37.3° because the measure of its congruent alternate interior angle is 37.3°. To find $m\angle 1$, I can find the sum of 79.4° and 37.3° and subtract that sum from 180°.

5. What are the measures of $\angle 3$ and $\angle 4$? Explain.
$m\angle 3 = 63.3°$, $m\angle 4 = 142.7°$;
Sample answer:
$m\angle 2 + m\angle 4 = 180°$, so $m\angle 4 = 142.7°$;
$m\angle 3 + 79.4° + 37.3° = 180°$,
so $m\angle 3 = 63.3°$

6. In $\triangle ABC$, $m\angle A = x°$, $m\angle B = (2x)°$, and $m\angle C = (6x + 18)°$. What is the measure of each angle?
$m\angle A = 18°$, $m\angle B = 36°$, $m\angle C = 126°$

368 6-9 Interior and Exterior Angles of Triangles

## ADDITIONAL EXAMPLE 3

Help students solve more complicated problems using algebra to find unknown angle measures in triangles with this additional example. Make sure students remember the rules about isosceles triangles and are careful with decimals.

**Q:** In the problem there are only two angle measures given. How can you find the other angle measures? [Sample answer: The triangle is isosceles and the $m\angle 2 = m\angle 3$. The sum of the measures of the angles in a triangle is 180 degrees, so $m\angle 2 + m\angle 3 + m\angle 4 = 180$ degrees.]

**Q:** How can you write an equation to find the value of the $x$ for this triangle? [Sample answer: Because the measure of an exterior angle is equal to the sum of its remote interior angles, I can write the equation $m\angle 1 = m\angle 2 + m\angle 3$, and then substitute the expressions for the measure of each angle.]

**Additional Examples** are available online.

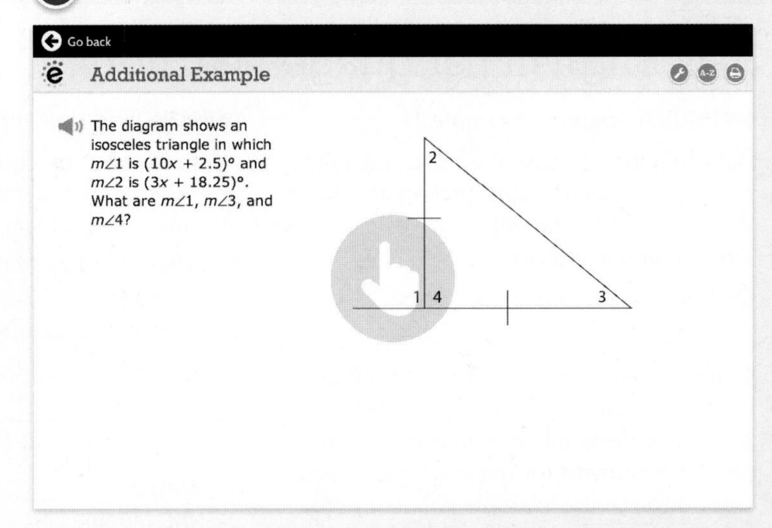


**Answer:** $m\angle 1 = 87.5°$, $m\angle 3 = 43.75°$, $m\angle 4 = 92.5°$

Go Online

 Practice  Tutorials  Math Tools

# Practice & Problem Solving  

**Interactive Practice** and **Virtual Nerd Tutorials** are available online.

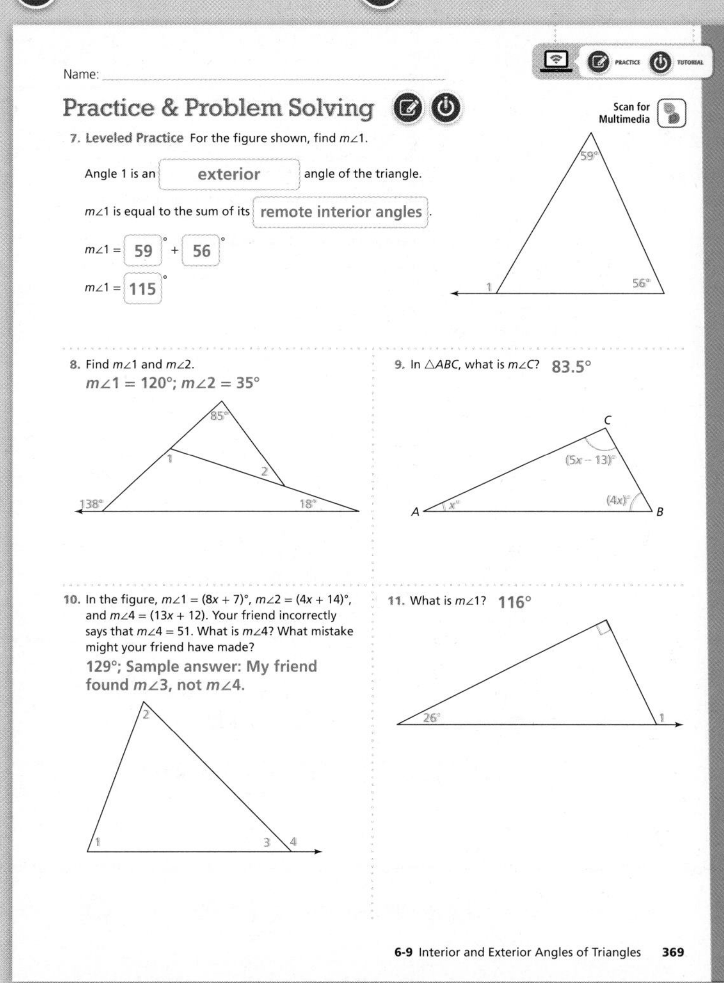

Name:

Practice & Problem Solving

Scan for Multimedia

7. Leveled Practice For the figure shown, find $m\angle 1$.

Angle 1 is an exterior angle of the triangle.

$m\angle 1$ is equal to the sum of its remote interior angles.

$m\angle 1 = 59° + 56°$

$m\angle 1 = 115°$

8. Find $m\angle 1$ and $m\angle 2$.
$m\angle 1 = 120°$; $m\angle 2 = 35°$

9. In $\triangle ABC$, what is $m\angle C$? 83.5°

10. In the figure, $m\angle 1 = (8x + 7)°$, $m\angle 2 = (4x + 14)°$, and $m\angle 4 = (13x + 12)$. Your friend incorrectly says that $m\angle 4 = 51$. What is $m\angle 4$? What mistake might your friend have made?
129°; Sample answer: My friend found $m\angle 3$, not $m\angle 4$.

11. What is $m\angle 1$? 116°

6-9 Interior and Exterior Angles of Triangles 369

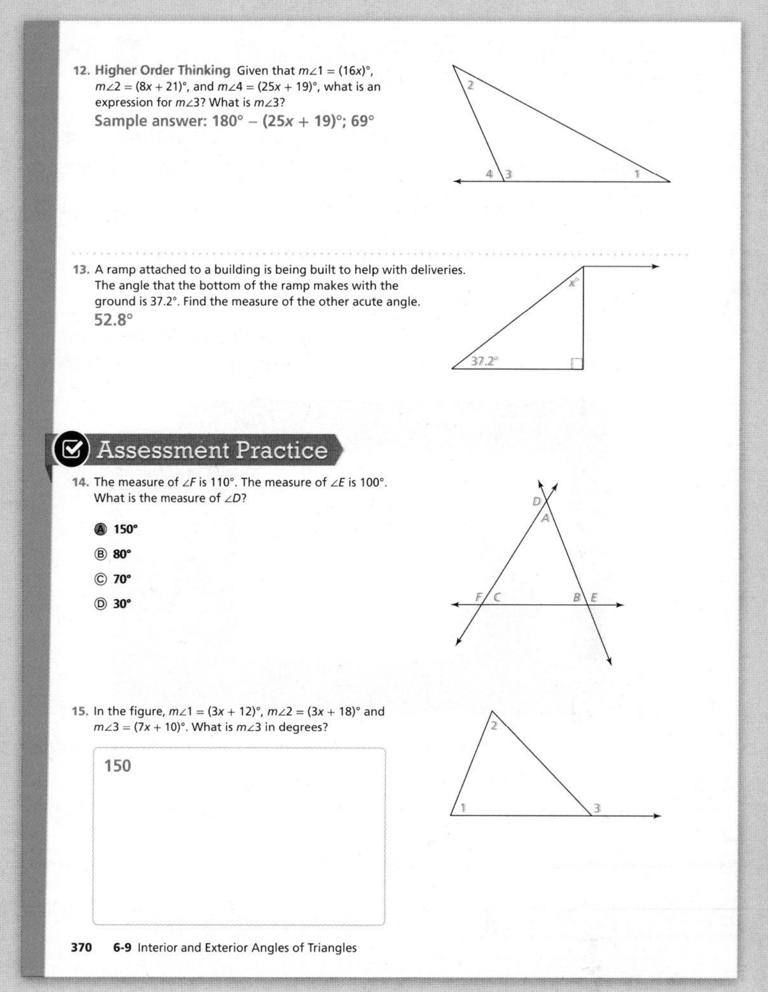

12. Higher Order Thinking Given that $m\angle 1 = (16x)°$, $m\angle 2 = (8x + 21)°$, and $m\angle 4 = (25x + 19)°$, what is an expression for $m\angle 3$? What is $m\angle 3$?
Sample answer: $180° - (25x + 19)°$; 69°

13. A ramp attached to a building is being built to help with deliveries. The angle that the bottom of the ramp makes with the ground is 37.2°. Find the measure of the other acute angle.
52.8°

Assessment Practice

14. The measure of $\angle F$ is 110°. The measure of $\angle E$ is 100°. What is the measure of $\angle D$?

Ⓐ 150°
Ⓑ 80°
Ⓒ 70°
Ⓓ 30°

15. In the figure, $m\angle 1 = (3x + 12)°$, $m\angle 2 = (3x + 18)°$ and $m\angle 3 = (7x + 10)°$. What is $m\angle 3$ in degrees?

150

370 6-9 Interior and Exterior Angles of Triangles

## Error Intervention

**ITEM 12 Higher Order Thinking** Students may have difficulty thinking of an expression because they do not realize they need to use two constants for the expression.

**Q:** What is the relationship of ∠1, ∠2, and ∠3? Explain. [Sample answer: Since they are the interior angles of the triangle, they have a sum of 180°.]

**Q:** What is the relationship of ∠1, ∠2, and ∠4? Explain. [Sample answer: ∠1 and ∠2 are remote interior angles, and ∠4 is an exterior angle.]

## English Language Learners

**ITEM 13** Use this question to increase students' understanding of mathematical situations in the real-world. Have students label each section of the drawing with *ramp*, *ground*, or *loading area*.

**Q:** What is a ramp? [Sample answer: A sloping surface connecting two levels]

You may opt to have students complete the automatically scored Practice & Problem Solving items online.

### Item Analysis

| Example | Items | DOK |
|---|---|---|
| 1 | 9 | 1 |
| | 13 | 2 |
| 2 | 7, 8 | 1 |
| | 11, 14 | 2 |
| 3 | 15 | 2 |
| | 10, 12 | 3 |

# STEP 3 | Assess & Differentiate

Go Online

Assess Tutorials Worksheets

## Lesson Quiz

**Formative** Assessment

Use the student scores on the Lesson Quiz to prescribe differentiated assignments.

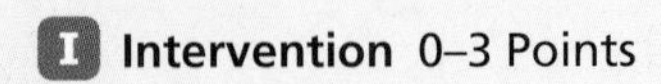

**I Intervention** 0–3 Points **O On-Level** 4 Points **A Advanced** 5 Points

You may opt to have students take the Lesson Quiz online. The Lesson Quiz will be automatically scored and appropriate remediation, practice, or enrichment will be assigned based on student performance.

**Lesson Quiz** is available online.

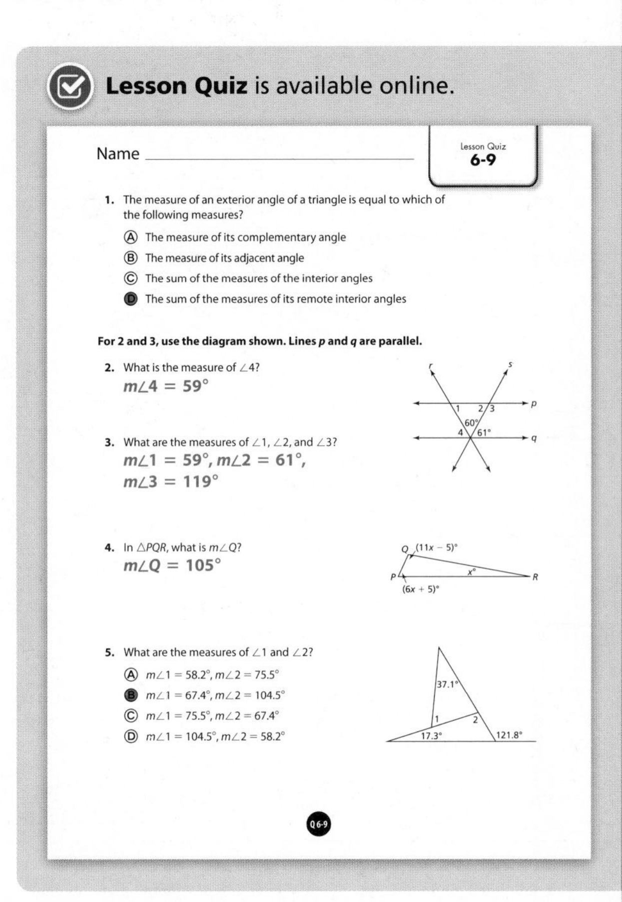

Name ______________ Lesson Quiz 6-9

1. The measure of an exterior angle of a triangle is equal to which of the following measures?
   Ⓐ The measure of its complementary angle
   Ⓑ The measure of its adjacent angle
   Ⓒ The sum of the measures of the interior angles
   Ⓓ The sum of the measures of its remote interior angles

**For 2 and 3, use the diagram shown. Lines p and q are parallel.**

2. What is the measure of $\angle 4$?
   $m\angle 4 = 59°$
3. What are the measures of $\angle 1$, $\angle 2$, and $\angle 3$?
   $m\angle 1 = 59°, m\angle 2 = 61°,$
   $m\angle 3 = 119°$
4. In $\triangle PQR$, what is $m\angle Q$?
   $m\angle Q = 105°$
5. What are the measures of $\angle 1$ and $\angle 2$?
   Ⓐ $m\angle 1 = 58.2°, m\angle 2 = 75.5°$
   Ⓑ $m\angle 1 = 67.4°, m\angle 2 = 104.5°$
   Ⓒ $m\angle 1 = 75.5°, m\angle 2 = 67.4°$
   Ⓓ $m\angle 1 = 104.5°, m\angle 2 = 58.2°$

Q6-9

## Video Tutorials

Students can access instructional tutorials using the **Virtual Nerd app**.

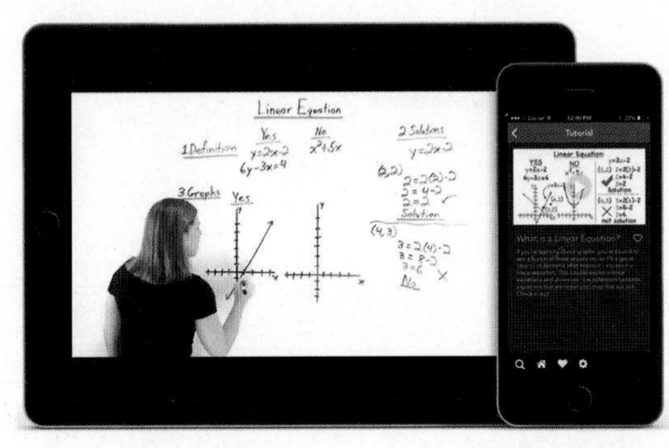

Students can also access the videos using the **BouncePages app** to scan exercise pages marked with this icon. Students can download both apps for free in their mobile devices' app store.

## Differentiated Intervention

**I** = Intervention **O** = On-Level **A** = Advanced

### Reteach to Build Understanding I

Provides scaffolded reteaching for the key lesson concepts.

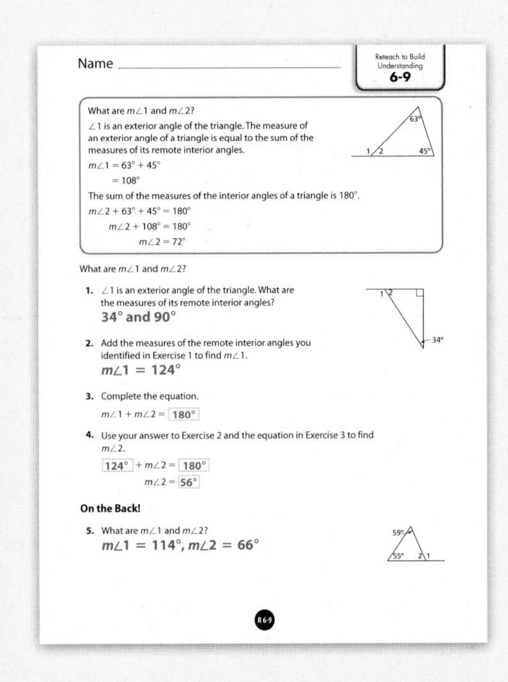

Name ______________ Reteach to Build Understanding 6-9

What are $m\angle 1$ and $m\angle 2$?
$\angle 1$ is an exterior angle of the triangle. The measure of an exterior angle of a triangle is equal to the sum of the measures of its remote interior angles.
$m\angle 1 = 63° + 45°$
$= 108°$
The sum of the measures of the interior angles of a triangle is 180°.
$m\angle 2 + 63° + 45° = 180°$
$m\angle 2 + 108° = 180°$
$m\angle 2 = 72°$

What are $m\angle 1$ and $m\angle 2$?

1. $\angle 1$ is an exterior angle of the triangle. What are the measures of its remote interior angles?
   34° and 90°
2. Add the measures of the remote interior angles you identified in Exercise 1 to find $m\angle 1$.
   $m\angle 1 = 124°$
3. Complete the equation.
   $m\angle 1 + m\angle 2 = 180°$
4. Use your answer to Exercise 2 and the equation in Exercise 3 to find $m\angle 2$.
   $124° + m\angle 2 = 180°$
   $m\angle 2 = 56°$

**On the Back!**

5. What are $m\angle 1$ and $m\angle 2$?
   $m\angle 1 = 114°, m\angle 2 = 66°$

R6-9

### Additional Vocabulary Support I O

Helps students develop and reinforce understanding of key terms and concepts.

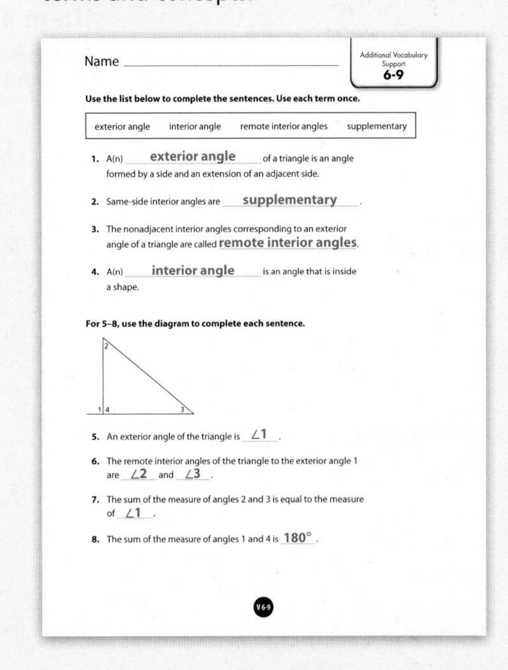

Name ______________ Additional Vocabulary Support 6-9

**Use the list below to complete the sentences. Use each term once.**

exterior angle | interior angle | remote interior angles | supplementary

1. A(n) **exterior angle** of a triangle is an angle formed by a side and an extension of an adjacent side.
2. Same-side interior angles are **supplementary**.
3. The nonadjacent interior angles corresponding to an exterior angle of a triangle are called **remote interior angles**.
4. A(n) **interior angle** is an angle that is inside a shape.

**For 5–8, use the diagram to complete each sentence.**

5. An exterior angle of the triangle is $\angle 1$.
6. The remote interior angles of the triangle to the exterior angle 1 are $\angle 2$ and $\angle 3$.
7. The sum of the measure of angles 2 and 3 is equal to the measure of $\angle 1$.
8. The sum of the measure of angles 1 and 4 is 180°.

V6-9

### Build Mathematical Literacy I O

Provides support for struggling readers to build mathematical literacy.

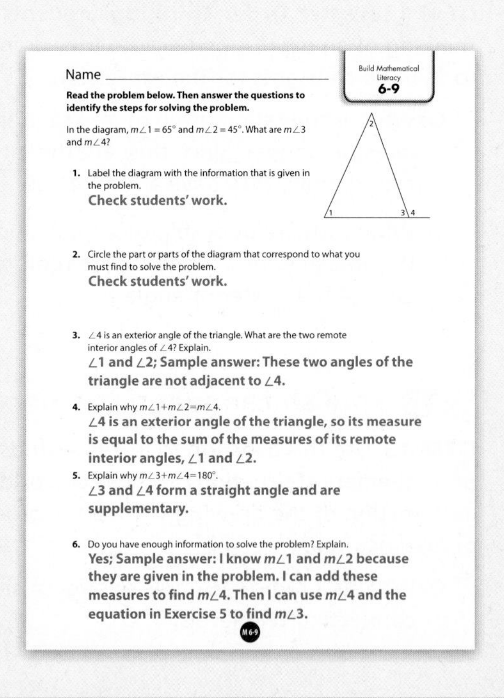

Name ______________ Build Mathematical Literacy 6-9

**Read the problem below. Then answer the questions to identify the steps for solving the problem.**

In the diagram, $m\angle 1 = 65°$ and $m\angle 2 = 45°$. What are $m\angle 3$ and $m\angle 4$?

1. Label the diagram with the information that is given in the problem.
   Check students' work.
2. Circle the part or parts of the diagram that correspond to what you must find to solve the problem.
   Check students' work.
3. $\angle 4$ is an exterior angle of the triangle. What are the two remote interior angles of $\angle 4$? Explain.
   $\angle 1$ and $\angle 2$; Sample answer: These two angles of the triangle are not adjacent to $\angle 4$.
4. Explain why $m\angle 1 + m\angle 2 = m\angle 4$.
   $\angle 4$ is an exterior angle of the triangle, so its measure is equal to the sum of the measures of its remote interior angles, $\angle 1$ and $\angle 2$.
5. Explain why $m\angle 3 + m\angle 4 = 180°$.
   $\angle 3$ and $\angle 4$ form a straight angle and are supplementary.
6. Do you have enough information to solve the problem? Explain.
   Yes; Sample answer: I know $m\angle 1$ and $m\angle 2$ because they are given in the problem. I can add these measures to find $m\angle 4$. Then I can use $m\angle 4$ and the equation in Exercise 5 to find $m\angle 3$.

M6-9

Go Online

 Practice  Worksheets  Math Tools  Math Games

# Additional Practice

You may opt to have students complete the automatically scored Additional Practice items online.

### Item Analysis

| Example | Items | DOK |
|---|---|---|
| 1 | 2, 5 | 2 |
| | 4 | 3 |
| 2 | 1 | 1 |
| | 7 | 2 |
| 3 | 3, 8 | 2 |
| | 6 | 3 |

**Interactive Practice** is available online.

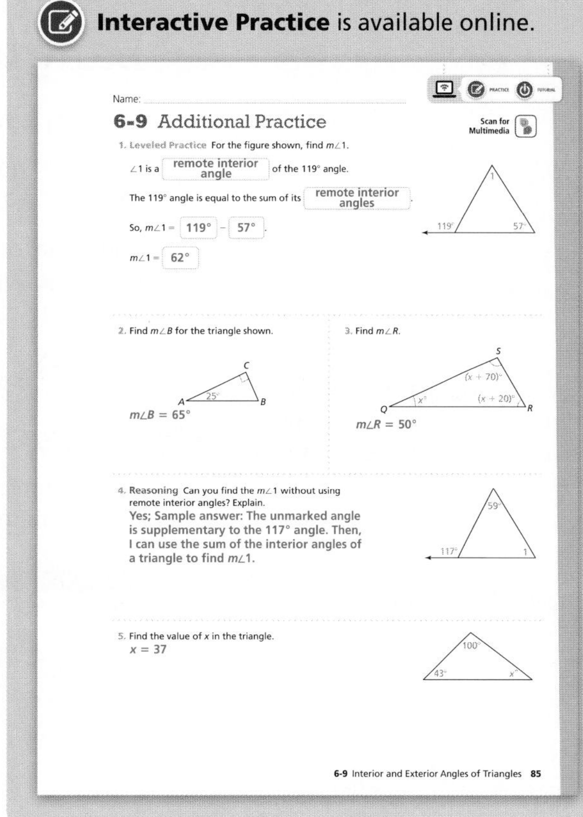

Name:

**6-9** Additional Practice

Scan for Multimedia

1. Leveled Practice For the figure shown, find $m\angle 1$.

$\angle 1$ is a remote interior angle of the 119° angle.

The 119° angle is equal to the sum of its remote interior angles.

So, $m\angle 1 =$ 119° − 57°.

$m\angle 1 =$ 62°

2. Find $m\angle B$ for the triangle shown.

$m\angle B = 65°$

3. Find $m\angle R$.

$m\angle R = 50°$

4. Reasoning Can you find the $m\angle 1$ without using remote interior angles? Explain.
Yes; Sample answer: The unmarked angle is supplementary to the 117° angle. Then, I can use the sum of the interior angles of a triangle to find $m\angle 1$.

5. Find the value of $x$ in the triangle.
$x = 37$

6-9 Interior and Exterior Angles of Triangles 85

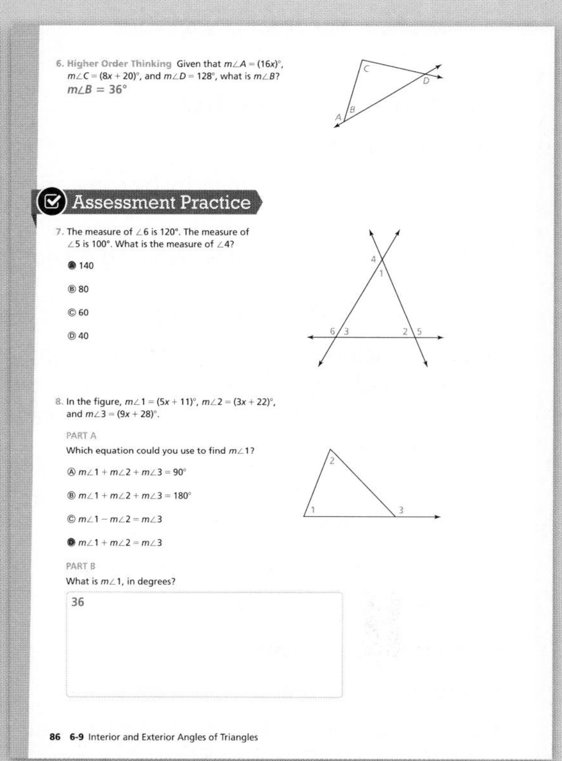

6. Higher Order Thinking Given that $m\angle A = (16x)°$, $m\angle C = (8x + 20)°$, and $m\angle D = 128°$, what is $m\angle B$?
$m\angle B = 36°$

Assessment Practice

7. The measure of $\angle 6$ is 120°. The measure of $\angle 5$ is 100°. What is the measure of $\angle 4$?

Ⓐ 140
Ⓑ 80
Ⓒ 60
Ⓓ 40

8. In the figure, $m\angle 1 = (5x + 11)°$, $m\angle 2 = (3x + 22)°$, and $m\angle 3 = (9x + 28)°$.

PART A
Which equation could you use to find $m\angle 1$?

Ⓐ $m\angle 1 + m\angle 2 + m\angle 3 = 90°$
Ⓑ $m\angle 1 + m\angle 2 + m\angle 3 = 180°$
Ⓒ $m\angle 1 - m\angle 2 = m\angle 3$
Ⓓ $m\angle 1 + m\angle 2 = m\angle 3$

PART B
What is $m\angle 1$, in degrees?

36

86 6-9 Interior and Exterior Angles of Triangles

# Differentiated Intervention

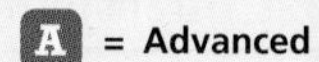

I = Intervention O = On-Level A = Advanced

## Enrichment O A

Presents engaging problems and activities that extend the lesson concepts.

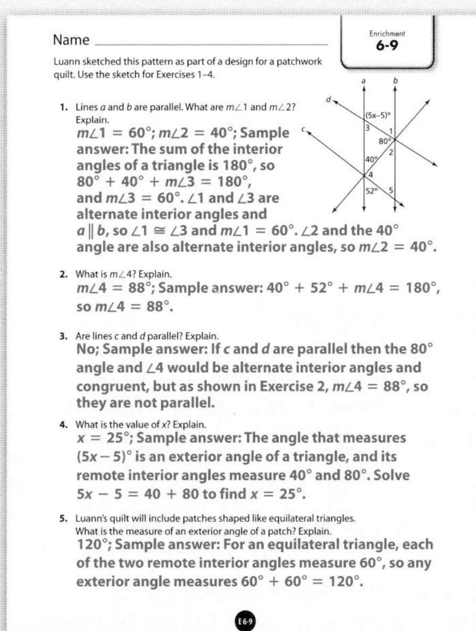

Name

Enrichment 6-9

Luann sketched this pattern as part of a design for a patchwork quilt. Use the sketch for Exercises 1–4.

1. Lines $a$ and $b$ are parallel. What are $m\angle 1$ and $m\angle 2$? Explain.
$m\angle 1 = 60°$; $m\angle 2 = 40°$; Sample answer: The sum of the interior angles of a triangle is 180°, so $80° + 40° + m\angle 3 = 180°$, and $m\angle 3 = 60°$. $\angle 1$ and $\angle 3$ are alternate interior angles and $a \parallel b$, so $\angle 1 \cong \angle 3$ and $m\angle 1 = 60°$. $\angle 2$ and the 40° angle are also alternate interior angles, so $m\angle 2 = 40°$.

2. What is $m\angle 4$? Explain.
$m\angle 4 = 88°$; Sample answer: $40° + 52° + m\angle 4 = 180°$, so $m\angle 4 = 88°$.

3. Are lines $c$ and $d$ parallel? Explain.
No; Sample answer: If $c$ and $d$ are parallel then the 80° angle and $\angle 4$ would be alternate interior angles and congruent, but as shown in Exercise 2, $m\angle 4 = 88°$, so they are not parallel.

4. What is the value of $x$? Explain.
$x = 25°$; Sample answer: The angle that measures $(5x - 5)°$ is an exterior angle of a triangle, and its remote interior angles measure 40° and 80°. Solve $5x - 5 = 40 + 80$ to find $x = 25°$.

5. Luann's quilt will include patches shaped like equilateral triangles. What is the measure of an exterior angle of a patch? Explain.
120°; Sample answer: For an equilateral triangle, each of the two remote interior angles measure 60°, so any exterior angle measures $60° + 60° = 120°$.

E 6-9

## Math Tools and Games I O A

Offers additional activities and games to build understanding and fluency.

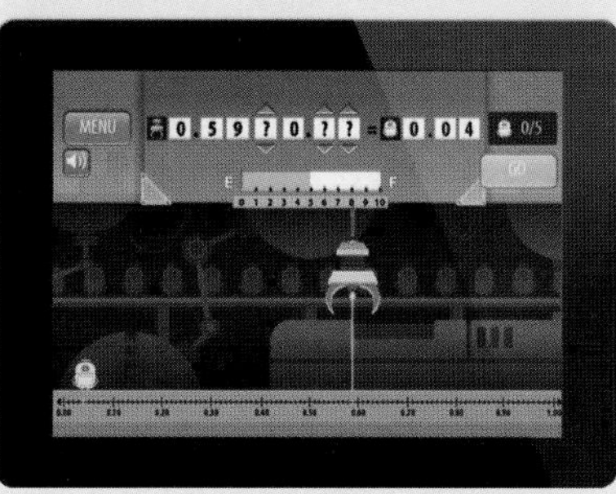


## Pick a Project and STEM Project I O A

Provides an additional opportunity for students to demonstrate understanding of key mathematical concepts.

Lesson 6-10

# Angle-Angle Triangle Similarity

Go Online

## Lesson Overview

FOCUS

### Mathematics Objective

**Students will be able to:**

✔ determine triangle similarity by comparing the angle measures of the triangles.

✔ solve algebraic problems involving similar triangles.

### Essential Understanding

You can conclude that two triangles are similar by showing that two angles of one triangle are congruent to two angles of the other triangle using the Angle-Angle Criterion. Triangle similarity can be used to determine unknown angle measures.

COHERENCE

**Previously in this topic, students:**

- found the measures of interior and exterior angles of a triangle.
- explored the concept of similar figures.

**In this lesson, students:**

- determine whether triangles are similar.
- use triangle similarity to find angle measures.

**In high school, students will:**

- learn other methods for proving triangles are similar.
- extend their understanding of similarity in terms of similarity transformations.

**Cross-Cluster Connection** Work with congruent and similar figures (8.G.1) connects to work with proportional relationships (8.EE.2).

RIGOR

This lesson emphasizes a blend of **procedural skill and fluency** and **application**.

- Students become fluent in comparing angle measures in two triangles to determine if they are similar.
- Students apply the concepts of triangle similarity to find the measures of angles in similar triangles.

## Language Support

### Lesson Language Objective

Explain how to use angle measures to determine whether two triangles are similar.

Additional resources are available in the **Language Support Handbook**.

## Math Anytime

### Today's Challenge

Use the Topic 6 problems any time during this topic.

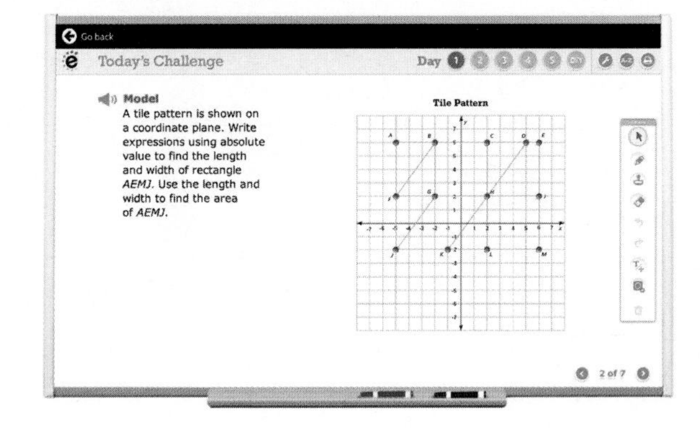


## Mathematics Overview | Common Core Standards

### Content Standards

In this lesson you will focus on Common Core Standard **8.G.A.5**.

- **8.G.A.5** Use informal arguments to establish facts about the angle sum and exterior angle of triangles, about the angles created when parallel lines are cut by a transversal, and the angle-angle criterion for similarity of triangles.

### Mathematical Practice Standards

**MP.3 Construct Arguments and Critique Reasoning**
Students will analyze problems related to triangle similarity to construct arguments. Students will justify their conclusions with mathematical concepts and vocabulary.

**MP.8 Generalize**
Students will understand the broader application of the Angle-Angle Criterion in the angle measures of similar triangles.

## STEP 1 | Problem-Based Learning

15-20 min

Go Online

Activity

# Explore It!

Formative Assessment

**Purpose** Students engage in productive struggle to compare the side lengths and angle measures of two triangles and connect it to determining whether triangles are similar in the Visual Learning Bridge.

## ETP Before

WHOLE CLASS

### 1 Introduce the Problem

Provide rulers, compasses, and protractors, as needed.

### 2 Check for Understanding of the Problem

Engage students with the problem by asking: What different shapes of flags have you seen?

## ETP During

SMALL GROUP

### 3 Observe Students at Work

- **How do students draw the triangles?** Students might trace the flags, or they might use a ruler and a protractor.
- **How do students describe how the side lengths are related?** Students might describe a sequence of transformations that maps one triangle onto the other to show that the triangles are similar which means the side lengths are proportional, or they might measure the side lengths.
- **How do students describe how the angle measures are related?** Students might use the fact that the sum of the angles of a triangle is 180° to calculate the measures of the missing angles, or they might measure the angles to determine that they are equal.

If needed, ask Is there anything you learned in previous lessons that can help you solve this problem?

### Early Finishers

How would the problem change if the labeled angle in the larger flag measured 50°? [Sample answer: The triangles would not be similar because their angles are not equal, and their side lengths would not be proportional.]

## ETP After

WHOLE CLASS

### 4 Discuss Solution Strategies and Key Ideas

Consider having groups share their solutions to part (A) first, followed by part (B), and then part (C). Have students discuss how they know that the flags are similar; if you translate and dilate the smaller flag it maps onto the larger flag. Have students make a conjecture about the angles of two similar triangles; two similar triangles have equal angle measures.

### 5 Consider Instructional Implications

After presenting Example 1, have students refer back to the conjecture they made in the Explore It and describe how it fits with the Angle-Angle Criterion for triangle similarity; since the angles of two similar triangles have equal measures, and the sum of the angles in a triangle is always 180°, if triangles have two corresponding angles with equal measures then the triangles are similar.

## Analyze Student Work

**Explore It!** Activity is available online.

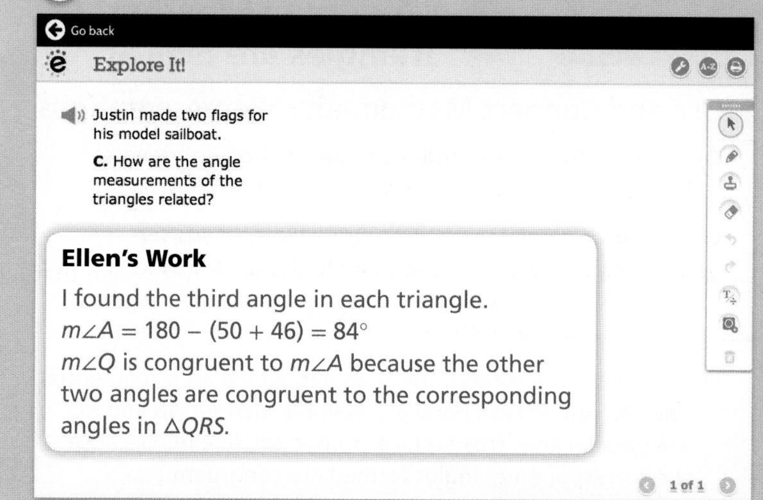


**Ellen** uses the definition of similar triangles and congruent angles to describe how the angle measures of the triangles are related.

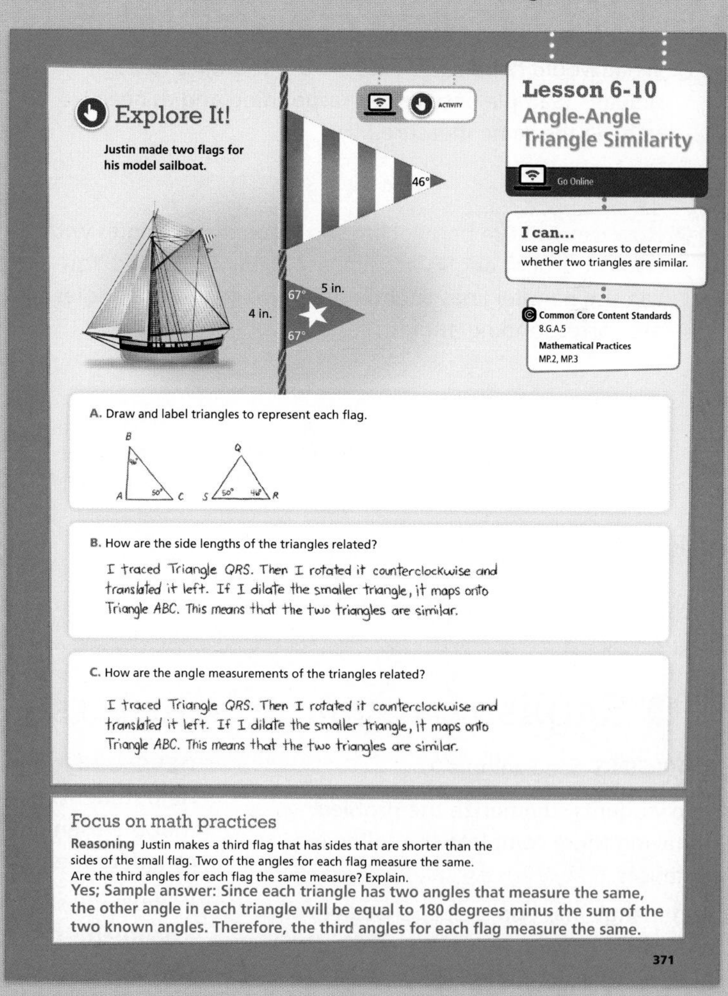
Explore It!

Justin made two flags for his model sailboat.

Lesson 6-10
Angle-Angle Triangle Similarity

Go Online

I can...
use angle measures to determine whether two triangles are similar.

Common Core Content Standards 8.G.A.5
Mathematical Practices MP.2, MP.3

46°
5 in.
4 in.
67°
67°

A. Draw and label triangles to represent each flag.

B. How are the side lengths of the triangles related?

I traced Triangle QRS. Then I rotated it counterclockwise and translated it left. If I dilate the smaller triangle, it maps onto Triangle ABC. This means that the two triangles are similar.

C. How are the angle measurements of the triangles related?

I traced Triangle QRS. Then I rotated it counterclockwise and translated it left. If I dilate the smaller triangle, it maps onto Triangle ABC. This means that the two triangles are similar.

Focus on math practices

**Reasoning** Justin makes a third flag that has sides that are shorter than the sides of the small flag. Two of the angles for each flag measure the same. Are the third angles for each flag the same measure? Explain.
Yes; Sample answer: Since each triangle has two angles that measure the same, the other angle in each triangle will be equal to 180 degrees minus the sum of the two known angles. Therefore, the third angles for each flag measure the same.

371

**Gavin** starts with the given measures and shows which are equal. Then he uses the sum of the interior angles of triangles to show that the unlabeled angles are also equal.

Go Online

Visual Learning

Assess

# STEP 2 | Visual Learning

## ETP Establish Mathematics Goals to Focus Learning

Engage students in a discussion about the ***Essential Question***. Make sure students understand the concepts of rotations, reflections, translations, dilations, and similar figures before you begin Example 1.

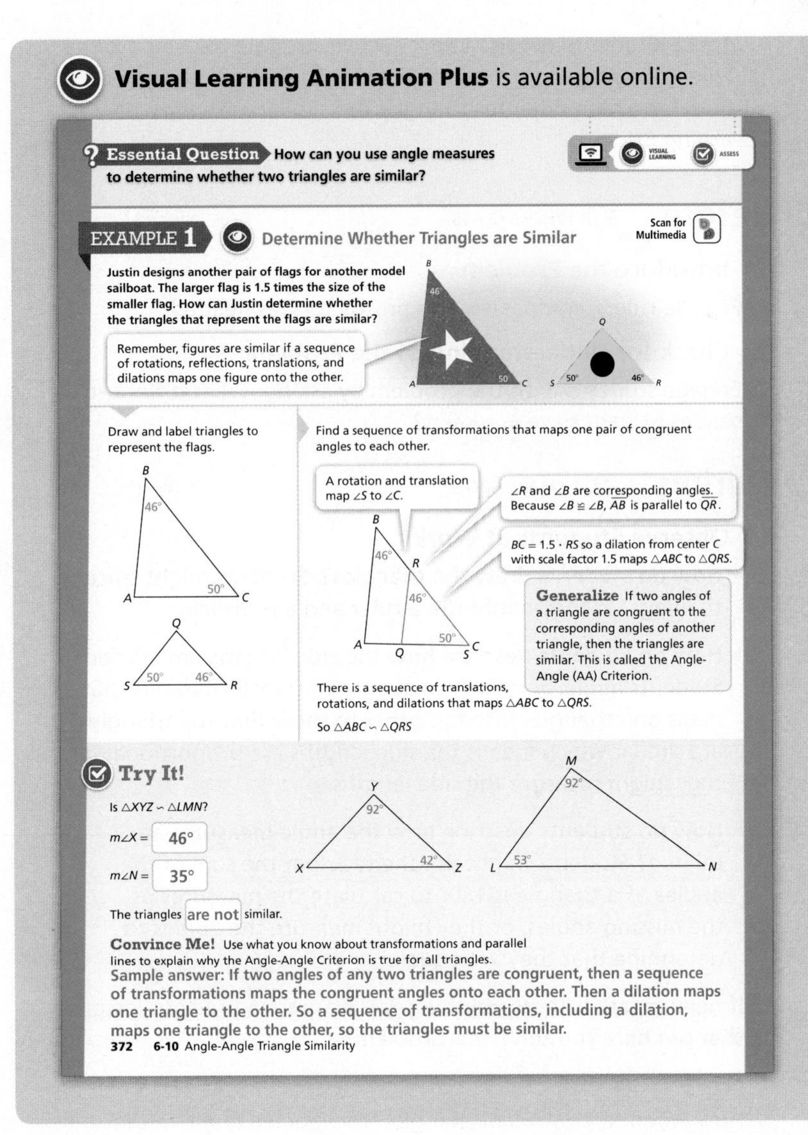

**Visual Learning Animation Plus** is available online.

**Essential Question** How can you use angle measures to determine whether two triangles are similar?

EXAMPLE 1 Determine Whether Triangles are Similar

Scan for Multimedia

Justin designs another pair of flags for another model sailboat. The larger flag is 1.5 times the size of the smaller flag. How can Justin determine whether the triangles that represent the flags are similar?

Remember, figures are similar if a sequence of rotations, reflections, translations, and dilations maps one figure onto the other.

Draw and label triangles to represent the flags.

Find a sequence of transformations that maps one pair of congruent angles to each other.

A rotation and translation map $\angle S$ to $\angle C$.

$\angle R$ and $\angle B$ are corresponding angles. Because $\angle B \cong \angle B$, $\overline{AB}$ is parallel to $\overline{QR}$.

$BC = 1.5 \cdot RS$ so a dilation from center $C$ with scale factor 1.5 maps $\triangle ABC$ to $\triangle QRS$.

**Generalize** If two angles of a triangle are congruent to the corresponding angles of another triangle, then the triangles are similar. This is called the Angle-Angle (AA) Criterion.

There is a sequence of translations, rotations, and dilations that maps $\triangle ABC$ to $\triangle QRS$.

So $\triangle ABC \sim \triangle QRS$

**Try It!**

Is $\triangle XYZ \sim \triangle LMN$?

$m\angle X =$ 46°

$m\angle N =$ 35°

The triangles are not similar.

**Convince Me!** Use what you know about transformations and parallel lines to explain why the Angle-Angle Criterion is true for all triangles.

Sample answer: If two angles of any two triangles are congruent, then a sequence of transformations maps the congruent angles onto each other. Then a dilation maps one triangle to the other. So a sequence of transformations, including a dilation, maps one triangle to the other, so the triangles must be similar.

372 6-10 Angle-Angle Triangle Similarity



## EXAMPLE 1  Determine Whether Triangles are Similar

## ETP Use and Connect Mathematical Representations

**Q:** What are the corresponding angles in the two triangles? [$\angle A$ and $\angle Q$; $\angle B$ and $\angle R$; and $\angle C$ and $\angle S$]

**Q:** Why do you need to rotate $\triangle QRS$? [Sample answer: Rotating $\triangle QRS$ orients the triangle the same way as $\triangle ABC$, with the 46° angle as the top vertex and the 50° angle on the bottom right.]

**Q:** Once you have rotated the triangles, why does it follow that lines $AB$ and $RQ$ are parallel? [Sample answer: $AB$ and $RQ$ are parallel lines crossed by a transversal, line $BC$, because the corresponding angles formed are congruent.]

##  Try It!  Formative Assessment

##  ETP Elicit and Use Evidence of Student Thinking

**Q:** What would have to be true for the triangles to be similar? [Sample answer: Corresponding angles need to have the same measure.]

### Convince Me!

**Q:** How can you use parallel lines to show two triangles with two congruent angles are similar? [Sample answer: You can use parallel lines to show that two congruent angles are corresponding angles.]

Students can access the ***Visual Learning Animation Plus*** by using the **Bounce Pages app** to scan this page. Students can download the app for free in their mobile devices' app store.

## ELL English Language Learners

**EMERGING** See Example 1.

Help students summarize the problem by having them complete the following sentences.

Each triangle has two ______ labeled, one labeled 46° and the other labeled 50°. [angles] After translating and ______ [rotating] one triangle on top of the other, you can see that $\triangle ABC$ maps to $\triangle$______. [$QRS$] Because the ______ [corresponding] angles of the triangles are congruent, the triangles are ______. [similar]

**DEVELOPING** See Example 2, part (a).

Help students understand how to show that the triangles are similar. Have them complete the following sentences.

If two angles in one triangle are ______ [congruent] to two angles in another triangle, then those ______ [angles] have equal measure. If this ______ [criterion] or information is true about two triangles, then those triangles are ______. [similar]

Tell students we call this the Angle-Angle Criterion.

**BRIDGING** See Example 2.

Have students write what the Angle-Angle Criterion means in their own words. Ask students to exchange their papers and critique each other's work.

Activity

Assess

# EXAMPLE 2  Determine Whether Triangles are Similar

## ETP Pose Purposeful Questions

**Q:** Do you need to find the measures of $\angle B$ and $\angle N$? Explain. [No; Sample answer: Because two angles have the same measures, you can apply the AA Criterion to prove similarity.]

**Q:** Is it necessary to find the measures of $\angle Z$ and $\angle S$ to determine similarity in Part b? [No; Sample answer: The sum of the angles of a triangle is 180°. By inspection, you know that the angles cannot be equal because $180 - (85 + 42) \neq 180 - (85 + 45)$.]

 **Try It!**  Formative Assessment

##  Elicit and Use Evidence of Student Thinking

**Q:** What properties of parallel lines crossed by a transversal help you to determine congruent angles in this situation? [Sample answer: When two parallel lines are crossed by a transversal, the alternate interior angles formed are equal.]

# EXAMPLE 3  Solve Problems Involving Similar Triangles

##  Pose Purposeful Questions

**Q:** Which are the corresponding angles in the two triangles? Explain. [Sample answer: $\angle A$ and $\angle E$, $\angle BCA$ and $\angle DCE$, and $\angle B$ and $\angle D$; Sample answer: They are in corresponding positions in the similarity statement.]

**Q:** Why can you say that $2x + x = 180$? [Sample answer: $\angle BCD$ and $\angle DCE$ form a straight line, so they are supplementary.]

 **Try It!**  Formative Assessment

##  Elicit and Use Evidence of Student Thinking

**Q:** What given information helped you prove similarity? Explain. [Sample answer: The smaller triangle has a right angle and two congruent angles. This enabled me to start off by writing the equation $15x = 45$ because one of the smaller angles and the $(15x)°$ angle are equal, as they are alternate interior angles.]

**Examples and Try Its!** are available online.

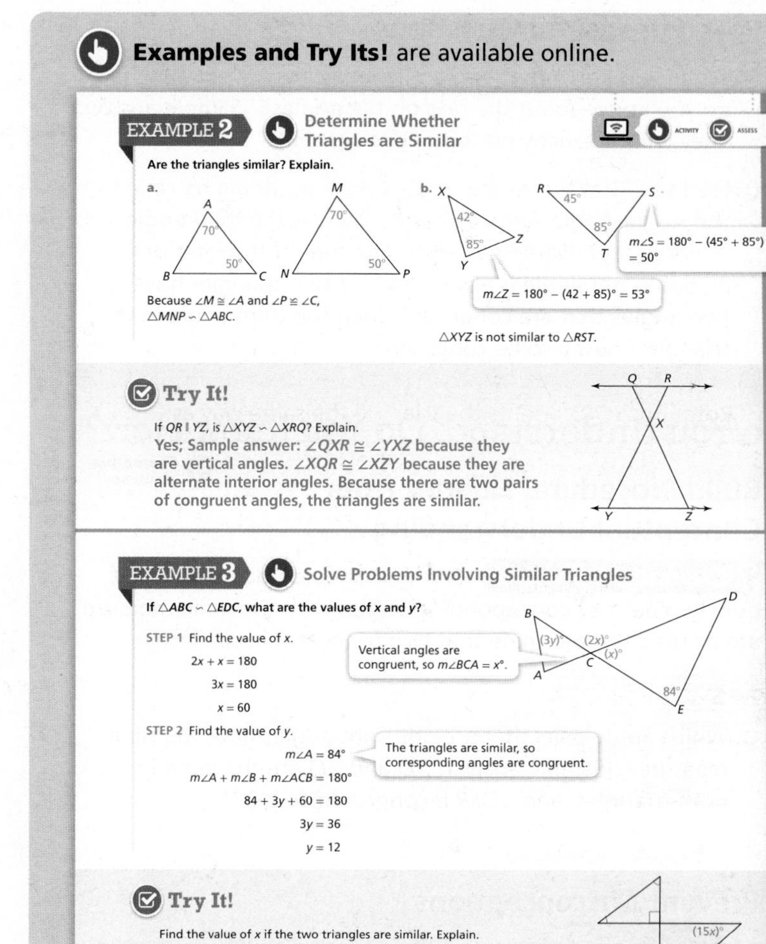
EXAMPLE 2 Determine Whether Triangles are Similar

Are the triangles similar? Explain.

a. Because $\angle M \cong \angle A$ and $\angle P \cong \angle C$, $\triangle MNP \sim \triangle ABC$.

b. $m\angle Z = 180° - (42 + 85)° = 53°$

$m\angle S = 180° - (45° + 85°) = 50°$

$\triangle XYZ$ is not similar to $\triangle RST$.

Try It!

If $QR \parallel YZ$, is $\triangle XYZ \sim \triangle XRQ$? Explain.

Yes; Sample answer: $\angle QXR \cong \angle YXZ$ because they are vertical angles. $\angle XQR \cong \angle XZY$ because they are alternate interior angles. Because there are two pairs of congruent angles, the triangles are similar.

EXAMPLE 3 Solve Problems Involving Similar Triangles

If $\triangle ABC \sim \triangle EDC$, what are the values of $x$ and $y$?

STEP 1 Find the value of $x$.

$2x + x = 180$

$3x = 180$

$x = 60$

Vertical angles are congruent, so $m\angle BCA = x°$.

STEP 2 Find the value of $y$.

$m\angle A = 84°$

The triangles are similar, so corresponding angles are congruent.

$m\angle A + m\angle B + m\angle ACB = 180°$

$84 + 3y + 60 = 180$

$3y = 36$

$y = 12$

Try It!

Find the value of $x$ if the two triangles are similar. Explain.

3; Sample answer: Since vertical angles are congruent, one angle is 90 degrees. The two marked angles are equal and each angle measures 45 degrees. So the other triangle must also have two equal 45-degree angles. Since $15x = 45$, then $x = 3$.

6-10 Angle-Angle Triangle Similarity 373

ADDITIONAL EXAMPLES 

**For additional examples go online.**

##  Response to Intervention

**USE WITH EXAMPLE 2** Review the relationship between angles when two parallel lines are crossed by a transversal. Use the Example 2 *Try It!*

**Q:** What do you know about side $QR$ and side $YZ$? [Sample answer: They are parallel to each other.]

**Q:** What type of angles are $\angle Q$ and $\angle Z$ and $\angle R$ and $\angle Y$? Explain. [Alternate interior angles; Sample answer: They are on opposite sides of a transversal that crosses two parallel lines.]

##  Enrichment

**USE WITH EXAMPLE 1** You may wish to challenge advanced students with this situation and question.

Draw a triangle. Draw another triangle that is similar but not congruent. Cut out the sides for each triangle, and keep the sides for each triangle separate.

**Q:** Can you draw two figures whose sides are proportional and the triangles are not similar? Explain. [No; Sample answer: If corresponding side lengths are proportional then the triangles will be similar.]

Go Online

Key Concept Assess Activity

# KEY CONCEPT

## ETP Pose Purposeful Questions

**Q:** When you know that two angle measures are equal, what do you know about the rays on the angles? [Sample answer: They will fit exactly on top of each other.]

**Q:** Fred said that the Angle-Angle Criterion should be called the Angle-Angle-Angle Criterion. Why is the third angle unnecessary? [Sample answer: The sum of the interior angles in a triangle is always 180°. If two triangles have two angles that are congruent, then the third angle in the triangles must also be congruent.]

# Do You Understand/Do You Know How?

**Formative** Assessment

## ETP Build Procedural Fluency from Conceptual Understanding

**Essential Question** Students should understand that only two pairs of corresponding angles with the same measure are needed to determine that two triangles are similar.

**ITEM 5**

**Q:** Which angle pairs that are not right angles have the same measure? [Sample answer: $\angle Q$ and $\angle Q$ are the same in both triangles, and $\angle QSR$ is congruent to $\angle QML$.]

## Prevent Misconceptions

**ITEM 4** Students may have the misconception that because a triangle does not have an angle marked as a right angle, then it must not have one.

**Q:** How can it be that the two triangles are similar when only one triangle has an angle labeled as a right angle? [Sample answer: Both triangles have a right angle. In one triangle the right angle is labeled, but in the other the smallest angle is labeled.]

Available Online

KEY CONCEPT

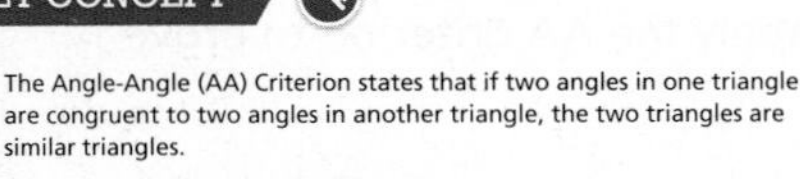

The Angle-Angle (AA) Criterion states that if two angles in one triangle are congruent to two angles in another triangle, the two triangles are similar triangles.

$\angle A \cong \angle D$ and $\angle B \cong \angle E$, so $\triangle ABC \sim \triangle DEF$.

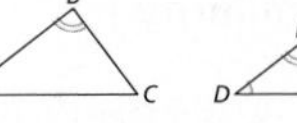


### Do You Understand?

1. **Essential Question** How can you use angle measures to determine whether two triangles are similar?
Sample answer: If two triangles have two pairs of angles with the same measure, then the two pairs of angles are congruent and the triangles are similar.

2. **Construct Arguments** Claire says that the AA Criterion should be called the AAA Criterion. Explain why Claire might say this. Do you agree? Explain.
Sample answer: She might have said this because if two pairs of angles in two triangles are congruent, then all three are. I would not agree since it only needs to be established that two pairs of angles are congruent.

3. **Reasoning** Which triangle pairs below are always similar? Explain.
Two right triangles
Two isosceles right triangles
Two equilateral triangles
Two isosceles right triangles and two equilateral triangles; Sample answer: Two isosceles right triangles are always similar because they have two 45° angles. Two equilateral triangles are always similar because all of their angle measures are 60°. Two right triangles are not always similar because the other two pairs of angles could have different measures.

### Do You Know How?

4. Are the two triangles similar? Explain.

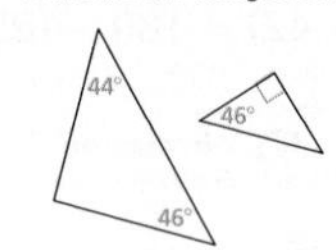


Yes; Sample answer: The missing angle measure in the first triangle is $180° - 46° - 44° = 90°$. Since the triangles have two congruent angles, they are similar triangles.

5. Is $\triangle QRS \sim \triangle QLM$? Explain.

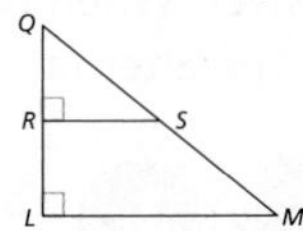


Yes; Sample answer: Both of the triangles are right triangles and they share a vertex. They are similar under the AA Criterion.

6. Are the triangles similar? What is the value of $x$?

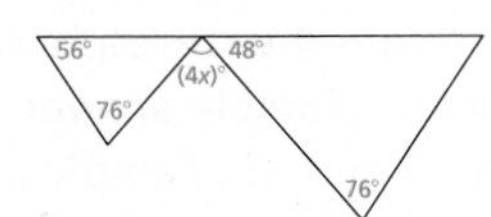


Yes, the triangles are similar.
$x = 21$

374 6-10 Angle-Angle Triangle Similarity

# ADDITIONAL EXAMPLE 3

Help students solve more problems using algebra to find unknown angle measures in triangles, when no interior angles are given. Make sure they remember the rules about vertical angles and linear pairs.

**Q:** What rules about angles can you use to find the measure of interior angles in the triangles? [Sample answer: The fact that all vertical angles are congruent, and that linear pairs are supplementary can help you find the measure of some of the angles in the triangles.]

**Q:** Which interior angles are corresponding? [$\angle A$ and $\angle L$, $\angle ACB$ and $\angle LCM$, and $\angle B$ and $\angle M$]

**Additional Examples** are available online.

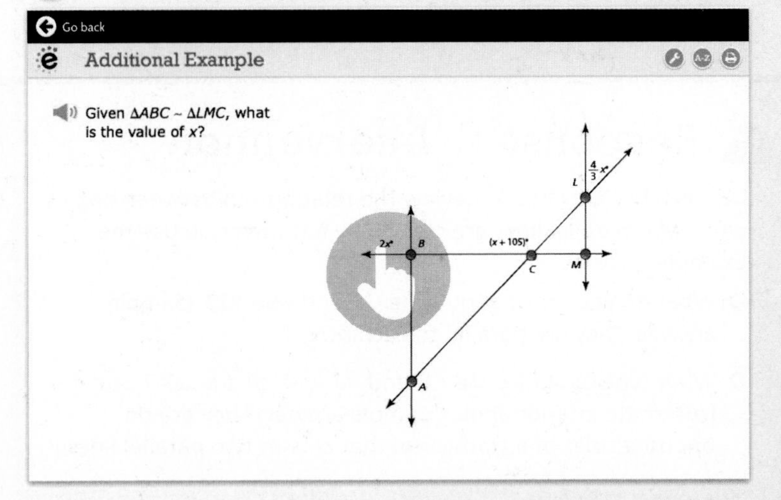


**Answer:** $x = 45$

 Practice  Tutorials  Math Tools

# Practice & Problem Solving  

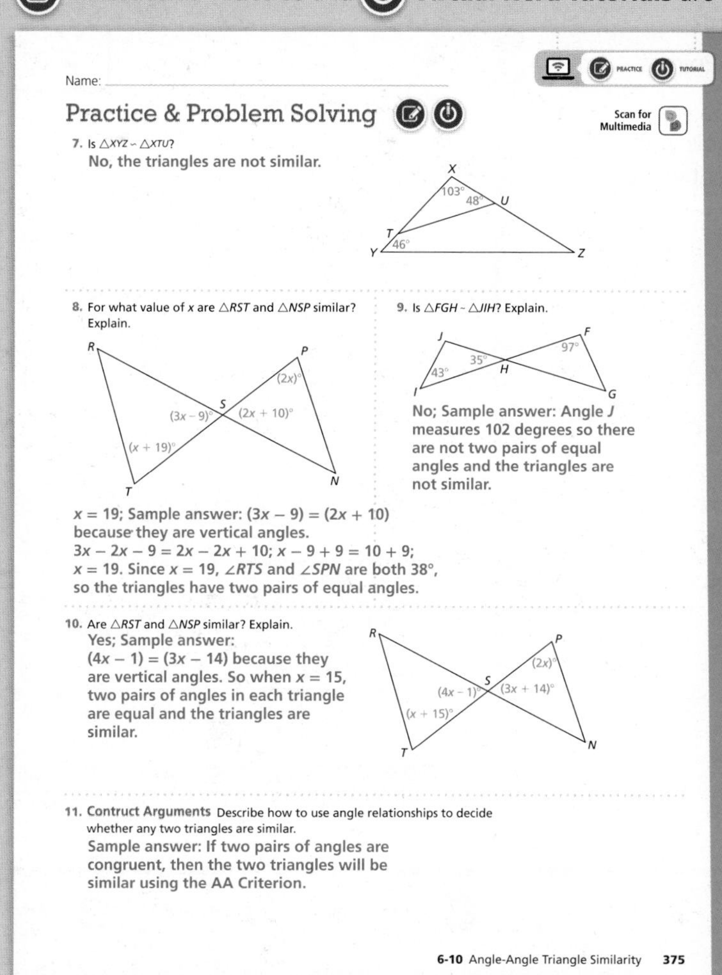

Name:

Practice & Problem Solving

Scan for Multimedia

7. Is $\triangle XYZ \sim \triangle XTU$?
No, the triangles are not similar.

8. For what value of $x$ are $\triangle RST$ and $\triangle NSP$ similar? Explain.
$x = 19$; Sample answer: $(3x - 9) = (2x + 10)$ because they are vertical angles.
$3x - 2x - 9 = 2x - 2x + 10$; $x - 9 + 9 = 10 + 9$;
$x = 19$. Since $x = 19$, $\angle RTS$ and $\angle SPN$ are both 38°, so the triangles have two pairs of equal angles.

9. Is $\triangle FGH \sim \triangle JIH$? Explain.
No; Sample answer: Angle $J$ measures 102 degrees so there are not two pairs of equal angles and the triangles are not similar.

10. Are $\triangle RST$ and $\triangle NSP$ similar? Explain.
Yes; Sample answer: $(4x - 1) = (3x - 14)$ because they are vertical angles. So when $x = 15$, two pairs of angles in each triangle are equal and the triangles are similar.

11. Contruct Arguments Describe how to use angle relationships to decide whether any two triangles are similar.
Sample answer: If two pairs of angles are congruent, then the two triangles will be similar using the AA Criterion.

6-10 Angle-Angle Triangle Similarity 375

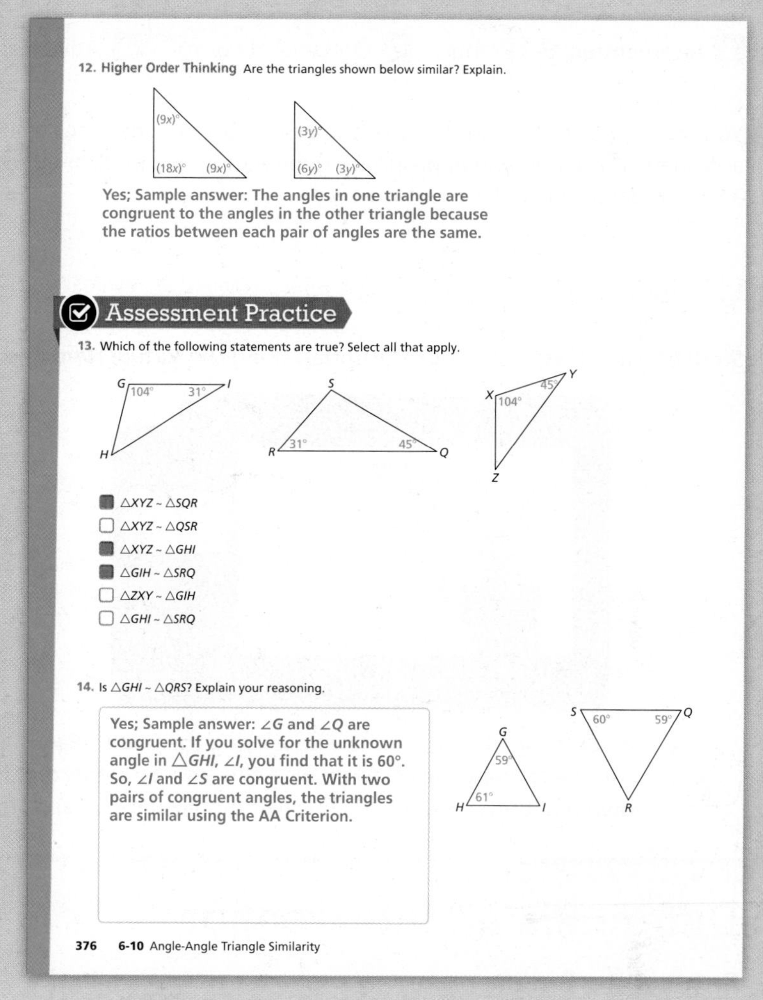

12. Higher Order Thinking Are the triangles shown below similar? Explain.
Yes; Sample answer: The angles in one triangle are congruent to the angles in the other triangle because the ratios between each pair of angles are the same.

Assessment Practice

13. Which of the following statements are true? Select all that apply.

- [x] $\triangle XYZ \sim \triangle SQR$
- [ ] $\triangle XYZ \sim \triangle QSR$
- [x] $\triangle XYZ \sim \triangle GHI$
- [x] $\triangle GIH \sim \triangle SRQ$
- [ ] $\triangle ZXY \sim \triangle GIH$
- [ ] $\triangle GHI \sim \triangle SRQ$

14. Is $\triangle GHI \sim \triangle QRS$? Explain your reasoning.
Yes; Sample answer: $\angle G$ and $\angle Q$ are congruent. If you solve for the unknown angle in $\triangle GHI$, $\angle I$, you find that it is 60°. So, $\angle I$ and $\angle S$ are congruent. With two pairs of congruent angles, the triangles are similar using the AA Criterion.

376 6-10 Angle-Angle Triangle Similarity

## Error Intervention

**ITEM 10** Students may have difficulty deciding how to begin solving this problem.

**Q:** Which two angles must be congruent? Explain. [Sample answer: $\angle RST$ and $\angle NSP$, since they are vertical angles]

**Q:** How can you find the value of $x$? [Sample answer: Set the expressions $4x - 1$ and $3x + 14$ equal to each other.]

**Q:** Once you have found the value of $x$, what is the next step? [Sample answer: Substitute the value of $x$ into all four expressions. Check for equal corresponding angle measures.]

## Challenge

You can challenge advanced students with this problem.

**ITEM 10**

**Q:** Draw a pair of non-similar triangles that share a common point. Label some of the angles with variable expressions. Make sure that the solution determines that the triangles are not similar. [Check students' work.]

You may opt to have students complete the automatically scored Practice & Problem Solving items online.

### Item Analysis

| Example | Items | DOK |
|---|---|---|
| 1 | 7 | 1 |
| | 13, 14 | 2 |
| 2 | 9 | 1 |
| | 11 | 2 |
| 3 | 8, 10 | 2 |
| | 12 | 3 |

# Lesson Quiz

Use the student scores on the Lesson Quiz to prescribe differentiated assignments.

**I Intervention** 0–3 Points **O On-Level** 4 Points **A Advanced** 5 Points

You may opt to have students take the Lesson Quiz online. The Lesson Quiz will be automatically scored and appropriate remediation, practice, or enrichment will be assigned based on student performance.

**Lesson Quiz** is available online.

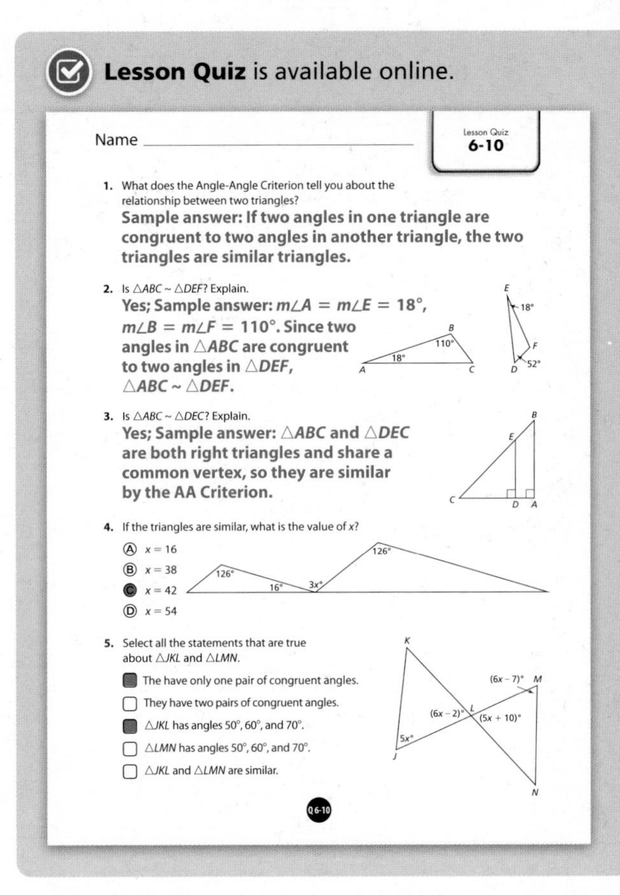

Name ____________ Lesson Quiz 6-10

1. What does the Angle-Angle Criterion tell you about the relationship between two triangles?
   **Sample answer: If two angles in one triangle are congruent to two angles in another triangle, the two triangles are similar triangles.**
2. Is $\triangle ABC \sim \triangle DEF$? Explain.
   **Yes; Sample answer: $m\angle A = m\angle E = 18°$, $m\angle B = m\angle F = 110°$. Since two angles in $\triangle ABC$ are congruent to two angles in $\triangle DEF$, $\triangle ABC \sim \triangle DEF$.**
3. Is $\triangle ABC \sim \triangle DEC$? Explain.
   **Yes; Sample answer: $\triangle ABC$ and $\triangle DEC$ are both right triangles and share a common vertex, so they are similar by the AA Criterion.**
4. If the triangles are similar, what is the value of $x$?
   Ⓐ $x = 16$
   Ⓑ $x = 38$
   Ⓒ $x = 42$
   Ⓓ $x = 54$
5. Select all the statements that are true about $\triangle JKL$ and $\triangle LMN$.
   - ■ The have only one pair of congruent angles.
   - □ They have two pairs of congruent angles.
   - ■ $\triangle JKL$ has angles 50°, 60°, and 70°.
   - □ $\triangle LMN$ has angles 50°, 60°, and 70°.
   - □ $\triangle JKL$ and $\triangle LMN$ are similar.

Q 6-10

# Video Tutorials

Students can access instructional tutorials using the **Virtual Nerd app**.

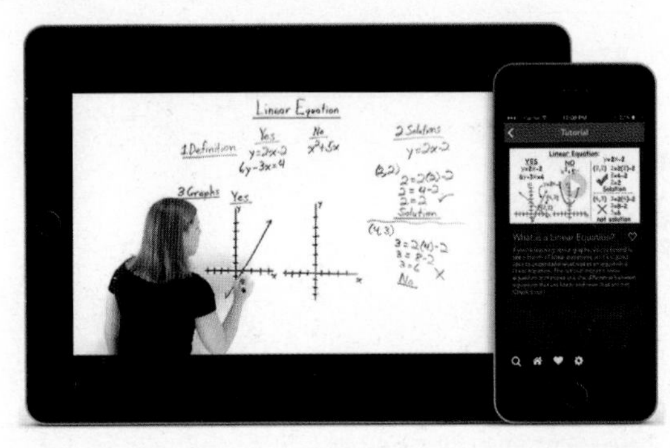


Students can also access the videos using the **BouncePages app** to scan exercise pages marked with this icon. Students can download both apps for free in their mobile devices' app store.

# Differentiated Intervention

**I** = Intervention **O** = On-Level **A** = Advanced

## Reteach to Build Understanding I

Provides scaffolded reteaching for the key lesson concepts.

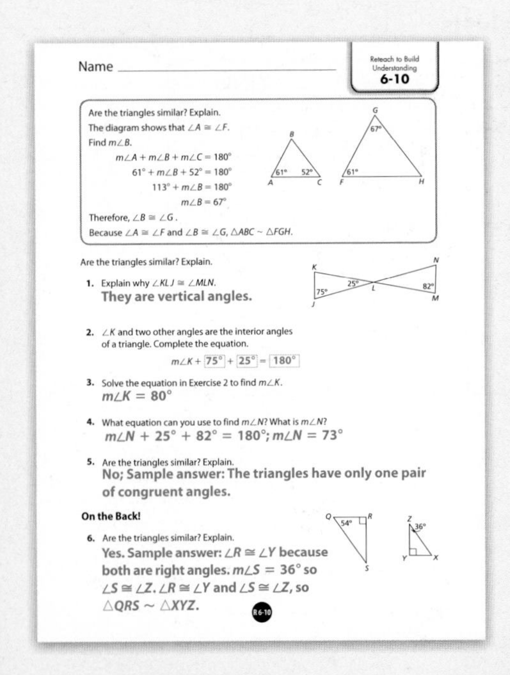

Name ____________ Reteach to Build Understanding 6-10

Are the triangles similar? Explain.
The diagram shows that $\angle A \cong \angle F$.
Find $m\angle B$.

$m\angle A + m\angle B + m\angle C = 180°$
$61° + m\angle B + 52° = 180°$
$113° + m\angle B = 180°$
$m\angle B = 67°$

Therefore, $\angle B \cong \angle G$.
Because $\angle A \cong \angle F$ and $\angle B \cong \angle G$, $\triangle ABC \sim \triangle FGH$.

Are the triangles similar? Explain.

1. Explain why $\angle KLJ \cong \angle MLN$.
   **They are vertical angles.**
2. $\angle K$ and two other angles are the interior angles of a triangle. Complete the equation.
   $m\angle K +$ **75°** $+$ **25°** $=$ **180°**
3. Solve the equation in Exercise 2 to find $m\angle K$.
   **$m\angle K = 80°$**
4. What equation can you use to find $m\angle N$? What is $m\angle N$?
   **$m\angle N + 25° + 82° = 180°; m\angle N = 73°$**
5. Are the triangles similar? Explain.
   **No; Sample answer: The triangles have only one pair of congruent angles.**

**On the Back!**

6. Are the triangles similar? Explain.
   **Yes. Sample answer: $\angle R \cong \angle Y$ because both are right angles. $m\angle S = 36°$ so $\angle S \cong \angle Z$. $\angle R \cong \angle Y$ and $\angle S \cong \angle Z$, so $\triangle QRS \sim \triangle XYZ$.**

R 6-10

## Additional Vocabulary Support I O

Helps students develop and reinforce understanding of key terms and concepts.

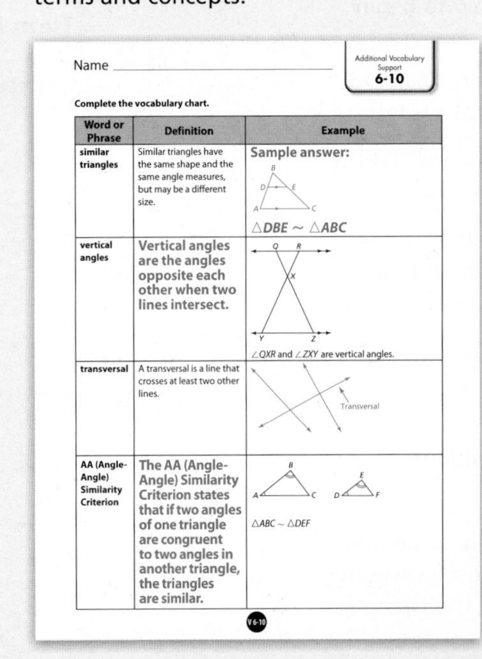

Name ____________ Additional Vocabulary Support 6-10

**Complete the vocabulary chart.**

| Word or Phrase | Definition | Example |
| --- | --- | --- |
| similar triangles | Similar triangles have the same shape and the same angle measures, but may be a different size. | **Sample answer:** $\triangle DBE \sim \triangle ABC$ |
| vertical angles | **Vertical angles are the angles opposite each other when two lines intersect.** | $\angle QXR$ and $\angle ZXY$ are vertical angles. |
| transversal | A transversal is a line that crosses at least two other lines. | Transversal |
| AA (Angle-Angle) Similarity Criterion | **The AA (Angle-Angle) Similarity Criterion states that if two angles of one triangle are congruent to two angles in another triangle, the triangles are similar.** | $\triangle ABC \sim \triangle DEF$ |

V 6-10

## Build Mathematical Literacy I O

Provides support for struggling readers to build mathematical literacy.

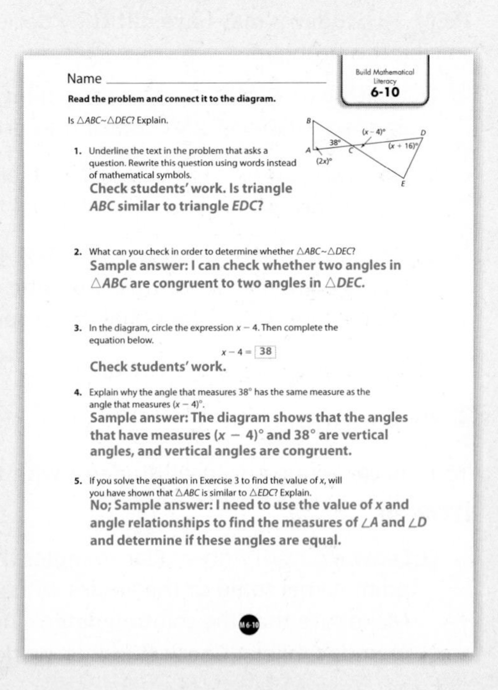

Name ____________ Build Mathematical Literacy 6-10

**Read the problem and connect it to the diagram.**

Is $\triangle ABC \sim \triangle DEC$? Explain.

1. Underline the text in the problem that asks a question. Rewrite this question using words instead of mathematical symbols.
   **Check students' work. Is triangle ABC similar to triangle EDC?**
2. What can you check in order to determine whether $\triangle ABC \sim \triangle DEC$?
   **Sample answer: I can check whether two angles in $\triangle ABC$ are congruent to two angles in $\triangle DEC$.**
3. In the diagram, circle the expression $x - 4$. Then complete the equation below.
   $x - 4 =$ **38**
   **Check students' work.**
4. Explain why the angle that measures 38° has the same measure as the angle that measures $(x - 4)°$.
   **Sample answer: The diagram shows that the angles that have measures $(x - 4)°$ and 38° are vertical angles, and vertical angles are congruent.**
5. If you solve the equation in Exercise 3 to find the value of $x$, will you have shown that $\triangle ABC$ is similar to $\triangle EDC$? Explain.
   **No; Sample answer: I need to use the value of $x$ and angle relationships to find the measures of $\angle A$ and $\angle D$ and determine if these angles are equal.**

M 6-10

Go Online

Practice | Worksheets | Math Tools | Math Games

# Additional Practice

You may opt to have students complete the automatically scored Additional Practice items online.

### Item Analysis

| Example | Items | DOK |
|---|---|---|
| 1 | 1 | 1 |
| | 4 | 2 |
| 2 | 3, 7 | 2 |
| 3 | 2, 5 | 2 |
| | 6 | 3 |

**Interactive Practice** is available online.

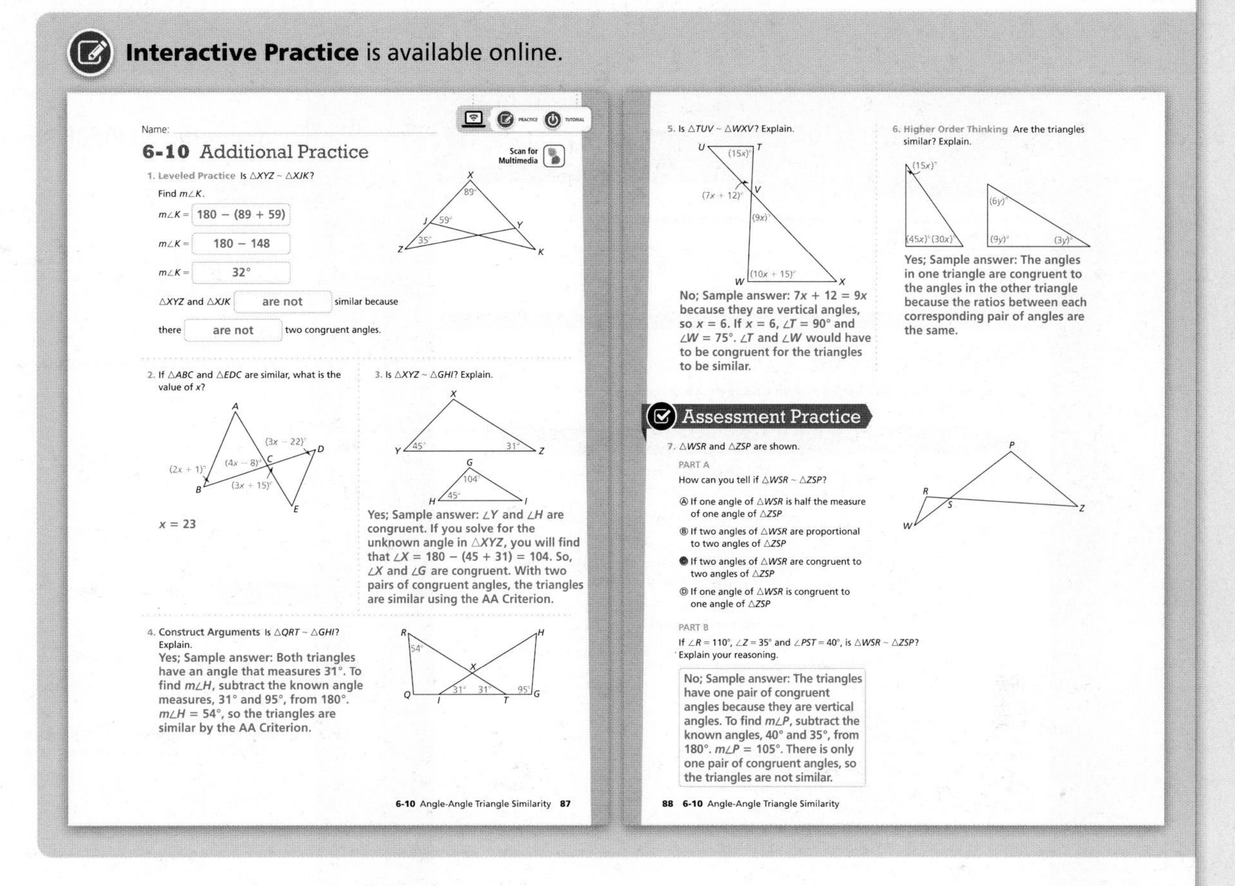

Name:

**6-10** Additional Practice

Scan for Multimedia

1. Leveled Practice Is $\triangle XYZ \sim \triangle XJK$?

Find $m\angle K$.

$m\angle K = 180 - (89 + 59)$

$m\angle K = 180 - 148$

$m\angle K = 32°$

$\triangle XYZ$ and $\triangle XJK$ are not similar because there are not two congruent angles.

2. If $\triangle ABC$ and $\triangle EDC$ are similar, what is the value of $x$?

$x = 23$

3. Is $\triangle XYZ \sim \triangle GHI$? Explain.

Yes; Sample answer: $\angle Y$ and $\angle H$ are congruent. If you solve for the unknown angle in $\triangle XYZ$, you will find that $\angle X = 180 - (45 + 31) = 104$. So, $\angle X$ and $\angle G$ are congruent. With two pairs of congruent angles, the triangles are similar using the AA Criterion.

4. Construct Arguments Is $\triangle QRT \sim \triangle GHI$? Explain.

Yes; Sample answer: Both triangles have an angle that measures 31°. To find $m\angle H$, subtract the known angle measures, 31° and 95°, from 180°. $m\angle H = 54°$, so the triangles are similar by the AA Criterion.

6-10 Angle-Angle Triangle Similarity 87

5. Is $\triangle TUV \sim \triangle WXV$? Explain.

No; Sample answer: $7x + 12 = 9x$ because they are vertical angles, so $x = 6$. If $x = 6$, $\angle T = 90°$ and $\angle W = 75°$. $\angle T$ and $\angle W$ would have to be congruent for the triangles to be similar.

6. Higher Order Thinking Are the triangles similar? Explain.

Yes; Sample answer: The angles in one triangle are congruent to the angles in the other triangle because the ratios between each corresponding pair of angles are the same.

Assessment Practice

7. $\triangle WSR$ and $\triangle ZSP$ are shown.

PART A

How can you tell if $\triangle WSR \sim \triangle ZSP$?

Ⓐ If one angle of $\triangle WSR$ is half the measure of one angle of $\triangle ZSP$

Ⓑ If two angles of $\triangle WSR$ are proportional to two angles of $\triangle ZSP$

● If two angles of $\triangle WSR$ are congruent to two angles of $\triangle ZSP$

Ⓓ If one angle of $\triangle WSR$ is congruent to one angle of $\triangle ZSP$

PART B

If $\angle R = 110°$, $\angle Z = 35°$ and $\angle PST = 40°$, is $\triangle WSR \sim \triangle ZSP$? Explain your reasoning.

No; Sample answer: The triangles have one pair of congruent angles because they are vertical angles. To find $m\angle P$, subtract the known angles, 40° and 35°, from 180°. $m\angle P = 105°$. There is only one pair of congruent angles, so the triangles are not similar.

88 6-10 Angle-Angle Triangle Similarity

# Differentiated Intervention

I = Intervention   O = On-Level   A = Advanced

## Enrichment O A

Presents engaging problems and activities that extend the lesson concepts.

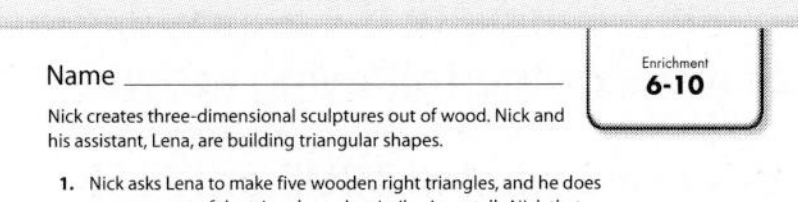

Name ______ Enrichment 6-10

Nick creates three-dimensional sculptures out of wood. Nick and his assistant, Lena, are building triangular shapes.

1. Nick asks Lena to make five wooden right triangles, and he does not want any of the triangles to be similar. Lena tells Nick that this is impossible, because all right triangles are similar. Is Lena correct? Explain.
**No; Sample answer: Although every right triangle has a 90° angle, the other pairs of angles could have different measures, so the triangles would not have two pairs of congruent angles.**

2. Nick builds $\triangle PST$ and then adds $\overline{QR}$ so that $\overline{QR} \parallel \overline{ST}$. Is $\triangle PQR \sim \triangle PST$? Explain.
**Yes; Sample answer: Two angles in $\triangle PQR$ are congruent to two angles in $\triangle PTS$. $\angle PRQ$ and $\angle PTS$ are corresponding angles and $\overline{QR} \parallel \overline{ST}$, so $\angle PRQ \cong \angle PTS$. $\angle QPR$ and $\angle SPT$ are the same angle, so $\angle QPR \cong \angle SPT$.**

3. Lena tells Nick that she has created two isosceles triangles, and each triangle contains a 45° angle but they are not similar. Nick says that Lena's triangles must be similar. Is he correct? Explain.
**No; Sample answer: One triangle could be an isosceles right triangle with a 90° angle and two 45° angles. The other triangle could be an isosceles triangle with a 45° angle and two 67.5° angles.**

4. Nick builds a triangle with a 71° angle and an angle that measures $(8x)°$. Lena builds a triangle in which the measures of two angles are 71° and $(7y)°$. Find a set of values for $x$ and $y$ which result in the two triangles being similar. Explain.
**Sample answer: If $x = 7$ and $y = 8$, then the two triangles have two congruent angles with measures of 71° and 56° and are similar by the Angle-Angle Criterion.**

E 6-10

## Math Tools and Games I O A

Offers additional activities and games to build understanding and fluency.

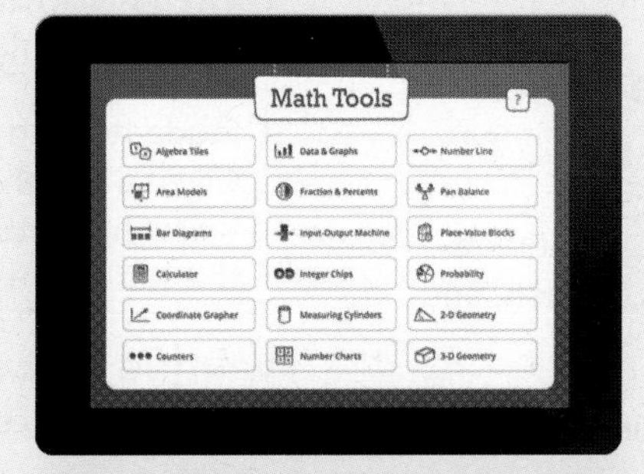


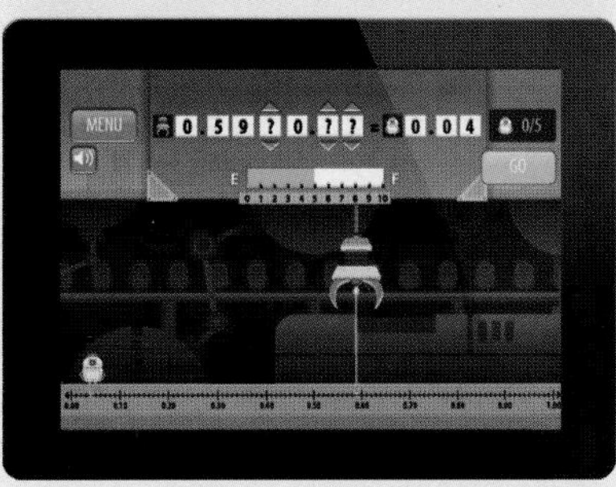


## Pick a Project and STEM Project I O A

Provides an additional opportunity for students to demonstrate understanding of key mathematical concepts.

# Congruence and Similarity

Go Online

Glossary

Available Online

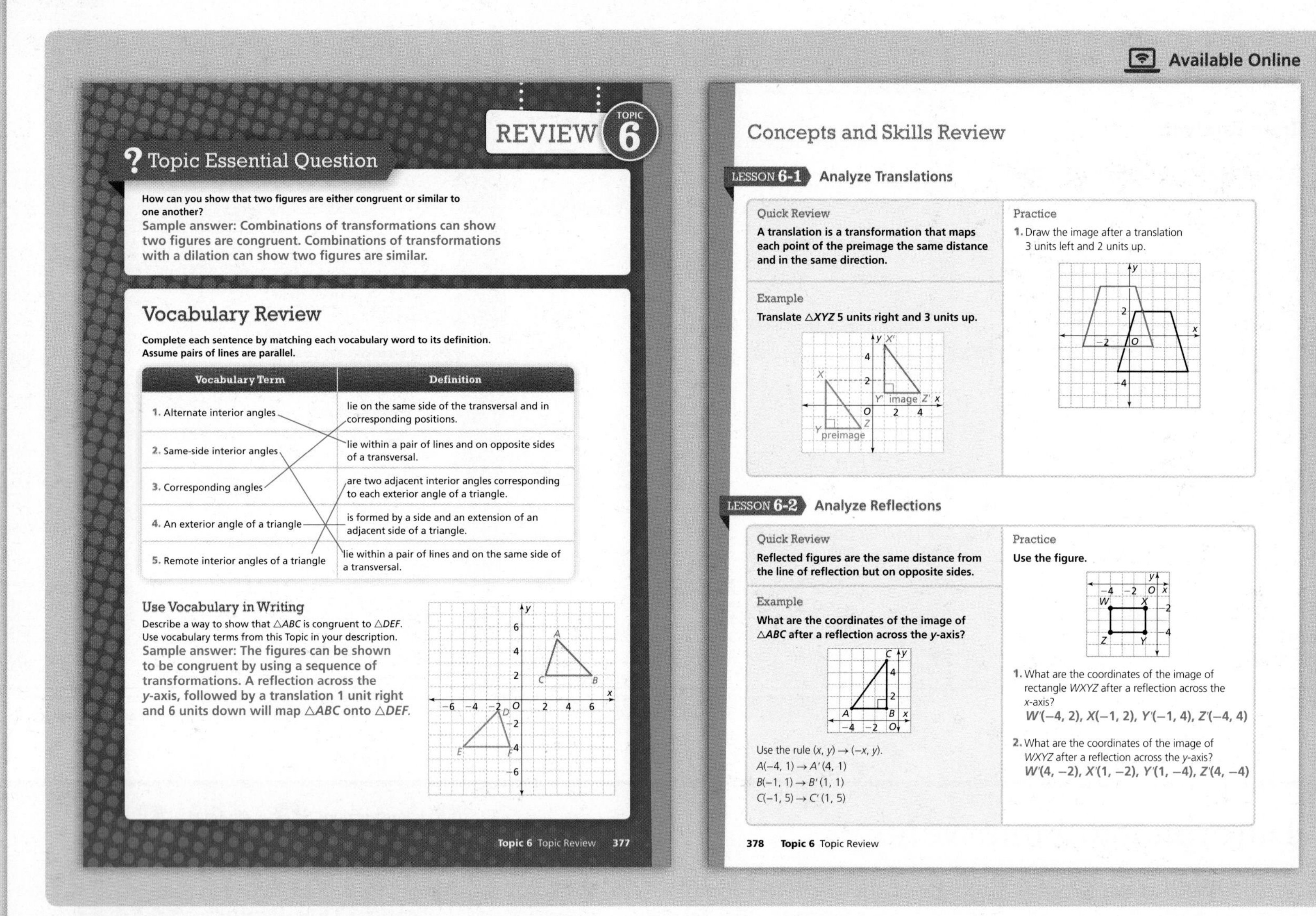

REVIEW TOPIC 6

## Topic Essential Question

How can you show that two figures are either congruent or similar to one another?
Sample answer: Combinations of transformations can show two figures are congruent. Combinations of transformations with a dilation can show two figures are similar.

## Vocabulary Review

Complete each sentence by matching each vocabulary word to its definition. Assume pairs of lines are parallel.

| Vocabulary Term | Definition |
|---|---|
| 1. Alternate interior angles | lie on the same side of the transversal and in corresponding positions. |
| 2. Same-side interior angles | lie within a pair of lines and on opposite sides of a transversal. |
| 3. Corresponding angles | are two adjacent interior angles corresponding to each exterior angle of a triangle. |
| 4. An exterior angle of a triangle | is formed by a side and an extension of an adjacent side of a triangle. |
| 5. Remote interior angles of a triangle | lie within a pair of lines and on the same side of a transversal. |

### Use Vocabulary in Writing

Describe a way to show that $\triangle ABC$ is congruent to $\triangle DEF$. Use vocabulary terms from this Topic in your description.
Sample answer: The figures can be shown to be congruent by using a sequence of transformations. A reflection across the $y$-axis, followed by a translation 1 unit right and 6 units down will map $\triangle ABC$ onto $\triangle DEF$.



Topic 6 Topic Review 377

## Concepts and Skills Review

LESSON 6-1 Analyze Translations

Quick Review
A translation is a transformation that maps each point of the preimage the same distance and in the same direction.

Example
Translate $\triangle XYZ$ 5 units right and 3 units up.



Practice
1. Draw the image after a translation 3 units left and 2 units up.



LESSON 6-2 Analyze Reflections

Quick Review
Reflected figures are the same distance from the line of reflection but on opposite sides.

Example
What are the coordinates of the image of $\triangle ABC$ after a reflection across the $y$-axis?



Use the rule $(x, y) \rightarrow (-x, y)$.
$A(-4, 1) \rightarrow A'(4, 1)$
$B(-1, 1) \rightarrow B'(1, 1)$
$C(-1, 5) \rightarrow C'(1, 5)$

Practice
Use the figure.



1. What are the coordinates of the image of rectangle $WXYZ$ after a reflection across the $x$-axis?
$W'(-4, 2)$, $X'(-1, 2)$, $Y'(-1, 4)$, $Z'(-4, 4)$

2. What are the coordinates of the image of $WXYZ$ after a reflection across the $y$-axis?
$W'(4, -2)$, $X'(1, -2)$, $Y'(1, -4)$, $Z'(4, -4)$

378 Topic 6 Topic Review

## ? Topic Essential Question

**How can you show that two figures are either congruent or similar to one another?**

As students answer the Essential Question in writing, encourage them to include definitions, examples, non-examples, models, and other representations that support their answers.

Be sure the following are made explicit while discussing students' answers.

- A transformation, such as a translation, a reflection, and a rotation, changes the position, shape, or size of a figure.
- Parallel lines intersected by a transversal produce congruent and supplementary angles.
- Triangles are similar if they have two congruent angles, by the AA Criterion.

## Vocabulary Review

**ORAL LANGUAGE** Before students complete the page, reinforce oral language by using one or more of the following activities.

- Students each have two index cards labeled TRUE or FALSE. Given a statement, drawing, or example of each vocabulary word, have students use their cards to determine whether the statement is true or false.

**WRITING IN MATH** After students complete the page, you can further reinforce writing in math by doing the following activity.

- Have students work in pairs to describe each vocabulary term. Draw a grid with four boxes labeled *Definition*, *Characteristics*, *Examples*, and *Non-examples*. Assign a vocabulary term to each group and have them fill out the chart.

# Concepts and Skills Review

Available Online

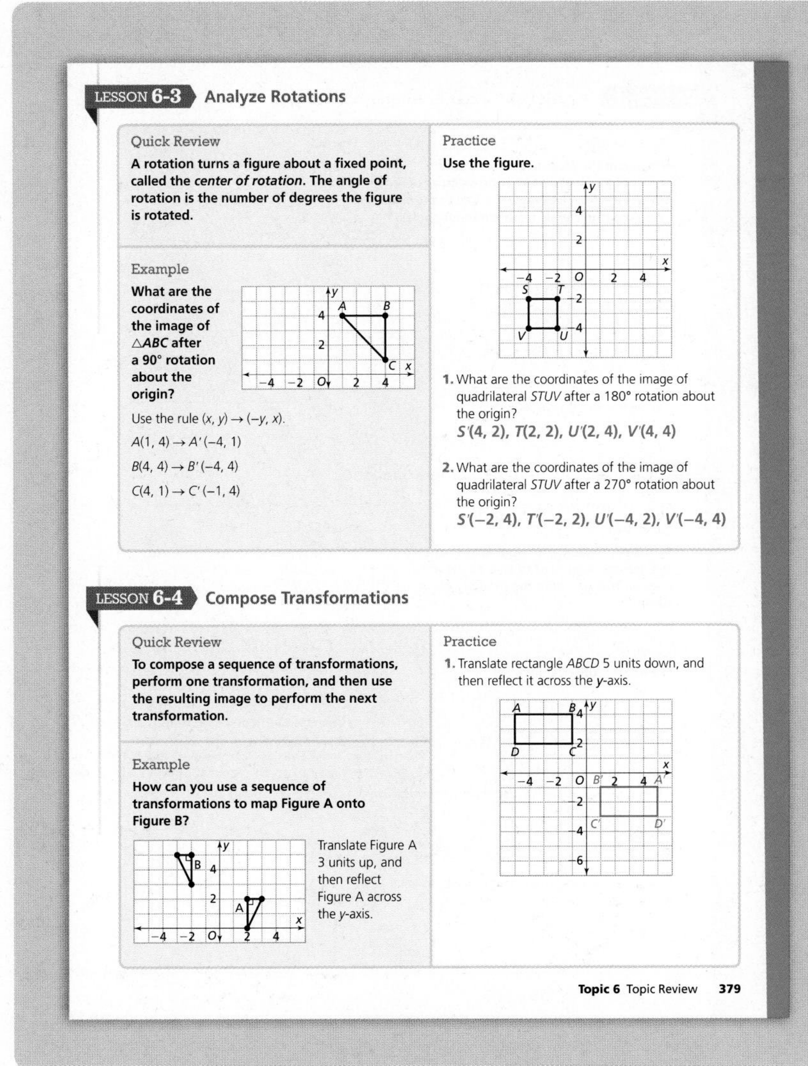

LESSON 6-3 Analyze Rotations

Quick Review

**A rotation turns a figure about a fixed point, called the *center of rotation*. The angle of rotation is the number of degrees the figure is rotated.**

Example

**What are the coordinates of the image of $\triangle ABC$ after a 90° rotation about the origin?**

Use the rule $(x, y) \rightarrow (-y, x)$.

$A(1, 4) \rightarrow A'(-4, 1)$

$B(4, 4) \rightarrow B'(-4, 4)$

$C(4, 1) \rightarrow C'(-1, 4)$

Practice

**Use the figure.**

1. What are the coordinates of the image of quadrilateral *STUV* after a 180° rotation about the origin?
   $S'(4, 2), T'(2, 2), U'(2, 4), V'(4, 4)$
2. What are the coordinates of the image of quadrilateral *STUV* after a 270° rotation about the origin?
   $S'(-2, 4), T'(-2, 2), U'(-4, 2), V'(-4, 4)$

LESSON 6-4 Compose Transformations

Quick Review

**To compose a sequence of transformations, perform one transformation, and then use the resulting image to perform the next transformation.**

Example

**How can you use a sequence of transformations to map Figure A onto Figure B?**

Translate Figure A 3 units up, and then reflect Figure A across the *y*-axis.

Practice

1. Translate rectangle *ABCD* 5 units down, and then reflect it across the *y*-axis.

**Topic 6** Topic Review 379

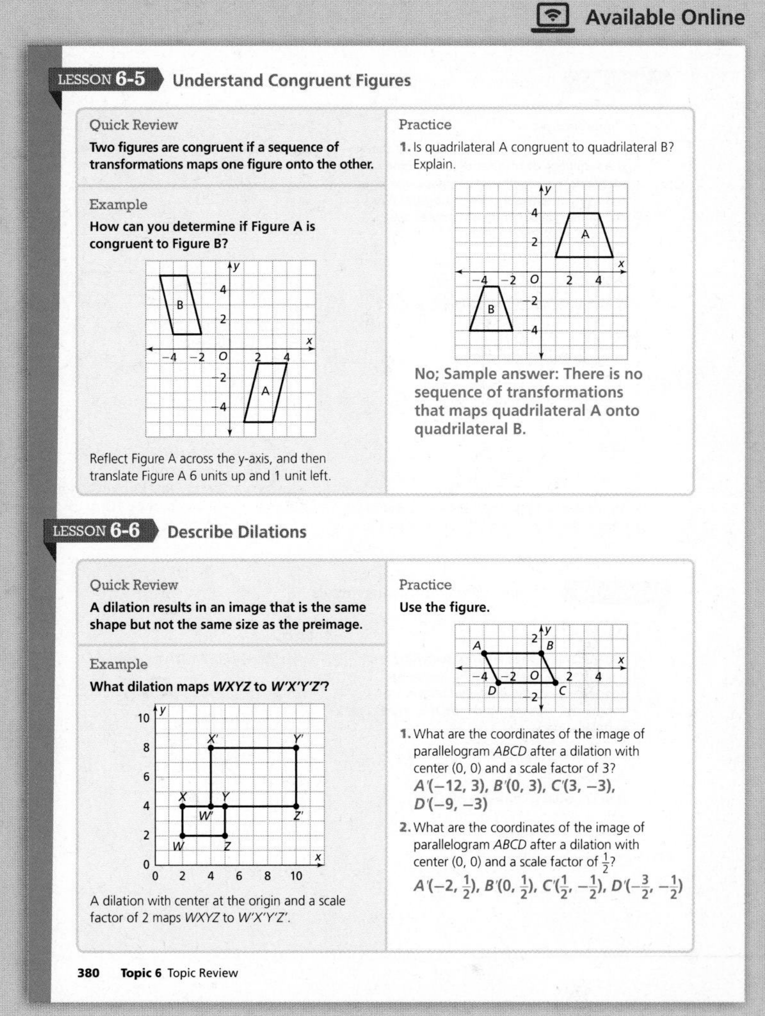

LESSON 6-5 Understand Congruent Figures

Quick Review

**Two figures are congruent if a sequence of transformations maps one figure onto the other.**

Example

**How can you determine if Figure A is congruent to Figure B?**

Reflect Figure A across the y-axis, and then translate Figure A 6 units up and 1 unit left.

Practice

1. Is quadrilateral A congruent to quadrilateral B? Explain.

   No; Sample answer: There is no sequence of transformations that maps quadrilateral A onto quadrilateral B.

LESSON 6-6 Describe Dilations

Quick Review

**A dilation results in an image that is the same shape but not the same size as the preimage.**

Example

**What dilation maps *WXYZ* to *W'X'Y'Z'*?**

A dilation with center at the origin and a scale factor of 2 maps *WXYZ* to *W'X'Y'Z'*.

Practice

**Use the figure.**

1. What are the coordinates of the image of parallelogram *ABCD* after a dilation with center (0, 0) and a scale factor of 3?
   $A'(-12, 3), B'(0, 3), C'(3, -3), D'(-9, -3)$
2. What are the coordinates of the image of parallelogram *ABCD* after a dilation with center (0, 0) and a scale factor of $\frac{1}{2}$?
   $A'(-2, \frac{1}{2}), B'(0, \frac{1}{2}), C'(\frac{1}{2}, -\frac{1}{2}), D'(-\frac{3}{2}, -\frac{1}{2})$

380 **Topic 6** Topic Review

Available Online

## LESSON 6-7 Understand Similar Figures

**Quick Review**

**Two-dimensional figures are similar if there is a sequence of translations, reflections, rotations, and dilations that maps one figure onto the other figure. Similar figures have the same shape, congruent angles, and proportional side lengths.**

**Example**

**Is rectangle $ABCD \sim$ rectangle $A'B'C'D'$?**

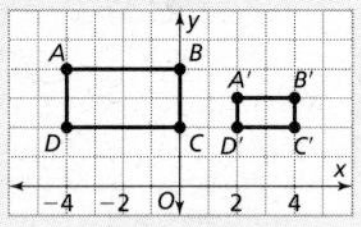

All the angles are right angles.

$$\frac{AB}{A'B'} = \frac{BC}{B'C'} = \frac{CD}{C'D'} = \frac{AD}{A'D'} = \frac{2}{1} = 2$$

The figures have congruent angle measures and proportional side lengths, so they are similar.

**Practice**

**Use the figure.**

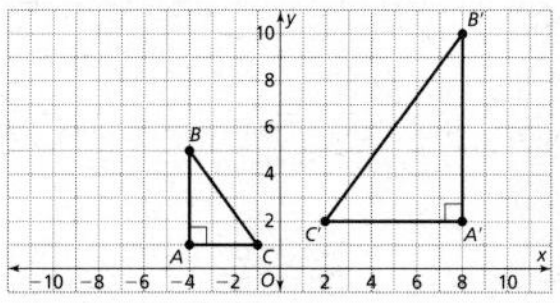

1. Is $\triangle ABC$ similar to $\triangle A'B'C'$? Explain.
   Yes; Sample answer: Corresponding angles are congruent and corresponding side lengths are proportional.

2. What sequence of transformations shows that $\triangle ABC$ is similar to $\triangle A'B'C'$?
   Sample answer: Dilation with center (0,0) and a scale factor of 2, and then a reflection across the $y$-axis

## LESSON 6-8 Angles, Lines, and Transversals

**Quick Review**

**When parallel lines are intersected by a transversal, corresponding angles are congruent, alternate interior angles are congruent, and same-side interior angles are supplementary.**

**Example**

**If $m \parallel n$, what is the value of $x$?**

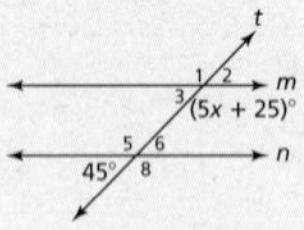

$m\angle 3 = 45°$

$45 + (5x + 25) = 180$

$x = 22$

**Practice**

In the figure, $a \parallel b$. What is the value of $x$?

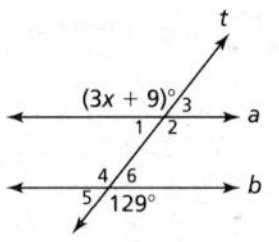

$x = 40$



## LESSON 6-9 Interior and Exterior Angles of Triangles

**Quick Review**

**The sum of the measures of the interior angles of a triangle is 180°. The measure of an exterior angle of a triangle is equal to the sum of the measures of its remote interior angles.**

**Example**

**Find the missing angle measure.**

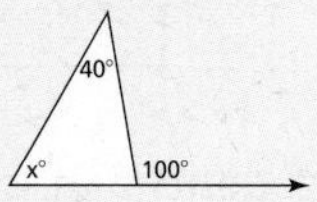

$x + 40 = 100$, so $x = 60$

**Practice**

1. Find the missing angle measure. 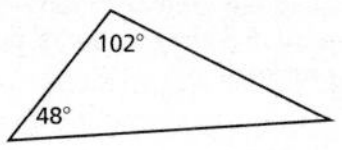
   30°

2. Find the value of $x$. 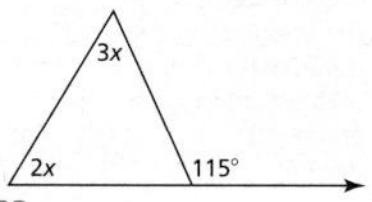
   $x = 23$

## LESSON 6-10 Angle-Angle Triangle Similarity

**Quick Review**

**By the AA Criterion, if two angles in one triangle are congruent to two angles in another triangle, then the triangles are similar.**

**Example**

**Is $\triangle ABC \sim \triangle DEF$? Explain.**

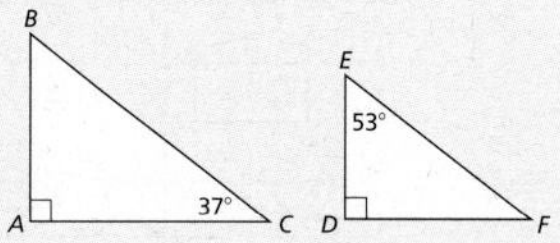

$m\angle B = 180° - 90° - 37° = 53°$

$m\angle A = m\angle D = 90°$ and $m\angle B = m\angle E = 53°$

Because two angles of the triangles are congruent, the triangles are similar by the AA Criterion.

**Practice**

1. $AB \parallel XY$. Is $\triangle ABC \sim \triangle XYC$? Explain. 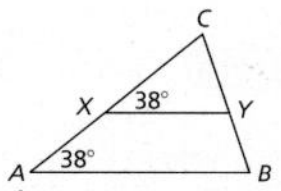
   Yes; Sample answer: $\angle C \cong \angle C$ because an angle is congruent to itself, and $\angle BAC \cong \angle YXC$. Because there are two congruent angles, the triangles are similar under the AA Criterion.

2. Find the values of $x$ and $y$ given that $\triangle ABC$ is similar to $\triangle MNC$. $x = 30$, $y = 12$

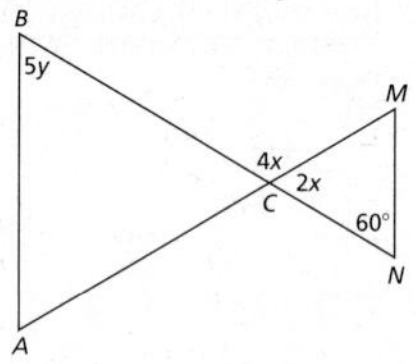

# Fluency Practice

Go Online

Games

## Crisscrossed

Students maintain fluency with solving multi-step equations as they complete a crossword-style activity that reinforces mathematical practices.

**Getting Started** Students may work independently or with a partner. Go over the directions. Point out that the decimal point in each solution should be placed in its own box in the puzzle.

Students should solve each problem and complete their own puzzle. Encourage students to record their work on a separate sheet of paper.

**As Students Do the Activity** Remind students that the puzzle works like a crossword puzzle, so intersecting solutions share a common digit. If the digit isn't the same, students need to check their work and correct as needed.

Some students may find all of the answers first and then fill in the puzzle. Allow this strategy, as it provides the same fluency practice.

**Another Activity** Have students work together to write a new set of clues that results in the same solutions in the puzzle. Ask them to record the new clues on a separate sheet of paper.

Extra Challenge Create your own Crisscrossed puzzle activity. Write a new problem for each clue, and use grid paper to create the puzzle. Then trade your activity with a partner and complete your partner's Crisscrossed activity.

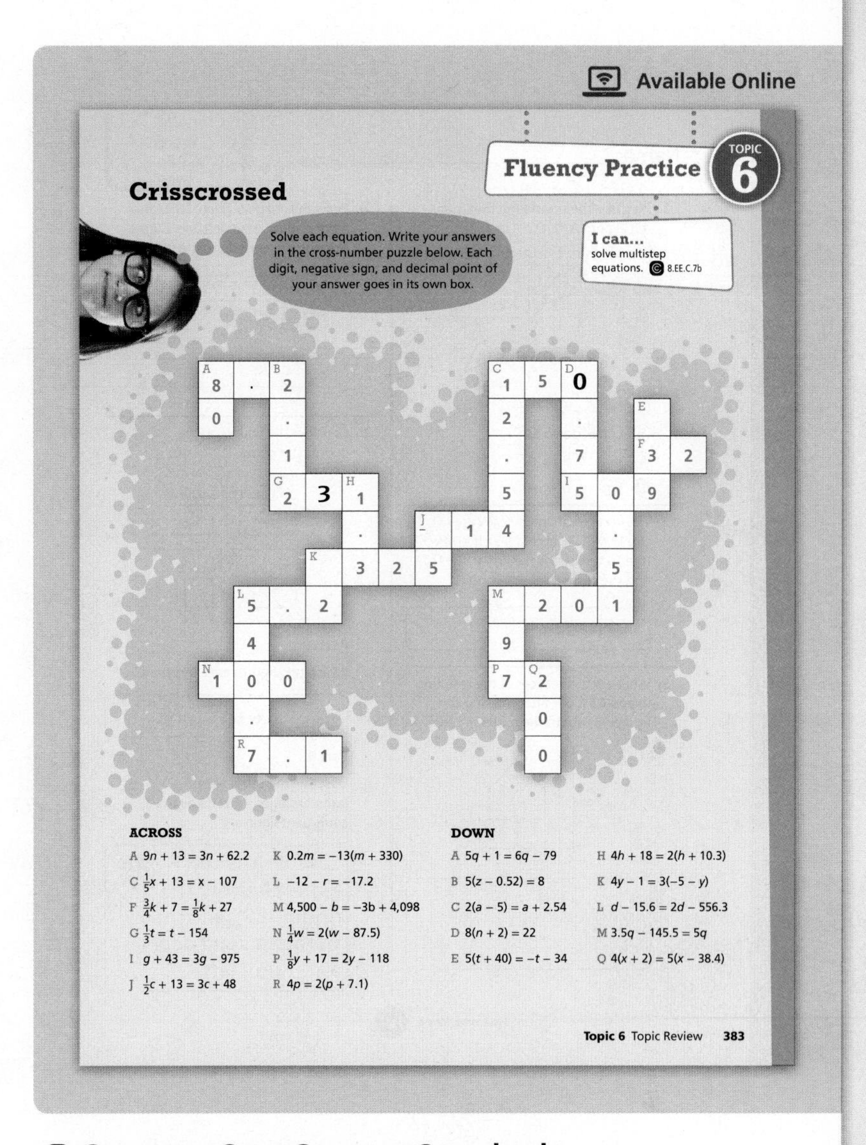


### Common Core Content Standards

**8.EE.C.7b** Solve linear equations with rational number coefficients, including equations whose solutions require expanding expressions using the distributive property and collecting like terms.

### Mathematical Practices

MP.2, MP.6, MP.7

# TOPIC 6 Assessment

Go Online

Assess

Available Online

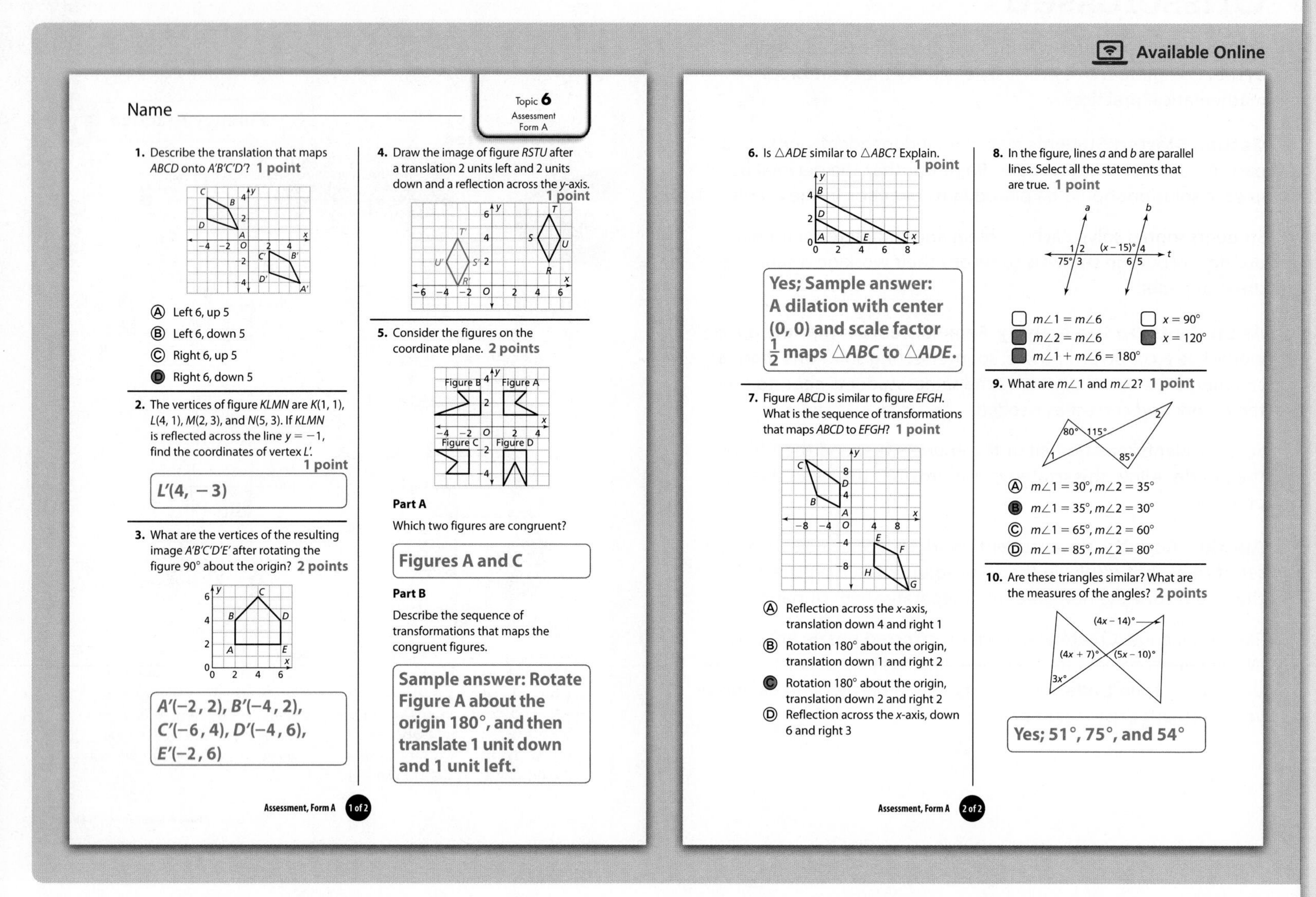

Name ______________________

Topic 6 Assessment Form A

1. Describe the translation that maps ABCD onto A′B′C′D′? **1 point**

Ⓐ Left 6, up 5
Ⓑ Left 6, down 5
Ⓒ Right 6, up 5
Ⓓ Right 6, down 5

2. The vertices of figure KLMN are K(1, 1), L(4, 1), M(2, 3), and N(5, 3). If KLMN is reflected across the line $y = -1$, find the coordinates of vertex L′. **1 point**

**L′(4, −3)**

3. What are the vertices of the resulting image A′B′C′D′E′ after rotating the figure 90° about the origin? **2 points**

**A′(−2, 2), B′(−4, 2), C′(−6, 4), D′(−4, 6), E′(−2, 6)**

4. Draw the image of figure RSTU after a translation 2 units left and 2 units down and a reflection across the y-axis. **1 point**

5. Consider the figures on the coordinate plane. **2 points**

**Part A**

Which two figures are congruent?

**Figures A and C**

**Part B**

Describe the sequence of transformations that maps the congruent figures.

**Sample answer: Rotate Figure A about the origin 180°, and then translate 1 unit down and 1 unit left.**

Assessment, Form A 1 of 2

6. Is △ADE similar to △ABC? Explain. **1 point**

**Yes; Sample answer: A dilation with center (0, 0) and scale factor $\frac{1}{2}$ maps △ABC to △ADE.**

7. Figure ABCD is similar to figure EFGH. What is the sequence of transformations that maps ABCD to EFGH? **1 point**

Ⓐ Reflection across the x-axis, translation down 4 and right 1
Ⓑ Rotation 180° about the origin, translation down 1 and right 2
Ⓒ Rotation 180° about the origin, translation down 2 and right 2
Ⓓ Reflection across the x-axis, down 6 and right 3

8. In the figure, lines a and b are parallel lines. Select all the statements that are true. **1 point**

☐ $m\angle 1 = m\angle 6$ ☐ $x = 90°$
■ $m\angle 2 = m\angle 6$ ■ $x = 120°$
■ $m\angle 1 + m\angle 6 = 180°$

9. What are $m\angle 1$ and $m\angle 2$? **1 point**

Ⓐ $m\angle 1 = 30°, m\angle 2 = 35°$
Ⓑ $m\angle 1 = 35°, m\angle 2 = 30°$
Ⓒ $m\angle 1 = 65°, m\angle 2 = 60°$
Ⓓ $m\angle 1 = 85°, m\angle 2 = 80°$

10. Are these triangles similar? What are the measures of the angles? **2 points**

**Yes; 51°, 75°, and 54°**

Assessment, Form A 2 of 2

Assess students' understanding of the topic concepts and skills using the Topic Assessments found online.

Use the Item Analysis Chart on the facing page to assign intervention to students based on their scores on the paper and pencil version of the Topic Assessments.

You may opt to have students take the Topic Assessment online. The online assessment is auto-scored, with differentiated intervention automatically assigned to students based on their scores.

You can use ExamView to generate additional Topic Assessments. There are two versions of the Topic Assessment, Form A and Form B. These parallel versions assess the same content item for item. The Item Analysis chart on the next page can be used with both versions.

## Scoring Guide: Forms A and B

| Score | Recommendations |
|---|---|
| Greater Than 85% | Assign the corresponding MDIS for items answered incorrectly. Use Enrichment activities with the student. |
| 70%–85% | Assign the corresponding MDIS for items answered incorrectly. You may also assign Reteach to Build Understanding and Virtual Nerd Video assets for the lessons correlated to the items the student answered incorrectly. |
| Less Than 70% | Assign the corresponding MDIS for items answered incorrectly. Assign appropriate intervention lessons available online. You may also assign Reteach to Build Understanding, Additional Vocabulary Support, Build Mathematical Literacy, and Virtual Nerd Video assets for the lessons correlated to the items the student answered incorrectly. |

Go Online

Assess

Available Online

Name ________________

Topic 6 Assessment Form B

**1.** Which figure is a translation of Figure 1? **1 point**

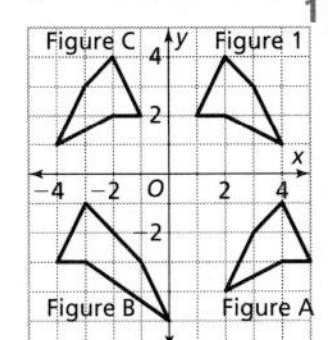


Ⓐ Figure A
Ⓑ Figure B
Ⓒ Figure C
Ⓓ None of the above

**2.** The vertices of figure *KLMN* are $K(-2, -1)$, $L(-2, -3)$, $M(-5, -3)$, and $N(-5, -1)$. If figure *KLMN* is reflected across the line $x = 2$, find the coordinates of vertex $N'$. **1 point**

**$N'(9, -1)$**

**3.** What are the vertices of the resulting image $A'B'C'D'E'$ after rotating the figure 90° about the origin? **2 points**

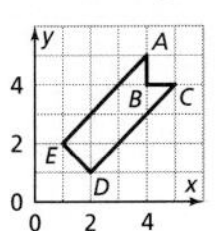

**$A'(-5, 4)$, $B'(-4, 4)$, $C'(-4, 5)$, $D'(-1, 2)$, $E'(-2, 1)$**

**4.** Draw the image of $\triangle ABC$ after a translation of 3 units right and 1 unit down and a reflection across the *y*-axis. **1 point**

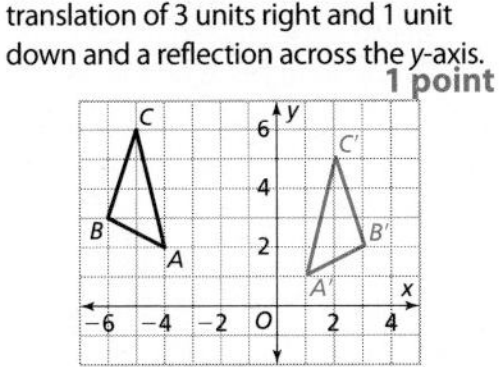

**5.** Consider the figures on the coordinate plane. **2 points**

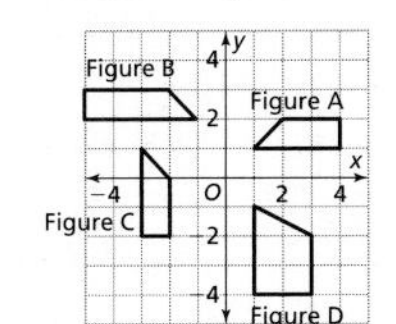


**Part A**

Which two figures are congruent?

**Figures A and C**

**Part B**

Describe the sequence of transformations that maps the congruent figures.

**Sample answer: Rotate Figure A 270° about the origin, and then translate 4 units left and 2 units up.**



**6.** Is Figure *AEFG* similar to Figure *ABCD*? Explain. **1 point**

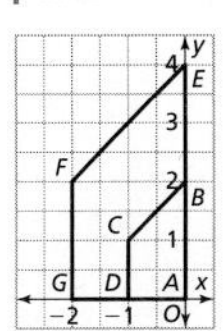

**Yes; Sample answer: A dilation with center (0, 0) and scale factor 2 maps *ABCD* to *AEFG*.**

**7.** $\triangle ABC$ is similar to $\triangle DEF$. What is the sequence of transformations that maps $\triangle ABC$ to $\triangle DEF$? **1 point**

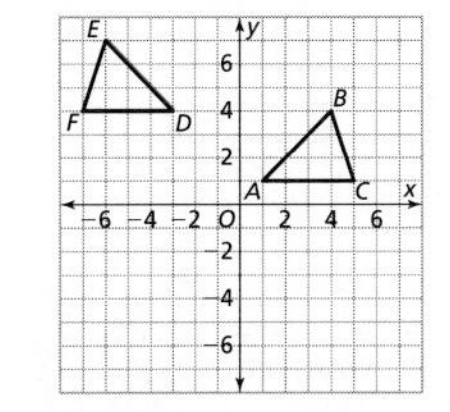

Ⓐ Rotation 90° about the origin, translation up 3 and left 2
Ⓑ Reflection across $x = -1$ and translation up 3
Ⓒ Reflection across the *y*-axis, translation up 2 and left 1
Ⓓ Rotation 180° about the origin, translation up 4 and left 8

**8.** In the figure, *b* and *c* are parallel lines. Select all the statements that are true. **1 point**

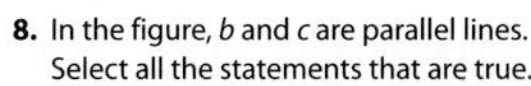

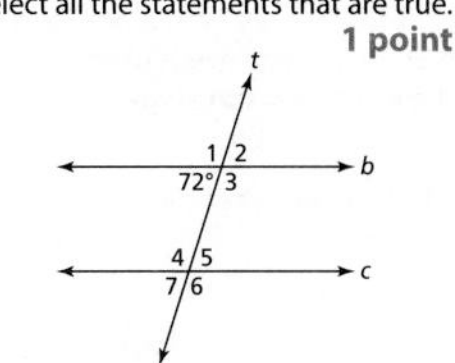

■ $m\angle 2 = m\angle 7$
□ $m\angle 1 = m\angle 5$
■ $m\angle 5 = 72°$
□ $m\angle 3 = 90°$
■ $m\angle 6 = 108°$

**9.** What is the value of *x*? **1 point**

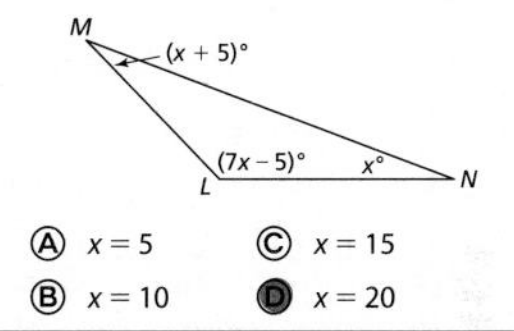

Ⓐ $x = 5$
Ⓑ $x = 10$
Ⓒ $x = 15$
Ⓓ $x = 20$

**10.** Are these triangles similar? What are the measurements of the angles? **1 point**

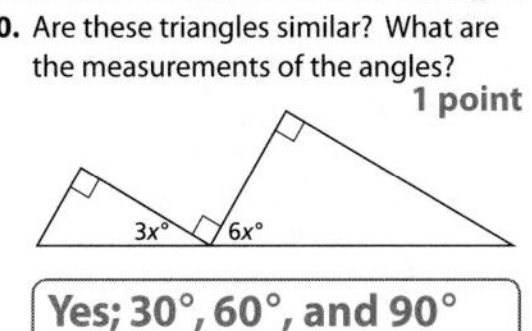

**Yes; 30°, 60°, and 90°**



## Item Analysis for Diagnosis and Intervention: Forms A and B

| Item | Points | DOK | MDIS | Standard |
|---|---|---|---|---|
| 1 | 1 | 1 | N58 | 8.G.A.3 |
| 2 | 1 | 2 | N58 | 8.G.A.3 |
| 3 | 1 | 2 | N58 | 8.G.A.3 |
| 4 | 1 | 2 | N59 | 8.G.A.3 |
| 5 | 2 | 2 | N60, N59 | 8.G.A.2 |

| Item | Points | DOK | MDIS | Standard |
|---|---|---|---|---|
| 6 | 1 | 2 | N62 | 8.G.A.4 |
| 7 | 1 | 2 | N59 | 8.G.A.4 |
| 8 | 1 | 2 | N5 | 8.G.A.5 |
| 9 | 1 | 2 | N3 | 8.G.A.5 |
| 10 | 1 | 3 | N62 | 8.G.A.4 |

TOPIC 6

# Performance Task

Go Online

Assess

Assess students' ability to apply the topic concepts and skills using the Topic Performance Tasks found online.

Available Online

Name ______________________

Topic 6
Performance Task
Form A

An art teacher and a math teacher challenge students in the eighth-grade class to make designs for note cards to sell as a class fundraiser. The rule is that each design needs to be created from congruent or similar figures. Also, students need to explain how their design follows the rule.

Figure B, Figure A, Figure C, Figure D

1. Taryn says she used transformations to make her design.

**Part A**

What sequence of transformations maps Figure A onto Figure C? **2 points**

**Sample answer: Figure A can be mapped onto Figure C through a reflection across the *x*-axis and then a translation 1 unit down and 5 units left.**

**Part B**

What sequence of transformations maps Figure A onto Figure D? **2 points**

**Sample answer: Figure A can be mapped onto Figure D through a 270° rotation about the origin and then a translation 2 units down.**

2. Kyle submits a design for the contest, but his explanation was misplaced. How can Figure A be mapped onto Figure B? Can any other transformation be used to map Figure A onto Figure B? **2 points**

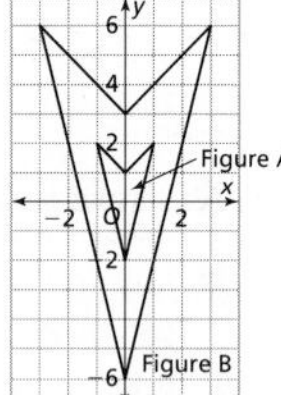


**Figure A can be mapped onto Figure B through a dilation with center (0, 0) and a scale factor 3. No other transformation can be applied.**

Performance Task, Form A  1 of 2

3. Jonathan drew $\overline{ED}$ parallel to $\overline{JH}$ and $\overline{AB}$ parallel to $\overline{FG}$. He says that, because the line segments are parallel, his design forms two pairs of similar triangles. Is he correct? Explain. **3 points**

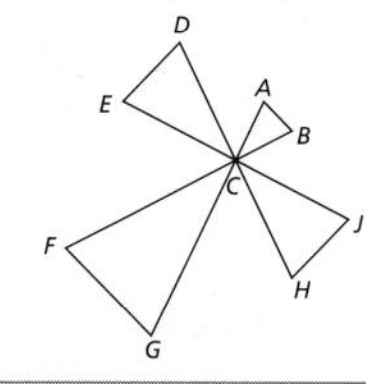


**Yes; Sample answer: Since vertical angles are congruent, $m\angle ACB = m\angle FCG$. Then, since alternate interior angles are congruent, $m\angle CBA = m\angle CFG$. Because two pairs of angles are congruent, $\triangle ABC \cong \triangle GFC$ by the AA Criterion. Similarly, $m\angle ECD = m\angle HCJ$ and $m\angle EDC = m\angle JHC$, so $\triangle EDC \cong \triangle JHC$.**

4. Design your own note card. Draw four congruent or similar figures, including at least two different transformations. Explain your design. **4 points**

**Check students' work.**

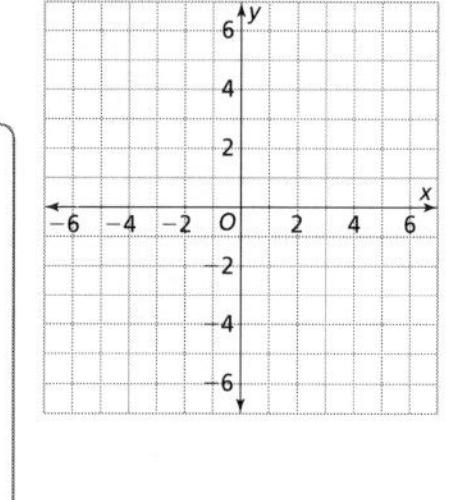

Performance Task, Form A  2 of 2

## RtI Item Analysis for Diagnosis and Intervention: Form A

| Item | DOK | MDIS | Standard |
|---|---|---|---|
| 1A | 2 | N58, N59 | 8.G.A.1, 8.G.A.2 |
| 1B | 2 | N58, N59 | 8.G.A.1, 8.G.A.2 |
| 2 | 2 | N61, N62 | 8.G.A.3, 8.G.A.4 |
| 3 | 3 | N58, N59, N63 | 8.G.A.4, 8.G.A.5 |
| 4 | 4 | N58–N62 | 8.G.A.2, 8.G.A.3, 8.G.A.4 |

## Scoring Rubric: Forms A and B

| Item | Points (Form A) | Points (Form B) |
|---|---|---|
| 1 | **A/B** 2: Correct sequence of transformations<br>1: Partially correct sequence of transformations | **A** 2: Correct dimensions and angle measures<br>1: Correct dimensions or angle measures<br>**B** 2: Correct answer and explanation<br>1: Correct answer or explanation |
| 2 | 2: Correct answer and explanation<br>1: Correct answer or explanation | **A/B** 2: Correct answer and explanation<br>1: Correct answer or explanation |
| 3 | 3: Correctly shows all four triangles are similar<br>2: Correctly shows three of four triangles are similar<br>1: Correctly shows two of four triangles are similar | 4: Complete design and explanation of how four images are mapped<br>3: Complete design and explanation of how three images are mapped<br>2: Complete design and explanation of how two images are mapped |
| 4 | 4: Complete design and explanation of how four images are mapped<br>3: Complete design and explanation of how three images are mapped<br>2: Complete design and explanation of how two images are mapped | N/A |

Go Online

Assess

Available Online

Name ______________________

Topic 6
Performance Task
Form B

Students in Mr. Messi's art classes are designing panes for a stained-glass window. The window will have the shape of a parallelogram, with nine congruent panes. Mr. Messi gives the class this sketch of the window.

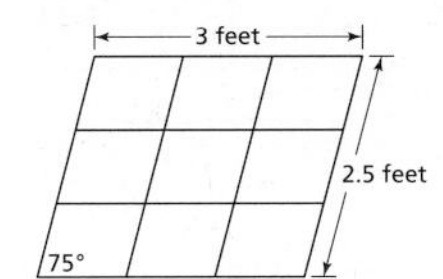


**1.** Ella will design the center pane of the window.

**Part A**

Sketch and label the dimensions and angle measurements of Ella's windowpane. **2 points**

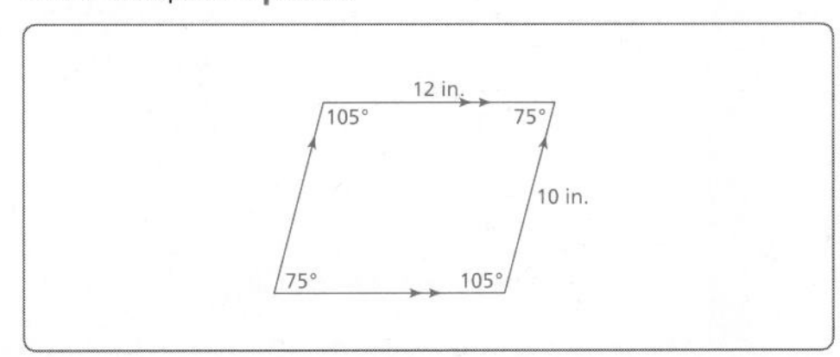


**Part B**

Is Ella's windowpane similar to the entire stained-glass window? Explain. **2 points**

**Yes; Sample answer: The measures for the corresponding angles of Ella's windowpane and the stained-glass window are equal. Ella's windowpane is a dilation of the stained-glass window with scale factor $\frac{1}{3}$.**

Performance Task, Form B 1 of 2

**2.** Ella sketches the design for her pane on a coordinate plane.

**Part A**

Ella says that Figure A can be transformed onto Figure B through a 180° rotation about the origin. Her friend Asha says that she can use a different transformation to map Figure A onto Figure B. What transformation could Asha apply? **2 points**

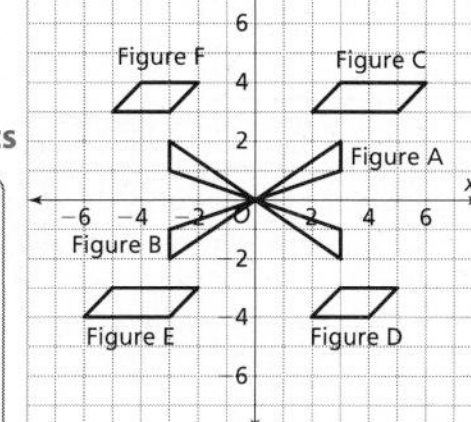


**Sample answer: Asha could transform Figure A onto Figure B through a reflection across the *x*-axis, and then a reflection over the y-axis.**

**Part B**

Ella says that Figure C can be mapped onto any of the parallelograms on the coordinate plane. Asha disagrees. Who is correct? Explain. **2 points**

**Asha; Sample answer: Figure C cannot be mapped onto Figures D or F because the parallelograms are not similar.**

**3.** Design your own pattern for a stained-glass windowpane. Draw four similar or congruent figures. Then describe two separate transformations that can be used to map images in your pattern. **4 points**

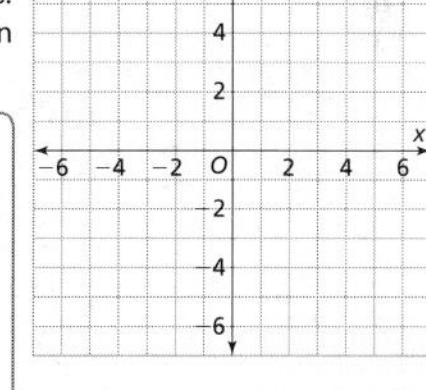

**Check students' work.**

Performance Task, Form B 2 of 2

## Item Analysis for Diagnosis and Intervention: Form B

| Item | DOK | MDIS | Standard |
|---|---|---|---|
| **1A** | 2 | N60 | 8.G.A.3 |
| **1B** | 2 | N61, N62 | 8.G.A.4 |
| **2A** | 2 | N58–N62 | 8.G.A.1, 8.G.A.2, 8.G.A.3 |
| **2B** | 3 | N58–N62 | 8.G.A.3, 8.G.A.4 |
| **3** | 3 | N58–N62 | 8.G.A.2, 8.G.A.3, 8.G.A.4 |

## Scoring Guide: Forms A and B

| Score | Recommendations |
|---|---|
| Greater Than 85% | Assign the corresponding MDIS for items answered incorrectly. Use Enrichment activities with the student. |
| 70%–85% | Assign the corresponding MDIS for items answered incorrectly. You may also assign Reteach to Build Understanding and Virtual Nerd Video assets for the lessons correlated to the items the student answered incorrectly. |
| Less Than 70% | Assign the corresponding MDIS for items answered incorrectly. Assign appropriate intervention lessons available online. You may also assign Reteach to Build Understanding, Additional Vocabulary Support, Build Mathematical Literacy, and Virtual Nerd Video assets for the lessons correlated to the items the student answered incorrectly. |

TOPICS 1-6

# CUMULATIVE/BENCHMARK ASSESSMENT

Available Online

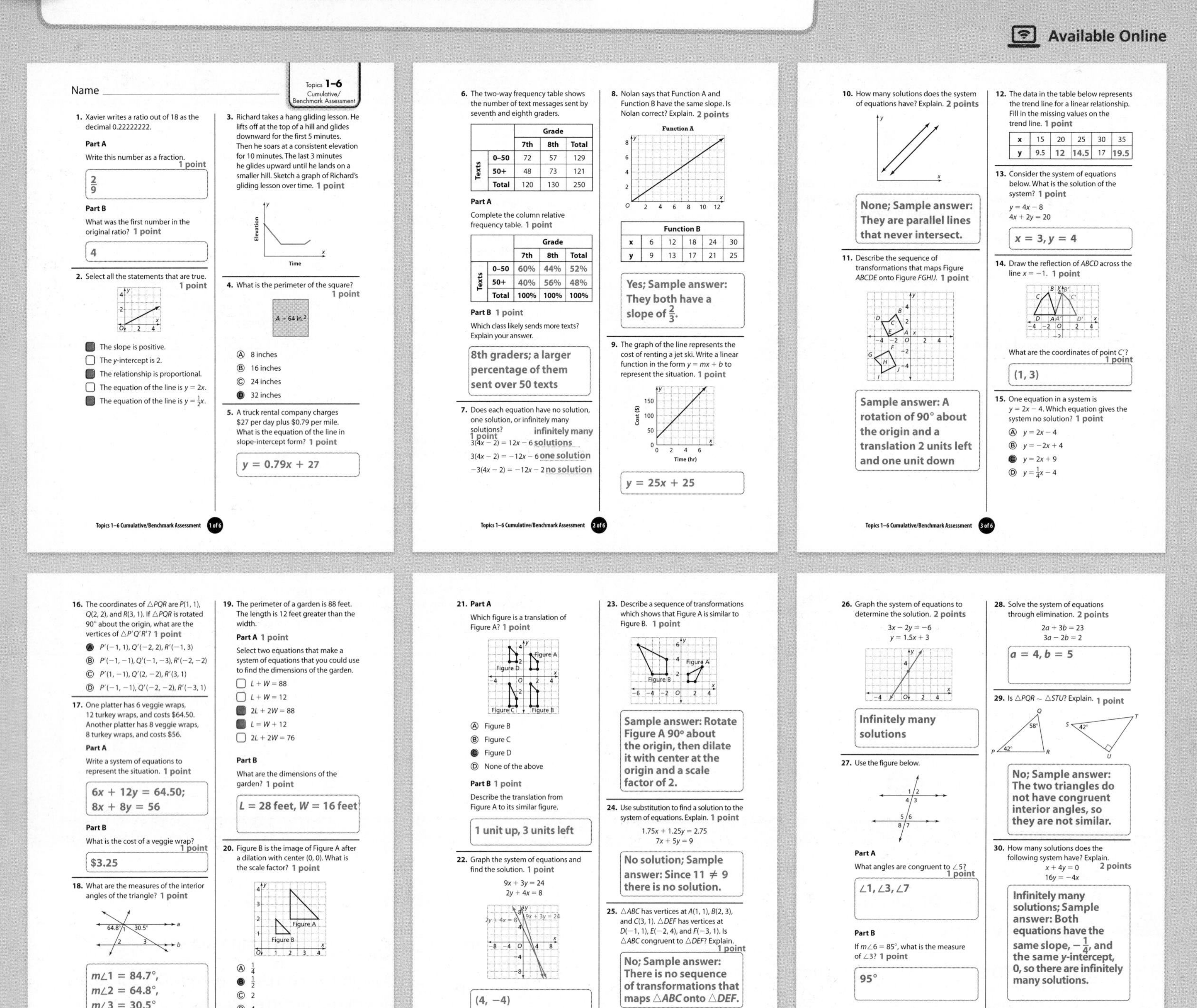

Name

Topics 1–6 Cumulative/Benchmark Assessment

1. Xavier writes a ratio out of 18 as the decimal 0.22222222.

Part A

Write this number as a fraction. 1 point

$\frac{2}{9}$

Part B

What was the first number in the original ratio? 1 point

4

2. Select all the statements that are true. 1 point

- [x] The slope is positive.
- [ ] The y-intercept is 2.
- [x] The relationship is proportional.
- [ ] The equation of the line is $y = 2x$.
- [x] The equation of the line is $y = \frac{1}{2}x$.

3. Richard takes a hang gliding lesson. He lifts off at the top of a hill and glides downward for the first 5 minutes. Then he soars at a consistent elevation for 10 minutes. The last 3 minutes he glides upward until he lands on a smaller hill. Sketch a graph of Richard's gliding lesson over time. 1 point

4. What is the perimeter of the square? 1 point

$A = 64$ in.²

Ⓐ 8 inches
Ⓑ 16 inches
Ⓒ 24 inches
Ⓓ 32 inches

5. A truck rental company charges $27 per day plus $0.79 per mile. What is the equation of the line in slope-intercept form? 1 point

$y = 0.79x + 27$

Topics 1–6 Cumulative/Benchmark Assessment 1 of 6

6. The two-way frequency table shows the number of text messages sent by seventh and eighth graders.

| Texts | Grade 7th | 8th | Total |
|---|---|---|---|
| 0–50 | 72 | 57 | 129 |
| 50+ | 48 | 73 | 121 |
| Total | 120 | 130 | 250 |

Part A

Complete the column relative frequency table. 1 point

| Texts | Grade 7th | 8th | Total |
|---|---|---|---|
| 0–50 | 60% | 44% | 52% |
| 50+ | 40% | 56% | 48% |
| Total | 100% | 100% | 100% |

Part B 1 point

Which class likely sends more texts? Explain your answer.

8th graders; a larger percentage of them sent over 50 texts

7. Does each equation have no solution, one solution, or infinitely many solutions? 1 point

$3(4x - 2) = 12x - 6$ infinitely many solutions

$3(4x - 2) = -12x - 6$ one solution

$-3(4x - 2) = -12x - 2$ no solution

8. Nolan says that Function A and Function B have the same slope. Is Nolan correct? Explain. 2 points

Function A

Function B

| x | 6 | 12 | 18 | 24 | 30 |
|---|---|---|---|---|---|
| y | 9 | 13 | 17 | 21 | 25 |

Yes; Sample answer: They both have a slope of $\frac{2}{3}$.

9. The graph of the line represents the cost of renting a jet ski. Write a linear function in the form $y = mx + b$ to represent the situation. 1 point

$y = 25x + 25$

Topics 1–6 Cumulative/Benchmark Assessment 2 of 6

10. How many solutions does the system of equations have? Explain. 2 points

None; Sample answer: They are parallel lines that never intersect.

11. Describe the sequence of transformations that maps Figure ABCDE onto Figure FGHIJ. 1 point

Sample answer: A rotation of 90° about the origin and a translation 2 units left and one unit down

12. The data in the table below represents the trend line for a linear relationship. Fill in the missing values on the trend line. 1 point

| x | 15 | 20 | 25 | 30 | 35 |
|---|---|---|---|---|---|
| y | 9.5 | 12 | 14.5 | 17 | 19.5 |

13. Consider the system of equations below. What is the solution of the system? 1 point

$y = 4x - 8$
$4x + 2y = 20$

$x = 3, y = 4$

14. Draw the reflection of ABCD across the line $x = -1$. 1 point

What are the coordinates of point C′? 1 point

(1, 3)

15. One equation in a system is $y = 2x - 4$. Which equation gives the system no solution? 1 point

Ⓐ $y = 2x - 4$
Ⓑ $y = -2x + 4$
Ⓒ $y = 2x + 9$
Ⓓ $y = \frac{1}{2}x - 4$

Topics 1–6 Cumulative/Benchmark Assessment 3 of 6

16. The coordinates of △PQR are P(1, 1), Q(2, 2), and R(3, 1). If △PQR is rotated 90° about the origin, what are the vertices of △P′Q′R′? 1 point

Ⓐ P′(−1, 1), Q′(−2, 2), R′(−1, 3)
Ⓑ P′(−1, −1), Q′(−1, −3), R′(−2, −2)
Ⓒ P′(1, −1), Q′(2, −2), R′(3, 1)
Ⓓ P′(−1, −1), Q′(−2, −2), R′(−3, 1)

17. One platter has 6 veggie wraps, 12 turkey wraps, and costs $64.50. Another platter has 8 veggie wraps, 8 turkey wraps, and costs $56.

Part A

Write a system of equations to represent the situation. 1 point

$6x + 12y = 64.50$; $8x + 8y = 56$

Part B

What is the cost of a veggie wrap? 1 point

$3.25

18. What are the measures of the interior angles of the triangle? 1 point

$m\angle 1 = 84.7°$, $m\angle 2 = 64.8°$, $m\angle 3 = 30.5°$

19. The perimeter of a garden is 88 feet. The length is 12 feet greater than the width.

Part A 1 point

Select two equations that make a system of equations that you could use to find the dimensions of the garden.

- [ ] $L + W = 88$
- [ ] $L + W = 12$
- [x] $2L + 2W = 88$
- [x] $L = W + 12$
- [ ] $2L + 2W = 76$

Part B

What are the dimensions of the garden? 1 point

$L = 28$ feet, $W = 16$ feet

20. Figure B is the image of Figure A after a dilation with center (0, 0). What is the scale factor? 1 point

Ⓐ $\frac{1}{4}$
Ⓑ $\frac{1}{2}$
Ⓒ 2
Ⓓ 4

Topics 1–6 Cumulative/Benchmark Assessment 4 of 6

21. Part A

Which figure is a translation of Figure A? 1 point

Ⓐ Figure B
Ⓑ Figure C
Ⓒ Figure D
Ⓓ None of the above

Part B 1 point

Describe the translation from Figure A to its similar figure.

1 unit up, 3 units left

22. Graph the system of equations and find the solution. 1 point

$9x + 3y = 24$
$2y + 4x = 8$

(4, −4)

23. Describe a sequence of transformations which shows that Figure A is similar to Figure B. 1 point

Sample answer: Rotate Figure A 90° about the origin, then dilate it with center at the origin and a scale factor of 2.

24. Use substitution to find a solution to the system of equations. Explain. 1 point

$1.75x + 1.25y = 2.75$
$7x + 5y = 9$

No solution; Sample answer: Since $11 \neq 9$ there is no solution.

25. △ABC has vertices at A(1, 1), B(2, 3), and C(3, 1). △DEF has vertices at D(−1, 1), E(−2, 4), and F(−3, 1). Is △ABC congruent to △DEF? Explain. 1 point

No; Sample answer: There is no sequence of transformations that maps △ABC onto △DEF.

Topics 1–6 Cumulative/Benchmark Assessment 5 of 6

26. Graph the system of equations to determine the solution. 2 points

$3x - 2y = -6$
$y = 1.5x + 3$

Infinitely many solutions

27. Use the figure below.

Part A

What angles are congruent to ∠5? 1 point

∠1, ∠3, ∠7

Part B

If $m\angle 6 = 85°$, what is the measure of ∠3? 1 point

95°

28. Solve the system of equations through elimination. 2 points

$2a + 3b = 23$
$3a - 2b = 2$

$a = 4, b = 5$

29. Is △PQR ~ △STU? Explain. 1 point

No; Sample answer: The two triangles do not have congruent interior angles, so they are not similar.

30. How many solutions does the following system have? Explain. 2 points

$x + 4y = 0$
$16y = -4x$

Infinitely many solutions; Sample answer: Both equations have the same slope, $-\frac{1}{4}$, and the same y-intercept, 0, so there are infinitely many solutions.

Topics 1–6 Cumulative/Benchmark Assessment 6 of 6

Items 1–10 assess content taught in Topics 1–4. Items 11–30 assess content taught in Topics 5 and 6.

Go Online

Assess

## Item Analysis for Topics 1–6 Benchmark Assessment

| Item | Points | DOK | MDIS | Standard |
|---|---|---|---|---|
| **1A** | 1 | 1 | M23 | 8.NS.A.1 |
| **1B** | 1 | 2 | L45 | 8.NS.A.1 |
| **2** | 1 | 2 | K50 | 8.EE.B.5 |
| **3** | 1 | 2 | K54 | 8.F.B.5 |
| **4** | 1 | 1 | L83 | 8.EE.A.2 |
| **5** | 1 | 3 | K52 | 8.F.B.4 |
| **6** | 6 | 3 | N90 | 8.SP.A.4 |
| **7** | 1 | 2 | K33 | 8.EE.C.7a |
| **8** | 1 | 2 | K52 | 8.F.A.2 |
| **9** | 1 | 3 | K52 | 8.F.B.4 |
| **10** | 1 | 1 | K51 | 8.EE.C.8a |
| **11** | 1 | 2 | N59 | 8.G.A.2, 8.G.A.3 |
| **12** | 1 | 2 | N72 | 8.SP.A.2 |
| **13** | 1 | 2 | K36 | 8.EE.C.8b |
| **14** | 1 | 2 | N59 | 8.G.A.3 |
| **15** | 1 | 2 | K33 | 8.EE.C.8a |
| **16** | 1 | 2 | N59 | 8.G.A.3 |

| Item | Points | DOK | MDIS | Standard |
|---|---|---|---|---|
| **17A** | 1 | 3 | K33 | 8.EE.C.8b |
| **17B** | 1 | 2 | K35 | 8.EE.C.8b |
| **18** | 1 | 2 | N11 | 8.G.A.5 |
| **19A** | 1 | 2 | K33 | 8.EE.C.8b |
| **19B** | 1 | 2 | K35 | 8.EE.C.8b |
| **20** | 1 | 1 | N61 | 8.G.A.3 |
| **21** | 2 | 2 | N58 | 8.G.A.4 |
| **22** | 1 | 2 | K34 | 8.EE.C.8b |
| **23** | 1 | 2 | N59 | 8.G.A.3 |
| **24** | 1 | 2 | K35 | 8.EE.C.8b |
| **25** | 1 | 2 | N60 | 8.G.A.4 |
| **26** | 1 | 2 | K34 | 8.EE.C.8b |
| **27A** | 1 | 1 | N5 | 8.G.A.5 |
| **27B** | 1 | 2 | N5 | 8.G.A.5 |
| **28** | 1 | 2 | K35 | 8.EE.C.8b |
| **29** | 1 | 2 | N60 | 8.G.A.4 |
| **30** | 1 | 1 | K36 | 8.EE.C.8b |

You may opt to have students take the Cumulative/Benchmark Assessment online. The online assessment is auto-scored, with differentiated intervention automatically assigned to students based on their scores.

### Scoring Rubric

| Item | Points | Benchmark Assessment Scoring Guide |
|---|---|---|
| **9** | 2<br>1 | Correct answer and explanation<br>Correct answer or explanation |
| **11** | 2<br>1 | Correct number of solutions and explanation<br>Correct number of solutions or explanation |
| **26** | 2<br>1 | Correct graph and number of solutions<br>Correct graph or number of solutions |
| **28** | 2<br>1 | Correct answer and explanation<br>Correct answer or explanation |
| **30** | 2<br>1 | Correct number of solutions and explanation<br>Correct number of solutions or explanation |

### Scoring Guide

| Score | Recommendations |
|---|---|
| Greater Than 85% | Assign the corresponding MDIS for items answered incorrectly. |
| 70%–85% | Assign the corresponding MDIS for items answered incorrectly. Monitor the student during Step 1 and Try It! parts of the lessons for personalized remediation needs. |
| Less Than 70% | Assign the corresponding MDIS for items answered incorrectly.<br>Assign appropriate intervention lessons available online. |

# TOPIC 7 Understand and Apply the Pythagorean Theorem

## Math Background Focus

### Pythagorean Theorem Concepts

- **Pythagorean Theorem** In Lesson 7-1, students investigate and prove the Pythagorean Theorem using the area of a square. This lesson develops the procedural skills students need to use the Pythagorean Theorem in Lesson 7-3 where they solve problems in both two and three dimensions.

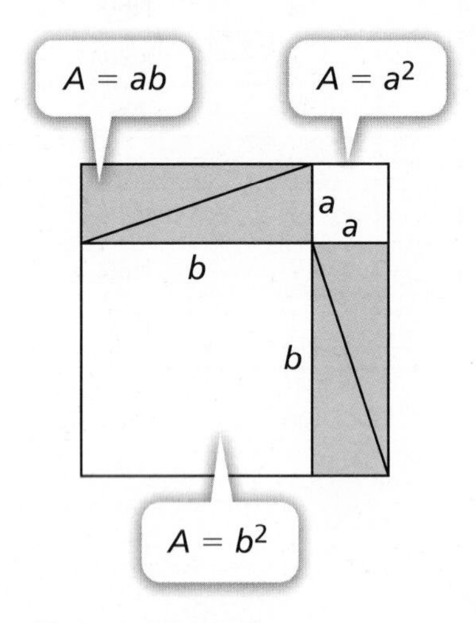


The total area of the large square is $A = ab + ab + a^2 + b^2$

Find the missing lengths in the rectangular prism.

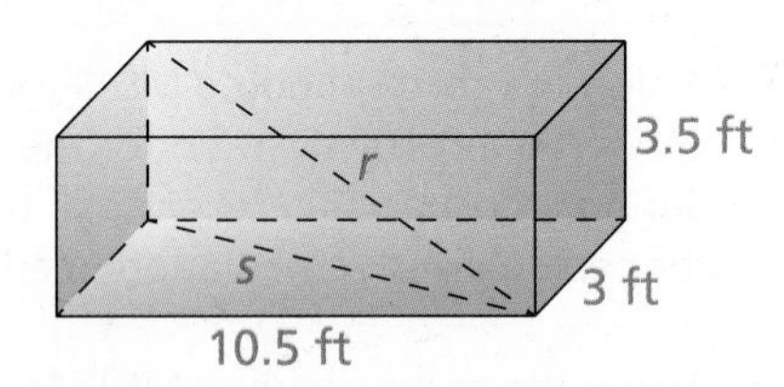


- **Converse of the Pythagorean Theorem** In Lesson 7-2, students explore the Converse of the Pythagorean Theorem. Students first investigate lengths of sides of triangles and which combination will ensure the triangle is a right triangle. Students are shown the proof of the Converse of the Pythagorean Theorem by supposing that a given triangle is a right triangle. They develop a logical argument to prove that a given triangle is congruent to a given right triangle, and thus whenever $a^2 + b^2 = c^2$, the triangle in question is a right triangle.

### Apply the Pythagorean Theorem

- **Pythagorean Theorem** In Lesson 7-1, students apply their knowledge of the Pythagorean Theorem to determine unknown side lengths of a right triangle. In Lesson 7-2, students apply their knowledge of the Converse of the Pythagorean Theorem to identify right triangles. In Lesson 7-3, students apply their knowledge of the Pythagorean Theorem and its converse to solve application problems.

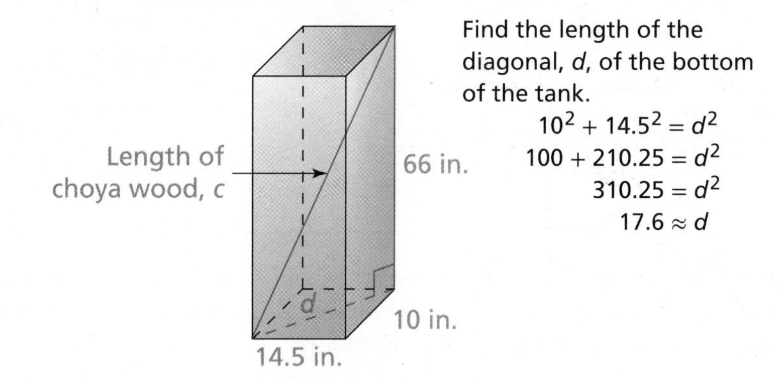


Find the length of the diagonal, $d$, of the bottom of the tank.

$$10^2 + 14.5^2 = d^2$$
$$100 + 210.25 = d^2$$
$$310.25 = d^2$$
$$17.6 \approx d$$

Use the Pythagorean Theorem to find the length of the choya wood.

$$66^2 + 17.6^2 = c^2$$
$$4{,}356 + 310.25 = c^2$$
$$4{,}666.25 = c^2$$
$$68.3 \approx c$$

Go Online

Video

- **Distance between Two Points** In Lesson 7-4, students apply their understanding of the Pythagorean Theorem to find the distance between two points on a coordinate plane and use the distance to find a missing coordinate. Students also extend their knowledge of the Pythagorean Theorem to find the perimeter of a figure.

**Find the length of side *AB* of $\Delta ABC$.**

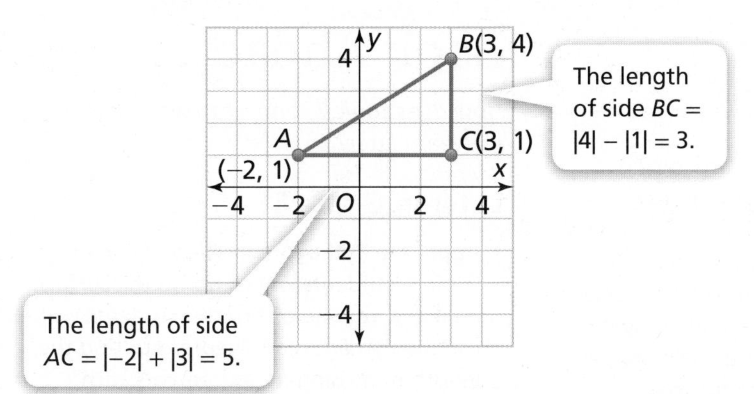


Use absolute value to find the length of side *AC* and side *BC*. Find the length of the hypotenuse *AB*.

$$c^2 = 5^2 + 32$$
$$c^2 = 25 + 9$$
$$c^2 = 34$$
$$\sqrt{c^2} = \sqrt{34}$$
$$c \approx 5.83$$

The distance between point *A* and point *B* is about 5.83 units.

**Professional Development Videos** Topic Overview Videos and Listen and Look For Lesson Videos present additional important information about the content.

# Advanced Concepts for the Teacher

The Pythagorean Theorem is an important theorem in mathematics. Because of this, many different geometric and algebraic proofs have been made of its properties.

- **Bhaskara's Proof** Bhaskara proved the Pythagorean Theorem by constructing a square using four copies of right triangle *ABC* and one smaller square.

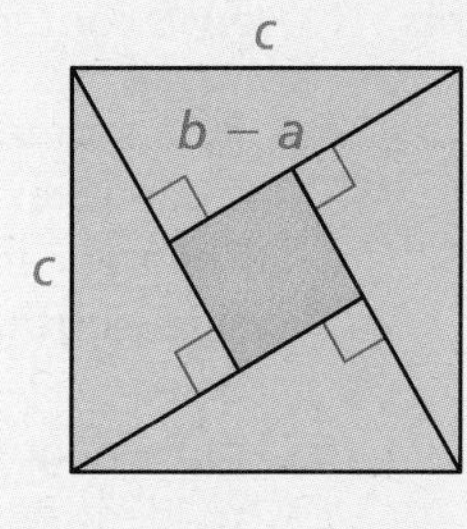


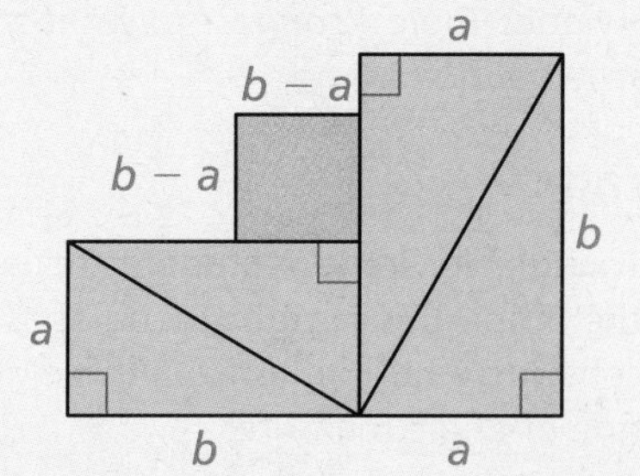


The hypotenuse of each triangle forms a side of the square with length *c*. If the long leg of the triangle is side *b* and the short leg side *a*, then the side length of the smaller square is $b - a$.

Combine pairs of triangles to form rectangles with side lengths *a* and *b*, and area *ab*. The area of the small square is $(b - a)^2 = b^2 - 2ab + a^2$.

The area of the large square, $c^2$, is equal to the area of composed figure on the right, therefore:

$$c^2 = b^2 - 2ab + a^2 + 2ab$$
$$= b^2 + a^2$$

- **President James Garfield's Proof** U.S. President Garfield composed right triangles into a trapezoid to prove the Pythagorean Theorem.

  Two of the triangles have legs with length *a* and *b* and hypotenuse *c*. The legs of the third triangle have length *c*.

  The trapezoid has base lengths *a* and *b* and height $a + b$.

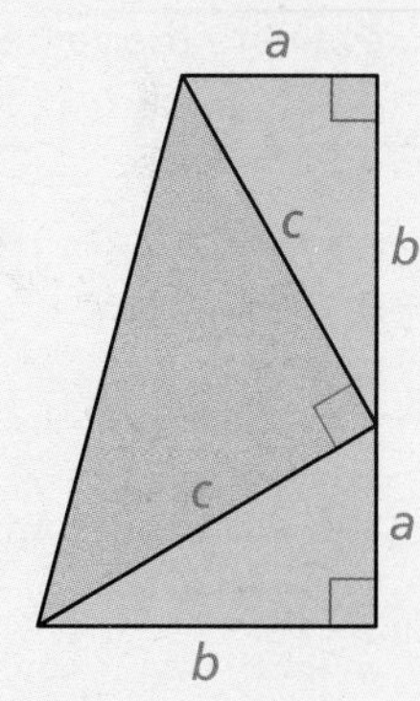


The area of the trapezoid is:

$$A = \frac{a + b}{2}(a + b)$$
$$= \frac{1}{2}(a^2 + 2ab + b^2)$$

The total area of the individual triangles is:

$$A = \frac{1}{2}(ab) + \frac{1}{2}(ab) + \frac{1}{2}(c^2)$$
$$= \frac{1}{2}(2ab + c^2)$$

The areas must be equal so:

$$\frac{1}{2}(a^2 + 2ab + b^2) = \frac{1}{2}(2ab + c^2)$$
$$a^2 + 2ab + b^2 = 2ab + c^2$$
$$a^2 + b^2 = c^2$$

# Math Background Coherence

Students learn best when concepts are connected throughout the curriculum. This coherence is achieved within clusters, across clusters, across domains, and across grade levels.

## Look Back

*How does Topic 7 connect to what students learned earlier?*

### Grade 7

- **Triangle** In Grade 7, students reviewed the properties of right triangles as they constructed triangles from three given side or angle measures.
- **Solve Problems Using Equations** Students learned to write equations to represent problem situations. Students also learned approaches to solving two-step equations.

### Earlier in Grade 8

- **Number System** In Topic 1, students extended their knowledge of rational and irrational numbers, including $\pi$. They used square roots to represent solutions to equations of the form $x^2 = p$, where $p$ is a positive rational number, and evaluate the value of that expression.

## Topic 7

*How is content connected within Topic 7?*

- **Pythagorean Theorem** In Lesson 7-1, students examine the Pythagorean Theorem and use it to find the unknown side lengths of triangles and solids. In Lesson 7-2, students learn the Converse of Pythagorean Theorem and apply it to identify triangles and analyze shapes. In Lesson 7-3, students apply their knowledge of the Pythagorean Theorem to solve two- and three-dimensional problems, including real-world problems. In Lesson 7-4, students apply their understanding of the Pythagorean Theorem to find the distance between two points on a coordinate plane, and then use the distance to find a missing point and perimeter of a figure on a coordinate plane.

  What is the height of the square pyramid shown?

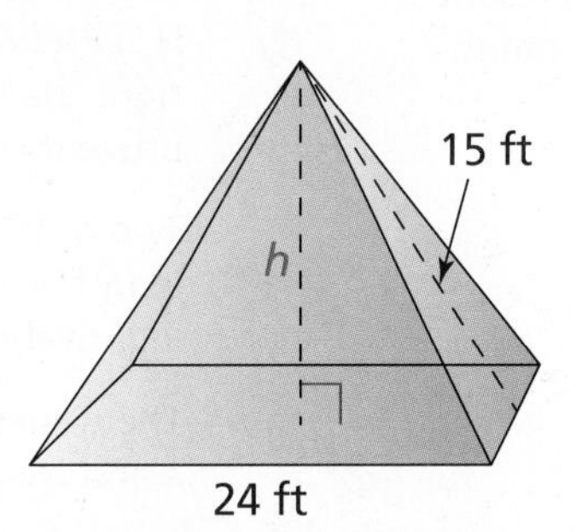


The height $h$ of the pyramid is one leg of a right triangle. The other leg has a length that is half of 24 feet, or 12 feet. Use the Pythagorean Theorem to find $h$.

$$h^2 + 12^2 = 15^2$$
$$h^2 + 144 = 225$$
$$h^2 = 81$$
$$h = \sqrt{81}$$
$$h = 9$$

The height of the pyramid is 9 feet.

## Look Ahead

*How does Topic 7 connect to what students will learn later?*

### Later in Grade 8

- **Apply the Pythagorean Theorem** In Topic 8, students will compute the surface area and volume of figures. Students will use the Pythagorean Theorem to find the length of missing measurements such as the radius, height, or slant height of a cone.

### Algebra I

- **Pythagorean Theorem** In Algebra I, students use the Pythagorean Theorem to formally prove triangle similarity, and to solve application problems.

Go Online

Video

# Math Background **Rigor**

A rigorous curriculum emphasizes conceptual understanding, procedural skill and fluency, and applications.

## Conceptual Understanding

- **Recognize Legs and Hypotenuse** In order for students to be successful in using the Pythagorean Theorem, they must recognize that the hypotenuse of a right triangle is the longest side and is opposite the right angle. The legs are adjacent to the right angle and can have equal or different measures.
- **Understand Distance on the Coordinate Plane** Students understand that absolute value can be used to find vertical and horizontal distances on the coordinate plane. They learn that the Pythagorean Theorem can be used to find any distance on the coordinate plane, including diagonal distances.

  Find the distance between the points labeled with stars on the graph below.

Remember, you can use absolute values to find the vertical distance. $|3| - |1| = 2$

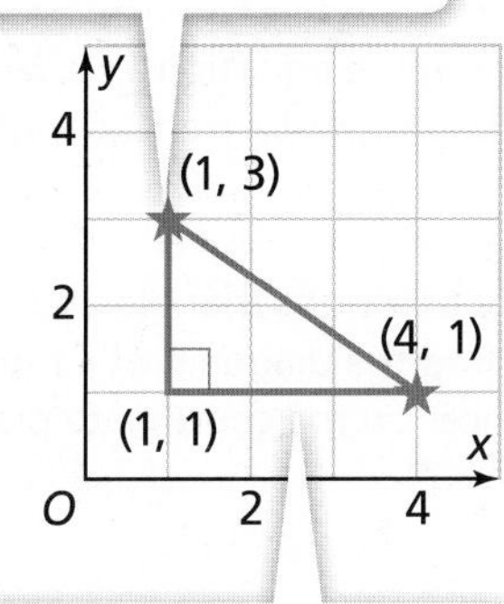


The horizontal distance is $|4| - |1| = 3$.

Use the Pythagorean Theorem to find the distance between the two points.

$$a^2 + b^2 = c^2$$

$$2^2 + 3^2 = c^2$$

Substitute the known lengths.

$$13 = c^2$$

$$\sqrt{13} = c$$

$$3.61 \approx c$$

## Procedural Skill and Fluency

There are no standards in this cluster that call for fluency.

- **Find the Missing Length** In Lesson 7-1, students learn how to substitute values into the equation $a^2 + b^2 = c^2$ and solve for a missing value. In Lesson 7-2, they substitute three values into the equation and solve to identify right triangles.

  What is the length of the hypotenuse of the triangle when $x = 15$? Round your answer to the nearest tenth.

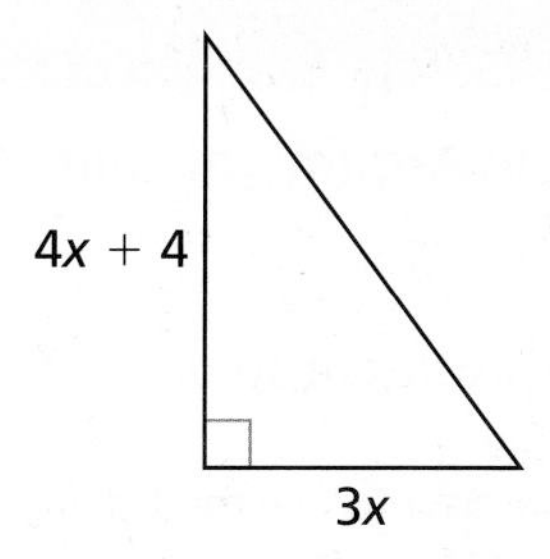


Use the Pythagorean Theorem to find the unknown side length of the right triangle.

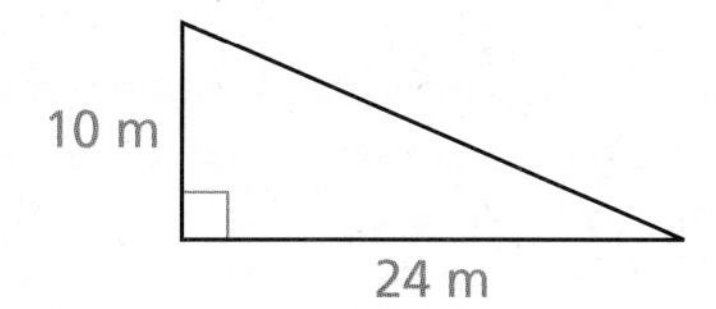


## Applications

- **Pythagorean Theorem** Throughout Topic 7, students apply the Pythagorean Theorem to various types of problems. In Lessons 7-1 and 7-2, the problems are primarily straight math problems. Lessons 7-3 and 7-4 include many practical applications, such as determining if an object will fit in a box and finding distances on a map.

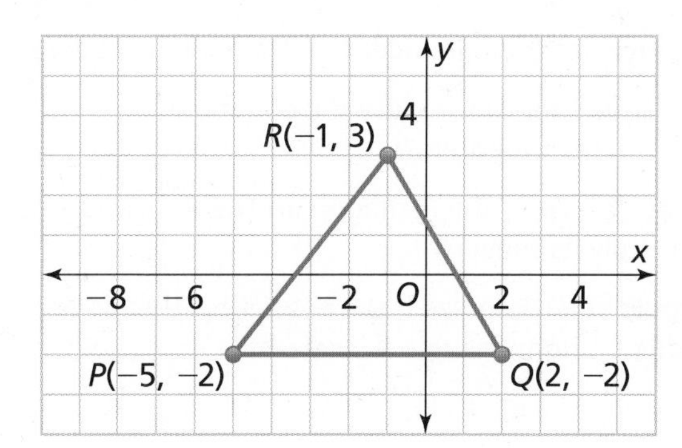

# Math Practices

The math practices and processes describe the behaviors and thinking habits that mathematically proficient students demonstrate when actively engaged in mathematics work. Opportunities for engagement in the practices and to develop expertise with these important behaviors and thinking habits exist throughout the topic and program. The focus below is on mathematical reasoning and explanation.

As students solve Pythagorean Theorem problems, look for these behaviors to assess and identify students who demonstrate proficiency with mathematical reasoning and explaining.

**Math Practices Within Topic 7 Lessons**

| **Construct Viable Arguments and Critique Reasoning** (MP.3) | **Look for and Make Use of Structure** (MP.7) |
|---|---|
| Mathematically proficient students: | Mathematically proficient students: |
| • Justify when and how to use the Pythagorean Theorem and the Converse of the Pythagorean Theorem. | • Have a conceptual and practical understanding of the structure of the equation $a^2 + b^2 = c^2$. |
| • Identify and explain the steps of substituting a value into the equation $a^2 + b^2 = c^2$ and solving for the unknown. | • Recognize mathematical and real-world problems that can be represented by the equation $a^2 + b^2 = c^2$. |
| • Develop logical arguments that include definitions, properties, and given facts to support their application of the equation $a^2 + b^2 = c^2$. | • Use the structure of the equation $a^2 + b^2 = c^2$ to find an unknown side length of a right triangle and to identify right triangles. |
| • Recognize faulty claims about the application of the Pythagorean Theorem and articulate the conceptual or procedural error involved. | • Use the structure of a right triangle and the equation $a^2 + b^2 = c^2$ to find the diagonal of a right rectangular prism and distances on the coordinate plane. |

Help students become more proficient with mathematical reasoning and explanation.

If students are not able to apply the Pythagorean Theorem appropriately, then use these questioning strategies to help them develop reasoning and explaining skills as they solve problems throughout the topic.

**Q:** To what type of triangles does the Pythagorean Theorem apply?

**Q:** In what situations can you use the equation of the Pythagorean theorem?

**Q:** When do you apply the Pythagorean Theorem and when do you apply its converse?

**Q:** How could you recognize if the answer for the length of a side of a right triangle is incorrect?

**Q:** What are the characteristics of the hypotenuse of a right triangle?

**Q:** How can you identify what value to substitute for *a*, *b*, or *c* in the equation $a^2 + b^2 = c^2$?

**Q:** When is the hypotenuse of a right triangle also the diagonal of a rectangular prism?

**Q:** How is the equation for the Pythagorean Theorem related to distance on the coordinate plane?

# Topic Readiness Assessment

Topic Readiness Assessment Masters

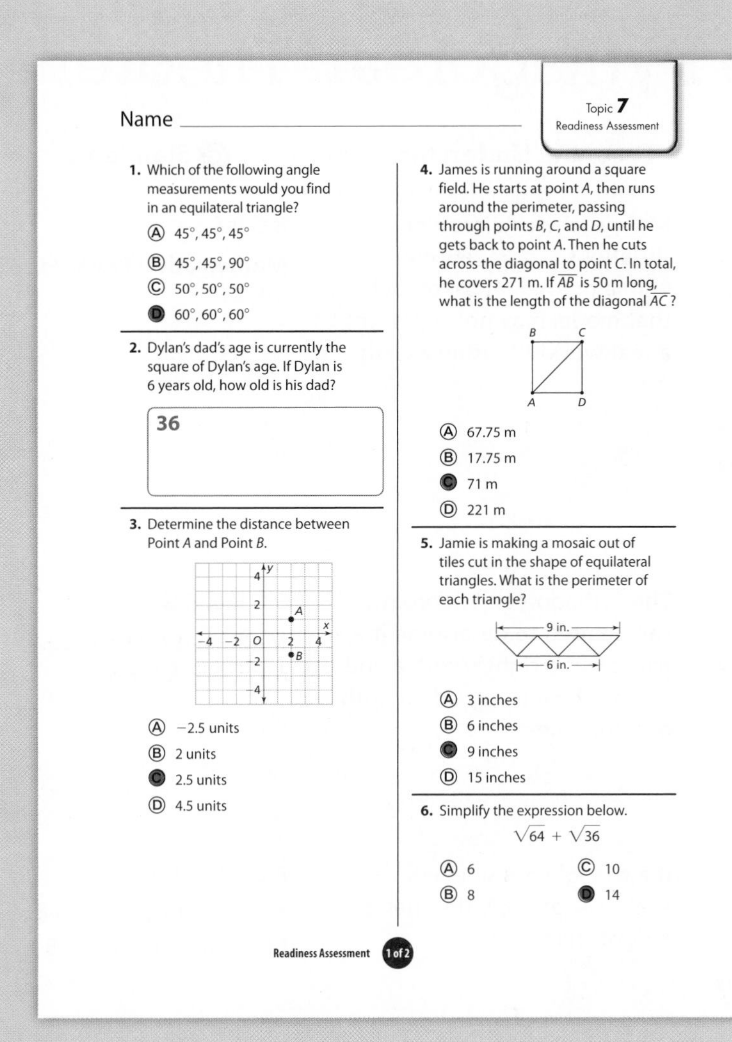

Name ______________________

Topic 7 Readiness Assessment

**1.** Which of the following angle measurements would you find in an equilateral triangle?

Ⓐ 45°, 45°, 45°
Ⓑ 45°, 45°, 90°
Ⓒ 50°, 50°, 50°
Ⓓ 60°, 60°, 60°

**2.** Dylan's dad's age is currently the square of Dylan's age. If Dylan is 6 years old, how old is his dad?

36

**3.** Determine the distance between Point *A* and Point *B*.

Ⓐ −2.5 units
Ⓑ 2 units
Ⓒ 2.5 units
Ⓓ 4.5 units

**4.** James is running around a square field. He starts at point *A*, then runs around the perimeter, passing through points *B*, *C*, and *D*, until he gets back to point *A*. Then he cuts across the diagonal to point *C*. In total, he covers 271 m. If $\overline{AB}$ is 50 m long, what is the length of the diagonal $\overline{AC}$?

Ⓐ 67.75 m
Ⓑ 17.75 m
Ⓒ 71 m
Ⓓ 221 m

**5.** Jamie is making a mosaic out of tiles cut in the shape of equilateral triangles. What is the perimeter of each triangle?

Ⓐ 3 inches
Ⓑ 6 inches
Ⓒ 9 inches
Ⓓ 15 inches

**6.** Simplify the expression below.

$\sqrt{64} + \sqrt{36}$

Ⓐ 6
Ⓑ 8
Ⓒ 10
Ⓓ 14

Readiness Assessment 1 of 2

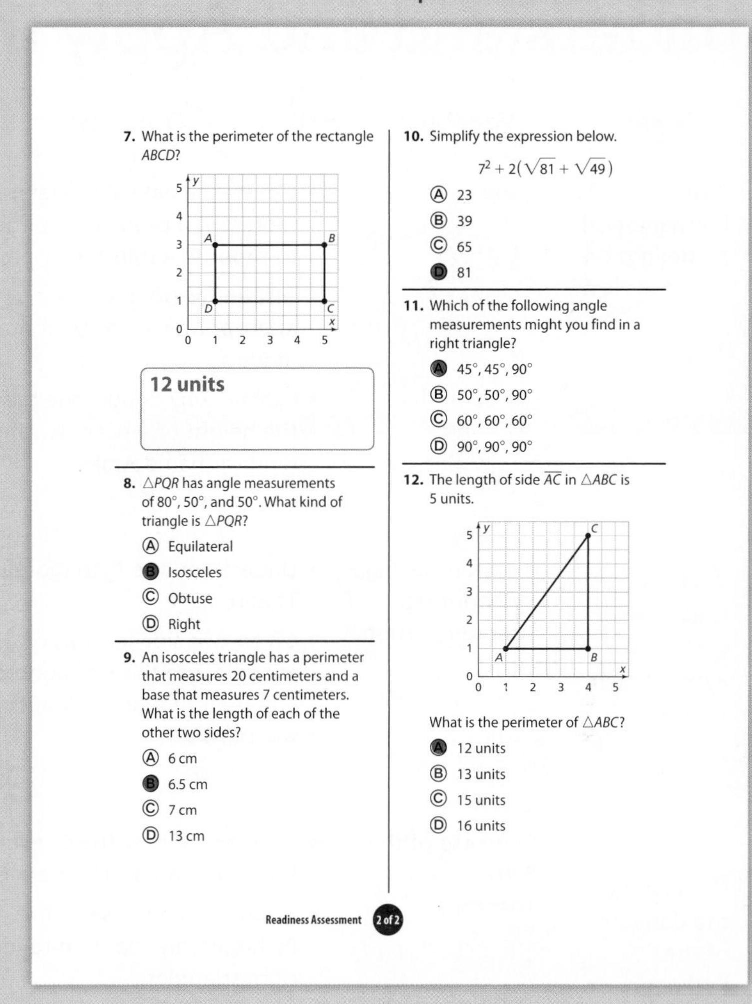

**7.** What is the perimeter of the rectangle *ABCD*?

12 units

**8.** $\triangle PQR$ has angle measurements of 80°, 50°, and 50°. What kind of triangle is $\triangle PQR$?

Ⓐ Equilateral
Ⓑ Isosceles
Ⓒ Obtuse
Ⓓ Right

**9.** An isosceles triangle has a perimeter that measures 20 centimeters and a base that measures 7 centimeters. What is the length of each of the other two sides?

Ⓐ 6 cm
Ⓑ 6.5 cm
Ⓒ 7 cm
Ⓓ 13 cm

**10.** Simplify the expression below.

$7^2 + 2(\sqrt{81} + \sqrt{49})$

Ⓐ 23
Ⓑ 39
Ⓒ 65
Ⓓ 81

**11.** Which of the following angle measurements might you find in a right triangle?

Ⓐ 45°, 45°, 90°
Ⓑ 50°, 50°, 90°
Ⓒ 60°, 60°, 60°
Ⓓ 90°, 90°, 90°

**12.** The length of side $\overline{AC}$ in $\triangle ABC$ is 5 units.

What is the perimeter of $\triangle ABC$?

Ⓐ 12 units
Ⓑ 13 units
Ⓒ 15 units
Ⓓ 16 units

Readiness Assessment 2 of 2

Assess students' understanding of prerequisite concepts and skills using the Topic Readiness Assessment.

You may opt to have students take the Topic Readiness Assessment online.

## Scoring Guide

| Score | Recommendations |
|---|---|
| Greater Than 85% | Assign the corresponding MDIS for items answered incorrectly. Use Enrichment activities with the student during the topic. |
| 70%–85% | Assign the corresponding MDIS for items answered incorrectly. Monitor the student during Step 1 and Try It! parts of the lessons for personalized remediation needs. |
| Less Than 70% | Assign the corresponding MDIS for items answered incorrectly. Assign appropriate intervention lessons available online. |

## Item Analysis for Diagnosis and Remediation

| Item | DOK | MDIS | Standard |
|---|---|---|---|
| 1 | 2 | N8 | 7.G.A.2 |
| 2 | 2 | L2, L83 | 6.EE.A.2c |
| 3 | 2 | N66 | 6.G.A.3 |
| 4 | 2 | N2 | 7.G.A.1 |
| 5 | 2 | N8 | 7.G.A.1 |
| 6 | 1 | L81, K9 | 8.EE.A.2 |
| 7 | 2 | N66 | 6.G.A.3 |
| 8 | 1 | N8 | 7.G.A.2 |
| 9 | 2 | N8, N37 | 7.G.A.2 |
| 10 | 2 | L2, L81, K9 | 6.EE.A.2c, 8.EE.A.2 |
| 11 | 2 | N8 | 7.G.A.2 |
| 12 | 2 | N37, N7 | 6.G.A.3 |

# TOPIC 7 Topic Planner

## Understand and Apply the Pythagorean Theorem

| Lesson | Vocabulary | Objective | Essential Understanding | Standards |
|---|---|---|---|---|
| **3-Act Mathematical Modeling: Go with the Flow** | none | • Use mathematical modeling to represent a problem situation and to propose a solution.<br>• Test and verify the appropriateness of their math models.<br>• Explain why double the base and the height of a triangle, the area is more than double. | Many real-world problem situations can be represented with a mathematical model, but that model may not represent a real-world situation exactly. | 8.G.B.6<br>**Mathematical Practices**<br>MP.4 |
| **7-1 Understand the Pythagorean Theorem** | hypotenuse, leg, Pythagorean Theorem, proof | • Understand the Pythagorean Theorem.<br>• Given two side lengths of a right triangle, use the Pythagorean Theorem to find the length of the third side. | The Pythagorean Theorem can be used to determine if a triangle is a right triangle and to find the missing side length of a triangle. | 8.G.B.6, 8.G.B.7<br>**Mathematical Practices**<br>MP.3, MP.7, MP.8 |
| **7-2 Understand the Converse of the Pythagorean Theorem** | Converse of the Pythagorean Theorem | • Understand why the Converse of the Pythagorean Theorem is true.<br>• Apply the Converse of the Pythagorean Theorem to identify right triangles.<br>• Use the Converse of the Pythagorean Theorem to analyze two-dimensional shapes. | If a triangle has side length such that $a^2 + b^2 = c^2$, the triangle is a right triangle. | 8.G.B.6, 8.G.B.7<br>**Mathematical Practices**<br>MP.3, MP.4, MP.7, MP.8 |

## Lesson Resources

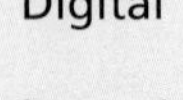
Digital

Print

**Student's Edition**

**Additional Practice Workbook**

**Teaching Resources**
- Reteach to Build Understanding
- Additional Vocabulary Support
- Build Mathematical Literacy
- Enrichment

**Assessment Resources**
- Lesson Quiz

Digital

**Digital Lesson Courseware**
- Today's Challenge
- Visual Learning Animation Plus
- Key Concept
- Additional Examples
- 3-Act Mathematical Modeling
- Online Practice powered by MathXL for School
- Adaptive Practice
- Virtual Nerd Video Tutorials
- Animated Glossary
- Digital Math Tools
- Online Math Games

**Lesson Support for Teachers**
- Listen and Look For PD Lesson Video

Go Online

Digital

The suggested pacing for each lesson is 2 days for a 45-minute math class and 1 day for a 90-minute class.

| Lesson | Vocabulary | Objective | Essential Understanding | Standards |
|---|---|---|---|---|
| **7-3** **Apply the Pythagorean Theorem to Solve Problems** | none | • Apply the Pythagorean Theorem and its converse to solve real-world problems.<br>• Apply the Pythagorean Theorem to solve problems that involve three dimensions. | The Pythagorean Theorem and its converse can be used to solve real-world problems that involve right triangles. Both can be used to determine the unknown leg lengths of a right triangle, or to identify or verify whether a triangle is a right triangle. | 8.G.B.7<br>**Mathematical Practices**<br>MP.1, MP.2, MP.3, MP.7, MP.8 |
| **7-4** **Find Distance in the Coordinate Plane** | none | • Apply the Pythagorean Theorem to find the distance between two points on a map or coordinate plane.<br>• Find the perimeter of a figure on a coordinate plane.<br>• Identify the coordinates of the third vertex of a triangle on the coordinate plane. | The Pythagorean Theorem can be used to find the distance between any two points on a coordinate plane by drawing a line to connect the points and using it as the hypotenuse of a right triangle where the legs are the horizontal and vertical distances. | 8.G.B.8<br>**Mathematical Practices**<br>MP.3, MP.4, MP.7, MP.8 |

## Topic Resources

Digital

Print

### Student's Edition

- Review What You Know
- Language Development Activity
- Mid-Topic Checkpoint and Performance Task
- Topic Review
- Fluency Practice Activity
- enVision® STEM Project
- Pick a Project

### Assessment Resources

- Topic Readiness Assessment
- Mid-Topic Assessment
- Topic Assessment
- Topic Performance Task

Digital

### Topic Support for Students

- Math Practice Animations
- enVision® STEM Project
- 3-Act Mathematical Modeling Lesson

### Topic Support for Teachers

- Topic Overview Video
- ExamView Test Generator

# Understand and Apply the Pythagorean Theorem

Available Online

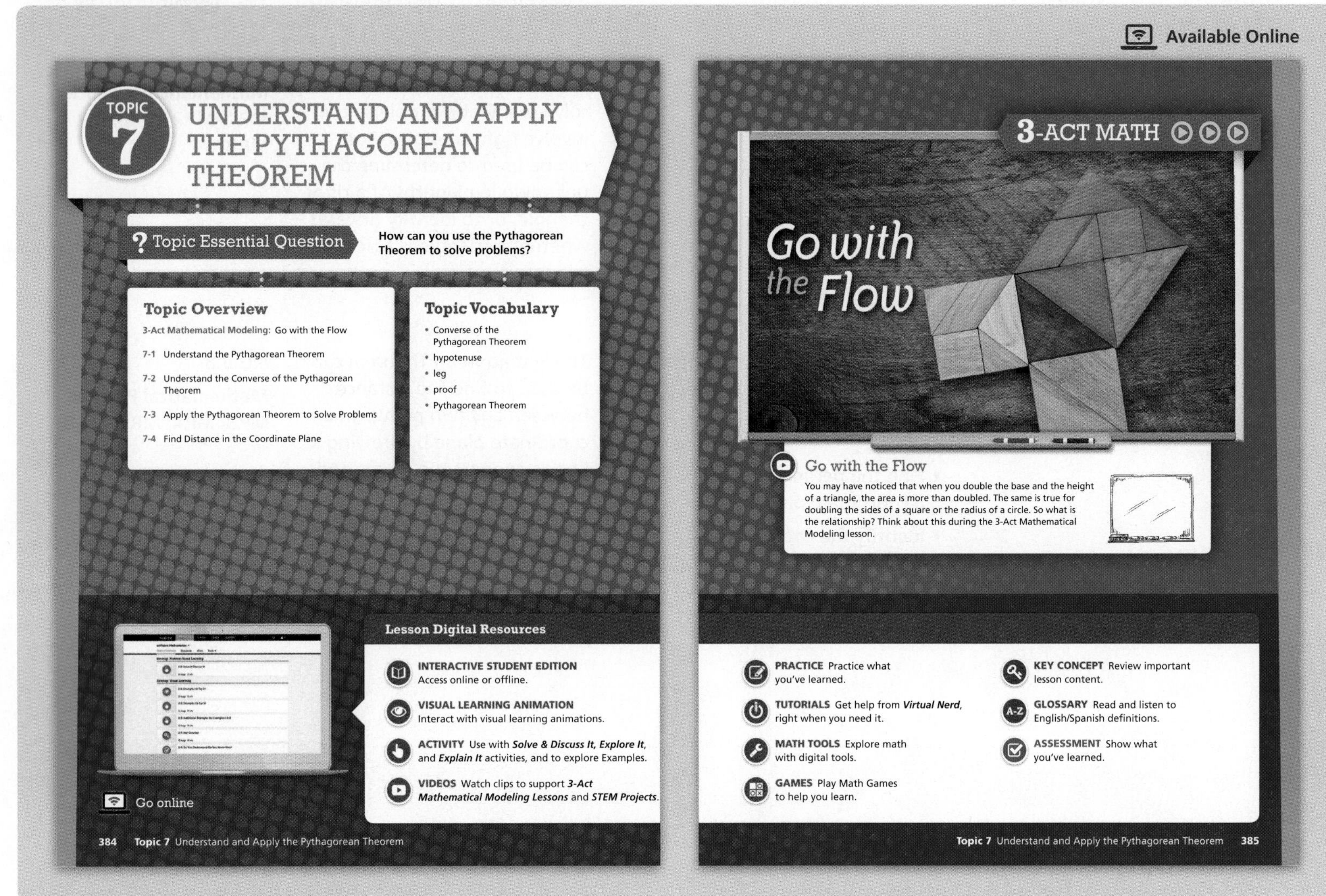

TOPIC 7 UNDERSTAND AND APPLY THE PYTHAGOREAN THEOREM

? Topic Essential Question

How can you use the Pythagorean Theorem to solve problems?

**Topic Overview**

3-Act Mathematical Modeling: Go with the Flow

7-1 Understand the Pythagorean Theorem

7-2 Understand the Converse of the Pythagorean Theorem

7-3 Apply the Pythagorean Theorem to Solve Problems

7-4 Find Distance in the Coordinate Plane

**Topic Vocabulary**

- Converse of the Pythagorean Theorem
- hypotenuse
- leg
- proof
- Pythagorean Theorem

Go online

**Lesson Digital Resources**

**INTERACTIVE STUDENT EDITION** Access online or offline.

**VISUAL LEARNING ANIMATION** Interact with visual learning animations.

**ACTIVITY** Use with ***Solve & Discuss It, Explore It,*** and ***Explain It*** activities, and to explore Examples.

**VIDEOS** Watch clips to support ***3-Act Mathematical Modeling Lessons*** and ***STEM Projects.***

384 **Topic 7** Understand and Apply the Pythagorean Theorem

3-ACT MATH

Go with the Flow

Go with the Flow

You may have noticed that when you double the base and the height of a triangle, the area is more than doubled. The same is true for doubling the sides of a square or the radius of a circle. So what is the relationship? Think about this during the 3-Act Mathematical Modeling lesson.

**PRACTICE** Practice what you've learned.

**TUTORIALS** Get help from ***Virtual Nerd,*** right when you need it.

**MATH TOOLS** Explore math with digital tools.

**GAMES** Play Math Games to help you learn.

**KEY CONCEPT** Review important lesson content.

**GLOSSARY** Read and listen to English/Spanish definitions.

**ASSESSMENT** Show what you've learned.

**Topic 7** Understand and Apply the Pythagorean Theorem 385

## Topic Essential Question

**How can you use the Pythagorean Theorem to solve problems?**

Revisit the Topic Essential Question throughout the topic. See the Teacher's Edition for the Topic Review for notes about answering the question.

## 3-Act Mathematical Modeling

**Generate excitement about the upcoming 3-Act Mathematical Modeling lesson by having students read about the math modeling problem for this topic.**

See the Teacher's Edition lesson support for notes about how to use the lesson video in your classroom.

# enVision® STEM Project

Go Online

Video

## Rainy Days

In this project, students will discuss inexpensive ways to save water in areas where water is scarce and research the necessary components of a rainwater collection system as an alternative. They will design a slanted roof system that will be used to collect rainwater.

### What's the Math?

Students use what they already know about right triangles and the Pythagorean Theorem to design a slanted roof system to collect rainwater. They will use the dimensions of the roof to calculate its area and determine the numbers of gallons of rainwater that will be collected for every inch of rainfall.

### What's the Science?

Students apply the engineering design process to find possible solutions to water shortage problems. They research and gather data on the impact of water shortages and the need for alternative water sources. They explore a rainwater collection system as an alternative measure.

### What's the Engineering and Technology?

Students think like engineers as they work toward a proposed solution. The solution may require researching the necessary components of a rainwater collection system, designing a slanted roof system to collect rainwater, and examining the efficiency of the designed system.

### Introduce the Project

Present the project by having students discuss what they know about water shortages, using water wisely, and alternative water sources.

**Q:** Why is using water wisely important? [Sample answers: Saves money on water and energy bills, extends the life of supply and wastewater facilities]

**Q:** What are some examples of ways stored rainwater can be used in everyday life? [Sample answer: Washing, flushing toilets, watering gardens, purified for drinking]

**Q:** What are the steps in the engineering design process? [Sample answer: Define the problem, do background research, brainstorm solutions, choose the best solution, develop a prototype, test the prototype, and redesign as necessary]

**Q:** What criteria might you consider when designing your slanted roof system to collect rainwater? [Sample answers: The area of the roof; how many gallons of rainwater it collects for every inch of rainfall]

You can launch this project any time during Topic 7.

Show the Topic 7 STEM video to generate interest in the project.

Teacher resources that provide students with project details and support are available online.

**enVision STEM Project Video** is available online.

TOPIC 7 enVision® STEM Project

Did You Know?

Over two billion people will face **water shortages** by 2050 according to a 2015 United Nations Environment Program report.

Using **water wisely** saves money on water and energy bills and extends the life of supply and wastewater facilities.

Rainwater can be **collected** and stored for use in irrigation, industrial uses, flushing toilets, washing clothes and cars, or it can be purified for use as everyday drinking water.

This **alternative water source** reduces the use of fresh water from reservoirs and wells.

**Roofs of buildings** or large tarps are used to collect rainwater.

A rainwater **collection system** for a building roof that measures 28 feet by 40 feet can provide 700 gallons of water—enough water to support two people for a year—from a rainfall of 1.0 inch.

Even a **5 foot by 7 foot tarp** can collect **2 gallons** of water from a rainfall total of only 0.1 in.

The **rainwater harvesting** market is expected to **grow 5%** from 2016 to 2020.

Your Task: Rainy Days

Rainwater collection is an inexpensive way to save water in areas where it is scarce. One inch of rain falling on a square roof with an area of 100 $ft^2$ collects 62 gallons of water that weighs over 500 pounds. You and your classmates will research the necessary components of a rainwater collection system. Then you will use what you know about right triangles to design a slanted roof system that will be used to collect rainwater.

386 Topic 7 enVision STEM Project

### Common Core Content Standards

8.G.B.6, 8.G.B.7, 8.G.B.8

### Mathematical Practices Standards

MP.1, MP.2, MP.3, MP.4

### Next Generation Science Standards

MS-ESS3-1, MS-ESS3-3, MS-ETS1-1, MS-ETS1-2, MS-ETS1-3, MS-ETS1-4

# TOPIC 7 Get Ready!

Go Online

Glossary

## Review What You Know!

Assign the Review What You Know to activate prior knowledge and to practice prerequisite concepts and skills needed for success in this topic.

Encourage students to work independently or with a partner. Use these questioning strategies to help them get started.

### Simplify Expressions with Exponents

**Q:** When simplifying an expression, how do you know if you should square the number or add the values first? [Sample answer: Follow the order of operations. Use the exponent first and square each number. Then add or subtract.]

**Q:** Why are addition and subtraction completed in the same step? [Sample answer: Subtraction can be changed to addition by adding the opposite value.]

### Square Roots

**Q:** What does it mean for a number to be a perfect square? [Sample answer: A number is a perfect square when the value of the square root is a whole number.]

### Distance on a Coordinate Plane

**Q:** What are you finding when you find the distance between the two points on the coordinate plane? [Sample answer: The length between the two points.]

**Q:** Why can you simply count between the points? [Sample answer: If the points were connected they would form a horizontal or vertical segment.]

Available Online

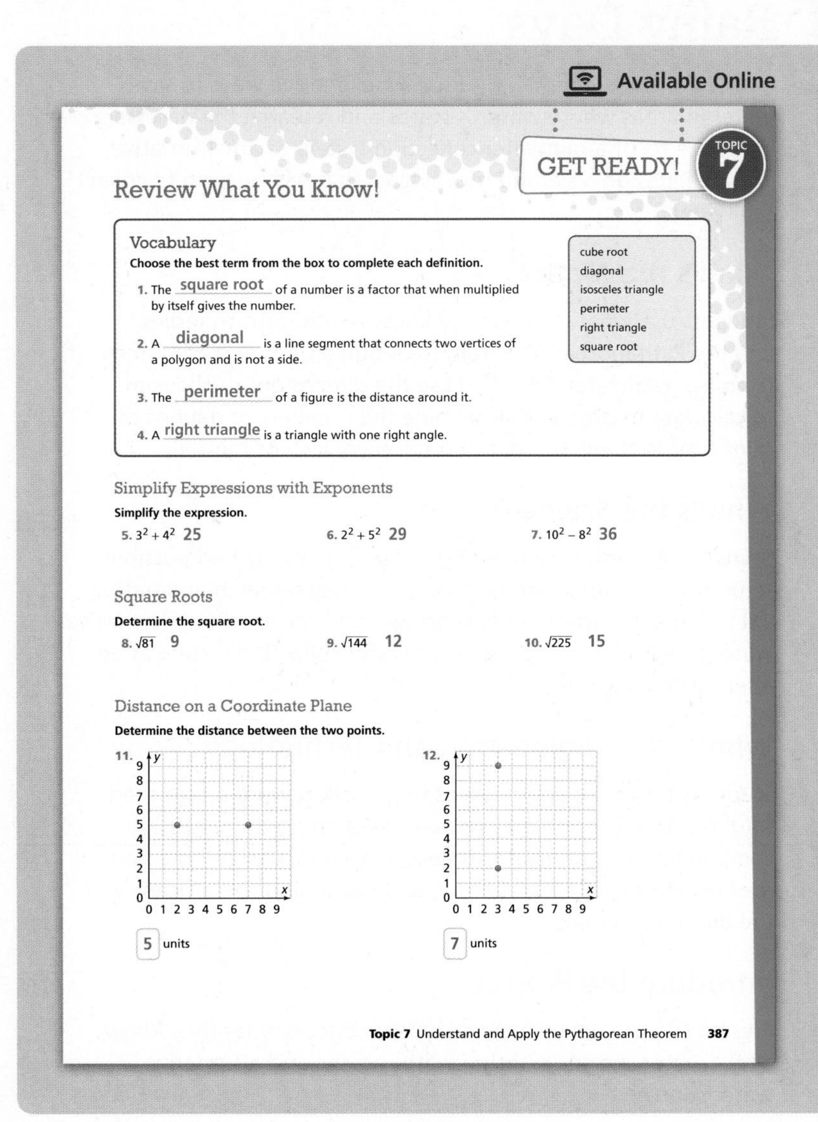

GET READY! TOPIC 7

Review What You Know!

Vocabulary

Choose the best term from the box to complete each definition.

cube root
diagonal
isosceles triangle
perimeter
right triangle
square root

1. The square root of a number is a factor that when multiplied by itself gives the number.
2. A diagonal is a line segment that connects two vertices of a polygon and is not a side.
3. The perimeter of a figure is the distance around it.
4. A right triangle is a triangle with one right angle.

Simplify Expressions with Exponents

Simplify the expression.

5. $3^2 + 4^2$ 25
6. $2^2 + 5^2$ 29
7. $10^2 - 8^2$ 36

Square Roots

Determine the square root.

8. $\sqrt{81}$ 9
9. $\sqrt{144}$ 12
10. $\sqrt{225}$ 15

Distance on a Coordinate Plane

Determine the distance between the two points.

11. 5 units
12. 7 units

Topic 7 Understand and Apply the Pythagorean Theorem 387

### Item Analysis for Diagnosis and Remediation

| Item | MDIS | Standard |
|---|---|---|
| 1 | L81 | 8.EE.A.2 |
| 2 | N2 | 7.G.A.1 |
| 3 | N7, N37 | 6.NS.C.8, 7.G.A.2 |
| 4 | N8 | 7.G.A.2 |
| 5–7 | L83 | 8.EE.A.2 |
| 8–10 | L81 | 8.EE.A.2 |
| 11–12 | N66 | 6.NS.C.8 |

## Vocabulary Review

You may choose to strengthen vocabulary with the following activity.

- Have students work individually or in pairs to complete a poster with the definition and a variety of representations of one of the vocabulary terms. Make sure students have the materials they need to create the posters. The posters should be displayed as a good visual aid as students work through the topic.

Go Online

Glossary

# Language Development

As students progress through this topic, have them fill in the word map with key terms and phrases related to the Pythagorean Theorem and its Converse. For each key term or phrase listed, have them draw a related illustration or cite an example. This will help students to build a deeper understanding of the new math vocabulary.

**Q:** How does providing an example or illustration with each new vocabulary term or phrase help you understand the word(s)? [Sample answer: It makes the meaning of the word or phrase easier to understand because it is a visual representation.]

Encourage students to pay careful attention to text features and visuals in each lesson, as these frequently provide important clues and communicate ideas.

**Q:** How can you determine the word meaning by using text and graphic features on the page? [Sample answer: Look for definitions, restatements, examples, or descriptions of the words, and for pictures and diagrams that illustrate the concept.]

As students progress through the topic, encourage them to add important ideas and details to their word maps to clarify their understanding of new terms and phrases related to the Pythagorean Theorem and its Converse.

## Extension for Language Development

Challenge students to use their completed word maps to write a problem that can be solved using the Pythagorean Theorem or its Converse. Then have the students take a partner's problem and solve it.

## Word Wall

To help students comprehend the meaning of *hypotenuse*, assist them in making a word wall. Invite students to write examples that represent hypotenuse along with illustrations on index cards, and display them under the word *Hypotenuse*. Remind students that the hypotenuse is the longest side of a right triangle. Instructions on how to design a word wall are included in the Language Support Handbook.

**Available Online**

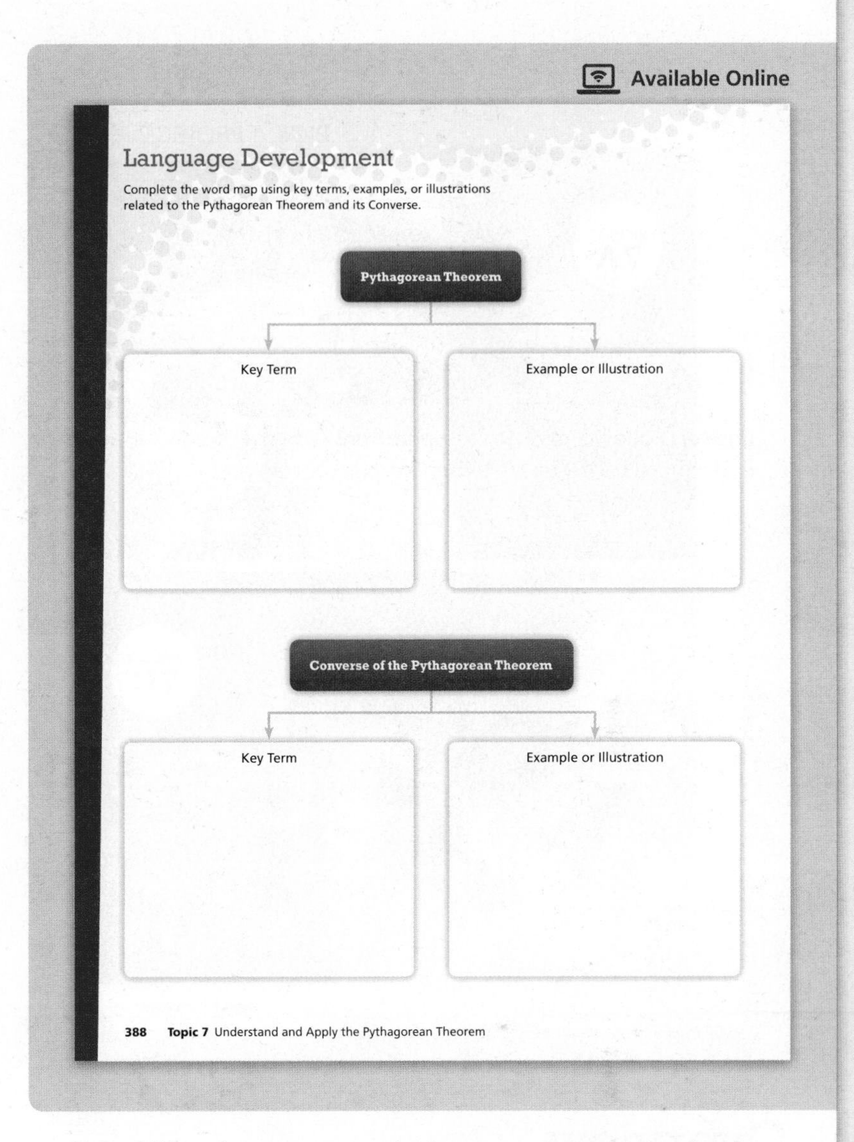
Language Development

Complete the word map using key terms, examples, or illustrations related to the Pythagorean Theorem and its Converse.

Pythagorean Theorem

Key Term

Example or Illustration

Converse of the Pythagorean Theorem

Key Term

Example or Illustration

388 **Topic 7** Understand and Apply the Pythagorean Theorem

For additional resources, see the **Language Support Handbook.**

TOPIC 7

# Pick a Project

Available Online

## Overview

A variety of rich projects is provided for each topic. Students may select the project that is most interesting to them.

| Project | Different Engaging Contexts | Different Activity Modalities | Different Final Products |
|---|---|---|---|
| **7A** | Century bike rides | Plan | Map |
| **7B** | Kites | Build | Kite and instruction manual |
| **7C** | Triangles | Make | Scrapbook |
| **7D** | Textile design | Design | Sketch for fabric design with templates |

## Selecting a Project

Introduce each project option with the students. Sharing the resource masters with students might help them choose.

## During the Project

**Pacing** Projects will be completed over a number of lessons. The amount of time students spend on each project will vary. You may wish to let early finishers choose an additional project.

**Grouping** You might have students work independently, with a partner, or in small groups.

**Content** Projects are related to the content of this topic. As students continue their work on projects throughout the topic, new math ideas should be incorporated.

**Project Sharing** Invite students to share their completed projects with a partner, a small group, or with the whole class. Encourage students to discuss how they demonstrated math practices during the project. Provide students an opportunity for reflection by asking what interesting information they learned and what math they used in the project.

**Extensions** Extension suggestions are included for each project.

**Look For** Did students achieve the goal of the project? Did they apply math correctly in the project?

Go Online

Worksheets

## Project 7A 8.G.B.8

**Materials** grid paper

**Guidelines** Students should wait until after learning about finding distances in the coordinate plane to map out their routes on a coordinate grid.

**Extension** Ask students to shorten the bike route to half the distance. Have them review the route and stops. Ask them what they would need to change. Have students write a paragraph describing the new bike route.

## Project 7B 8.G.A.2, 8.G.B.7

**Materials** wooden dowels or plastic rods, arts and crafts supplies

**Guidelines** Students will be able to work on their kites and do calculations after each lesson.

**Extension** Ask students to suppose that the perimeter of the kite doubles. Ask them to write a paragraph describing how much material would now be needed and whether the same-length crossbars would work to support the new kite.

## Project 7C 8.G.B.6, 8.G.B.7

**Materials** camera (optional)

**Guidelines** Students can update their scrapbooks after each lesson.

**Extension** Ask students to review the triangles that were not right triangles. Have them think about how many side lengths would need to change for each triangle to become a right triangle. Ask students to write a paragraph describing this in detail and show all calculations.

## Project 7D 8.G.A.2, 8.G.B.7

**Materials** construction paper, poster board

**Guidelines** Students can update their templates and models after each lesson.

**Extension** Ask students to think about how to make a quilt from the fabric they designed. How would they modify the design so that the pattern repeats in a square or triangular format? Show how the pieces would fit together.

# Scoring Guide

Provide a scoring rubric to students as they begin work on the project.

For students who score Below Expectations for any criteria, review the rubric score with them in detail. Encourage them to update their project, or select a different project, to demonstrate their understanding of the mathematics in this topic.

**Available Online**

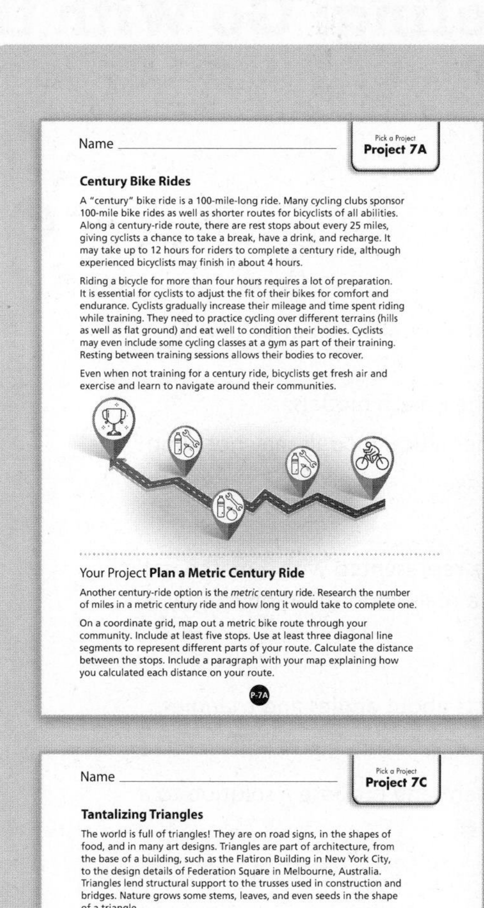

Name ______________

Pick a Project
Project 7A

**Century Bike Rides**

A "century" bike ride is a 100-mile-long ride. Many cycling clubs sponsor 100-mile bike rides as well as shorter routes for bicyclists of all abilities. Along a century-ride route, there are rest stops about every 25 miles, giving cyclists a chance to take a break, have a drink, and recharge. It may take up to 12 hours for riders to complete a century ride, although experienced bicyclists may finish in about 4 hours.

Riding a bicycle for more than four hours requires a lot of preparation. It is essential for cyclists to adjust the fit of their bikes for comfort and endurance. Cyclists gradually increase their mileage and time spent riding while training. They need to practice cycling over different terrains (hills as well as flat ground) and eat well to condition their bodies. Cyclists may even include some cycling classes at a gym as part of their training. Resting between training sessions allows their bodies to recover.

Even when not training for a century ride, bicyclists get fresh air and exercise and learn to navigate around their communities.

Your Project **Plan a Metric Century Ride**

Another century-ride option is the *metric* century ride. Research the number of miles in a metric century ride and how long it would take to complete one.

On a coordinate grid, map out a metric bike route through your community. Include at least five stops. Use at least three diagonal line segments to represent different parts of your route. Calculate the distance between the stops. Include a paragraph with your map explaining how you calculated each distance on your route.

P-7A

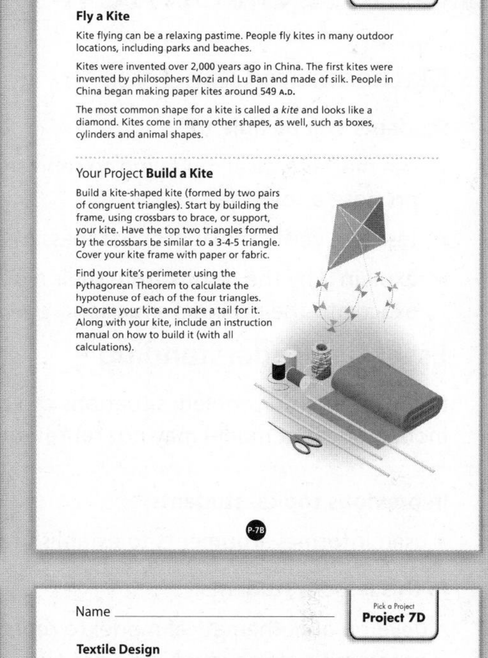

Name ______________

Pick a Project
Project 7B

**Fly a Kite**

Kite flying can be a relaxing pastime. People fly kites in many outdoor locations, including parks and beaches.

Kites were invented over 2,000 years ago in China. The first kites were invented by philosophers Mozi and Lu Ban and made of silk. People in China began making paper kites around 549 A.D.

The most common shape for a kite is called a *kite* and looks like a diamond. Kites come in many other shapes, as well, such as boxes, cylinders and animal shapes.

Your Project **Build a Kite**

Build a kite-shaped kite (formed by two pairs of congruent triangles). Start by building the frame, using crossbars to brace, or support, your kite. Have the top two triangles formed by the crossbars be similar to a 3-4-5 triangle. Cover your kite frame with paper or fabric.

Find your kite's perimeter using the Pythagorean Theorem to calculate the hypotenuse of each of the four triangles. Decorate your kite and make a tail for it. Along with your kite, include an instruction manual on how to build it (with all calculations).

P-7B

Name ______________

Pick a Project
Project 7C

**Tantalizing Triangles**

The world is full of triangles! They are on road signs, in the shapes of food, and in many art designs. Triangles are part of architecture, from the base of a building, such as the Flatiron Building in New York City, to the design details of Federation Square in Melbourne, Australia. Triangles lend structural support to the trusses used in construction and bridges. Nature grows some stems, leaves, and even seeds in the shape of a triangle.

Your Project **Make a Scrapbook**

Make a scrapbook of triangular shapes in the real world. Begin by finding at least six real-world triangles. Take pictures of the triangular shapes for your scrapbook or download pictures of the shapes from the Internet.

Find the dimensions of each triangle. Use the Pythagorean Theorem and the Converse of the Pythagorean Theorem to determine whether or not any of the triangles are right triangles. Each photo should include a description; details about the triangle, including lengths and angles; and your calculations. Include at least two triangles that appear to be right triangles but are not.

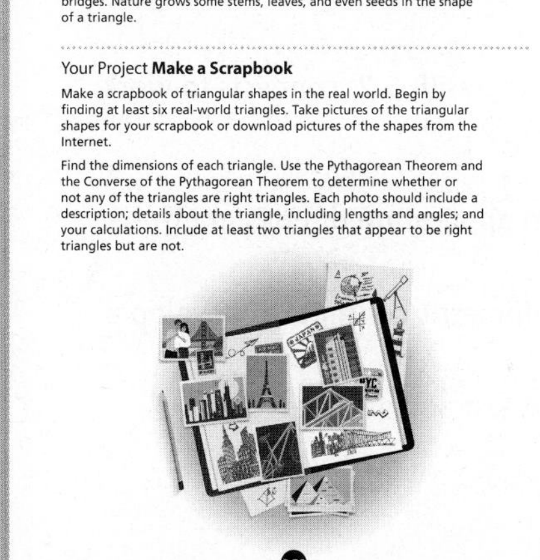

P-7C

Name ______________

Pick a Project
Project 7D

**Textile Design**

From clothing to curtains to car-seat covers, fabric (or cloth) is a part of everyday life. Some fabrics are designed specifically for warmth. Others are designed for comfort or fashion. Fabrics may be knitted or woven, hand-painted or printed. *Textile* is another word for fabric. Cotton, wool, silk, and linen are all textiles.

Textile designers are responsible for creating interesting and unique designs for fabrics. A design might include a pattern that repeats across the fabric. A designer sometimes makes a template for the pattern, making sure that the design is offset correctly to make a larger pattern across the width of the fabric.

Your Project **Design a Fabric Template**

Think about how fabric and clothing are used to showcase your culture. Design some templates for a geometric fabric pattern using at least five different sizes and types of right triangles. Decide how to move and repeat at least one of your templates across fabric to make a larger design. Plan to cover a piece of fabric that is 45 inches wide by 20 inches long. Use the Pythagorean Theorem to calculate the lengths of the legs and hypotenuses of your right triangles.

Pass in your templates and final fabric design model to your teacher. Include all the calculations you did to ensure that the piece of fabric is filled with your templated design.

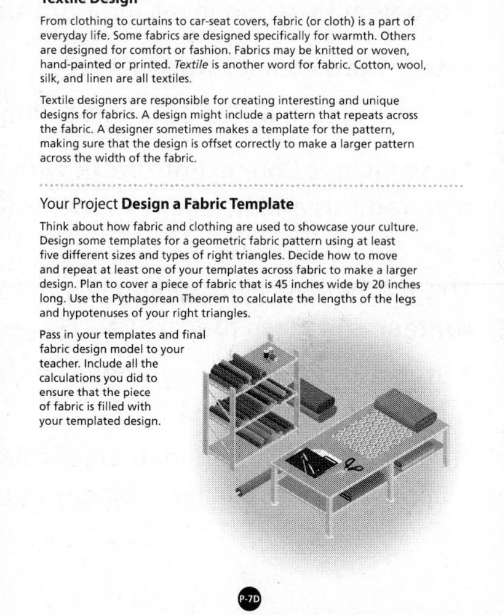

P-7D

**Sample Scoring Rubric**

| Below Expectations (0–1 point: Explain.) | Meets Goal (2 points) | Above Expectations (3–4 points: Explain.) |
|---|---|---|
| | **Mathematics:** The project accurately demonstrates understanding of a key mathematical concept from the topic. | |
| | **Context:** The mathematics from the topic connects to the project context in a logical and natural way. | |
| | **Presentation:** The directions and guidelines were accurately followed. | |

# 3-ACT MATH

# 3-Act Mathematical Modeling: Go With the Flow

Go Online

Video Activity

## Lesson Overview

FOCUS

### Mathematics Objectives

**Students will be able to:**

- ✔ use mathematical modeling to represent a problem situation and to propose a solution.
- ✔ test and verify the appropriateness of their math models.
- ✔ explain why the results from their mathematical models may not align exactly to the problem situation.

### Essential Understanding

Many real-world problem situations can be represented with a mathematical model, but that model may not represent a real-world situation exactly.

COHERENCE

**In previous topics, students:**

- used informal arguments to establish facts about angles and triangles.

**In this lesson, students:**

- develop a mathematical model to represent and propose a solution to a problem situation involving right triangles.

**Later in this course, students will:**

- refine their mathematical modeling skills.

**Cross-Cluster Connection** Work with right triangles (8.G.2) connects to work with radicals and integer exponents (8.EE.1).

RIGOR

This mathematical modeling lesson focuses on **application** of both **math content** and **math practices and processes**.

- Students draw on their understanding of geometric concepts to develop a representative model.
- Students apply their mathematical model to test and validate its applicability to similar problem situations.

## Math Anytime

### Today's Challenge

Use the Topic 7 problems any time during this topic.

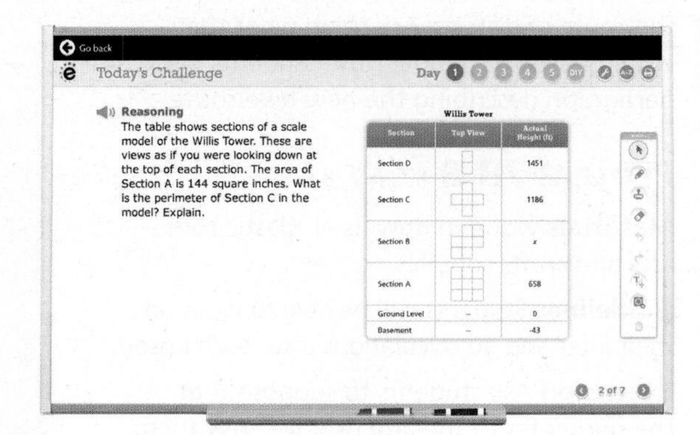


## Mathematics Overview — Common Core Standards

### Content Standards

In this lesson, students apply concepts and skills related to Common Core Standard **8.G.B.6**.

- **8.G.B.6** Explain a proof of the Pythagorean Theorem and its converse.

### Mathematical Practice Standards

**MP.4 Model with Mathematics**

The focus of this lesson is on mathematical modeling. Students identify the relationship among variables, develop a model that represents the situation, and use the model to propose a solution. Students interpret their solutions and propose explanations for why their answers may not match the real-world answer.

As students carry out mathematical modeling, they will also engage in sense-making **(MP.1)**, abstract and quantitative reasoning **(MP.2)**, and mathematical communication and argumentation **(MP.3)**. In testing and validating their models, students look for patterns and structure **(MP.7, MP.8)**.

Go Online

Video

# 3-Act Mathematical Modeling

## ACT 1 The Hook 

**3-Act Math Video** is available online.

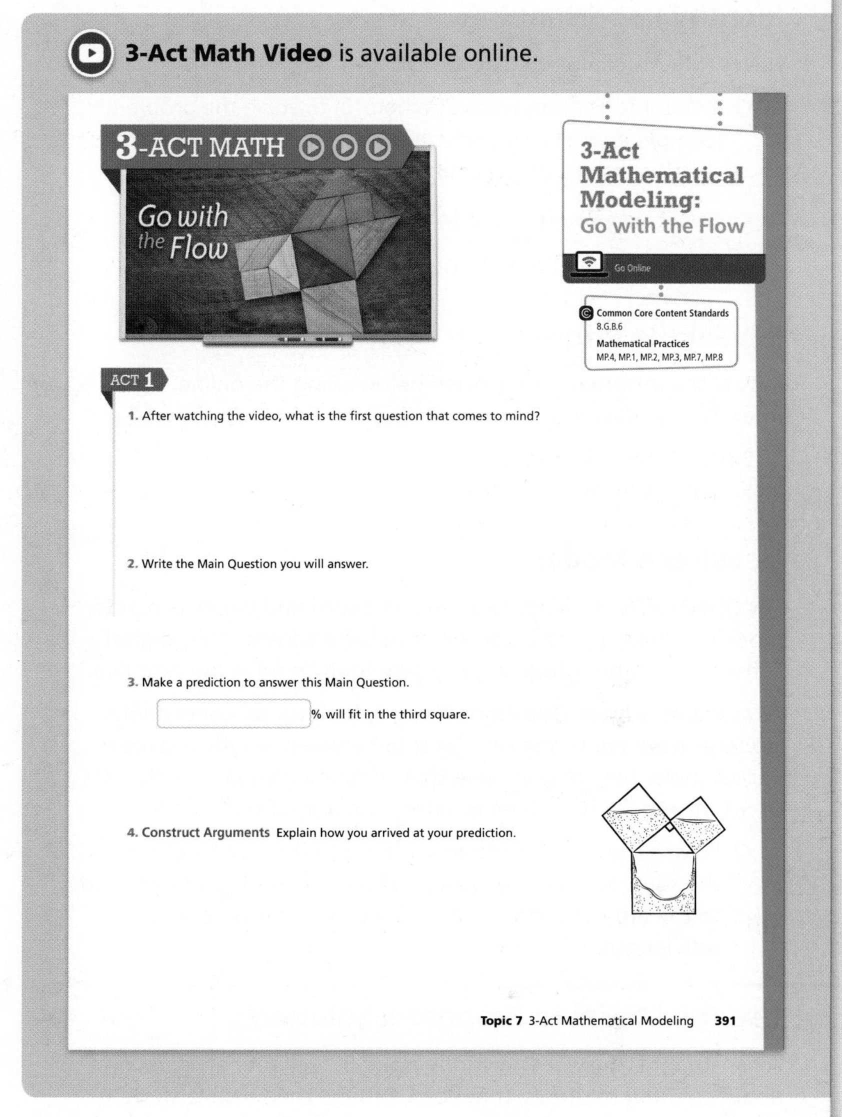

3-ACT MATH

Go with the Flow

3-Act Mathematical Modeling:
Go with the Flow

Go Online

Common Core Content Standards
8.G.B.6

Mathematical Practices
MP.4, MP.1, MP.2, MP.3, MP.7, MP.8

ACT 1

1. After watching the video, what is the first question that comes to mind?

2. Write the Main Question you will answer.

3. Make a prediction to answer this Main Question.

______% will fit in the third square.

4. **Construct Arguments** Explain how you arrived at your prediction.

Topic 7 3-Act Mathematical Modeling 391

Students will be tasked with deciding how much of the sand in the smaller boxes will fit in the large box.

### Play the Video and Brainstorm Questions

Have students complete **Question 1**. Encourage them to consider the situation and ask any questions that arise. Listen for interesting mathematical and non-mathematical questions. Ask students what makes each question interesting.

**Q:** What questions do you have? [Sample questions: How fast is the sand flowing? How long will it take? How big are the squares?]

### Pose the Main Question

After the question brainstorming, pose the Main Question students will be tasked with answering. Have students complete **Question 2**.

**Main Question**

**Q:** Will the sand fit in the large square?

### Ask about Predictions

Have students complete **Questions 3 and 4**. This problem can be difficult to predict an answer from the visual alone. Look for students to make intuitive, informal arguments at this point.

You can survey the class for the range of predictions.

**Q:** Why do you think your prediction is the answer to the Main Question?

**Q:** Who had a similar prediction?

**Q:** How many of you agree with that prediction?

**Q:** Who has a different prediction?

Go Online

Activity

## ACT 2 The Model 

### Identify Important Info

Have students complete **Question 5**.

**Q:** What information would be helpful to solve the problem? [Sample answers: How much sand is in each square; What the dimensions of the squares are]

**Q:** How could you get that information?

**Q:** Why do you need that information?

### Reveal the Information

Reveal the information provided below using the online interactivity. Have students record information in **Question 5**.

Sides of the triangle:
5.1 in., 6.8 in., 8.5 in.

### Develop a Model

For **Question 6**, students might select pencil and paper, concrete models, a ruler, a protractor, a calculator, a spreadsheet, digital software, or other grade-appropriate tools to solve the problem.

As students answer **Questions 7 and 8**, look for misconceptions students have about the relationship between length and area. For example, they may assume that combining squares with sides of 5.1 in. and 6.8 in. will be greater than a square of side 8.5 in.

**Q:** How is the amount of sand related to the side length of the square? [Sample answer: The amount of sand is related to the area of the square, and area is the square of the side length.]

### Use the Model to Propose a Solution

After students answer **Questions 7 and 8**, facilitate a discussion about solution methods. If needed, project the possible student solutions (shown below).

**3-Act Math Activity** is available online.

ACT 2

5. What information in this situation would be helpful to know? How would you use that information?

6. **Use Appropriate Tools** What tools can you use to solve the problem? Explain how you would use them strategically.

7. **Model With Math** Represent the situation using mathematics. Use your representation to answer the Main Question.

8. What is your answer to the Main Question? Does it differ from your prediction? Explain.

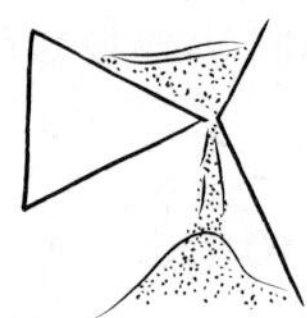

392 **Topic 7** 3-Act Mathematical Modeling

### Possible Student Solutions

**Simone's Work**

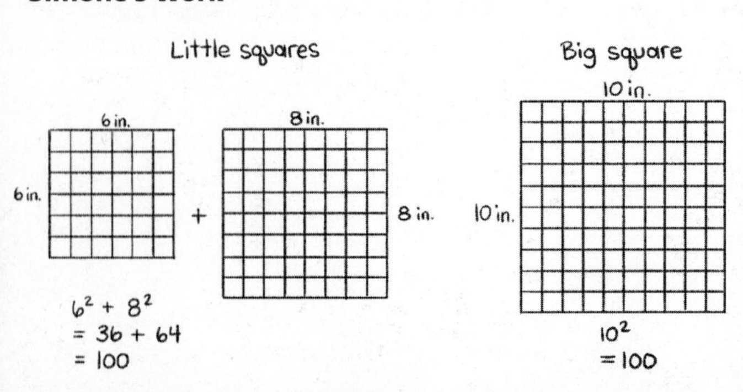


**Simone** compares the area of the two smaller squares to the area of the largest square. She uses 1-square-inch grids to compare the number of square inches.

**Kurt's Work**

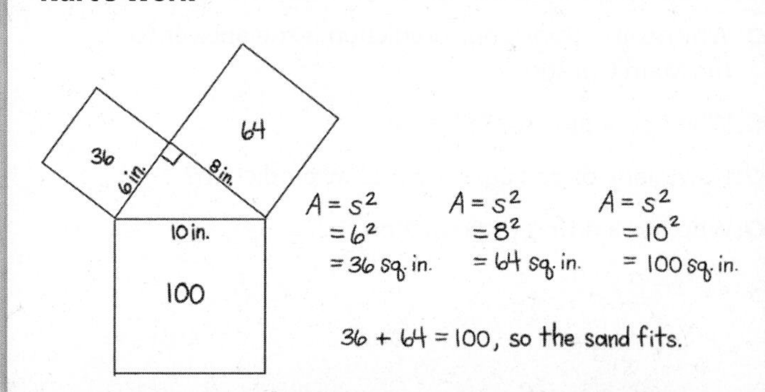


**Kurt** uses the formula for the area of a square three times. He draws and labels a diagram to compare the areas.

Go Online

Video

# ACT 3 The Solution and Sequel 

**3-Act Math Video** is available online.

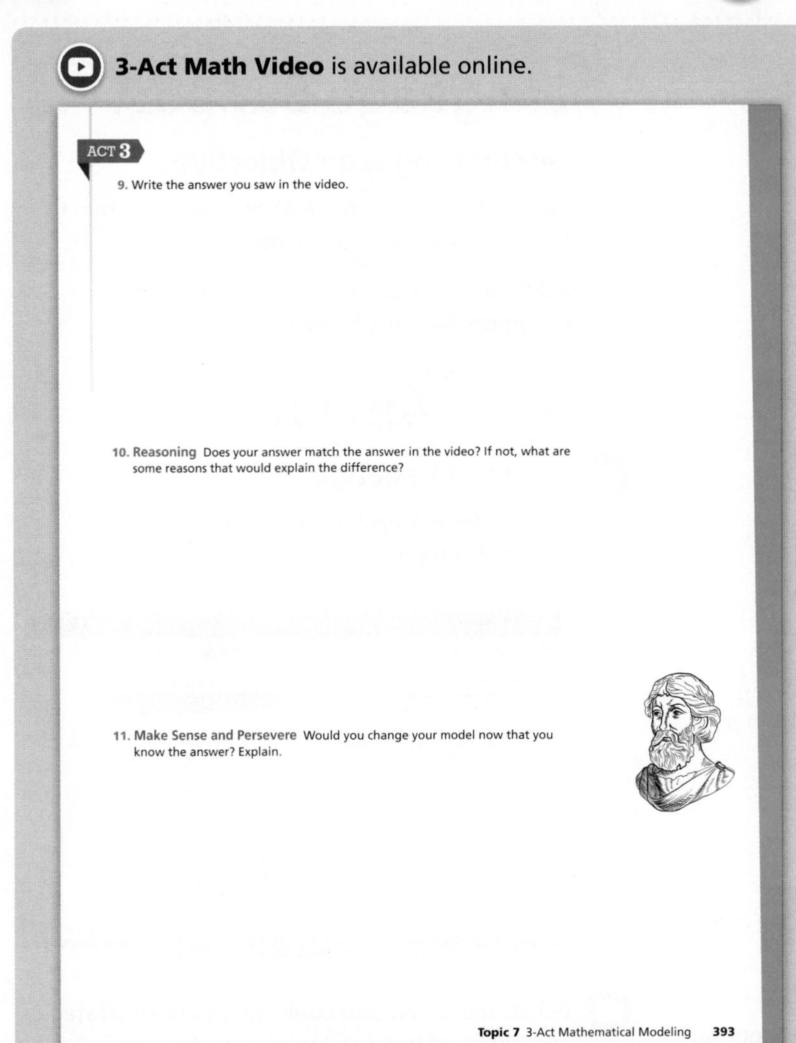

ACT 3

9. Write the answer you saw in the video.

10. Reasoning Does your answer match the answer in the video? If not, what are some reasons that would explain the difference?

11. Make Sense and Persevere Would you change your model now that you know the answer? Explain.

Topic 7 3-Act Mathematical Modeling 393

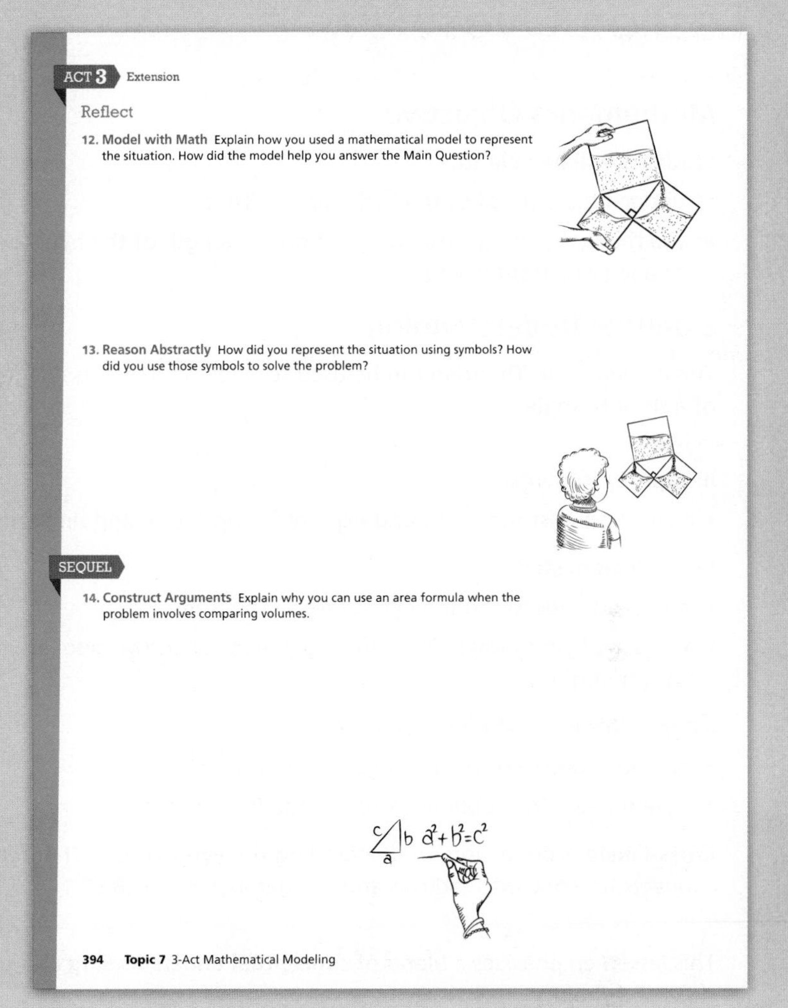

ACT 3 Extension

Reflect

12. Model with Math Explain how you used a mathematical model to represent the situation. How did the model help you answer the Main Question?

13. Reason Abstractly How did you represent the situation using symbols? How did you use those symbols to solve the problem?

SEQUEL

14. Construct Arguments Explain why you can use an area formula when the problem involves comparing volumes.



394 Topic 7 3-Act Mathematical Modeling

## Use the Video to Reveal the Answer

The final part of the video shows the entire process of pouring the sand into the large square. Have students complete **Question 9**. Congratulate the students who were closest to the actual answer.

### Main Question Answer

**The sand fits almost exactly in the large square.**

## Validate Conclusions

After students complete **Questions 10 and 11**, encourage them to discuss possible sources of error inherent in using math to model real-world situations. Look for students to point out that their models are still useful even though they are not perfect.

**Q:** Why does your answer not match the answer in the video? [Sample answers: The squares may not be exact squares. The depth of each square may not be the same; I only considered the area of the bottom.]

**Q:** How useful was your model at predicting the answer?

**Q:** How could your model better represent the situation?

## Reflect on Thinking

**Reason Abstractly** If time allows, have students complete **Questions 12 and 13** as an extension. Use this opportunity to discuss how students incorporate mathematical processes during the task.

## Pose the Sequel

**Construct Arguments** Use **Question 14** to present a similar problem situation involving the relationship between the area of the base of a prism and its volume. You can assign to early finishers or as homework so students can test the usefulness of their models.

**Q:** Explain why you can use an area formula when the problem involves comparing volumes.

Look for students to mention that they are comparing volumes, not finding volumes. If all three prisms have the same height, then they only need to use the areas of the bases.

Lesson **7-1**

# Understand the Pythagorean Theorem

## Lesson Overview

**FOCUS**

### Mathematics Objective

**Students will be able to:**

✔ understand a proof of the Pythagorean Theorem.

✔ use the Pythagorean Theorem to find the length of the hypotenuse or a leg of a right triangle.

### Essential Understanding

The Pythagorean Theorem can be used to find an unknown side length of a right triangle.

**COHERENCE**

**In Topic 6, students:**

- analyzed transformations and explored congruence and similarity.

**In this lesson, students:**

- learn and understand the Pythagorean Theorem.
- apply the Pythagorean Theorem to solve for unknown side lengths in a right triangle.

**Later in this topic, students will:**

- use the converse of the Pythagorean Theorem.
- solve real-world problems involving the Pythagorean Theorem.

**Cross-Cluster Connection** Understanding the Pythagorean Theorem (8.G.2) connects to work with radicals and integer exponents (8.EE.1).

**RIGOR**

This lesson emphasizes a blend of **conceptual understanding** and **procedural skills and fluency**.

- Students construct a logical argument to derive a proof of the Pythagorean Theorem.
- Students apply their understanding of the Pythagorean Theorem, $a^2 + b^2 = c^2$, to calculate a missing side length or hypotenuse of a right triangle.

## Language Support

### Lesson Language Objective

Explain how to use the Pythagorean Theorem to find unknown sides of triangles.

Additional resources are available in the **Language Support Handbook**.

## Math Anytime

### Today's Challenge

Use the Topic 7 problems any time during this topic.

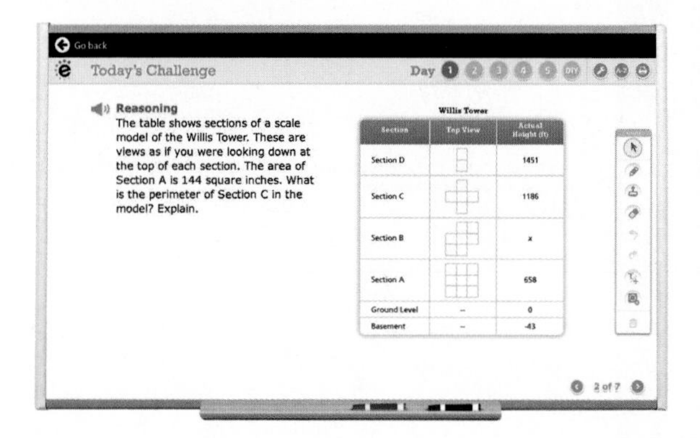

Watch the **Listen and Look For Video** for strategies and habits of mind to look for as students complete work on this lesson.

## Mathematics Overview | Common Core Standards

### Content Standards

In this lesson, you will focus on **8.G.B.6** and **8.G.B.7**.

- **8.G.B.6** Explain a proof of the Pythagorean Theorem and its converse.
- **8.G.B.7** Apply the Pythagorean Theorem to determine unknown side lengths in right triangles in real-world and mathematical problems in two and three dimensions.

### Mathematical Practice Standards

**MP.3 Construct Viable Arguments and Critique the Reasoning of Others**
Students understand and can explain a proof of the Pythagorean Theorem.

**MP.7 Look for and Make Use of Structure**
Students discover how the Pythagorean Theorem can be used to solve for different right triangle side lengths.

STEP 1 | Problem-Based Learning

15-20 min

Go Online

Activity

# Explain It!

**Purpose** Students explore the relationship between the sides of a right triangle to prove the Pythagorean Theorem in the Visual Learning Bridge.

## ETP Before — WHOLE CLASS

### 1 Introduce the Problem

Provide rulers and grid paper, as needed.

### 2 Check for Understanding of the Problem

Activate prior knowledge by asking: What do you know about right triangles?

## ETP During — SMALL GROUP

### 3 Observe Students at Work

Observe students while they work, noting the strategies that students use to explain their conclusions. Students may draw their own right triangles and squares and check if the rule applies by finding the area of the squares. Encourage students to use grid paper to ensure that the triangles they draw are right angle triangles. If needed, ask How can you calculate the area of a square?

### Early Finishers

If the lengths of the legs of the right triangle are doubled, what is the area of the square of the hypotenuse? Explain. [Sample answer: The new side lengths would be $2a$ and $2b$. The area of the largest square would be $4a^2 + 4b^2 = 4(a^2 + b^2) = 4c^2$.]

## ETP After — WHOLE CLASS

### 4 Discuss Solution Strategies and Key Ideas

Have students present their conclusions about Kelly's theory. Students may conclude that because the hypotenuse is the longest side, a square that has the hypotenuse as a side will have the greatest area. They might then reason that the area of the largest square is equal to the sum of the area of the smaller squares. Other students may draw different examples of right triangles and squares to show that they followed Kelly's conjecture.

Have students discuss what expressions represent the areas of the three squares and what equation they could write to relate them: the area of the square with side $a$ is $a^2$, the area of the square with side $b$ is $b^2$, the area of the square with side $c$ is $c^2$, and the equation that relates them is $a^2 + b^2 = c^2$.

### 5 Consider Instructional Implications

When presenting Example 1, connect the diagrams in the proof of the Pythagorean Theorem to the diagrams students drew of the right triangles and squares in the Explain It. Point out how the square with side length $c$ now has a right triangle on each side and how the diagram itself forms a new square with side length $a + b$.

## Analyze Student Work

**Explain It!** Activity is available online.

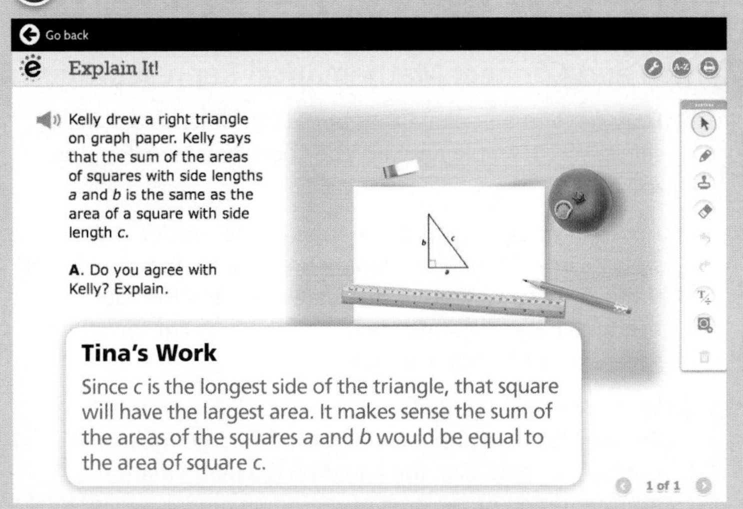


**Tina** understands that the square for the longest side has the largest area and that it is equal to the sum of the areas of the two smaller squares.

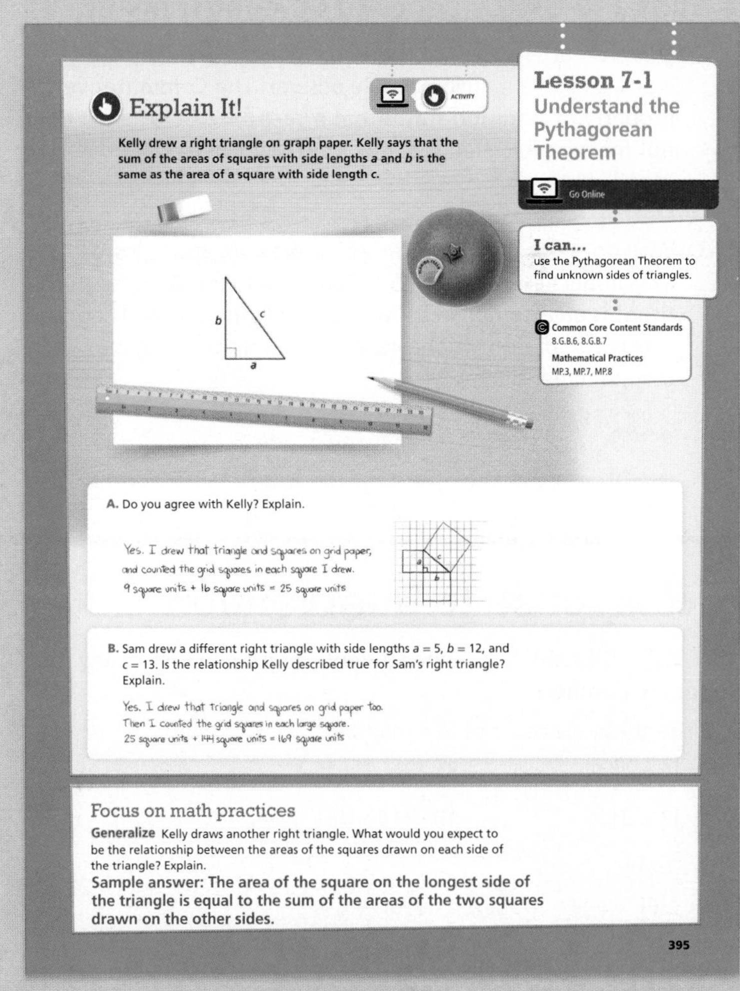


**Matt** calculates the answer and realizes that the sum of the areas of the two small squares is equal to the area of the largest square.

# STEP 2 | Visual Learning

Go Online

## ETP Establish Mathematics Goals to Focus Learning

Engage students in a discussion about the ***Essential Question***. Make sure they understand the Pythagorean Theorem and how it relates the side lengths of a right triangle.

## EXAMPLE 1 Understand the Pythagorean Theorem

### ETP Use and Connect Mathematical Representations

**Q:** How can you be certain that both large squares are the same size? [Sample answer: They both have side lengths $a + b$.]

**Q:** How can you justify that the areas of the smaller white squares inside the larger square are equal? [Sample answer: If the large squares have the same area, and the four triangles have the same area, then the areas of the white squares must be equal in size.]

**Q:** What does the equation in the last section represent? Explain. [Sample answer: Because both large squares are exactly the same size, the equation is a mathematical representation of the area of these two models set as equal.]

## Try It!

Formative Assessment

### ETP Elicit and Use Evidence of Student Thinking

**Q:** Does it matter which of the two leg lengths you assign to $a$ and $b$? Explain. [No; Sample answer: The Commutative Property of Addition states that $a^2 + b^2 = b^2 + a^2$, so it does not matter which leg is $a$ and which is $b$.]

### Convince Me!

**Q:** Why does the proof use variables like $a$, $b$, and $c$, instead of numbers like 3, 4, and 5? [Sample answer: Because the proof is an attempt to show that the Pythagorean Theorem is true for *all* right triangles, not just a right triangle of certain dimensions.]

**Visual Learning Animation Plus** is available online.

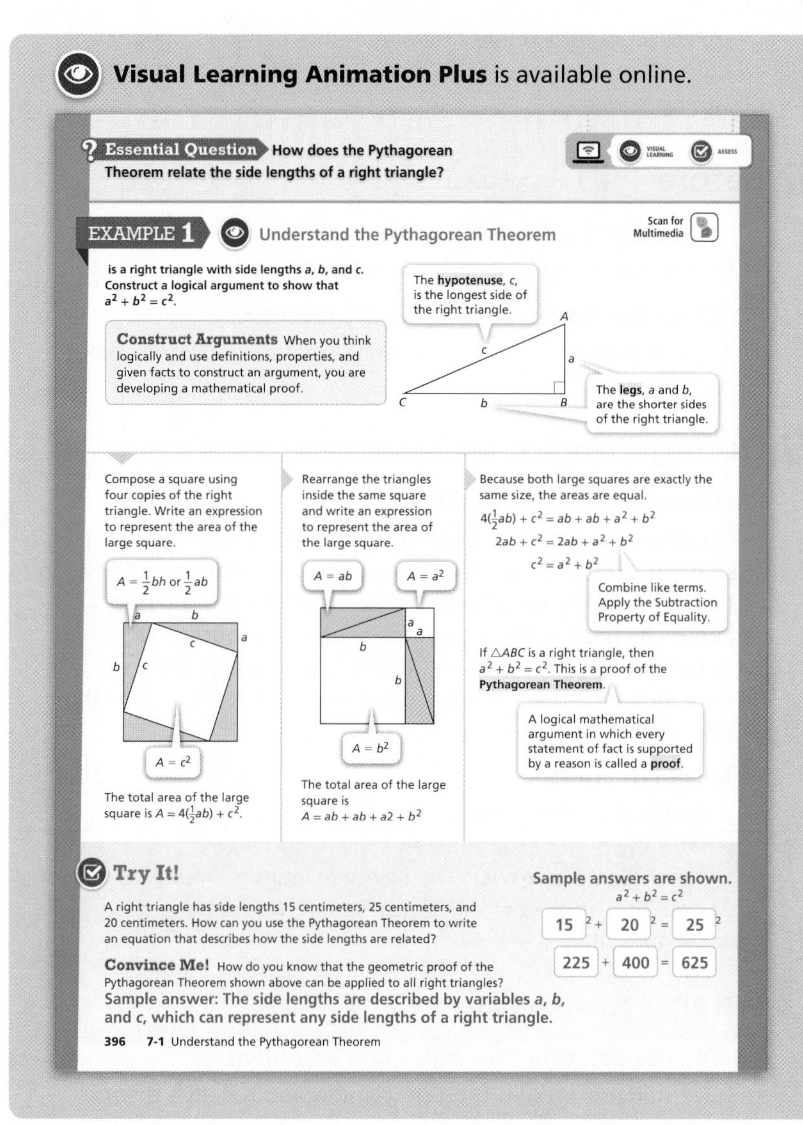

Essential Question How does the Pythagorean Theorem relate the side lengths of a right triangle?

EXAMPLE 1 Understand the Pythagorean Theorem

Scan for Multimedia

$\triangle ABC$ is a right triangle with side lengths $a$, $b$, and $c$. Construct a logical argument to show that $a^2 + b^2 = c^2$.

**Construct Arguments** When you think logically and use definitions, properties, and given facts to construct an argument, you are developing a mathematical proof.



Compose a square using four copies of the right triangle. Write an expression to represent the area of the large square.



The total area of the large square is $A = 4(\frac{1}{2}ab) + c^2$.

Rearrange the triangles inside the same square and write an expression to represent the area of the large square.



The total area of the large square is $A = ab + ab + a2 + b^2$

Because both large squares are exactly the same size, the areas are equal.

$4(\frac{1}{2}ab) + c^2 = ab + ab + a^2 + b^2$

$2ab + c^2 = 2ab + a^2 + b^2$

$c^2 = a^2 + b^2$

Combine like terms. Apply the Subtraction Property of Equality.

If $\triangle ABC$ is a right triangle, then $a^2 + b^2 = c^2$. This is a proof of the **Pythagorean Theorem**.

A logical mathematical argument in which every statement of fact is supported by a reason is called a **proof**.

Try It! Sample answers are shown.

A right triangle has side lengths 15 centimeters, 25 centimeters, and 20 centimeters. How can you use the Pythagorean Theorem to write an equation that describes how the side lengths are related?

$a^2 + b^2 = c^2$

$15^2 + 20^2 = 25^2$

$225 + 400 = 625$

**Convince Me!** How do you know that the geometric proof of the Pythagorean Theorem shown above can be applied to all right triangles?
Sample answer: The side lengths are described by variables $a$, $b$, and $c$, which can represent any side lengths of a right triangle.

396 7-1 Understand the Pythagorean Theorem

Students can access the ***Visual Learning Animation Plus*** by using the **BouncePages app** to scan this page. Students can download the app for free in their mobile devices' app store.

## Response to Intervention

**USE WITH EXAMPLE 2** Some students might need to review how to square numbers.

- Write these expressions in expanded form.

| | |
|---|---|
| $4^2$ [$4 \times 4$] | $3^2$ [$3 \times 3$] |
| $7^2$ [$7 \times 7$] | $16^2$ [$16 \times 16$] |

- Evaluate.

| | |
|---|---|
| $6^2$ [36] | $4^2$ [16] |
| $5^2$ [25] | $10^2$ [100] |

## Enrichment

**USE WITH EXAMPLE 1** Challenge students to extend their knowledge of the Pythagorean Theorem.

- Think about a specific right triangle.

**Q:** The hypotenuse of a right triangle is 4 inches long and its legs are equal in length. Using the Pythagorean Theorem, write an equation that represents the relationship between the sides of this right triangle using only two variables. [Sample answers: $2a^2 = c^2$; $2b^2 = c^2$]

**Q:** Solve for the lengths of the legs of this right triangle. [$\sqrt{8}$ or $2\sqrt{2}$ in.]

**Q:** What specific type of right triangle has two legs with equal lengths? [Isosceles right triangle]

Go Online

Activity Assess

## EXAMPLE 2  Use the Pythagorean Theorem to Find the Length of the Hypotenuse

### ETP Pose Purposeful Questions

**Q:** Why is it possible to solve this problem using the Pythagorean Theorem? [Sample answer: Because the triangle is a right triangle and two side lengths are given]

**Q:** Would the Pythagorean Theorem still apply if one or more of the three side lengths were not a whole number? Explain. [Yes; Sample answer: A right triangle with leg lengths that measure 3 inches and 5 inches has a hypotenuse that measures $\sqrt{34}$ inches.]

## EXAMPLE 3  Use the Pythagorean Theorem to Find the Length of a Leg

### ETP Pose Purposeful Questions

**Q:** How do you know where to substitute the value 29 in the equation? [Sample answer: In the diagram of the right triangle, the measurement of 29 inches is opposite from the right angle, so it must be the hypotenuse rather than a leg. The measure 29 inches corresponds to *c*.]

**Q:** What Property of Equality do you use in the fourth step when isolating $b^2$? [Subtraction Property of Equality]

##  Try It!  Formative Assessment

### ETP Elicit and Use Evidence of Student Thinking

**Q:** What is one way to determine which of the legs is the longer leg? [Sample answer: $18^2 = 324$, so you can think of 18 as $\sqrt{324}$. Since $\sqrt{324} < \sqrt{700}$, the leg that measures $\sqrt{700}$ is the longer leg.]

**Examples and Try Its!** are available online.

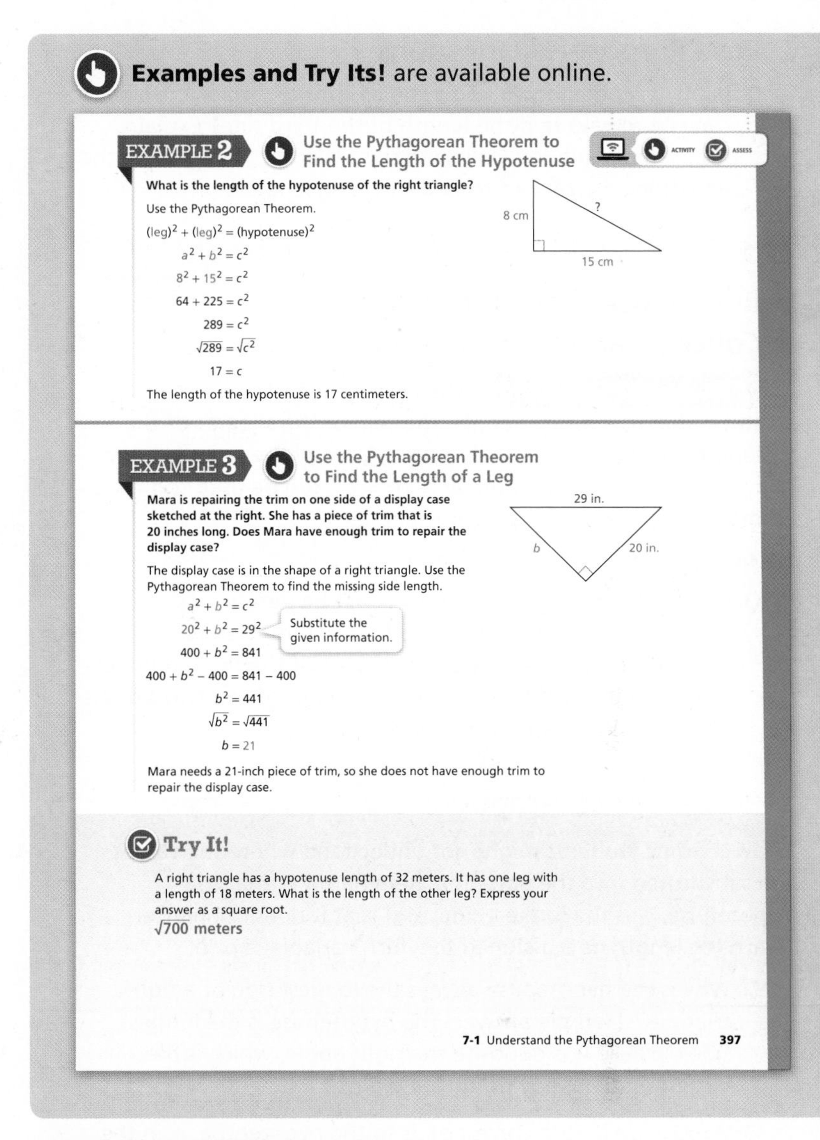

EXAMPLE 2 Use the Pythagorean Theorem to Find the Length of the Hypotenuse

**What is the length of the hypotenuse of the right triangle?**

Use the Pythagorean Theorem.

$(\text{leg})^2 + (\text{leg})^2 = (\text{hypotenuse})^2$

$a^2 + b^2 = c^2$

$8^2 + 15^2 = c^2$

$64 + 225 = c^2$

$289 = c^2$

$\sqrt{289} = \sqrt{c^2}$

$17 = c$

The length of the hypotenuse is 17 centimeters.



EXAMPLE 3 Use the Pythagorean Theorem to Find the Length of a Leg

**Mara is repairing the trim on one side of a display case sketched at the right. She has a piece of trim that is 20 inches long. Does Mara have enough trim to repair the display case?**

The display case is in the shape of a right triangle. Use the Pythagorean Theorem to find the missing side length.

$a^2 + b^2 = c^2$

$20^2 + b^2 = 29^2$ — Substitute the given information.

$400 + b^2 = 841$

$400 + b^2 - 400 = 841 - 400$

$b^2 = 441$

$\sqrt{b^2} = \sqrt{441}$

$b = 21$

Mara needs a 21-inch piece of trim, so she does not have enough trim to repair the display case.



Try It!

A right triangle has a hypotenuse length of 32 meters. It has one leg with a length of 18 meters. What is the length of the other leg? Express your answer as a square root.

$\sqrt{700}$ meters

7-1 Understand the Pythagorean Theorem 397

ADDITIONAL EXAMPLES 

**For additional examples go online.**

## ELL English Language Learners

**ENTERING** Ask students to review Example 1.

**Q:** What is a *right triangle*? [A right triangle is a triangle that has an angle that measures 90°.]

**Q:** What word(s) describe the sides that form the right angle? [Sample answer: Perpendicular, adjacent]

Write $c^2$ on the board. Then erase the *c* and write 5. Say: *Substitute 5 for c.*

**Q:** What does *substitute* mean? [Sample answers: Change or replace]

**DEVELOPING** Ask students to read Example 3.

Have students work together to define the following words:

*repair trim display case enough*

Students should first practice saying the definitions to each other. Then volunteers can define the words for the group. When possible, encourage students to use each word in a sentence.

**EXPANDING** Ask students to read Example 3.

Ask students to explain in their own words how they know that there is not enough trim to repair the display case.

**Q:** In this problem, what is the meaning of *trim*? [Sample answer: *Trim* is an additional decoration that usually runs along the edges or sides of something.]

**Q:** How do you find *b* if you know the lengths of the other legs and the hypotenuse? [Sample answer: Substitute the given values of the other leg and the hypotenuse into the Pythagorean Theorem equation and solve.]

Go Online

Key Concept   Assess   Activity

## KEY CONCEPT

### ETP Pose Purposeful Questions

**Q:** In any triangle, if you know the lengths of two of the sides, can you always find the length of the third side? Explain. [No; Sample answer: Only with right triangles can you use the equation $a^2 + b^2 = c^2$ to find a missing length.]

## Do You Understand/Do You Know How?

**Formative** Assessment

### ETP Build Procedural Fluency from Conceptual Understanding

**Essential Question** The Pythagorean Theorem states that in a right triangle, the sum of the squares of the lengths of the legs is equal to the square of the length of the hypotenuse. This equation, $a^2 + b^2 = c^2$, can be used to find a missing side length of a right triangle.

**ITEM 2**

**Q:** Given any three numbers, how can it be determined whether they represent the sides of a right triangle? [Sample answer: Calculate the squares of the three numbers. Then determine if the sum of the squares of any two sides is equal to the square of the third side.]

### Prevent Misconceptions

**ITEM 3** Some students might not understand where the values are substituted into the equation. Remind them that the hypotenuse, $c$, is the longest side, and that it does not matter which leg length gets assigned to which variable, $a$ or $b$.

**Q:** Why is the hypotenuse always the longest side of a right triangle? [Sample answer: The hypotenuse is the longest side because it is opposite the right angle, which is the largest angle in any right triangle.]

**Q:** Which side length corresponds to the hypotenuse, $c$, in the equation for the Pythagorean Theorem?

3, 4, 5 [5]   6.25, 3.75, 5 [6.25]

**Available Online**

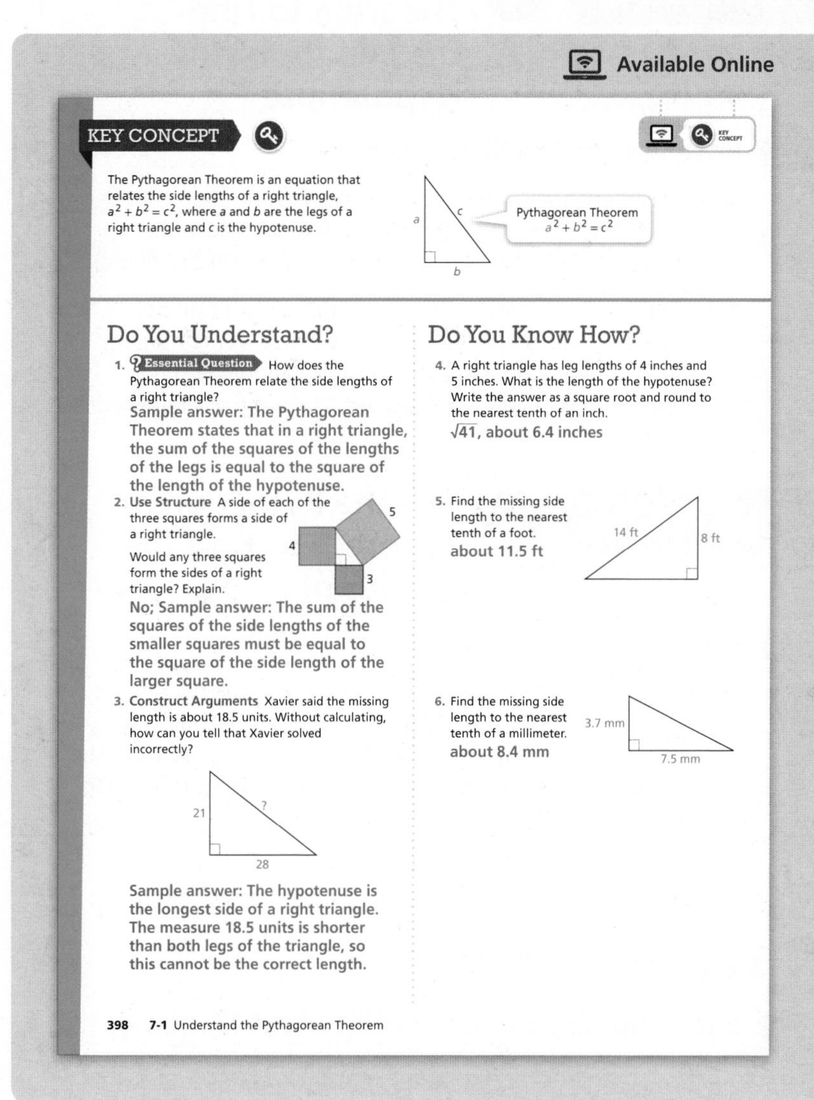

KEY CONCEPT

The Pythagorean Theorem is an equation that relates the side lengths of a right triangle, $a^2 + b^2 = c^2$, where $a$ and $b$ are the legs of a right triangle and $c$ is the hypotenuse.

Pythagorean Theorem $a^2 + b^2 = c^2$

**Do You Understand?**

1. **Essential Question** How does the Pythagorean Theorem relate the side lengths of a right triangle?
Sample answer: The Pythagorean Theorem states that in a right triangle, the sum of the squares of the lengths of the legs is equal to the square of the length of the hypotenuse.

2. **Use Structure** A side of each of the three squares forms a side of a right triangle.
Would any three squares form the sides of a right triangle? Explain.
No; Sample answer: The sum of the squares of the side lengths of the smaller squares must be equal to the square of the side length of the larger square.

3. **Construct Arguments** Xavier said the missing length is about 18.5 units. Without calculating, how can you tell that Xavier solved incorrectly?
Sample answer: The hypotenuse is the longest side of a right triangle. The measure 18.5 units is shorter than both legs of the triangle, so this cannot be the correct length.

**Do You Know How?**

4. A right triangle has leg lengths of 4 inches and 5 inches. What is the length of the hypotenuse? Write the answer as a square root and round to the nearest tenth of an inch.
$\sqrt{41}$, about 6.4 inches

5. Find the missing side length to the nearest tenth of a foot.
about 11.5 ft

6. Find the missing side length to the nearest tenth of a millimeter.
about 8.4 mm

398 7-1 Understand the Pythagorean Theorem

## ADDITIONAL EXAMPLE 1

Help students determine whether a set of side length measurements describes a right triangle.

**Q:** How do you know which side length is possibly the hypotenuse and which side lengths are possibly the legs? [Sample answer: The longest side length is the possible hypotenuse, and the other two side lengths are the possible legs.]

**Q:** How can you determine if three side lengths form a right triangle? [Sample answer: Substitute the side length values into the Pythagorean Theorem. If the side lengths make a true statement, the lengths make a right triangle.]

**Additional Examples** are available online.

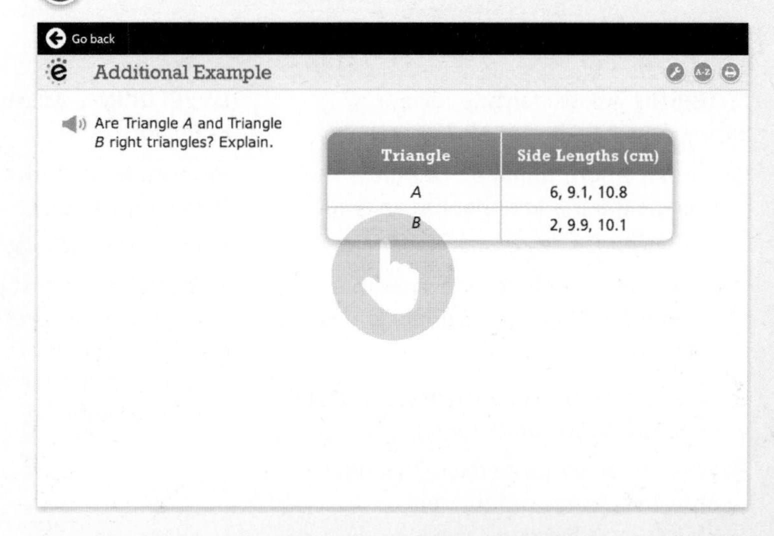

Go back

Additional Example

Are Triangle $A$ and Triangle $B$ right triangles? Explain.

| Triangle | Side Lengths (cm) |
|---|---|
| $A$ | 6, 9.1, 10.8 |
| $B$ | 2, 9.9, 10.1 |

**Answer:** Triangle A is not a right triangle. Triangle B is a right triangle.

Go Online

Practice | Tutorials | Math Tools

# Practice & Problem Solving  

**Interactive Practice** and **Virtual Nerd Tutorials** are available online.

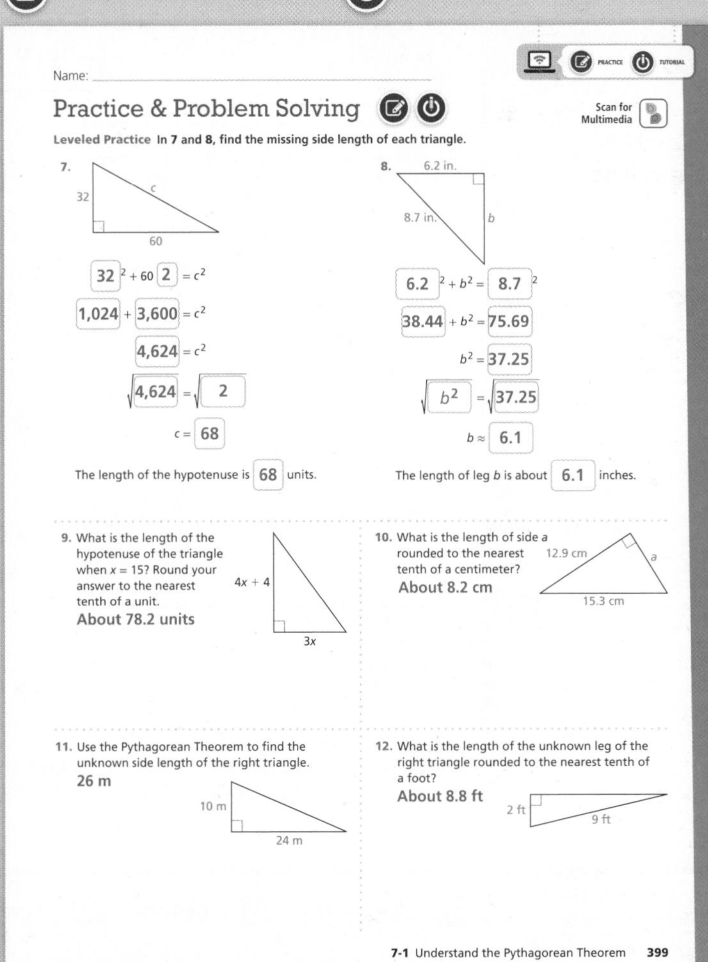

Name: ______

## Practice & Problem Solving

Scan for Multimedia

**Leveled Practice** In 7 and 8, find the missing side length of each triangle.

7. (triangle with legs 32 and 60, hypotenuse $c$)

$32^2 + 60^2 = c^2$

$1{,}024 + 3{,}600 = c^2$

$4{,}624 = c^2$

$\sqrt{4{,}624} = \sqrt{c^2}$

$c = 68$

The length of the hypotenuse is 68 units.

8. (triangle with leg 6.2 in., hypotenuse 8.7 in., leg $b$)

$6.2^2 + b^2 = 8.7^2$

$38.44 + b^2 = 75.69$

$b^2 = 37.25$

$\sqrt{b^2} = \sqrt{37.25}$

$b \approx 6.1$

The length of leg $b$ is about 6.1 inches.

9. What is the length of the hypotenuse of the triangle when $x = 15$? Round your answer to the nearest tenth of a unit.
About 78.2 units



10. What is the length of side $a$ rounded to the nearest tenth of a centimeter?
About 8.2 cm



11. Use the Pythagorean Theorem to find the unknown side length of the right triangle.
26 m



12. What is the length of the unknown leg of the right triangle rounded to the nearest tenth of a foot?
About 8.8 ft





13. A student is asked to find the length of the hypotenuse of a right triangle. The length of one leg is 32 centimeters, and the length of the other leg is 26 centimeters. The student incorrectly says that the length of the hypotenuse is 7.6 centimeters.

a. Find the length of the hypotenuse of the right triangle to the nearest tenth of a centimeter. About 41.2 cm

b. What mistake might the student have made?
Sample answer: She added the lengths of the legs and then took the square root of the sum instead of squaring each length first and then taking the square root of the sum.

14. Find the length of the unknown leg of the right triangle.
35 units

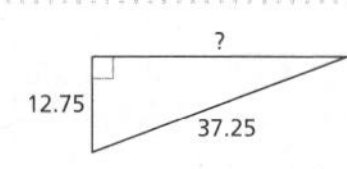


15. Higher Order Thinking A right triangle has side lengths 12 centimeters and 14 centimeters. Name two possible side lengths for the third side, and explain how you solved for each.
Sample answer: If these are the lengths of the legs of the triangle, then the length of the hypotenuse is about 18.4 centimeters long. If the hypotenuse is 14 centimeters, then the second leg is about 7.2 centimeters long. The side length 12 centimeters cannot be the hypotenuse because it is shorter than 14 centimeters.

### Assessment Practice

16. Which right triangle has a hypotenuse that is about 39 feet long?

17. Which right triangle does NOT have an unknown leg length of about 33 cm?

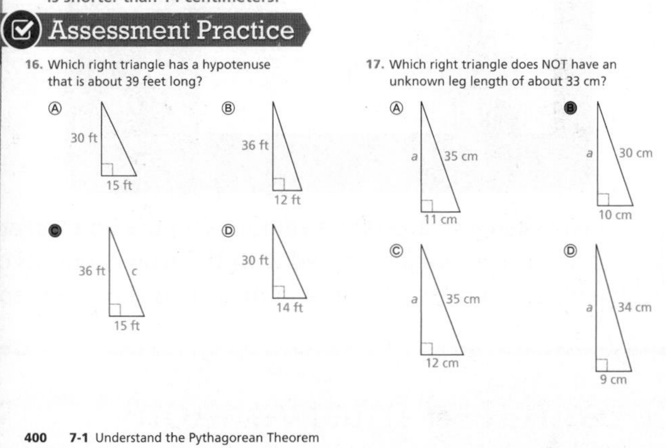




## English Language Learners

**ITEM 9** Work with a partner. Take turns explaining to each other the steps you would take to solve the problem.

**Q:** How do you find the *lengths* of each of the legs? Explain. [Sample answer: Substitute 15 for $x$ into each expression and simplify. $4x + 4 = 4(15) + 4 = 60 + 4 = 64$, and $3x = 3(15) = 45$. The lengths of the legs are 64 units and 45 units.]

**Q:** Why is the answer expressed in *units*? [This problem did not specify the unit of measure for the sides.]

## Challenge

**ITEM 9** Use this item to extend students' understanding of side lengths of right triangles.

**Q:** The lengths of the legs of a right triangle are $3x$ and $4x$. In terms of $x$, what is the length of the hypotenuse? [$5x$]

You may opt to have students complete the automatically scored Practice & Problem Solving items online.

### Item Analysis

| Example | Items | DOK |
|---|---|---|
| 1 | 15 | 3 |
| 2 | 7, 11 | 1 |
| | 9, 16 | 2 |
| | 13 | 3 |
| 3 | 8, 10, 12, 14 | 1 |
| | 17 | 2 |

# STEP 3 | Assess & Differentiate

Go Online

Assess Tutorials Worksheets

## Lesson Quiz

**Formative** Assessment

Use the student scores on the Lesson Quiz to prescribe differentiated assignments.

**I Intervention** 0–3 Points **O On-Level** 4 Points **A Advanced** 5 Points

You may opt to have students take the Lesson Quiz online. The Lesson Quiz will be automatically scored, and appropriate remediation, practice, or enrichment will be assigned based on student performance.

**Lesson Quiz** is available online.

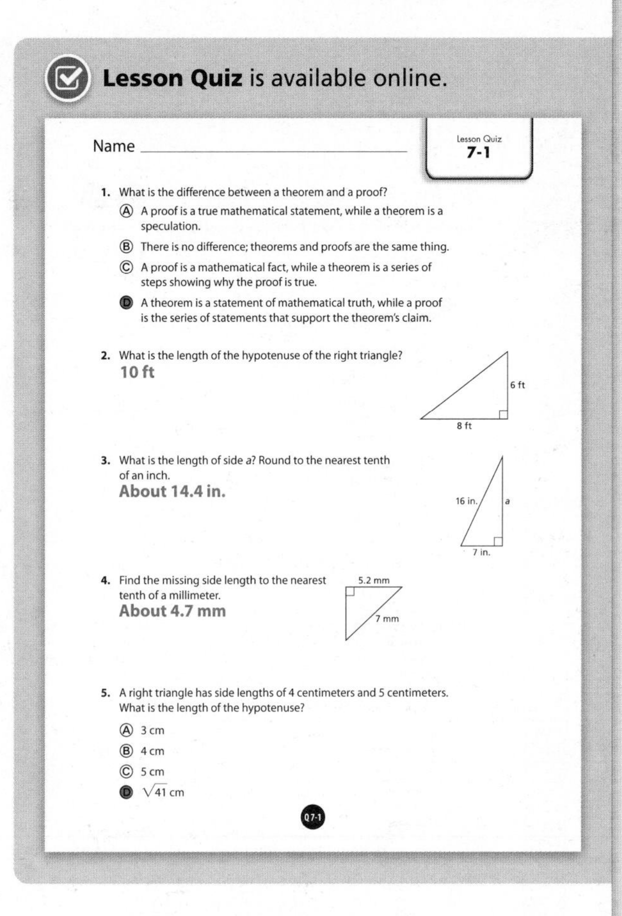

Name ________________ Lesson Quiz 7-1

1. What is the difference between a theorem and a proof?
   - Ⓐ A proof is a true mathematical statement, while a theorem is a speculation.
   - Ⓑ There is no difference; theorems and proofs are the same thing.
   - Ⓒ A proof is a mathematical fact, while a theorem is a series of steps showing why the proof is true.
   - Ⓓ A theorem is a statement of mathematical truth, while a proof is the series of statements that support the theorem's claim.
2. What is the length of the hypotenuse of the right triangle? (6 ft, 8 ft)
   **10 ft**
3. What is the length of side $a$? Round to the nearest tenth of an inch. (16 in., 7 in.)
   **About 14.4 in.**
4. Find the missing side length to the nearest tenth of a millimeter. (5.2 mm, 7 mm)
   **About 4.7 mm**
5. A right triangle has side lengths of 4 centimeters and 5 centimeters. What is the length of the hypotenuse?
   - Ⓐ 3 cm
   - Ⓑ 4 cm
   - Ⓒ 5 cm
   - Ⓓ $\sqrt{41}$ cm

Q7-1

## Video Tutorials

Students can access instructional tutorials using the **Virtual Nerd app**.

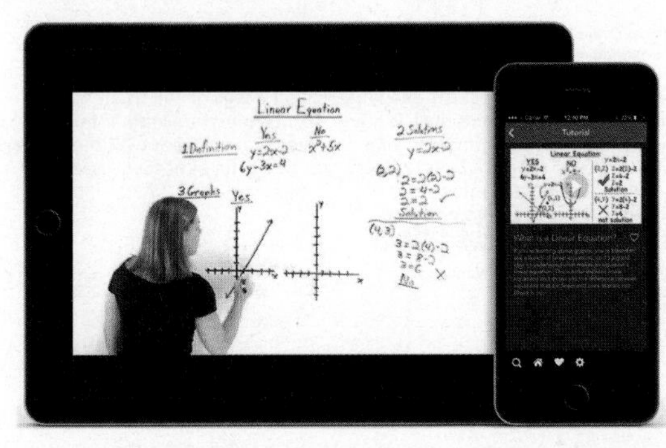

Students can also access the videos using the **BouncePages app** to scan exercise pages marked with this icon. Students can download both apps for free in their mobile devices' app store.

## Differentiated Intervention

**I** = Intervention **O** = On-Level **A** = Advanced

### Reteach to Build Understanding I

Provides scaffolded reteaching for the key lesson concepts.

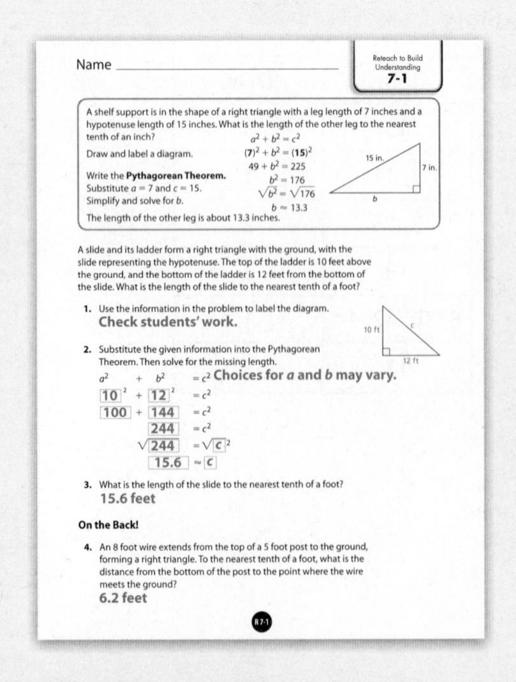

Name ________________ Reteach to Build Understanding 7-1

A shelf support is in the shape of a right triangle with a leg length of 7 inches and a hypotenuse length of 15 inches. What is the length of the other leg to the nearest tenth of an inch?

Draw and label a diagram.
Write the **Pythagorean Theorem.**
Substitute $a = 7$ and $c = 15$.
Simplify and solve for $b$.

$a^2 + b^2 = c^2$
$(7)^2 + b^2 = (15)^2$
$49 + b^2 = 225$
$b^2 = 176$
$\sqrt{b^2} = \sqrt{176}$
$b \approx 13.3$

(15 in., 7 in., $b$)

The length of the other leg is about 13.3 inches.

A slide and its ladder form a right triangle with the ground, with the slide representing the hypotenuse. The top of the ladder is 10 feet above the ground, and the bottom of the ladder is 12 feet from the bottom of the slide. What is the length of the slide to the nearest tenth of a foot?

1. Use the information in the problem to label the diagram. (10 ft, 12 ft, $c$)
   **Check students' work.**
2. Substitute the given information into the Pythagorean Theorem. Then solve for the missing length.
   $a^2 + b^2 = c^2$ **Choices for $a$ and $b$ may vary.**
   $10^2 + 12^2 = c^2$
   $100 + 144 = c^2$
   $244 = c^2$
   $\sqrt{244} = \sqrt{c^2}$
   $15.6 \approx c$
3. What is the length of the slide to the nearest tenth of a foot?
   **15.6 feet**

**On the Back!**

4. An 8 foot wire extends from the top of a 5 foot post to the ground, forming a right triangle. To the nearest tenth of a foot, what is the distance from the bottom of the post to the point where the wire meets the ground?
   **6.2 feet**

R7-1

### Additional Vocabulary Support I O

Helps students develop and reinforce understanding of key terms and concepts.

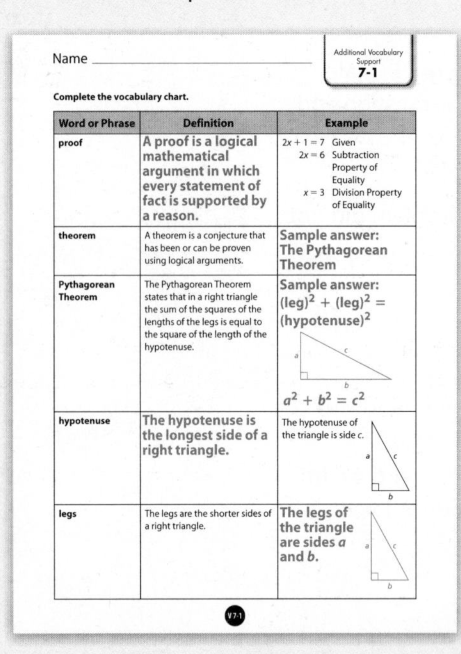

Name ________________ Additional Vocabulary Support 7-1

**Complete the vocabulary chart.**

| Word or Phrase | Definition | Example |
| --- | --- | --- |
| proof | **A proof is a logical mathematical argument in which every statement of fact is supported by a reason.** | $2x + 1 = 7$ Given<br>$2x = 6$ Subtraction Property of Equality<br>$x = 3$ Division Property of Equality |
| theorem | A theorem is a conjecture that has been or can be proven using logical arguments. | **Sample answer: The Pythagorean Theorem** |
| Pythagorean Theorem | The Pythagorean Theorem states that in a right triangle the sum of the squares of the lengths of the legs is equal to the square of the length of the hypotenuse. | **Sample answer: $(\text{leg})^2 + (\text{leg})^2 = (\text{hypotenuse})^2$**<br>($a$, $b$, $c$)<br>$a^2 + b^2 = c^2$ |
| hypotenuse | **The hypotenuse is the longest side of a right triangle.** | The hypotenuse of the triangle is side $c$. ($a$, $b$, $c$) |
| legs | The legs are the shorter sides of a right triangle. | **The legs of the triangle are sides $a$ and $b$.** ($a$, $b$, $c$) |

V7-1

### Build Mathematical Literacy I O

Provides support for struggling readers to build mathematical literacy.

Name ________________ Build Mathematical Literacy 7-1

**Read the problem below. Then answer the questions to identify the steps for solving the problem.**

What is the missing side length of the triangle, rounded to the nearest tenth of a foot? (6 ft, 15 ft)

1. How do you know that you can use the Pythagorean Theorem to find the missing side length?
   **The given triangle is a right triangle because the diagram shows a right angle marker.**
2. Is the unknown side a leg of the triangle or the hypotenuse? Explain how you know.
   **Leg; The unknown side is not opposite the right angle, so it is not the hypotenuse. Therefore, it is a leg.**
3. Fill in the boxes to show which values to substitute into the Pythagorean Theorem.
   $a^2 + b^2 = c^2$
   $\boxed{6}^2 + b^2 = \boxed{15}^2$
4. Using the information from Exercise 3, you can solve for the variable $b$. Once you have solved for this variable, will you have answered the question? Explain.
   **Yes; The value of $b$ is the missing side length.**
5. Would substituting 6 for $b$ and solving for $a$ change the result in this problem? Explain.
   **No; Sample Answer: Since there is no coefficient for $a$ or $b$, the result will be the same.**

M7-1

Go Online

 Practice  Worksheets  Math Tools  Math Games

# Additional Practice

You may opt to have students complete the automatically scored Additional Practice items online.

### Item Analysis

| Example | Items | DOK |
|---|---|---|
| 1 | 5, 7 | 2 |
| | 8 | 3 |
| 2 | 1 | 1 |
| | 4, 6, 9 | 2 |
| 3 | 2 | 1 |
| | 3, 10 | 2 |

**Interactive Practice** is available online.

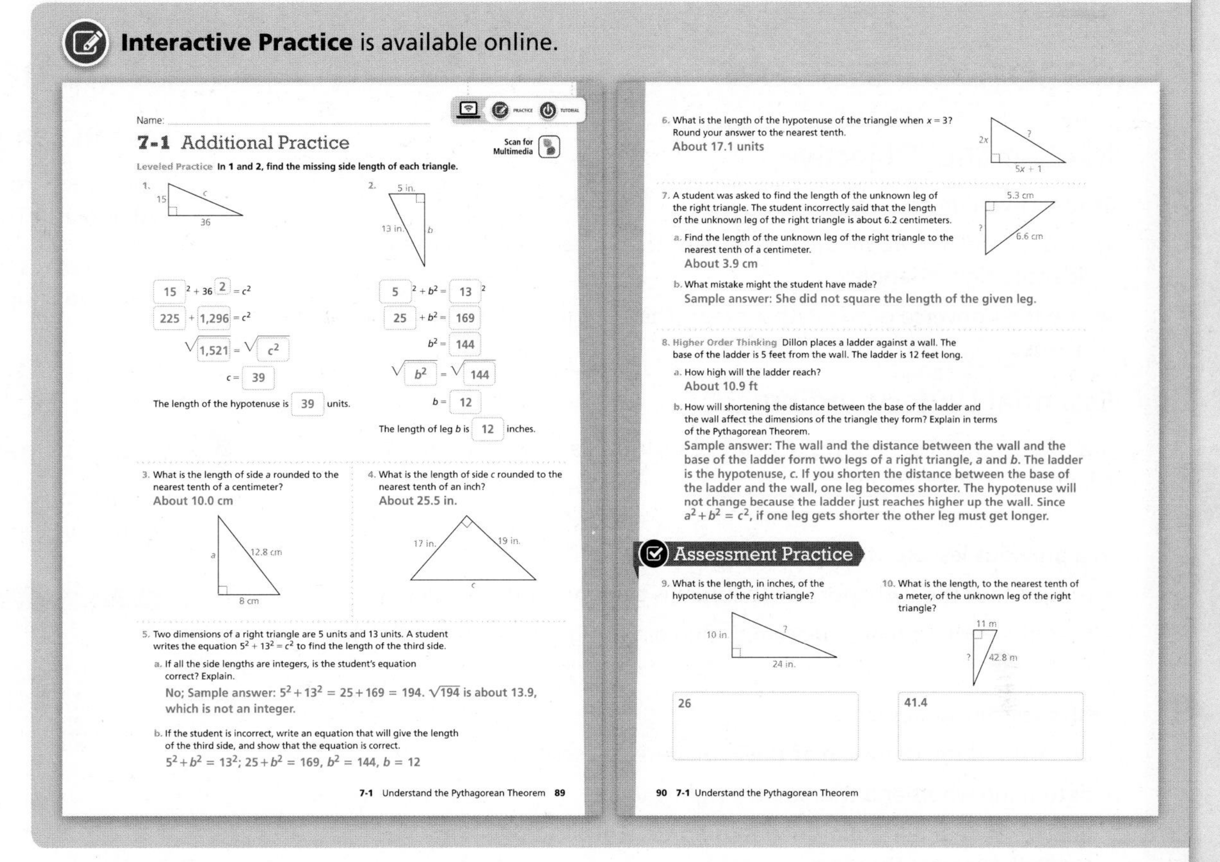

Name:

**7-1** Additional Practice

Scan for Multimedia

Leveled Practice In 1 and 2, find the missing side length of each triangle.

1. $15^2 + 36^2 = c^2$
$225 + 1{,}296 = c^2$
$\sqrt{1{,}521} = \sqrt{c^2}$
$c = 39$
The length of the hypotenuse is 39 units.

2. $5^2 + b^2 = 13^2$
$25 + b^2 = 169$
$b^2 = 144$
$\sqrt{b^2} = \sqrt{144}$
$b = 12$
The length of leg $b$ is 12 inches.

3. What is the length of side $a$ rounded to the nearest tenth of a centimeter?
About 10.0 cm

4. What is the length of side $c$ rounded to the nearest tenth of an inch?
About 25.5 in.

5. Two dimensions of a right triangle are 5 units and 13 units. A student writes the equation $5^2 + 13^2 = c^2$ to find the length of the third side.
a. If all the side lengths are integers, is the student's equation correct? Explain.
No; Sample answer: $5^2 + 13^2 = 25 + 169 = 194$. $\sqrt{194}$ is about 13.9, which is not an integer.
b. If the student is incorrect, write an equation that will give the length of the third side, and show that the equation is correct.
$5^2 + b^2 = 13^2$; $25 + b^2 = 169$, $b^2 = 144$, $b = 12$

7-1 Understand the Pythagorean Theorem 89

6. What is the length of the hypotenuse of the triangle when $x = 3$? Round your answer to the nearest tenth.
About 17.1 units

7. A student was asked to find the length of the unknown leg of the right triangle. The student incorrectly said that the length of the unknown leg of the right triangle is about 6.2 centimeters.
a. Find the length of the unknown leg of the right triangle to the nearest tenth of a centimeter.
About 3.9 cm
b. What mistake might the student have made?
Sample answer: She did not square the length of the given leg.

8. Higher Order Thinking Dillon places a ladder against a wall. The base of the ladder is 5 feet from the wall. The ladder is 12 feet long.
a. How high will the ladder reach?
About 10.9 ft
b. How will shortening the distance between the base of the ladder and the wall affect the dimensions of the triangle they form? Explain in terms of the Pythagorean Theorem.
Sample answer: The wall and the distance between the wall and the base of the ladder form two legs of a right triangle, $a$ and $b$. The ladder is the hypotenuse, $c$. If you shorten the distance between the base of the ladder and the wall, one leg becomes shorter. The hypotenuse will not change because the ladder just reaches higher up the wall. Since $a^2 + b^2 = c^2$, if one leg gets shorter the other leg must get longer.

Assessment Practice

9. What is the length, in inches, of the hypotenuse of the right triangle?
26

10. What is the length, to the nearest tenth of a meter, of the unknown leg of the right triangle?
41.4

90 7-1 Understand the Pythagorean Theorem

# Differentiated Intervention

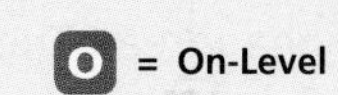

I = Intervention O = On-Level A = Advanced

## Enrichment O A

Presents engaging problems and activities that extend the lesson concepts.

## Math Tools and Games I O A

Offers additional activities and games to build understanding and fluency.

## Pick a Project and STEM Project I O A

Provides an additional opportunity for students to demonstrate understanding of key mathematical concepts.

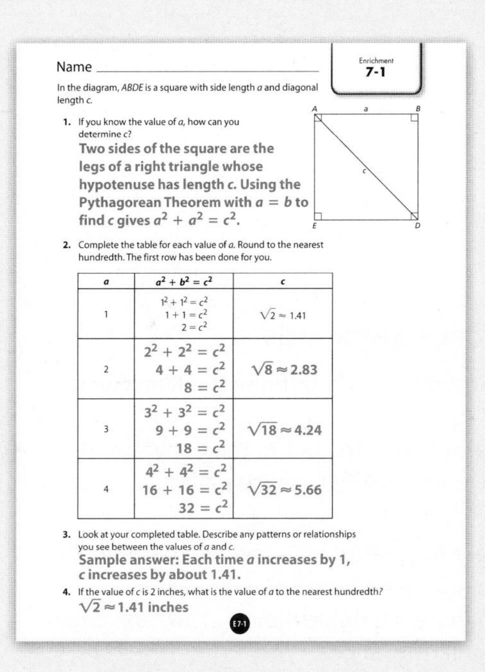

Name

Enrichment 7-1

In the diagram, $ABDE$ is a square with side length $a$ and diagonal length $c$.

1. If you know the value of $a$, how can you determine $c$?
Two sides of the square are the legs of a right triangle whose hypotenuse has length $c$. Using the Pythagorean Theorem with $a = b$ to find $c$ gives $a^2 + a^2 = c^2$.

2. Complete the table for each value of $a$. Round to the nearest hundredth. The first row has been done for you.

| $a$ | $a^2 + b^2 = c^2$ | $c$ |
|---|---|---|
| 1 | $1^2 + 1^2 = c^2$; $1 + 1 = c^2$; $2 = c^2$ | $\sqrt{2} \approx 1.41$ |
| 2 | $2^2 + 2^2 = c^2$; $4 + 4 = c^2$; $8 = c^2$ | $\sqrt{8} \approx 2.83$ |
| 3 | $3^2 + 3^2 = c^2$; $9 + 9 = c^2$; $18 = c^2$ | $\sqrt{18} \approx 4.24$ |
| 4 | $4^2 + 4^2 = c^2$; $16 + 16 = c^2$; $32 = c^2$ | $\sqrt{32} \approx 5.66$ |

3. Look at your completed table. Describe any patterns or relationships you see between the values of $a$ and $c$.
Sample answer: Each time $a$ increases by 1, $c$ increases by about 1.41.

4. If the value of $c$ is 2 inches, what is the value of $a$ to the nearest hundredth?
$\sqrt{2} \approx 1.41$ inches

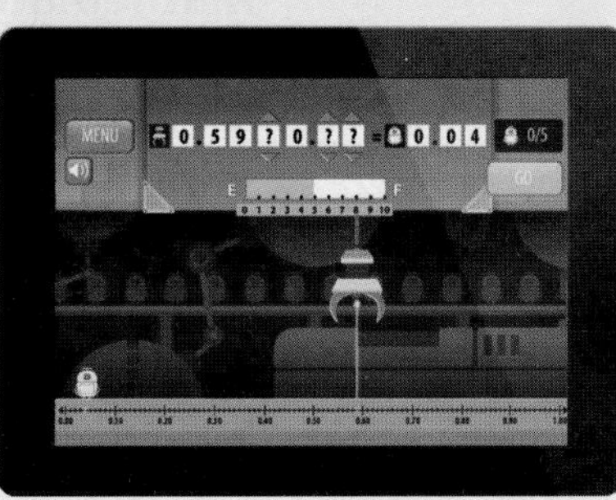

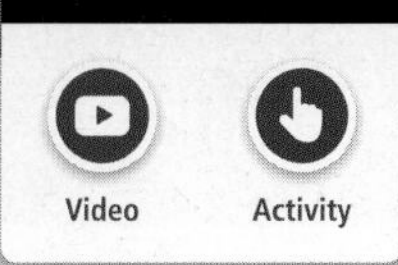


# Lesson 7-2 Understand the Converse of the Pythagorean Theorem

## Lesson Overview

FOCUS

### Mathematics Objective

**Students will be able to:**

- ✔ understand and apply the Converse of the Pythagorean Theorem to identify right triangles.
- ✔ use the Converse of the Pythagorean Theorem to analyze two-dimensional shapes.

### Essential Understanding

If a triangle has side lengths $a$, $b$, and $c$ such that $a^2 + b^2 = c^2$, then the triangle is a right triangle.

COHERENCE

**In a previous lesson, students:**

- proved that the Pythagorean Theorem is true for right triangles.
- used the Pythagorean Theorem to find a missing side length of a right triangle.

**In this lesson, students:**

- understand the Converse of the Pythagorean Theorem.
- determine whether a triangle is a right triangle.
- analyze two-dimensional shapes using the Converse of the Pythagorean Theorem.

**Later in this topic, students will:**

- apply the Pythagorean Theorem to solve real-world problems.
- apply the Pythagorean Theorem to find distances on a coordinate plane.

**Cross-Cluster Connection** Understanding the Converse of the Pythagorean Theorem (8.G.2) connects to work with radicals and integer exponents (8.EE.1).

RIGOR

This lesson emphasizes a blend of **procedural skills and fluency** and **conceptual understanding**.

- Students practice using the Converse of the Pythagorean Theorem to identify right triangles in different situations.
- Students understand the proof of the Converse of the Pythagorean Theorem and how it can be used to identify a right triangle.

## Language Support

### Lesson Language Objective

Explain how to use the Converse of the Pythagorean Theorem to identify right triangles.

Additional resources are available in the Language Support Handbook.

## Math Anytime

### Today's Challenge

Use the Topic 7 problems any time during this topic.

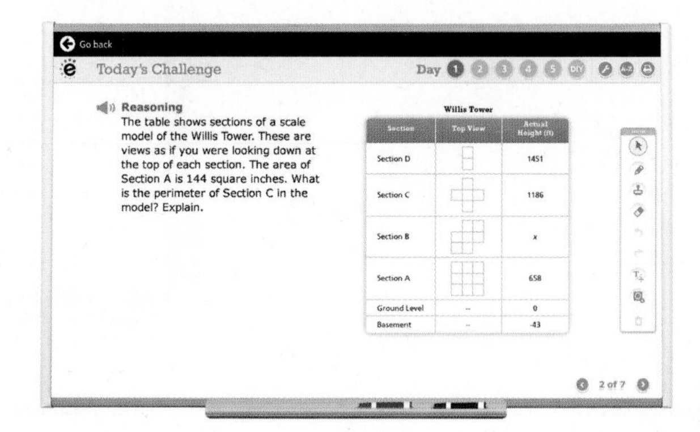


## Mathematics Overview | Common Core Standards

### Content Standards

In this lesson, you will focus on **8.G.B.6** and **8.G.B.7**.

- **8.G.B.6** Explain a proof of the Pythagorean Theorem and its converse.
- **8.G.B.7** Apply the Pythagorean Theorem to determine unknown side lengths in right triangles in real-world and mathematical problems in two and three dimensions.

### Mathematical Practice Standards

**MP.3 Construct Viable Arguments and Critique the Reasoning of Others**
Students will construct arguments related to the Converse of the Pythagorean Theorem and justify their reasoning.

**MP.8 Look for and Express Regularity in Repeated Reasoning**
Students will practice using the equation $a^2 + b^2 = c^2$ to determine whether a triangle is a right triangle. They will begin to see the patterns in similar situations.

## STEP 1 | Problem-Based Learning

15-20 min

Go Online

Activity

# Solve & Discuss It!

Formative Assessment

**Purpose** Students engage in productive struggle, identifying combinations of side lengths that form right triangles. They connect and apply this to the Converse of the Pythagorean Theorem in Example 2.

## ETP Before — WHOLE CLASS

**1 Introduce the Problem**

Provide grid paper and rulers, as needed.

**2 Check for Understanding of the Problem**

Activate prior knowledge by asking: How do you know if a triangle is a right triangle?

## ETP During — SMALL GROUP

**3 Observe Students at Work**

Observe students while they work, noting the strategies that students used to identify the combinations of side lengths that make a right triangle. Students may use grid paper and draw possible options. Other students may apply the Pythagorean Theorem, identifying combinations of side lengths that make the equation true. If needed, ask Is there anything you learned in the previous lesson you could apply to this problem?

**Early Finishers**

How would the problem change if Kayla used scissors to cut the 5 cm and 13 cm straws in half? [Sample answer: You could make a triangle using 2.5 cm, 6 cm, and 6.5 cm straws.]

## ETP After — WHOLE CLASS

**4 Discuss Solution Strategies and Key Ideas**

Have students give the side lengths of all the right triangles they found and discuss their strategies for finding those triangles. Have them discuss the methods they could use to check whether the triangles are in fact right triangles; they may suggest drawing the triangle and measuring the angles or using the Pythagorean Theorem.

Have students discuss how they know which side length must be the hypotenuse; the hypotenuse is the longest side of a right triangle.

**5 Consider Instructional Implications**

When presenting Example 2, discuss with students how they used the Converse of the Pythagorean Theorem to identify whether triangles were right triangles in the Solve & Discuss It.

## Analyze Student Work

**Solve and Discuss It!** Activity is available online.

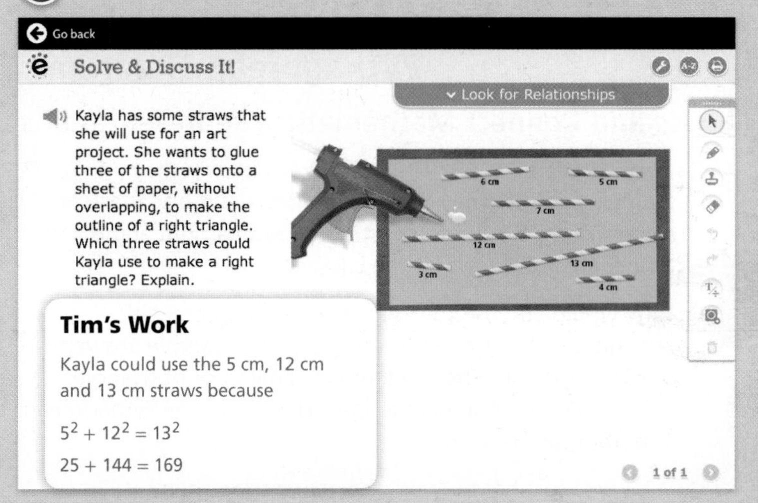


**Tim** uses the Pythagorean Theorem to determine what combinations of sides work to make a true equation.

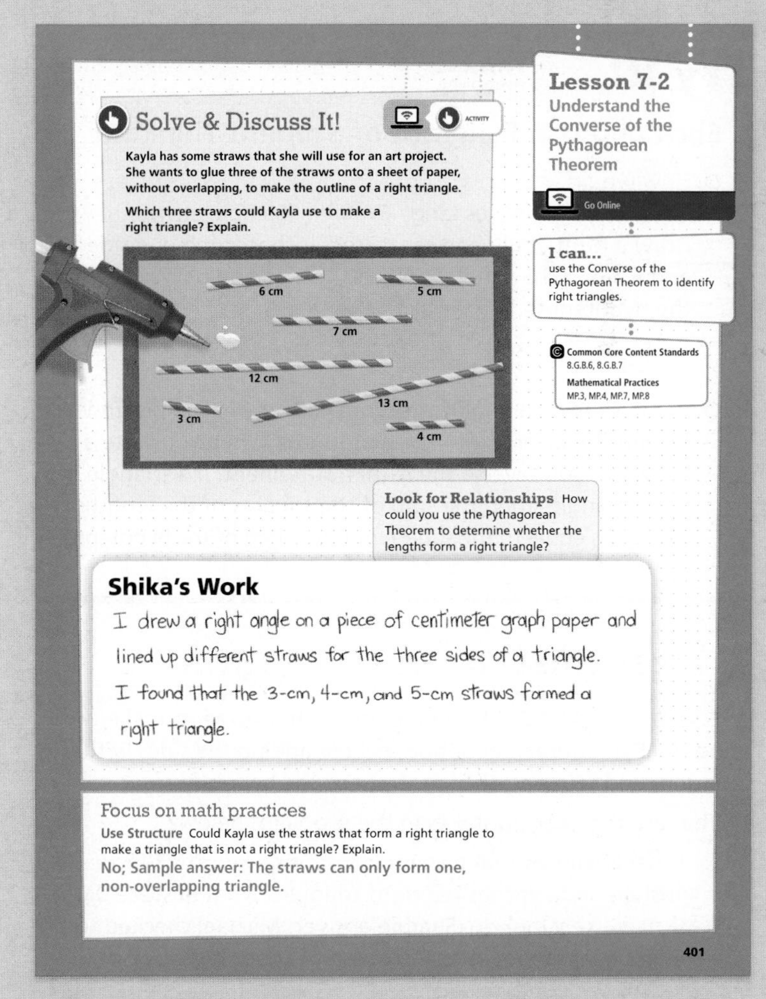


**Shika** uses a right angle drawn on a piece of paper to line up the legs of the triangle, and then she lines up the leg that corresponds to the hypotenuse. She finds that the 3-centimeter, 4-centimeter, and 5-centimeter straws form a right triangle.

# STEP 2 | Visual Learning

Go Online

Visual Learning

Assess

## Establish Mathematics Goals to Focus Learning

Engage students in a discussion about the ***Essential Question***. Make sure they understand what a right triangle is and review the Pythagorean Theorem.

## EXAMPLE 1 Understand the Converse of the Pythagorean Theorem

## Use and Connect Mathematical Representations

**Q:** How are triangles *ABC* and *DEF* alike? How are they different? [Sample answer: They both have sides *a* and *b* that are the same. Triangle *DEF* was constructed with a right angle and a side labeled *x*, rather than *c*.]

**Q:** Why would you use the Pythagorean Theorem with triangle *DEF* but not with triangle *ABC*? [Sample answer: The Pythagorean Theorem applies only to right triangles. Triangle *DEF* is defined as a right triangle, so the Pythagorean Theorem can be used.]

**Q:** Why are you able to make the assumption that $c = x$?] [Sample answer: Triangle *DEF* is known to be a right triangle. Therefore in the equation $a^2 + b^2 = c^2$, you can substitute *c* for *x*.]

## Try It!

Formative Assessment

## Elicit and Use Evidence of Student Thinking

**Q:** How would you draw a right triangle with legs that are 4 inches and 5 inches long? Explain. [Sample answer: Draw a right angle and measure 4 inches along one side and 5 along the other. Connect the two end points to form the hypotenuse.]

## Convince Me!

**Q:** What is the meaning of the word *converse*? [Sample answers: "Opposite, inverse, or switch around"; When you state a converse, you reverse the if-then statement. *If* a triangle is a right triangle, *then* the sum of the squares of the lengths of the legs is equal to the square of the length of the hypotenuse.]

**Visual Learning Animation Plus** is available online.

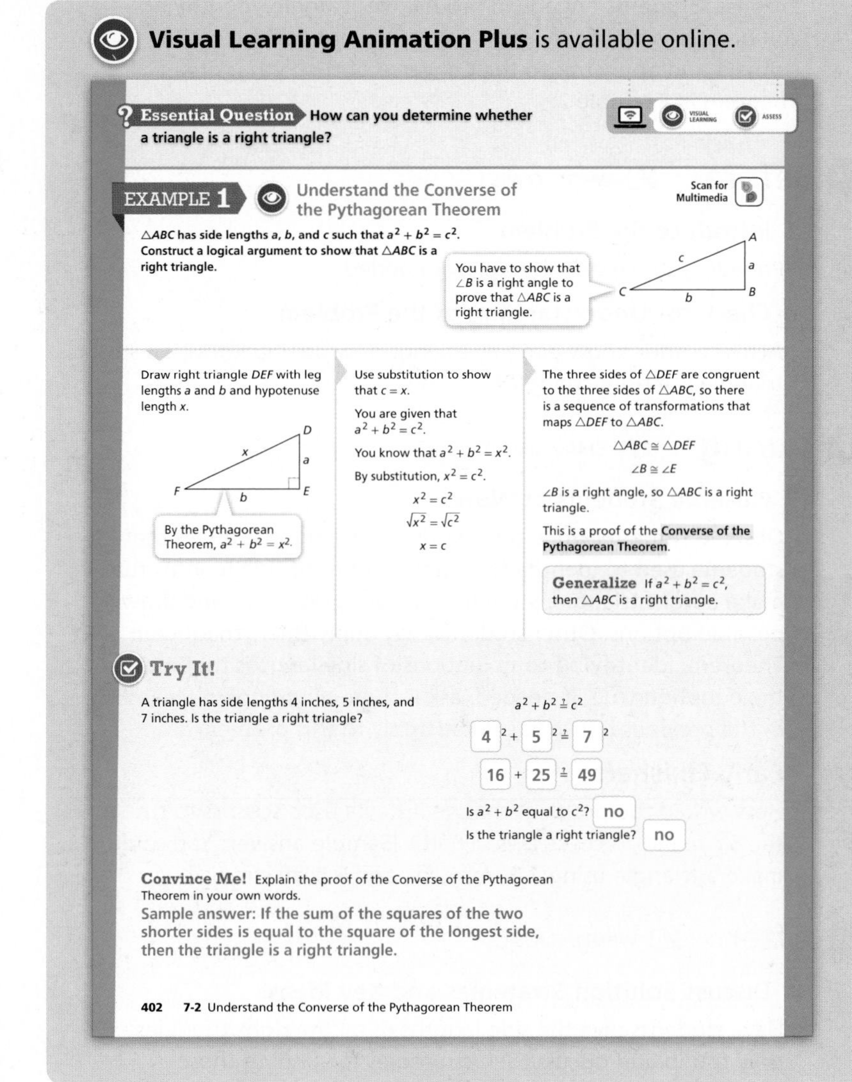


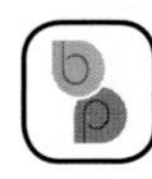

Students can access the ***Visual Learning Animation Plus*** by using the **BouncePages app** to scan this page. Students can download the app for free in their mobile devices' app store.

## Response to Intervention

**USE WITH EXAMPLE 2** Common errors that students make when using the Pythagorean equation include adding the sides without squaring, and squaring the legs but not the hypotenuse.

- What are the likely mistakes in the problems below?

**Q:** Michael believes that a triangle with side lengths 3 inches, 4 inches, and 7 inches is a right triangle. What mistake did Michael likely make? [Sample answer: Michael checked to see if 3 + 4 was equal to 7, instead of checking to see if $3^2 + 4^2$ was equal to $7^2$.]

**Q:** Janie thinks that a triangle with side lengths 1 cm, 2 cm, and 5 cm is a right triangle. What mistake did she likely make? [Janie checked to see if $1^2 + 2^2$ was equal to 5, instead of checking to see if $1^2 + 2^2$ was equal to $5^2$.]

## Enrichment

**USE WITH EXAMPLE 2** Have students investigate Pythagorean triples, which are sets of whole numbers that satisfy the equation $a^2 + b^2 = c^2$.

- The whole numbers 3, 4, and 5 are whole-number unit lengths **that could be the side lengths of a right triangle.**

**Q:** Do the following side lengths form a right triangle? Explain.
6 cm, 8 cm, and 10 cm — 7, 10, 12
15 cm, 36 cm, and 39 cm — 16, 30, 34
[Yes; Sample answer: 36 + 64 = 100, 225 + 1,296 = 1,521, and 256 + 900 = 1,156. Side lengths 7, 10, and 12 do not form a right triangle.]

**Q:** What are some other Pythagorean triples? [Answers will vary.]

Go Online

Activity Assess

# EXAMPLE 2

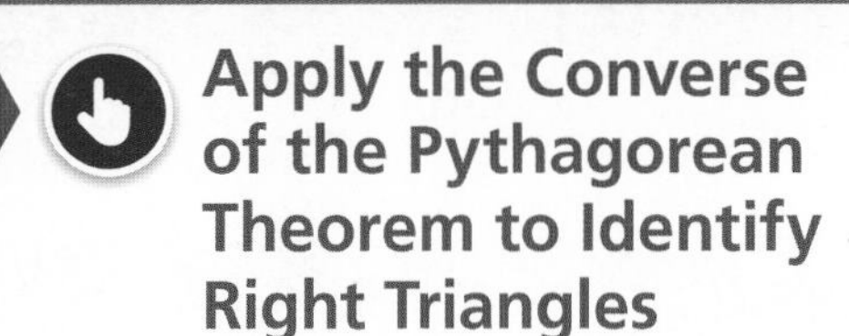

## Apply the Converse of the Pythagorean Theorem to Identify Right Triangles

### ETP Pose Purposeful Questions

**Q:** Why do you use the Converse of the Pythagorean Theorem in this example instead of the Pythagorean Theorem? [Sample answer: You are asking if the triangle is a right triangle. Therefore if the sum of the squares of the lengths of the legs is equal to the square of the length of the hypotenuse, you have determined that the triangle is a right triangle.]

## Try It! Formative Assessment

### ETP Elicit and Use Evidence of Student Thinking

**Q:** What if the side length is 11 feet instead of 10 feet. Is the triangle still a right triangle? Explain. [No; Sample answer: $121 + (\sqrt{105})^2 \neq (\sqrt{205})^2$]

**Q:** If you change the length of any one of the sides of a right triangle, even by the slightest amount, is it still a right triangle? Explain. [No; Sample answer: $a^2 + b^2 = c^2$ will no longer hold true.]

# EXAMPLE 3

## Use the Converse of the Pythagorean Theorem to Analyze Shapes

### ETP Pose Purposeful Questions

**Q:** Which of the sides corresponds to the possible hypotenuse in triangle *NLP*? Explain. [Sample answer: In triangle *NLP*, the possible hypotenuse is *NL*, because it is the longest side. None of them. The triangle is not a right triangle.]

## Try It! Formative Assessment

### ETP Elicit and Use Evidence of Student Thinking

**Q:** What might be the first line of an answer to this question? [Sample answer: $17^2 + 15^2 \stackrel{?}{=} \sqrt{514}$]

**Examples and Try Its!** are available online.

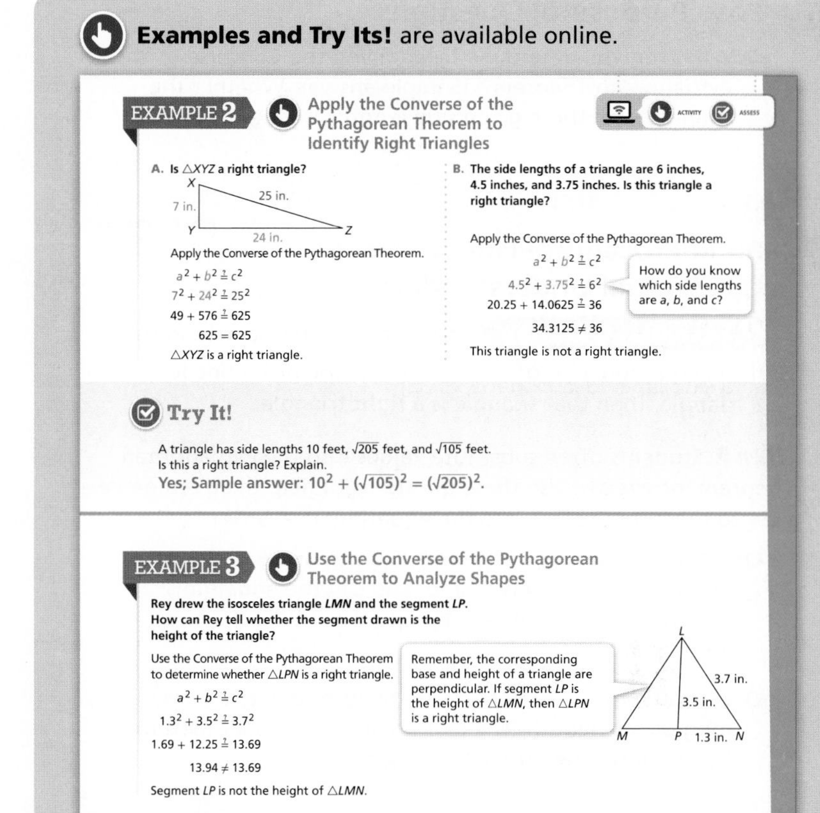

EXAMPLE 2 Apply the Converse of the Pythagorean Theorem to Identify Right Triangles

A. Is $\triangle XYZ$ a right triangle?

Apply the Converse of the Pythagorean Theorem.

$a^2 + b^2 \stackrel{?}{=} c^2$

$7^2 + 24^2 \stackrel{?}{=} 25^2$

$49 + 576 \stackrel{?}{=} 625$

$625 = 625$

$\triangle XYZ$ is a right triangle.

B. The side lengths of a triangle are 6 inches, 4.5 inches, and 3.75 inches. Is this triangle a right triangle?

Apply the Converse of the Pythagorean Theorem.

$a^2 + b^2 \stackrel{?}{=} c^2$

$4.5^2 + 3.75^2 \stackrel{?}{=} 6^2$

$20.25 + 14.0625 \stackrel{?}{=} 36$

$34.3125 \neq 36$

This triangle is not a right triangle.

How do you know which side lengths are *a*, *b*, and *c*?

Try It!

A triangle has side lengths 10 feet, $\sqrt{205}$ feet, and $\sqrt{105}$ feet. Is this a right triangle? Explain.

Yes; Sample answer: $10^2 + (\sqrt{105})^2 = (\sqrt{205})^2$.

EXAMPLE 3 Use the Converse of the Pythagorean Theorem to Analyze Shapes

Rey drew the isosceles triangle *LMN* and the segment *LP*. How can Rey tell whether the segment drawn is the height of the triangle?

Use the Converse of the Pythagorean Theorem to determine whether $\triangle LPN$ is a right triangle.

$a^2 + b^2 \stackrel{?}{=} c^2$

$1.3^2 + 3.5^2 \stackrel{?}{=} 3.7^2$

$1.69 + 12.25 \stackrel{?}{=} 13.69$

$13.94 \neq 13.69$

Segment *LP* is not the height of $\triangle LMN$.

Remember, the corresponding base and height of a triangle are perpendicular. If segment *LP* is the height of $\triangle LMN$, then $\triangle LPN$ is a right triangle.

Try It!

A triangle is inside a trapezoid. Is the triangle a right triangle? Explain.

Yes; Sample answer: $17^2 + 15^2 = (\sqrt{514})^2$.



7-2 Understand the Converse of the Pythagorean Theorem 403

ADDITIONAL EXAMPLES 

**For additional examples go online.**

## English Language Learners

**EMERGING** Read Example 1.

Write the following on the board:

Theorem: If a triangle is a right triangle, then $a^2 + b^2 = c^2$.

Converse: If $a^2 + b^2 = c^2$, then a triangle is a right triangle.

Draw a circle around the "If" statement and a circle around the "then" statement in the theorem. Draw arrows to show how they are switched in the converse.

**DEVELOPING** Review Example 3.

Have students work in pairs to review and discuss what is needed in order to solve this problem.

**Q:** What is an isosceles triangle? [A triangle with two congruent sides]

**Q:** How do you know if a triangle is a right triangle? [If $a^2 + b^2 = c^2$, then the triangle is a right triangle.]

**Q:** What theorem does this represent? [The Converse of the Pythagorean Theorem]

**EXPANDING** Read Example 1. Have students work in pairs to review and discuss what is needed in order to solve this problem.

**Q:** The word *converse* is similar to the word *reverse*. How can you use that to remember what a converse is? [Sample answers: To find a converse, take the first part and second part of an if-then statement and reverse the order.]

Go Online

 Key Concept  Assess  Activity

## KEY CONCEPT

### ETP Pose Purposeful Questions

**Q:** What can you determine by applying the Converse of the Pythagorean Theorem? [Sample answer: Whether the triangle with three given side lengths is a right triangle]

## Do You Understand/Do You Know How?

Formative Assessment

### ETP Build Procedural Fluency from Conceptual Understanding

**Essential Question** Students should understand that if the equation $a^2 + b^2 = c^2$ is true for the given side lengths of a triangle, then that triangle is a right triangle.

**ITEM 2** Students often substitute values into the Pythagorean Theorem incorrectly. Use these questions to help them remember how to substitute values into the equation $a^2 + b^2 = c^2$.

**Q:** A triangle has sides of 4 units, 5 units, and 3 units. What numbers corresponds to *a*, *b*, and *c* in the equation $a^2 + b^2 = c^2$? [$a = 4$, $b = 3$, and $c = 5$, or $a = 3$, $b = 4$, and $c = 5$]

**Q:** Do you notice a pattern? [The hypotenuse, *c*, is always the longest side length. The legs are always smaller than the hypotenuse, and either can be *a* or *b*.]

###  Prevent Misconceptions

**ITEM 5**

**Q:** What are the squares of the lengths of the sides of the triangle? [26, 28, and 64]

Available Online

KEY CONCEPT

The Converse of the Pythagorean Theorem states that if the sum of the squares of the lengths of two sides of a triangle is equal to the square of the length of the third side, the triangle is a right triangle.

**Converse of Pythagorean Theorem**
If $a^2 + b^2 = c^2$, then a triangle is a right triangle.

**Do You Understand?**

1. **Essential Question** How can you determine whether a triangle is a right triangle?
Sample answer: If the lengths of the three sides of a triangle satisfy the equation $a^2 + b^2 = c^2$, then the triangle is a right triangle.

2. **Construct Arguments** A triangle has side lengths of 3 centimeters, 5 centimeters, and 4 centimeters. Abe used the Converse of the Pythagorean Theorem to determine whether it is a right triangle.

$$3^2 + 5^2 \stackrel{?}{=} 4^2$$
$$9 + 25 \stackrel{?}{=} 16$$
$$34 \neq 16$$

Abe concluded that it is not a right triangle. Is Abe correct? Explain.
No; Sample answer: Abe used $\text{leg}^2 + \text{hypotenuse}^2 = \text{leg}^2$ instead of $\text{leg}^2 + \text{leg}^2 = \text{hypotenuse}^2$ when solving. Since $9 + 16 = 25$, Abe can make a right triangle.

3. **Use Structure** When you are given three side lengths for a triangle, how do you know which length to substitute for *a*, *b*, or *c* in the Pythagorean Theorem?
Sample answer: The longest side length will always be substituted for *c*. The other two lengths can be either *a* or *b*. It does not matter which is which because of the Commutative Property of Addition.

**Do You Know How?**

4. Is the triangle a right triangle? Explain.
Yes; Sample answer: $6^2 + 8^2 = 10^2$.
(6 cm, 8 cm, 10 cm)

5. Is the triangle a right triangle? Explain.
No; Sample answer: $(\sqrt{26})^2 + (\sqrt{28})^2 \neq 8^2$.

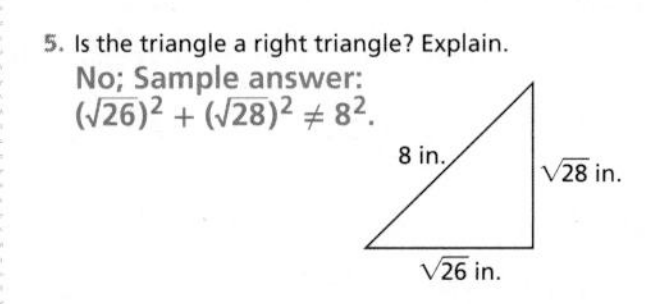


6. Is the purple triangle a right triangle? Explain.
No; Sample answer: $15.5^2 + 14^2 \neq 20.8^2$.
(15.5 m, 20.8 m, 14.0 m)

404 7-2 Understand the Converse of the Pythagorean Theorem

## ADDITIONAL EXAMPLE 2

Help students apply the Converse of the Pythagorean Theorem to triangles with one leg that is the height of a parallelogram.

Make sure students understand why subtracting the length of *AB* from *DC* gives the length of the shorter leg of both triangles.

**Q:** What information is needed to tell if the triangles are right triangles? [The length of the shorter leg of the triangles]

**Q:** Why is the missing side length the same for both triangles? [It is given that the triangles are congruent.]

**Q:** How will this information be used? [Sample answer: The length of the shorter leg along with the given lengths of the other two sides will be substituted into the formula $a^2 + b^2 = c^2$.]

**Additional Examples** are available online.

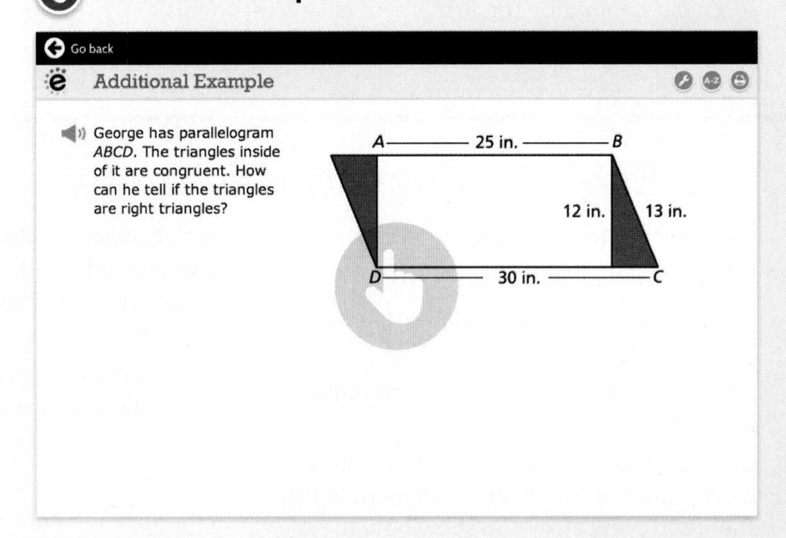


**Answer:** The triangles are right triangles.

Go Online

Practice Tutorials Math Tools

# Practice & Problem Solving  

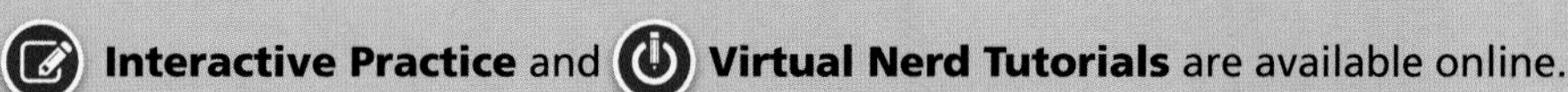


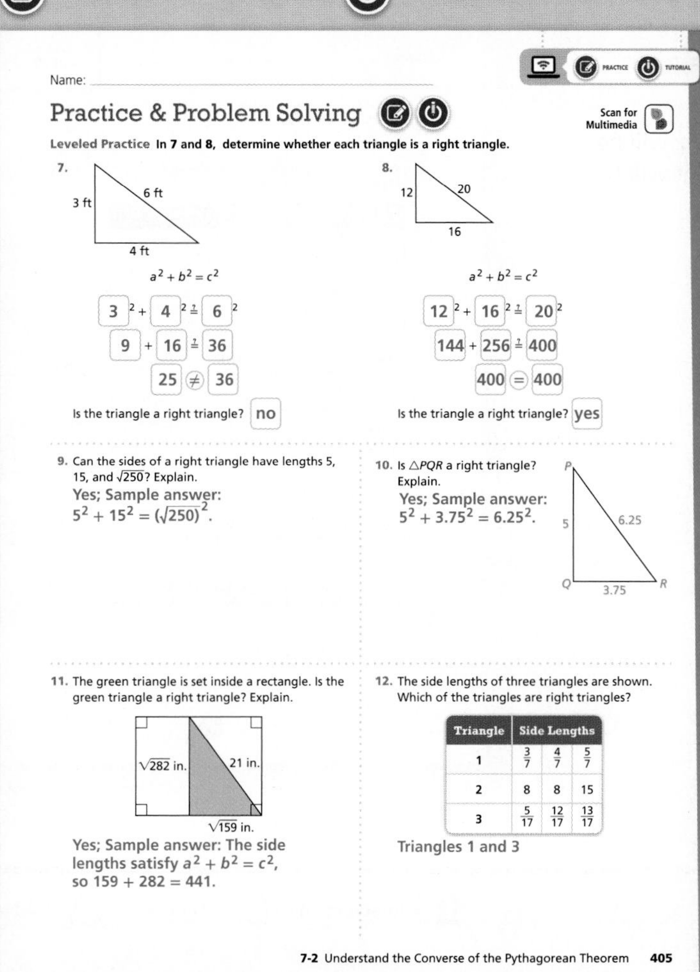

Name:

## Practice & Problem Solving

Scan for Multimedia

**Leveled Practice** In 7 and 8, determine whether each triangle is a right triangle.

7. (triangle: 3 ft, 4 ft, 6 ft)

$a^2 + b^2 = c^2$

$3^2 + 4^2 \stackrel{?}{=} 6^2$

$9 + 16 \stackrel{?}{=} 36$

$25 \neq 36$

Is the triangle a right triangle? no

8. (triangle: 12, 16, 20)

$a^2 + b^2 = c^2$

$12^2 + 16^2 \stackrel{?}{=} 20^2$

$144 + 256 \stackrel{?}{=} 400$

$400 = 400$

Is the triangle a right triangle? yes

9. Can the sides of a right triangle have lengths 5, 15, and $\sqrt{250}$? Explain.
Yes; Sample answer: $5^2 + 15^2 = (\sqrt{250})^2$.

10. Is $\triangle PQR$ a right triangle? Explain.
Yes; Sample answer: $5^2 + 3.75^2 = 6.25^2$.

11. The green triangle is set inside a rectangle. Is the green triangle a right triangle? Explain.
(labels: $\sqrt{282}$ in., 21 in., $\sqrt{159}$ in.)
Yes; Sample answer: The side lengths satisfy $a^2 + b^2 = c^2$, so $159 + 282 = 441$.

12. The side lengths of three triangles are shown. Which of the triangles are right triangles?

| Triangle | Side Lengths | | |
|---|---|---|---|
| 1 | $\frac{3}{7}$ | $\frac{4}{7}$ | $\frac{5}{7}$ |
| 2 | 8 | 8 | 15 |
| 3 | $\frac{5}{17}$ | $\frac{12}{17}$ | $\frac{13}{17}$ |

Triangles 1 and 3

7-2 Understand the Converse of the Pythagorean Theorem 405

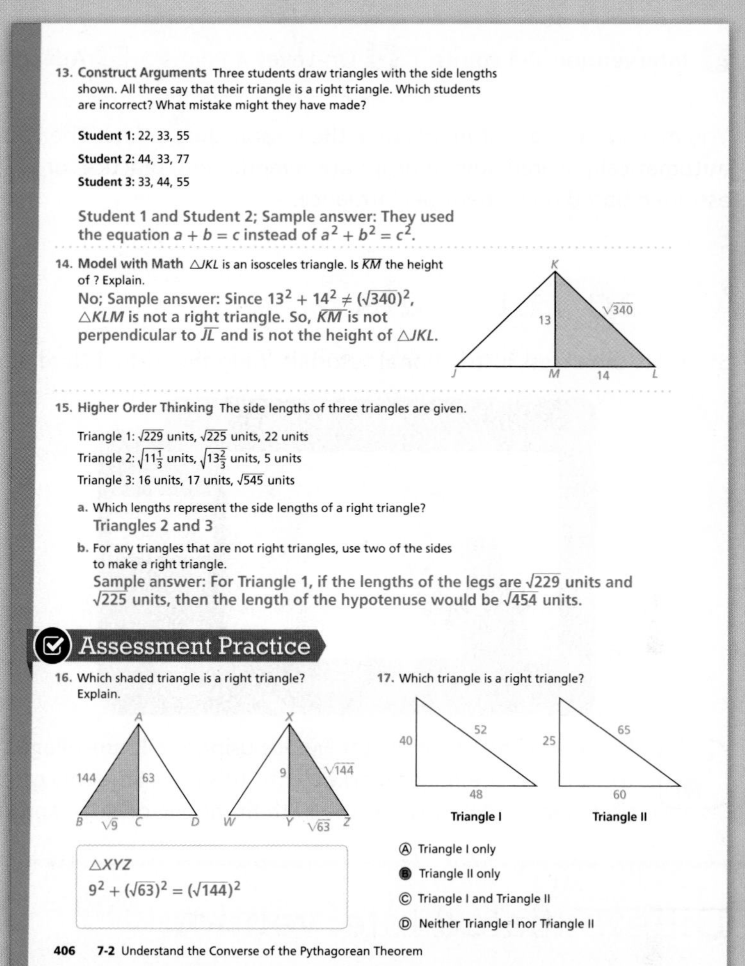

13. **Construct Arguments** Three students draw triangles with the side lengths shown. All three say that their triangle is a right triangle. Which students are incorrect? What mistake might they have made?

**Student 1:** 22, 33, 55
**Student 2:** 44, 33, 77
**Student 3:** 33, 44, 55

Student 1 and Student 2; Sample answer: They used the equation $a + b = c$ instead of $a^2 + b^2 = c^2$.

14. **Model with Math** $\triangle JKL$ is an isosceles triangle. Is $\overline{KM}$ the height of ? Explain.
No; Sample answer: Since $13^2 + 14^2 \neq (\sqrt{340})^2$, $\triangle KLM$ is not a right triangle. So, $\overline{KM}$ is not perpendicular to $\overline{JL}$ and is not the height of $\triangle JKL$.
(figure labels: K, J, M, L, 13, 14, $\sqrt{340}$)

15. **Higher Order Thinking** The side lengths of three triangles are given.
Triangle 1: $\sqrt{229}$ units, $\sqrt{225}$ units, 22 units
Triangle 2: $\sqrt{11\frac{1}{3}}$ units, $\sqrt{13\frac{2}{3}}$ units, 5 units
Triangle 3: 16 units, 17 units, $\sqrt{545}$ units

a. Which lengths represent the side lengths of a right triangle?
Triangles 2 and 3

b. For any triangles that are not right triangles, use two of the sides to make a right triangle.
Sample answer: For Triangle 1, if the lengths of the legs are $\sqrt{229}$ units and $\sqrt{225}$ units, then the length of the hypotenuse would be $\sqrt{454}$ units.

### Assessment Practice

16. Which shaded triangle is a right triangle? Explain.
(figure labels: A, B, C, D, 144, 63, $\sqrt{9}$; X, W, Y, Z, 9, $\sqrt{144}$, $\sqrt{63}$)
$\triangle XYZ$
$9^2 + (\sqrt{63})^2 = (\sqrt{144})^2$

17. Which triangle is a right triangle?
(Triangle I: 40, 48, 52; Triangle II: 25, 60, 65)
Ⓐ Triangle I only
Ⓑ Triangle II only
Ⓒ Triangle I and Triangle II
Ⓓ Neither Triangle I nor Triangle II

406 7-2 Understand the Converse of the Pythagorean Theorem

## Challenge

**ITEM 11** Encourage students to think about what conclusions they can draw from the information given in the problem.

**Q:** Is there enough information to determine the side lengths of the white triangle? Explain. [Yes; Sample answer: The white triangle has to have the same measurements as the green triangle. Once you know that the green triangle is a right triangle, the legs of both triangles form a rectangle.]

## Error Intervention

**ITEM 13** Help students realize that using the side lengths rather than the squares of the side lengths will not satisfy the Pythagorean Theorem.

**Q:** What happens when you try to draw a triangle with side lengths 3 units, 2 units, and 5 units? Explain. [Sample answer: It is impossible, because the 5-unit side can only sit on top of the lined up 2- and 3-unit sides.]

You may opt to have students complete the automatically scored Practice & Problem Solving items online.

### Item Analysis

| Example | Items | DOK |
|---|---|---|
| 1 | 15 | 3 |
| 2 | 7, 8, 10 | 1 |
| | 9, 12, 13, 16, 17 | 2 |
| 3 | 11, 14 | 2 |

## STEP 3 | Assess & Differentiate

Go Online

 Assess  Tutorials  Worksheets

# Lesson Quiz

Formative Assessment

Use the student scores on the Lesson Quiz to prescribe differentiated assignments.

**I Intervention** 0-3 Points **O On-Level** 4 Points **A Advanced** 5 Points

You may opt to have students take the Lesson Quiz online. The Lesson Quiz will be automatically scored, and appropriate remediation, practice, or enrichment will be assigned based on student performance.

**Lesson Quiz** is available online.

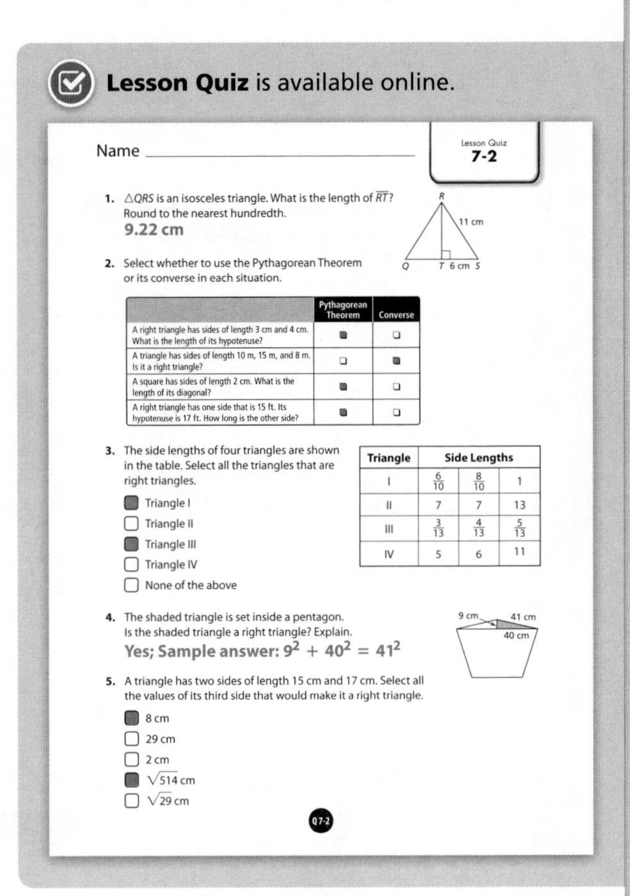

Name ______

Lesson Quiz 7-2

1. $\triangle QRS$ is an isosceles triangle. What is the length of $\overline{RT}$? Round to the nearest hundredth.
**9.22 cm**

2. Select whether to use the Pythagorean Theorem or its converse in each situation.

| | Pythagorean Theorem | Converse |
|---|---|---|
| A right triangle has sides of length 3 cm and 4 cm. What is the length of its hypotenuse? | ■ | ☐ |
| A triangle has sides of length 10 m, 15 m, and 8 m. Is it a right triangle? | ☐ | ■ |
| A square has sides of length 2 cm. What is the length of its diagonal? | ■ | ☐ |
| A right triangle has one side that is 15 ft. Its hypotenuse is 17 ft. How long is the other side? | ■ | ☐ |

3. The side lengths of four triangles are shown in the table. Select all the triangles that are right triangles.

| Triangle | Side Lengths | | |
|---|---|---|---|
| I | $\frac{6}{10}$ | $\frac{8}{10}$ | 1 |
| II | 7 | 7 | 13 |
| III | $\frac{3}{13}$ | $\frac{4}{13}$ | $\frac{5}{13}$ |
| IV | 5 | 6 | 11 |

■ Triangle I
☐ Triangle II
■ Triangle III
☐ Triangle IV
☐ None of the above

4. The shaded triangle is set inside a pentagon. Is the shaded triangle a right triangle? Explain.
**Yes; Sample answer: $9^2 + 40^2 = 41^2$**

5. A triangle has two sides of length 15 cm and 17 cm. Select all the values of its third side that would make it a right triangle.

■ 8 cm
☐ 29 cm
☐ 2 cm
■ $\sqrt{514}$ cm
☐ $\sqrt{29}$ cm

Q7-2

# Video Tutorials

Students can access instructional tutorials using the **Virtual Nerd app**.

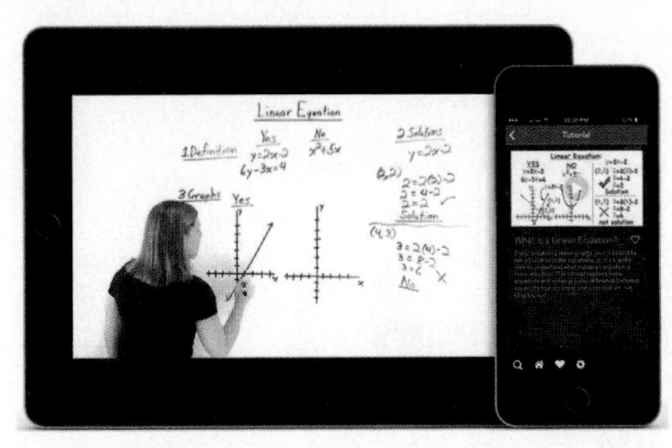

Students can also access the videos using the **BouncePages app** to scan exercise pages marked with this icon. Students can download both apps for free in their mobile devices' app store.

# Differentiated Intervention

**I** = Intervention **O** = On-Level **A** = Advanced

## Reteach to Build Understanding I

Provides scaffolded reteaching for the key lesson concepts.

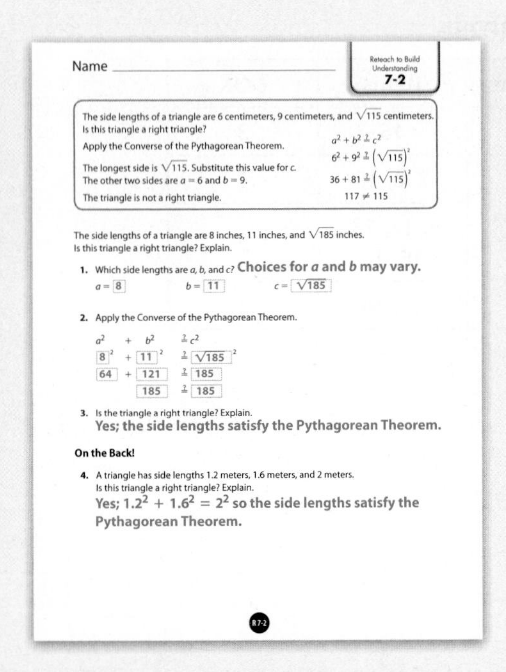

Name ______

Reteach to Build Understanding 7-2

The side lengths of a triangle are 6 centimeters, 9 centimeters, and $\sqrt{115}$ centimeters. Is this triangle a right triangle?

Apply the Converse of the Pythagorean Theorem. $a^2 + b^2 \stackrel{?}{=} c^2$

The longest side is $\sqrt{115}$. Substitute this value for $c$. The other two sides are $a = 6$ and $b = 9$. $6^2 + 9^2 \stackrel{?}{=} (\sqrt{115})^2$

$36 + 81 \stackrel{?}{=} (\sqrt{115})^2$

The triangle is not a right triangle. $117 \neq 115$

The side lengths of a triangle are 8 inches, 11 inches, and $\sqrt{185}$ inches. Is this triangle a right triangle? Explain.

1. Which side lengths are $a$, $b$, and $c$? **Choices for $a$ and $b$ may vary.**
$a =$ 8 $b =$ 11 $c =$ $\sqrt{185}$

2. Apply the Converse of the Pythagorean Theorem.
$a^2 + b^2 \stackrel{?}{=} c^2$
$8^2 + 11^2 \stackrel{?}{=} (\sqrt{185})^2$
$64 + 121 \stackrel{?}{=} 185$
$185 \stackrel{?}{=} 185$

3. Is the triangle a right triangle? Explain.
**Yes; the side lengths satisfy the Pythagorean Theorem.**

**On the Back!**

4. A triangle has side lengths 1.2 meters, 1.6 meters, and 2 meters. Is this triangle a right triangle? Explain.
**Yes; $1.2^2 + 1.6^2 = 2^2$ so the side lengths satisfy the Pythagorean Theorem.**

R7-2

## Additional Vocabulary Support I O

Helps students develop and reinforce understanding of key terms and concepts.

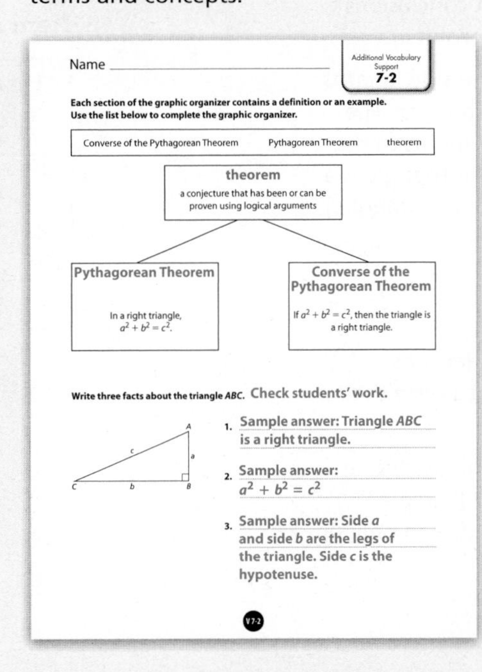

Name ______

Additional Vocabulary Support 7-2

**Each section of the graphic organizer contains a definition or an example. Use the list below to complete the graphic organizer.**

Converse of the Pythagorean Theorem Pythagorean Theorem theorem

**theorem**
a conjecture that has been or can be proven using logical arguments

**Pythagorean Theorem**
In a right triangle, $a^2 + b^2 = c^2$.

**Converse of the Pythagorean Theorem**
If $a^2 + b^2 = c^2$, then the triangle is a right triangle.

**Write three facts about the triangle *ABC*.** **Check students' work.**

1. **Sample answer: Triangle *ABC* is a right triangle.**
2. **Sample answer: $a^2 + b^2 = c^2$**
3. **Sample answer: Side *a* and side *b* are the legs of the triangle. Side *c* is the hypotenuse.**

V7-2

## Build Mathematical Literacy I O

Provides support for struggling readers to build mathematical literacy.

Name ______

Build Mathematical Literacy 7-2

**Read the problem below. Then answer the questions to understand the problem.**

Is the triangle in the diagram a right triangle?

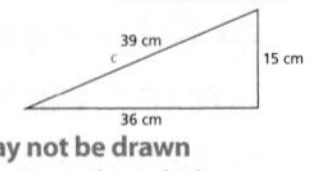

39 cm, 15 cm, 36 cm

1. Explain why you cannot answer the question simply by looking at the diagram.
**Sample answer: The diagram may not be drawn completely accurately or to scale. Even though the triangle appears to be a right triangle, there is no right angle marker in the diagram, so I cannot assume that the triangle contains a right angle.**

2. What do the three measurements in the diagram represent?
**The side lengths of the triangle**

3. The Converse of the Pythagorean Theorem states that if $a^2 + b^2 = c^2$, then the triangle is a right triangle. In the diagram, write the letter $c$ next to the side length that should be substituted for $c$. Explain.
**Check students' work. The variable $c$ represents the longest side length and the length 39 cm is the longest side.**

4. Explain how to substitute the remaining two side lengths into the equation $a^2 + b^2 = c^2$.
**Sample answer: Substitute either of the remaining side lengths for $a$ and then substitute the other side length for $b$.**

5. Once you have substituted all given values into the equation, will you need to solve for a variable? Explain.
**No; Sample answer: Each variable represents a side length, and all three side lengths are given in this problem. To answer the question, I need to check that the equation is true.**

M7-2

Go Online

 Practice   Worksheets   Math Tools Math Games

# Additional Practice

You may opt to have students complete the automatically scored Additional Practice items online.

### Item Analysis

| Example | Items | DOK |
|---|---|---|
| 1 | 5 | 2 |
| | 7 | 3 |
| 2 | 1, 2 | 1 |
| | 4, 8, 9 | 2 |
| 3 | 3, 6 | 2 |

**Interactive Practice** is available online.

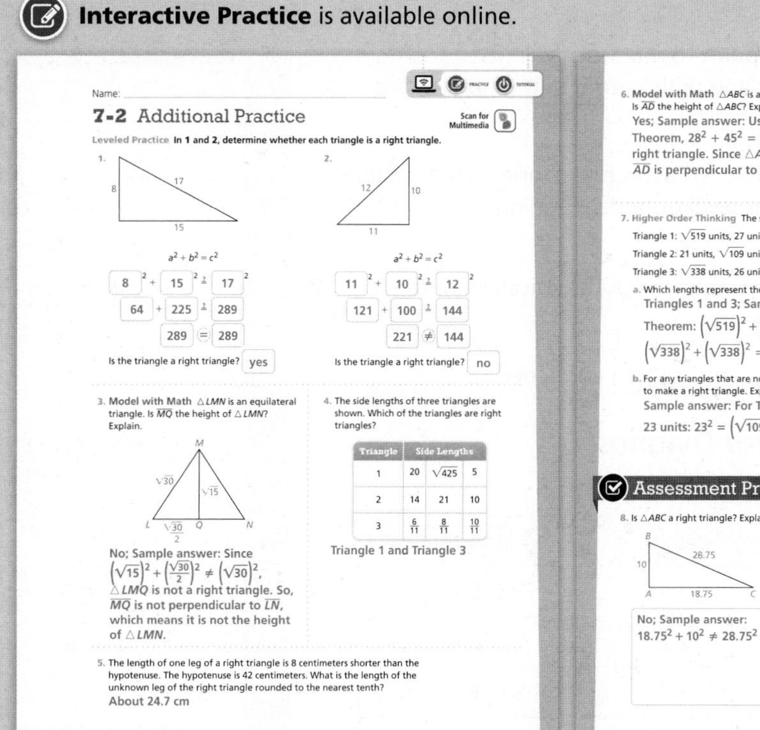

Name:

**7-2** Additional Practice

Scan for Multimedia

Leveled Practice In **1** and **2**, determine whether each triangle is a right triangle.

1. (triangle with sides 8, 15, 17)

$a^2 + b^2 = c^2$

$8^2 + 15^2 \stackrel{?}{=} 17^2$

$64 + 225 \stackrel{?}{=} 289$

$289 = 289$

Is the triangle a right triangle? yes

2. (triangle with sides 12, 10, 11)

$a^2 + b^2 = c^2$

$11^2 + 10^2 \stackrel{?}{=} 12^2$

$121 + 100 \stackrel{?}{=} 144$

$221 \neq 144$

Is the triangle a right triangle? no

3. Model with Math $\triangle LMN$ is an equilateral triangle. Is $\overline{MQ}$ the height of $\triangle LMN$? Explain.

No; Sample answer: Since $(\sqrt{15})^2 + \left(\frac{\sqrt{30}}{2}\right)^2 \neq (\sqrt{30})^2$, $\triangle LMQ$ is not a right triangle. So, $\overline{MQ}$ is not perpendicular to $\overline{LN}$, which means it is not the height of $\triangle LMN$.

4. The side lengths of three triangles are shown. Which of the triangles are right triangles?

| Triangle | Side Lengths | | |
|---|---|---|---|
| 1 | 20 | $\sqrt{425}$ | 5 |
| 2 | 14 | 21 | 10 |
| 3 | $\frac{6}{11}$ | $\frac{8}{11}$ | $\frac{10}{11}$ |

Triangle 1 and Triangle 3

5. The length of one leg of a right triangle is 8 centimeters shorter than the hypotenuse. The hypotenuse is 42 centimeters. What is the length of the unknown leg of the right triangle rounded to the nearest tenth?

About 24.7 cm

7-2 Understand the Converse of the Pythagorean Theorem 91

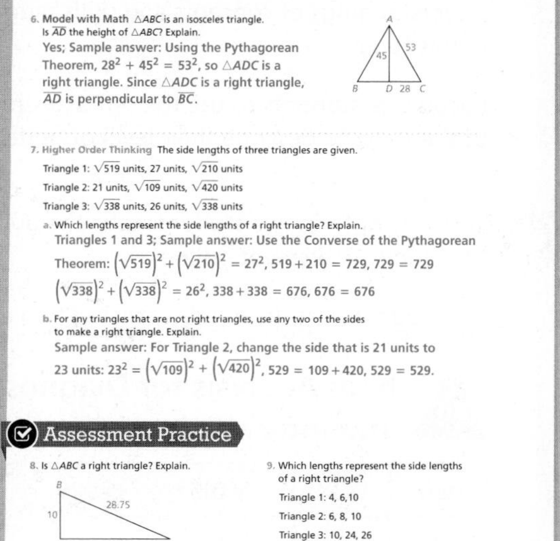

6. Model with Math $\triangle ABC$ is an isosceles triangle. Is $\overline{AD}$ the height of $\triangle ABC$? Explain.

Yes; Sample answer: Using the Pythagorean Theorem, $28^2 + 45^2 = 53^2$, so $\triangle ADC$ is a right triangle. Since $\triangle ADC$ is a right triangle, $\overline{AD}$ is perpendicular to $\overline{BC}$.

7. Higher Order Thinking The side lengths of three triangles are given.

Triangle 1: $\sqrt{519}$ units, 27 units, $\sqrt{210}$ units

Triangle 2: 21 units, $\sqrt{109}$ units, $\sqrt{420}$ units

Triangle 3: $\sqrt{338}$ units, 26 units, $\sqrt{338}$ units

a. Which lengths represent the side lengths of a right triangle? Explain.

Triangles 1 and 3; Sample answer: Use the Converse of the Pythagorean Theorem: $(\sqrt{519})^2 + (\sqrt{210})^2 = 27^2$, $519 + 210 = 729$, $729 = 729$

$(\sqrt{338})^2 + (\sqrt{338})^2 = 26^2$, $338 + 338 = 676$, $676 = 676$

b. For any triangles that are not right triangles, use any two of the sides to make a right triangle. Explain.

Sample answer: For Triangle 2, change the side that is 21 units to 23 units: $23^2 = (\sqrt{109})^2 + (\sqrt{420})^2$, $529 = 109 + 420$, $529 = 529$.

Assessment Practice

8. Is $\triangle ABC$ a right triangle? Explain.

No; Sample answer: $18.75^2 + 10^2 \neq 28.75^2$

9. Which lengths represent the side lengths of a right triangle?

Triangle 1: 4, 6, 10

Triangle 2: 6, 8, 10

Triangle 3: 10, 24, 26

Ⓐ Triangle 1 and Triangle 3 are right triangles.

● Triangle 2 and Triangle 3 are right triangles.

Ⓒ All of the triangles are right triangles.

Ⓓ None of the triangles are right triangles.

92 7-2 Understand the Converse of the Pythagorean Theorem

# Differentiated Intervention

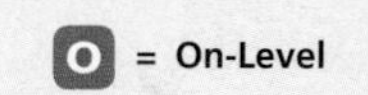 

I = Intervention O = On-Level A = Advanced

## Enrichment O A

Presents engaging problems and activities that extend the lesson concepts.

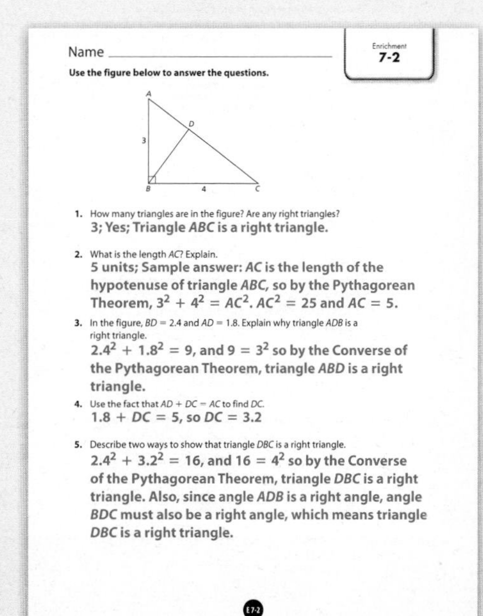

Name

Enrichment 7-2

Use the figure below to answer the questions.

1. How many triangles are in the figure? Are any right triangles?
**3; Yes; Triangle *ABC* is a right triangle.**

2. What is the length *AC*? Explain.
**5 units; Sample answer: *AC* is the length of the hypotenuse of triangle *ABC*, so by the Pythagorean Theorem, $3^2 + 4^2 = AC^2$. $AC^2 = 25$ and $AC = 5$.**

3. In the figure, $BD = 2.4$ and $AD = 1.8$. Explain why triangle *ADB* is a right triangle.
**$2.4^2 + 1.8^2 = 9$, and $9 = 3^2$ so by the Converse of the Pythagorean Theorem, triangle *ABD* is a right triangle.**

4. Use the fact that $AD + DC = AC$ to find *DC*.
**$1.8 + DC = 5$, so $DC = 3.2$**

5. Describe two ways to show that triangle *DBC* is a right triangle.
**$2.4^2 + 3.2^2 = 16$, and $16 = 4^2$ so by the Converse of the Pythagorean Theorem, triangle *DBC* is a right triangle. Also, since angle *ADB* is a right angle, angle *BDC* must also be a right angle, which means triangle *DBC* is a right triangle.**

## Math Tools and Games I O A

Offers additional activities and games to build understanding and fluency.

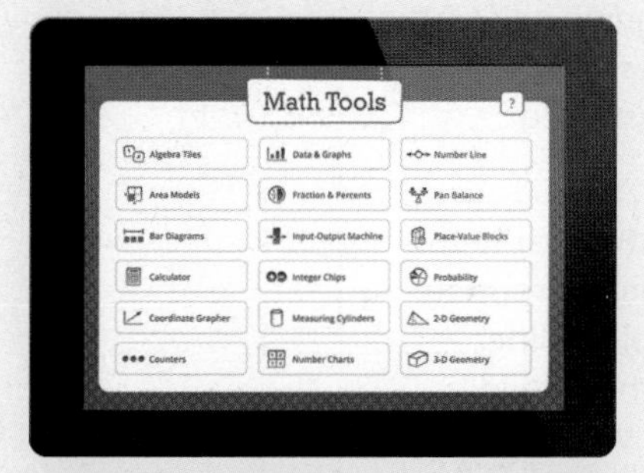


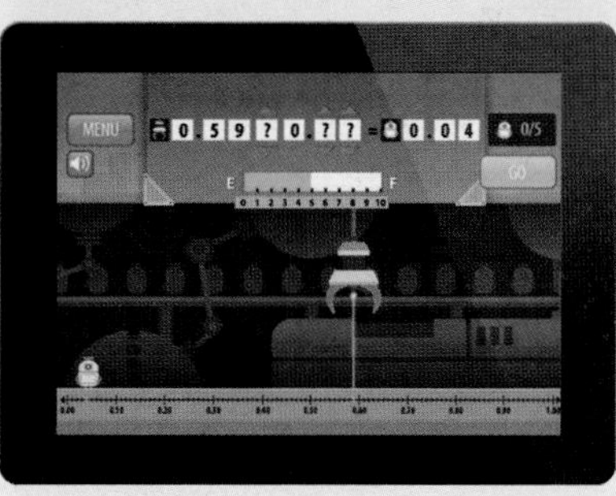

## Pick a Project and STEM Project I O A

Provides an additional opportunity for students to demonstrate understanding of key mathematical concepts.

# MID-TOPIC CHECKPOINT

Go Online

Assess

Assign the Mid-Topic Checkpoint to monitor students' understandings of concepts and skills taught in the first lessons in this topic.

Encourage students to use the self-assessment form at the bottom of the page to describe their level of understanding.

You may opt to have students take the automatically scored Mid-Topic Assessment online.

Use students' results to adjust instruction as needed.

## Item Analysis for Diagnosis and Intervention

| Item | DOK | MDIS | Lesson | Standard |
|---|---|---|---|---|
| 1 | 2 | N64 | 7-1 | 8.G.B.6 |
| 2 | 3 | N65 | 7-2 | 8.G.B.6 |
| 3 | 3 | N64 | 7-1 | 8.G.B.6, 8.G.B.7 |
| 4 | 2 | N64 | 7-1 | 8.G.B.7 |
| 5 | 2 | N64 | 7-1 | 8.G.B.7 |
| 6 | 1 | N64, N65 | 7-2 | 8.G.B.7 |

## Scoring Guide

| Score | Recommendations |
|---|---|
| Greater Than 85% | Assign the corresponding MDIS for items answered incorrectly. Use Enrichment activities with the student. |
| 70%–85% | Assign the corresponding MDIS for items answered incorrectly. You may also assign Reteach to Build Understanding and Virtual Nerd Video assets for the lessons correlated to the items the student answered incorrectly. |
| Less Than 70% | Assign the corresponding MDIS for items answered incorrectly. Assign appropriate intervention lessons available online. You may also assign Reteach to Build Understanding, Additional Vocabulary Support, Build Mathematical Literacy, and Virtual Nerd Video assets for the lessons correlated to the items the student answered incorrectly. |

Available Online

Name: ____________

MID-TOPIC CHECKPOINT

TOPIC 7

1. **Vocabulary** How are the hypotenuse and the legs of a right triangle related? *Lesson 7-1*
   **Sample answer: The hypotenuse is the longest side of a right triangle, and the legs are the shorter sides. The square of the hypotenuse is equal to the sum of the squares of the legs.**

2. Given that $\triangle PQR$ has side lengths of 12.5 centimeters, 30 centimeters, and 32.5 centimeters, prove $\triangle PQR$ is a right triangle. *Lesson 7-2*
   **Sample answer: Apply the Converse of the Pythagorean Theorem.**
   $a^2 + b^2 \stackrel{?}{=} c^2$
   $12.5^2 + 30^2 \stackrel{?}{=} 32.5^2$
   $156.25 + 900 \stackrel{?}{=} 1056.25$
   $1056.25 = 1056.25$

3. Ella said that if she knows the lengths of just two sides of any triangle, then she can find the length of the third side by using the Pythagorean Theorem. Is Ella correct? Explain. *Lesson 7-1*
   **No; Sample answer: It is true that if you know the lengths of two sides of a right triangle, then you can find the length of the third side by substituting the two known side lengths into the equation $a^2 + b^2 = c^2$ and solving for the third side length. But you cannot use this relationship if the triangle is not a right triangle.**

4. Find the unknown side length. Round to the nearest tenth. *Lesson 7-1*
   **About 6.9 cm**
   8 cm
   4 cm

5. The height of a shed is 6 m. A ladder leans against the shed with its base 4.5 m away, and its top just reaching the roof. What is the length of the ladder? *Lesson 7-1*
   **7.5 m**

6. Select all the sets of lengths that could represent the sides of a right triangle. *Lesson 7-2*
   - ☐ 5 cm, 10 cm, 15 cm
   - ☐ 7 in., 14 in., 25 in.
   - ■ 13 m, 84 m, 85 m
   - ☐ 5 ft, 11 ft, 12 ft
   - ■ 6 ft, 9 ft, $\sqrt{117}$ ft

How well did you do on the mid-topic checkpoint? Fill in the stars. ☆☆☆

Topic 7 Understand and Apply the Pythagorean Theorem 407

### Mid-Topic Assessment Master

Name ____________

Topic 7 Mid-Topic Assessment

1. **Vocabulary** What is the hypotenuse, and where is it found?
   **Sample answer: The hypotenuse is the longest side of a right triangle, opposite the 90° angle. The square of the hypotenuse equals the sum of the squares of the other two sides.**

2. Triangle *LMN* has side lengths of 18.5 inches, 10 inches, and 15.5 inches. Use the Converse of the Pythagorean Theorem to prove that *LMN* is not a right triangle. Write numbers 1-4 to order the steps.
   **3** $100 + 240.25 \stackrel{?}{=} 342.25$
   **1** $a^2 + b^2 \stackrel{?}{=} c^2$
   **4** $340.25 \neq 342.25$
   **2** $10^2 + 15.5^2 \stackrel{?}{=} 18.5^2$
   Therefore, triangle *LMN* is not a right triangle.

3. What information must you know about a triangle in order to use the Pythagorean Theorem to find the length of a missing side?
   **Sample answer: In order to use the Pythagorean Theorem, you must know the lengths of any two sides of the triangle and know that one of the angles measures 90°.**

4. Find the unknown side length. Round to the nearest tenth.
   **About 24.5 ft**
   5 ft
   25 ft

5. The lengths of the legs of a right triangle are 8 inches and 9 inches. What is the length of the hypotenuse? Round to the nearest inch.
   **12 in.**

6. Select all the sets of lengths that could represent the sides of a right triangle.
   - ☐ 6 cm, 7 cm, 8 cm
   - ☐ 7 in., 17 in., 11 in.
   - ☐ 9 m, 12 m, 14 m
   - ■ 11 ft, 60 ft, 61 ft
   - ■ 3 mm, 9 mm, $\sqrt{90}$ mm

Mid-Topic Assessment 1 of 1

# MID-TOPIC PERFORMANCE TASK

Go Online

Assess

Assess students' ability to apply the concepts and skills in the first part of the topic using the Mid-Topic Performance Task, found in the Student's Edition or online.

## Item Analysis for Diagnosis and Intervention

| Part | DOK | MDIS | Lesson | Standard |
|---|---|---|---|---|
| A | 3 | N64 | 7-1 | 8.G.B.7 |
| B | 1 | N64 | 7-1 | 8.G.B.7 |
| C | 3 | N64 | 7-1 | 8.G.B.7 |
| D | 3 | N64 | 7-1 | 8.G.B.7 |

## Scoring Rubric

| Part | Points | Mid-Topic Performance Task |
|---|---|---|
| A | 2 | Correct answer and explanation |
| | 1 | Correct answer or explanation |
| B | 2 | Correct answer and explanation |
| | 1 | Correct answer |
| C | 2 | Correct answer and explanation |
| | 1 | Correct answer or explanation |
| D | 2 | Correct answer and explanation |
| | 1 | Correct answer or explanation |

## Scoring Guide

| Score | Recommendations |
|---|---|
| Greater Than 85% | Assign the corresponding MDIS for items answered incorrectly. Use Enrichment activities with the student. |
| 70%–85% | Assign the corresponding MDIS for items answered incorrectly. You may also assign Reteach to Build Understanding and Virtual Nerd Video assets for the lessons correlated to the items the student answered incorrectly. |
| Less Than 70% | Assign the corresponding MDIS for items answered incorrectly. Assign appropriate intervention lessons available online. You may also assign Reteach to Build Understanding, Additional Vocabulary Support, Build Mathematical Literacy, and Virtual Nerd Video assets for the lessons correlated to the items the student answered incorrectly. |

Available Online

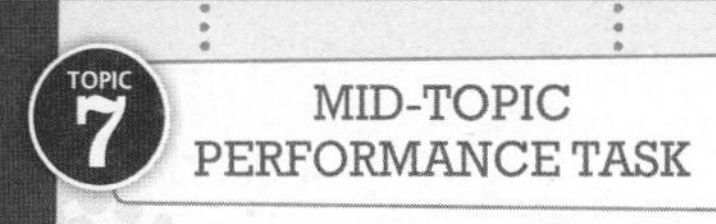

TOPIC 7 MID-TOPIC PERFORMANCE TASK

Javier is standing near a palm tree. He holds an electronic tape measure near his eyes and finds the three distances shown.

25 ft
?
7 ft
9 ft

**PART A**

Javier says that he can now use the Pythagorean Theorem to find the height of the tree. Explain. Use vocabulary terms in your explanation.

Sample answer: The lines formed by Javier's measurements and by the height of the tree form two right triangles. He knows the lengths of the hypotenuse and one leg of each triangle. For each triangle, he can use the Pythagorean Theorem to find the unknown length of the other leg. If he adds the lengths of those legs, he will know the height of the tree.

**PART B**

Find the height of the tree. Round to the nearest tenth. Show your work.

About 29.7 ft; Sample answer: For the upper triangle: $a^2 + 7^2 = 25^2$; $a^2 + 49 = 625$; $a^2 = 576$; $a = 24$. For the lower triangle: $a^2 + 7^2 = 9^2$; $a^2 + 49 = 81$; $a^2 = 32$; $a \approx 5.7$. Height of the tree: $24 + 5.7 = 29.7$.

**PART C**

Javier moves backward so that his horizontal distance from the palm tree is 3 feet greater. Will the distance from his eyes to the top of the tree also be 3 feet greater? Explain.

No; Sample answer: Javier's move backward changes the upper right triangle so that the length of the shorter leg is now 10 feet. From Part B, the length of the longer leg of this triangle is 24 feet. Use the Pythagorean Theorem to find the hypotenuse of the new triangle: $10^2 + 24^2 = c^2$; $100 + 576 = c^2$; $676 = c^2$; $26 = c$. The distance from Javier's eyes to the top of the tree will only be 1 foot greater.

**PART D**

Could Javier change his horizontal distance from the tree so that the distance from his eyes to the top of the tree is only 20 feet? Explain.

No; Sample answer: The 20-foot distance from Javier's eyes to the top of the tree would be the length of the hypotenuse of the upper right triangle. From Part B, the length of one leg of this triangle is 24 feet. But the hypotenuse is the longest side of a right triangle. So, it is impossible for the distance from Javier's eyes to the top of the tree to be 20 feet.

408 **Topic 7** Understand and Apply the Pythagorean Theorem

Go Online

Video Activity

# Lesson 7-3 Apply the Pythagorean Theorem to Solve Problems

## Lesson Overview

FOCUS

### Mathematics Objective

**Students will be able to:**

✔ use the Pythagorean Theorem and its converse to solve problems.

### Essential Understanding

The Pythagorean Theorem and its converse can be used to solve real-world problems that involve right triangles.

COHERENCE

**Previously in this topic, students:**

- learned and applied the Pythagorean Theorem and its converse.

**In this lesson, students:**

- apply their knowledge of the Pythagorean Theorem to solve real-world problems, including problems about triangles in three dimensions.
- verify right triangles to solve real-world situations.

**Later in this topic, students will:**

- apply their knowledge of the Pythagorean Theorem to solve for distance in a coordinate plane.

**Cross-Cluster Connection** Using the Pythagorean Theorem (8.G.2) connects to using radicals and integer exponents (8.EE.1).

RIGOR

This lesson emphasizes a blend of **application** and **procedural skill and fluency**.

- Students practice using the Pythagorean Theorem and its converse in a variety of contexts.
- Students apply their understanding of the Pythagorean Theorem and its converse to solve real-world problems in two and three dimensions.

## Language Support

### Lesson Language Objective

Explain how to use the Pythagorean Theorem to solve problems.

Additional resources are available in the **Language Support Handbook**.

## Math Anytime

### Today's Challenge

Use the Topic 7 problems any time during this topic.

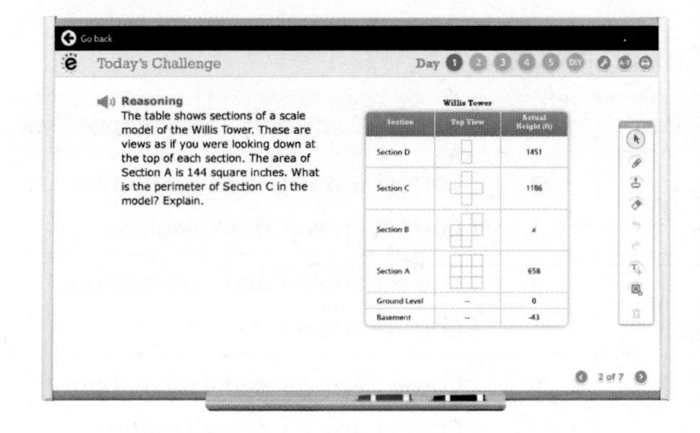


## Mathematics Overview — Common Core Standards

### Content Standards

In this lesson, you will focus on **8.G.B.7.**

- **8.G.B.7** Apply the Pythagorean Theorem to determine unknown side lengths in right triangles in real-world and mathematical problems in two and three dimensions.

### Mathematical Practice Standards

**MP.3 Construct Viable Arguments and Critique the Reasoning of Others**
Students learn to justify their conclusions about missing side lengths and about triangle properties using their mathematical knowledge about right triangles.

**MP.7 Look for and Make Use of Structure**
Students extend their knowledge of the Pythagorean Theorem in two dimensions to applications involving figures in three dimensions.

**MP.8 Look for and Express Regularity in Repeated Reasoning**
Students practice using the Pythagorean Theorem and its converse to solve for unknown side lengths and to determine whether a triangle is a right triangle. They will begin to see the patterns in similar situations.

STEP 1 | Problem-Based Learning

15-20 min

Go Online

Activity

# Solve & Discuss It!

Formative Assessment

**Purpose** Students calculate the hypotenuse in a real-world situation and connect it to applying the Pythagorean Theorem to solve problems in the Visual Learning Bridge and Example 2.

## ETP Before — WHOLE CLASS

**1 Introduce the Problem**

**2 Check for Understanding of the Problem**

Ask students: Have you ever packed a long object in a box or suitcase?

## ETP During — SMALL GROUP

**3 Observe Students at Work**

Observe students while they work, noting the strategies that students take to identify how the umbrella could be placed in a box. Students may reason that the umbrella cannot be laid down flat but instead needs to be placed on a diagonal. Students will then identify, using the Pythagorean Theorem, if the umbrella could fit in any of the boxes. If needed, ask Could the umbrella lay flat in any of the boxes?

### Early Finishers

How would the problem change if the umbrella was 40 inches long? [Sample answer: The umbrella would only fit along the inside diagonal of the box that measures 27 × 14 × 27 inches.]

## ETP After — WHOLE CLASS

**4 Discuss Solution Strategies and Key Ideas**

Have students discuss the ways the umbrella could be placed in the boxes; none of the sides are long enough for it to lay flat, so the umbrella needs to be placed on either the side diagonal or on the inside diagonal. Then have them discuss how they determined that the diagonals of the boxes were the hypotenuses of right triangles.

Have students share their calculations for each of these diagonals, then discuss which boxes the umbrella could fit in; all of them.

Have them discuss which box would be the most practical to ship the umbrella in; while the umbrella fits into the larger box, using one of the smaller boxes would be more practical as shipping rates can be calculated not just on weight but on the size of the package as well.

**5 Consider Instructional Implications**

When presenting Example 1, remind them how they used the Pythagorean Theorem to calculate the diagonals of rectangular prisms in the Solve & Discuss It. The problem in Example 1 is exactly like solving for the bottom diagonal in the boxes. When presenting Example 2, ask students to consider the boxes given in the Solve & Discuss It and find the largest umbrella Carlos could ship using the boxes he already has; about 40.7 inches long.

## Analyze Student Work

**Solve and Discuss It!** Activity is available online.

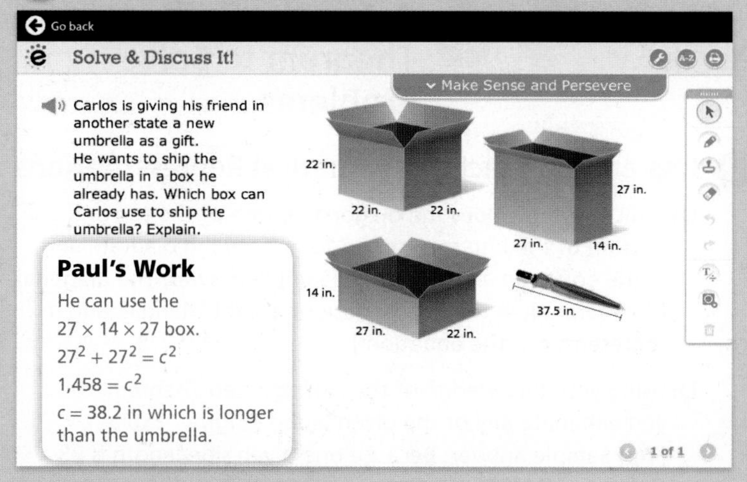


**Paul** calculates the diagonal of one of the sides of the boxes and finds that it is longer than the umbrella. Therefore, he determines that the umbrella can fit in that box.

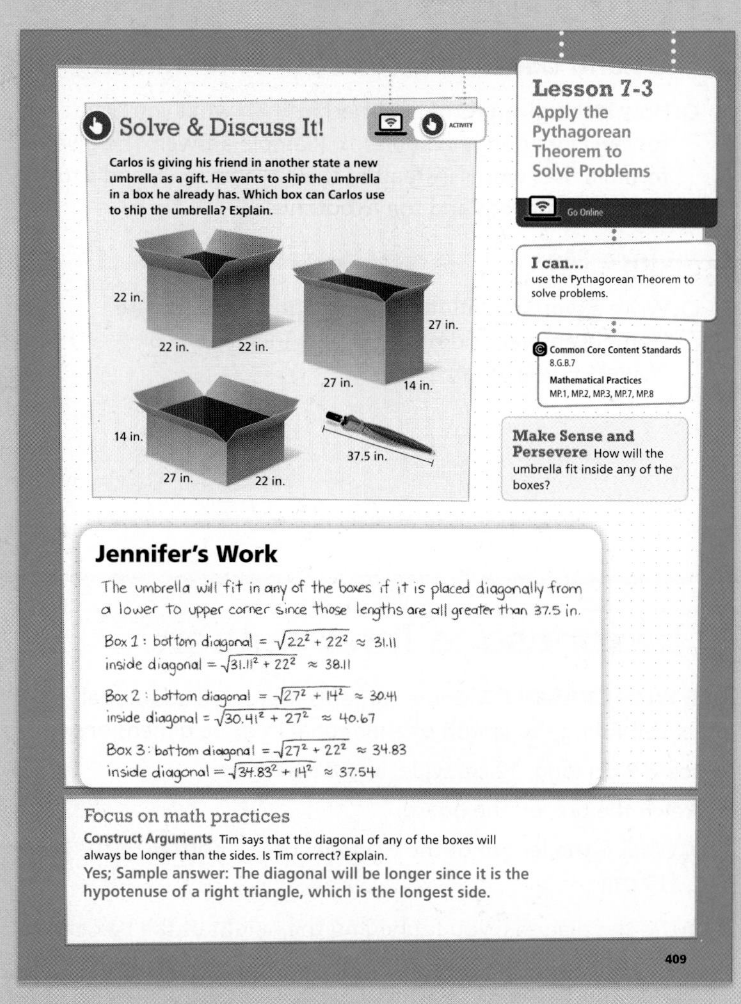


**Jennifer** sees that the inside diagonal of each box is the largest dimension, and calculates it by first computing the hypotenuse of the bottom diagonal and using this as one of the side lengths for the inside triangle.

# STEP 2 | Visual Learning

Go Online

## ETP Establish Mathematics Goals to Focus Learning

Engage students in a discussion about the ***Essential Question***. Make sure they understand the equation for the Pythagorean Theorem and how it can be used to solve for unknown side lengths and to identify right triangles.

## EXAMPLE 1

## Apply the Pythagorean Theorem to Solve Problems

### ETP Use and Connect Mathematical Representations

**Q:** Which variable does the diagonal length of the top and bottom of the kite correspond to in both the diagram and in the equation $a^2 + b^2 = c^2$? [Sample answer: The diagonal of a rectangle is the hypotenuse of a right triangle, and it represents *c* in the equation.]

**Q:** Using your knowledge of the Pythagorean Theorem, can you eliminate any of the given wood lengths? Explain. [Yes; Sample answer: Because one given side length is 28 inches, and the hypotenuse is always longer than either leg, the diagonal brace (hypotenuse) cannot be 28 inches.]

## Try It!

**Formative** Assessment

### ETP Elicit and Use Evidence of Student Thinking

**Q:** How is the given formula different than what you have seen for the Pythagorean Theorem? [Sample answer: The given formula uses words instead of the variables *a*, *b*, and *c* to represent the legs and the hypotenuse.]

### Convince Me!

**Q:** Write a word equation for the diagonal of a square. [Sample answer: $(\text{side})^2 + (\text{side})^2 = (\text{diagonal})^2$ or $2(\text{side})^2 = (\text{diagonal})^2$]

**Visual Learning Animation Plus** is available online.

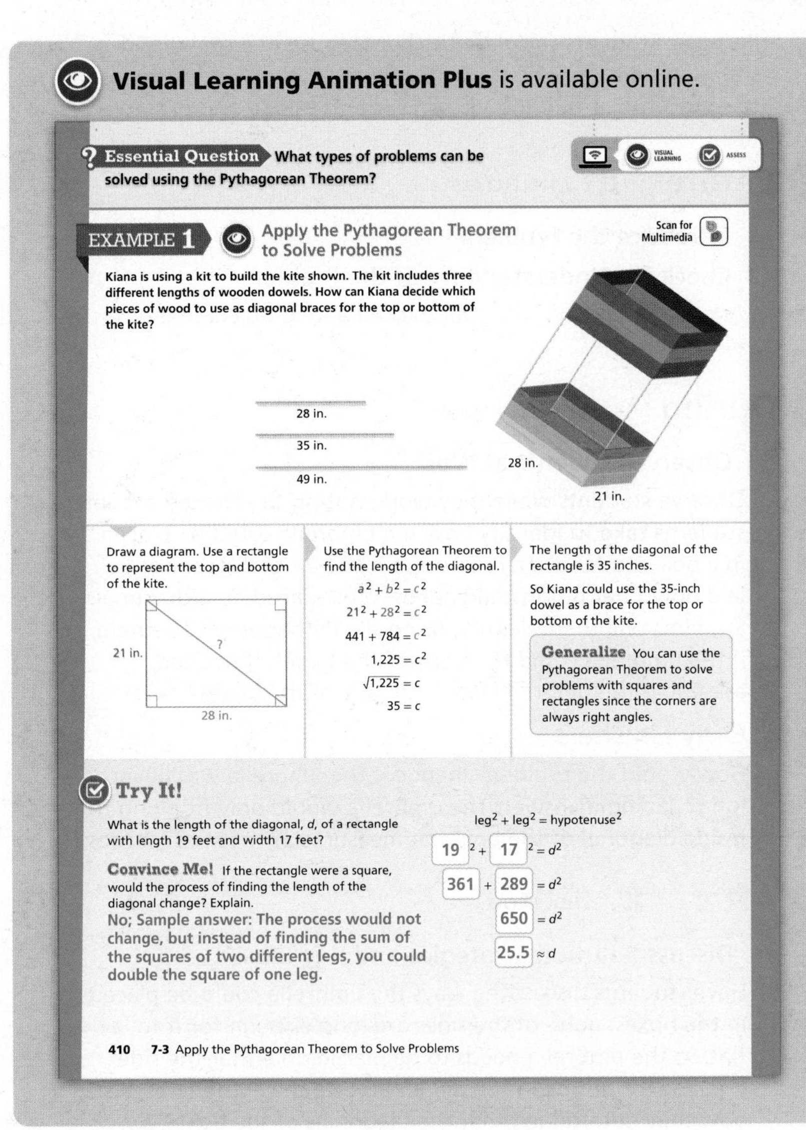

**Essential Question** What types of problems can be solved using the Pythagorean Theorem?

EXAMPLE 1 Apply the Pythagorean Theorem to Solve Problems

Scan for Multimedia

Kiana is using a kit to build the kite shown. The kit includes three different lengths of wooden dowels. How can Kiana decide which pieces of wood to use as diagonal braces for the top or bottom of the kite?

28 in.
35 in.
49 in.

28 in.
21 in.

Draw a diagram. Use a rectangle to represent the top and bottom of the kite.

21 in.
?
28 in.

Use the Pythagorean Theorem to find the length of the diagonal.

$a^2 + b^2 = c^2$
$21^2 + 28^2 = c^2$
$441 + 784 = c^2$
$1{,}225 = c^2$
$\sqrt{1{,}225} = c$
$35 = c$

The length of the diagonal of the rectangle is 35 inches.

So Kiana could use the 35-inch dowel as a brace for the top or bottom of the kite.

**Generalize** You can use the Pythagorean Theorem to solve problems with squares and rectangles since the corners are always right angles.

**Try It!**

What is the length of the diagonal, *d*, of a rectangle with length 19 feet and width 17 feet?

$\text{leg}^2 + \text{leg}^2 = \text{hypotenuse}^2$
$19^2 + 17^2 = d^2$
$361 + 289 = d^2$
$650 = d^2$
$25.5 \approx d$

**Convince Me!** If the rectangle were a square, would the process of finding the length of the diagonal change? Explain.

No; Sample answer: The process would not change, but instead of finding the sum of the squares of two different legs, you could double the square of one leg.

410 7-3 Apply the Pythagorean Theorem to Solve Problems

Students can access the ***Visual Learning Animation Plus*** by using the **BouncePages app** to scan this page. Students can download the app for free in their mobile devices' app store.

## Response to Intervention

**USE WITH EXAMPLE 2** Some students may need additional practice finding the length of a diagonal in three dimensions.

A box is 9 cm long, 12 cm wide, and 8 cm high.

- Sketch the box on the board.

**Q:** What is the length of the diagonal of the bottom of the box? [15 cm]

**Q:** Use the diagonal you found and the height of the box as the legs of a right triangle. What is the length of the diagonal of this right triangle? [17 cm]

## Enrichment

**USE WITH EXAMPLE 1** Challenge students to find patterns and make generalizations across the situations described.

- Assume all the dimensions of the kite were doubled.

**Q:** Predict what would happen to the length of the diagonal brace. [It would double in length.]

**Q:** Test your prediction. Solve to determine the length of the diagonal brace. [70 inches]

- Assume all the dimensions of the kite were cut in half.

**Q:** Predict what would happen to the length of the diagonal. [It would also be cut in half.]

**Q:** Solve for the length of the diagonal. [17.5 inches]

Go Online

Activity

Assess

## EXAMPLE 2  Apply the Pythagorean Theorem to Triangles in Three Dimensions

### ETP Pose Purposeful Questions

**Q:** Why is it necessary to determine the diagonal of the bottom of the tank first? [Sample answer: To use the Pythagorean Theorem, you must know two side lengths of a right triangle. The height of the aquarium is one side length, and *d* is the other side length. Together, they create a right triangle with the unknown length of the hypotenuse.]

## EXAMPLE 3  Apply the Converse of the Pythagorean Theorem to Solve Problems

###  Pose Purposeful Questions

**Q:** If the triangular shelf is a right triangle, how do you know which value would represent the hypotenuse? [Sample answer: The hypotenuse is always the longest side, so in this case, the 30-inch side would be the hypotenuse.]

**Q:** Why do you use the Converse of the Pythagorean Theorem instead of the Pythagorean Theorem to solve this problem? [Sample answer: You use the Converse of the Pythagorean Theorem because you know the three side lengths, and you need to determine whether the triangle is a right triangle.]

##  Try It!  Formative Assessment

###  Elicit and Use Evidence of Student Thinking

**Q:** The height, *h*, represents the length of one leg of a right triangle with a hypotenuse of 15 ft. What is the length of the other leg? [Half the base length, or 12 ft]

**Examples and Try Its!** are available online.

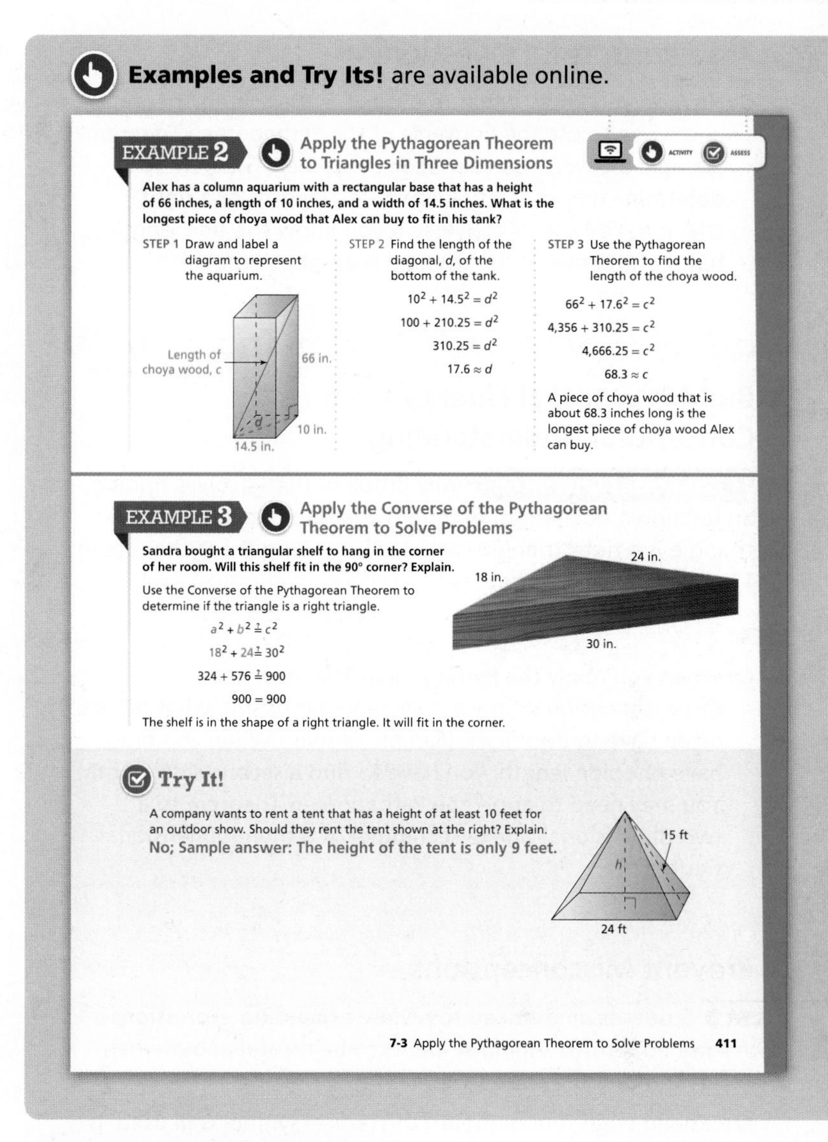
EXAMPLE 2 Apply the Pythagorean Theorem to Triangles in Three Dimensions

Alex has a column aquarium with a rectangular base that has a height of 66 inches, a length of 10 inches, and a width of 14.5 inches. What is the longest piece of choya wood that Alex can buy to fit in his tank?

STEP 1 Draw and label a diagram to represent the aquarium.



STEP 2 Find the length of the diagonal, *d*, of the bottom of the tank.

$10^2 + 14.5^2 = d^2$

$100 + 210.25 = d^2$

$310.25 = d^2$

$17.6 \approx d$

STEP 3 Use the Pythagorean Theorem to find the length of the choya wood.

$66^2 + 17.6^2 = c^2$

$4{,}356 + 310.25 = c^2$

$4{,}666.25 = c^2$

$68.3 \approx c$

A piece of choya wood that is about 68.3 inches long is the longest piece of choya wood Alex can buy.

EXAMPLE 3 Apply the Converse of the Pythagorean Theorem to Solve Problems

Sandra bought a triangular shelf to hang in the corner of her room. Will this shelf fit in the 90° corner? Explain.

Use the Converse of the Pythagorean Theorem to determine if the triangle is a right triangle.

$a^2 + b^2 \stackrel{?}{=} c^2$

$18^2 + 24^2 \stackrel{?}{=} 30^2$

$324 + 576 \stackrel{?}{=} 900$

$900 = 900$



The shelf is in the shape of a right triangle. It will fit in the corner.

Try It!

A company wants to rent a tent that has a height of at least 10 feet for an outdoor show. Should they rent the tent shown at the right? Explain.
No; Sample answer: The height of the tent is only 9 feet.



7-3 Apply the Pythagorean Theorem to Solve Problems 411

## ADDITIONAL EXAMPLES 

**For additional examples go online.**

## ELL English Language Learners

**ENTERING** Review Example 1.
Help students use the illustrations as supports to understand the problem.

**Q:** Look at the second sentence. It says "The kit includes three different lengths of wooden dowels." Which part of the illustration shows this? [Students should point to the dowels shown.] What do you think a dowel is? [Sample answer: A stick or rod]

**Q:** What do you think the question is asking you to do? [Sample answer: Choose which of the three dowels is the same length as the diagonal.]

**EMERGING** Review Example 1.
English Language Learners may struggle with words like *dowel* and *brace*. Explain what these words mean and how they fit into the context of the problem. Help them understand how they can use the diagram as support to understand the problem.

**Q:** Could you solve this problem without understanding what all of the words mean? Explain. [Yes; Sample answer: You can use context to figure out meanings of words you don't know. You can use the diagram to see that you need to find the hypotenuse of a right triangle given the measurements shown.]

**EXPANDING** Complete Example 3.
Have students summarize the important information in their own words.

**Q:** What values should you substitute for *a* and *b*? Explain. [18 in., 24 in.; Sample answers: The legs of the triangle or the shorter side lengths of the shelf]

**Q:** What is the 30-inch side called? [Hypotenuse]

**Q:** How do you know the triangle is a right triangle? [Sample answers: because of the converse of the Pythagorean Theorem, because the numbers make the Pythagorean equation true.]

Go Online

Key Concept

Assess

Activity

## KEY CONCEPT

### ETP Pose Purposeful Questions

**Q:** How do you know when to use the Pythagorean Theorem and when to use the Converse of the Pythagorean Theorem? [Sample answer: You use the Pythagorean Theorem to determine one of the unknown side lengths of a right triangle. You use its converse if you know the side lengths, but do not know if the triangle is a right triangle.]

## Do You Understand/Do You Know How?

Formative Assessment

### ETP Build Procedural Fluency from Conceptual Understanding

**Essential Question** Any problem that involves finding an unknown side length of a right triangle or determining if a triangle is a right triangle can be solved using the Pythagorean Theorem or its converse.

**ITEM 2**

**Q:** When you apply the Pythagorean Theorem to a three-dimensional figure (a rectangular prism), what do you often have to find first? [Sample answer: When you only have one side length, you have to find a second side length. You may need to apply the Pythagorean Theorem to a two-dimensional side (a rectangle) of a three-dimensional figure.]

### Prevent Misconceptions

**ITEM 3** Students might need to review expanding expressions with squared terms. Remind students to be careful about when they can and cannot group factors.

**Q:** Expand what is underneath the radical symbol Gigi used. Is it equal to the expression Glen used? Explain. [No; Sample answer: $a^2 + 2ab + b^2 \neq a^2 + b^2$]

Available Online

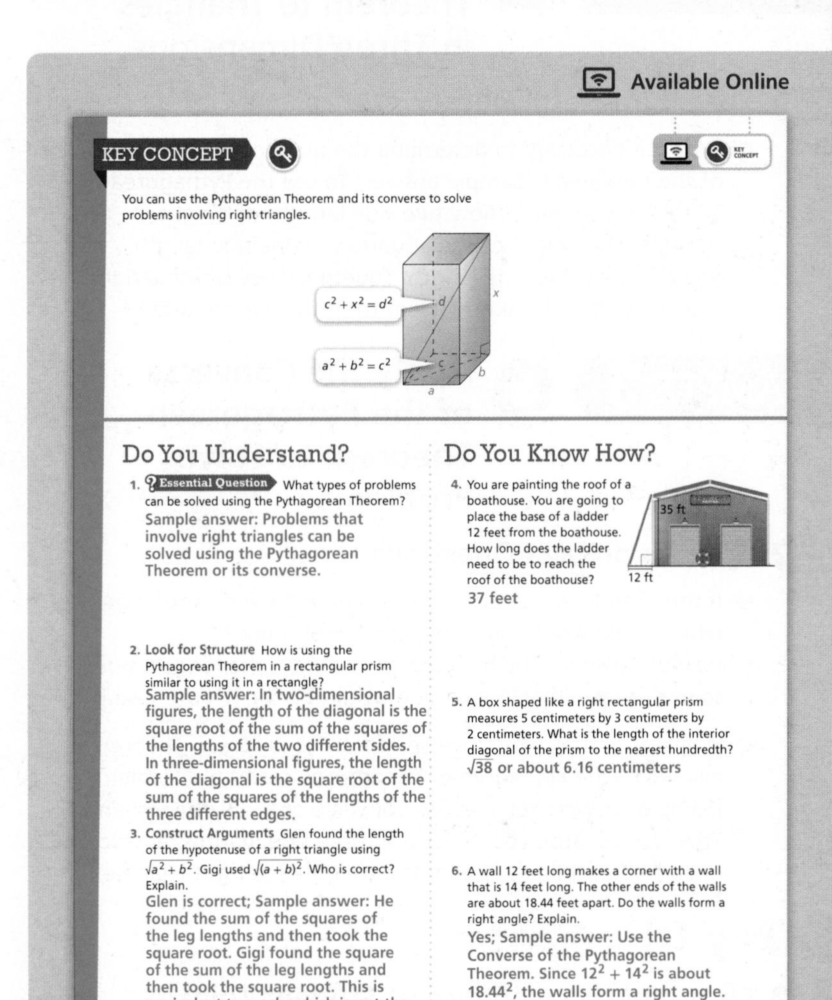

KEY CONCEPT

You can use the Pythagorean Theorem and its converse to solve problems involving right triangles.



**Do You Understand?**

1. **Essential Question** What types of problems can be solved using the Pythagorean Theorem? Sample answer: Problems that involve right triangles can be solved using the Pythagorean Theorem or its converse.

2. **Look for Structure** How is using the Pythagorean Theorem in a rectangular prism similar to using it in a rectangle? Sample answer: In two-dimensional figures, the length of the diagonal is the square root of the sum of the squares of the lengths of the two different sides. In three-dimensional figures, the length of the diagonal is the square root of the sum of the squares of the lengths of the three different edges.

3. **Construct Arguments** Glen found the length of the hypotenuse of a right triangle using $\sqrt{a^2 + b^2}$. Gigi used $\sqrt{(a + b)^2}$. Who is correct? Explain. Glen is correct; Sample answer: He found the sum of the squares of the leg lengths and then took the square root. Gigi found the square of the sum of the leg lengths and then took the square root. This is equivalent to $a + b$, which is not the length of the hypotenuse.

**Do You Know How?**

4. You are painting the roof of a boathouse. You are going to place the base of a ladder 12 feet from the boathouse. How long does the ladder need to be to reach the roof of the boathouse? 37 feet



5. A box shaped like a right rectangular prism measures 5 centimeters by 3 centimeters by 2 centimeters. What is the length of the interior diagonal of the prism to the nearest hundredth? $\sqrt{38}$ or about 6.16 centimeters

6. A wall 12 feet long makes a corner with a wall that is 14 feet long. The other ends of the walls are about 18.44 feet apart. Do the walls form a right angle? Explain. Yes; Sample answer: Use the Converse of the Pythagorean Theorem. Since $12^2 + 14^2$ is about $18.44^2$, the walls form a right angle.

412 7-3 Apply the Pythagorean Theorem to Solve Problems

## ADDITIONAL EXAMPLE 2

**Q:** What is the difference between the height and the slant height of a square pyramid? [Sample answer: The height is the distance from the top of the pyramid straight down to the middle of the base. The slant height is the distance from the top down the side to the middle of one side of the base.]

**Q:** A right triangle is formed by the height, the slant height, and a third length. What is that third length? Explain. [12.5 cm; Sample answer: It is the length from the center of the base to the edge of the base where it meets the slant height. It is half the length of one side of the base.]

**Additional Examples** are available online.

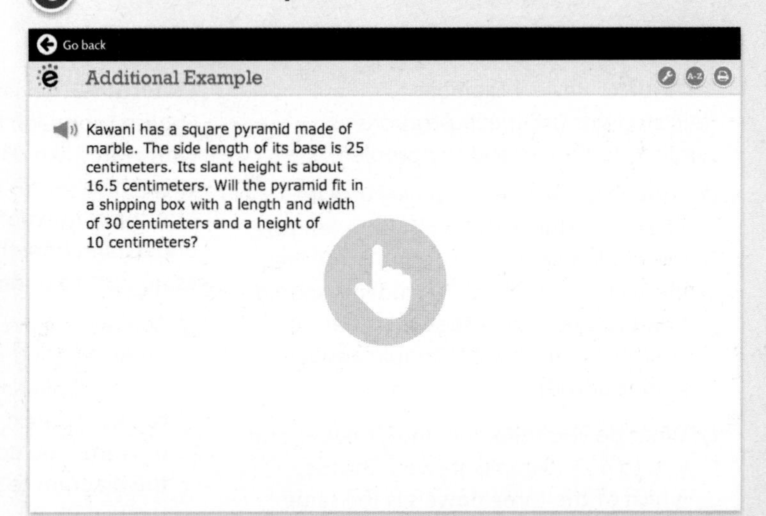



**Answer:** No

Practice Tutorials Math Tools

# Practice & Problem Solving

**Interactive Practice** and **Virtual Nerd Tutorials** are available online.

Name:

## Practice & Problem Solving

Scan for Multimedia

**Leveled Practice** In 7 and 8, use the Pythagorean Theorem to solve.

7. You are going to use an inclined plane to lift a heavy object to the top of a shelving unit with a height of 6 feet. The base of the inclined plane is 16 feet from the shelving unit. What is the length of the inclined plane? Round to the nearest tenth of a foot.

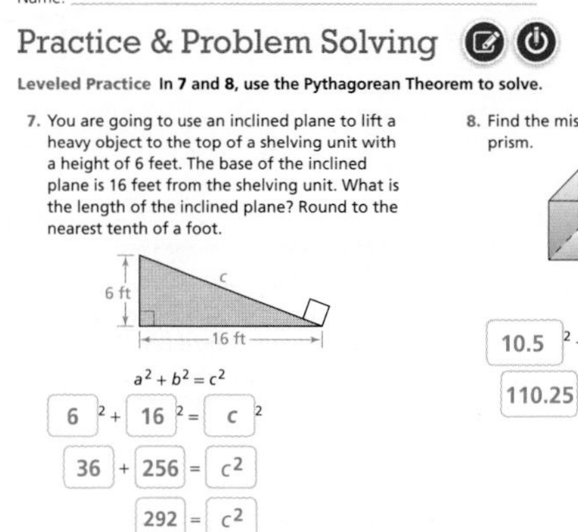


$a^2 + b^2 = c^2$

$6^2 + 16^2 = c^2$

$36 + 256 = c^2$

$292 = c^2$

$17.1 \approx c$

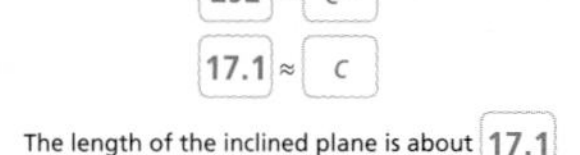

The length of the inclined plane is about 17.1 feet.

8. Find the missing lengths in the rectangular prism.

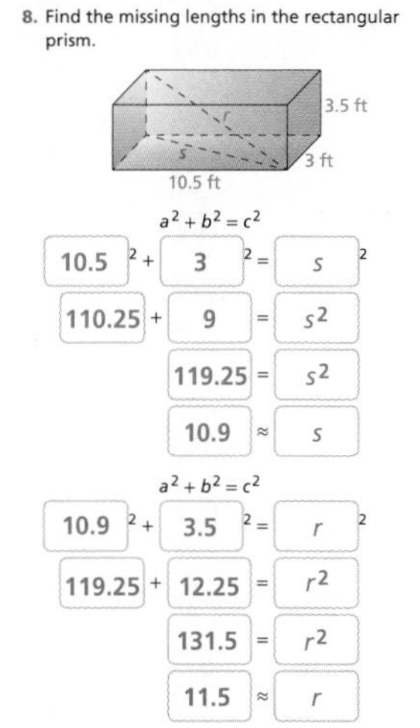


$a^2 + b^2 = c^2$

$10.5^2 + 3^2 = s^2$

$110.25 + 9 = s^2$

$119.25 = s^2$

$10.9 \approx s$

$a^2 + b^2 = c^2$

$10.9^2 + 3.5^2 = r^2$

$119.25 + 12.25 = r^2$

$131.5 = r^2$

$11.5 \approx r$

9. A stainless steel patio heater is shaped like a square pyramid. The length of one side of the base is 19.8 inches. The slant height is 92.8 inches. What is the height of the heater? Round to the nearest tenth of an inch.

About 92.3 inches

10. **Reasoning** What is the measurement of the longest line segment in a right rectangular prism that is 16 centimeters long, 9 centimeters wide, and 7 centimeters tall? Round to the nearest tenth of a centimeter.

About 19.6 cm

11. Felipe is making triangles for a stained glass window. He made the design shown, but wants to change it. Felipe wants to move the purple triangle to the corner. The purple piece has side lengths of 4.5 inches, 6 inches, and 7 inches. Can the purple piece be moved to the corner? Explain.

No; The purple piece is not a right triangle, $4.5^2 + 6^2 \neq 72$, so the purple triangle will not fit in the corner.

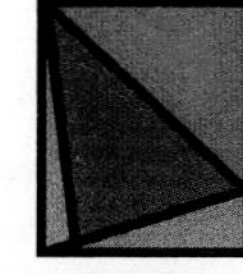



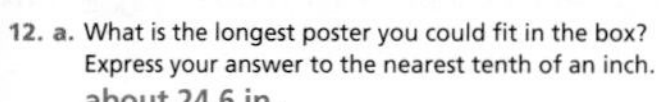

12. a. What is the longest poster you could fit in the box? Express your answer to the nearest tenth of an inch.

About 24.6 in.

b. Explain why you can fit only one maximum-length poster in the box, but you can fit multiple 21.5-inch posters in the same box.

Sample answer: The interior diagonal of the box can only take one poster, but the diagonal of the base of the box can have multiple posters stacked on top of one another.

12 in.
20 in.
8 in.

13. The corner of a room where two walls meet the floor should be a right angle. Jeff makes a mark along each wall. One mark is 3 inches from the corner. The other is 4 inches from the corner. How can Jeff use the Pythagorean Theorem to see if the walls form a right angle?

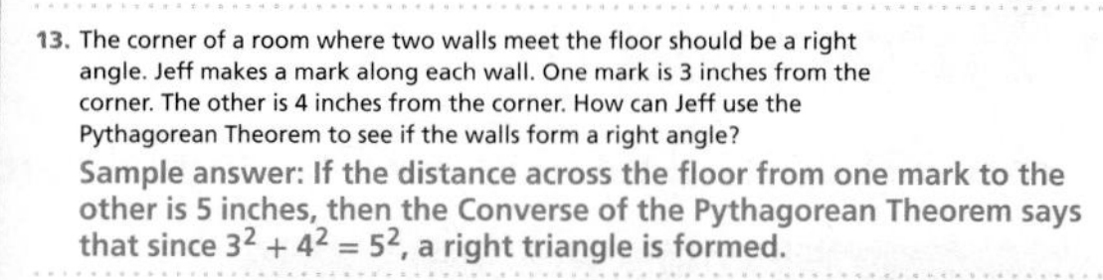

Sample answer: If the distance across the floor from one mark to the other is 5 inches, then the Converse of the Pythagorean Theorem says that since $3^2 + 4^2 = 5^2$, a right triangle is formed.

14. **Higher Order Thinking** It is recommended that a ramp have at least 6 feet of horizontal distance for every 1 foot of vertical rise along an incline. The ramp shown has a vertical rise of 2 feet. Does the ramp shown match the recommended specifications? Explain.

21 ft

Yes; Sample answer: To meet the recommendation the ramp needs to have a horizontal distance of 12 feet. The ramp shown has a horizontal distance of 21 feet.

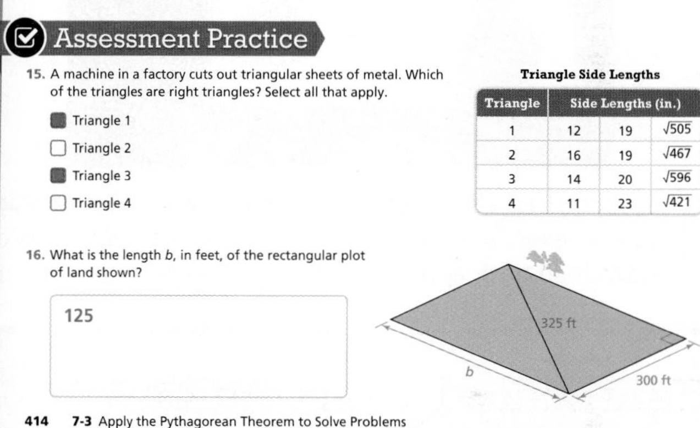

### Assessment Practice

15. A machine in a factory cuts out triangular sheets of metal. Which of the triangles are right triangles? Select all that apply.

- ■ Triangle 1
- ☐ Triangle 2
- ■ Triangle 3
- ☐ Triangle 4

**Triangle Side Lengths**

| Triangle | Side Lengths (in.) | | |
|---|---|---|---|
| 1 | 12 | 19 | $\sqrt{505}$ |
| 2 | 16 | 19 | $\sqrt{467}$ |
| 3 | 14 | 20 | $\sqrt{596}$ |
| 4 | 11 | 23 | $\sqrt{421}$ |

16. What is the length *b*, in feet, of the rectangular plot of land shown?

125

325 ft
b
300 ft



## Error Intervention

**ITEM 9** Some students may be confused about which lengths represent the leg lengths and which length represents the hypotenuse. Ask the following questions:

**Q:** Using your knowledge of height and slant height, will the missing height be a leg or the hypotenuse of the right triangle formed? [Sample answer: The missing height will be a leg of the right triangle formed.]

## English Language Learners

**ITEM 10** Some English Language Learners may struggle when reading word problems. Encourage them to summarize the problem and look for key words that can be used to determine the task(s) necessary to solve the problem.

**Q:** What word or words indicate that it is possible to form a right triangle from the given information in the problem? Explain. [Sample answer: You know that the prism has right angles because it is called a right rectangular prism. You also know that a rectangle can be divided into two equal right triangles.]

You may opt to have students complete the automatically scored Practice & Problem Solving items online.

### Item Analysis

| Example | Items | DOK |
|---|---|---|
| 1 | 7 | 1 |
| | 15, 16 | 2 |
| | 14 | 3 |
| 2 | 8 | 1 |
| | 9, 10, 12 | 2 |
| 3 | 11, 13 | 2 |

# STEP 3 | Assess & Differentiate

Go Online

 Assess  Tutorials  Worksheets

## Lesson Quiz

**Formative** Assessment

Use the student scores on the Lesson Quiz to prescribe differentiated assignments.

**I Intervention** 0–3 Points **O On-Level** 4 Points **A Advanced** 5 Points

You may opt to have students take the Lesson Quiz online. The Lesson Quiz will be automatically scored, and appropriate remediation, practice, or enrichment will be assigned based on student performance.

**Lesson Quiz** is available online.

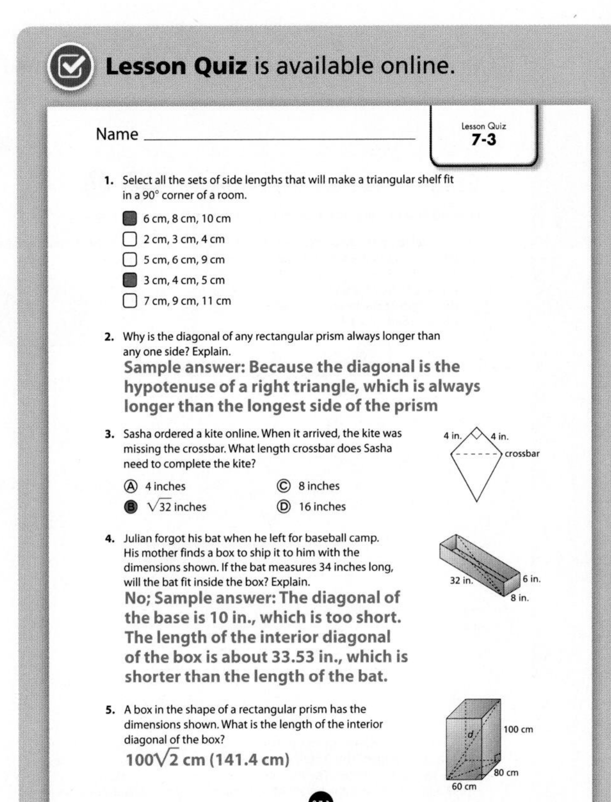

Name ________ Lesson Quiz 7-3

1. Select all the sets of side lengths that will make a triangular shelf fit in a 90° corner of a room.
   - ■ 6 cm, 8 cm, 10 cm
   - ☐ 2 cm, 3 cm, 4 cm
   - ☐ 5 cm, 6 cm, 9 cm
   - ■ 3 cm, 4 cm, 5 cm
   - ☐ 7 cm, 9 cm, 11 cm
2. Why is the diagonal of any rectangular prism always longer than any one side? Explain.
   **Sample answer: Because the diagonal is the hypotenuse of a right triangle, which is always longer than the longest side of the prism**
3. Sasha ordered a kite online. When it arrived, the kite was missing the crossbar. What length crossbar does Sasha need to complete the kite?
   Ⓐ 4 inches Ⓒ 8 inches
   Ⓑ $\sqrt{32}$ inches Ⓓ 16 inches
4. Julian forgot his bat when he left for baseball camp. His mother finds a box to ship it to him with the dimensions shown. If the bat measures 34 inches long, will the bat fit inside the box? Explain.
   **No; Sample answer: The diagonal of the base is 10 in., which is too short. The length of the interior diagonal of the box is about 33.53 in., which is shorter than the length of the bat.**
5. A box in the shape of a rectangular prism has the dimensions shown. What is the length of the interior diagonal of the box?
   **$100\sqrt{2}$ cm (141.4 cm)**

## Video Tutorials

Students can access instructional tutorials using the **Virtual Nerd app**.

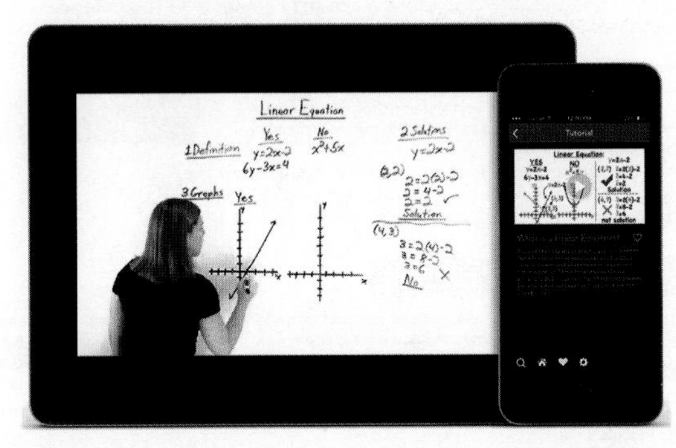

Students can also access the videos using the **BouncePages app** to scan exercise pages marked with this icon. Students can download both apps for free in their mobile devices' app store.

## Differentiated Intervention

**I** = Intervention **O** = On-Level **A** = Advanced

### Reteach to Build Understanding I

Provides scaffolded reteaching for the key lesson concepts.

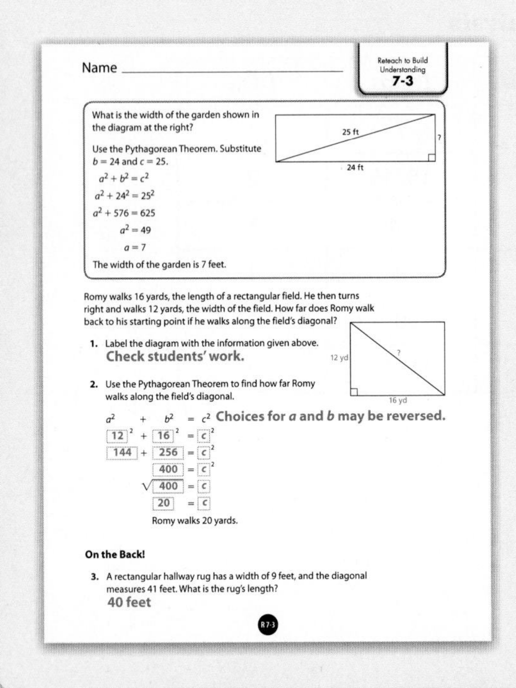

Name ________ Reteach to Build Understanding 7-3

What is the width of the garden shown in the diagram at the right?

Use the Pythagorean Theorem. Substitute $b = 24$ and $c = 25$.

$a^2 + b^2 = c^2$
$a^2 + 24^2 = 25^2$
$a^2 + 576 = 625$
$a^2 = 49$
$a = 7$

The width of the garden is 7 feet.

Romy walks 16 yards, the length of a rectangular field. He then turns right and walks 12 yards, the width of the field. How far does Romy walk back to his starting point if he walks along the field's diagonal?

1. Label the diagram with the information given above.
   **Check students' work.**
2. Use the Pythagorean Theorem to find how far Romy walks along the field's diagonal.
   $a^2 + b^2 = c^2$ **Choices for $a$ and $b$ may be reversed.**
   $12^2 + 16^2 = c^2$
   $144 + 256 = c^2$
   $400 = c^2$
   $\sqrt{400} = c$
   $20 = c$
   Romy walks 20 yards.

**On the Back!**

3. A rectangular hallway rug has a width of 9 feet, and the diagonal measures 41 feet. What is the rug's length?
   **40 feet**



### Additional Vocabulary Support I O

Helps students develop and reinforce understanding of key terms and concepts.

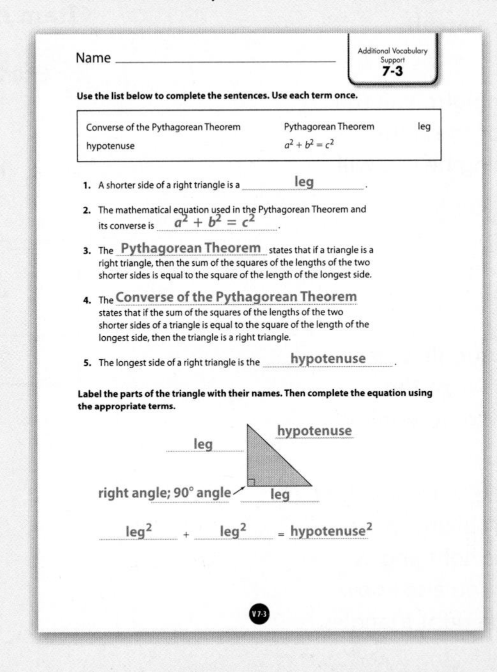

Name ________ Additional Vocabulary Support 7-3

**Use the list below to complete the sentences. Use each term once.**

Converse of the Pythagorean Theorem | Pythagorean Theorem | leg | hypotenuse | $a^2 + b^2 = c^2$

1. A shorter side of a right triangle is a **leg**.
2. The mathematical equation used in the Pythagorean Theorem and its converse is **$a^2 + b^2 = c^2$**.
3. The **Pythagorean Theorem** states that if a triangle is a right triangle, then the sum of the squares of the lengths of the two shorter sides is equal to the square of the length of the longest side.
4. The **Converse of the Pythagorean Theorem** states that if the sum of the squares of the lengths of the two shorter sides of a triangle is equal to the square of the length of the longest side, then the triangle is a right triangle.
5. The longest side of a right triangle is the **hypotenuse**.

**Label the parts of the triangle with their names. Then complete the equation using the appropriate terms.**



### Build Mathematical Literacy I O

Provides support for struggling readers to build mathematical literacy.

Name ________ Build Mathematical Literacy 7-3

**Read the problem below. Then answer the questions to understand the problem.**

A small heater is in the shape of a square pyramid. Each side of the pyramid's base measures 30.5 centimeters. The slant height of the pyramid is 164.8 centimeters. What is the height of the pyramid?

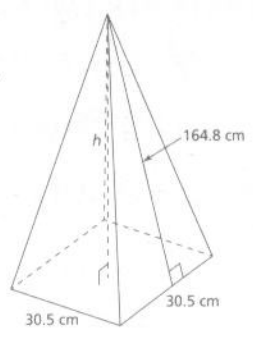

1. Draw and label a diagram of the given information.
   **Check students' work.**
2. In the problem, underline the quantity that you are asked to find. Choose a variable to represent this quantity and add this information to your diagram in Exercise 1.
   **Check students' work.**
3. How is the slant height of a pyramid different from its height?
   **The slant height is the length of a line drawn on the face of the pyramid from the middle of the side of the base of the pyramid to the vertex of the pyramid. Sample answer: The height is the length of a line drawn from the vertex to the base. The line intersects the base at a right angle.**
4. How does drawing and labeling a diagram help you solve the problem?
   **Sample answer: It helps me see the relationships between the quantities described in the problem. For example, I can see which lengths form which parts of the right triangles.**
5. How can you find the height of the pyramid?
   **Take half the length of the base and square it and subtract this from the square of the slant height. Take the square root of that number and express the resulting length in centimeters.**

h
164.8 cm
30.5 cm
30.5 cm
M7-3

Go Online

Practice

Worksheets

Math Tools

Math Games

# Additional Practice

You may opt to have students complete the automatically scored Additional Practice items online.

### Item Analysis

| Example | Items | DOK |
|---|---|---|
| 1 | 1 | 1 |
| | 3 | 2 |
| 2 | 2 | 1 |
| | 4, 5, 8 | 2 |
| | 7 | 3 |
| 3 | 6, 9 | 2 |

**Interactive Practice** is available online.

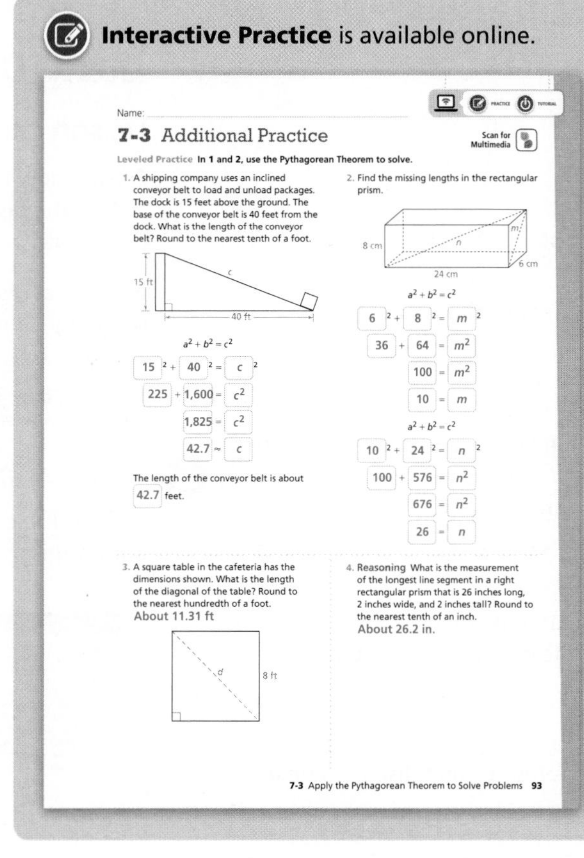

Name:

PRACTICE TUTORIAL

## 7-3 Additional Practice

Scan for Multimedia

Leveled Practice **In 1 and 2, use the Pythagorean Theorem to solve.**

1. A shipping company uses an inclined conveyor belt to load and unload packages. The dock is 15 feet above the ground. The base of the conveyor belt is 40 feet from the dock. What is the length of the conveyor belt? Round to the nearest tenth of a foot.

   15 ft, 40 ft, c

   $a^2 + b^2 = c^2$

   $15^2 + 40^2 = c^2$

   $225 + 1{,}600 = c^2$

   $1{,}825 = c^2$

   $42.7 \approx c$

   The length of the conveyor belt is about 42.7 feet.

2. Find the missing lengths in the rectangular prism.

   8 cm, 24 cm, 6 cm, m, n

   $a^2 + b^2 = c^2$

   $6^2 + 8^2 = m^2$

   $36 + 64 = m^2$

   $100 = m^2$

   $10 = m$

   $a^2 + b^2 = c^2$

   $10^2 + 24^2 = n^2$

   $100 + 576 = n^2$

   $676 = n^2$

   $26 = n$

3. A square table in the cafeteria has the dimensions shown. What is the length of the diagonal of the table? Round to the nearest hundredth of a foot.
   About 11.31 ft

   d, 8 ft

4. **Reasoning** What is the measurement of the longest line segment in a right rectangular prism that is 26 inches long, 2 inches wide, and 2 inches tall? Round to the nearest tenth of an inch.
   About 26.2 in.

**7-3** Apply the Pythagorean Theorem to Solve Problems **93**

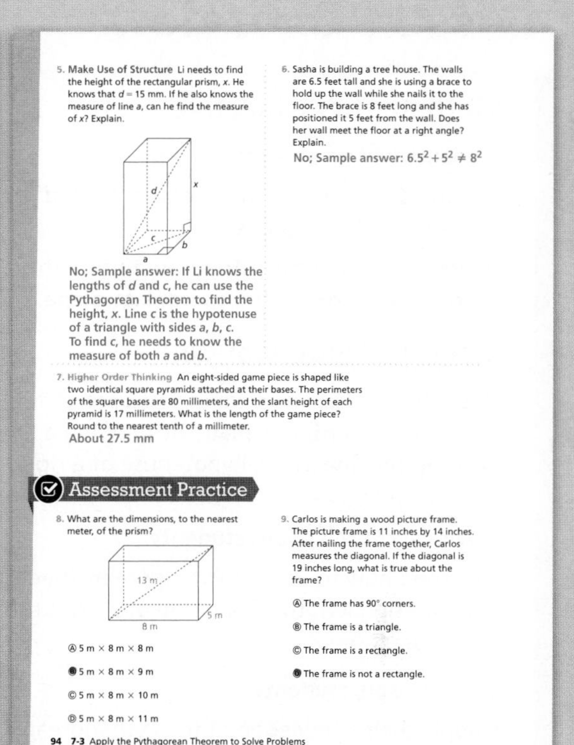

5. **Make Use of Structure** Li needs to find the height of the rectangular prism, $x$. He knows that $d = 15$ mm. If he also knows the measure of line $a$, can he find the measure of $x$? Explain.

   d, x, c, b, a

   No; Sample answer: If Li knows the lengths of $d$ and $c$, he can use the Pythagorean Theorem to find the height, $x$. Line $c$ is the hypotenuse of a triangle with sides $a$, $b$, $c$. To find $c$, he needs to know the measure of both $a$ and $b$.

6. Sasha is building a tree house. The walls are 6.5 feet tall and she is using a brace to hold up the wall while she nails it to the floor. The brace is 8 feet long and she has positioned it 5 feet from the wall. Does her wall meet the floor at a right angle? Explain.
   No; Sample answer: $6.5^2 + 5^2 \neq 8^2$

7. Higher Order Thinking An eight-sided game piece is shaped like two identical square pyramids attached at their bases. The perimeters of the square bases are 80 millimeters, and the slant height of each pyramid is 17 millimeters. What is the length of the game piece? Round to the nearest tenth of a millimeter.
   About 27.5 mm

### Assessment Practice

8. What are the dimensions, to the nearest meter, of the prism?

   13 m, 8 m, 5 m

   Ⓐ 5 m × 8 m × 8 m

   Ⓑ 5 m × 8 m × 9 m

   Ⓒ 5 m × 8 m × 10 m

   Ⓓ 5 m × 8 m × 11 m

9. Carlos is making a wood picture frame. The picture frame is 11 inches by 14 inches. After nailing the frame together, Carlos measures the diagonal. If the diagonal is 19 inches long, what is true about the frame?

   Ⓐ The frame has 90° corners.

   Ⓑ The frame is a triangle.

   Ⓒ The frame is a rectangle.

   Ⓓ The frame is not a rectangle.

**94** **7-3** Apply the Pythagorean Theorem to Solve Problems

# Differentiated Intervention

I = Intervention   O = On-Level   A = Advanced

## Enrichment O A

Presents engaging problems and activities that extend the lesson concepts.

Name ______________________

Enrichment 7-3

**Max makes and sells custom walking sticks for hikers. Each stick is packed in a rectangular box with length $l$, width $w$, and height $h$.**

x, h, w, l

1. On the diagram, draw a segment that represents the longest walking stick that can be packed in the box. Label the segment $x$. How is $x$ related to the length, width, and height of the box?
   **Check students work. Sample answer: $x$ is the hypotenuse of a right triangle. One leg is the box's height $h$, and the other leg is the diagonal of the box's base.**

2. What is the longest walking stick that can be packed in a box with length 3 inches, width 4 inches, and height 40 inches? Round your answer to the nearest hundredth. Explain.
   **about 40.31 in.; By the Pythagorean Theorem, the diagonal of the base is 5 in. ($3^2 + 4^2 = 25; \sqrt{25} = 5$). The hypotenuse of a right triangle with legs 5 in. and 40 in. is about 40.31 in. ($5^2 + 40^2 = 1{,}625; \sqrt{1{,}625} \approx 40.31$).**

3. To pack a 48-inch walking stick, what is the minimum height for a packing box with a width of 15 inches and length of 8 inches? Round your answer to the nearest hundredth. Explain.
   **about 44.89 in.; By the Pythagorean Theorem, the diagonal of the base is 17 in. ($8^2 + 15^2 = 289; \sqrt{289} = 17$). Use the Pythagorean Theorem to find $h$, the leg of a right triangle with one leg 17 in. and hypotenuse 48 in.:**

$$17^2 + h^2 = 48^2$$
$$h^2 = 48^2 - 17^2$$
$$= 2{,}304 - 289$$
$$= 2{,}015$$
$$h = \sqrt{2{,}015} \approx 44.89$$

E7-3

## Math Tools and Games I O A

Offers additional activities and games to build understanding and fluency.

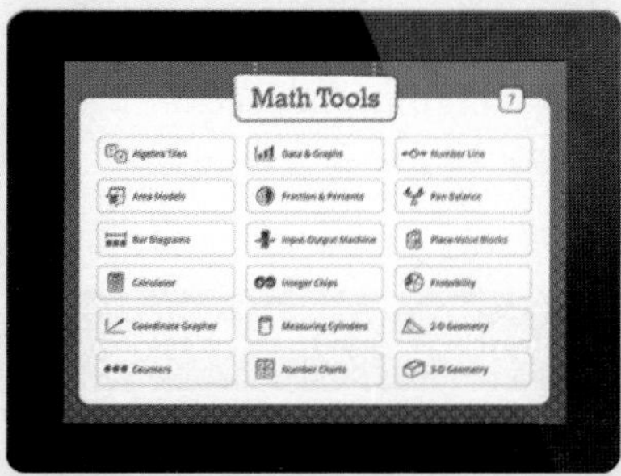


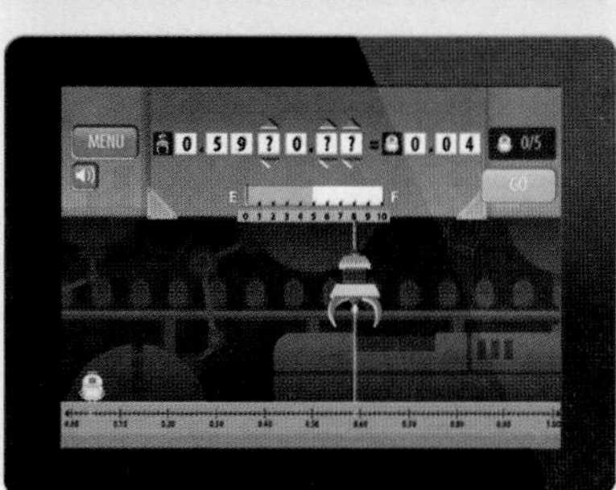

## Pick a Project and STEM Project I O A

Provides an additional opportunity for students to demonstrate understanding of key mathematical concepts.

Go Online

Video Activity

# Lesson 7-4 Find Distance in the Coordinate Plane

## Lesson Overview

FOCUS

### Mathematics Objective

**Students will be able to:**

✔ apply the Pythagorean Theorem to find the distance between two points on a coordinate plane.

✔ use the Pythagorean Theorem to find the perimeter of a figure and to solve problems on the coordinate plane.

### Essential Understanding

The Pythagorean Theorem can be used to find the distance between any two points on a coordinate plane by drawing a line to connect the two points and by using the line as the hypotenuse of a right triangle.

COHERENCE

**Previously in this topic, students:**

- learned how to use the Pythagorean Theorem and its converse to find the missing length of one side of a right triangle given the other two side measurements.

**In this lesson, students:**

- apply their knowledge of the Pythagorean Theorem to find distances on a coordinate plane.

**In High School, students will:**

- use trigonometry to solve problems with right triangles.

**Cross-Cluster Connection** Using the Pythagorean Theorem to find distances in the coordinate plane (8.G.2) connects to lines and linear equations (8.EE.2).

RIGOR

This lesson emphasizes a blend of **procedural skills and fluency** and **application.**

- Students practice finding distances between two points on the coordinate plane, thus becoming fluent in the use of coordinate planes and the Pythagorean Theorem.
- Students apply the Pythagorean Theorem to solve real-world problems involving distances on maps and between points on a coordinate grid.

## Language Support

### Lesson Language Objective

Explain how to use the Pythagorean Theorem to find the distance between two points in a coordinate plane.

Additional resources are available in the **Language Support Handbook.**

## Math Anytime

### Today's Challenge

Use the Topic 7 problems any time during this topic.

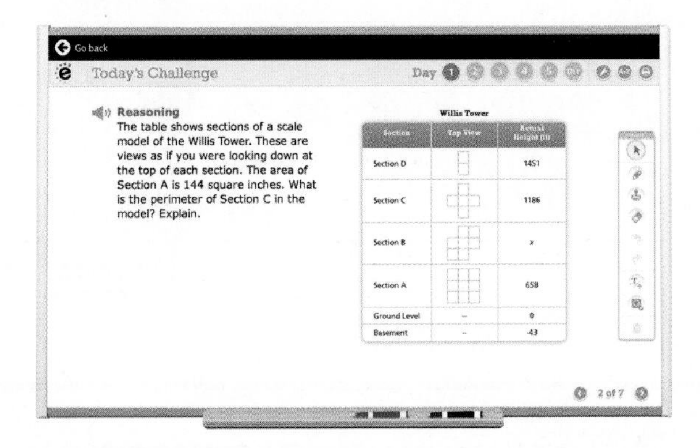


Watch the **Listen and Look For Video** for strategies and habits of mind to look for as students complete work on this lesson.

## Mathematics Overview — Common Core Standards

### Content Standards

In this lesson, you will focus on **8.G.B.8**.

- **8.G.B.8** Apply the Pythagorean Theorem to find the distance between two points in a coordinate system.

### Mathematical Practice Standards

**MP.4 Model with Mathematics**
Students will use maps to model the relationship and distance between points on a coordinate plane.

**MP.7 Look for and Make Use of Structure**
Students will apply the structure of the Pythagorean Theorem in conjunction with the structure of a coordinate plane to find the distance between two points.

**MP.8 Look for and Express Regularity in Repeated Reasoning**
Students will practice using the equation $a^2 + b^2 = c^2$ to determine the distance between two points on a coordinate plane. They begin to see the patterns in similar situations, but still pay attention to the details every time the process is repeated.

# STEP 1 | Problem-Based Learning

15-20 min

Go Online

Activity

## Explore It!

Formative Assessment

**Purpose** Students find the sum of the horizontal and vertical distance between two points on a grid and use this as an introduction to finding distance in the coordinate plane using the Pythagorean Theorem in the Visual Learning Bridge.

### ETP Before

WHOLE CLASS

**1 Introduce the Problem**

Provide grid paper and rulers, as needed.

**2 Check for Understanding of the Problem**

Ask students: Have you ever found the distance between two places using a scaled map?

### ETP During

SMALL GROUP

**3 Observe Students at Work**

Observe students while they work, noting the strategies that students take to find the distance. Students may represent the entire map on a coordinate plane, using the bottom left corner of the map as (0, 0). Students may also use the point (1, 1) on the map as (0, 0) on the coordinate plane, reasoning that the first row and first column on the map are not used. If needed, ask Which point on the map is represented by the origin on the graph?

After plotting the points students will draw a path between the haunted castle and the clown tent and find the distance between them. A common mistake students may make is writing an expression for the distance between the locations using centimeters instead of feet. If needed, ask What unit of measurement is used on the map?

**Early Finishers**

How would the problem change if they were traveling from the clown tent to the roller coaster? [Sample answer: The distance would be 2(500) + 2(500) + 2(500) = 3,000 feet.]

### ETP After

WHOLE CLASS

**4 Discuss Solution Strategies and Key Ideas**

Have students discuss how they modeled the map on the coordinate plane. Record their points on a projector or on the board then connect the points to show the path. Have students discuss how they found the distance between the two points on the map and how they converted that distance (in centimeters) to the actual distance (in feet).

Record students' expressions on the board. After all the different expressions have been recorded have students discuss how the expressions are equivalent, for example: 3(500) + 2(500) = 500(2 + 3).

**5 Consider Instructional Implications**

The same map is used in Example 1 where students find the shortest distance between the points, the diagonal. Once the length of the diagonal is calculated, remind students of the total distance they found between the two points in the Explore It by traveling only horizontally and vertically. Have students discuss why it makes sense that the diagonal is shorter than the total.

## Analyze Student Work

**Explore It!** Activity is available online.

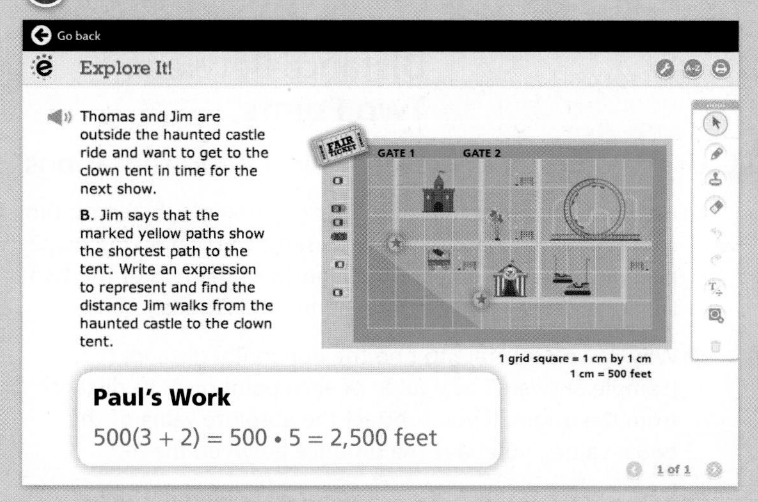


**Paul** counts the units across the map and down to the clown tent. Then he multiplies the sum by 500, the actual distance, in feet, each unit represents.

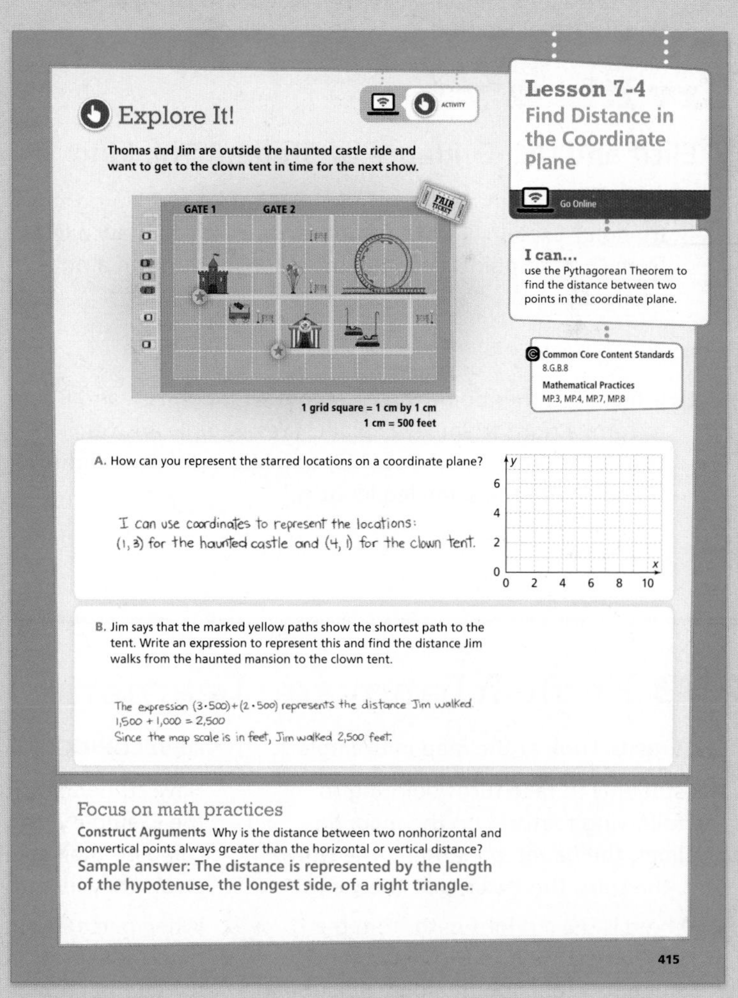


**Mia** counts the total number of squares along Jim's path. Then she uses the map scale to write two products to represent the distance Jim walked.

# STEP 2 | Visual Learning

Go Online

Visual Learning

Assess

## Establish Mathematics Goals to Focus Learning

Engage students in a discussion about the ***Essential Question***. Make sure they understand how to locate points on a coordinate plane, and understand the Pythagorean Theorem.

## EXAMPLE 1  Apply the Pythagorean Theorem to Find the Distance Between Two Points

### ETP Use and Connect Mathematical Representations

**Q:** How can you be certain that the right triangle shown on the coordinate plane accurately represents the one on the map? [Sample answer: Compare the lengths of the legs of the two triangles. They both measure 3 units and 2 units.]

**Q:** Why do you subtract to find the horizontal distance? [Sample answer: The *x*-value of each point gives its distance from the origin. If you subtract the absolute value of the two *x*-values, you have the distance between them.]

**Q:** How is the path that Thomas suggests related to the right triangle on the map and on the grid? [Sample answer: The path is the hypotenuse of the two right triangles. Once you know its length on the map, you can use the map scale to find its actual length.]

## Try It!

Formative Assessment

### Elicit and Use Evidence of Student Thinking

**Q:** What third point along with points *A* and *B* forms a right triangle? Explain. [(2, 1); Sample answer: If you draw a line from (2, 1) to points *A* and *B*, the three points form a right triangle.]

### Convince Me!

**Q:** Is there another point you could use with points A and B to form a right triangle? Explain. [Yes; Sample answer: You could draw a point at (4, 3) to make a different right triangle with the same leg lengths.]

**Visual Learning Animation Plus** is available online.

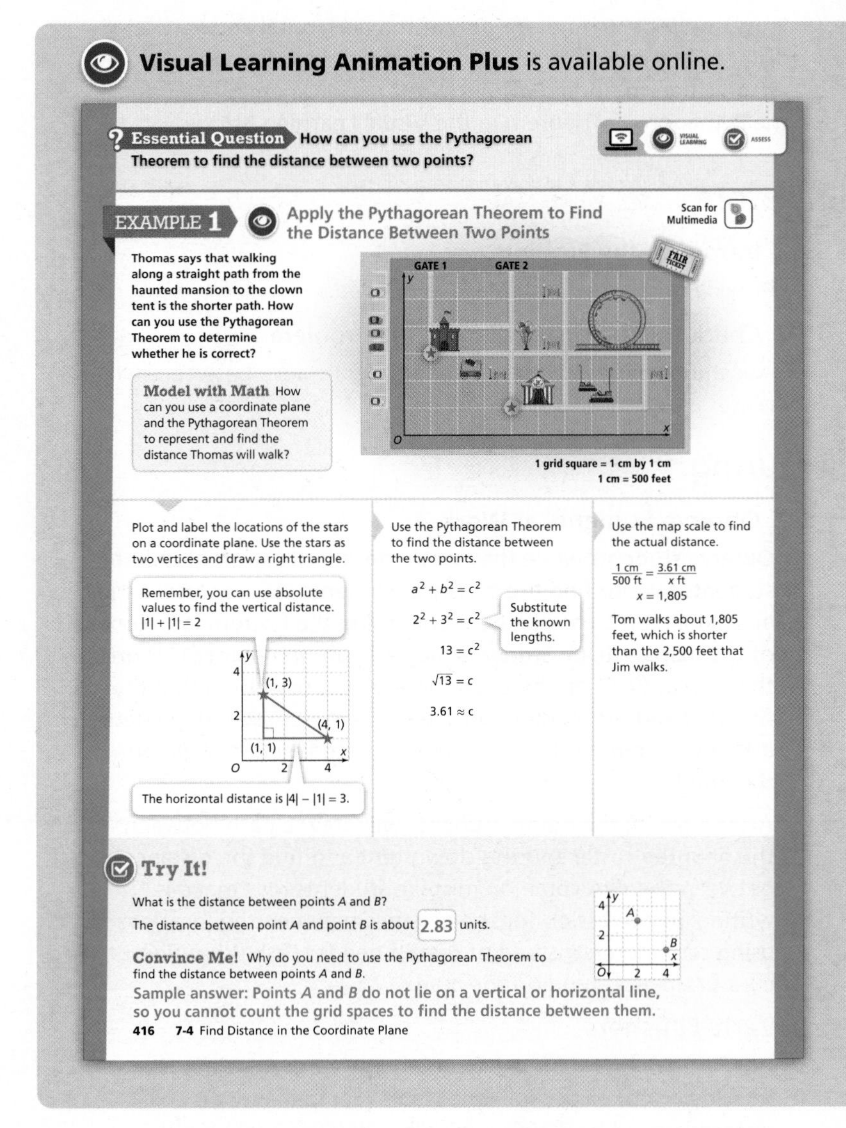

Essential Question How can you use the Pythagorean Theorem to find the distance between two points?

EXAMPLE 1 Apply the Pythagorean Theorem to Find the Distance Between Two Points

Scan for Multimedia

Thomas says that walking along a straight path from the haunted mansion to the clown tent is the shorter path. How can you use the Pythagorean Theorem to determine whether he is correct?

Model with Math How can you use a coordinate plane and the Pythagorean Theorem to represent and find the distance Thomas will walk?



Plot and label the locations of the stars on a coordinate plane. Use the stars as two vertices and draw a right triangle.

Remember, you can use absolute values to find the vertical distance. |1| + |1| = 2



The horizontal distance is |4| − |1| = 3.

Use the Pythagorean Theorem to find the distance between the two points.

$a^2 + b^2 = c^2$

$2^2 + 3^2 = c^2$

$13 = c^2$

$\sqrt{13} = c$

$3.61 \approx c$

Substitute the known lengths.

Use the map scale to find the actual distance.

$\frac{1 \text{ cm}}{500 \text{ ft}} = \frac{3.61 \text{ cm}}{x \text{ ft}}$

$x = 1{,}805$

Tom walks about 1,805 feet, which is shorter than the 2,500 feet that Jim walks.

Try It!

What is the distance between points *A* and *B*?

The distance between point *A* and point *B* is about 2.83 units.

Convince Me! Why do you need to use the Pythagorean Theorem to find the distance between points *A* and *B*.

Sample answer: Points *A* and *B* do not lie on a vertical or horizontal line, so you cannot count the grid spaces to find the distance between them.

416 7-4 Find Distance in the Coordinate Plane

Students can access the ***Visual Learning Animation Plus*** by using the **BouncePages app** to scan this page. Students can download the app for free in their mobile devices' app store.

## English Language Learners

**ENTERING** Look at the map in Example 1.

Ask students to take turns pointing to the following features on the map: the gridlines, the *haunted mansion*, the *clown tent*, the *stars*, the *x*-axis, and the *y*-axis.

**Q:** Where is the straight path from the haunted mansion to the clown tent? [Students should point along a diagonal line from the star on the left to the star on the right.]

**DEVELOPING** Solve Example 2.

Have students write their own solutions to the Example 2 *Try It!* Then have partners compare their solutions, correcting any errors they identify.

When partners agree on a solution, have them practice explaining how they solved the problem. Listen for the use of mathematical terms such as *perimeter*, *absolute value*, *hypotenuse*, and *substitute*.

**EXPANDING** Solve Example 3.

Have students restate the problem in their own words.

Then have students work with a partner and take turns explaining how to solve for the third vertex of Li's triangle.

Listen for students who use academic vocabulary and develop fluency.

## EXAMPLE 2  Find the Perimeter of a Figure on a Coordinate Plane

### Pose Purposeful Questions

**Q:** To find the length of *AC*, could you use $|-2| + |3|$? Explain. [Yes; Sample answer: *AC* goes from $x = -2$ to $x = 3$. Add to find the total length: $|-2| + |3| = 2 + 3 = 5$. To check, count the distance and see that it is 5 units in length.]

## Try It!  Formative Assessment

### Elicit and Use Evidence of Student Thinking

**Q:** Can you tell which distance is horizontal and which is vertical by looking at the coordinates? Explain? [Yes; Sample answer: Points (5, −1) and (2, −1) have the same *y*-coordinate; they are on the horizontal line $y = -1$. Points (2, 5) and (2, −1) have the same x-coordinate; they are on the line $x = 2$.]

**Q:** Can you find the perimeter without drawing the figure? Explain. [Yes; Sample answer: Find the distance between the given points. Then apply the Pythagorean Theorem.]

## EXAMPLE 3  Use the Pythagorean Theorem to Solve Problems on the Coordinate Plane

### Pose Purposeful Questions

**Q:** Are you using the Pythagorean Theorem differently here than in Example 2? Explain. [Yes; Sample answer: Here, you know the length of the hypotenuse and you are finding the length of a leg, *a*.]

**Q:** What does the value *a* represent? Explain. [Sample answer: It is the length of the longer leg of the right triangle and the height of the equilateral triangle.]

## Try It!  Formative Assessment

### Elicit and Use Evidence of Student Thinking

**Q:** Why can you use the same method you used to find the perimeter in Example 2 to find the third vertex in Example 3? [Sample answer: In both examples you are finding the missing measure of one leg of a right triangle.]

**Examples and Try Its!** are available online.

Find the perimeter of $\triangle ABC$.

STEP 1 Use absolute value to find the lengths of side *AC* and side *BC*.

STEP 2 Find the length of the hypotenuse *AB*.

$c^2 = 5^2 + 3^2$

$c^2 = 25 + 9$

$c^2 = 34$

$\sqrt{c^2} = \sqrt{34}$

$c \approx 5.83$

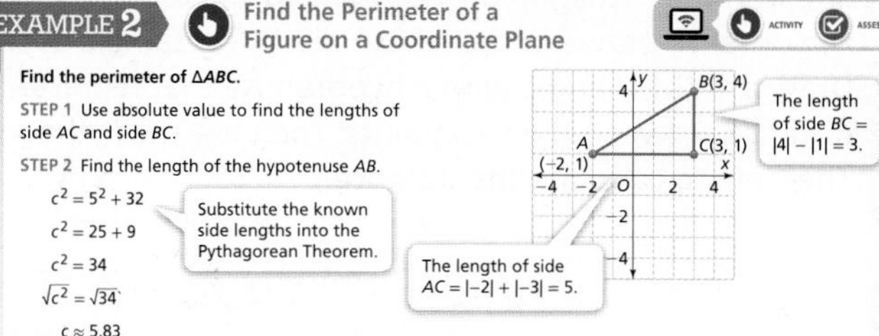


The distance between point *A* and point *B* is about 5.83 units.

STEP 3 Add the lengths of all three sides to find the perimeter.

$5 + 3 + 5.83 = 13.83$

The perimeter of $\triangle ABC$ is about 13.83 units.

**Try It!**

Find the perimeter of $\triangle ABC$ with vertices (2, 5), (5, −1), and (2, −1).
About 15.71 units

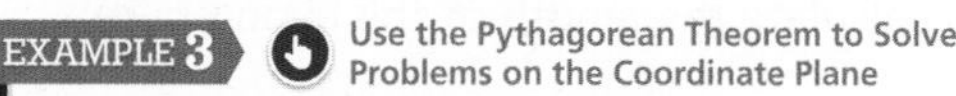


**Li draws one side of an equilateral triangle with vertices (−1, 1) and (3, 1) on the coordinate plane. The third vertex is in the first quadrant. What are the coordinates of the third vertex of Li's triangle?**

STEP 1 Find the length of the side drawn.

STEP 2 Use the Pythagorean Theorem to find the height of Li's triangle to the nearest tenth.

STEP 3 Complete the triangle by drawing the height to locate and label the third vertex.

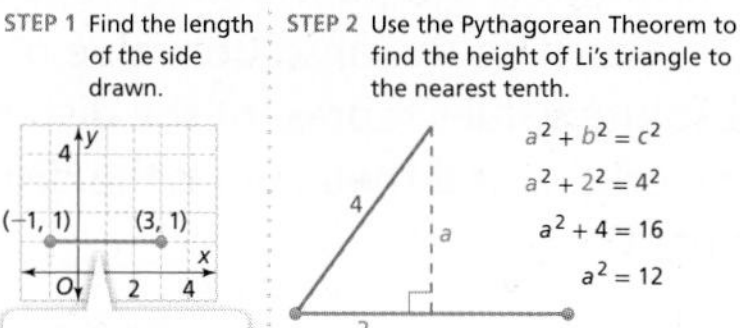


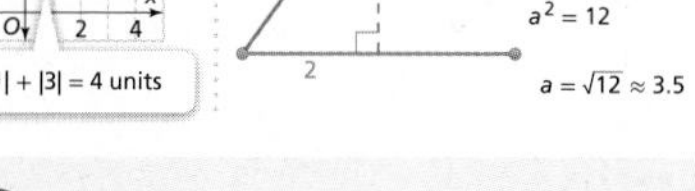


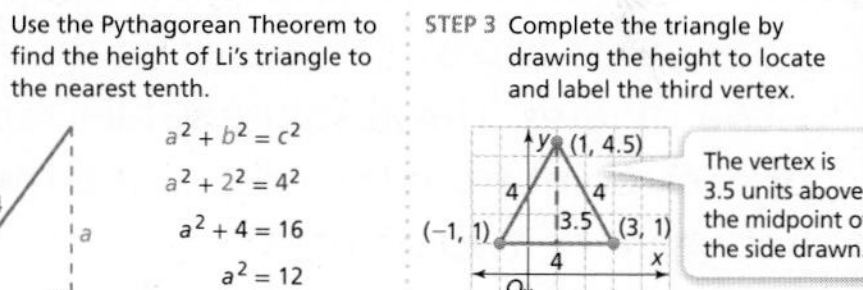


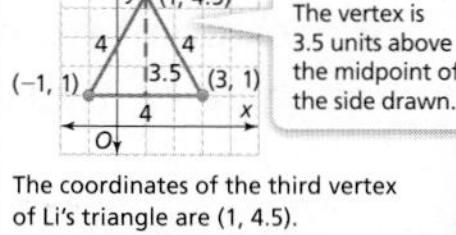


The coordinates of the third vertex of Li's triangle are (1, 4.5).

**Try It!**

What are the coordinates, to the nearest tenth, of the third vertex in an isosceles triangle that has one side length of 2 and two side lengths of 5, with vertices at (1, 0) and (1, 2)? The third vertex is in the first quadrant. (5.9, 1)

7-4 Find Distance in the Coordinate Plane 417

## ADDITIONAL EXAMPLES 

**For additional examples go online.**

## Response to Intervention

**USE WITH EXAMPLE 1** Students might need to review absolute value to accurately calculate distances on a coordinate plane.

- Use absolute value to solve each expression.

$-6 + (-8) =$ [$|-6| + |-8| = 6 + 8 = 14$]

$7 + (-5) =$ [$|7| + |-5| = 7 + 5 = 12$]

$-2 + 7 =$ [$|-2| + |7| = 2 + 7 = 9$]

## Enrichment

**USE WITH EXAMPLE 2** Challenge students to look for patterns and generalize how to find the perimeter on a coordinate plane.

**Q:** For any right triangle in the coordinate plane, how would you use the Pythagorean Theorem to find the perimeter? [Sample answer: If you know the measures of two sides, you can use them to calculate to measure of the third side.]

# STEP 2 | Visual Learning *continued*

Go Online

Key Concept

Assess

Activity

## KEY CONCEPT

### ETP Pose Purposeful Questions

**Q:** When two points are not on the same vertical or horizontal line, can the Pythagorean Theorem always be used to find the distance between them? Explain. [Yes. Sample answer: Draw a right triangle with a hypotenuse that represents the distance between the two points. Then use the Pythagorean Theorem to calculate the distance.]

## Do You Understand/Do You Know How?

**Formative** Assessment

### ETP Build Procedural Fluency from Conceptual Understanding

**Essential Question** Given two nonhorizontal and nonvertical points on a coordinate plane, draw a right triangle using the line that connects the two points as the hypotenuse, and the lines that run parallel to the axes as the legs. Then use $a^2 + b^2 = c^2$ to calculate the length of the hypotenuse.

**ITEM 3**

**Q:** How do you find the distance if the points are on opposite sides of the *x*-axis? Explain. [Use the absolute value of the *y*-coordinates. The absolute values represent the distance of each point from the origin, and their sum is the distance between the two points.]

### Prevent Misconceptions

**ITEM 4** Some students may try to use point *E* to solve this problem.

**Q:** Do you need point *E* to solve this problem? Explain. [No; Sample answer: Point *E* is not part of a triangle with hypotenuse *CD*.]

Available Online

KEY CONCEPT

You can use the Pythagorean Theorem to find the distance between any two points, *P* and *Q*, on the coordinate plane.

Draw a right triangle with side *PQ* as its hypotenuse.

**Do You Understand?**

1. **Essential Question** How can you use the Pythagorean Theorem to find the distance between two points?
Sample answer: For any two points that are not on a vertical or horizontal line, you can draw a right triangle so that its hypotenuse represents the distance between two points. Then you can use the Pythagorean Theorem to find the length of the hypotenuse.
2. **Model with Math** Can you use a right triangle to represent the distance between any two points on the coordinate plane? Explain.
Yes; Sample answer: The distance between two horizontal points or two vertical points could be represented by a horizontal or vertical leg of a right triangle, and the distance between two nonhorizontal and nonvertical points could be represented by the hypotenuse.
3. **Generalize** How does the fact that the points are on opposite sides of the *y*-axis affect the process of finding the distance between the two points?
Sample answer: When two points are on opposite sides of the *y*-axis, you need to use the absolute values of the *x*-coordinates to determine the horizontal distance between the points.

**Do You Know How?**

**In 4–6, use the coordinate plane below.**

C(1, 2), E(−2, 1), D(2, −1)

4. Find the distance between points *C* and *D*. Round to the nearest hundredth.
About 3.16 units
5. Find the perimeter of $\triangle CDE$.
About 11.4 units
6. Point *B* is plotted on the coordinate plane above the *x*-axis. $\triangle BDE$ is equilateral. What are the coordinates of point *B* to the nearest hundredth?
(0, 2.46)

418 7-4 Find Distance in the Coordinate Plane

## ADDITIONAL EXAMPLE 3

Help students solve a problem on the coordinate plane when none of the given sides of a triangle are on a horizontal or vertical line.

**Q:** How is this triangle different from the other triangles in this lesson? [Sample answer: None of the sides are horizontal or vertical on the coordinate plane, and none of the angles are right angles.]

**Q:** Suppose each side of the given triangle is part of another triangle that is a right triangle. How could you use this information to answer the question? [Sample answer: You could use the sides of the given triangle as the hypotenuse of three right triangles. The legs of these right triangles would be vertical and horizontal lines whose length you could calculate. If two of the legs are the same length, Angela is correct.]

**Additional Examples** are available online.

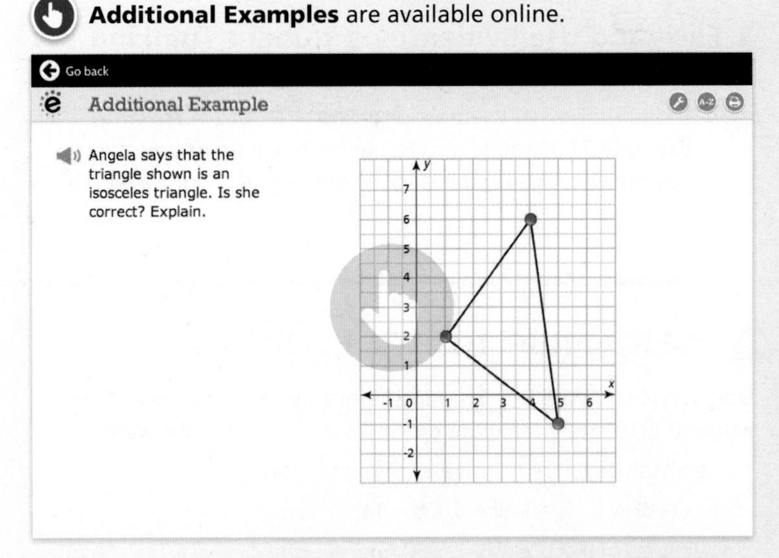


**Answer:** The triangle is an isosceles triangle because Angela can prove that two side lengths are equal, and one side length is not equal.

Go Online

Practice Tutorials Math Tools

# Practice & Problem Solving  

**Interactive Practice** and **Virtual Nerd Tutorials** are available online.

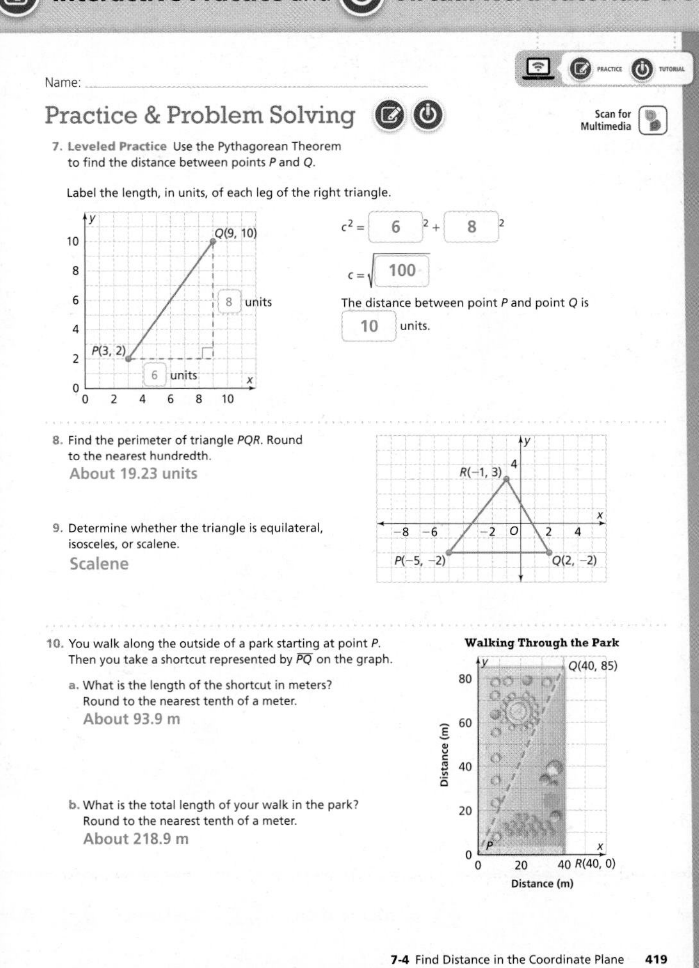
Name:

Practice & Problem Solving

Scan for Multimedia

7. **Leveled Practice** Use the Pythagorean Theorem to find the distance between points $P$ and $Q$.

Label the length, in units, of each leg of the right triangle.



$c^2 = 6^2 + 8^2$

$c = \sqrt{100}$

The distance between point $P$ and point $Q$ is 10 units.

8. Find the perimeter of triangle $PQR$. Round to the nearest hundredth.
About 19.23 units

9. Determine whether the triangle is equilateral, isosceles, or scalene.
Scalene



10. You walk along the outside of a park starting at point $P$. Then you take a shortcut represented by $\overline{PQ}$ on the graph.

a. What is the length of the shortcut in meters? Round to the nearest tenth of a meter.
About 93.9 m

b. What is the total length of your walk in the park? Round to the nearest tenth of a meter.
About 218.9 m



7-4 Find Distance in the Coordinate Plane 419

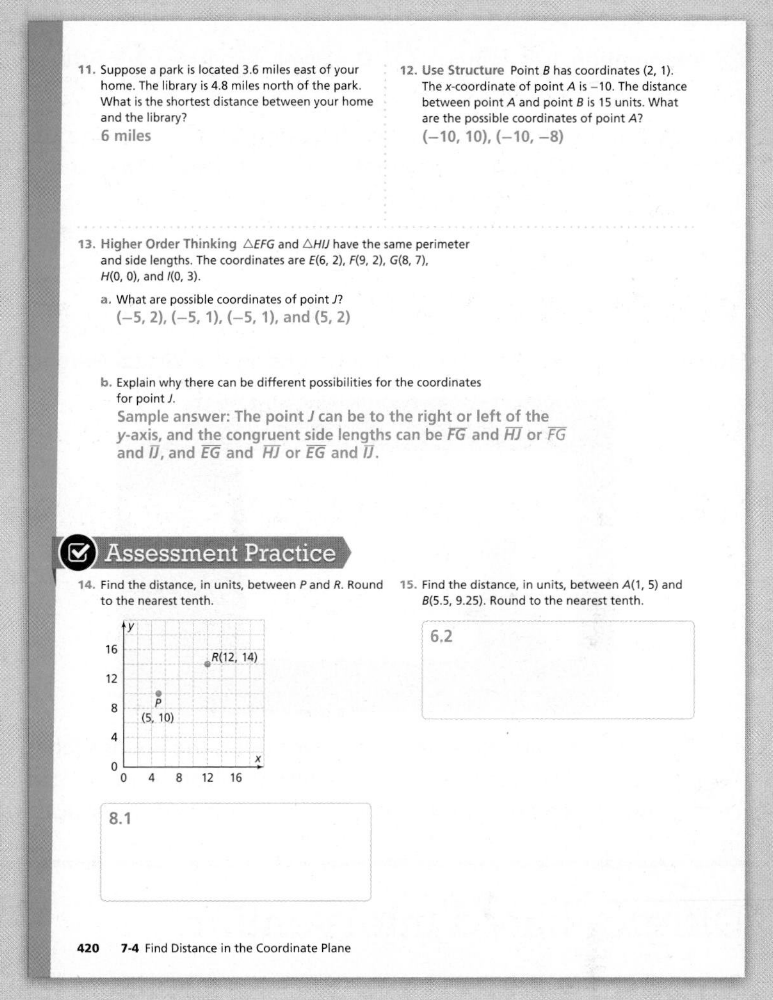
11. Suppose a park is located 3.6 miles east of your home. The library is 4.8 miles north of the park. What is the shortest distance between your home and the library?
6 miles

12. **Use Structure** Point $B$ has coordinates (2, 1). The $x$-coordinate of point $A$ is −10. The distance between point $A$ and point $B$ is 15 units. What are the possible coordinates of point $A$?
(−10, 10), (−10, −8)

13. **Higher Order Thinking** $\triangle EFG$ and $\triangle HIJ$ have the same perimeter and side lengths. The coordinates are $E(6, 2)$, $F(9, 2)$, $G(8, 7)$, $H(0, 0)$, and $I(0, 3)$.

a. What are possible coordinates of point $J$?
(−5, 2), (−5, 1), (−5, 1), and (5, 2)

b. Explain why there can be different possibilities for the coordinates for point $J$.
Sample answer: The point $J$ can be to the right or left of the $y$-axis, and the congruent side lengths can be $\overline{FG}$ and $\overline{HJ}$ or $\overline{FG}$ and $\overline{IJ}$, and $\overline{EG}$ and $\overline{HJ}$ or $\overline{EG}$ and $\overline{IJ}$.

**Assessment Practice**

14. Find the distance, in units, between $P$ and $R$. Round to the nearest tenth.



8.1

15. Find the distance, in units, between $A(1, 5)$ and $B(5.5, 9.25)$. Round to the nearest tenth.
6.2

420 7-4 Find Distance in the Coordinate Plane

## English Language Learners

**ITEM 7** Explain to a partner the answers to these questions.

**Q:** Why do you need to draw a right triangle? [Sample answer: If you know the lengths of the two legs, you can can use the equation $a^2 + b^2 = c^2$ to find the distance between points $P$ and $Q$.]

**Q:** Where should you draw the lines to make a right triangle? [Sample answer: Draw a horizontal line that goes right from (3, 2). Draw a vertical line that goes down from (9, 10).]

## Challenge

**ITEM 12** Challenge advanced student with this problem.

**Q:** Point $B$ has coordinates (2, 1). What points in Quadrant 1 are 5 units from point $B$? [Sample answer: (2, 6), (7, 1), (5, 5), (6, 4)]

You may opt to have students complete the automatically scored Practice & Problem Solving items online.

### Item Analysis

| Example | Items | DOK |
|---|---|---|
| 1 | 7, 9, 12, 14, 15 | 2 |
| 2 | 8, 10 | 2 |
| 3 | 11 | 2 |
| | 13 | 3 |

## STEP 3 | Assess & Differentiate

Go Online

 Assess  Tutorials  Worksheets

# Lesson Quiz

**Formative** Assessment

Use the student scores on the Lesson Quiz to prescribe differentiated assignments.

**I Intervention** 0–3 Points **O On-Level** 4 Points **A Advanced** 5 Points

You may opt to have students take the Lesson Quiz online. The Lesson Quiz will be automatically scored and appropriate remediation, practice, or enrichment will be assigned based on student performance.

# Video Tutorials

Students can access instructional tutorials using the **Virtual Nerd app**.

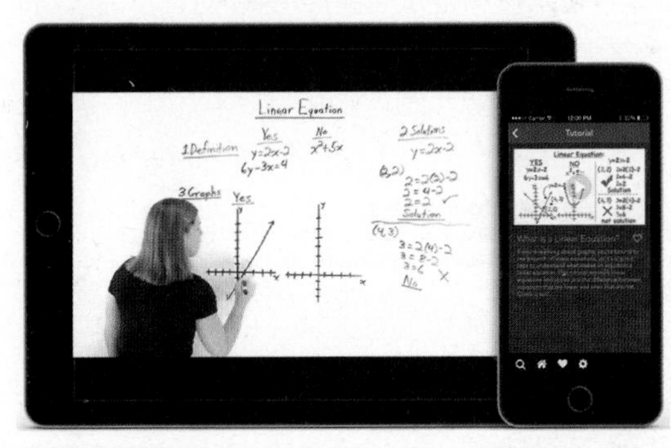

Students can also access the videos using the **BouncePages app** to scan exercise pages marked with this icon. Students can download both apps for free in their mobile devices' app store.

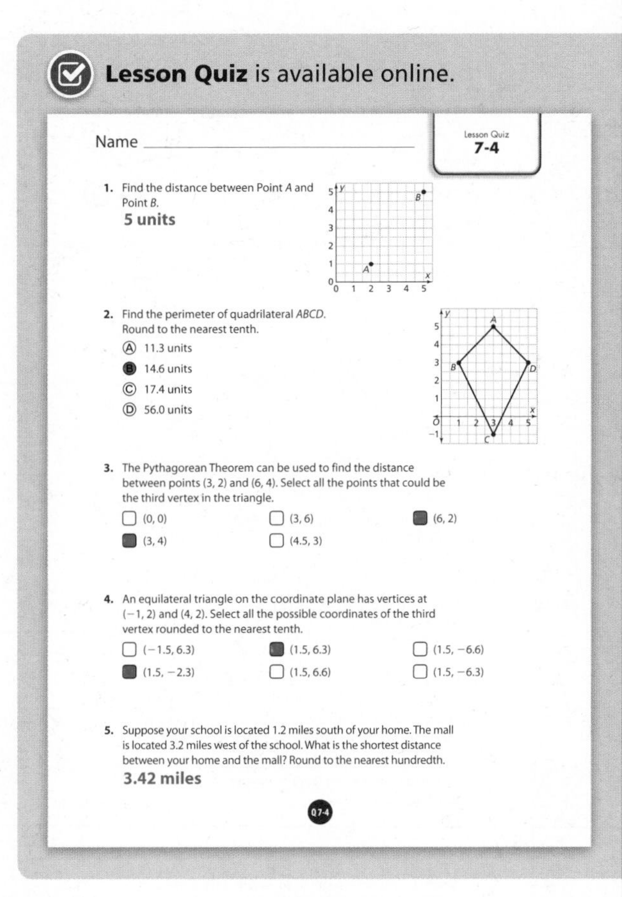

**Lesson Quiz** is available online.

Name ______________________

Lesson Quiz **7-4**

1. Find the distance between Point *A* and Point *B*.
   **5 units**

2. Find the perimeter of quadrilateral *ABCD*. Round to the nearest tenth.
   Ⓐ 11.3 units
   Ⓑ 14.6 units
   Ⓒ 17.4 units
   Ⓓ 56.0 units

3. The Pythagorean Theorem can be used to find the distance between points (3, 2) and (6, 4). Select all the points that could be the third vertex in the triangle.
   ☐ (0, 0) ☐ (3, 6) ■ (6, 2)
   ■ (3, 4) ☐ (4.5, 3)

4. An equilateral triangle on the coordinate plane has vertices at (−1, 2) and (4, 2). Select all the possible coordinates of the third vertex rounded to the nearest tenth.
   ☐ (−1.5, 6.3) ■ (1.5, 6.3) ☐ (1.5, −6.6)
   ■ (1.5, −2.3) ☐ (1.5, 6.6) ☐ (1.5, −6.3)

5. Suppose your school is located 1.2 miles south of your home. The mall is located 3.2 miles west of the school. What is the shortest distance between your home and the mall? Round to the nearest hundredth.
   **3.42 miles**

Q7-4

# Differentiated Intervention

**I** = Intervention **O** = On-Level **A** = Advanced

## Reteach to Build Understanding I

Provides scaffolded reteaching for the key lesson concepts.

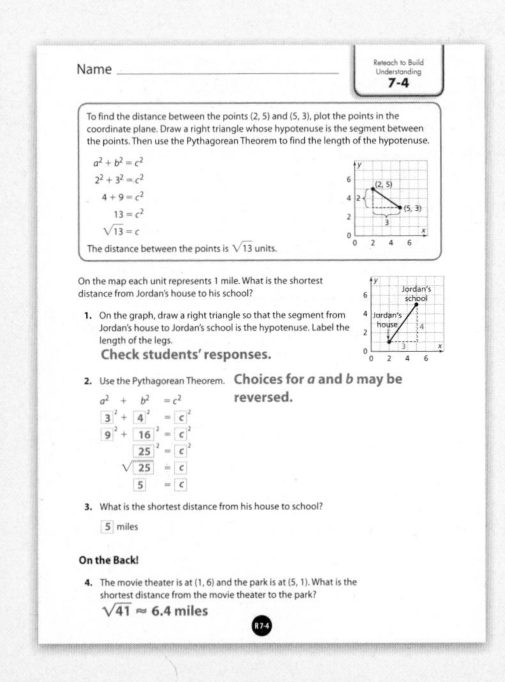

Name ______________________

Reteach to Build Understanding **7-4**

To find the distance between the points (2, 5) and (5, 3), plot the points in the coordinate plane. Draw a right triangle whose hypotenuse is the segment between the points. Then use the Pythagorean Theorem to find the length of the hypotenuse.

$a^2 + b^2 = c^2$
$2^2 + 3^2 = c^2$
$4 + 9 = c^2$
$13 = c^2$
$\sqrt{13} = c$

The distance between the points is $\sqrt{13}$ units.

On the map each unit represents 1 mile. What is the shortest distance from Jordan's house to his school?

1. On the graph, draw a right triangle so that the segment from Jordan's house to Jordan's school is the hypotenuse. Label the length of the legs.
   **Check students' responses.**
2. Use the Pythagorean Theorem. **Choices for *a* and *b* may be reversed.**
   $a^2 + b^2 = c^2$
   $3^2 + 4^2 = c^2$
   $9 + 16 = c^2$
   $25 = c^2$
   $\sqrt{25} = c$
   $5 = c$
3. What is the shortest distance from his house to school?
   5 miles

**On the Back!**

4. The movie theater is at (1, 6) and the park is at (5, 1). What is the shortest distance from the movie theater to the park?
   **$\sqrt{41} \approx 6.4$ miles**

R7-4

## Additional Vocabulary Support I O

Helps students develop and reinforce understanding of key terms and concepts.

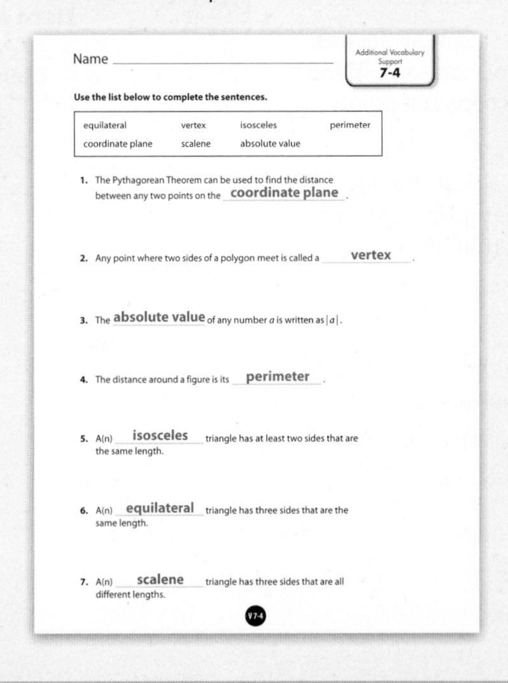

Name ______________________

Additional Vocabulary Support **7-4**

**Use the list below to complete the sentences.**

| equilateral | vertex | isosceles | perimeter |
|---|---|---|---|
| coordinate plane | scalene | absolute value | |

1. The Pythagorean Theorem can be used to find the distance between any two points on the **coordinate plane**.
2. Any point where two sides of a polygon meet is called a **vertex**.
3. The **absolute value** of any number $a$ is written as $|a|$.
4. The distance around a figure is its **perimeter**.
5. A(n) **isosceles** triangle has at least two sides that are the same length.
6. A(n) **equilateral** triangle has three sides that are the same length.
7. A(n) **scalene** triangle has three sides that are all different lengths.

V7-4

## Build Mathematical Literacy I O

Provides support for struggling readers to build mathematical literacy.

Name ______________________

Build Mathematical Literacy **7-4**

**Read the problem below and connect it to the graph.**

Find the perimeter of $\triangle ABC$.

1. What is the perimeter of a triangle? How can you find a triangle's perimeter?
   **The perimeter is the total distance around the triangle; add the lengths of the triangle's sides.**
2. How can you find the distance between points *A* and *C*?
   **Sample answer: Count the number of units between points *A* and *C*.**
3. What other distances do you need to find in order to solve the problem?
   **The distance between points *B* and *C* and the distance between points *A* and *B***
4. Can you find the distances between points *B* and *C* and *A* and *B* by counting the units? Explain.
   **No. Sample answer: The lines are not parallel to the lines on the coordinate plane.**
5. Once you have found the distances between points *B* and *C* and points *A* and *B*, can you solve the problem? Explain.
   **Yes; Sample answer: I will now be able to add the lengths of all the sides.**

M7-4

Go Online

Practice

Worksheets

Math Tools

Math Games

# Additional Practice

You may opt to have students complete the automatically scored Additional Practice items online.

### Item Analysis

| Example | Items | DOK |
|---|---|---|
| 1 | 1, 7, 9, 10 | 2 |
| 2 | 2, 6 | 2 |
| 3 | 3, 5 | 2 |
|  | 4, 8 | 3 |

**Interactive Practice** is available online.

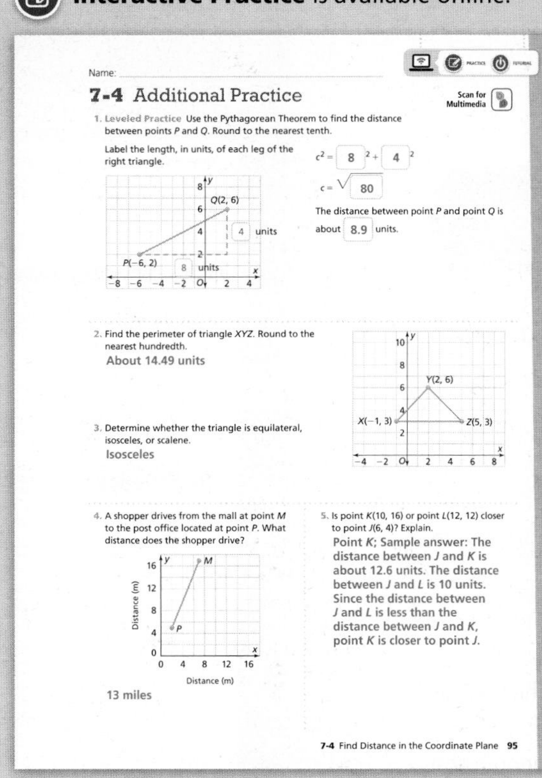

Name:

**7-4** Additional Practice

Scan for Multimedia

1. Leveled Practice Use the Pythagorean Theorem to find the distance between points $P$ and $Q$. Round to the nearest tenth.

Label the length, in units, of each leg of the right triangle.

$c^2 = 8^2 + 4^2$

$c = \sqrt{80}$

The distance between point $P$ and point $Q$ is about 8.9 units.

2. Find the perimeter of triangle $XYZ$. Round to the nearest hundredth.
About 14.49 units

3. Determine whether the triangle is equilateral, isosceles, or scalene.
Isosceles

4. A shopper drives from the mall at point $M$ to the post office located at point $P$. What distance does the shopper drive?
13 miles

5. Is point $K(10, 16)$ or point $L(12, 12)$ closer to point $J(6, 4)$? Explain.
Point $K$; Sample answer: The distance between $J$ and $K$ is about 12.6 units. The distance between $J$ and $L$ is 10 units. Since the distance between $J$ and $L$ is less than the distance between $J$ and $K$, point $K$ is closer to point $J$.

7-4 Find Distance in the Coordinate Plane 95

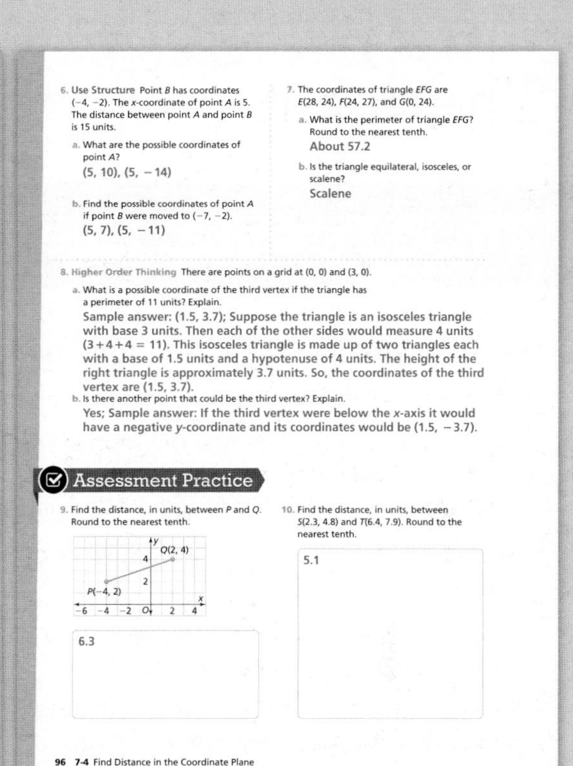

6. Use Structure Point $B$ has coordinates $(-4, -2)$. The $x$-coordinate of point $A$ is 5. The distance between point $A$ and point $B$ is 15 units.
a. What are the possible coordinates of point $A$?
(5, 10), (5, −14)
b. Find the possible coordinates of point $A$ if point $B$ were moved to $(-7, -2)$.
(5, 7), (5, −11)

7. The coordinates of triangle $EFG$ are $E(28, 24)$, $F(24, 27)$, and $G(0, 24)$.
a. What is the perimeter of triangle $EFG$? Round to the nearest tenth.
About 57.2
b. Is the triangle equilateral, isosceles, or scalene?
Scalene

8. Higher Order Thinking There are points on a grid at (0, 0) and (3, 0).
a. What is a possible coordinate of the third vertex if the triangle has a perimeter of 11 units? Explain.
Sample answer: (1.5, 3.7); Suppose the triangle is an isosceles triangle with base 3 units. Then each of the other sides would measure 4 units $(3 + 4 + 4 = 11)$. This isosceles triangle is made up of two triangles each with a base of 1.5 units and a hypotenuse of 4 units. The height of the right triangle is approximately 3.7 units. So, the coordinates of the third vertex are (1.5, 3.7).
b. Is there another point that could be the third vertex? Explain.
Yes; Sample answer: If the third vertex were below the $x$-axis it would have a negative $y$-coordinate and its coordinates would be (1.5, −3.7).

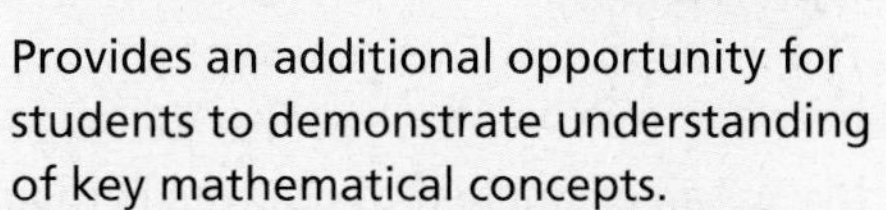
Assessment Practice

9. Find the distance, in units, between $P$ and $Q$. Round to the nearest tenth.
6.3

10. Find the distance, in units, between $S(2.3, 4.8)$ and $T(6.4, 7.9)$. Round to the nearest tenth.
5.1

96 7-4 Find Distance in the Coordinate Plane

# Differentiated Intervention

I = Intervention O = On-Level A = Advanced

## Enrichment  

Presents engaging problems and activities that extend the lesson concepts.

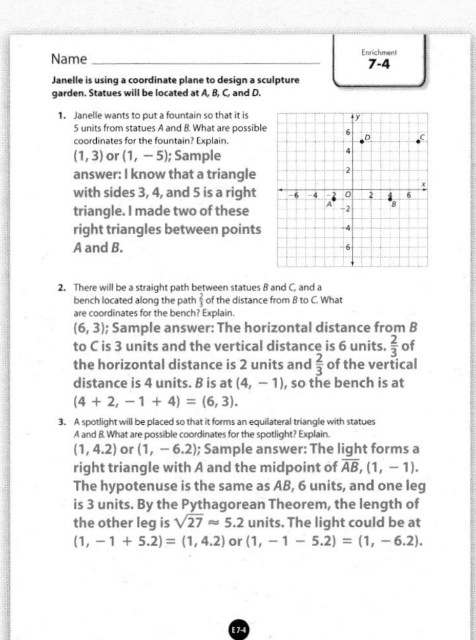

Name

Enrichment 7-4

Janelle is using a coordinate plane to design a sculpture garden. Statues will be located at $A$, $B$, $C$, and $D$.

1. Janelle wants to put a fountain so that it is 5 units from statues $A$ and $B$. What are possible coordinates for the fountain? Explain.
(1, 3) or (1, −5); Sample answer: I know that a triangle with sides 3, 4, and 5 is a right triangle. I made two of these right triangles between points $A$ and $B$.

2. There will be a straight path between statues $B$ and $C$, and a bench located along the path $\frac{2}{3}$ of the distance from $B$ to $C$. What are coordinates for the bench? Explain.
(6, 3); Sample answer: The horizontal distance from $B$ to $C$ is 3 units and the vertical distance is 6 units. $\frac{2}{3}$ of the horizontal distance is 2 units and $\frac{2}{3}$ of the vertical distance is 4 units. $B$ is at (4, −1), so the bench is at $(4 + 2, -1 + 4) = (6, 3)$.

3. A spotlight will be placed so that it forms an equilateral triangle with statues $A$ and $B$. What are possible coordinates for the spotlight? Explain.
(1, 4.2) or (1, −6.2); Sample answer: The light forms a right triangle with $A$ and the midpoint of $\overline{AB}$, (1, −1). The hypotenuse is the same as $AB$, 6 units, and one leg is 3 units. By the Pythagorean Theorem, the length of the other leg is $\sqrt{27} \approx 5.2$ units. The light could be at $(1, -1 + 5.2) = (1, 4.2)$ or $(1, -1 - 5.2) = (1, -6.2)$.

E74

## Math Tools and Games I O A

Offers additional activities and games to build understanding and fluency.

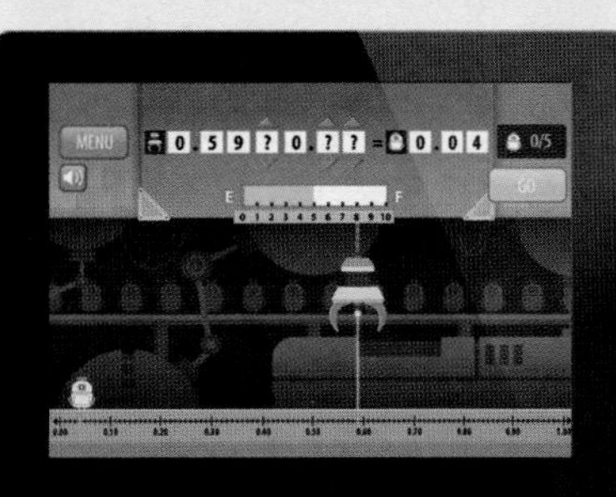


## Pick a Project and STEM Project I O A

Provides an additional opportunity for students to demonstrate understanding of key mathematical concepts.

Go Online

Glossary

# Understand and Apply the Pythagorean Theorem

## ? Topic Essential Question

### How can you use the Pythagorean Theorem to solve problems?

As students answer the Essential Question in writing, encourage them to include definitions, examples, non-examples, models, and other representations that support their answers.

Be sure the following are made explicit while discussing students' answers.

- A proof is a logical argument in which every statement of fact is supported by a reason.
- Review an example of a proof that includes a mathematical reason for each step in the proof.
- The Pythagorean Theorem states that in a right triangle the sum of the squares of the lengths of the legs is equal to the square of the length of the hypotenuse ($a^2 + b^2 = c^2$).
- Present an example that uses the Pythagorean Theorem.
- The Converse of the Pythagorean Theorem states that if $a^2 + b^2 = c^2$ for side lengths $a$, $b$, and $c$ of a triangle, then the triangle is a right triangle.
- Present an example that uses the Converse of the Pythagorean Theorem.
- The Pythagorean Theorem can be used to find the distance between two points on the coordinate plane.
- Discuss an example that uses the Pythagorean Theorem to find distance in the coordinate plane.

## Vocabulary Review

**ORAL LANGUAGE** Before students complete the page, reinforce oral language by using one or more of the following activities.

- Have students work in pairs to write a real-world problem using vocabulary terms. Then have them exchange their problems and solve. Share their solutions with the class.
- Play a guessing game in which a clue or example about one of the vocabulary terms is given and other students guess the word.

**WRITING IN MATH** After students complete the page, you can further reinforce writing in math by doing the following activity.

- Have students work in pairs to create a word search using vocabulary terms from this topic and previous topics. Encourage students to use definitions and examples, rather than the terms, for the clues. Provide grid paper for the students to create their word search.

Available Online

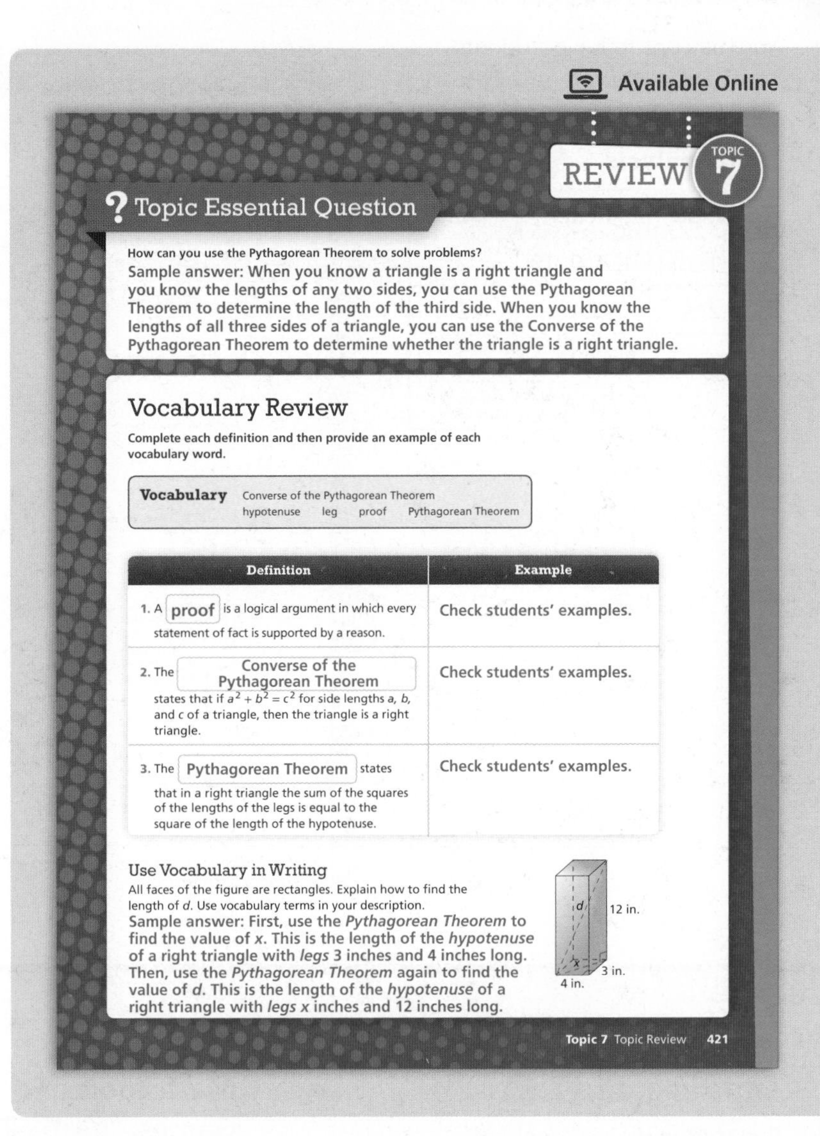
TOPIC 7 REVIEW

? Topic Essential Question

How can you use the Pythagorean Theorem to solve problems?

Sample answer: When you know a triangle is a right triangle and you know the lengths of any two sides, you can use the Pythagorean Theorem to determine the length of the third side. When you know the lengths of all three sides of a triangle, you can use the Converse of the Pythagorean Theorem to determine whether the triangle is a right triangle.

Vocabulary Review

Complete each definition and then provide an example of each vocabulary word.

**Vocabulary** Converse of the Pythagorean Theorem hypotenuse leg proof Pythagorean Theorem

| Definition | Example |
|---|---|
| 1. A proof is a logical argument in which every statement of fact is supported by a reason. | Check students' examples. |
| 2. The Converse of the Pythagorean Theorem states that if $a^2 + b^2 = c^2$ for side lengths $a$, $b$, and $c$ of a triangle, then the triangle is a right triangle. | Check students' examples. |
| 3. The Pythagorean Theorem states that in a right triangle the sum of the squares of the lengths of the legs is equal to the square of the length of the hypotenuse. | Check students' examples. |

Use Vocabulary in Writing

All faces of the figure are rectangles. Explain how to find the length of $d$. Use vocabulary terms in your description.

Sample answer: First, use the *Pythagorean Theorem* to find the value of $x$. This is the length of the *hypotenuse* of a right triangle with *legs* 3 inches and 4 inches long. Then, use the *Pythagorean Theorem* again to find the value of $d$. This is the length of the *hypotenuse* of a right triangle with *legs* $x$ inches and 12 inches long.



Topic 7 Topic Review 421

# Concepts and Skills Review

Available Online

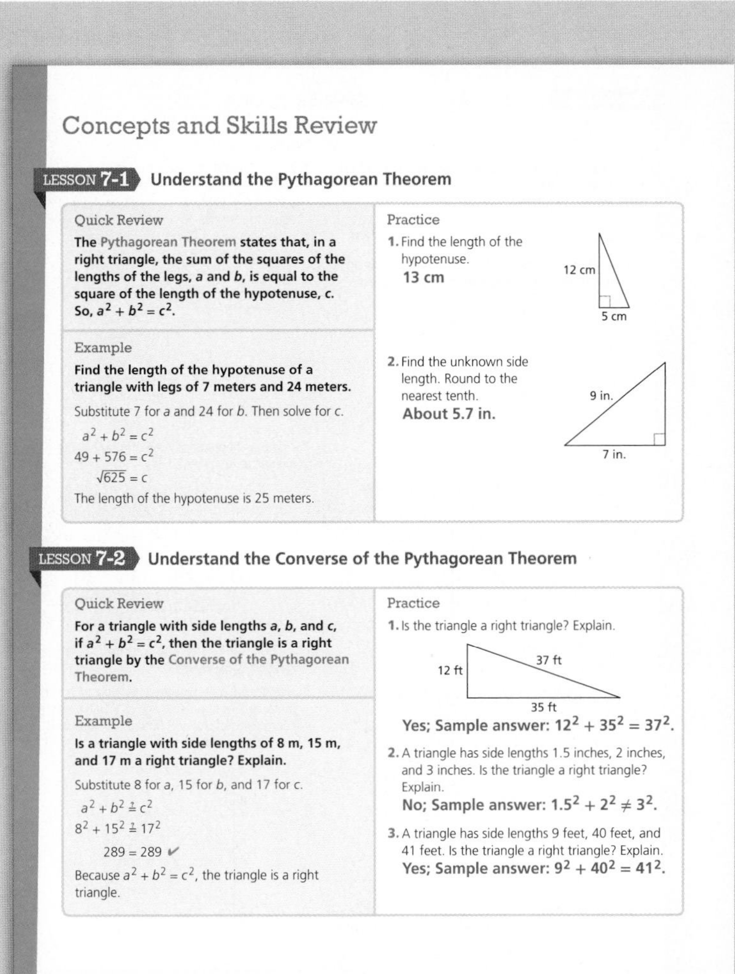

## Concepts and Skills Review

### LESSON 7-1 Understand the Pythagorean Theorem

**Quick Review**

**The Pythagorean Theorem states that, in a right triangle, the sum of the squares of the lengths of the legs, *a* and *b*, is equal to the square of the length of the hypotenuse, *c*. So, $a^2 + b^2 = c^2$.**

**Example**

**Find the length of the hypotenuse of a triangle with legs of 7 meters and 24 meters.**

Substitute 7 for *a* and 24 for *b*. Then solve for *c*.

$a^2 + b^2 = c^2$

$49 + 576 = c^2$

$\sqrt{625} = c$

The length of the hypotenuse is 25 meters.

**Practice**

1. Find the length of the hypotenuse.
   **13 cm**



2. Find the unknown side length. Round to the nearest tenth.
   **About 5.7 in.**



### LESSON 7-2 Understand the Converse of the Pythagorean Theorem

**Quick Review**

**For a triangle with side lengths *a*, *b*, and *c*, if $a^2 + b^2 = c^2$, then the triangle is a right triangle by the Converse of the Pythagorean Theorem.**

**Example**

**Is a triangle with side lengths of 8 m, 15 m, and 17 m a right triangle? Explain.**

Substitute 8 for *a*, 15 for *b*, and 17 for *c*.

$a^2 + b^2 \stackrel{?}{=} c^2$

$8^2 + 15^2 \stackrel{?}{=} 17^2$

$289 = 289$ ✓

Because $a^2 + b^2 = c^2$, the triangle is a right triangle.

**Practice**

1. Is the triangle a right triangle? Explain.



   **Yes; Sample answer: $12^2 + 35^2 = 37^2$.**

2. A triangle has side lengths 1.5 inches, 2 inches, and 3 inches. Is the triangle a right triangle? Explain.
   **No; Sample answer: $1.5^2 + 2^2 \neq 3^2$.**
3. A triangle has side lengths 9 feet, 40 feet, and 41 feet. Is the triangle a right triangle? Explain.
   **Yes; Sample answer: $9^2 + 40^2 = 41^2$.**

422 Topic 7 Topic Review

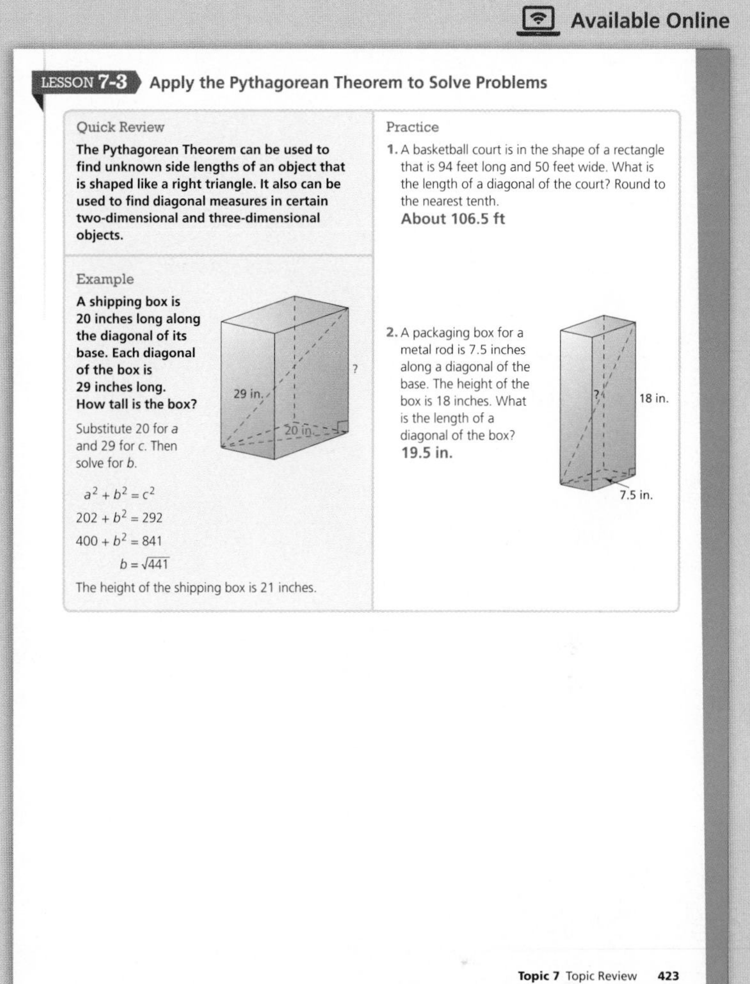

### LESSON 7-3 Apply the Pythagorean Theorem to Solve Problems

**Quick Review**

**The Pythagorean Theorem can be used to find unknown side lengths of an object that is shaped like a right triangle. It also can be used to find diagonal measures in certain two-dimensional and three-dimensional objects.**

**Example**

**A shipping box is 20 inches long along the diagonal of its base. Each diagonal of the box is 29 inches long. How tall is the box?**



Substitute 20 for *a* and 29 for *c*. Then solve for *b*.

$a^2 + b^2 = c^2$

$202 + b^2 = 292$

$400 + b^2 = 841$

$b = \sqrt{441}$

The height of the shipping box is 21 inches.

**Practice**

1. A basketball court is in the shape of a rectangle that is 94 feet long and 50 feet wide. What is the length of a diagonal of the court? Round to the nearest tenth.
   **About 106.5 ft**
2. A packaging box for a metal rod is 7.5 inches along a diagonal of the base. The height of the box is 18 inches. What is the length of a diagonal of the box?
   **19.5 in.**



Topic 7 Topic Review 423

Available Online

## LESSON 7-4 Find Distance in the Coordinate Plane

**Quick Review**

**The Pythagorean Theorem can be used to find the distance between any two points on the coordinate plane.**

**Example**

**Find the distance between the two points on the coordinate plane. Round to the nearest tenth.**

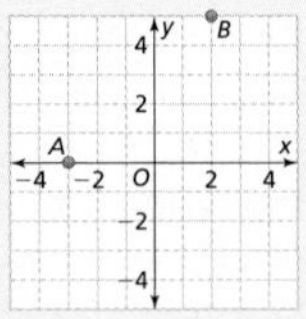

Draw a right triangle. Determine the lengths of its legs.

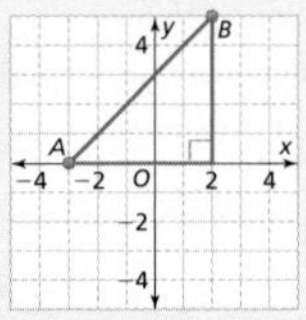

The length of the horizontal leg is 5 units.

The length of the vertical leg is 5 units.

Use the relationship $a^2 + b^2 = c^2$. Substitute 5 for $a$ and 5 for $b$. Then solve for $c$.

$a^2 + b^2 = c^2$

$5^2 + 5^2 = c^2$

$25 + 25 = c^2$

$50 = c^2$

$\sqrt{50} = c$

$7.1 \approx c$

The distance between the two points is about 7.1 units.

**Practice**

1. Points $C$ and $D$ represent the location of two parks on a map. Find the distance between the parks if the length of each unit on the grid is equal to 25 miles. Round to the nearest mile.

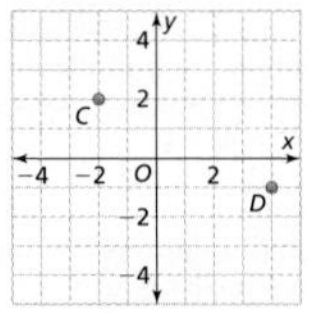

   **About 168 miles**

2. Find the perimeter of $\triangle ABC$. Round to the nearest tenth.

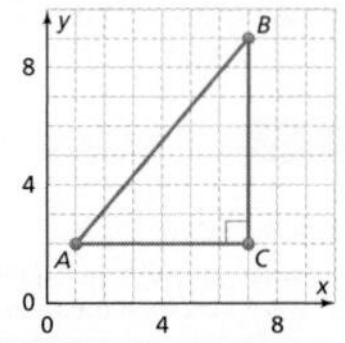

   **About 22.2 units**

3. Triangle $JKL$ is an equilateral triangle with two of its vertices at points $J$ and $K$. What are the coordinates of point $L$? Round to the nearest tenth as needed.

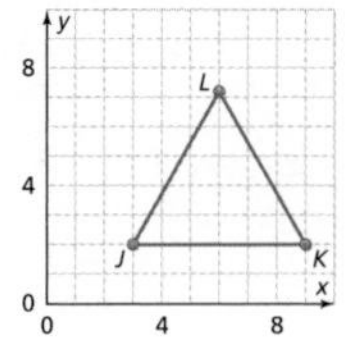

   **(6, 7.2)**

424 **Topic 7** Topic Review

# Fluency Practice

Go Online

Games

## Riddle Rearranging

Students maintain fluency with solving multi-step equations as they complete a riddle style activity that reinforces mathematical practices.

**Getting Started** Students may work independently or with a partner. Go over the directions. Remind students to solve all the equations first before rearranging the answers from least to greatest.

Students should solve each problem and complete their own riddle. Encourage students to record their work on a separate sheet of paper.

**As Students Do the Activity** Remind the students to arrange the answers in order from least to greatest. The letters corresponding to each equation will spell out the answer to the riddle below.

**Another Activity** Have students work together to write a new riddle. Then arrange the answers in order from greatest to least to solve the riddle. The letters should spell out one sentence.

Extra Challenge Create your own riddle activity. Write a new equation for each box. Then trade your activity with a partner and complete your partner's riddle.

Available Online

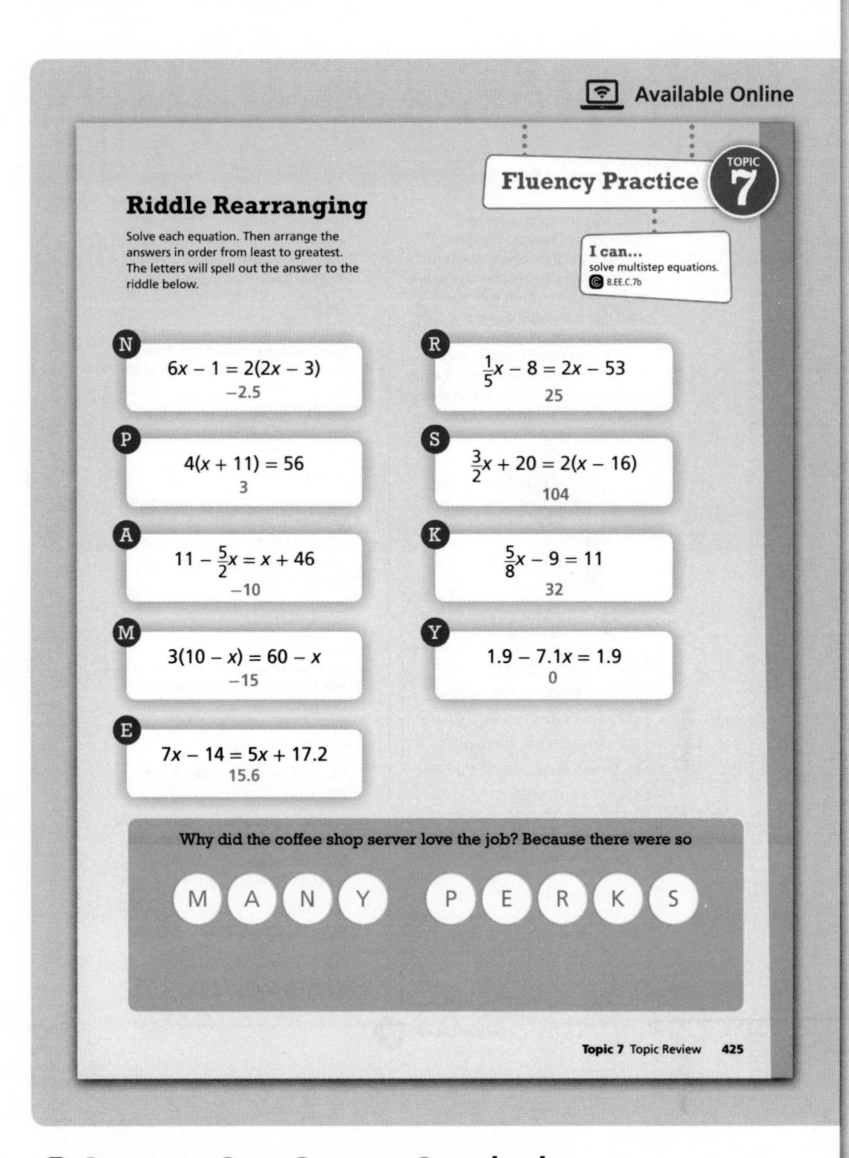

Fluency Practice TOPIC 7

**Riddle Rearranging**

Solve each equation. Then arrange the answers in order from least to greatest. The letters will spell out the answer to the riddle below.

I can... solve multistep equations. 8.EE.C.7b

N $6x - 1 = 2(2x - 3)$ −2.5

R $\frac{1}{5}x - 8 = 2x - 53$ 25

P $4(x + 11) = 56$ 3

S $\frac{3}{2}x + 20 = 2(x - 16)$ 104

A $11 - \frac{5}{2}x = x + 46$ −10

K $\frac{5}{8}x - 9 = 11$ 32

M $3(10 - x) = 60 - x$ −15

Y $1.9 - 7.1x = 1.9$ 0

E $7x - 14 = 5x + 17.2$ 15.6

Why did the coffee shop server love the job? Because there were so

M A N Y P E R K S

Topic 7 Topic Review 425

### Common Core Content Standards

**8.EE.C.7b** Solve linear equations with rational number coefficients, including equations whose solutions require expanding expressions using the distributive property and collecting like terms.

### Mathematical Practices

MP.2, MP.6, MP.7

# Assessment

Go Online

Assess

Available Online

Name ____________________

Topic 7 Assessment Form A

1. Emily says she can prove the Pythagorean Theorem using the following diagram. She explains that she can divide the squares on the two shorter sides into grids with equal-sized grid squares. She says she can then rearrange the grid squares to cover the area of the square on the hypotenuse, which proves that the sum of the squares on the two shorter sides equals the square on the hypotenuse.

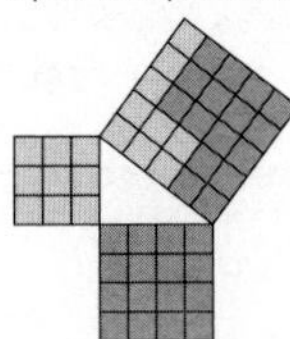

**1 point**

Is this a valid geometrical proof that $a^2 + b^2 = c^2$ for all right triangles?

**No; Sample answer: This proof only works when you can draw grids on the squares. It does not work for all right triangles.**

2. A triangular piece of fabric has side lengths of 1.2 feet, 2 feet, and 1.6 feet. Will it fit in the corner of a rectangular quilt? Explain. **1 point**

**Yes; Sample answer: It is a right triangle, $1.2^2 + 1.6^2 = 2^2$.**

3. Town Hall is located 4.3 miles directly east of the middle school. The fire station is located 1.7 miles directly north of Town Hall. **2 points**

**Part A**

What is the length of a straight line between the school and the fire station? Round to the nearest tenth.

**4.6 miles**

**Part B**

The hospital is 3.1 miles west of the fire station. What is the length of a straight line between the school and the hospital? Round to the nearest tenth.

**2.1 miles**

4. What is the length of the diagonal of a poster board with dimensions 22 inches by 28 inches? Round to the nearest tenth. **1 point**

Ⓐ 24.8 in.
Ⓑ 28.4 in.
● 35.6 in.
Ⓓ 50 in.

5. The three side lengths of four triangles are given. Which triangle is a right triangle? **1 point**

● Triangle 1: $\sqrt{13}$, 6, 7
Ⓑ Triangle 2: 7, 8, 13
Ⓒ Triangle 3: 10, 11, 12
Ⓓ Triangle 4: $\sqrt{10}$, 9, 8



6. Seraphina says that $\triangle KLM$ is a right triangle. Is she correct? Explain. **1 point**

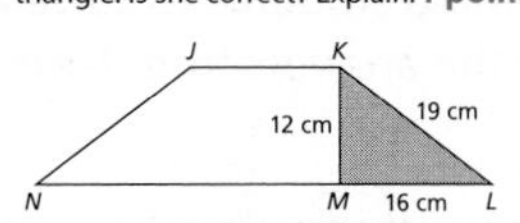


**No; Sample answer: Since $12^2 + 16^2 \neq 19^2$, it is not a right triangle.**

7. Lana draws $\triangle LMN$ on the coordinate plane.

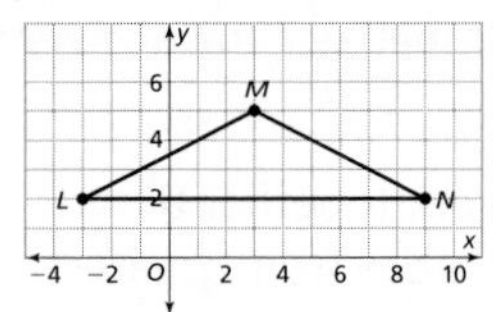


What is the perimeter of $\triangle LMN$? Round to the nearest unit. **1 point**

**25 units**

8. The top of a ladder rests at a height of 15 feet against the side of a house. If the base of the ladder is 6 feet from the house, what is the length of the ladder? Round to the nearest foot. **1 point**

Ⓐ 9 ft
Ⓑ 14 ft
● 16 ft
Ⓓ 21 ft

9. Kylie needs to pack her baton for a color-guard competition. The baton is 38 inches long. She has a rectangular box with a base of 13 inches by 35 inches and a height of 13 inches. **3 points**

**Part A**

Could the baton lie flat on a diagonal along the base of the box? Explain.

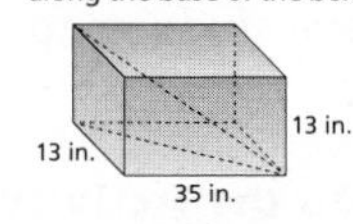


**No; The diagonal is about 37.3 in. long.**

**Part B**

Could the baton fit along the interior diagonal of the box?

**Yes; Sample answer: The interior diagonal is about 39.5 in., so the baton will fit.**

10. Vanessa draws one side of equilateral $\triangle ABC$ on the coordinate plane at points $A(-2, 1)$ and $B(4,1)$. What are the two possible coordinates of vertex $C$? Round to the nearest tenth. **2 points**

**(1, −4.2) and (1, 6.2)**



Assess students' understanding of the topic concepts and skills using the Topic Assessments found online.

Use the Item Analysis Chart on the facing page to assign an intervention to students based on their scores on the paper and pencil version of the Topic Assessments.

You may opt to have students take the Topic Assessment online. The online assessment is auto-scored, with a differentiated intervention automatically assigned to students based on their scores.

You can use ExamView to generate additional Topic Assessments.

There are two versions of the Topic Assessment, Form A and Form B. These parallel versions assess the same content item for each item. The Item Analysis chart on the next page can be used with both versions.

## Scoring Guide: Forms A and B

| Score | Recommendations |
|---|---|
| Greater Than 85% | Assign the corresponding MDIS for items answered incorrectly. Use Enrichment activities with the student. |
| 70%–85% | Assign the corresponding MDIS for items answered incorrectly. You may also assign Reteach to Build Understanding and Virtual Nerd Video assets for the lessons correlated to the items the student answered incorrectly. |
| Less Than 70% | Assign the corresponding MDIS for items answered incorrectly. Assign appropriate intervention lessons available online. You may also assign Reteach to Build Understanding, Additional Vocabulary Support, Build Mathematical Literacy, and Virtual Nerd Video assets for the lessons correlated to the items the student answered incorrectly. |

Go Online

Assess

Available Online

Name ______________________

Topic 7 Assessment Form B

**1.** Mark says he can prove the Pythagorean Theorem using the following diagram. He explains that he can fill the squares on the two shorter sides with equal-sized circles. He can then rearrange the circles to fill the square on the hypotenuse, which proves that the sum of the squares on the two shorter sides equals the square on the hypotenuse.

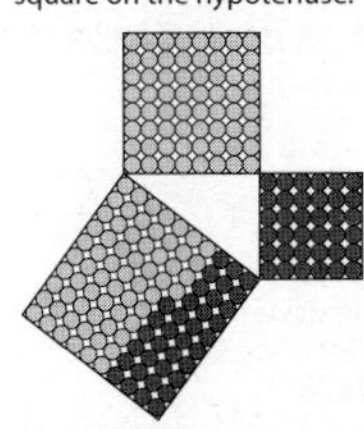

**1 point**

Is this a valid geometrical proof that $a^2 + b^2 = c^2$ for all right triangles?

**No; Sample answer: The circles do not completely fill the squares, and you do not know whether the space between is the same.**

**2.** A triangular bookshelf has a base of 10 inches, 12 inches, and 18 inches. Will the bookshelf fit in the corner of a square living room? Explain. **1 point**

**No; Sample answer: Since $10^2 + 12^2 \neq 18^2$, the base is not a right triangle.**

**3.** Calvin's school is 2.3 miles directly south of his house. After school, he takes a bus 1.8 miles directly west to the sports complex. **2 points**

**Part A**

What is the length of a straight line between Calvin's house and the sports complex? Round to the nearest tenth.

**2.9 miles**

**Part B**

Calvin takes piano lessons at a community music school located 3.7 miles directly north of the sports complex. What is the length of a straight line between Calvin's house and the music school? Round to the nearest tenth.

**2.3 miles**

**4.** A rectangular swimming pool is 19 meters wide by 35 meters long. What is the length of the diagonal of the pool? Round to the nearest tenth. **1 point**

Ⓐ 37.3 m
● 39.8 m
Ⓑ 38.9 m
Ⓓ 54 m

**5.** The three side lengths of four triangles are given. Which triangle is a right triangle? **1 point**

Ⓐ Triangle 1: 10, $\sqrt{65}$, 14
● Triangle 2: 8, 15, 17
Ⓒ Triangle 3: 15, 16, 23
Ⓓ Triangle 4: 9, $\sqrt{260}$, 19

Assessment, Form B 1 of 2

**6.** Brian says that $\triangle BCD$ is a right triangle. Is he correct? Explain. **1 point**

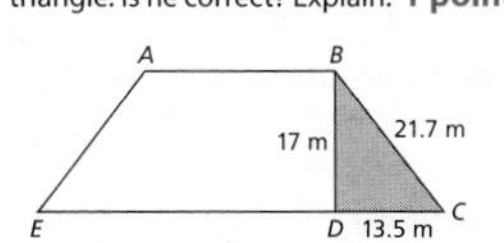


**Yes; Sample answer: $13.5^2 + 17^2 = 21.7^2$**

**7.** Ivan draws $\triangle PQR$ on the coordinate plane.

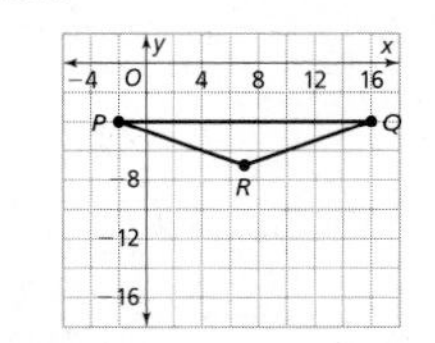


What is the perimeter of $\triangle PQR$? Round to the nearest unit. **1 point**

**37 units**

**8.** Maliki is building a ramp with a base of 4 feet and a vertical height of 2 feet. What is the length of the ramp? Round to the nearest tenth. **1 point**

Ⓐ 2.0 ft
 4.5 ft
Ⓑ 3.5 ft
Ⓓ 6.0 ft

**9.** A pair of drumsticks is 15.25 inches long. They need to fit in a rectangular box with a base of 13 inches by 7.5 inches and a height of 4 inches. **3 points**

**Part A**

Could the drumsticks lie flat on a diagonal along the base of the box? Explain.

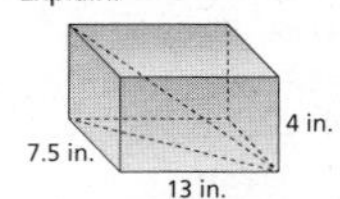


**No; The diagonal is about 15 in. long.**

**Part B**

Could the drumsticks fit along the interior diagonal of the box? Explain.

**Yes; Sample answer: The interior diagonal is about 15.52 in., so the drumsticks will fit.**

**10.** Victor draws one side of equilateral $\triangle PQR$ on the coordinate plane at points $P(-9, -2)$ and $Q(-2, -2)$. What are the two possible coordinates of vertex $R$? Round to the nearest tenth. **2 points**

**$(-5.5, -8.1)$ and $(-5.5, 4.1)$**

Assessment, Form B 2 of 2

## Item Analysis for Diagnosis and Intervention: Forms A and B

| Item | Points | DOK | MDIS | Standard |
|---|---|---|---|---|
| 1 | 1 | 3 | N64 | 8.G.B.6 |
| 2 | 1 | 2 | N65 | 8.G.B.7 |
| 3A | 1 | 2 | N64, N66 | 8.G.B.8 |
| 3B | 1 | 2 | N64, N66 | 8.G.B.8 |
| 4 | 1 | 2 | N64 | 8.G.B.7 |
| 5 | 1 | 2 | N65 | 8.G.B.7 |

| Item | Points | DOK | MDIS | Standard |
|---|---|---|---|---|
| 6 | 1 | 2 | N65 | 8.G.B.7 |
| 7 | 1 | 2 | N66, N65, N37 | 8.G.B.8 |
| 8 | 1 | 2 | N64 | 8.G.B.7 |
| 9A | 1 | 2 | N64 | 8.G.B.7 |
| 9B | 1 | 2 | N64 | 8.G.B.7 |
| 10 | 1 | 2 | N66 | 8.G.B.8 |

# Performance Task

Go Online

Assess students' ability to apply the topic concepts and skills using the Topic Performance Task found online.

Available Online

Name ______________________

Topic **7**
Performance Task
Form A

Cameron is designing a table for his game room. He wants the table to have a square top with triangular leaves that fold on hinges.

**1.** Cameron makes a sketch of the tabletop, with the leaves open, on the coordinate plane as shown.

**Part A**

If each unit on the grid represents 1 foot, what are the lengths of each side of each leaf? Round to the nearest tenth of a foot. **1 point**

**1.4 feet, 1.4 feet, and 2 feet**

**Part B**

What are the dimensions of the tabletop with the leaves open? Round to the nearest tenth of a foot. **1 point**

**2.8 feet by 2.8 feet**

**2.** Each leaf of Cameron's tabletop will be connected to the table by a support hinge that holds the leaf up. What is the length, *h*, of each support hinge? Explain. **2 points**

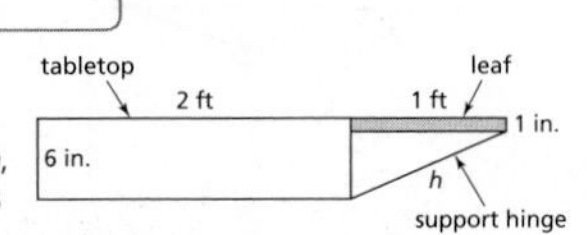


**13 inches ; Sample answer: The support hinge forms the hypotenuse of a right triangle with legs of lengths 5 in. and 12 in. $5^2 + 12^2 = h^2$; $169 = h^2$; $h = 13$.**

**3.** Cameron decides to make the center part of the tabletop out of inlaid wood. He sketches the design shown, where four trapezoids form a square with 6-inch sides in the middle of the table. What is the length, *d*, of the side of each trapezoid? Round to the nearest tenth of an inch. Explain. **2 points**

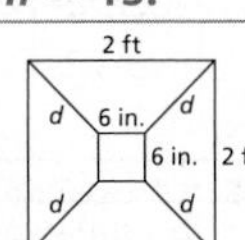


**12.7 inches; Sample answer: First, find the length of the diagonal of the tabletop; $24^2 + 24^2 = t^2$; $1152 = t^2$; $t = 33.9$. Then find the length of the diagonal of the square; $6^2 + 6^2 = c^2$; $72 = c^2$; $c = 8.5$. Subtract and divide by 2; $33.9 - 8.5 = 25.4$, $25.4 \div 2 = 12.7$.**

Performance Task, Form A 

**4.** Once he has completed the table, Cameron decides to make corner shelves from left-over triangular boards. The side lengths of the boards are 18 inches, 18 inches, and 24 inches.

**Part A**

Can Cameron use the boards as they are for his corner shelves? Explain. **2 points**

**No; Sample answer: The longest side is the hypotenuse, so check that $18^2 + 18^2 \stackrel{?}{=} c^2$; $648 \neq 576$. The boards are not right triangles and will not fit properly in the corner of the room.**

**Part B**

Cameron decides to cut down the left-over boards. He wants two sides of each shelf, which will fit in the corner, to have the same side length. To the nearest whole inch, what is the length of each side of the largest corner shelf Cameron can make using the boards? **1 point**

**17 inches, 17 inches, 24 inches**

**5.** Cameron makes a blueprint for his game room to decide how to set up the room. He places the table in the center of the sketched room. How far away is each corner of the table from each closest corner of the room? Explain. **2 points**

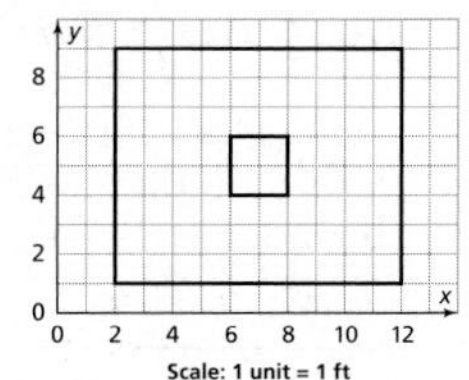


**5 feet; Sample answer: The distance from the corner of the table (6, 4) to the closest corner of the room (2, 1) is $3^2 + 4^2 = c^2$; $c = 5$.**

Performance Task, Form A 

## Item Analysis for Diagnosis and Intervention: Form A

| Item | DOK | MDIS | Standard |
|---|---|---|---|
| 1A | 2 | N64, N66 | 8.G.B.7, 8.G.B.8, MP.2 |
| 1B | 2 | N64 | 8.G.B.8, MP.7 |
| 2 | 2 | N64 | 8.G.B.7, MP.8 |
| 3 | 3 | N64 | 8.G.B.7, MP.1 |
| 4A | 2 | N65 | 8.G.B.7, MP.3 |
| 4B | 2 | N65 | 8.G.B.7, MP.6 |
| 5 | 3 | N64, N66 | 8.G.B.8, 8.G.B.7, MP.4 |

## Scoring Rubric: Forms A and B

| Item | Points (Form A) | Points (Form B) |
|---|---|---|
| 1 | **A** 1: Correct answer<br>**B** 1: Correct answer | 2: Correct answer and explanation<br>1: Correct answer or explanation |
| 2 | 2: Correct answer and explanation<br>1: Correct answer or explanation | **A** 1: Correct answer<br>**B** 2: Correct answer and explanation<br>1: Correct answer or explanation |
| 3 | 2: Correct answer and explanation<br>1: Correct answer or explanation | 2: Correct answer and explanation<br>1: Correct answer or explanation |
| 4 | **A** 2: Correct answer and explanation<br>1: Correct answer or explanation<br>**B** 1: Correct answer | 2: Correct answer and explanation<br>1: Correct answer or explanation |
| 5 | 2: Correct answer and explanation<br>1: Correct answer or explanation | 2: Correct answer and explanation<br>1: Correct answer or explanation |

Available Online

Name ______________________

Topic 7
Performance Task
Form B

Dani is hosting a party at her beach house for the kite festival. She is designing paper lanterns to hang in her yard.

1. Dani makes a sketch of her lantern. She adds side sails in the shape of an isosceles triangle like those on a box kite. What is the length of the congruent sides of the sails? Explain. **2 points**

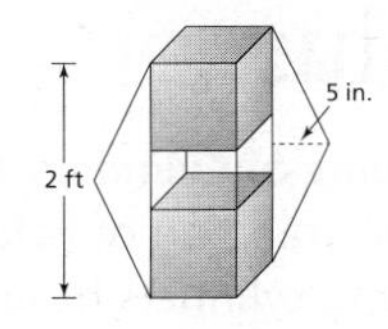


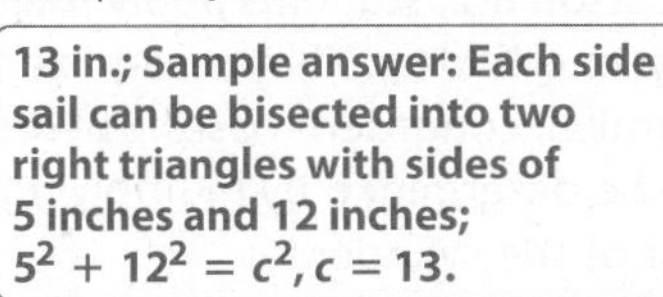

**13 in.; Sample answer: Each side sail can be bisected into two right triangles with sides of 5 inches and 12 inches; $5^2 + 12^2 = c^2, c = 13$.**

2. The main body of the paper lantern will consist of two rectangular prisms, each with a height of 0.75 feet and side lengths of 0.75 feet.

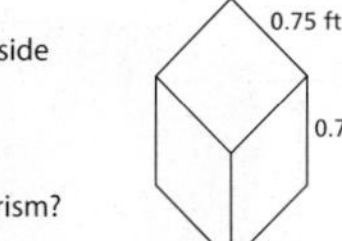
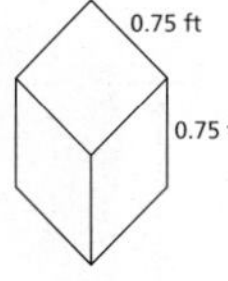


**Part A**

What is the length of the diagonal of the end of each prism? Round to the nearest foot. **1 point**

**1 foot**

**Part B**

Dani decides the top box will need an interior vertical diagonal brace to help hold its shape. What is the length of the brace? Explain. **2 points**

**1.25 ft; Sample answer: The diagonal brace is the hypotenuse of a right triangle with sides 1 and 0.75, so $1^2 + 0.75^2 = c^2, c = 1.25$.**



3. The festival sends Dani a map of where people will launch their kites. A portion of the map is shown. How far apart does each kite flyer stand? Round to the nearest foot. Explain. **2 points**

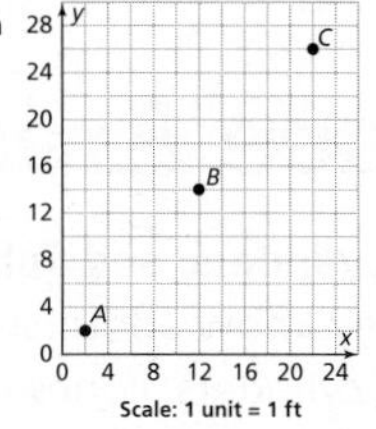


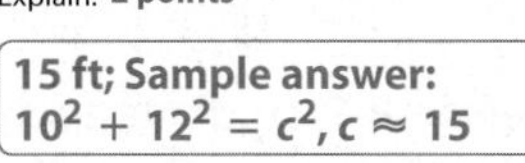

**15 ft; Sample answer: $10^2 + 12^2 = c^2, c \approx 15$**

4. Dani decides to make a kite for the festival. This kite will have a traditional kite shape, with a horizontal cross bar of 18 inches and a vertical cross bar of 36 inches. The cross bars are perpendicular. What are the outside dimensions of the kite? Round to the nearest tenth Explain. **2 points**

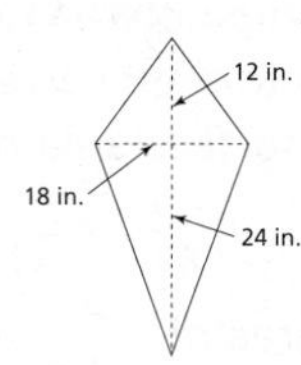


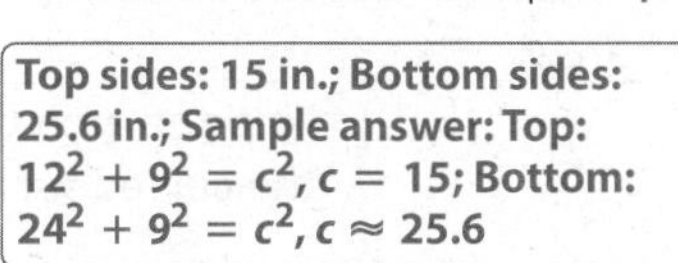

**Top sides: 15 in.; Bottom sides: 25.6 in.; Sample answer: Top: $12^2 + 9^2 = c^2, c = 15$; Bottom: $24^2 + 9^2 = c^2, c \approx 25.6$**

5. Dani decides to cut triangular pieces of nylon fabric that she will attach to the tail of her kite.

3 ft
3 in.

She uses a 3 inch by 3 feet strip of nylon. She will cut 12 separate pieces. What are the side lengths of each piece? Round to the nearest tenth. Explain. **2 points**

**5.5 in., 4.1 in., 4.1 in.; Sample answer: Each triangle has a base of $36 \div 6.5 = 5.5$. Each triangle can be bisected into two right triangles with sides of 3 in. and 2.75 in.; $3^2 + 2.75^2 = c^2, c \approx 4.1$.**

## Item Analysis for Diagnosis and Intervention: Form B

| Item | DOK | MDIS | Standard |
|---|---|---|---|
| 1 | 3 | N64 | 8.G.B.7, MP.2 |
| 2A | 2 | N64 | 8.G.B.7, MP.7 |
| 2B | 3 | N64 | 8.G.B.7, MP.6 |
| 3 | 3 | N64, N66 | 8.G.B.8, MP.4 |
| 4 | 2 | N64 | 8.G.B.7, MP.2 |
| 5 | 2 | N64 | 8.G.B.7, MP.8 |

## Scoring Guide: Forms A and B

| Score | Recommendations |
|---|---|
| Greater Than 85% | Assign the corresponding MDIS for items answered incorrectly. Use Enrichment activities with the student. |
| 70%–85% | Assign the corresponding MDIS for items answered incorrectly. You may also assign Reteach to Build Understanding and Virtual Nerd Video assets for the lessons correlated to the items the student answered incorrectly. |
| Less Than 70% | Assign the corresponding MDIS for items answered incorrectly. Assign appropriate intervention lessons available online. You may also assign Reteach to Build Understanding, Additional Vocabulary Support, Build Mathematical Literacy, and Virtual Nerd Video assets for the lessons correlated to the items the student answered incorrectly. |

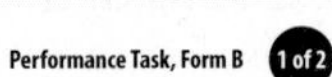

TOPIC 8

# Solve Problems Involving Surface Area and Volume

## Math Background Focus

### Surface Area

- **Cones, Cylinders, and Spheres** In Lesson 8-1, students apply what they know about surface area to determine the surface areas of cylinders, cones, and spheres. They examine the relationship between the surface area formulas of cones and cylinders to their corresponding nets. Students use reasoning to find the surface area of spheres.

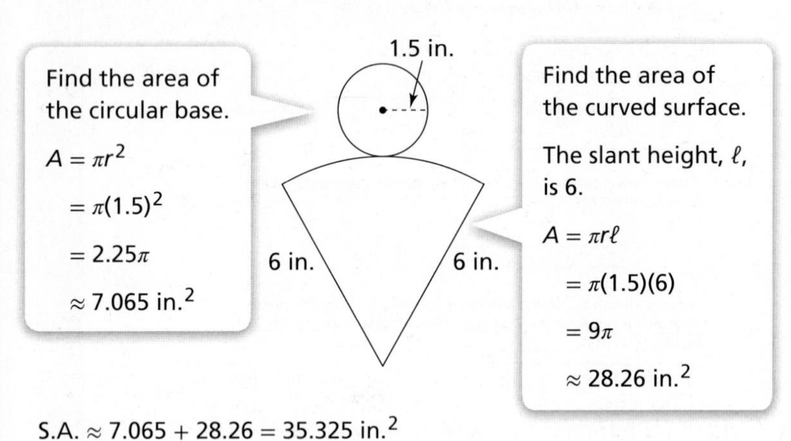


S.A. $\approx 7.065 + 28.26 = 35.325$ in.$^2$

### Volume

- **Volume of Cylinders** In Lesson 8-2, students apply their understanding of volume to cylinders. They recognize that, like prisms, cylinders have parallel, congruent bases. Therefore, the volume of a cylinder can be determined by multiplying the area of the base by the height of the cylinder.

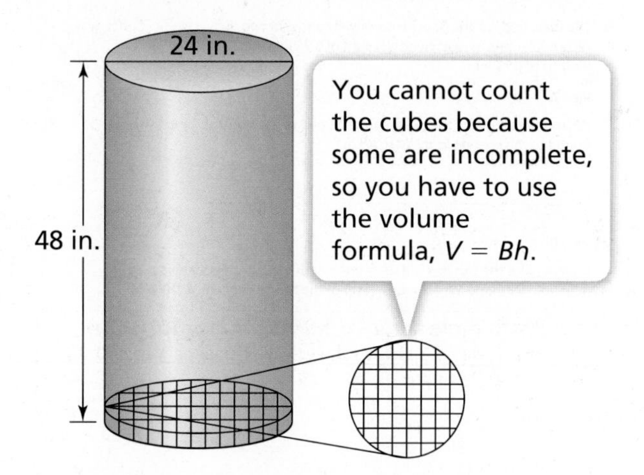


Use the formula to find the volume of the cylinder. Use 3.14 for $\pi$.

$V = Bh$
$= \pi r^2 \cdot h$
$= 3.14 \cdot (12)^2 \cdot 48$
$= 21{,}703.68$ in.$^3$

The cylindrical tank is large enough for the 25 zebra fish.

- **Volume of Cones** In Lesson 8-3, students relate the volume of cylinders to the volume of cones. They recognize that the relationship between the volumes of prisms and pyramids with the same base and height is the same between the volumes of cylinders and cones with the same base and height. This relationship is generalized to write the volume formula for a cone.

  A city engineer determines that 5,500 cubic meters of sand will be needed to treat the roadways this winter. Does the city have enough sand to treat the roadways? Use $\frac{22}{7}$ for $\pi$. Explain.

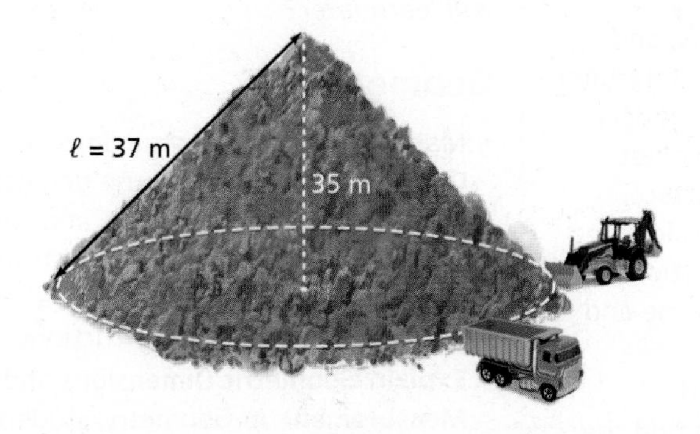


- **Volume of Spheres** In Lesson 8-4, students learn that the volume of a sphere is the same as twice the volume of a cone that has a base diameter and height that is the same as the sphere diameter.

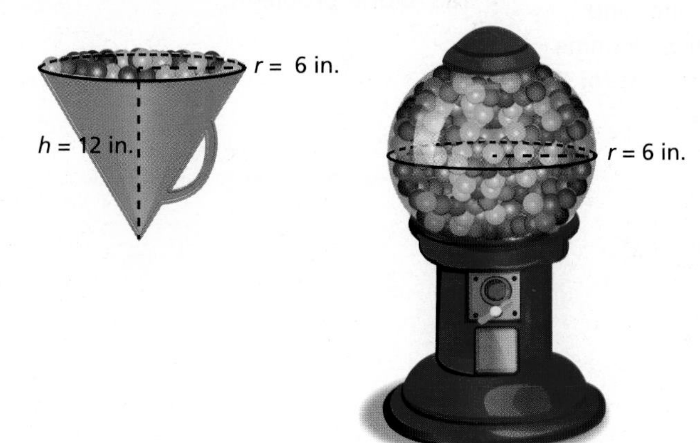


Go Online

Video

# Advanced Concepts for the Teacher

- **Volume of a Cone** The volume of a cylinder can be used to derive the formula for the volume of a cone. Estimate the volume of a cone with radius $r$ and height $h$ by dividing the cone into $n$ levels. Each section will have height $\frac{h}{n}$.

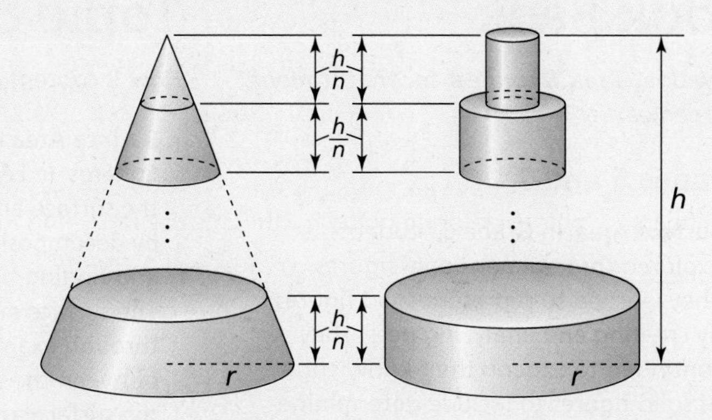


The volume of the compound figure composed of cylinders is the sum of the volumes of the individual cylinders. The largest cylinder has radius $r$, and the radius of each smaller cylinder is a fraction of the original radius, determined by $n$. As the volume of one cylinder is $\pi r^2 h$, the volume of the shape with $n$ divisions is:

$$V_n = \pi\left(\frac{r}{n}\right)^2\left(\frac{h}{n}\right) + \pi\left(\frac{2r}{n}\right)^2\left(\frac{h}{n}\right) + \ldots + \pi\left(\frac{nr}{n}\right)^2\left(\frac{h}{n}\right)$$

Simplify the volume expression by factoring.

$$V_n = \frac{\pi r^2 h}{n^3}\left(1^2 + 2^2 + \ldots + n^2\right)$$

The expression in the parentheses is sum of the squares of integers from 1 to $n$. Substitute the formula for the sum of this series.

$$V_n = \frac{\pi r^2 h}{n^3} \cdot \frac{n(n+1)(2n+1)}{6}$$

Divide each factor in the numerator that includes $n$ by one factor of $n$ from $n^3$.

$$V_n = \frac{1}{6}\pi r^2 h \cdot \left(\frac{n}{n}\right)\left(\frac{n+1}{n}\right)\left(\frac{2n+1}{n}\right)$$
$$= \frac{1}{6}\pi r^2 h(1)\left(1 + \frac{1}{n}\right)\left(2 + \frac{1}{n}\right)$$

As $n$ gets greater and greater, the value of $\frac{1}{n}$ approaches 0, and the value of the two expressions with $n$ approach 1 and 2, respectively.

$$V = \frac{1}{6}\pi r^2 h(1)(1)(2)$$
$$= \frac{1}{3}\pi r^2 h$$

This is the volume formula for a cone with radius $r$.

# Math Background Coherence

Students learn best when concepts are connected throughout the curriculum. This coherence is achieved within topics, across topics, across domains, and across grade levels.

## Look Back

*How does Topic 8 connect to what students learned earlier?*

### Grades 6 and 7

- **Surface Area** In Grade 6, students explored three-dimensional figures. They learned to represent solid figures by creating and analyzing nets. They continued to expand their knowledge of solid figures to include determining the surface areas for prisms and pyramids. In Grade 7, students reinforced and applied their knowledge of surface area of prisms to solve real-world problems.
- **Volume** In Grade 6, students were introduced to the concept of volume of three-dimensional figures. In Grade 7, students applied their knowledge of volume by solving real-world problems involving cubes and right prisms.

## Topic 8

*How is content connected within Topic 8?*

- **Surface Area of Cones, Cylinders, and Spheres** In Lesson 8-1, students determine the surface area of cones and cylinders by decomposing the shape into a net and finding the area of each surface. The surface area of a sphere is calculated through examination of the relationship between the surface area of a cone and the surface area of a sphere.
- **Volume of Cones, Cylinders, and Spheres** In Lesson 8-2, students find the volume of a cone by applying a similar procedure to the volume of a right prism. In Lesson 8-3, students examine the differences and similarities between the formulas for volumes of cones and cylinders. In Lesson 8-4, students examine the similarity between the formulas for volumes of cones and spheres.

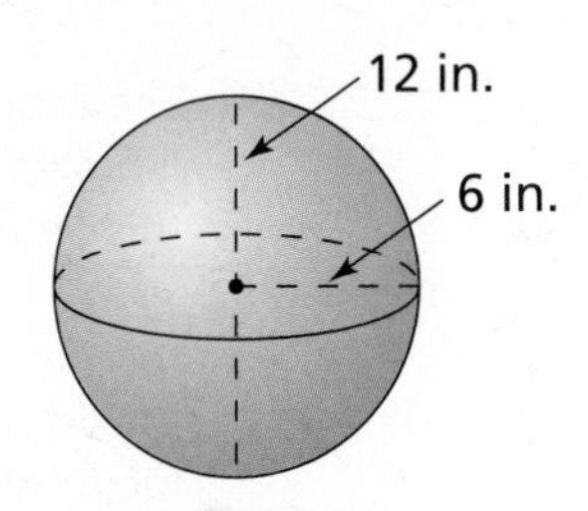


The volume of a sphere is the same as twice the volume of a cone with the same circular base and height.

Volume of a sphere = 2(Volume of a cone)

$$V = 2\left(\frac{1}{3}Bh\right)$$
$$= 2\left(\frac{1}{3}\pi r^2 h\right)$$
$$= 2\left(\frac{1}{3}\pi r^2 \cdot 2r\right)$$
$$= \frac{4}{3}\pi r^3$$

The height of a sphere is twice its radius.

**Generalize** The formula for the volume of a sphere is $V = \frac{4}{3}\pi r^3$.

## Look Ahead

*How does Topic 8 connect to what students will learn later?*

### Geometry

- **Make Geometric Constructions** In Geometry, students will use geometric tools such as a straightedge and compass to make formal geometric constructions. They will learn the difference between sketches and formal constructions.
- **Explain Geometric Dimensions and Measurement** In Geometry, students expand their knowledge of formulas for the volume of cylinders, cones, and spheres to providing explanations for volume formulas and apply them to solve real-world problems.

# Math Background Rigor

A rigorous curriculum emphasizes conceptual understanding, procedural skill and fluency, and applications.

## Conceptual Understanding

- **Surface Area of Cylinders and Cones** Students further their conceptual understanding of surface area by applying what they know to find the surface area of cylinders and cones. They identify the two-dimensional surfaces that make up three-dimensional figures and draw nets as a strategy for finding surface areas of cylinders and cones.

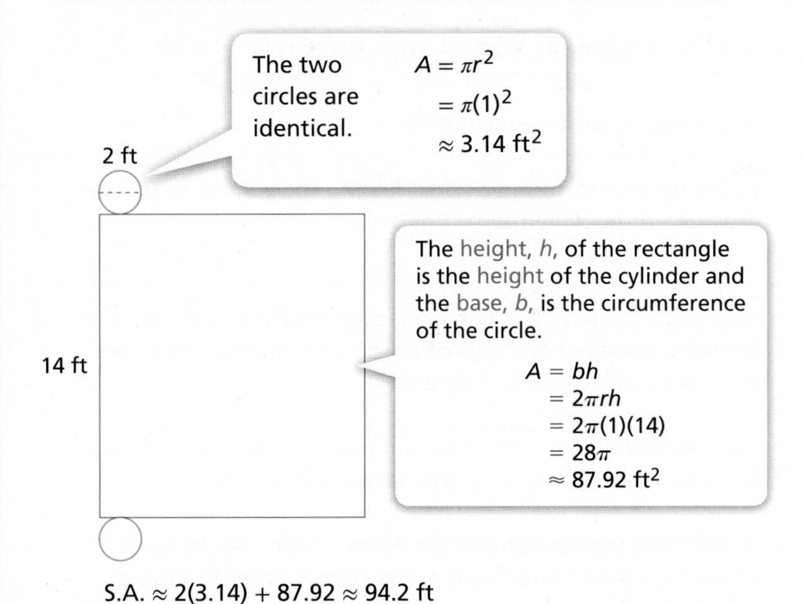


S.A. $\approx 2(3.14) + 87.92 \approx 94.2$ ft

- **Volume of Cones, Cylinders, and Spheres** Students understand that volume is a measure of capacity. They relate volumes of cones, cylinders, and spheres to the volumes of three-dimensional figures they know. They use these relationships to generalize volume formulas for cones, cylinders, and spheres.

## Procedural Skill and Fluency

- **Formulas for Surface Area** Students demonstrate procedural fluency when they apply calculating areas of two-dimensional figures to find surface areas of cylinders, cones, and spheres.
- **Formulas for Volume** Students will connect their understanding of volume and three-dimensional figures to procedures for calculating volume. They demonstrate procedural skill and fluency by using formulas to calculate volumes.

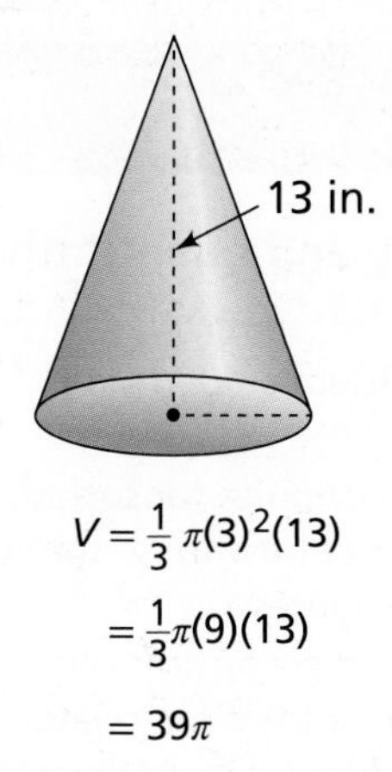


$$V = \frac{1}{3}\pi(3)^2(13)$$
$$= \frac{1}{3}\pi(9)(13)$$
$$= 39\pi$$

The volume of the cone is $39\pi$ inches.

## Applications

- **Surface Area and Volume of Cones, Cylinders, and Spheres** Students apply their understanding of surface area and volume of cylinders, cones, and spheres to solve real-world and mathematical problems. They have opportunities to solve problems involving composite figures and to apply the Pythagorean Theorem to find needed measures.

$$V = Bh$$
$$300 = \pi r^2 \cdot 14$$
$$300 = 43.96r^2$$
$$6.82 \approx r^2$$
$$2.6 \approx r$$

The radius of the can is about 2.6 centimeters.

# Math Practices

The math practices and processes describe the behaviors and thinking habits that mathematically proficient students demonstrate when actively engaged in mathematics work. Opportunities for engagement in the practices and to develop expertise with these important behaviors and thinking habits exist throughout the topic and program. Here we focus on mathematical reasoning and explaining.

As students solve volume and surface area problems, look for these behaviors to assess and identify students who demonstrate proficiency with mathematical reasoning and explaining.

**Math Practices Within Topic 8 Lessons**

| **Reason abstractly and quantitatively. (MP.2)** | **Look for and make use of structure. (MP.7)** |
|---|---|
| Mathematically proficient students: | Mathematically proficient students: |
| • Make sense of the formulas for surface area and volume and recognize how these formulas are related in three-dimensional figures. | • Apply the correct formula when finding the volume or surface area of a three-dimensional figure. |
| • Understand how quantities are related when using volume and surface area formulas in mathematical and real-world situations. | • Recognize the patterns and connections between the formulas for the volumes of rectangular prisms and cylinders, cylinders and cones, and cones and spheres. |
| • Analyze three-dimensional figures and their corresponding nets to find their surface areas. | • Use the overall structure of the volume or surface area formula to determine the unknown dimension of a figure. |
| • Consider units as they solve problems that involve volume and surface area. | • Understand the structure of the Pythagorean Theorem and when it is used to find needed measures in order to solve a volume problem. |
| • Recognize how to find an unknown dimension in order to solve volume and surface area problems. | • Recognize how to apply the different volume formulas when finding the volume of a composite figure. |

Help students become more proficient with mathematical reasoning and explanation.

If students do not understand how to determine volume and surface area of three-dimensional figures, then use these questioning strategies to help them develop reasoning and explaining skills as they solve problems throughout the topic.

**Q:** What does each quantity used in the problem represent?

**Q:** What is the relationship between the quantities?

**Q:** How is finding the area of a two-dimensional figure related to finding the surface area of a three-dimensional figure?

**Q:** What is the relationship between the surface area of a three-dimensional figure and the areas of the shapes in its net?

**Q:** What do square units represent when solving problems? What do cubic units represent when solving problems?

**Q:** What patterns do you recognize in the formulas for the volume of a rectangular prism and the volume of a cylinder?

**Q:** What patterns do you recognize in the formulas for the volume of a cylinder and the volume of a cone?

**Q:** What patterns do you recognize in the formulas for the volume of a cone and the volume of a sphere?

**Q:** What surface area or volume formula(s) do you need to apply in order to solve this problem?

**Q:** In what ways does this problem connect to other volume or surface area formulas?

# Topic Readiness Assessment

Go Online

Assess

Topic Readiness Assessment Masters

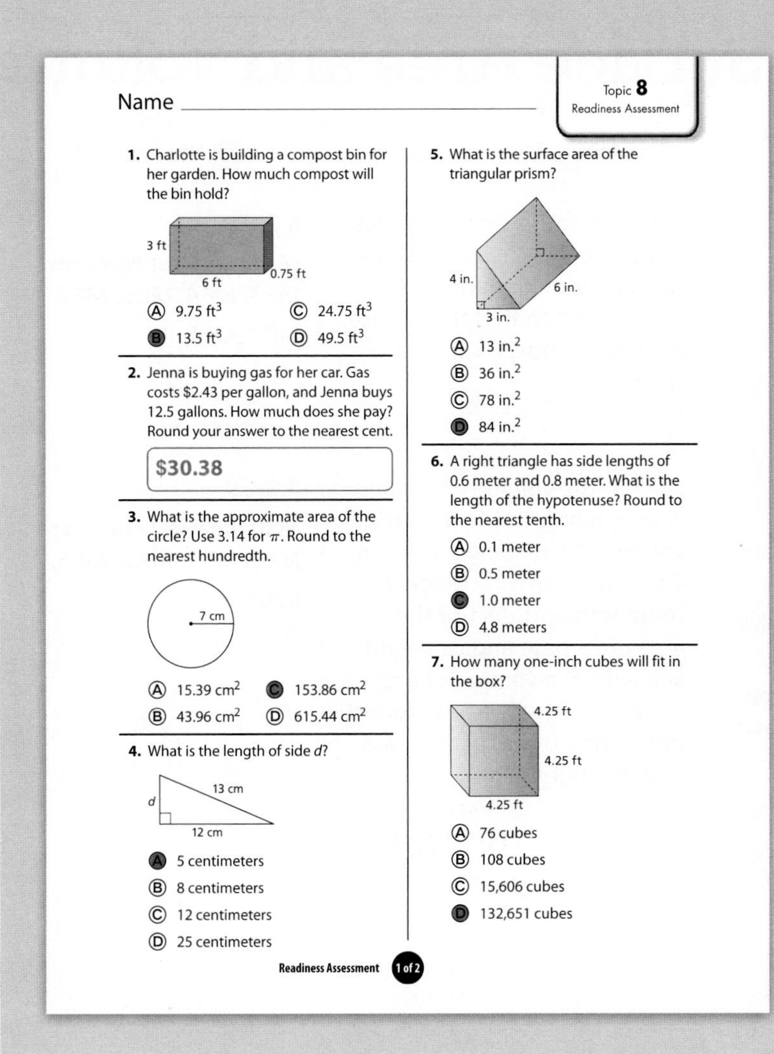

Name ____________________

Topic 8
Readiness Assessment

1. Charlotte is building a compost bin for her garden. How much compost will the bin hold?

3 ft, 6 ft, 0.75 ft

Ⓐ 9.75 $ft^3$
Ⓑ 13.5 $ft^3$
Ⓒ 24.75 $ft^3$
Ⓓ 49.5 $ft^3$

2. Jenna is buying gas for her car. Gas costs $2.43 per gallon, and Jenna buys 12.5 gallons. How much does she pay? Round your answer to the nearest cent.

$30.38

3. What is the approximate area of the circle? Use 3.14 for $\pi$. Round to the nearest hundredth.

7 cm

Ⓐ 15.39 $cm^2$
Ⓑ 43.96 $cm^2$
Ⓒ 153.86 $cm^2$
Ⓓ 615.44 $cm^2$

4. What is the length of side *d*?

13 cm, *d*, 12 cm

Ⓐ 5 centimeters
Ⓑ 8 centimeters
Ⓒ 12 centimeters
Ⓓ 25 centimeters

5. What is the surface area of the triangular prism?

4 in., 6 in., 3 in.

Ⓐ 13 $in.^2$
Ⓑ 36 $in.^2$
Ⓒ 78 $in.^2$
Ⓓ 84 $in.^2$

6. A right triangle has side lengths of 0.6 meter and 0.8 meter. What is the length of the hypotenuse? Round to the nearest tenth.

Ⓐ 0.1 meter
Ⓑ 0.5 meter
Ⓒ 1.0 meter
Ⓓ 4.8 meters

7. How many one-inch cubes will fit in the box?

4.25 ft, 4.25 ft, 4.25 ft

Ⓐ 76 cubes
Ⓑ 108 cubes
Ⓒ 15,606 cubes
Ⓓ 132,651 cubes

Readiness Assessment 1 of 2

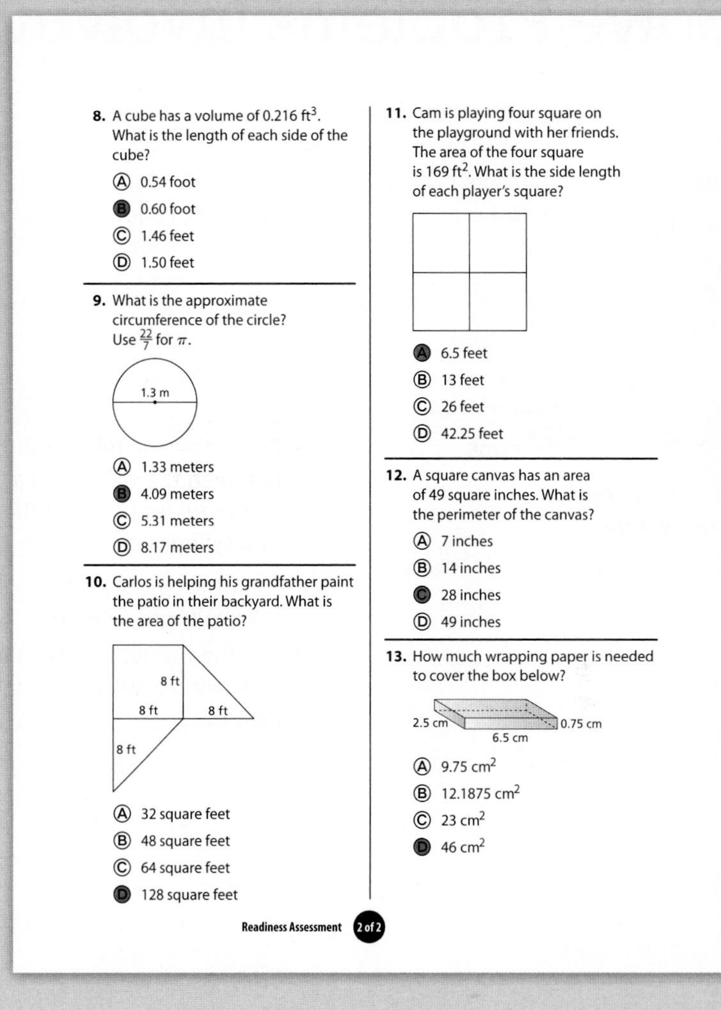

8. A cube has a volume of 0.216 $ft^3$. What is the length of each side of the cube?

Ⓐ 0.54 foot
Ⓑ 0.60 foot
Ⓒ 1.46 feet
Ⓓ 1.50 feet

9. What is the approximate circumference of the circle? Use $\frac{22}{7}$ for $\pi$.

1.3 m

Ⓐ 1.33 meters
Ⓑ 4.09 meters
Ⓒ 5.31 meters
Ⓓ 8.17 meters

10. Carlos is helping his grandfather paint the patio in their backyard. What is the area of the patio?

8 ft, 8 ft, 8 ft, 8 ft

Ⓐ 32 square feet
Ⓑ 48 square feet
Ⓒ 64 square feet
Ⓓ 128 square feet

11. Cam is playing four square on the playground with her friends. The area of the four square is 169 $ft^2$. What is the side length of each player's square?

Ⓐ 6.5 feet
Ⓑ 13 feet
Ⓒ 26 feet
Ⓓ 42.25 feet

12. A square canvas has an area of 49 square inches. What is the perimeter of the canvas?

Ⓐ 7 inches
Ⓑ 14 inches
Ⓒ 28 inches
Ⓓ 49 inches

13. How much wrapping paper is needed to cover the box below?

2.5 cm, 6.5 cm, 0.75 cm

Ⓐ 9.75 $cm^2$
Ⓑ 12.1875 $cm^2$
Ⓒ 23 $cm^2$
Ⓓ 46 $cm^2$

Readiness Assessment 2 of 2

Assess students' understanding of prerequisite concepts and skills using the Topic Readiness Assessment.

You may opt to have students take the Topic Readiness Assessment online.

## Scoring Guide

| Score | Recommendations |
|---|---|
| Greater Than 85% | Assign the corresponding MDIS for items answered incorrectly. Use Enrichment activities with the student during the topic. |
| 70%–85% | Assign the corresponding MDIS for items answered incorrectly. Monitor the student during Step 1 and Try It! parts of the lessons for personalized remediation needs. |
| Less Than 70% | Assign the corresponding MDIS for items answered incorrectly. Assign appropriate intervention lessons available online. |

## Item Analysis for Diagnosis and Remediation

| Item | DOK | MDIS | Standard |
|---|---|---|---|
| 1 | 2 | N52 | 7.G.B.6 |
| 2 | 2 | L64 | 6.NS.B.3 |
| 3 | 2 | N47 | 7.G.B.4 |
| 4 | 2 | N64 | 8.G.B.7 |
| 5 | 2 | N49 | 7.G.B.6 |
| 6 | 2 | N64 | 8.G.B.7 |
| 7 | 2 | N51 | 7.G.B.6 |
| 8 | 2 | N52 | 7.G.B.6, 8.EE.A.2 |
| 9 | 2 | N46 | 7.G.B.4 |
| 10 | 2 | N42 | 8.G.B.6 |
| 11 | 2 | N41 | 7.G.B.6 |
| 12 | 2 | N41 | 7.G.B.6, 8.EE.A.2 |
| 13 | 2 | N48 | 7.G.B.6 |

TOPIC 8

# Topic Planner

## Solve Problems Involving Surface Area and Volume

| Lesson | Vocabulary | Objective | Essential Understanding | Standards |
|---|---|---|---|---|
| **8-1** Find Surface Area of Three-Dimensional Figures | cone, cylinder, sphere | • Find the surface areas of cylinders, cones, and spheres. | Formulas for finding the areas of polygons, such as rectangles, squares, triangles and circles, can be used to find the surface areas of cylinders, cones, and spheres. | 8.G.C.9<br>**Mathematical Practices** MP.3, MP.4, MP.5, MP.6, MP.7, MP.8 |
| **8-2** Find Volume of Cylinders | none | • Recognize the relationship between the volume of a rectangular prism and the volume of a cylinder.<br>• Solve real-world problems involving the volume of a cylinder.<br>• Use the formula for the volume of a cylinder to find an unknown measure. | Finding the volume of a cylinder is an extension of finding the volume of a rectangular prism. The volume of a rectangular prism is the product of the area of its base and its height. Similarly, the volume of a cylinder is equal to the product of the area of its circular base and its height. | 8.G.C.9<br>**Mathematical Practices** MP.2, MP.3, MP.5, MP.6, MP.7 |

## Lesson Resources

Digital

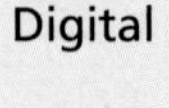
Print

**Student's Edition**

**Additional Practice Workbook**

**Teaching Resources**
- Reteach to Build Understanding
- Additional Vocabulary Support
- Build Mathematical Literacy
- Enrichment

**Assessment Resources**
- Lesson Quiz

Digital

**Digital Lesson Courseware**
- Today's Challenge
- Visual Learning Animation Plus
- Key Concept
- Additional Examples
- 3-Act Mathematical Modeling
- Online Practice powered by MathXL for School
- Adaptive Practice
- Virtual Nerd Video Tutorials
- Animated Glossary
- Digital Math Tools
- Online Math Games

**Lesson Support for Teachers**
- Listen and Look For PD Lesson Video

The suggested pacing for each lesson is 2 days for a 45-minute math class and 1 day for a 90-minute class.

Go Online

Digital

| Lesson | Vocabulary | Objective | Essential Understanding | Standards |
|---|---|---|---|---|
| **8-3** Find Volume of Cones | none | • Recognize the relationship between the volume of a cylinder and the volume of a cone.<br>• Use the Pythagorean Theorem when solving volume problems.<br>• Find the volume of a cone. Given the circumference of the base, find the volume of a cone. | The volume of a cone is $\frac{1}{3}$ the volume of a cylinder given that the bases have the same radius and the heights are the same. The formula for the volume of a cone is $V = \frac{1}{3}Bh$, where $B$ is the area of its circular base and $h$ is the height of the cone. | 8.G.C.9<br>**Mathematical Practices**<br>MP.1, MP.2, MP.7 |
| **8-4** Find Volume of Spheres | composite figure | • Recognize the relationship between the volume of a cone and the volume of a sphere.<br>• Find the volume of a sphere. Given the surface area, find the volume of a sphere.<br>• Find the volume of a composite figure. | The volumes of a sphere and cone are proportionally related. The volume of a sphere is twice the volume of a cone that has the same circular base and height. The formula for the volume of a sphere is $V = \frac{4}{3}\pi r^3$, where $r$ is the radius of the sphere. | 8.G.C.9<br>**Mathematical Practices**<br>MP.2, MP.3, MP.6, MP.7, MP.8 |
| 3-Act Mathematical Modeling: Measure Up | none | • Use mathematical modeling to represent a problem situation and to propose a solution.<br>• Test and verify the appropriateness of their math models.<br>• Explain why the results from their mathematical models may not align to the problem situation. | Many real-word problem situations can be represented with a mathematical model, but that model may not represent a real-world situation exactly. | 8.G.C.9<br>**Mathematical Practices**<br>MP.4 |

# Topic Resources

Digital

Print

### Student's Edition
- Review What You Know
- Language Development Activity
- Mid-Topic Checkpoint and Performance Task
- Topic Review
- Fluency Practice Activity
- enVision® STEM Project
- Pick a Project

### Assessment Resources
- Topic Readiness Assessment
- Mid-Topic Assessment
- Topic Assessment
- Topic Performance Task

Digital

### Topic Support for Students
- Math Practice Animations
- enVision® STEM Project
- 3-Act Mathematical Modeling Lesson

### Topic Support for Teachers
- Topic Overview Video
- ExamView Test Generator

# TOPIC 8 Topic Opener

# Solve Problems Involving Surface Area and Volume

Available Online

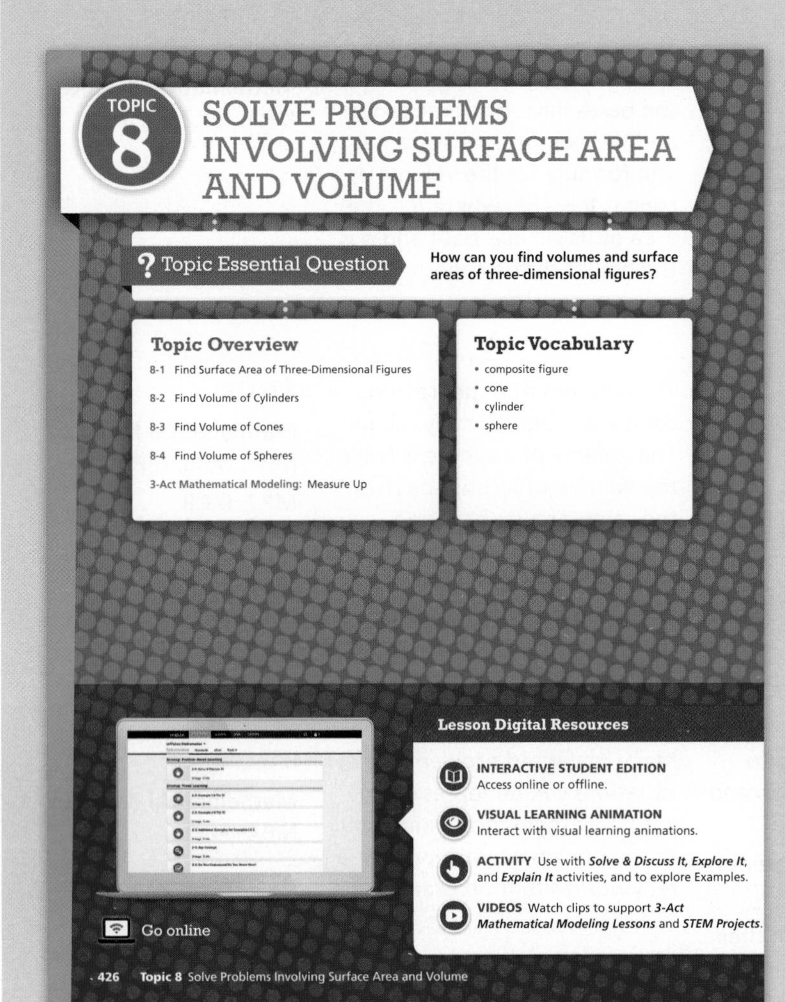

TOPIC 8 SOLVE PROBLEMS INVOLVING SURFACE AREA AND VOLUME

? Topic Essential Question — How can you find volumes and surface areas of three-dimensional figures?

**Topic Overview**

- 8-1 Find Surface Area of Three-Dimensional Figures
- 8-2 Find Volume of Cylinders
- 8-3 Find Volume of Cones
- 8-4 Find Volume of Spheres
- 3-Act Mathematical Modeling: Measure Up

**Topic Vocabulary**

- composite figure
- cone
- cylinder
- sphere

Go online

**Lesson Digital Resources**

- **INTERACTIVE STUDENT EDITION** Access online or offline.
- **VISUAL LEARNING ANIMATION** Interact with visual learning animations.
- **ACTIVITY** Use with *Solve & Discuss It, Explore It,* and *Explain It* activities, and to explore Examples.
- **VIDEOS** Watch clips to support *3-Act Mathematical Modeling Lessons* and *STEM Projects.*

426 Topic 8 Solve Problems Involving Surface Area and Volume

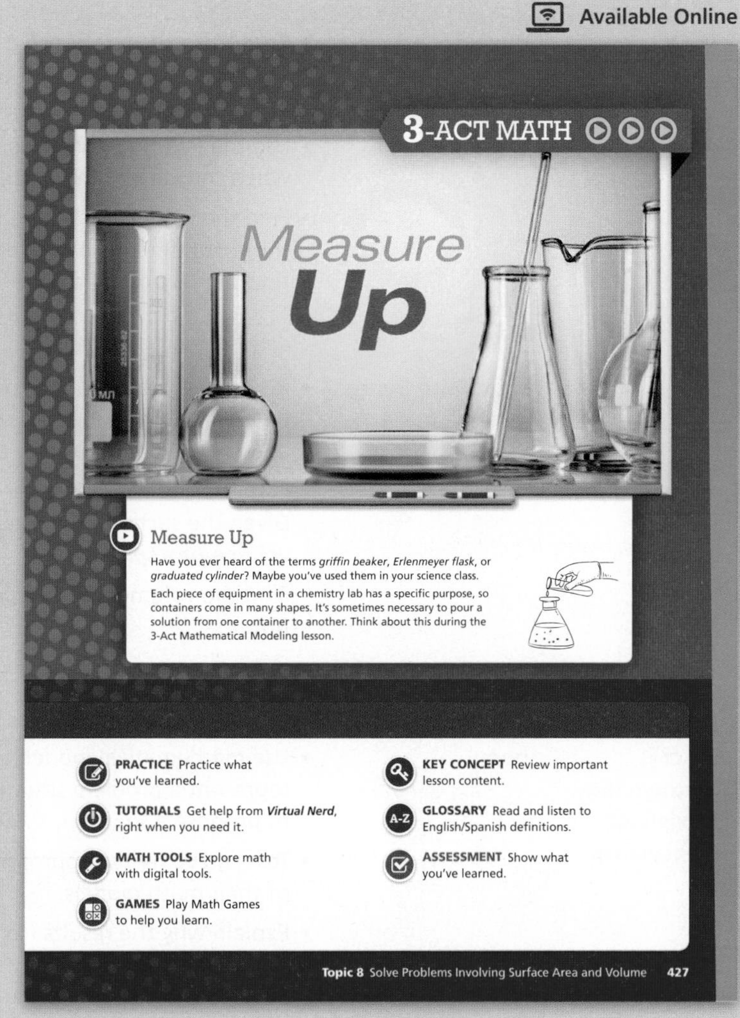

3-ACT MATH

Measure Up

**Measure Up**

Have you ever heard of the terms *griffin beaker, Erlenmeyer flask,* or *graduated cylinder*? Maybe you've used them in your science class. Each piece of equipment in a chemistry lab has a specific purpose, so containers come in many shapes. It's sometimes necessary to pour a solution from one container to another. Think about this during the 3-Act Mathematical Modeling lesson.

- **PRACTICE** Practice what you've learned.
- **TUTORIALS** Get help from *Virtual Nerd,* right when you need it.
- **MATH TOOLS** Explore math with digital tools.
- **GAMES** Play Math Games to help you learn.
- **KEY CONCEPT** Review important lesson content.
- **GLOSSARY** Read and listen to English/Spanish definitions.
- **ASSESSMENT** Show what you've learned.

Topic 8 Solve Problems Involving Surface Area and Volume 427

## Topic Essential Question

**How are the formulas for volume of a cylinder, cone, and sphere related to one another?**

Revisit the Topic Essential Question throughout the topic. See the Teacher's Edition for the Topic Review for notes about answering the question.

## 3-Act Mathematical Modeling

**Generate excitement about the upcoming 3-Act Mathematical Modeling lesson by having students read about the math modeling problem for this topic.**

See the Teacher's Edition lesson support for notes about how to use the lesson video in your classroom.

# enVision® STEM Project

Go Online

Video

## Wrap it Up!

In this project, students explore how engineers design packaging for water purifiers. They will use the engineer design process to determine an environmentally sound way to package water purifiers, taking into account cost efficiency and eco-friendly materials to use for packaging.

### What's the Math?

Students use geometry to determine how the volume and surface area of the packaging relates to the volume and surface area of the water purifier item being packed. Students will use the formulas for volume and surface area to determine the right size packaging to use.

### What's the Science?

Students use the engineering design process, as in Topic 7, to determine possible solutions in an environmentally sound way to package water purifiers. They will gather data, develop and find possible solutions, and redesign if needed.

### What's the Engineering and Technology?

Students think like engineers and apply the engineering design process as they work toward a viable solution. The solution may require implementation of established or innovative technologies.

### Introduce the Project

Present the project by having students discuss what they know about product packaging and its impact on the environment. Discuss how the students will apply the engineering design process in the development of an eco-friendly way to package water purifiers.

**Q:** What are the steps in the engineering design process? [Sample answer: Define the problem, do background research, brainstorm solutions, choose the best solution, develop a prototype, test the prototype, and redesign as necessary]

**Q:** Name some packaging materials that negatively impact the environment. [Sample answer: Plastic, Styrofoam]

**Q:** What are some materials used in eco-friendly packaging? [Sample answer: Mushrooms, bamboo]

**Q:** Why is an eco-friendly design important for packaging? [Sample answer: Materials are disposable, recyclable, biodegradable, and not wasted.]

**Q:** What data might be helpful in evaluating the solution? [Sample answer: Cost efficiency, functionality of the packaging, type of material]

You can launch this project any time after Topic 8 Lesson 2.

Show the Topic 8 STEM video to generate interest in the project.

Teacher resources that provide students with project details and support are available online.

**enVision STEM Project Video** is available online.

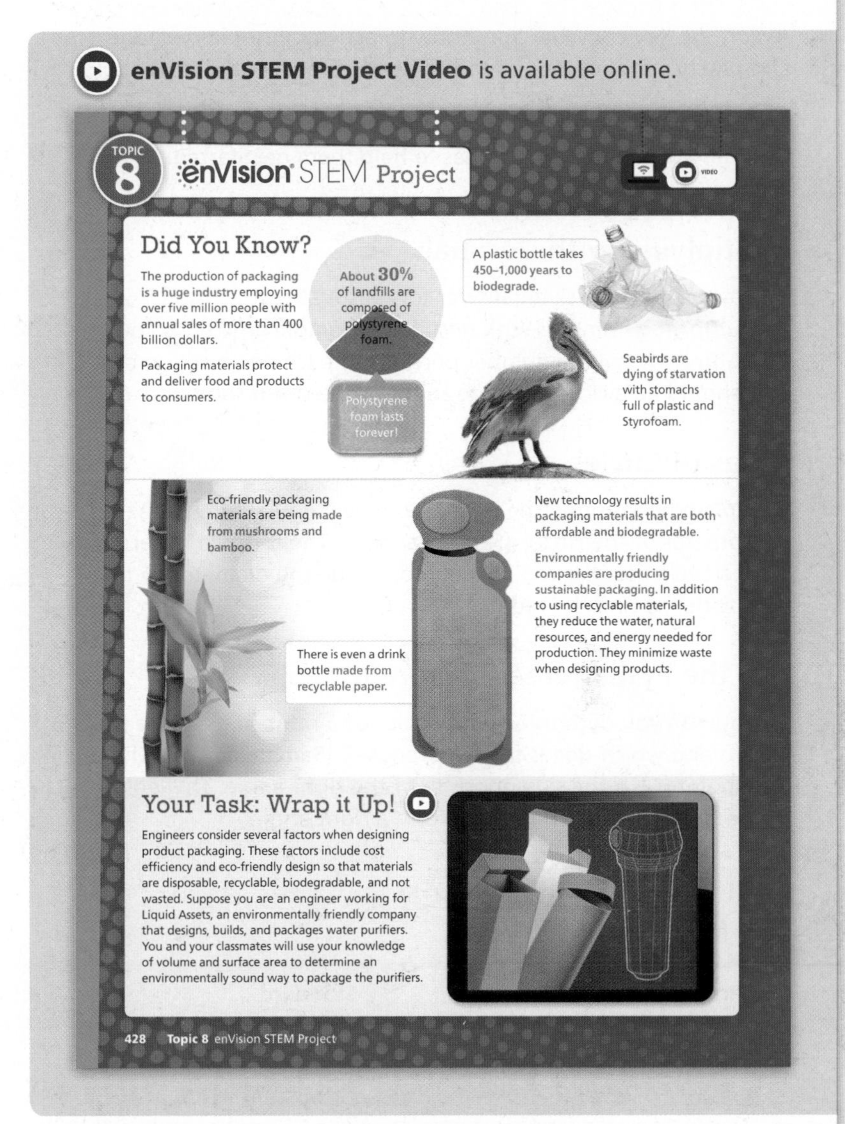

TOPIC 8 enVision STEM Project

Did You Know?

The production of packaging is a huge industry employing over five million people with annual sales of more than 400 billion dollars.

Packaging materials protect and deliver food and products to consumers.

About 30% of landfills are composed of polystyrene foam.

Polystyrene foam lasts forever!

A plastic bottle takes 450–1,000 years to biodegrade.

Seabirds are dying of starvation with stomachs full of plastic and Styrofoam.

Eco-friendly packaging materials are being made from mushrooms and bamboo.

There is even a drink bottle made from recyclable paper.

New technology results in packaging materials that are both affordable and biodegradable.

Environmentally friendly companies are producing sustainable packaging. In addition to using recyclable materials, they reduce the water, natural resources, and energy needed for production. They minimize waste when designing products.

Your Task: Wrap it Up!

Engineers consider several factors when designing product packaging. These factors include cost efficiency and eco-friendly design so that materials are disposable, recyclable, biodegradable, and not wasted. Suppose you are an engineer working for Liquid Assets, an environmentally friendly company that designs, builds, and packages water purifiers. You and your classmates will use your knowledge of volume and surface area to determine an environmentally sound way to package the purifiers.

428 Topic 8 enVision STEM Project

### Common Core Content Standards

8.G.C.9

### Mathematical Practices Standards

MP.1, MP.2, MP.3, MP.4

### Next Generation Science Standards

MS-ETS1-1, MS-ETS1-2, MS-ETS1-3, MS-ETS1-4, MS-ESS3-3

Go Online

Glossary

# Review What You Know!

Assign the Review What You Know to activate prior knowledge and practice the prerequisite skills needed for success in this topic.

Encourage students to work independently or with a partner. Use these questioning strategies to help them get started.

## Multiplying with Decimals

**Q:** How can you check an answer for reasonableness when multiplying numbers with decimals? [Sample answer: If you multiply the whole number portions of each decimal number, it should be a close estimate to the worked-out solution.]

## Areas of Circles

**Q:** Explain how to find the area of a circle if you are given the diameter of the circle. [Sample answer: The formula for area of a circle uses the radius squared. Divide the diameter by two in order to find the radius.]

## Use the Pythagorean Theorem

**Q:** How can you determine which sides of a right triangle are the legs and which side is the hypotenuse? [Sample answer: The hypotenuse is the side opposite of the right angle. The legs of the right triangle connect to form a right angle.]

## Item Analysis for Diagnosis and Intervention

| Item | MDIS | Standard |
|---|---|---|
| 1, 5 | N10 | 7.G.B.4 |
| 2, 3 | N14 | 6.G.A.4, 7.G.B.6 |
| 4 | N6 | 7.G.B.6 |
| 6, 7 | L60 | 6.NS.B.3 |
| 8 | L64 | 6.NS.B.3 |
| 9, 10 | N47 | 7.G.B.4 |
| 11, 12 | N64 | 8.G.B.7 |

Available Online

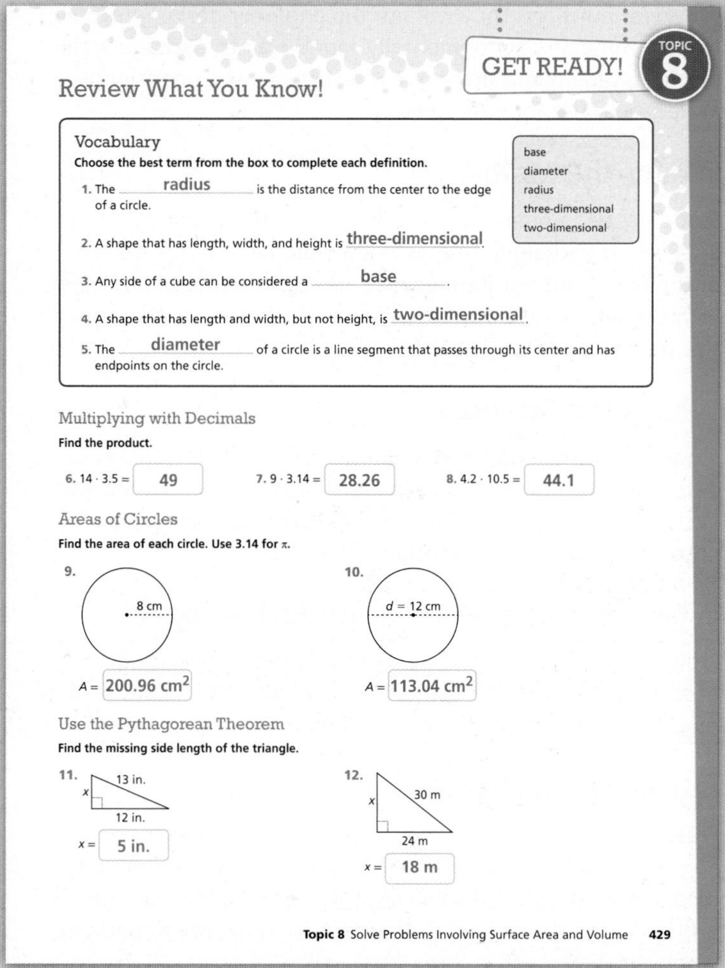

GET READY! TOPIC 8

Review What You Know!

**Vocabulary**

**Choose the best term from the box to complete each definition.**

base
diameter
radius
three-dimensional
two-dimensional

1. The radius is the distance from the center to the edge of a circle.
2. A shape that has length, width, and height is three-dimensional.
3. Any side of a cube can be considered a base.
4. A shape that has length and width, but not height, is two-dimensional.
5. The diameter of a circle is a line segment that passes through its center and has endpoints on the circle.

Multiplying with Decimals

**Find the product.**

6. $14 \cdot 3.5 =$ 49

7. $9 \cdot 3.14 =$ 28.26

8. $4.2 \cdot 10.5 =$ 44.1

Areas of Circles

**Find the area of each circle. Use 3.14 for $\pi$.**

9. 8 cm

$A =$ 200.96 $cm^2$

10. $d = 12$ cm

$A =$ 113.04 $cm^2$

Use the Pythagorean Theorem

**Find the missing side length of the triangle.**

11. 13 in., 12 in., $x$

$x =$ 5 in.

12. 30 m, 24 m, $x$

$x =$ 18 m

**Topic 8** Solve Problems Involving Surface Area and Volume 429

# Vocabulary Review

You may choose to strengthen vocabulary with the following activity.

- Have students work together in teams. Write two or more vocabulary terms on chart paper. Ask students to make connections between the terms. They can verbalize their connections and you can record their contributions using words or drawings. The students must be able to explain the connection between the terms. You may also ask other teams to critique the reasoning of others.

Go Online

Glossary

# Language Development

Have students use what they learned in this topic to write key words, ideas, examples, or illustrations that relate to each new vocabulary term in the connecting boxes. Encourage students to include surface area and volume in relation to these figures.

**Q:** How is the area of a two-dimensional figure related to the surface area of a three-dimensional figure? [Sample answer: You can identify the two-dimensional figures that make up a three-dimensional figure. Then you can find the area of each two-dimensional figure and add them to find the total surface area of the three-dimensional figure.]

**Q:** What are the differences and similarities between volumes of cones and volumes of cylinders? [Answers will vary.]

Encourage students to review the word web as they work through each lesson. Have students revise the details related to the new vocabulary terms with more pertinent ones if necessary.

**Q:** How does the listing key words, ideas, and related details for each new vocabulary term help you to better understand them? [Sample answer: It gives you a better foundation for understanding the vocabulary terms and can be used as a visual reference.]

Remind students to complete all the circles and connecting boxes in their word webs as they progress through the topic.

## Extension for Language Development

Challenge students to use their completed word webs to write a brief summary of the concepts they have learned in this topic. Encourage students to use sketches or models to help communicate their ideas about the new vocabulary words and how they relate to surface area and volume.

## Word Wall

To help students comprehend the meaning of *cylinder*, assist them in making a word wall. Invite students to write a description and draw an illustration of a cylinder on index cards, and display them under the word *Cylinder*. Remind students that they will learn to calculate the surface area and volume of a cylinder in this topic. Instructions on how to design a word wall are included in the Language Support Handbook.

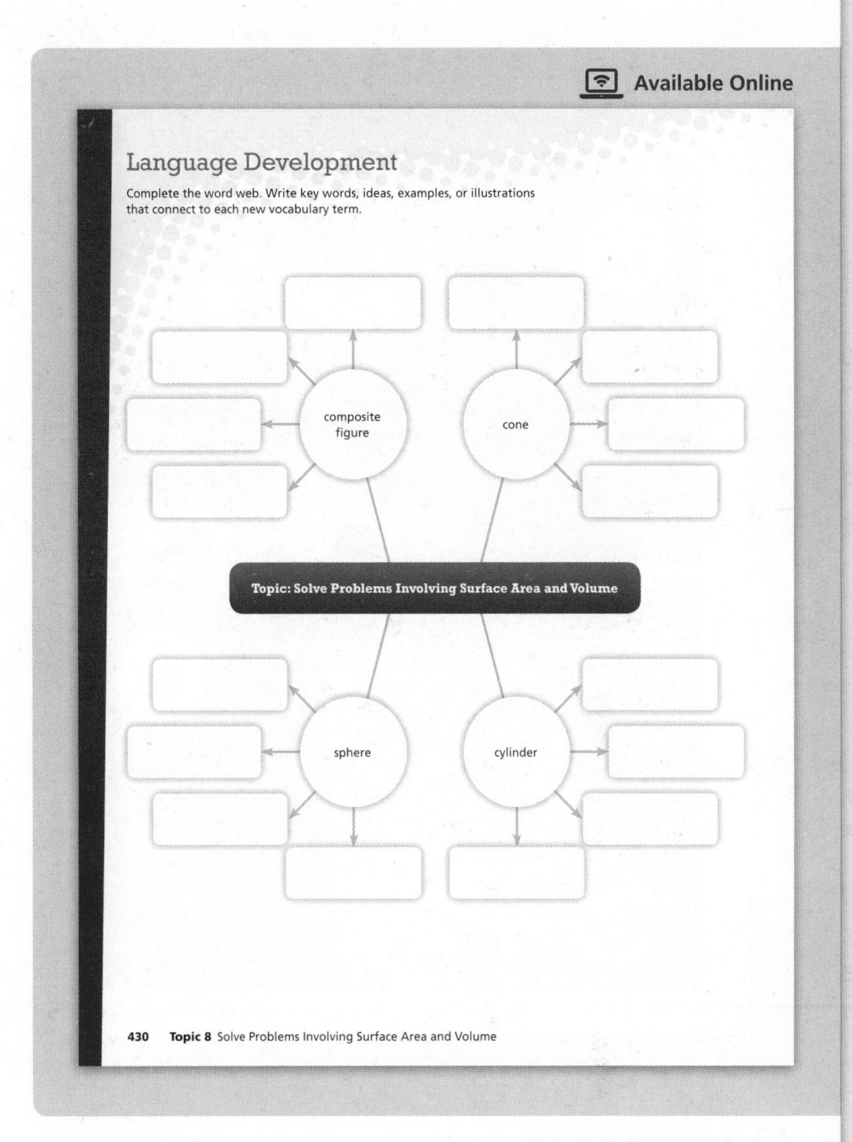


For additional resources, see the **Language Support Handbook.**

# Pick a Project

Available Online

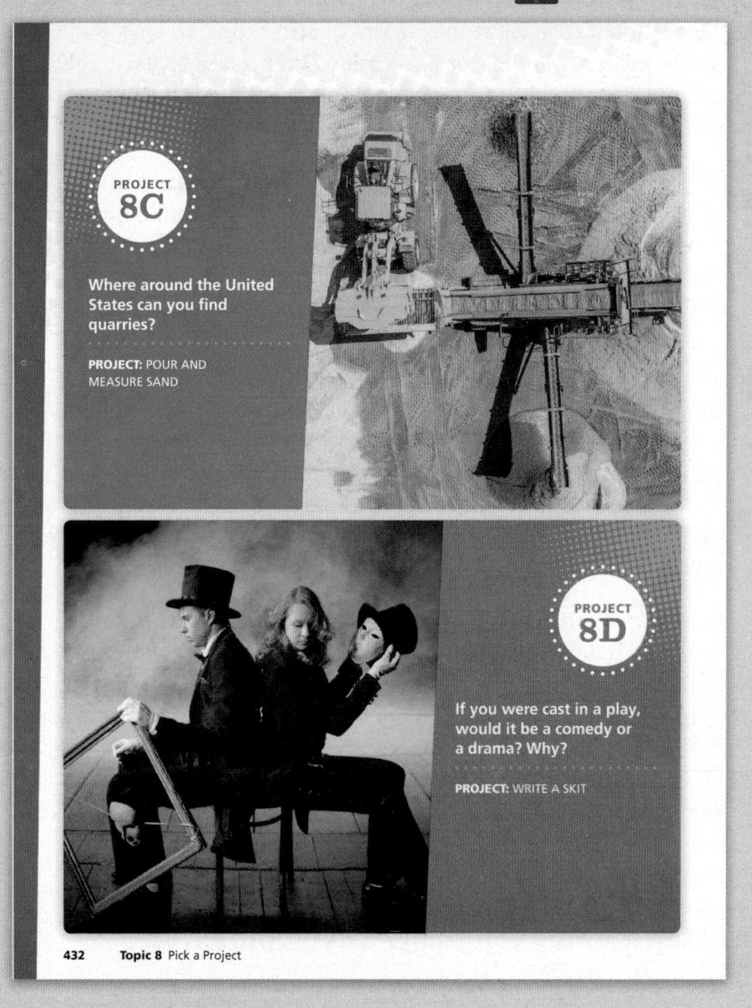


## Overview

A variety of rich projects is provided for each topic. Students may select the project that is most interesting to them.

| Project | Different Engaging Contexts | Different Activity Modalities | Different Final Products |
|---|---|---|---|
| 8A | Rock concerts | Design | Proposal |
| 8B | Museums | Make | Diorama |
| 8C | Quarries | Pour and measure | Report |
| 8D | Humor | Write | Skit |

## Selecting a Project

Introduce each project option with the students. Sharing the resource masters with students might help them choose.

## During the Project

**Pacing** Projects will be completed over a number of lessons. The amount of time students spend on each project will vary. You may wish to let early finishers choose an additional project.

**Grouping** You might have students work independently, with a partner, or in small groups.

**Content** Projects are related to the content of this topic. As students continue their work on projects throughout the topic, new math ideas should be incorporated.

**Project Sharing** Invite students to share their completed projects with a partner, a small group, or with the whole class. Encourage students to discuss how they demonstrated math practices during the project. Provide students an opportunity for reflection by asking what interesting information they learned and what math they used in the project.

**Extensions** Extension suggestions are included for each project.

**Look For** Did students achieve the goal of the project? Did they apply math correctly in the project?

Go Online

Worksheets

## PROJECT 8A ⓒ 8.G.C.9

**Materials** straightedge, grid paper

**Guidelines** Students will be able to update their designs after each lesson.

**Extension** Tell students that the production manager would like all of the cylinders and cones reduced to three-fourths of their original size. Have students determine how the dimensions and calculations would change and revise their proposals accordingly.

## PROJECT 8B ⓒ 8.G.C.9

**Materials** arts and crafts supplies

**Guidelines** Students will be able to update their models and reports after each lesson.

**Extension** Ask students to add three structures to their museum: a cylinder, a cone, and a sphere. Have them determine the size and volume of each structure.

## PROJECT 8C ⓒ 8.G.C.9

**Materials** cylinders, sand, measuring tape

**Guidelines** Students should do the experiment after they learn about volume of a cylinder but before they learn about volume of a cone.

**Extension** Have students refill the cylinders. Have them pour the sand into balloons to form spheres. Ask students to estimate the dimensions of each filled balloon. Have them compare the measurements of the spheres to the other volumes. What do they notice?

## PROJECT 8D ⓒ 8.G.C.9

**Materials** video recorder (optional)

**Guidelines** Students will be able to revise their skits after each lesson.

**Extension** Ask students how their skits would change if they introduced new characters with half the diameter of the original characters. How would the characters compare?

Available Online

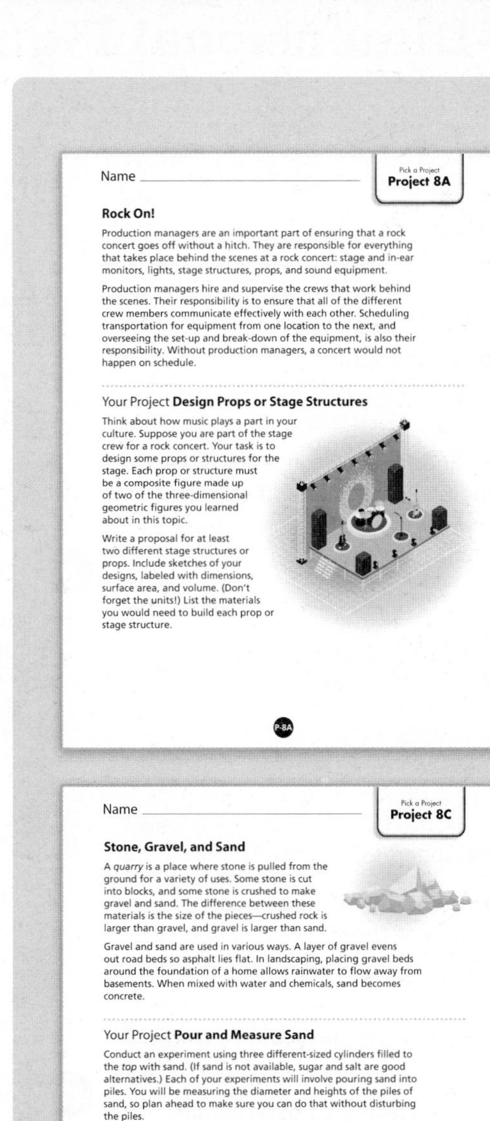

Name ______________________

Pick a Project
**Project 8A**

**Rock On!**

Production managers are an important part of ensuring that a rock concert goes off without a hitch. They are responsible for everything that takes place behind the scenes at a rock concert: stage and in-ear monitors, lights, stage structures, props, and sound equipment.

Production managers hire and supervise the crews that work behind the scenes. Their responsibility is to ensure that all of the different crew members communicate effectively with each other. Scheduling transportation for equipment from one location to the next, and overseeing the set-up and break-down of the equipment, is also their responsibility. Without production managers, a concert would not happen on schedule.

Your Project **Design Props or Stage Structures**

Think about how music plays a part in your culture. Suppose you are part of the stage crew for a rock concert. Your task is to design some props or structures for the stage. Each prop or structure must be a composite figure made up of two of the three-dimensional geometric figures you learned about in this topic.

Write a proposal for at least two different stage structures or props. Include sketches of your designs, labeled with dimensions, surface area, and volume. (Don't forget the units!) List the materials you would need to build each prop or stage structure.

P-8A

Name ______________________

Pick a Project
**Project 8B**

**Museum Mania**

A museum is a place people visit to see historical artifacts, artistic displays, or other items of importance. Some items are on permanent display while other items may be collected together for a temporary exhibit. Some museums have a theme, such as the Hershey Story Museum in Pennsylvania, which includes a chocolate lab for children. The Museum of American Railroad in Texas displays a large collection of railcars and railroad equipment and is the home of the world's largest diesel-electric locomotive.

Your Project **Make a Model of a Museum**

Suppose you are designing a new children's museum. Your museum will be a "hands-on" museum, where people can touch the items on display. Base the design of your building, your sculptures, and any art (displayed on your museum walls) on the geometric shapes you have learned throughout this topic.

Make a diorama of your museum, and write a report describing your museum and its features. Include in your report all your calculations for surface area (space available for wall displays) and volume. Remember, you need to save some space for people to walk through your museum!

P-8B

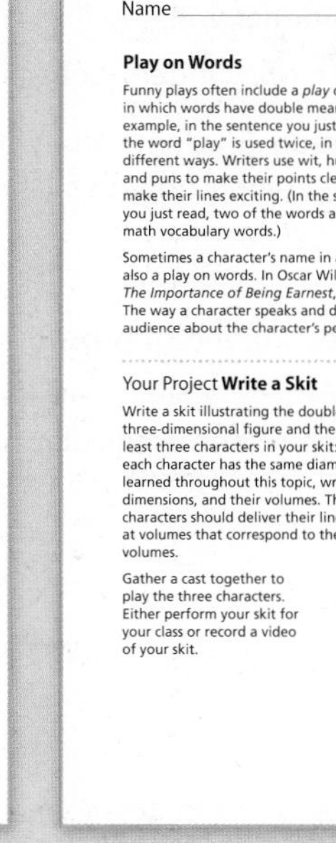

Name ______________________

Pick a Project
**Project 8C**

**Stone, Gravel, and Sand**

A *quarry* is a place where stone is pulled from the ground for a variety of uses. Some stone is cut into blocks, and some stone is crushed to make gravel and sand. The difference between these materials is the size of the pieces—crushed rock is larger than gravel, and gravel is larger than sand.

Gravel and sand are used in various ways. A layer of gravel evens out road beds so asphalt lies flat. In landscaping, placing gravel beds around the foundation of a home allows rainwater to flow away from basements. When mixed with water and chemicals, sand becomes concrete.

Your Project **Pour and Measure Sand**

Conduct an experiment using three different-sized cylinders filled to the *top* with sand. (If sand is not available, sugar and salt are good alternatives.) Each of your experiments will involve pouring sand into piles. You will be measuring the diameter and heights of the piles of sand, so plan ahead to make sure you can do that without disturbing the piles.

Pour the sand from each cylinder slowly into a cone-shaped pile. In a table, record the dimensions (radius and height) and volume of each cylinder and of each cone-shaped pile of sand. Make sure you pour from the same height each time.

Analyze your data. Determine the relationship between the volume of a cylinder and the volume of a cone. Write a paragraph summarizing your findings and conclusions.

P-8C

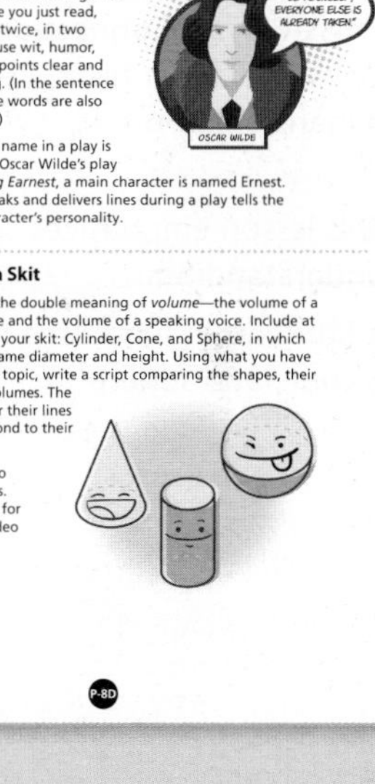


Name ______________________

Pick a Project
**Project 8D**

**Play on Words**

Funny plays often include a *play on words*, in which words have double meanings. For example, in the sentence you just read, the word "play" is used twice, in two different ways. Writers use wit, humor, and puns to make their points clear and make their lines exciting. (In the sentence you just read, two of the words are also math vocabulary words.)

Sometimes a character's name in a play is also a play on words. In Oscar Wilde's play *The Importance of Being Earnest*, a main character is named Ernest. The way a character speaks and delivers lines during a play tells the audience about the character's personality.

Your Project **Write a Skit**

Write a skit illustrating the double meaning of *volume*—the volume of a three-dimensional figure and the volume of a speaking voice. Include at least three characters in your skit: Cylinder, Cone, and Sphere, in which each character has the same diameter and height. Using what you have learned throughout this topic, write a script comparing the shapes, their dimensions, and their volumes. The characters should deliver their lines at volumes that correspond to their volumes.

Gather a cast together to play the three characters. Either perform your skit for your class or record a video of your skit.

P-8D

## Scoring Guide

Provide a scoring rubric to students as they begin work on the project.

For students who score Below Expectations for any criteria, review the rubric score with them in detail. Encourage them to update their project, or select a different project, to demonstrate their understanding of the mathematics in this topic.

**Sample Scoring Rubric**

| Below Expectations (0–1 point: Explain.) | Meets Goal (2 points) | Above Expectations (3–4 points: Explain.) |
| --- | --- | --- |
| | **Mathematics:** The project accurately demonstrates understanding of a key mathematical concept from the topic. | |
| | **Context:** The mathematics from the topic connects to the project context in a logical and natural way. | |
| | **Presentation:** The directions and guidelines were accurately followed. | |

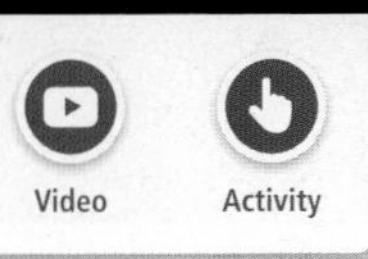


# Lesson 8-1 Find Surface Area of Three-Dimensional Figures

## Lesson Overview

FOCUS

### Mathematics Objective

**Students will be able to:**

✔ calculate the surface areas of cylinders, cones, and spheres.

### Essential Understanding

Determining surface areas of cylinders, cones, and spheres is an extension of finding the areas of rectangles, squares, triangles, and circles and also the surface areas of right prisms.

COHERENCE

**Previously in Grade 7, students:**

- found the surface areas of cubes and right prisms.
- calculated the area of a circle.

**In this lesson, students:**

- calculate the surface areas of cylinders, cones, and spheres.

**Later in this topic, students will:**

- calculate the volume of cylinders, cones, and spheres.

**Cross-Cluster Connection** Students apply previous work solving linear equations from Topic 2 when finding surface area of three-dimensional figures.

RIGOR

This lesson emphasizes a blend of **procedural skill and fluency** and **conceptual understanding.**

- Students will become fluent in calculating the surface area of a cylinder, cone, and sphere.

## Language Support

### Lesson Language Objective

Explain how to find the surface area of cylinders, cones, and spheres.

Additional resources are available in the **Language Support Handbook**.

## Math Anytime

### Today's Challenge

Use the Topic 8 problems any time during this topic.

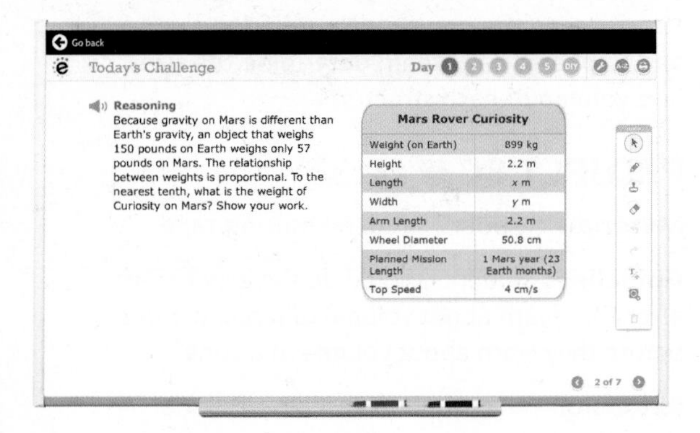


Watch the **Listen and Look For Video** for strategies and habits of mind to look for as students complete work on this lesson.

## Mathematics Overview | Common Core Standards

### Content Standards

In this lesson, you will focus on **8.G.C.9**.

- **8.G.C.9** Know the formulas for the volumes of cones, cylinders, and spheres and use them to solve real-world and mathematical problems.

### Mathematical Practice Standards

**MP.4 Model with Math**
Students will identify the different parts of a cylinder, cone, or sphere to use to determine the surface area formulas for these shapes. They will compute the surface area and justify the reasonableness of their results.

**MP.7 Look for and Make Use of Structure**
Students will look at the overall structure of the formulas for the surface areas of cylinders, cones, and spheres, and see the relationship between the surface area formulas and the formula for the area of a circle.

# STEP 1 | Problem-Based Learning

15-20 min

Go Online

Activity

## Explore It!

Formative Assessment

**Purpose** Students draw a net for a cylinder and describe how the measures of its parts are related. They then connect it to finding the surface area of a cylinder in the Visual Learning Bridge.

## ETP Before — WHOLE CLASS

### 1 Introduce the Problem

Provide scrap paper and scissors, as needed.

### 2 Check for Understanding of the Problem

Engage students with the problem by asking: What objects in the real world are shaped like tubes or cylinders?

## ETP During — SMALL GROUP

### 3 Observe Students at Work

- **How do students draw a net for the tube-shaped container?** Students might draw a rectangle to represent the tube and then draw a circle on each of the longer sides of the rectangle to represent the top and bottom of the container. If needed, ask What is a net?
- **How do students relate the measures of the circles to the measures of the rectangle?** Students might say that the circumference of each circle is equal to one side of the rectangle.

If needed, provide students with scrap paper and scissors to make their own nets.

#### Early Finishers

How would the problem change if the tube was longer? [Sample answer: The base of the rectangle, which touches one of the circular bases, would remain the same length (the circumference of the circle). The height of the rectangle would increase.

## ETP After — WHOLE CLASS

### 4 Discuss Solution Strategies and Key Ideas

Have students discuss how they could find the area of their net; they could find the area of the circles and the rectangle and then calculate the sum. Have them discuss the least amount of information they would need to calculate the area of the net; the circumference of the circle that forms the base is the width of the rectangle and the height of the cylinder is the height of the rectangle.

### 5 Consider Instructional Implications

After presenting Example 1, refer students back to the problem in the Explore It and have them calculate the surface area of the container if the diameter of the base is 5 cm and the height of the tube is 10 cm; about 196.35 $cm^2$.

## Analyze Student Work

**Explore It!** Activity is available online.

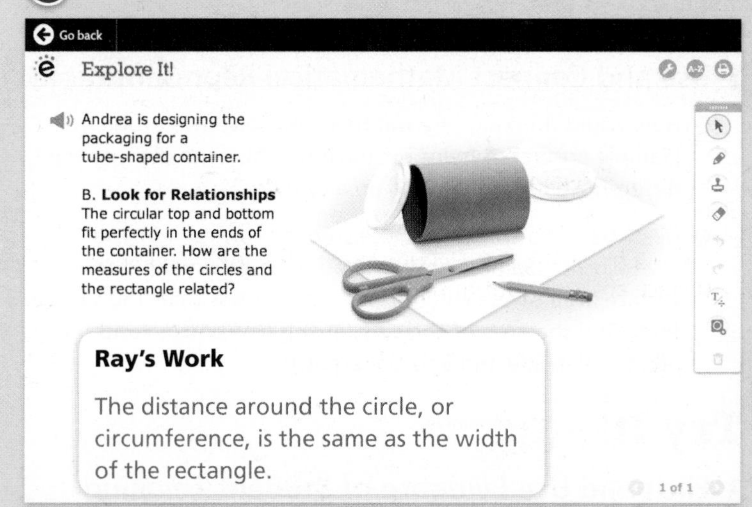


**Ray** describes the relationship between the length of the rectangle and the circumference of the circle.

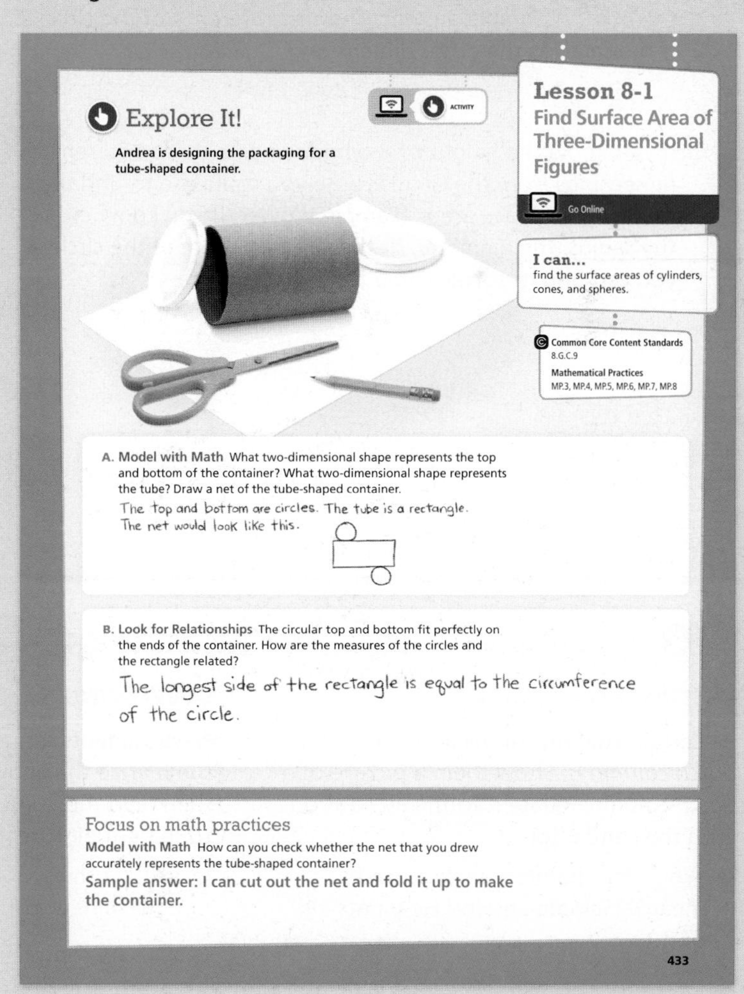
Explore It!

Andrea is designing the packaging for a tube-shaped container.

Lesson 8-1
Find Surface Area of Three-Dimensional Figures

Go Online

I can… find the surface areas of cylinders, cones, and spheres.

Common Core Content Standards 8.G.C.9
Mathematical Practices MP.3, MP.4, MP.5, MP.6, MP.7, MP.8

A. Model with Math What two-dimensional shape represents the top and bottom of the container? What two-dimensional shape represents the tube? Draw a net of the tube-shaped container.

The top and bottom are circles. The tube is a rectangle. The net would look like this.

B. Look for Relationships The circular top and bottom fit perfectly on the ends of the container. How are the measures of the circles and the rectangle related?

The longest side of the rectangle is equal to the circumference of the circle.

Focus on math practices

Model with Math How can you check whether the net that you drew accurately represents the tube-shaped container?

Sample answer: I can cut out the net and fold it up to make the container.

433

**Ky** explains the relationship between the shapes and their measurements in this cylinder.

# STEP 2 | Visual Learning

Go Online

Visual Learning

Assess

## Establish Mathematics Goals to Focus Learning

Engage students in a discussion about the ***Essential Question***. Make sure students understand that the surface area of a solid is the area that covers it, like wrapping paper.

## EXAMPLE 1 Find the Surface Area of a Cylinder

### ETP Use and Connect Mathematical Representations

**Q:** How could thinking of a net help you solve this problem? [Sample answer: It helps by making it easier to identify the different shapes that make up a cylinder.]

**Q:** Describe the problem and the steps to solving it in your own words. [Sample answer: You must determine if the surface area of the column is greater or less than 150 square feet. Find the area of the circular top and bottom and the rectangular side and add the areas.]

## Try It! Formative Assessment

### Elicit and Use Evidence of Student Thinking

**Q:** The height of the column makes up one dimension of the rectangular part of the net of the column. What makes up the other? [Sample answer: The circumference of the circle is the same as the other dimension.]

### Convince Me!

**Q:** If you know the height of a cylinder, name three different dimensions from the circular base you could use to find the rest of the surface area. [Sample answer: If you know either the radius, the diameter, or the circumference of the circle you can find its surface area.]

**Visual Learning Animation Plus** is available online.

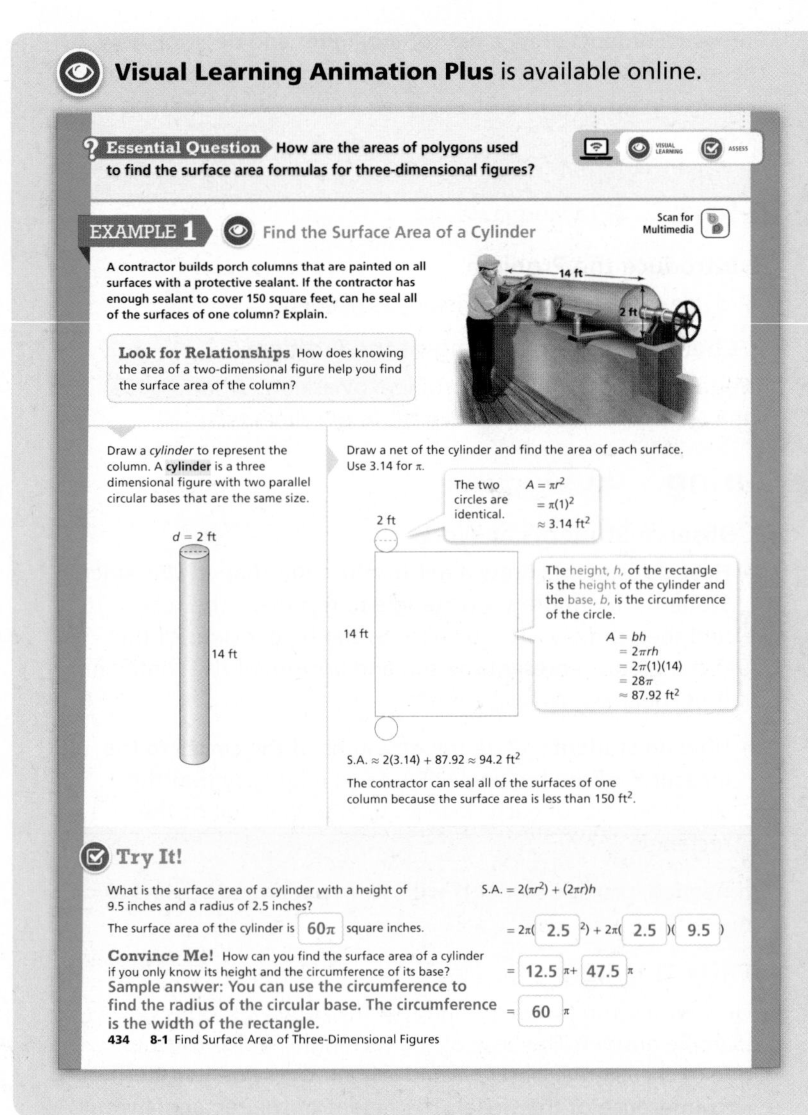

Essential Question How are the areas of polygons used to find the surface area formulas for three-dimensional figures?

EXAMPLE 1 Find the Surface Area of a Cylinder

Scan for Multimedia

A contractor builds porch columns that are painted on all surfaces with a protective sealant. If the contractor has enough sealant to cover 150 square feet, can he seal all of the surfaces of one column? Explain.

Look for Relationships How does knowing the area of a two-dimensional figure help you find the surface area of the column?



Draw a *cylinder* to represent the column. A **cylinder** is a three dimensional figure with two parallel circular bases that are the same size.



Draw a net of the cylinder and find the area of each surface. Use 3.14 for $\pi$.

The two circles are identical. $A = \pi r^2$ $= \pi(1)^2$ $\approx 3.14$ ft$^2$



The height, $h$, of the rectangle is the height of the cylinder and the base, $b$, is the circumference of the circle.

$A = bh$
$= 2\pi rh$
$= 2\pi(1)(14)$
$= 28\pi$
$\approx 87.92$ ft$^2$

S.A. $\approx 2(3.14) + 87.92 \approx 94.2$ ft$^2$

The contractor can seal all of the surfaces of one column because the surface area is less than 150 ft$^2$.

Try It!

What is the surface area of a cylinder with a height of 9.5 inches and a radius of 2.5 inches?

The surface area of the cylinder is $60\pi$ square inches.

S.A. $= 2(\pi r^2) + (2\pi r)h$

$= 2\pi(2.5^2) + 2\pi(2.5)(9.5)$

$= 12.5\pi + 47.5\pi$

$= 60\pi$

Convince Me! How can you find the surface area of a cylinder if you only know its height and the circumference of its base?
Sample answer: You can use the circumference to find the radius of the circular base. The circumference is the width of the rectangle.

434 8-1 Find Surface Area of Three-Dimensional Figures

Students can access the ***Visual Learning Animation Plus*** by using the **BouncePages app** to scan this page. Students can download the app for free in their mobile devices' app store.

## ELL English Language Learners

**ENTERING** See Example 1.

Be certain students understand what a *porch column* is. Show them a picture of a porch column. Relate it to the illustration with the contractor.

**Q:** What does *painted on all surfaces* mean? [Sample answer: He paints all of it.]

**Q:** What does it mean to have *enough sealant*? [Sample answer: He can paint all the surfaces.]

**DEVELOPING** See Example 1.

Have students reread the problem and summarize the known information and then read the question aloud. Ask students to share their summaries.

**Q:** Look at the problem again. How can you determine the surface area of a cylinder?

**Q:** Will the contractor be able to seal all the surfaces of the column?

**EXPANDING** See Example 1.

Have students reread the problem and verbally describe to a partner the process of finding the surface area of the column. Allow the partner to ask questions about the process. Then have the partners exchange roles. Have the second partner explain how to use the surface area to answer the questions in the example, while the first asks questions.

Go Online

Activity

Assess

## EXAMPLE 2  Find the Surface Area of a Cone

###  Pose Purposeful Questions

**Q:** What is the relationship between the parts of the cone and the net of the cone? [Sample answer: The circle is the base of the cone. The section of a circle is the curved side of the cone.]

**Q:** Why does the formula for the surface area of a cone involve addition? [Sample answer: You must add the surface area of the base and the curved area to find the surface area of the cone.]

## EXAMPLE 3  Find the Surface Area of a Sphere

###  Pose Purposeful Questions

**Q:** How do you know the height of the cylinder that contains the sphere is $2r$? [Sample answer: The diameter of the sphere is $2r$. Since the height of the cylinder that contains the sphere is exactly the diameter of the sphere, the height of the cylinder must also be $2r$.]

**Q:** What would a net of the open cylinder look like? [A rectangle]

**Q:** What are the dimensions of the net of the open cylinder? Explain. [Sample answer: Its length is $2\pi r$, which is the circumference of the circle, and its height is $2r$.]

##  Try It! 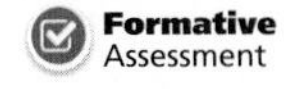 Formative Assessment

###  Elicit and Use Evidence of Student Thinking

**Q:** How can you find the surface area of a sphere when you only know the diameter? [Sample answer: You can find the circumference of the circle by using the diameter. The height of the open cylinder is equal to the diameter of the sphere.]

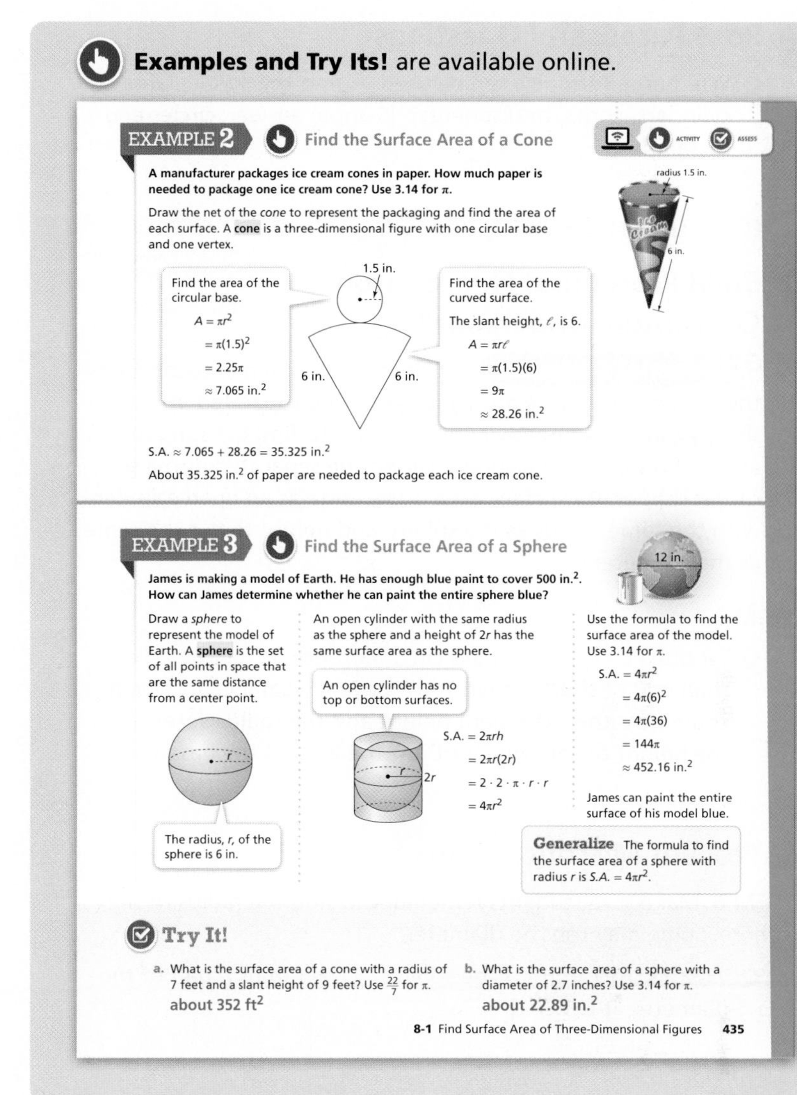

**Examples and Try Its!** are available online.

EXAMPLE 2 Find the Surface Area of a Cone

**A manufacturer packages ice cream cones in paper. How much paper is needed to package one ice cream cone? Use 3.14 for $\pi$.**

Draw the net of the *cone* to represent the packaging and find the area of each surface. A **cone** is a three-dimensional figure with one circular base and one vertex.

Find the area of the circular base.

$A = \pi r^2$
$= \pi(1.5)^2$
$= 2.25\pi$
$\approx 7.065$ in.$^2$

Find the area of the curved surface.

The slant height, $\ell$, is 6.

$A = \pi r \ell$
$= \pi(1.5)(6)$
$= 9\pi$
$\approx 28.26$ in.$^2$



S.A. $\approx 7.065 + 28.26 = 35.325$ in.$^2$

About 35.325 in.$^2$ of paper are needed to package each ice cream cone.

EXAMPLE 3 Find the Surface Area of a Sphere

**James is making a model of Earth. He has enough blue paint to cover 500 in.$^2$. How can James determine whether he can paint the entire sphere blue?**

Draw a *sphere* to represent the model of Earth. A **sphere** is the set of all points in space that are the same distance from a center point.

The radius, $r$, of the sphere is 6 in.

An open cylinder with the same radius as the sphere and a height of $2r$ has the same surface area as the sphere.

An open cylinder has no top or bottom surfaces.

S.A. $= 2\pi rh$
$= 2\pi r(2r)$
$= 2 \cdot 2 \cdot \pi \cdot r \cdot r$
$= 4\pi r^2$

Use the formula to find the surface area of the model. Use 3.14 for $\pi$.

S.A. $= 4\pi r^2$
$= 4\pi(6)^2$
$= 4\pi(36)$
$= 144\pi$
$\approx 452.16$ in.$^2$

James can paint the entire surface of his model blue.



**Generalize** The formula to find the surface area of a sphere with radius $r$ is $S.A. = 4\pi r^2$.

Try It!

a. What is the surface area of a cone with a radius of 7 feet and a slant height of 9 feet? Use $\frac{22}{7}$ for $\pi$.
about 352 ft$^2$

b. What is the surface area of a sphere with a diameter of 2.7 inches? Use 3.14 for $\pi$.
about 22.89 in.$^2$

**8-1** Find Surface Area of Three-Dimensional Figures 435

## ADDITIONAL EXAMPLES 

**For additional examples go online.**

##  Response to Intervention

**USE WITH EXAMPLE 2** Some students may not know what the slant height of a cone is. Emphasize that the slant height is the measurement directly along the slanted side of the cone.

- Identify the parts of the cone.

**Q:** The formula for the surface area of a cone is $A = \pi r^2 + \pi rl$. What do the variables $r$ and $l$ represent? [Sample answer: The $r$ represents the radius of the circle on the end and the $l$ represents the slant height of the cone.]

**Q:** What is $r$ in this problem? What is $l$? [$r = 1.5$ inches; $l = 6$ inches]

##  Enrichment

**USE WITH EXAMPLE 1** Challenge interested students to determine whether a cylinder with a diameter twice as long would have twice the surface area.

- Will a column that has a diameter of 4 feet have twice the surface area as this column?

**Q:** What is the area of the circle now? Use 3.14 for $\pi$. [12.56 ft$^2$]

**Q:** Is the area of this circle twice the area of the original circle? Will the column have twice the surface area? [No; Sample answer: The area of the rectangle is twice as large, but the area of the circle is 4 times as large. The larger column will have about 2.13 times the surface area.]

# STEP 2 | Visual Learning *continued*

Go Online

Key Concept

Assess

Activity

## KEY CONCEPT

### ETP Pose Purposeful Questions

**Q:** What area formulas can be used to find the surface area of cylinders, cones, and spheres? [Sample answer: circles and rectangles]

## Do You Understand/Do You Know How?

**Formative** Assessment

### ETP Build Procedural Fluency from Conceptual Understanding

**Essential Question** Students should demonstrate that the surfaces of a cone and cylinder can be separated into shapes that they already know in order to find the surface area. The surface of a sphere cannot be separated into a set of flat shapes. It's surface area is the same as an open cylinder with the same radius as the sphere and height that is the same as the diameter.]

**ITEM 3**

**Q:** Would a cone with a base circumference $6\pi$ feet be taller than you or shorter than you? Explain. [Sample answer. It could be either. The slant height and the radius determines the height of the cone, not just the area of the base.]

### Prevent Misconceptions

**ITEM 6** Make sure students remember to find the radius of the sphere. Some may use the diameter.

**Q:** What is the radius of the sphere? [The radius is half of the diameter; it is 1 cm.]

Available Online

KEY CONCEPT

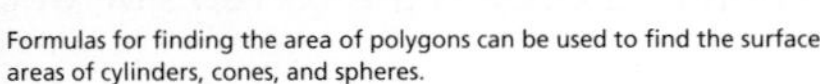

Formulas for finding the area of polygons can be used to find the surface areas of cylinders, cones, and spheres.

**Do You Understand?**

1. **Essential Question** How are the areas of polygons used to find the surface area formulas for three-dimensional figures?
Sample answer: The surface area of a three-dimensional figure is found by adding the areas of its two-dimensional faces.

2. **Reasoning** Why is the length of the base of the rectangle the same as the circumference of the circles in the net of a cylinder?
Sample answer: The length of the base of the rectangle will wrap around the outside of the circle in the net, showing that the base length is equal to the circumference of the circle.

3. **Construct Arguments** Aaron says that all cones with a base circumference of $8\pi$ inches will have the same surface area. Is Aaron correct? Explain.
No; Sample answer: The area of the bases will be the same, but different heights will produce cones with different surface areas.

**Do You Know How?**

4. What is the surface area of the cylinder? Use 3.14 for $\pi$, and round to the nearest tenth.

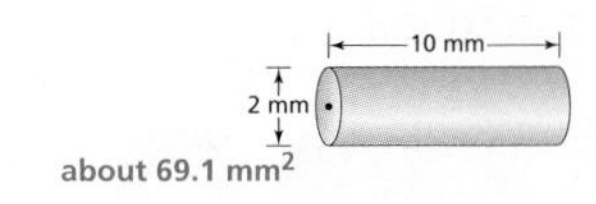


about 69.1 mm$^2$

5. What is the surface area of the cone to the nearest tenth? Use 3.14 for $\pi$.

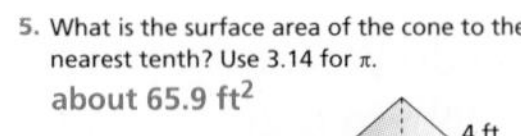

about 65.9 ft$^2$

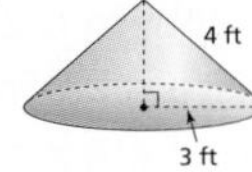


6. What is the surface area of the sphere in terms of $\pi$? $4\pi$ cm$^2$

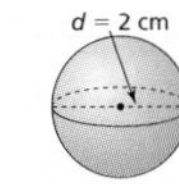


436 8-1 Find Surface Area of Three-Dimensional Figures

## ADDITIONAL EXAMPLE 1

Help students make the transition from finding the surface area of one cylinder to finding the surface area of the four cylinders glued together.

**Q:** When the cylinders are glued together will all the surfaces of each original cylinder be surface areas of this new large cylinder? Explain. [No; Sample answer: When the cylinders are glued together, the bases that are glued together will not be part of the surface area. There will only be two bases that are part of the surface area of the larger cylinder.]

**Q:** What will you need to do to find the total surface area? Explain. [Sample answer: I will need to find the height of the larger cylinder to find the area of the rectangle around the cylinder, and add two bases, one each for the top and bottom.]

**Additional Examples** are available online.

Go back

Additional Example

Benjamin had 4 cylinders with a height of 25 centimeters and a radius of 10 centimeters. He will glue them together to make one long cylinder. How can he find the total surface area of the cylinders once they are glued together? Use 3.14 for $\pi$, and round to the nearest whole number.

**Answer:** The surface area of the glued-together cylinder is about 6,908 square centimeters.

Go Online

Practice Tutorials Math Tools

# Practice & Problem Solving  

**Interactive Practice** and **Virtual Nerd Tutorials** are available online.

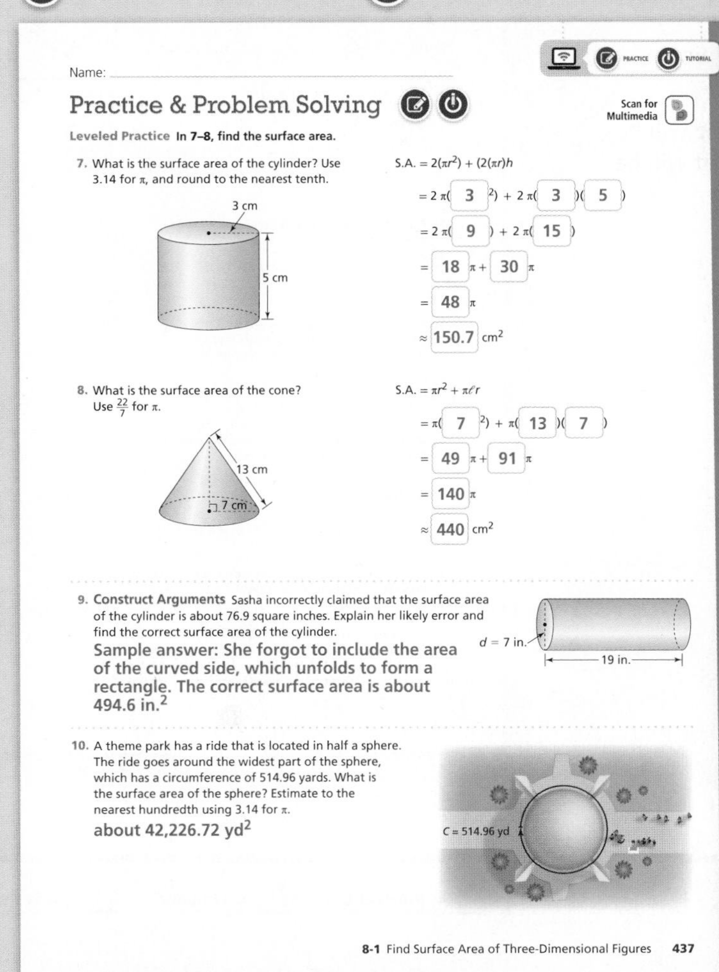

Name:

## Practice & Problem Solving

Scan for Multimedia

**Leveled Practice** In 7–8, find the surface area.

7. What is the surface area of the cylinder? Use 3.14 for $\pi$, and round to the nearest tenth.

$S.A. = 2(\pi r^2) + (2(\pi r)h$
$= 2\pi(3^2) + 2\pi(3)(5)$
$= 2\pi(9) + 2\pi(15)$
$= 18\pi + 30\pi$
$= 48\pi$
$\approx 150.7 \text{ cm}^2$



8. What is the surface area of the cone? Use $\frac{22}{7}$ for $\pi$.

$S.A. = \pi r^2 + \pi \ell r$
$= \pi(7^2) + \pi(13)(7)$
$= 49\pi + 91\pi$
$= 140\pi$
$\approx 440 \text{ cm}^2$



9. **Construct Arguments** Sasha incorrectly claimed that the surface area of the cylinder is about 76.9 square inches. Explain her likely error and find the correct surface area of the cylinder.
**Sample answer: She forgot to include the area of the curved side, which unfolds to form a rectangle. The correct surface area is about 494.6 in.²**



10. A theme park has a ride that is located in half a sphere. The ride goes around the widest part of the sphere, which has a circumference of 514.96 yards. What is the surface area of the sphere? Estimate to the nearest hundredth using 3.14 for $\pi$.
**about 42,226.72 yd²**





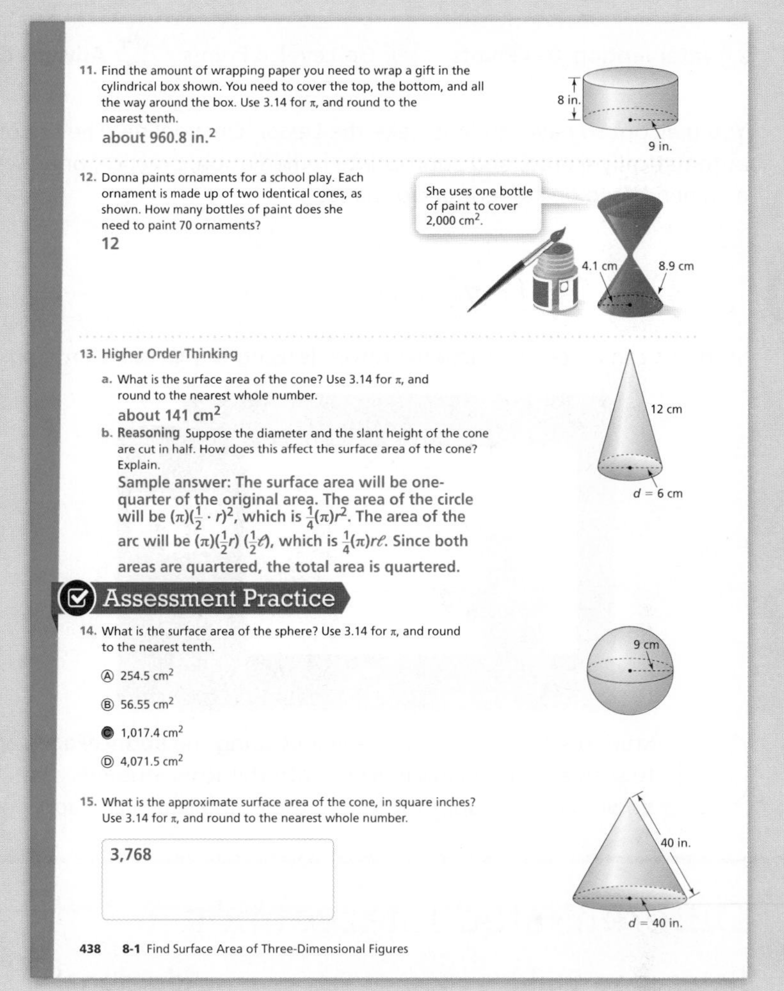

11. Find the amount of wrapping paper you need to wrap a gift in the cylindrical box shown. You need to cover the top, the bottom, and all the way around the box. Use 3.14 for $\pi$, and round to the nearest tenth.
**about 960.8 in.²**



12. Donna paints ornaments for a school play. Each ornament is made up of two identical cones, as shown. How many bottles of paint does she need to paint 70 ornaments?
**12**



13. **Higher Order Thinking**
a. What is the surface area of the cone? Use 3.14 for $\pi$, and round to the nearest whole number.
**about 141 cm²**
b. **Reasoning** Suppose the diameter and the slant height of the cone are cut in half. How does this affect the surface area of the cone? Explain.
**Sample answer: The surface area will be one-quarter of the original area. The area of the circle will be $(\pi)(\frac{1}{2} \cdot r)^2$, which is $\frac{1}{4}(\pi)r^2$. The area of the arc will be $(\pi)(\frac{1}{2}r)(\frac{1}{2}\ell)$, which is $\frac{1}{4}(\pi)r\ell$. Since both areas are quartered, the total area is quartered.**



### Assessment Practice

14. What is the surface area of the sphere? Use 3.14 for $\pi$, and round to the nearest tenth.
Ⓐ 254.5 cm²
Ⓑ 56.55 cm²
● 1,017.4 cm²
Ⓓ 4,071.5 cm²



15. What is the approximate surface area of the cone, in square inches? Use 3.14 for $\pi$, and round to the nearest whole number.
**3,768**





## Error Intervention

**ITEM 10** Students may have difficulty using the circumference of a sphere to find the surface area of the sphere.

**Q:** The circumference formula is $C = 2\pi r$. If the circumference is 514.96 yards, what is the radius? [The radius is about 82 yards.]

## English Language Learners

**ITEM 13** Students may have difficulty with the relationship between measurements in the problem. Make sure they understand what the phrase, 'cut in half' means.

**Q:** What is the radius of the base? How do you find it? [3 cm; Sample answer: It is half of the diameter.]

**Q:** In part b, what are the new radius and the new slant height? [$r = 1.5$ cm and $l = 6$ cm]

You may opt to have students complete the automatically scored Practice & Problem Solving items online.

### Item Analysis

| Example | Items | DOK |
|---|---|---|
| 1 | 7, 11 | 2 |
| | 9 | 3 |
| 2 | 8, 12, 15 | 2 |
| | 13 | 3 |
| 3 | 10, 14 | 2 |

# STEP 3 | Assess & Differentiate

Go Online

 Assess  Tutorials  Worksheets

## Lesson Quiz

RtI Use the student scores on the Lesson Quiz to prescribe differentiated assignments.

**I Intervention** 0–3 Points **O On-Level** 4 Points **A Advanced** 5 Points

You may opt to have students take the Lesson Quiz online. The Lesson Quiz will be automatically scored, and appropriate remediation, practice, or enrichment will be assigned based on student performance.

**Lesson Quiz** is available online.

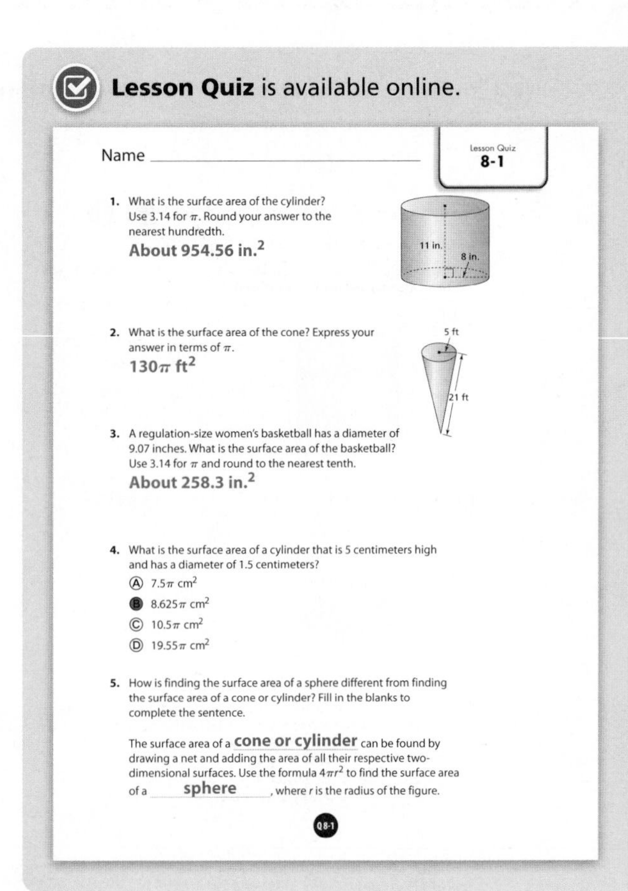

Name ______________ Lesson Quiz 8-1

1. What is the surface area of the cylinder? Use 3.14 for $\pi$. Round your answer to the nearest hundredth.
   **About 954.56 in.$^2$**
2. What is the surface area of the cone? Express your answer in terms of $\pi$.
   **$130\pi$ ft$^2$**
3. A regulation-size women's basketball has a diameter of 9.07 inches. What is the surface area of the basketball? Use 3.14 for $\pi$ and round to the nearest tenth.
   **About 258.3 in.$^2$**
4. What is the surface area of a cylinder that is 5 centimeters high and has a diameter of 1.5 centimeters?
   Ⓐ $7.5\pi$ cm$^2$
   Ⓑ $8.625\pi$ cm$^2$
   Ⓒ $10.5\pi$ cm$^2$
   Ⓓ $19.55\pi$ cm$^2$
5. How is finding the surface area of a sphere different from finding the surface area of a cone or cylinder? Fill in the blanks to complete the sentence.
   The surface area of a **cone or cylinder** can be found by drawing a net and adding the area of all their respective two-dimensional surfaces. Use the formula $4\pi r^2$ to find the surface area of a **sphere**, where $r$ is the radius of the figure.

Q8-1

## Video Tutorials

Students can access instructional tutorials using the **Virtual Nerd app**.

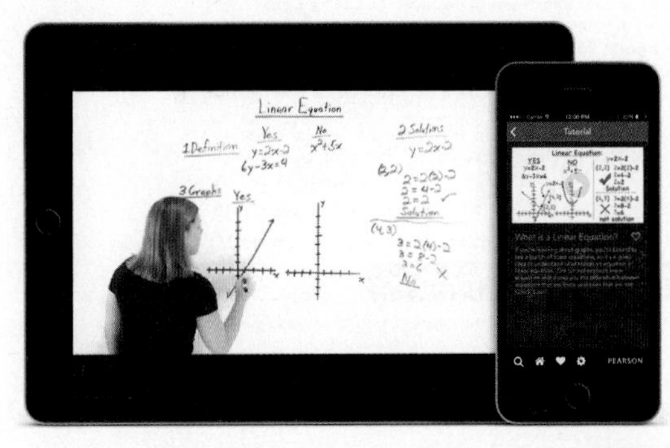

Students can also access the videos using the **BouncePages app** to scan exercise pages marked with this icon. Students can download both apps for free in their mobile devices' app store.

## Differentiated Intervention

I = Intervention O = On-Level A = Advanced

### Reteach to Build Understanding I

Provides scaffolded reteaching for the key lesson concepts.

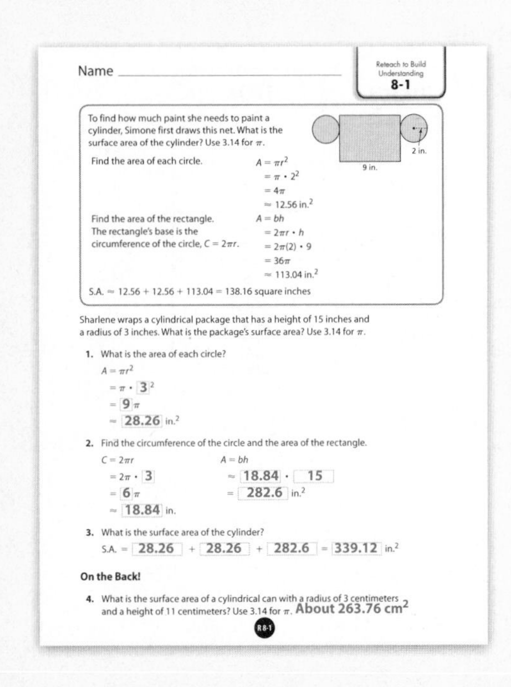

Name ______________ Reteach to Build Understanding 8-1

To find how much paint she needs to paint a cylinder, Simone first draws this net. What is the surface area of the cylinder? Use 3.14 for $\pi$.

Find the area of each circle. $A = \pi r^2 = \pi \cdot 2^2 = 4\pi \approx 12.56$ in.$^2$

Find the area of the rectangle. The rectangle's base is the circumference of the circle, $C = 2\pi r$. $A = bh = 2\pi r \cdot h = 2\pi(2) \cdot 9 = 36\pi \approx 113.04$ in.$^2$

S.A. ≈ 12.56 + 12.56 + 113.04 = 138.16 square inches

Sharlene wraps a cylindrical package that has a height of 15 inches and a radius of 3 inches. What is the package's surface area? Use 3.14 for $\pi$.

1. What is the area of each circle?
   $A = \pi r^2 = \pi \cdot 3^2 = 9\pi \approx 28.26$ in.$^2$
2. Find the circumference of the circle and the area of the rectangle.
   $C = 2\pi r = 2\pi \cdot 3 = 6\pi \approx 18.84$ in.
   $A = bh \approx 18.84 \cdot 15 = 282.6$ in.$^2$
3. What is the surface area of the cylinder?
   S.A. = 28.26 + 28.26 + 282.6 = 339.12 in.$^2$

**On the Back!**

4. What is the surface area of a cylindrical can with a radius of 3 centimeters and a height of 11 centimeters? Use 3.14 for $\pi$. **About 263.76 cm$^2$**

R8-1

### Additional Vocabulary Support I O

Helps students develop and reinforce understanding of key terms and concepts.

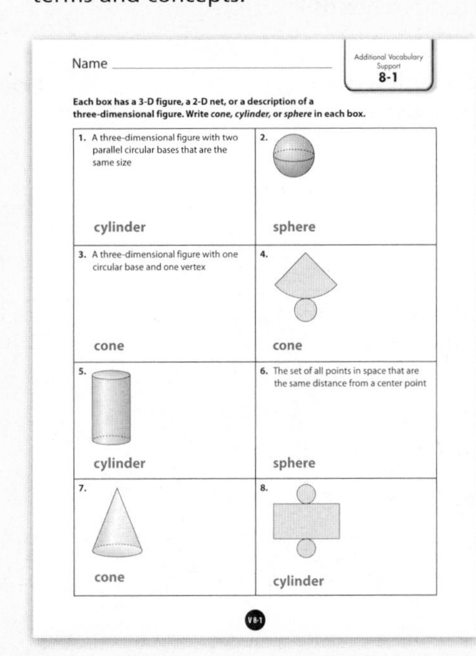

Name ______________ Additional Vocabulary Support 8-1

**Each box has a 3-D figure, a 2-D net, or a description of a three-dimensional figure. Write *cone, cylinder,* or *sphere* in each box.**

| | |
|---|---|
| 1. A three-dimensional figure with two parallel circular bases that are the same size — **cylinder** | 2. **sphere** |
| 3. A three-dimensional figure with one circular base and one vertex — **cone** | 4. **cone** |
| 5. **cylinder** | 6. The set of all points in space that are the same distance from a center point — **sphere** |
| 7. **cone** | 8. **cylinder** |

V8-1

### Build Mathematical Literacy I O

Provides support for struggling readers to build mathematical literacy.

Name ______________ Build Mathematical Literacy 8-1

A tent manufacturer makes a tent in the shape of a cone. How much canvas is used to make this tent, including the floor? Use 3.14 for $\pi$.

1. Underline the question you need to answer.
   **Check students' work.**
2. Highlight the information given in the diagram. Explain what each value represents.
   **Check students' work; The cone's radius is 2.5 feet, and the slant height is 6.5 feet.**
3. What formula can you use to solve this problem? Explain.
   **The formula for the surface area of the cone; The amount of canvas needed is equal to the area of the cone's curved surface and its base, which is the surface area of a cone.**
4. Describe the correct answer to this problem, including the units.
   **A number that represents the amount of canvas required for the tent in square feet**
5. Why does the problem tell you to use 3.14 for $\pi$? Explain how to use 3.14 to find the surface area.
   **Sample answer: Since 3.14 is an approximation of $\pi$, it can be used for $\pi$ in formulas. The formula for the surface area of a cone contains $\pi$; substitute 3.14 for each instance of $\pi$ and perform the necessary calculations.**

M8-1

Go Online

Practice | Worksheets | Math Tools | Math Games

# Additional Practice

You may opt to have students complete the automatically scored Additional Practice items online.

### Item Analysis

| Example | Items | DOK |
|---|---|---|
| 1 | 1, 5 | 2 |
| | 7 | 3 |
| 2 | 3, 6 | 2 |
| 3 | 2, 4 | 2 |
| | 8 | 3 |

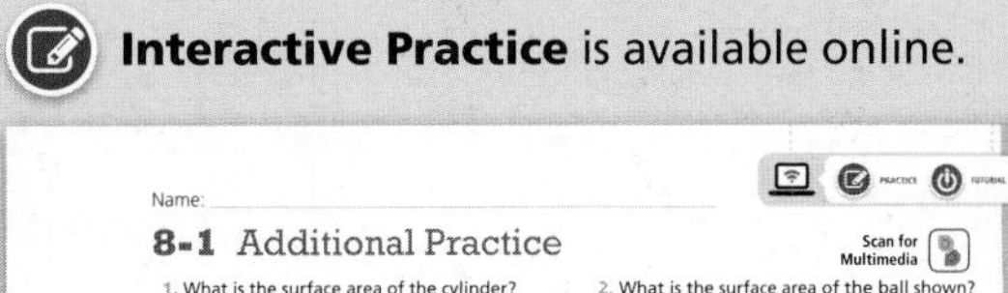

**Interactive Practice** is available online.

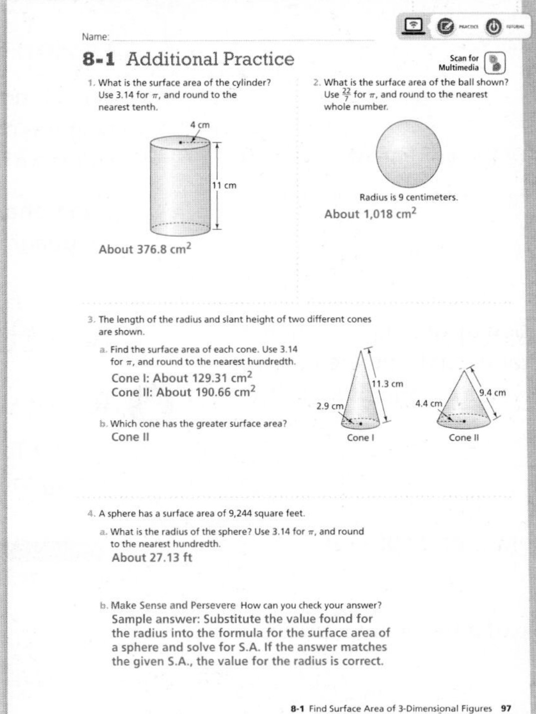

Name:

## 8-1 Additional Practice

Scan for Multimedia

1. What is the surface area of the cylinder? Use 3.14 for $\pi$, and round to the nearest tenth.
   About 376.8 cm²

2. What is the surface area of the ball shown? Use $\frac{22}{7}$ for $\pi$, and round to the nearest whole number.
   Radius is 9 centimeters.
   About 1,018 cm²

3. The length of the radius and slant height of two different cones are shown.
   a. Find the surface area of each cone. Use 3.14 for $\pi$, and round to the nearest hundredth.
   Cone I: About 129.31 cm²
   Cone II: About 190.66 cm²
   b. Which cone has the greater surface area?
   Cone II

4. A sphere has a surface area of 9,244 square feet.
   a. What is the radius of the sphere? Use 3.14 for $\pi$, and round to the nearest hundredth.
   About 27.13 ft
   b. Make Sense and Persevere How can you check your answer?
   Sample answer: Substitute the value found for the radius into the formula for the surface area of a sphere and solve for S.A. If the answer matches the given S.A., the value for the radius is correct.

8-1 Find Surface Area of 3-Dimensional Figures 97

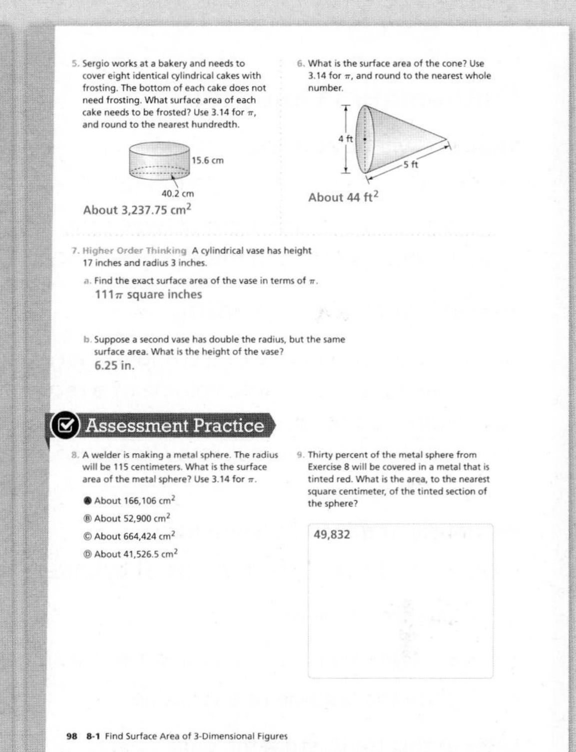

5. Sergio works at a bakery and needs to cover eight identical cylindrical cakes with frosting. The bottom of each cake does not need frosting. What surface area of each cake needs to be frosted? Use 3.14 for $\pi$, and round to the nearest hundredth.
   About 3,237.75 cm²

6. What is the surface area of the cone? Use 3.14 for $\pi$, and round to the nearest whole number.
   About 44 ft²

7. Higher Order Thinking A cylindrical vase has height 17 inches and radius 3 inches.
   a. Find the exact surface area of the vase in terms of $\pi$.
   $111\pi$ square inches
   b. Suppose a second vase has double the radius, but the same surface area. What is the height of the vase?
   6.25 in.

Assessment Practice

8. A welder is making a metal sphere. The radius will be 115 centimeters. What is the surface area of the metal sphere? Use 3.14 for $\pi$.
   ● About 166,106 cm²
   Ⓑ About 52,900 cm²
   Ⓒ About 664,424 cm²
   Ⓓ About 41,526.5 cm²

9. Thirty percent of the metal sphere from Exercise 8 will be covered in a metal that is tinted red. What is the area, to the nearest square centimeter, of the tinted section of the sphere?
   49,832

98 8-1 Find Surface Area of 3-Dimensional Figures

# Differentiated Intervention

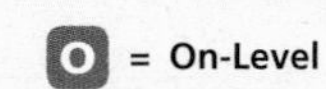 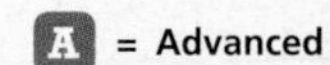

I = Intervention  O = On-Level  A = Advanced

## Enrichment O A

Presents engaging problems and activities that extend the lesson concepts.

Name

Enrichment 8-1

**Tell whether each statement is always true, never true, or sometimes true. Explain your reasoning.**

1. In the net of a cylinder, one dimension of the rectangle is the same as the circumference of each circular base.
   **Always true; Sample answer: To form the cylinder from the net, opposite sides of the rectangle wrap around each circle. Therefore, the base of the rectangle is equal to the circumference of the circle.**
2. If a cylinder and a cone have the same radius, $r$, and height, $h$, then the surface area of the cylinder is twice the surface area of the cone.
   **Never true; Sample answer: The bases have the same areas, so the base area of the cylinder is twice the base area of the cone. However, the area of the cylinder's curved surface is $2\pi rh$, and the area of the cone's curved surface is $\pi r\ell$, where $\ell$ is the slant height. The slant height is not equal to the height. So $2\pi rh$ is not twice $\pi r\ell$, and the cylinder's surface area is not twice the cone's surface area.**
3. The surface area of a sphere is greater than or equal to $4\pi$.
   **Sometimes true; Sample answer: The surface area of a sphere with radius $r$ is $4\pi r^2$. If $r = 1$, then $4\pi r = 4\pi$. If $r \geq 1$, then $4\pi r^2 \geq 4\pi$. If $0 < r < 1$, then $4\pi r^2 < 4\pi$.**
4. The area of the curved surface of a cone is greater than the area of its base.
   **Always true; Sample answer: The area of the curved surface is $\pi r\ell$, and the area of the base is $\pi r^2$. Since the slant height, $\ell$, must always be greater than the radius, $r$, $\pi r\ell > \pi r^2$.**
5. If a cylinder and sphere have the same radius, $r$, then the surface area of the cylinder is greater than or equal to the surface area of the sphere.
   **Sometimes true; Sample answer: If the cylinder's height, $h$, equals $r$, then its surface area is $2\pi r^2 + 2\pi r^2 = 4\pi r^2$, which is also the surface area of the sphere. If $r \geq h$, then the cylinder's surface area is greater than or equal to the sphere's surface area. If $r < h$, then the cylinder's surface area is less than the sphere's surface area.**

## Math Tools and Games I O A

Offers additional activities and games to build understanding and fluency.

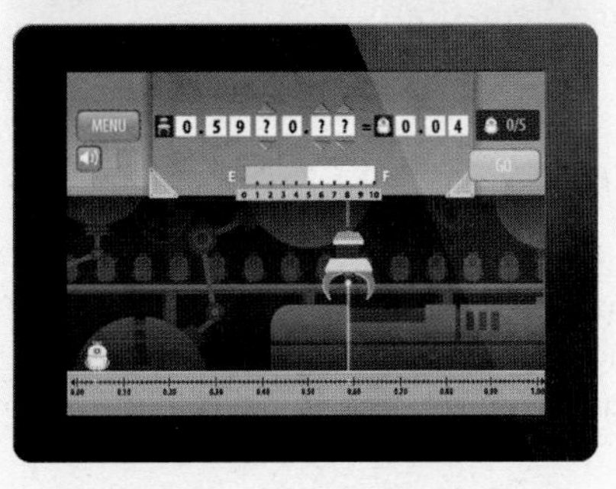


## Pick a Project and STEM Project I O A

Provides an additional opportunity for students to demonstrate understanding of key mathematical concepts.

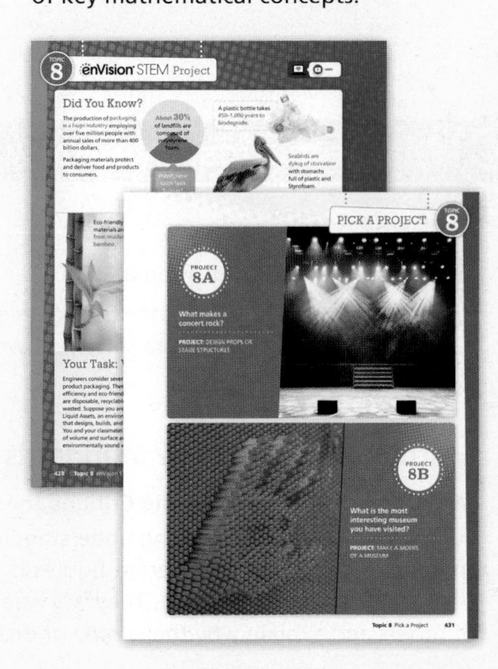

Lesson 8-2

# Find Volume of Cylinders

Go Online

Activity

## Lesson Overview

FOCUS

### Mathematics Objective

**Students will be able to:**

✔ identify and use the correct formula to calculate the volume of a cylinder.

✔ recognize the relationship between the formulas for the volume of a rectangular prism and the volume of a cylinder.

### Essential Understanding

Determining the volume of a cylinder is an extension of finding the volume of a rectangular prism. The volume of a rectangular prism is the area of its base multiplied by its height. Similarly, the volume of a cylinder is equal to the area of its base multiplied by its height.

COHERENCE

**Previously in this topic, students:**

- calculated the surface areas of cylinders, cones, and spheres.

**In this lesson, students:**

- compare the volume of a cylinder to the volume of a rectangular prism.
- calculate the volume of a cylinder.

**Later in this topic, students will:**

- calculate the volume of cones and spheres.

**Cross-Cluster Connection** Students apply previous work solving linear equations (8.EE.2) from Topic 2 when finding volume of cylinders (8.G.3).

RIGOR

This lesson emphasizes a blend of **procedural skill and fluency** and **conceptual understanding.**

- Students will become fluent in calculating the volume of a cylinder.

## Language Support

### Lesson Language Objective

Explain how to use what I know about finding volumes of rectangular prisms to find the volume of a cylinder.

Additional resources are available in the **Language Support Handbook**.

## Math Anytime

### Today's Challenge

Use the Topic 8 problems any time during this topic.

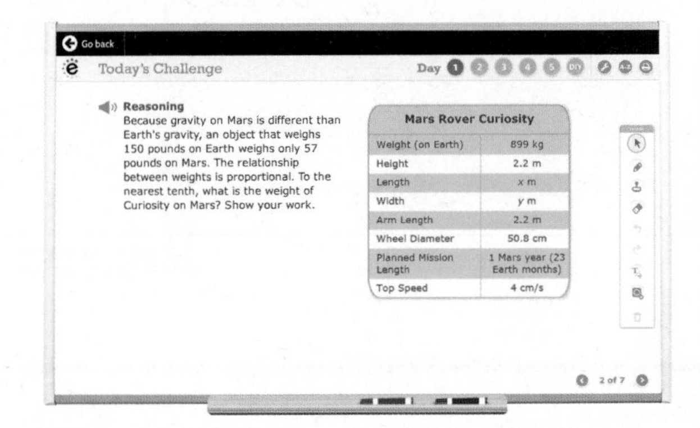


## Mathematics Overview | Common Core Standards

### Content Standards

In this lesson, you will focus on **8.G.C.9**.

- **8.G.C.9** Know the formulas for the volumes of cones, cylinders, and spheres and use them to solve real-world and mathematical problems.

### Mathematical Practice Standards

**MP.3 Construct Arguments and Critique the Reasoning of Others**
Students will use their growing understanding of volume to compare the volumes of different figures by reasoning about them and later by calculating. They will assess the arguments of others and explain why they agree or disagree.

**MP.7 Look For and Make Use of Structure**
Students will identify the different parts to a cylinder and understand how the product of the area of the base and the height of the cylinder calculates the volume.

# STEP 1 | Problem-Based Learning

15-20 min

Go Online

Activity

## Explain It!

**Purpose** Students engage in productive struggle comparing the volume of a cylinder and a rectangular prism with the same dimensions. They connect this comparison to working with volumes of rectangular prisms and cylinders in the Visual Learning Bridge.

### ETP Before — WHOLE CLASS

**1 Introduce the Problem**

**2 Check for Understanding of the Problem**

Engage students with the problem by showing them pictures of zebrafish and sharing some fun facts about them. Zebrafish share 70% of their genes with humans so they are widely used to study human genetics and disease. They have even been used for research on the International Space Station.

### ETP During — SMALL GROUP

**3 Observe Students at Work**

- **How do students compare and contrast the two fish tanks?** Students might say the tanks have the same height and width, but one tank is curved and has a circular base and the other has flat faces a square base.
- **How do students decide who is correct?** Students might sketch or describe the cylindrical tank inside the rectangular tank and conclude that the rectangular tank will hold more water. Alternatively, they might calculate the area of the base of each tank to see which is larger.

If needed, ask Is there anything you learned in a previous lesson that can help you solve this problem?

**Early Finishers**

How would the problem change if the diameter of the cylindrical tank was equal to the diagonal of the square base of the rectangular tank? [Sample answer: The tanks still have the same height, but the cylindrical tank would have a larger area at the base, so the cylindrical tank would hold more water.]

### After

**4 Discuss Solution Strategies and Key Ideas**

Consider having groups share their solutions to part (A) first, followed by part (B). Have students discuss what mathematical quantity is being compared in this problem; volume.

Have them discuss how to compute the volume of the rectangular tank; they can find the area of the square base and multiply it by the height of the prism.

Have students consider and discuss how they could find the volume of the cylindrical tank; they can find the area of the circular base and multiply it by the height of the cylinder.

**5 Consider Instructional Implications**

After presenting Example 1, have students refer back to the problem in the Explain It and have them calculate how much larger the volume of the rectangular tank is than the cylindrical tank; the rectangular tank has a volume of 27,648 in.$^3$ and the cylindrical tank has a volume of about 21,704 in.$^3$. The difference is about 5,944 in.$^3$.

## Analyze Student Work

**Explain It!** Activity is available online.

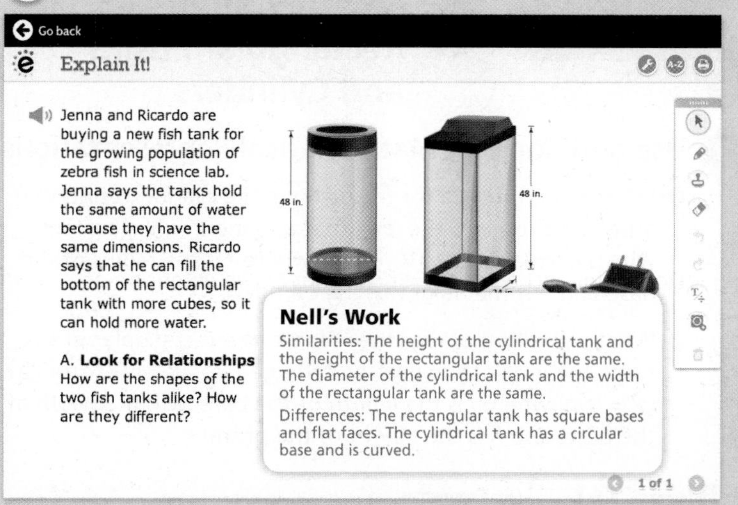


**Nell** notes that the tanks have the same height. Then she can see that the shapes of the bases are different.

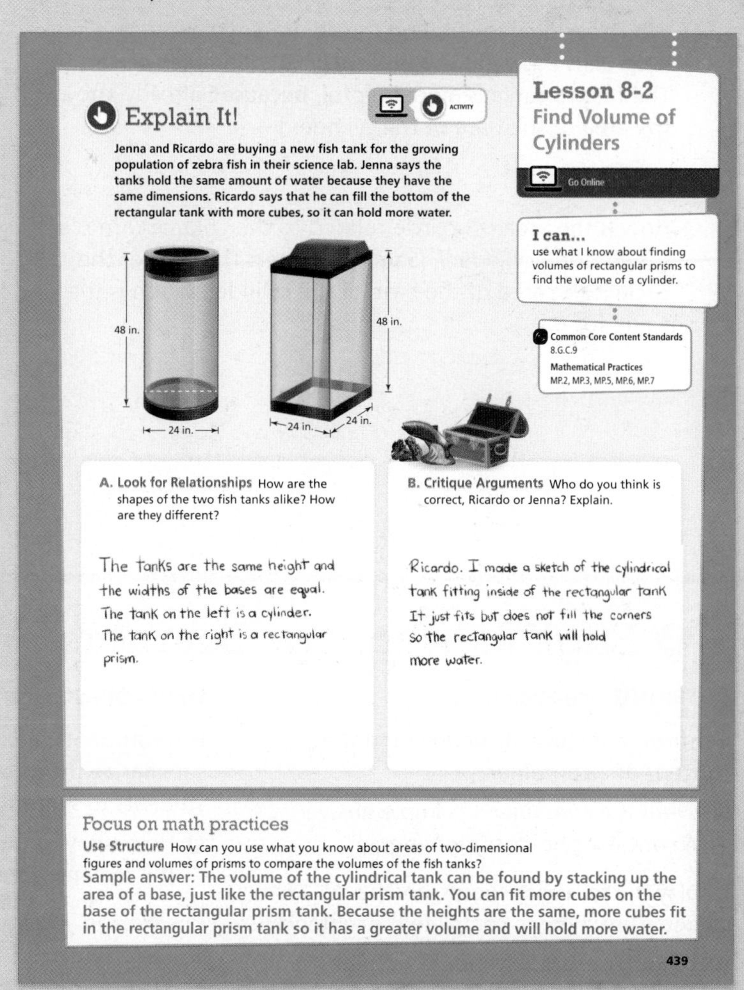


**José** sees that the cylindrical tank would fit completely inside the rectangular tank, with space left over.

Go Online

Visual Learning

Assess

# STEP 2 Visual Learning

## ETP Establish Mathematics Goals to Focus Learning

Engage students in a discussion about the ***Essential Question***. Encourage them to think of the volume of a cylinder and the volume of a rectangular prism in similar terms, as the product of the area of the base and the height.

Visual Learning Animation Plus is available online.

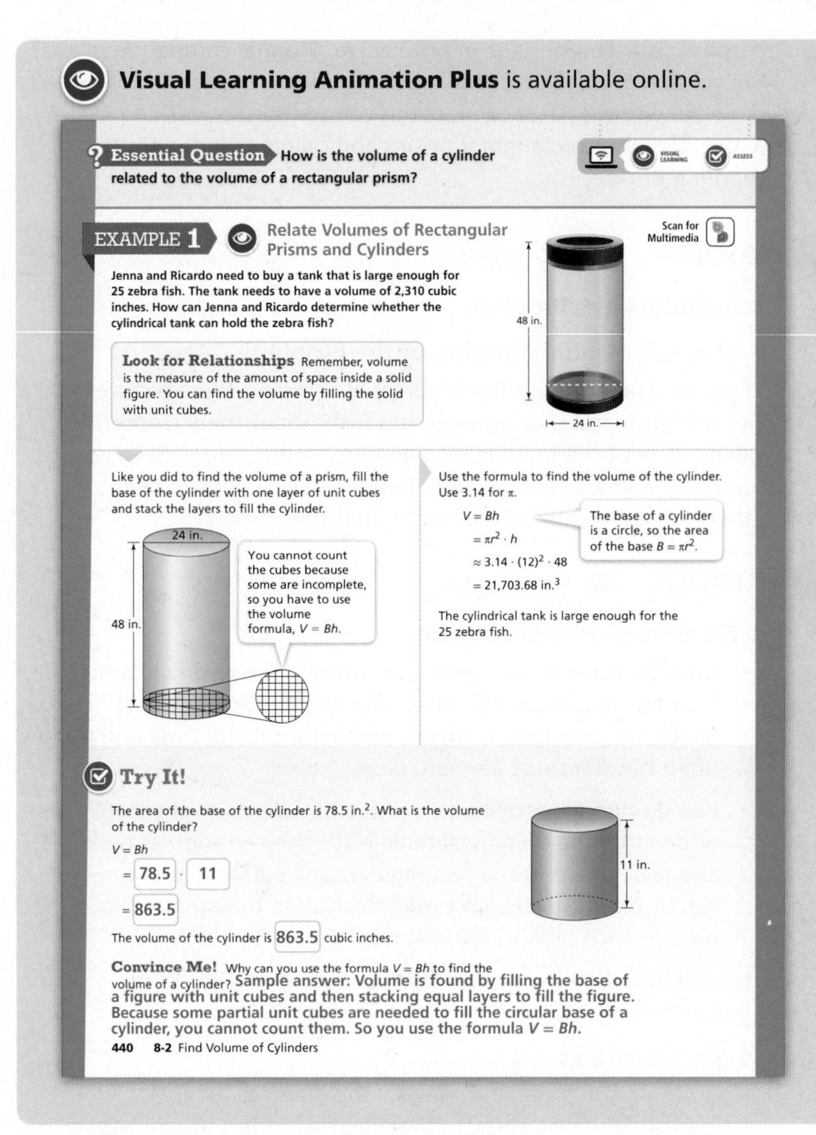

? Essential Question How is the volume of a cylinder related to the volume of a rectangular prism?

EXAMPLE 1 Relate Volumes of Rectangular Prisms and Cylinders

Scan for Multimedia

**Jenna and Ricardo need to buy a tank that is large enough for 25 zebra fish. The tank needs to have a volume of 2,310 cubic inches. How can Jenna and Ricardo determine whether the cylindrical tank can hold the zebra fish?**

**Look for Relationships** Remember, volume is the measure of the amount of space inside a solid figure. You can find the volume by filling the solid with unit cubes.



Like you did to find the volume of a prism, fill the base of the cylinder with one layer of unit cubes and stack the layers to fill the cylinder.



Use the formula to find the volume of the cylinder. Use 3.14 for $\pi$.

$V = Bh$

$= \pi r^2 \cdot h$

$\approx 3.14 \cdot (12)^2 \cdot 48$

$= 21{,}703.68 \text{ in.}^3$

The base of a cylinder is a circle, so the area of the base $B = \pi r^2$.

The cylindrical tank is large enough for the 25 zebra fish.

Try It!

The area of the base of the cylinder is 78.5 in.$^2$. What is the volume of the cylinder?



$V = Bh$

$= 78.5 \cdot 11$

$= 863.5$

The volume of the cylinder is 863.5 cubic inches.

**Convince Me!** Why can you use the formula $V = Bh$ to find the volume of a cylinder? **Sample answer: Volume is found by filling the base of a figure with unit cubes and then stacking equal layers to fill the figure. Because some partial unit cubes are needed to fill the circular base of a cylinder, you cannot count them. So you use the formula $V = Bh$.**

440 8-2 Find Volume of Cylinders

## EXAMPLE 1  Relate Volumes of Rectangular Prisms and Cylinders

## ETP Use and Connect Mathematical Representations

**Q:** What is the formula for the volume of a cylinder, using the area of a circle and the idea that a cylinder is like a prism with a circular base? [$V = \pi r^2 h$, where $r$ is the radius of the base and $h$ is the height of the cylinder]

**Q:** What is the formula for the volume of a rectangular prism, using the area of the base and the general volume formula? [$V = lwh$, where $l$ is the length of the base, $w$ is the width of the base, and $h$ is the height of the prism]

##  Try It!  Formative Assessment

## ETP Elicit and Use Evidence of Student Thinking

**Q:** Which formula for finding the volume of a cylinder is more helpful in this case: $V = Bh$ or $V \pi r^2 h$? [Sample answer: The first formula is more helpful, because I already know the area of the base of the cylinder.]

### Convince Me!

**Q:** How is the area of a circle related to the volume formula $V = Bh$ for a cylinder? [Sample answer: The area of the circle is the area of the base of the cylinder, which is the value for $B$.]

Students can access the ***Visual Learning Animation Plus*** by using the **BouncePages app** to scan this page. Students can download the app for free in their mobile devices' app store.

## ELL English Language Learners

**ENTERING** See Example 2.

Confirm that students understand the concept of a container.

**Q:** What is a *container*? [Sample answer: A container holds something.]

Display the following words, and have students use them to complete the sentences.

rectangular prism cylinder volume

A juice box is a ____________. The can of juice is a ____________. I need to find the ____________ of each container.

**DEVELOPING** See Example 1.

Have students reread the problem and summarize the known information. Ask students to share their summaries.

**Q:** How can you find the area of the base of the rectangular tank?

**Q:** How can you find the area of the base of the cylinder?

**Q:** How is finding the volume of a cylinder similar to finding the volume of a rectangular prism?

**BRIDGING** See Example 1.

Ask students to read the problem statement from Example 1 before you go over it as a class. Encourage students to make predictions about which container will hold more water based on the given information and illustrations. Then, after the class has completed the example, ask them to go back to their predictions and see whether they were correct. Ask students to speak about why they made the predictions they did and whether the calculations surprised them.

Go Online

 Activity  Assess

## EXAMPLE 2  Find an Unknown Measure

 **Pose Purposeful Questions**

**Q:** What steps are used to find the radius of the can of juice? [Sample answer: Use the volume formula. Substitute the given information into the formula: The volume, $V$, is 300 and the height, $h$, is 14. Then solve the equation for $r$.]

## EXAMPLE 3  Solve Problems Involving Volume of a Cylinder

 **Pose Purposeful Questions**

**Q:** In Step 2, why is 15 divided by the volume of the barrel? [Sample answer: Dividing the total amount of sand purchased by the volume of each barrel tells the number of barrels the sand will fill.]

**Q:** What does the remainder of 0.7 mean to the context of the problem? [Sample answer: It is the amount of sand left over after the barrels are full. There is enough sand left over to fill 0.7 of a barrel.]

##  Try It!  Formative Assessment

 **Elicit and Use Evidence of Student Thinking**

**Q:** Where should the values given in the problem be substituted into the volume equation? [Sample answer: The radius is 7.5 inches, the volume is 5,000 cubic inches, and $\pi$ is 3.14, so $r = 7.5$, $V = 5{,}000$, and $\pi = 3.14$.]

**Examples and Try Its!** are available online.

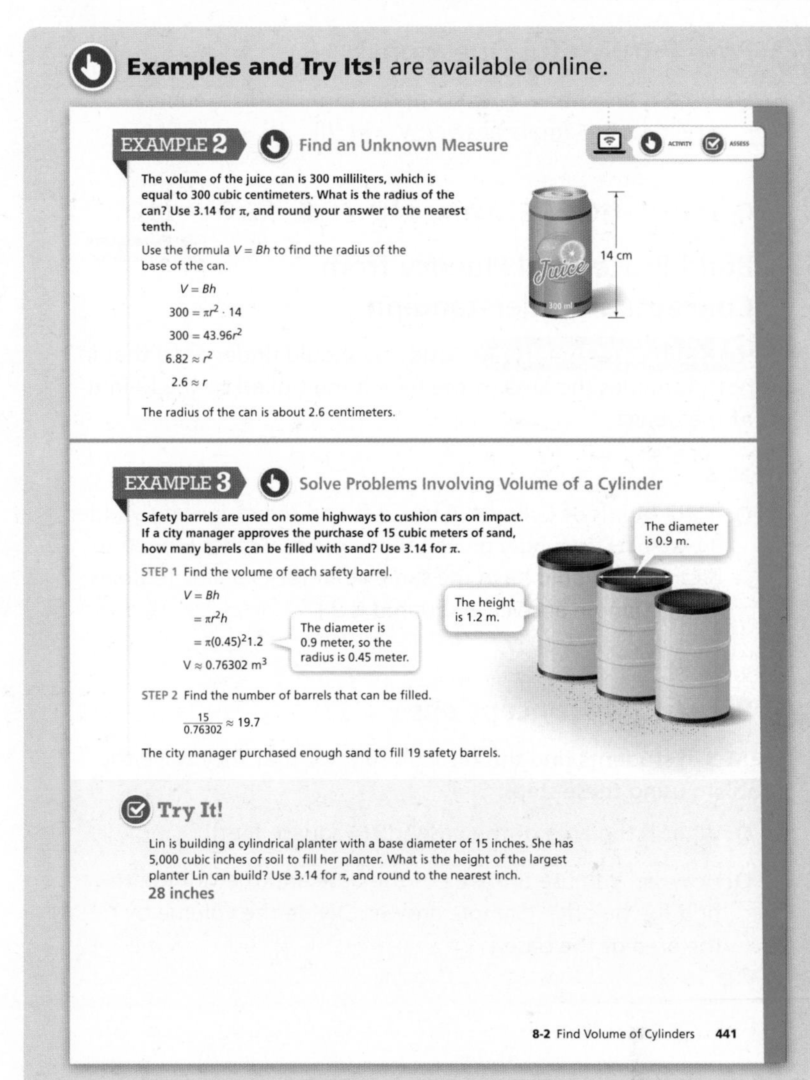

EXAMPLE 2 Find an Unknown Measure

**The volume of the juice can is 300 milliliters, which is equal to 300 cubic centimeters. What is the radius of the can? Use 3.14 for $\pi$, and round your answer to the nearest tenth.**

Use the formula $V = Bh$ to find the radius of the base of the can.

$V = Bh$

$300 = \pi r^2 \cdot 14$

$300 = 43.96r^2$

$6.82 \approx r^2$

$2.6 \approx r$

The radius of the can is about 2.6 centimeters.



EXAMPLE 3 Solve Problems Involving Volume of a Cylinder

**Safety barrels are used on some highways to cushion cars on impact. If a city manager approves the purchase of 15 cubic meters of sand, how many barrels can be filled with sand? Use 3.14 for $\pi$.**

STEP 1 Find the volume of each safety barrel.

$V = Bh$

$= \pi r^2 h$

$= \pi(0.45)^2 1.2$

$V \approx 0.76302 \text{ m}^3$

The diameter is 0.9 meter, so the radius is 0.45 meter.

STEP 2 Find the number of barrels that can be filled.

$\frac{15}{0.76302} \approx 19.7$

The city manager purchased enough sand to fill 19 safety barrels.



Try It!

Lin is building a cylindrical planter with a base diameter of 15 inches. She has 5,000 cubic inches of soil to fill her planter. What is the height of the largest planter Lin can build? Use 3.14 for $\pi$, and round to the nearest inch.
28 inches

8-2 Find Volume of Cylinders 441

**For additional examples go online.**

##  Response to Intervention

**USE WITH EXAMPLE 2** Some students may have difficulty understanding how to find the height or radius of a cylinder when the volume is given.

- Identify the parts of the formula.

**Q:** The formula for the volume of a cylinder is $V = \pi r^2 h$. What do the variables $r$ and $h$ represent? [$r$ represents the radius of the base and $h$ represents the height of the cylinder.]

**Q:** What amounts are given in the problem? [The height of 14 centimeters and the volume of 300 cubic centimeters]

**Q:** What can be substituted into the formula? [$V = 300$, $h = 14$, and $\pi = 3.14$]

##  Enrichment

**USE WITH EXAMPLE 3** Some students can be challenged to explore different-sized barrels.

- Answer the following:

**Q:** Suppose the height of each barrel was reduced to only 1 meter, but the diameter of each barrel was increased to 1 meter. How would this affect the volume of the barrel? [Sample answer: The volume of the barrel would increase to 0.785 cubic meters.]

**Q:** How does this change in the dimensions affect the number of barrels that can be filled with 15 cubic meters of sand? [Sample answer: Since 15 divided by the new volume is 19.108, the same number of barrels will be full of sand, but less sand will be left over.]

# STEP 2 | Visual Learning *continued*

Go Online

Key Concept

Assess

Activity

## KEY CONCEPT

### ETP Pose Purposeful Questions

**Q:** What is another way to write the formula for volume of a cylinder? [Sample answer: $V = \pi r^2 h$]

## Do You Understand/Do You Know How?

Formative Assessment

### ETP Build Procedural Fluency from Conceptual Understanding

**Essential Question** Students should understand that in both formulas the area of the base is multiplied by the height of the object.

**ITEM 3**

**Q:** If the radius of Cylinder A was 3 ft and the radius of Cylinder B was 1 ft, then how much taller would Cylinder B need to be so they would have the same volume? Explain. [9 times taller; Sample answer: 3 squared is 9.]

### Prevent Misconceptions

**ITEM 5** If students find this difficult suggest that they solve the problem using these steps.

**Q:** What is the area of the base? [314 square feet]

**Q:** How can you use the area of the base and the volume to find the height? [Sample answer: Divide the volume by the area of the base.]

Available Online

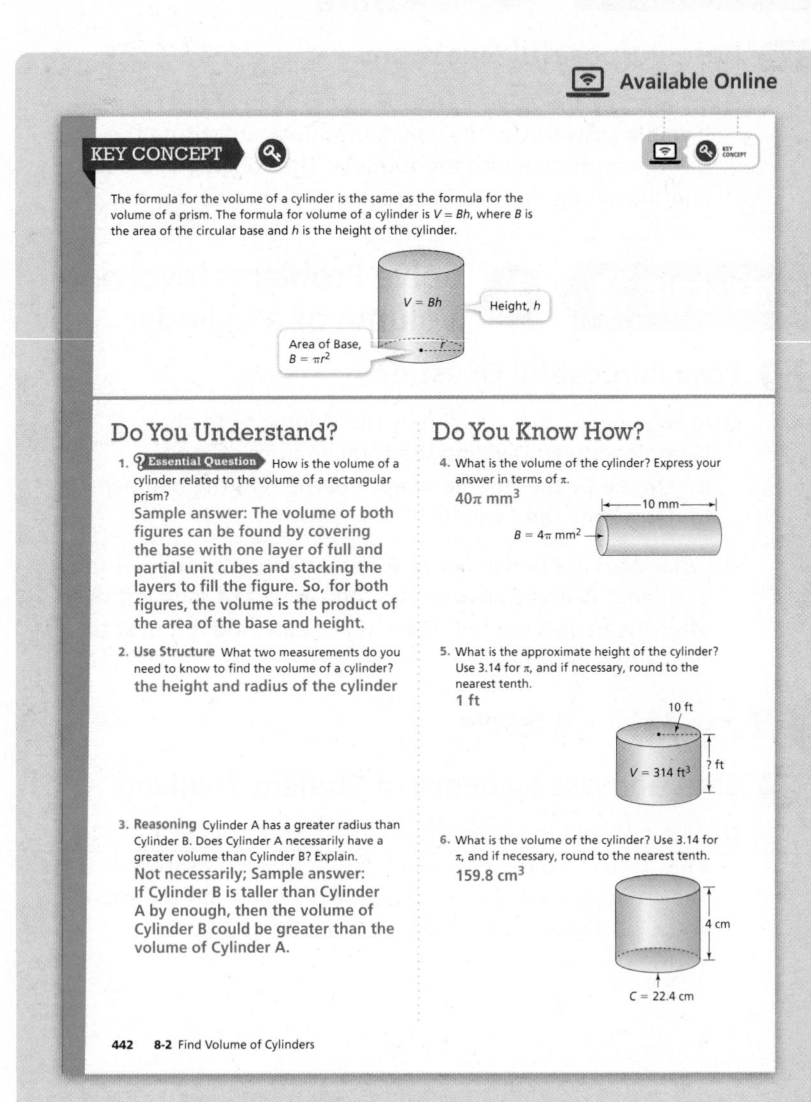

KEY CONCEPT

The formula for the volume of a cylinder is the same as the formula for the volume of a prism. The formula for volume of a cylinder is $V = Bh$, where $B$ is the area of the circular base and $h$ is the height of the cylinder.



**Do You Understand?**

1. **Essential Question** How is the volume of a cylinder related to the volume of a rectangular prism?
Sample answer: The volume of both figures can be found by covering the base with one layer of full and partial unit cubes and stacking the layers to fill the figure. So, for both figures, the volume is the product of the area of the base and height.

2. **Use Structure** What two measurements do you need to know to find the volume of a cylinder?
the height and radius of the cylinder

3. **Reasoning** Cylinder A has a greater radius than Cylinder B. Does Cylinder A necessarily have a greater volume than Cylinder B? Explain.
Not necessarily; Sample answer: If Cylinder B is taller than Cylinder A by enough, then the volume of Cylinder B could be greater than the volume of Cylinder A.

**Do You Know How?**

4. What is the volume of the cylinder? Express your answer in terms of $\pi$.
$40\pi$ mm$^3$



5. What is the approximate height of the cylinder? Use 3.14 for $\pi$, and if necessary, round to the nearest tenth.
1 ft



6. What is the volume of the cylinder? Use 3.14 for $\pi$, and if necessary, round to the nearest tenth.
159.8 cm$^3$



442 8-2 Find Volume of Cylinders

## ADDITIONAL EXAMPLE 3

Help students solve a different problem involving the volume of a cylinder with this additional example.

**Q:** What information are you given? [Volume and height]

**Q:** What information do you need to find out? [the circumference of the vase]

**Q:** How can you find the circumference of the vase? [Sample answer: Use the formula $V = \pi r^2 h$. Substitute 2,400 for the volume, 3.14 for $\pi$, and 20 for $h$. Find the radius and use it to find the circumference.]

**Additional Examples** are available online.

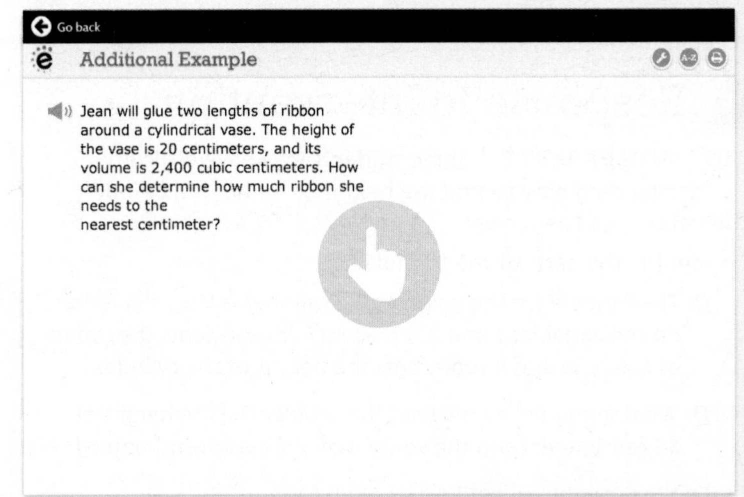



**Answer:** Jean will need about 78 centimeters of ribbon.

Go Online

Practice Tutorials Math Tools

# Practice & Problem Solving  

**Interactive Practice** and **Virtual Nerd Tutorials** are available online.

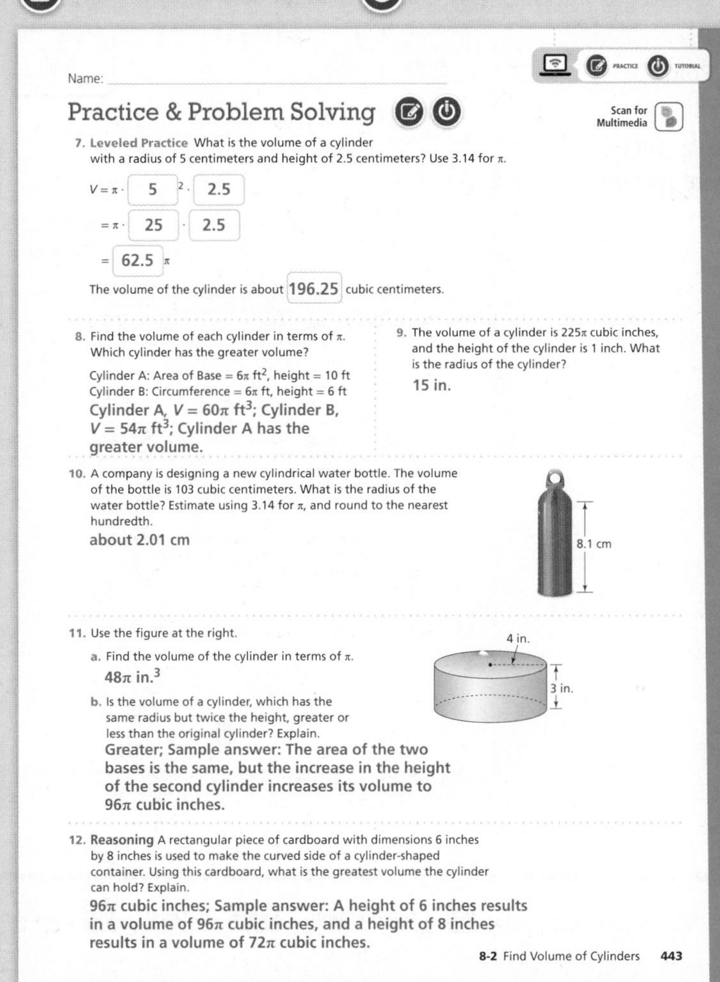

Name: ______

Practice & Problem Solving

Scan for Multimedia

7. **Leveled Practice** What is the volume of a cylinder with a radius of 5 centimeters and height of 2.5 centimeters? Use 3.14 for $\pi$.

$V = \pi \cdot 5^2 \cdot 2.5$

$= \pi \cdot 25 \cdot 2.5$

$= 62.5\pi$

The volume of the cylinder is about 196.25 cubic centimeters.

8. Find the volume of each cylinder in terms of $\pi$. Which cylinder has the greater volume?

Cylinder A: Area of Base = $6\pi$ ft$^2$, height = 10 ft
Cylinder B: Circumference = $6\pi$ ft, height = 6 ft

Cylinder A, $V = 60\pi$ ft$^3$; Cylinder B, $V = 54\pi$ ft$^3$; Cylinder A has the greater volume.

9. The volume of a cylinder is $225\pi$ cubic inches, and the height of the cylinder is 1 inch. What is the radius of the cylinder?

15 in.

10. A company is designing a new cylindrical water bottle. The volume of the bottle is 103 cubic centimeters. What is the radius of the water bottle? Estimate using 3.14 for $\pi$, and round to the nearest hundredth.

about 2.01 cm

8.1 cm

11. Use the figure at the right.

a. Find the volume of the cylinder in terms of $\pi$.

$48\pi$ in.$^3$

b. Is the volume of a cylinder, which has the same radius but twice the height, greater or less than the original cylinder? Explain.

Greater; Sample answer: The area of the two bases is the same, but the increase in the height of the second cylinder increases its volume to $96\pi$ cubic inches.

4 in.
3 in.

12. **Reasoning** A rectangular piece of cardboard with dimensions 6 inches by 8 inches is used to make the curved side of a cylinder-shaped container. Using this cardboard, what is the greatest volume the cylinder can hold? Explain.

$96\pi$ cubic inches; Sample answer: A height of 6 inches results in a volume of $96\pi$ cubic inches, and a height of 8 inches results in a volume of $72\pi$ cubic inches.

8-2 Find Volume of Cylinders 443

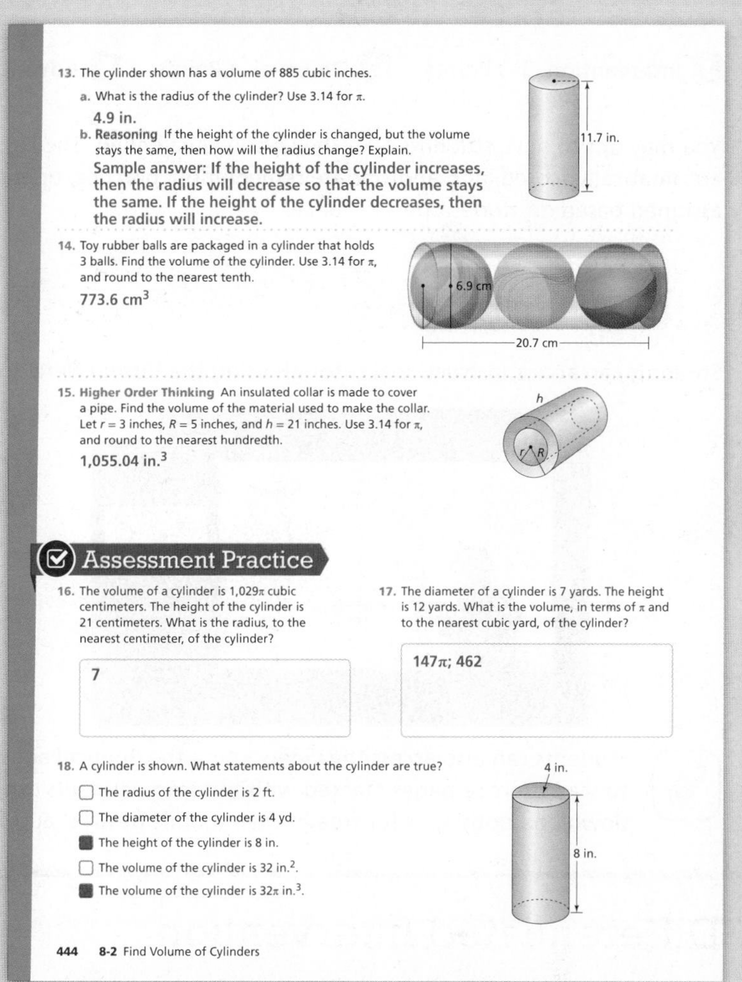

13. The cylinder shown has a volume of 885 cubic inches.

a. What is the radius of the cylinder? Use 3.14 for $\pi$.

4.9 in.

b. **Reasoning** If the height of the cylinder is changed, but the volume stays the same, then how will the radius change? Explain.

Sample answer: If the height of the cylinder increases, then the radius will decrease so that the volume stays the same. If the height of the cylinder decreases, then the radius will increase.

11.7 in.

14. Toy rubber balls are packaged in a cylinder that holds 3 balls. Find the volume of the cylinder. Use 3.14 for $\pi$, and round to the nearest tenth.

773.6 cm$^3$

6.9 cm
20.7 cm

15. **Higher Order Thinking** An insulated collar is made to cover a pipe. Find the volume of the material used to make the collar. Let $r = 3$ inches, $R = 5$ inches, and $h = 21$ inches. Use 3.14 for $\pi$, and round to the nearest hundredth.

1,055.04 in.$^3$

Assessment Practice

16. The volume of a cylinder is $1{,}029\pi$ cubic centimeters. The height of the cylinder is 21 centimeters. What is the radius, to the nearest centimeter, of the cylinder?

7

17. The diameter of a cylinder is 7 yards. The height is 12 yards. What is the volume, in terms of $\pi$ and to the nearest cubic yard, of the cylinder?

$147\pi$; 462

18. A cylinder is shown. What statements about the cylinder are true?

- ☐ The radius of the cylinder is 2 ft.
- ☐ The diameter of the cylinder is 4 yd.
- ☒ The height of the cylinder is 8 in.
- ☐ The volume of the cylinder is 32 in.$^2$.
- ☒ The volume of the cylinder is $32\pi$ in.$^3$.

4 in.
8 in.

444 8-2 Find Volume of Cylinders

## Error Intervention

**ITEM 11** Students may have difficulty understanding how to find an answer to the second part of the problem.

**Q:** How do you find the volume of the cylinder that is 3 inches high? [Sample answer: Multiply 3 in. by $16\pi$ in.$^2$]

**Q:** What number would you change to find the volume for the cylinder twice as tall? How would that change the result. [Sample answer: I would change the 3 to a 6. It would double the result.]

## Challenge

**ITEM 13 Reasoning Quantitatively** Interested students might want to explore how a change in the radius can impact the height of a cylinder when the volume is the same.

**Q:** Two cylinders have the same volume. Cylinder X has a height of 10 inches. The radius of Cylinder Y is twice as long as the radius of Cylinder X. What is the height of Cylinder Y? Explain. [Sample answer: The height of Cylinder Y is 2.5 inches. $10\pi r^2 = \pi(2r)^2 h$ because the cylinders have the same volume. If I divide both sides of the equation by $4\pi r^2$, I get $2.5 = h$.]

You may opt to have students complete the automatically scored Practice & Problem Solving items online.

### Item Analysis

| Example | Items | DOK |
|---|---|---|
| 1 | 7, 8, 17 | 2 |
| | 12 | 3 |
| 2 | 9, 16 | 2 |
| | 13, 18 | 3 |
| 3 | 10, 14 | 2 |
| | 11, 15 | 3 |

# STEP 3 Assess & Differentiate

Go Online

 Assess  Tutorials  Worksheets

##  Lesson Quiz

 **Formative** Assessment

 Use the student scores on the Lesson Quiz to prescribe differentiated assignments.

**I Intervention** 0–3 Points **O On-Level** 4 Points **A Advanced** 5 Points

You may opt to have students take the Lesson Quiz online. The Lesson Quiz will be automatically scored, and appropriate remediation, practice, or enrichment will be assigned based on student performance.

**Lesson Quiz** is available online.

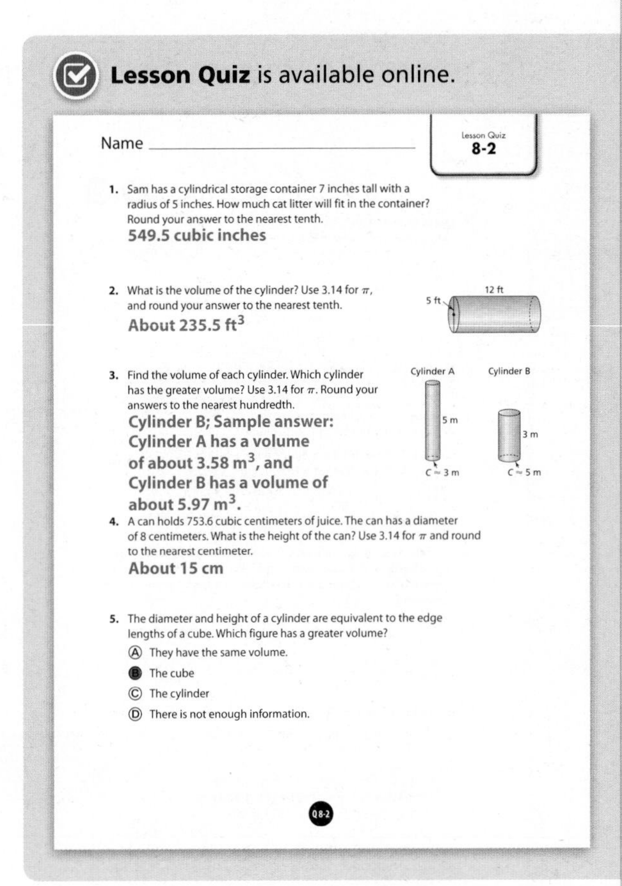

Name ______________ Lesson Quiz 8-2

1. Sam has a cylindrical storage container 7 inches tall with a radius of 5 inches. How much cat litter will fit in the container? Round your answer to the nearest tenth.
   549.5 cubic inches

2. What is the volume of the cylinder? Use 3.14 for $\pi$, and round your answer to the nearest tenth.
   About 235.5 $ft^3$



3. Find the volume of each cylinder. Which cylinder has the greater volume? Use 3.14 for $\pi$. Round your answers to the nearest hundredth.
   Cylinder B; Sample answer: Cylinder A has a volume of about 3.58 $m^3$, and Cylinder B has a volume of about 5.97 $m^3$.



4. A can holds 753.6 cubic centimeters of juice. The can has a diameter of 8 centimeters. What is the height of the can? Use 3.14 for $\pi$ and round to the nearest centimeter.
   About 15 cm

5. The diameter and height of a cylinder are equivalent to the edge lengths of a cube. Which figure has a greater volume?
   Ⓐ They have the same volume.
   Ⓑ The cube
   Ⓒ The cylinder
   Ⓓ There is not enough information.

Q8-2

## Video Tutorials

Students can access instructional tutorials using the **Virtual Nerd app**.

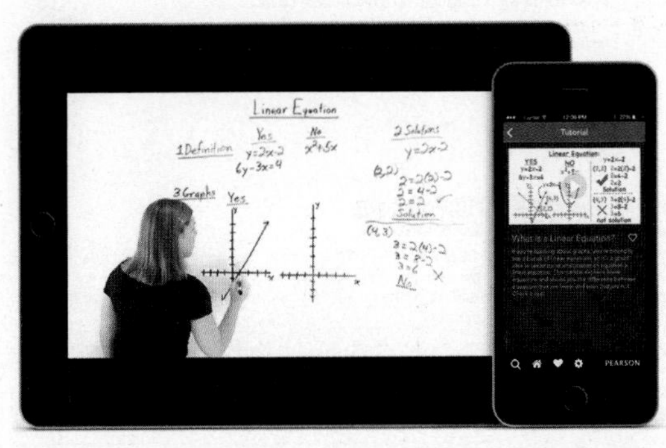

 Students can also access the videos using the **BouncePages app** to scan exercise pages marked with this icon. Students can download both apps for free in their mobile devices' app store.

## Differentiated Intervention

**I** = Intervention **O** = On-Level **A** = Advanced

### Reteach to Build Understanding I

Provides scaffolded reteaching for the key lesson concepts.

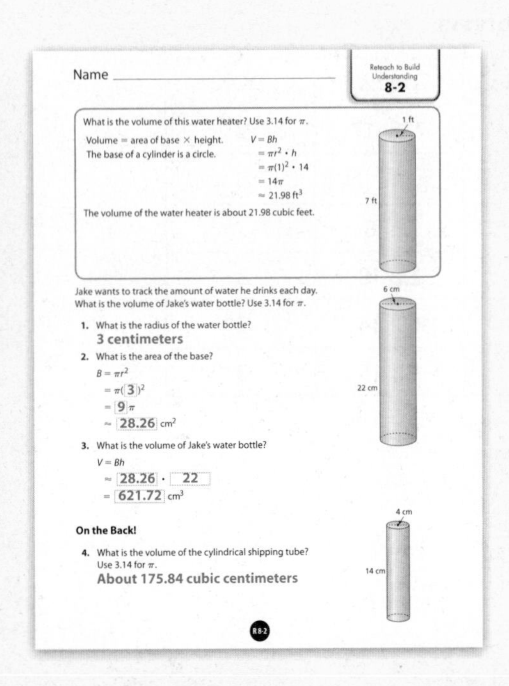

Name ______________ Reteach to Build Understanding 8-2

What is the volume of this water heater? Use 3.14 for $\pi$.

Volume = area of base × height. $V = Bh$
The base of a cylinder is a circle. $= \pi r^2 \cdot h$
$= \pi(1)^2 \cdot 14$
$= 14\pi$
$\approx 21.98$ $ft^3$

The volume of the water heater is about 21.98 cubic feet.



Jake wants to track the amount of water he drinks each day. What is the volume of Jake's water bottle? Use 3.14 for $\pi$.

1. What is the radius of the water bottle?
   3 centimeters
2. What is the area of the base?
   $B = \pi r^2$
   $= \pi(3)^2$
   $= 9\pi$
   $\approx 28.26$ $cm^2$
3. What is the volume of Jake's water bottle?
   $V = Bh$
   $\approx 28.26 \cdot 22$
   $= 621.72$ $cm^3$



On the Back!

4. What is the volume of the cylindrical shipping tube? Use 3.14 for $\pi$.
   About 175.84 cubic centimeters



R8-2

### Additional Vocabulary Support I O

Helps students develop and reinforce understanding of key terms and concepts.

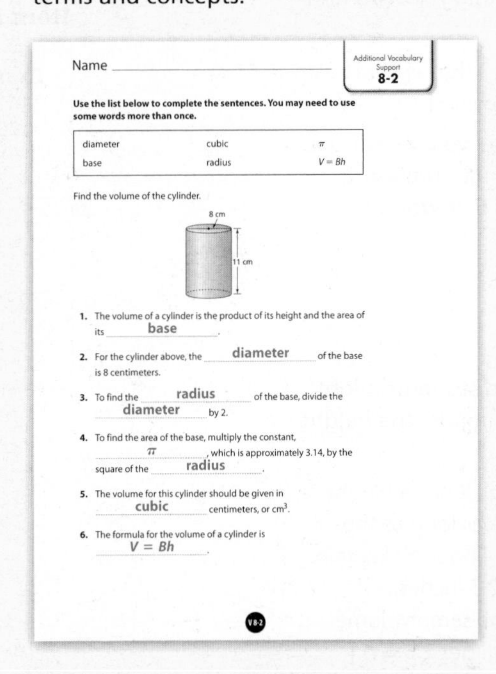

Name ______________ Additional Vocabulary Support 8-2

**Use the list below to complete the sentences. You may need to use some words more than once.**

| diameter | cubic | $\pi$ |
|---|---|---|
| base | radius | $V = Bh$ |

Find the volume of the cylinder.



1. The volume of a cylinder is the product of its height and the area of its base.
2. For the cylinder above, the diameter of the base is 8 centimeters.
3. To find the radius of the base, divide the diameter by 2.
4. To find the area of the base, multiply the constant, $\pi$, which is approximately 3.14, by the square of the radius.
5. The volume for this cylinder should be given in cubic centimeters, or $cm^3$.
6. The formula for the volume of a cylinder is $V = Bh$.

V8-2

### Build Mathematical Literacy I O

Provides support for struggling readers to build mathematical literacy.

Name ______________ Build Mathematical Literacy 8-2

Tiana compares the volumes of two different flour canisters. Which canister holds more flour?

1. How is the amount of flour that each container holds related to the volume?
   The volume of each container is equal to the amount of flour that each holds.

10 in.
6 in.
9 in.
6.5 in.
5 in.

2. Highlight the relevant information given in each diagram. Describe the dimensions of each container using the given information.
   Check students' work; The cylinder has a diameter of 6 inches, or radius of 3 inches, and a height of 10 inches. The rectangular prism has a length of 6.5 inches, a width of 5 inches, and a height of 9 inches.
3. Will you need to find the volumes of both containers to solve this problem? Explain.
   Yes; I cannot determine which container has the greater volume without calculating both volumes.
4. What is true about the volume of the container that holds more flour?
   The volume of the container that holds more flour is greater than the volume of the other container.
5. Do you have enough information to solve this problem? Explain.
   Yes; For each container, the volume can be found using the formula $V = Bh$, where $B$ is the area of the base and $h$ is the height. The diagram gives the heights and the necessary dimensions to calculate the base areas. So I can find both volumes and then compare them in order to determine which container holds more flour.

M8-2

Go Online

Practice Worksheets Math Tools Math Games

# Additional Practice

You may opt to have students complete the automatically scored Additional Practice items online.

### Item Analysis

| Example | Items | DOK |
|---|---|---|
| 1 | 1 | 1 |
| | 4, 6, 8 | 2 |
| | 5 | 3 |
| 2 | 2, 9 | 2 |
| 3 | 3 | 2 |
| | 7 | 3 |

**Interactive Practice** is available online.

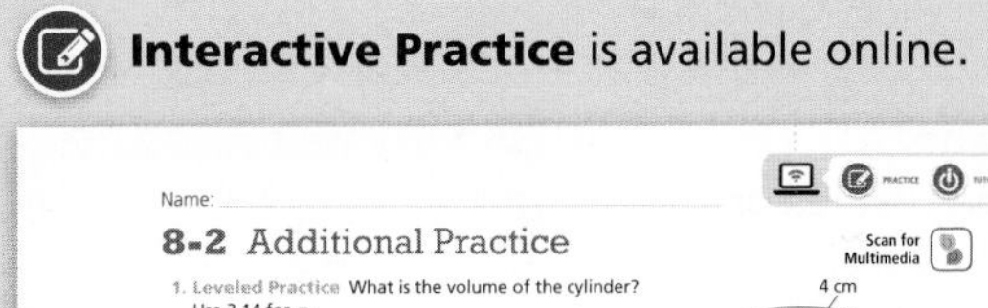

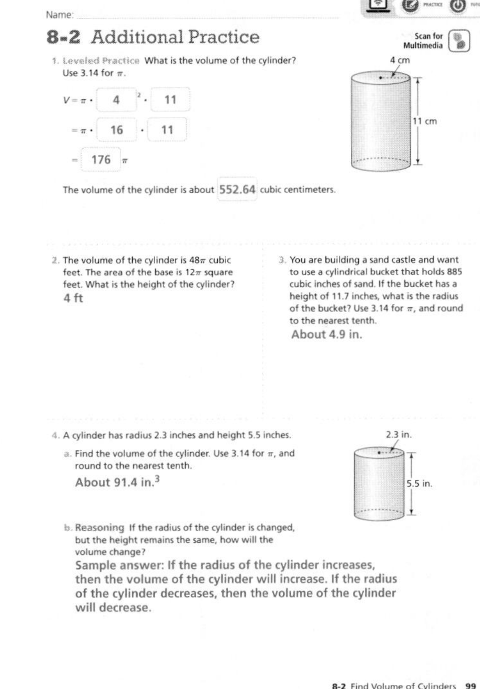

Name:

**8-2** Additional Practice

Scan for Multimedia

1. Leveled Practice What is the volume of the cylinder? Use 3.14 for $\pi$.

$V = \pi \cdot 4^2 \cdot 11$

$= \pi \cdot 16 \cdot 11$

$= 176\pi$

The volume of the cylinder is about 552.64 cubic centimeters.



2. The volume of the cylinder is $48\pi$ cubic feet. The area of the base is $12\pi$ square feet. What is the height of the cylinder?
4 ft

3. You are building a sand castle and want to use a cylindrical bucket that holds 885 cubic inches of sand. If the bucket has a height of 11.7 inches, what is the radius of the bucket? Use 3.14 for $\pi$, and round to the nearest tenth.
About 4.9 in.

4. A cylinder has radius 2.3 inches and height 5.5 inches.

a. Find the volume of the cylinder. Use 3.14 for $\pi$, and round to the nearest tenth.
About 91.4 in.$^3$



b. Reasoning If the radius of the cylinder is changed, but the height remains the same, how will the volume change?
Sample answer: If the radius of the cylinder increases, then the volume of the cylinder will increase. If the radius of the cylinder decreases, then the volume of the cylinder will decrease.

8-2 Find Volume of Cylinders 99

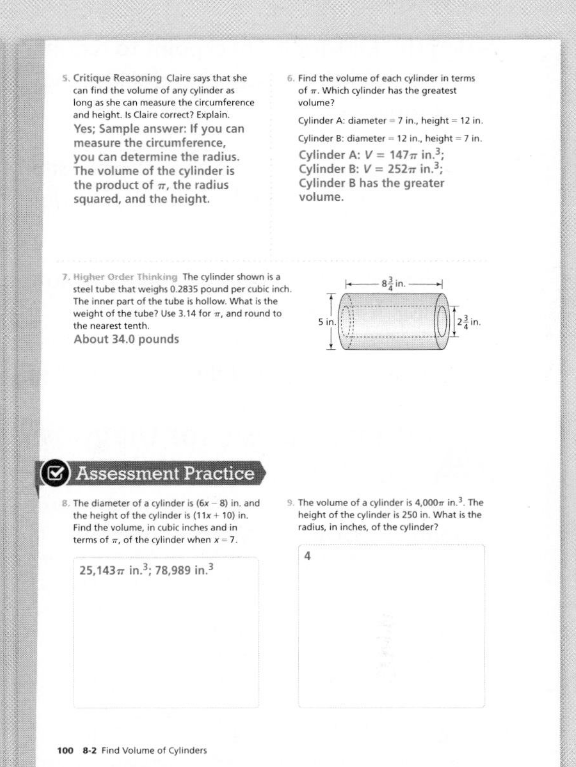

5. Critique Reasoning Claire says that she can find the volume of any cylinder as long as she can measure the circumference and height. Is Claire correct? Explain.
Yes; Sample answer: If you can measure the circumference, you can determine the radius. The volume of the cylinder is the product of $\pi$, the radius squared, and the height.

6. Find the volume of each cylinder in terms of $\pi$. Which cylinder has the greatest volume?
Cylinder A: diameter = 7 in., height = 12 in.
Cylinder B: diameter = 12 in., height = 7 in.
Cylinder A: $V = 147\pi$ in.$^3$;
Cylinder B: $V = 252\pi$ in.$^3$;
Cylinder B has the greater volume.

7. Higher Order Thinking The cylinder shown is a steel tube that weighs 0.2835 pound per cubic inch. The inner part of the tube is hollow. What is the weight of the tube? Use 3.14 for $\pi$, and round to the nearest tenth.
About 34.0 pounds



Assessment Practice

8. The diameter of a cylinder is $(6x - 8)$ in. and the height of the cylinder is $(11x + 10)$ in. Find the volume, in cubic inches and in terms of $\pi$, of the cylinder when $x = 7$.
$25,143\pi$ in.$^3$; 78,989 in.$^3$

9. The volume of a cylinder is $4,000\pi$ in.$^3$. The height of the cylinder is 250 in. What is the radius, in inches, of the cylinder?
4

100 8-2 Find Volume of Cylinders

# Differentiated Intervention

I = Intervention O = On-Level A = Advanced

## Enrichment O A

Presents engaging problems and activities that extend the lesson concepts.

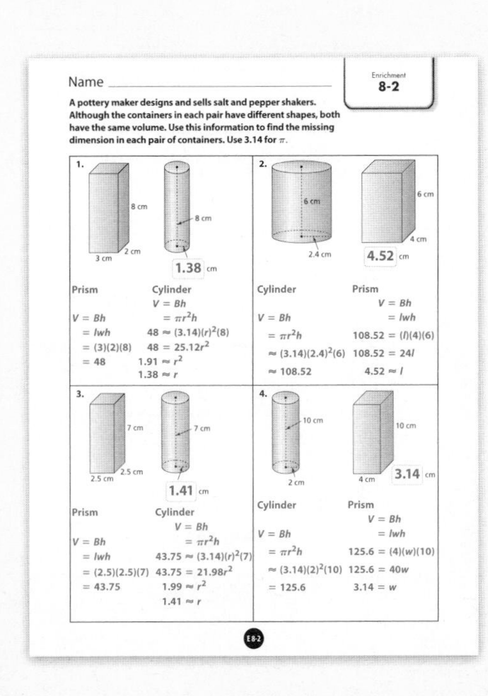

Name

Enrichment 8-2

A pottery maker designs and sells salt and pepper shakers. Although the containers in each pair have different shapes, both have the same volume. Use this information to find the missing dimension in each pair of containers. Use 3.14 for $\pi$.

1. Prism: $V = Bh = lwh = (3)(2)(8) = 48$; Cylinder: $V = Bh = \pi r^2 h$; $48 \approx (3.14)(r)^2(8)$; $48 = 25.12r^2$; $1.91 \approx r^2$; $1.38 \approx r$ — 1.38 cm

2. Cylinder: $V = Bh = \pi r^2 h \approx (3.14)(2.4)^2(6) \approx 108.52$; Prism: $V = Bh = lwh$; $108.52 = (l)(4)(6)$; $108.52 = 24l$; $4.52 \approx l$ — 4.52 cm

3. Prism: $V = Bh = lwh = (2.5)(2.5)(7) = 43.75$; Cylinder: $V = Bh = \pi r^2 h$; $43.75 \approx (3.14)(r)^2(7)$; $43.75 = 21.98r^2$; $1.99 \approx r^2$; $1.41 \approx r$ — 1.41 cm

4. Cylinder: $V = Bh = \pi r^2 h \approx (3.14)(2)^2(10) = 125.6$; Prism: $V = Bh = lwh$; $125.6 = (4)(w)(10)$; $125.6 = 40w$; $3.14 = w$ — 3.14 cm

## Math Tools and Games I O A

Offers additional activities and games to build understanding and fluency.

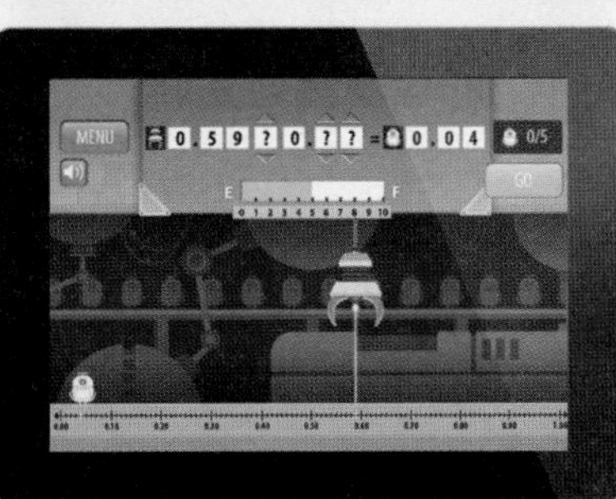

## Pick a Project and STEM Project I O A

Provides an additional opportunity for students to demonstrate understanding of key mathematical concepts.

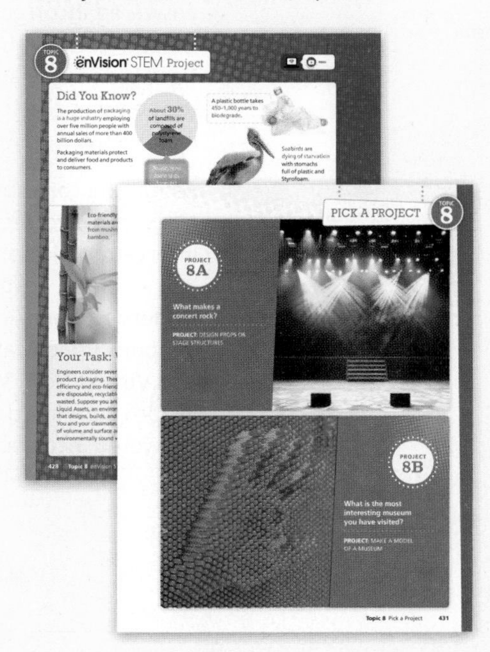

# MID-TOPIC CHECKPOINT

Go Online

Assess

Assign the Mid-Topic Checkpoint to monitor students' understandings of concepts and skills taught in the first lessons in this topic.

Encourage students to use the self-assessment form at the bottom of the page to describe their level of understanding.

You may opt to have students take the automatically-scored Mid-Topic Assessment online.

Use students' results to adjust instruction as needed.

## Item Analysis for Diagnosis and Intervention

| Item | DOK | MDIS | Lesson | Standard |
|---|---|---|---|---|
| 1 | 1 | N56 | 8-1, 8-2 | 8.G.C.9 |
| 2 | 2 | N50 | 8-1 | 8.G.C.9 |
| 3 | 2 | N49 | 8-1 | 8.G.C.9 |
| 4 | 2 | N53 | 8-1 | 8.G.C.9 |
| 5 | 2 | N50 | 8-1 | 8.G.C.9 |
| 6 | 2 | N53 | 8-2 | 8.G.C.9 |

## Scoring Guide

| Score | Recommendations |
|---|---|
| Greater Than 85% | Assign the corresponding MDIS for items answered incorrectly. Use Enrichment activities with the student. |
| 70%–85% | Assign the corresponding MDIS for items answered incorrectly. You may also assign Reteach to Build Understanding and Virtual Nerd Video assets for the lessons correlated to the items the student answered incorrectly. |
| Less Than 70% | Assign the corresponding MDIS for items answered incorrectly. Assign appropriate intervention lessons available online. You may also assign Reteach to Build Understanding, Additional Vocabulary Support, Build Mathematical Literacy, and Virtual Nerd Video assets for the lessons correlated to the items the student answered incorrectly. |

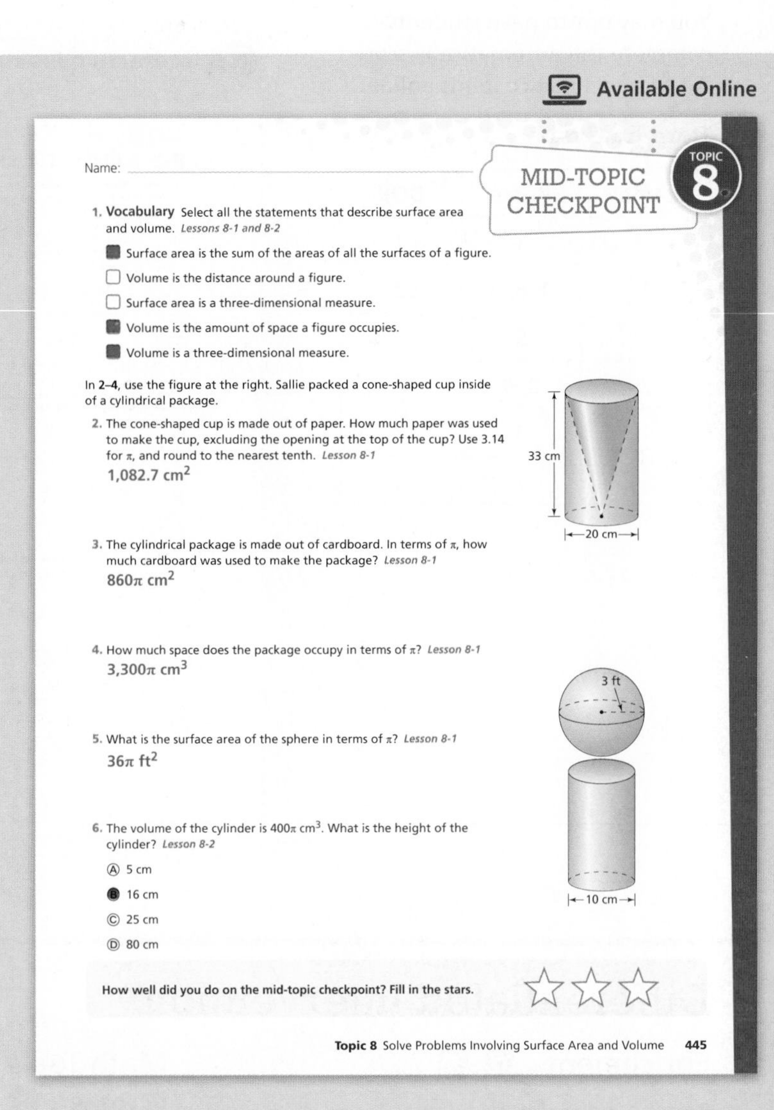

Available Online

Name:

MID-TOPIC CHECKPOINT

TOPIC 8

1. **Vocabulary** Select all the statements that describe surface area and volume. *Lessons 8-1 and 8-2*
   - ■ Surface area is the sum of the areas of all the surfaces of a figure.
   - □ Volume is the distance around a figure.
   - □ Surface area is a three-dimensional measure.
   - ■ Volume is the amount of space a figure occupies.
   - ■ Volume is a three-dimensional measure.

In **2–4**, use the figure at the right. Sallie packed a cone-shaped cup inside of a cylindrical package.

2. The cone-shaped cup is made out of paper. How much paper was used to make the cup, excluding the opening at the top of the cup? Use 3.14 for $\pi$, and round to the nearest tenth. *Lesson 8-1*
   1,082.7 cm$^2$

3. The cylindrical package is made out of cardboard. In terms of $\pi$, how much cardboard was used to make the package? *Lesson 8-1*
   $860\pi$ cm$^2$

4. How much space does the package occupy in terms of $\pi$? *Lesson 8-1*
   $3{,}300\pi$ cm$^3$

5. What is the surface area of the sphere in terms of $\pi$? *Lesson 8-1*
   $36\pi$ ft$^2$

6. The volume of the cylinder is $400\pi$ cm$^3$. What is the height of the cylinder? *Lesson 8-2*
   - Ⓐ 5 cm
   - ● 16 cm
   - Ⓒ 25 cm
   - Ⓓ 80 cm



How well did you do on the mid-topic checkpoint? Fill in the stars. ☆☆☆

**Topic 8** Solve Problems Involving Surface Area and Volume **445**

### Mid-Topic Assessment Master

Name

Topic 8 Mid-Topic Assessment

1. Vocabulary How is finding the surface area of a three-dimensional figure related to the net of the figure?
   **Sample answer: You can find the surface area of a three-dimensional figure by finding the area of its two-dimensional net.**

**Kenji packed an exercise ball into a cylindrical package. Use the figure for 2–4.**

2. The inflatable exercise ball is made out of vinyl. How much vinyl was used to make the exercise ball? Express your answer in terms of $\pi$.
   $36\pi$ ft$^2$

3. The cylindrical package is made out of plastic. In terms of $\pi$, how much plastic was used to make the package?
   $48\pi$ ft$^2$

4. How much space does the package occupy in terms of $\pi$?
   $45\pi$ ft$^3$

5. What is the surface area of the cone in terms of $\pi$?
   $76\pi$ m$^2$

6. The volume of the cylinder is $225\pi$ cm$^3$. What is the height of the cylinder?
   - Ⓐ 6.25 cm
   - ● 25 cm
   - Ⓒ 37.5 cm
   - Ⓓ 75 cm

5 feet · 3 ft · 15 m · 8 m · 6 cm

Mid-Topic Assessment 1 of 1

# MID-TOPIC PERFORMANCE TASK

Go Online

Assess

Assess students' ability to apply the concepts and skills in the first part of the topic using the Mid-Topic Performance Task, found in the Student's Edition or online.

## Item Analysis for Diagnosis and Intervention

| Part | DOK | MDIS | Lesson | Standard |
|---|---|---|---|---|
| A | 2 | N49 | 8-1 | 7.G.B.6 |
| B | 2 | N48, N49 | 8-1 | 7.G.B.6 |
| C | 2 | N52, N53 | 8-2 | 8.G.C.9 |

## Scoring Rubric

| Part | Points | Mid-Topic Performance Task |
|---|---|---|
| A | 2<br>1 | Correct solution and explanation<br>Correct solution |
| B | 2<br>1 | Correct solution and explanation<br>Correct solution |
| C | 2<br>1 | Correct solution and explanation<br>Correct solution |

## Scoring Guide

| Score | Recommendations |
|---|---|
| Greater Than 85% | Assign the corresponding MDIS for items answered incorrectly. Use Enrichment activities with the student. |
| 70%–85% | Assign the corresponding MDIS for items answered incorrectly. You may also assign Reteach to Build Understanding and Virtual Nerd Video assets for the lessons correlated to the items the student answered incorrectly. |
| Less Than 70% | Assign the corresponding MDIS for items answered incorrectly. Assign appropriate intervention lessons available online. You may also assign Reteach to Build Understanding, Additional Vocabulary Support, Build Mathematical Literacy, and Virtual Nerd Video assets for the lessons correlated to the items the student answered incorrectly. |

Available Online

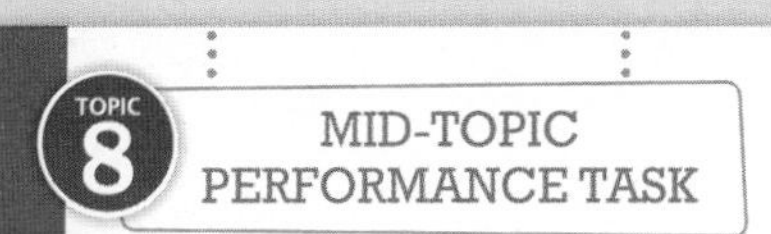

TOPIC 8 MID-TOPIC PERFORMANCE TASK

**Melissa designed a sculpture in which a cylinder-shaped section was removed from a cube.**

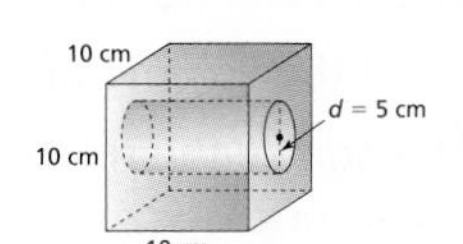


PART A

Before painting the surface of the sculpture, Melissa wants to sand the surface where the cylinder section was removed. What is the surface area of the section she will sand? Use 3.14 for $\pi$. Explain how you found the surface area.

157 $cm^2$; Sample answer: The section she will sand is the surface area of the cylinder that was removed, excluding both circular bases: $2(3.14)(2.5)(10) \approx 157$.

PART B

Melissa has a can of spray paint that covers about 6,500 square centimeters. Can Melissa apply two coats of paint to the entire sculpture? Explain. Use 3.14 for $\pi$.

Yes; Sample answer: Find the total surface area of the sculpture. Find the areas of the four square surfaces of the cube: $4(10 \cdot 10) = 400$. Find the area of the two surfaces where the cylinder was removed by subtracting the surface area of the circular base from the area of the square and multiplying the difference by two: $[(10)(10) - (3.14)(2.5)^2] \cdot 2 \approx 160.75$. Find the surface area where the cylinder-shaped section was removed, excluding both circular bases: $2(3.14)(2.5)(10) \approx 157$. Add the areas: $400 + 160.75 + 157 \approx 717.75$. Then multiply the surface area by 2 because Melissa will use two coats of paint: $717.75 \cdot 2 \approx 1{,}435.5$.

PART C

What is the volume of the sculpture? Use 3.14 for $\pi$.

803.75 $cm^3$

446 **Topic 8** Solve Problems Involving Surface Area and Volume

Go Online

Video Activity

# Lesson 8-3 Find Volume of Cones

## Lesson Overview

FOCUS

### Mathematics Objective

**Students will be able to:**

✔ find the volume of a cone.

✔ recognize the relationship between volume of a cylinder and volume of a cone.

### Essential Understanding

The volume of a cone is $\frac{1}{3}$ of the volume of a cylinder with the same radius and height. Students will examine this relationship and use it to determine the volume of any cone.

COHERENCE

**Previously in this topic, students:**

- compared the volume of a cylinder to the volume of a rectangular prism.

**In this lesson, students:**

- compare the volume of a cone to the volume of a cylinder.
- calculate the volume of a cone.

**Later in this topic, students will:**

- identify the relationship between the volume of a cone and the volume of a sphere.
- calculate the volume of spheres by using a formula.

**Cross-Cluster Connection** Students apply previous work solving linear equations (8.EE.2) from Topic 2 when finding volume of cones (8.G.3).

RIGOR

This lesson emphasizes a blend of **procedural skill and fluency** and **conceptual understanding.**

- Students will become fluent in calculating the volume of a cone.
- Students will understand the connections between the volume of a cone and the volume of a cylinder.

## Language Support

### Lesson Language Objective

Explain how to find the volume of cones.

Additional resources are available in the **Language Support Handbook**.

## Math Anytime

### Today's Challenge

Use the Topic 8 problems any time during this topic.

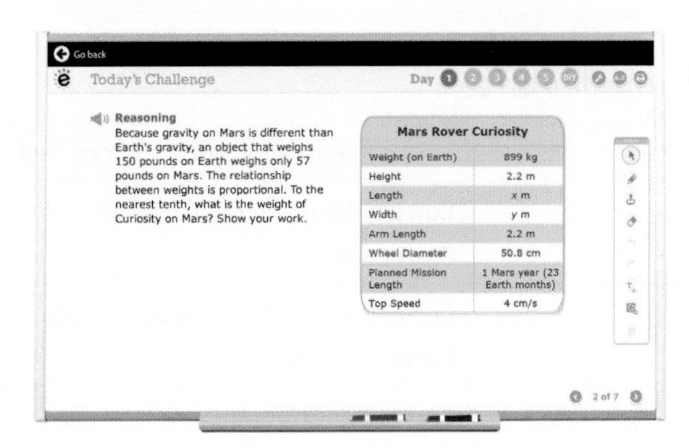


Watch the **Listen and Look For Video** for strategies and habits of mind to look for as students complete work on this lesson.

## Mathematics Overview — Common Core Standards

### Content Standards

This lesson focuses on **8.G.C.9**.

- **8.G.C.9** Know the formulas for the volumes of cones, cylinders, and spheres and use them to solve real-world and mathematical problems.

### Mathematical Practice Standards

**MP.1 Make Sense and Persevere**
Students will examine the mathematical relationship between the volumes of a cone and a cylinder.

**MP.7 Look for and Make Use of Structure**
Students will access existing knowledge of volume of cylinders and prisms to help them work through the task of finding the volume of pyramids and cones.

# STEP 1 | Problem-Based Learning

15-20 min

Go Online

Activity

## Solve & Discuss It!

**Purpose** Students compare the volume of a pyramid and a prism and connect it to finding the volume of a cone in the Visual Learning Bridge.

### Before — WHOLE CLASS

**1 Introduce the Problem**

**2 Check for Understanding of the Problem**

Engage students with the problem by asking: What objects in the real world are shaped like a rectangular pyramid? Like a rectangular prism?

### During — SMALL GROUP

**3 Observe Students at Work**

Students might conclude that the volume of one prism is 3 times the volume of one pyramid, or they might conclude that the volume of one pyramid is $\frac{1}{3}$ of the volume of one prism. Students may express these relationships using diagrams, verbal descriptions, or equations.

**Early Finishers**

How would the problem change if one batch of concrete mix makes 2 prisms or 6 pyramids? [Sample answer: The relationship between the volume of one pyramid and one prism remains the same.]

### ETP After — WHOLE CLASS

**4 Discuss Solution Strategies and Key Ideas**

Consider having groups who state that the volume of one pyramid is $\frac{1}{3}$ of the volume of one prism share first, followed by those who state that the volume of one prism is 3 times the volume of one pyramid. Have students discuss the connections between the responses; the responses are equivalent, since $3a = b$ is equivalent to $a = \frac{1}{3}b$ by the Multiplicative Property of Equality, where $a$ is the volume of the pyramid and $b$ is the volume of the prism.

Have students state how the pyramid and prism in this problem are the same; the dimensions of the bases are the same, and they have the same height. Have them describe the relationship between the volume of a pyramid and the volume of a prism given the same height and base; the volume of a pyramid is $\frac{1}{3}$ the volume of a prism.

**5 Consider Instructional Implications**

After presenting Example 1, refer students back to the problem in the Solve & Discuss It and have them discuss the relationships between the volume formulas for prism, pyramids, and cones;

$V_{prism} = Bh$

$V_{pyramid} = \frac{1}{3}(V_{prism}) = \frac{1}{3}Bh$

$V_{cone} = \frac{1}{3}Bh$.

## Analyze Student Work

**Solve and Discuss It!** Activity is available online.

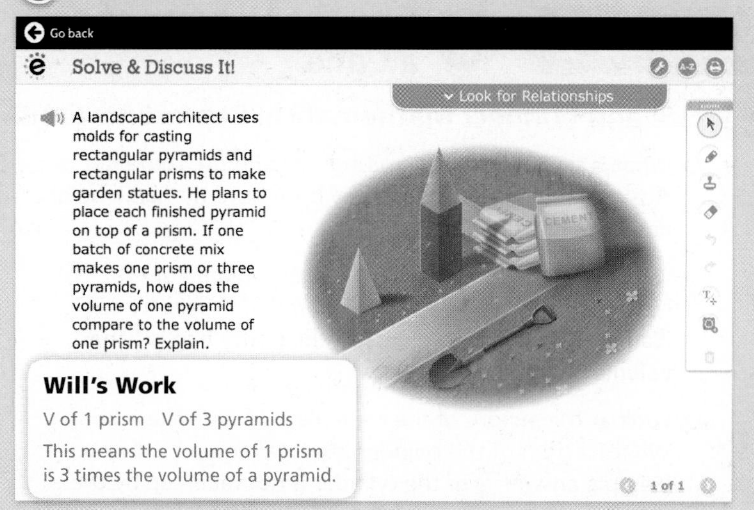


**Will** uses an equation to show the relationship between the volumes.

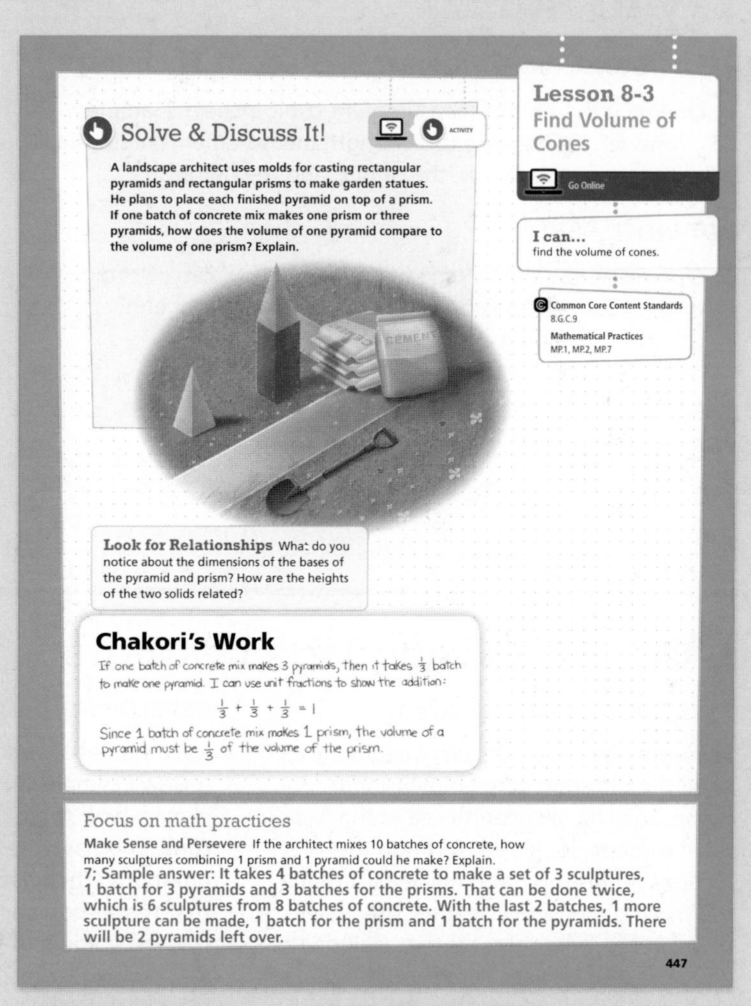

Lesson 8-3
Find Volume of Cones

Go Online

Solve & Discuss It! ACTIVITY

A landscape architect uses molds for casting rectangular pyramids and rectangular prisms to make garden statues. He plans to place each finished pyramid on top of a prism. If one batch of concrete mix makes one prism or three pyramids, how does the volume of one pyramid compare to the volume of one prism? Explain.

I can... find the volume of cones.

Common Core Content Standards 8.G.C.9
Mathematical Practices MP.1, MP.2, MP.7

**Look for Relationships** What do you notice about the dimensions of the bases of the pyramid and prism? How are the heights of the two solids related?

**Chakori's Work**

If one batch of concrete mix makes 3 pyramids, then it takes $\frac{1}{3}$ batch to make one pyramid. I can use unit fractions to show the addition:

$\frac{1}{3} + \frac{1}{3} + \frac{1}{3} = 1$

Since 1 batch of concrete mix makes 1 prism, the volume of a pyramid must be $\frac{1}{3}$ of the volume of the prism.

Focus on math practices

Make Sense and Persevere If the architect mixes 10 batches of concrete, how many sculptures combining 1 prism and 1 pyramid could he make? Explain.
7; Sample answer: It takes 4 batches of concrete to make a set of 3 sculptures, 1 batch for 3 pyramids and 3 batches for the prisms. That can be done twice, which is 6 sculptures from 8 batches of concrete. With the last 2 batches, 1 more sculpture can be made, 1 batch for the prism and 1 batch for the pyramids. There will be 2 pyramids left over.

447

**Chakori** uses the addition of unit fractions to show the relationship between the volumes of the prism and pyramids.

# STEP 2 | Visual Learning

Go Online

## ETP Establish Mathematics Goals to Focus Learning

Engage students in a discussion about the ***Essential Question***. Make sure students know how to identify the radius and the height of a cone. They should also be aware that the height of a cone is different from the slant height of a cone.

## EXAMPLE 1 Find the Volume of a Cone

### ETP Use and Connect Mathematical Representations

**Q:** What is similar about the pastry bag and the container of frosting? [Sample answer: They both have the same height and the same diameter.]

**Q:** What is the relationship between the volume of the container of frosting and the volume of the pastry bag? [Sample answer: The volume of the pastry bag is $\frac{1}{3}$ the volume of the container.]

**Q:** Look at the picture of the cone placed inside the cylinder. What fraction of the cylinder is not taken up by the cone. [Sample answer: $\frac{2}{3}$ of the cylinder is not taken up by the cone.]

## Try It!

Formative Assessment

### ETP Elicit and Use Evidence of Student Thinking

**Q:** Why is the unit of measurement cubic inches? [Sample answer: There were three length measurements multiplied together: the radius, the radius, and the height.]

### Convince Me!

**Q:** If you know the volume of a cylinder, how can you find the volume of a cone that has the same height and radius? [Sample answer: Multiply it by $\frac{1}{3}$.]

**Visual Learning Animation Plus** is available online.

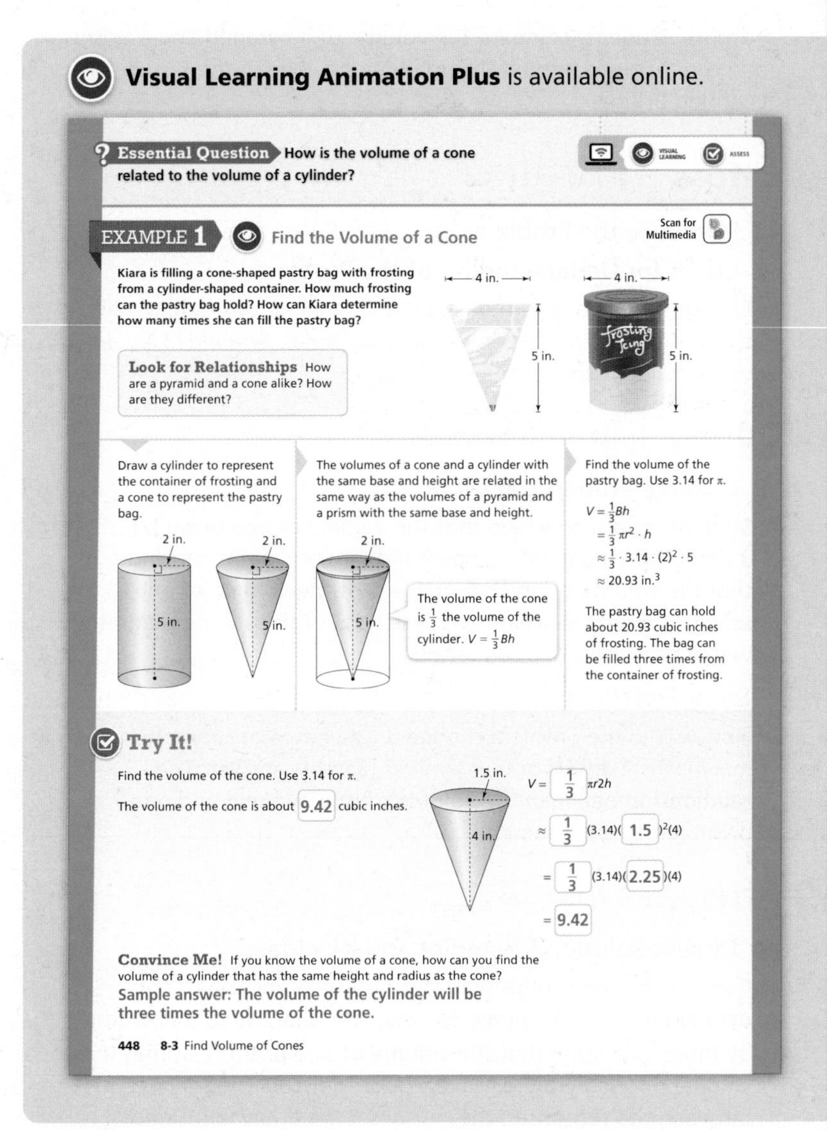

Essential Question How is the volume of a cone related to the volume of a cylinder?

EXAMPLE 1 Find the Volume of a Cone

Scan for Multimedia

Kiara is filling a cone-shaped pastry bag with frosting from a cylinder-shaped container. How much frosting can the pastry bag hold? How can Kiara determine how many times she can fill the pastry bag?

Look for Relationships How are a pyramid and a cone alike? How are they different?

Draw a cylinder to represent the container of frosting and a cone to represent the pastry bag.

The volumes of a cone and a cylinder with the same base and height are related in the same way as the volumes of a pyramid and a prism with the same base and height.

The volume of the cone is $\frac{1}{3}$ the volume of the cylinder. $V = \frac{1}{3}Bh$

Find the volume of the pastry bag. Use 3.14 for $\pi$.

$V = \frac{1}{3}Bh$
$= \frac{1}{3}\pi r^2 \cdot h$
$\approx \frac{1}{3} \cdot 3.14 \cdot (2)^2 \cdot 5$
$\approx 20.93$ in.$^3$

The pastry bag can hold about 20.93 cubic inches of frosting. The bag can be filled three times from the container of frosting.

Try It!

Find the volume of the cone. Use 3.14 for $\pi$.

The volume of the cone is about 9.42 cubic inches.

$V = \frac{1}{3}\pi r^2 h$
$\approx \frac{1}{3}(3.14)(1.5)^2(4)$
$= \frac{1}{3}(3.14)(2.25)(4)$
$= 9.42$

Convince Me! If you know the volume of a cone, how can you find the volume of a cylinder that has the same height and radius as the cone?
Sample answer: The volume of the cylinder will be three times the volume of the cone.

448 8-3 Find Volume of Cones

Students can access the ***Visual Learning Animation Plus*** by using the **BouncePages app** to scan this page. Students can download the app for free in their mobile devices' app store.

## ELL English Language Learners

**ENTERING** Use with Example 1.

Students may have difficulty keeping track of all the different three-dimensional shapes they have encountered in the topic. Have students look back through the sections in this topic and make a list of all the three-dimensional shapes. Then have them create memory cards that include the different shapes. Each card should include the shape name, a picture of the shape, a verbal description of the shape, and the formula for its volume.

**DEVELOPING** Use with Example 1.

Have students work with a partner to review Example 1. Have one partner explain how to find the volume of the cone, and have the other partner ask questions. Then have them switch roles so that the second partner explains how to find the volume of the cone, and the first asks questions. Encourage them both to refer back to the problem statement and illustrations as they work together.

**BRIDGING** Use with Example 2.

Have students draw pictures and write explanations to show the difference between the height and the slant height of a cone. Have them explain to a partner how to use the Pythagorean Theorem to use one of the measures to find the other.

Go Online

Activity

Assess

## EXAMPLE 2  Apply the Pythagorean Theorem to Solve Volume Problems

### ETP Pose Purposeful Questions

**Q:** What is the difference between the slant height of a cone and the height of a cone? [Sample answer: The slant height is the height along the outer edge of the cone from the bottom to the top. The height of a cone is the length of the cone from its tip perpendicular to its base.]

**Q:** If you know the slant height and radius of a cone how can the Pythagorean Theorem help you find its height? [Sample answer: The slant height, the radius, and the height form a right triangle. You can use the Pythagorean Theorem to find the missing leg, the height.]

## EXAMPLE 3  Find the Volume of a Cone Given the Circumference of the Base

### ETP Pose Purposeful Questions

**Q:** Why is it necessary to find the radius of the base of the cone? [Sample answer: You use the radius to find the area of the base so you can find the volume of the cone.]

**Q:** Do you need to use the Pythagorean Theorem to find the slant height of the cone? Explain. [No; Sample answer: The formula for the volume of a cone uses the height not the slant height, which is already given.]

##  Try It!  Formative Assessment

###  Elicit and Use Evidence of Student Thinking

**Q:** How can you find the radius of the base if you know the slant height and height? [Sample answer: You can use the Pythagorean Theorem.]

**Examples and Try Its!** are available online.

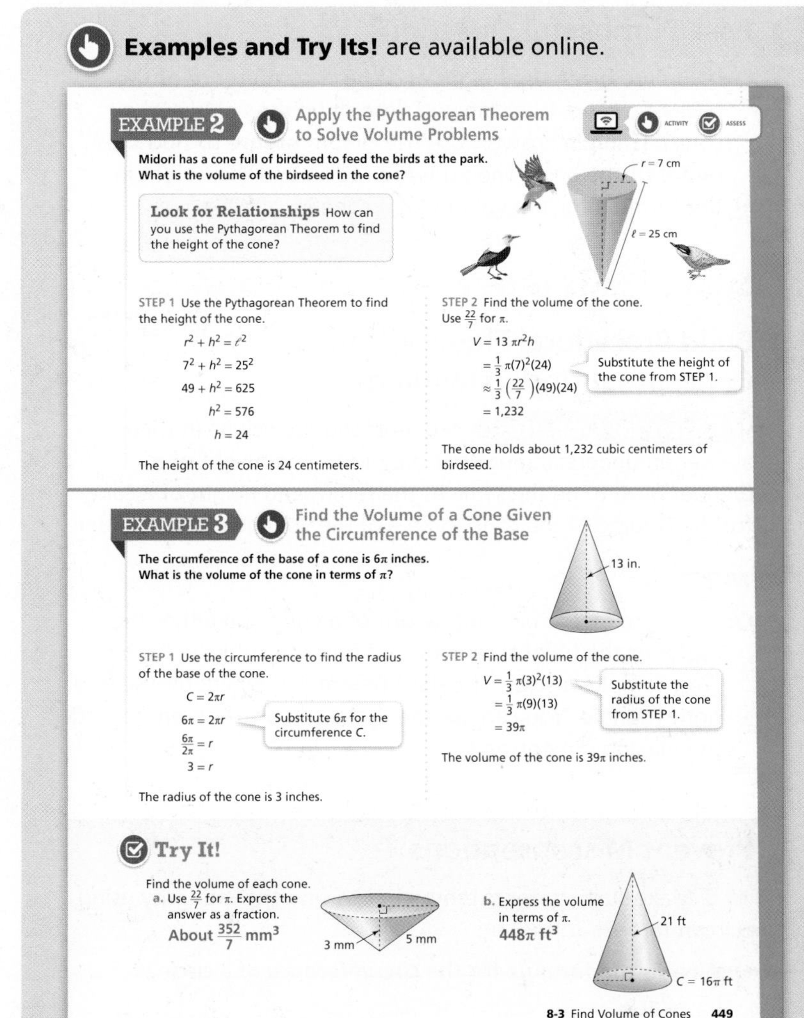

EXAMPLE 2 Apply the Pythagorean Theorem to Solve Volume Problems

ACTIVITY ASSESS

**Midori has a cone full of birdseed to feed the birds at the park. What is the volume of the birdseed in the cone?**

**Look for Relationships** How can you use the Pythagorean Theorem to find the height of the cone?

$r = 7$ cm

$\ell = 25$ cm

STEP 1 Use the Pythagorean Theorem to find the height of the cone.

$$r^2 + h^2 = \ell^2$$
$$7^2 + h^2 = 25^2$$
$$49 + h^2 = 625$$
$$h^2 = 576$$
$$h = 24$$

The height of the cone is 24 centimeters.

STEP 2 Find the volume of the cone. Use $\frac{22}{7}$ for $\pi$.

$$V = 13\ \pi r^2 h$$
$$= \frac{1}{3}\pi(7)^2(24)$$
$$\approx \frac{1}{3}\left(\frac{22}{7}\right)(49)(24)$$
$$= 1{,}232$$

Substitute the height of the cone from STEP 1.

The cone holds about 1,232 cubic centimeters of birdseed.

EXAMPLE 3 Find the Volume of a Cone Given the Circumference of the Base

**The circumference of the base of a cone is $6\pi$ inches. What is the volume of the cone in terms of $\pi$?**

13 in.

STEP 1 Use the circumference to find the radius of the base of the cone.

$$C = 2\pi r$$
$$6\pi = 2\pi r$$
$$\frac{6\pi}{2\pi} = r$$
$$3 = r$$

Substitute $6\pi$ for the circumference C.

The radius of the cone is 3 inches.

STEP 2 Find the volume of the cone.

$$V = \frac{1}{3}\pi(3)^2(13)$$
$$= \frac{1}{3}\pi(9)(13)$$
$$= 39\pi$$

Substitute the radius of the cone from STEP 1.

The volume of the cone is $39\pi$ inches.

Try It!

Find the volume of each cone.

a. Use $\frac{22}{7}$ for $\pi$. Express the answer as a fraction.
About $\frac{352}{7}$ mm$^3$

3 mm
5 mm

b. Express the volume in terms of $\pi$.
$448\pi$ ft$^3$

21 ft
$C = 16\pi$ ft

**8-3** Find Volume of Cones 449

ADDITIONAL EXAMPLES 

**For additional examples go online.**

##  Response to Intervention

**USE WITH EXAMPLE 2** Some students may need help remembering how to use the Pythagorean Theorem.

Draw a right triangle and label it with the information from the example. Place the slant height value as the hypotenuse of the right triangle and the radius of the circle as one of the leg values.

**Q:** What values are being substituted into the Pythagorean Theorem? [7 for *r* and 25 for *l*]

**Q:** What do you need to do to find the length of the leg which represents the height? [Sample answer: Subtract the value of the radius squared from the value of the slant height squared. The square root of that value is the length of the height.]

##  Enrichment

**USE WITH EXAMPLE 3** Challenge students to determine the circumference of the base of a cone if they are given the volume and height.

Answer the following:

**Q:** What is the circumference of a cone with a volume of $112.5\pi$ cubic centimeters and a height of 13.5 centimeters? Express the circumference in terms of $\pi$. Explain your steps. [$10\pi$; Sample answer: Find the radius by substituting the volume and the height in the formula for the volume of a cone. The radius is 5 centimeters. Then use this radius to find the circumference.]

Go Online

 Key Concept  Assess  Activity

# KEY CONCEPT 

## ETP Pose Purposeful Questions

**Q:** If you are given the height and the circumference of the base of a cone, how can you determine the volume of a cone? [Sample answer: Use the circumference to find the radius of the base. Then use the radius and the height in the formula for the volume of a cone.]

# Do You Understand/Do You Know How?

**Formative** Assessment

## ETP Build Procedural Fluency from Conceptual Understanding

**Essential Question** Students should include in their answer an understanding that the radius and height of a cylinder have to be the same as the radius and height of a cone for the volume of the cone to be $\frac{1}{3}$ of the volume of the cylinder.

**ITEM 2**

**Q:** If you are given the slant height of a cone and either the radius or the height, can you still find the volume? Explain. [Yes; Sample answer: The slant height is the hypotenuse of a right triangle. You can use the Pythagorean Theorem to find the missing dimension.]

## Prevent Misconceptions

**ITEM 6** Make sure students remember to find the radius by using the circumference formula.

**Q:** What is the formula for the circumference of a circle? [$C = 2\pi r$]

**Q:** What is the length of the radius? [0.7 feet]

Available Online

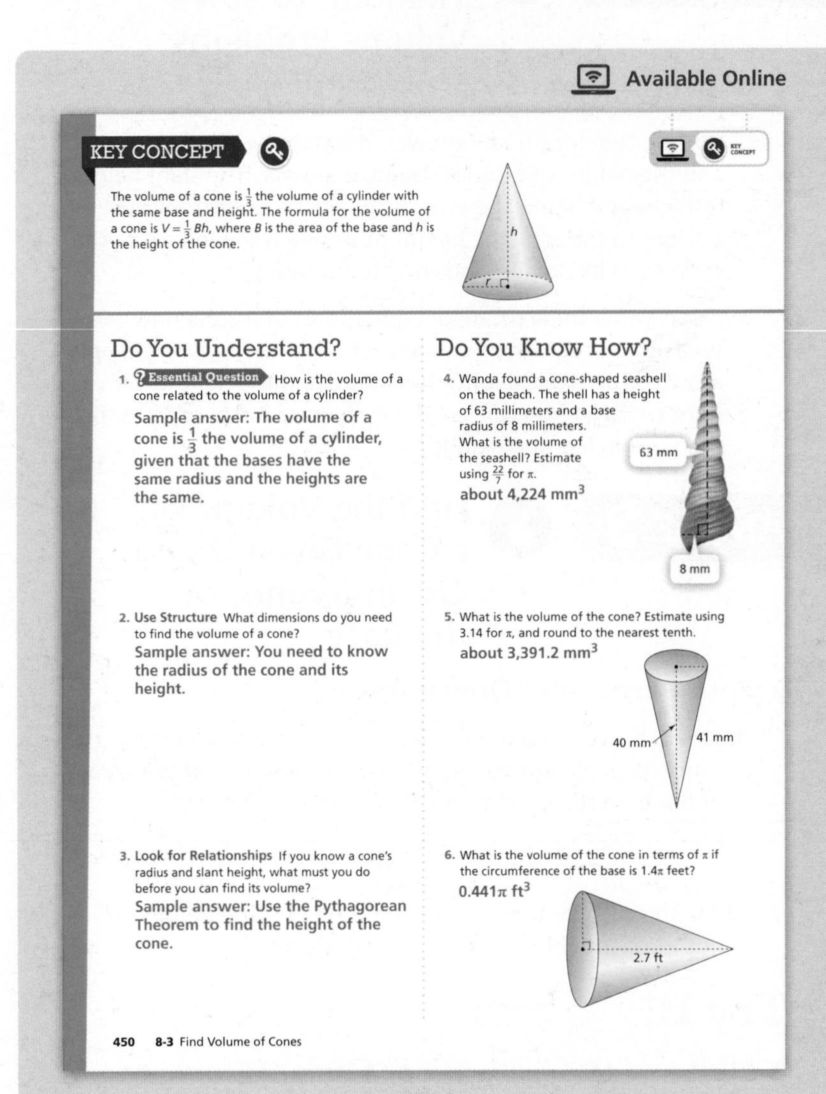

KEY CONCEPT

The volume of a cone is $\frac{1}{3}$ the volume of a cylinder with the same base and height. The formula for the volume of a cone is $V = \frac{1}{3}Bh$, where $B$ is the area of the base and $h$ is the height of the cone.



Do You Understand?

1. Essential Question How is the volume of a cone related to the volume of a cylinder?
Sample answer: The volume of a cone is $\frac{1}{3}$ the volume of a cylinder, given that the bases have the same radius and the heights are the same.

2. Use Structure What dimensions do you need to find the volume of a cone?
Sample answer: You need to know the radius of the cone and its height.

3. Look for Relationships If you know a cone's radius and slant height, what must you do before you can find its volume?
Sample answer: Use the Pythagorean Theorem to find the height of the cone.

Do You Know How?

4. Wanda found a cone-shaped seashell on the beach. The shell has a height of 63 millimeters and a base radius of 8 millimeters. What is the volume of the seashell? Estimate using $\frac{22}{7}$ for $\pi$.
about 4,224 mm$^3$



5. What is the volume of the cone? Estimate using 3.14 for $\pi$, and round to the nearest tenth.
about 3,391.2 mm$^3$



6. What is the volume of the cone in terms of $\pi$ if the circumference of the base is $1.4\pi$ feet?
$0.441\pi$ ft$^3$



450 8-3 Find Volume of Cones

# ADDITIONAL EXAMPLE 2 

Help students use the Pythagorean Theorem to solve this volume problem that includes decimals.

**Q:** Why might you want to use 3.14 as your approximation for $\pi$ in this problem? [Sample answer: Since there are other dimensions that are decimals, it could be easier to use this decimal approximation for $\pi$.]

**Q:** Why is it necessary to round numbers as you are working to find the final answer? [Sample answer: The height is an irrational number and it will need to be rounded so you can find an approximate volume.]

**Additional Examples** are available online.

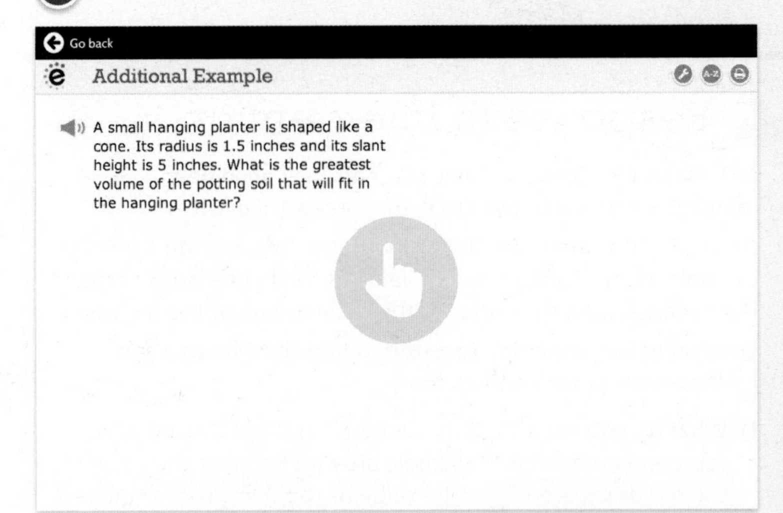



**Answer:** The greatest amount of potting soil that will fit in the hanging planter is about 11.3 cubic inches.

Go Online

Practice | Tutorials | Math Tools

# Practice & Problem Solving  

**Interactive Practice** and **Virtual Nerd Tutorials** are available online.

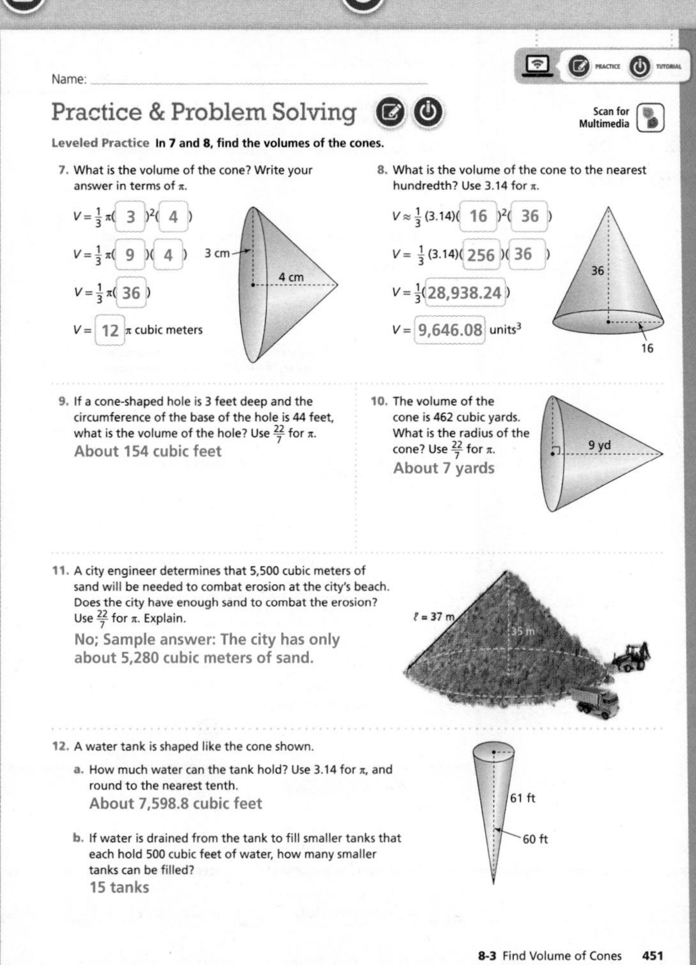
Name: ______

Practice & Problem Solving

Scan for Multimedia

**Leveled Practice** **In 7 and 8, find the volumes of the cones.**

7. What is the volume of the cone? Write your answer in terms of $\pi$.

$V = \frac{1}{3}\pi(3)^2(4)$

$V = \frac{1}{3}\pi(9)(4)$

$V = \frac{1}{3}\pi(36)$

$V = 12\pi$ cubic meters



8. What is the volume of the cone to the nearest hundredth? Use 3.14 for $\pi$.

$V \approx \frac{1}{3}(3.14)(16)^2(36)$

$V = \frac{1}{3}(3.14)(256)(36)$

$V = \frac{1}{3}(28{,}938.24)$

$V = 9{,}646.08$ units$^3$



9. If a cone-shaped hole is 3 feet deep and the circumference of the base of the hole is 44 feet, what is the volume of the hole? Use $\frac{22}{7}$ for $\pi$.
About 154 cubic feet

10. The volume of the cone is 462 cubic yards. What is the radius of the cone? Use $\frac{22}{7}$ for $\pi$.
About 7 yards



11. A city engineer determines that 5,500 cubic meters of sand will be needed to combat erosion at the city's beach. Does the city have enough sand to combat the erosion? Use $\frac{22}{7}$ for $\pi$. Explain.
No; Sample answer: The city has only about 5,280 cubic meters of sand.



12. A water tank is shaped like the cone shown.

a. How much water can the tank hold? Use 3.14 for $\pi$, and round to the nearest tenth.
About 7,598.8 cubic feet

b. If water is drained from the tank to fill smaller tanks that each hold 500 cubic feet of water, how many smaller tanks can be filled?
15 tanks



**8-3** Find Volume of Cones 451

13. An ice cream cone is filled exactly level with the top of a cone. The cone has a 9-centimeter depth and a base with a circumference of $9\pi$ centimeters. How much ice cream is in the cone in terms of $\pi$?
$60.75\pi$ cubic centimeters

14. In the scale model of a park, small green cones represent trees. What is the volume of one green cone? Use $\frac{22}{7}$ for $\pi$.
About 16,896 cubic millimeters

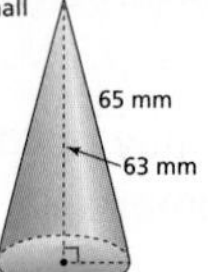


15. **Reasoning** Compare the volumes of two cones. One has a radius of 5 feet and a slant height of 13 feet. The other one has a height of 5 feet and a slant height of 13 feet.

a. Which cone has the greater volume?
The cone with a height of 5 feet

b. What is the volume of the larger cone in terms of $\pi$?
$240\pi$ cubic feet

16. An artist makes a cone-shaped sculpture for an art exhibit. If the sculpture is 7 feet tall and has a base with a circumference of 24.492 feet, what is the volume of the sculpture? Use 3.14 for $\pi$, and round to the nearest hundredth.
About 111.44 cubic feet

17. **Higher Order Thinking** A cone has a radius of 3 and a height of 11.

a. Suppose the radius is increased by 4 times its original measure. How many times greater is the volume of the larger cone than the smaller cone?
16

b. How would the volume of the cone change if the radius were divided by four?
The cone would have $\frac{1}{16}$ of its original volume.

## Assessment Practice

18. List the cones described below in order from least volume to greatest volume.

- Cone 1: radius 6 cm and height 12 cm
- Cone 2: radius 12 cm and height 6 cm
- Cone 3: radius 9 cm and height 8 cm

Ⓐ Cone 2, Cone 3, Cone 1

● Cone 1, Cone 3, Cone 2

Ⓒ Cone 2, Cone 1, Cone 3

Ⓓ Cone 1, Cone 2, Cone 3

19. What is the volume, in cubic inches, of a cone that has a radius of 8 inches and a height of 12 inches? Use 3.14 for $\pi$, and round to the nearest hundredth.

803.84

452 **8-3** Find Volume of Cones

## Error Intervention

**ITEM 15 Reasoning** Students may have difficulty understanding the difference between the height and slant height of a cone. Encourage them to focus on the word *slant* in slant height. Since a slant is on an angle, the slant height is the outside of the cone.

**Q:** What is the difference between the slant height and the height of a cone? [Sample answer: The slant height is the height along the cone's side from top to bottom; the height of the cone is a straight line down the middle of the cone that is perpendicular to the radius.]

## English Language Learners

**ITEM 12** Some ELL students may have difficulty understanding what is happening in the problem. Discuss with students that a water tank is a container that holds water, often to be used by residents of a city or town. Ask the students to tell what would happen if it is drained into smaller tanks.

You may opt to have students complete the automatically scored Practice & Problem Solving items online.

### Item Analysis

| Example | Items | DOK |
|---|---|---|
| 1 | 7, 8, 9 | 1 |
| | 12, 13, 14, 18, 19 | 2 |
| 2 | 11 | 2 |
| | 15 | 3 |
| 3 | 10, 16 | 2 |

# STEP 3 | Assess & Differentiate

Go Online

Assess Tutorials Worksheets

## Lesson Quiz

Formative Assessment

Use the student scores on the Lesson Quiz to prescribe differentiated assignments.

**I Intervention** 0–3 Points **O On-Level** 4 Points **A Advanced** 5 Points

You may opt to have students take the Lesson Quiz online. The Lesson Quiz will be automatically scored, and appropriate remediation, practice, or enrichment will be assigned based on student performance.

**Lesson Quiz** is available online.

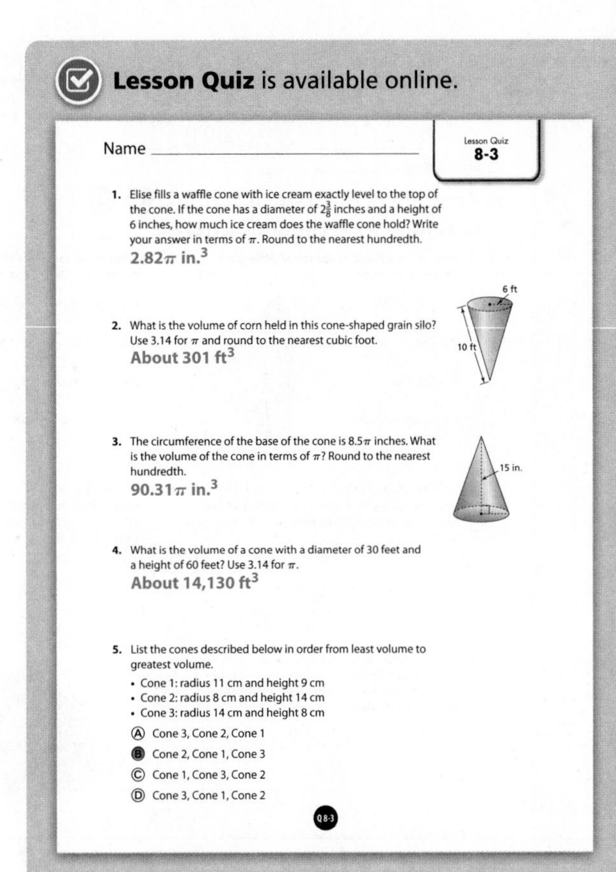

Name ______________ Lesson Quiz 8-3

1. Elise fills a waffle cone with ice cream exactly level to the top of the cone. If the cone has a diameter of $2\frac{3}{8}$ inches and a height of 6 inches, how much ice cream does the waffle cone hold? Write your answer in terms of $\pi$. Round to the nearest hundredth.
   $2.82\pi$ in.$^3$
2. What is the volume of corn held in this cone-shaped grain silo? Use 3.14 for $\pi$ and round to the nearest cubic foot.
   About 301 ft$^3$
3. The circumference of the base of the cone is $8.5\pi$ inches. What is the volume of the cone in terms of $\pi$? Round to the nearest hundredth.
   $90.31\pi$ in.$^3$
4. What is the volume of a cone with a diameter of 30 feet and a height of 60 feet? Use 3.14 for $\pi$.
   About 14,130 ft$^3$
5. List the cones described below in order from least volume to greatest volume.
   - Cone 1: radius 11 cm and height 9 cm
   - Cone 2: radius 8 cm and height 14 cm
   - Cone 3: radius 14 cm and height 8 cm

   Ⓐ Cone 3, Cone 2, Cone 1
   Ⓑ Cone 2, Cone 1, Cone 3
   Ⓒ Cone 1, Cone 3, Cone 2
   Ⓓ Cone 3, Cone 1, Cone 2



## Video Tutorials

Students can access instructional tutorials using the **Virtual Nerd app**.

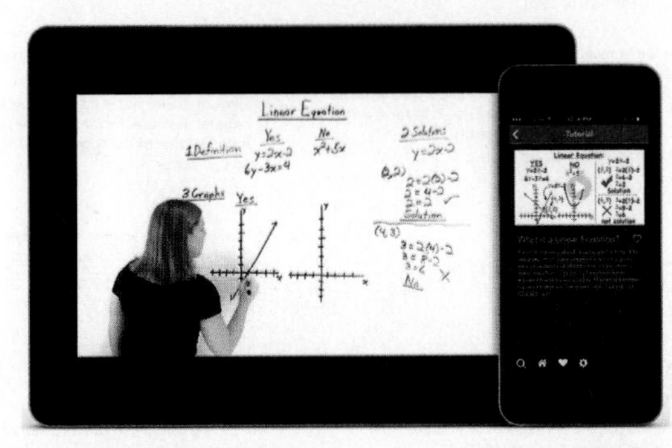

Students can also access the videos using the **BouncePages app** to scan exercise pages marked with this icon. Students can download both apps for free in their mobile devices' app store.

## Differentiated Intervention

I = Intervention O = On-Level A = Advanced

### Reteach to Build Understanding I

Provides scaffolded reteaching for the key lesson concepts.

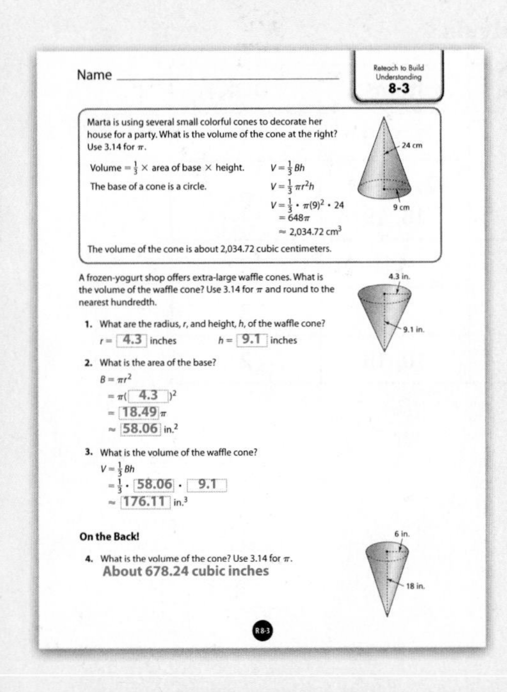

Name ______________ Reteach to Build Understanding 8-3

Marta is using several small colorful cones to decorate her house for a party. What is the volume of the cone at the right? Use 3.14 for $\pi$.

Volume = $\frac{1}{3}$ × area of base × height. $V = \frac{1}{3}Bh$
The base of a cone is a circle. $V = \frac{1}{3}\pi r^2 h$
$V = \frac{1}{3} \cdot \pi(9)^2 \cdot 24$
$= 648\pi$
$\approx 2{,}034.72$ cm$^3$

The volume of the cone is about 2,034.72 cubic centimeters.

A frozen-yogurt shop offers extra-large waffle cones. What is the volume of the waffle cone? Use 3.14 for $\pi$ and round to the nearest hundredth.

1. What are the radius, $r$, and height, $h$, of the waffle cone?
   $r$ = 4.3 inches $h$ = 9.1 inches
2. What is the area of the base?
   $B = \pi r^2$
   $= \pi(4.3)^2$
   $= 18.49\pi$
   $\approx 58.06$ in.$^2$
3. What is the volume of the waffle cone?
   $V = \frac{1}{3}Bh$
   $= \frac{1}{3} \cdot 58.06 \cdot 9.1$
   $\approx 176.11$ in.$^3$

**On the Back!**

4. What is the volume of the cone? Use 3.14 for $\pi$.
   About 678.24 cubic inches



### Additional Vocabulary Support I O

Helps students develop and reinforce understanding of key terms and concepts.

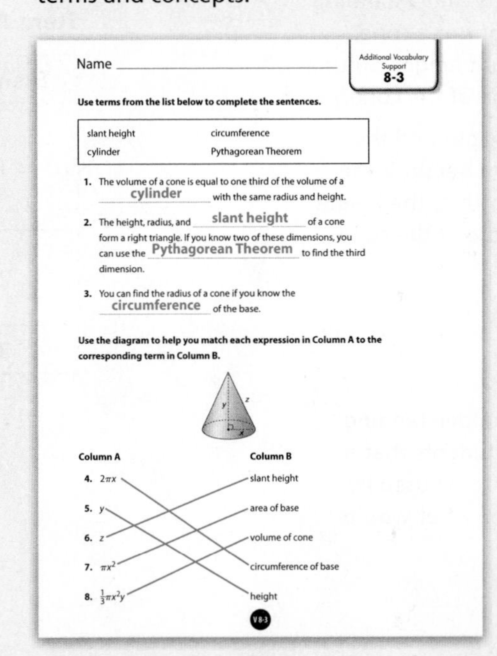

Name ______________ Additional Vocabulary Support 8-3

**Use terms from the list below to complete the sentences.**

| slant height | circumference |
|---|---|
| cylinder | Pythagorean Theorem |

1. The volume of a cone is equal to one third of the volume of a cylinder with the same radius and height.
2. The height, radius, and slant height of a cone form a right triangle. If you know two of these dimensions, you can use the Pythagorean Theorem to find the third dimension.
3. You can find the radius of a cone if you know the circumference of the base.

**Use the diagram to help you match each expression in Column A to the corresponding term in Column B.**

| Column A | Column B |
|---|---|
| 4. $2\pi x$ | slant height |
| 5. $y$ | area of base |
| 6. $z$ | volume of cone |
| 7. $\pi x^2$ | circumference of base |
| 8. $\frac{1}{3}\pi x^2 y$ | height |



### Build Mathematical Literacy I O

Provides support for struggling readers to build mathematical literacy.

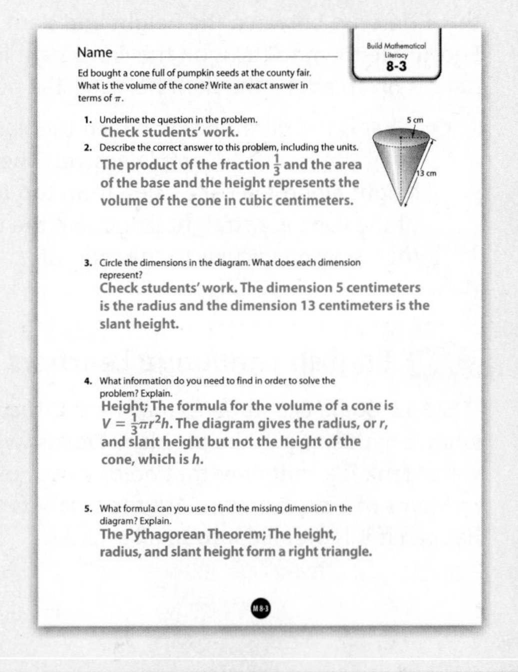

Name ______________ Build Mathematical Literacy 8-3

Ed bought a cone full of pumpkin seeds at the county fair. What is the volume of the cone? Write an exact answer in terms of $\pi$.

1. Underline the question in the problem.
   Check students' work.
2. Describe the correct answer to this problem, including the units.
   The product of the fraction $\frac{1}{3}$ and the area of the base and the height represents the volume of the cone in cubic centimeters.
3. Circle the dimensions in the diagram. What does each dimension represent?
   Check students' work. The dimension 5 centimeters is the radius and the dimension 13 centimeters is the slant height.
4. What information do you need to find in order to solve the problem? Explain.
   Height; The formula for the volume of a cone is $V = \frac{1}{3}\pi r^2 h$. The diagram gives the radius, or $r$, and slant height but not the height of the cone, which is $h$.
5. What formula can you use to find the missing dimension in the diagram? Explain.
   The Pythagorean Theorem; The height, radius, and slant height form a right triangle.

Go Online

 Practice  Worksheets  Math Tools   Math Games

# Additional Practice

You may opt to have students complete the automatically scored Additional Practice items online.

**Item Analysis**

| Example | Items | DOK |
|---|---|---|
| 1 | 1, 2 | 1 |
| | 12 | 2 |
| | 6, 11 | 3 |
| 2 | 3, 7, 8 | 2 |
| | 10 | 3 |
| 3 | 4, 5, 9 | 2 |

**Interactive Practice** is available online.

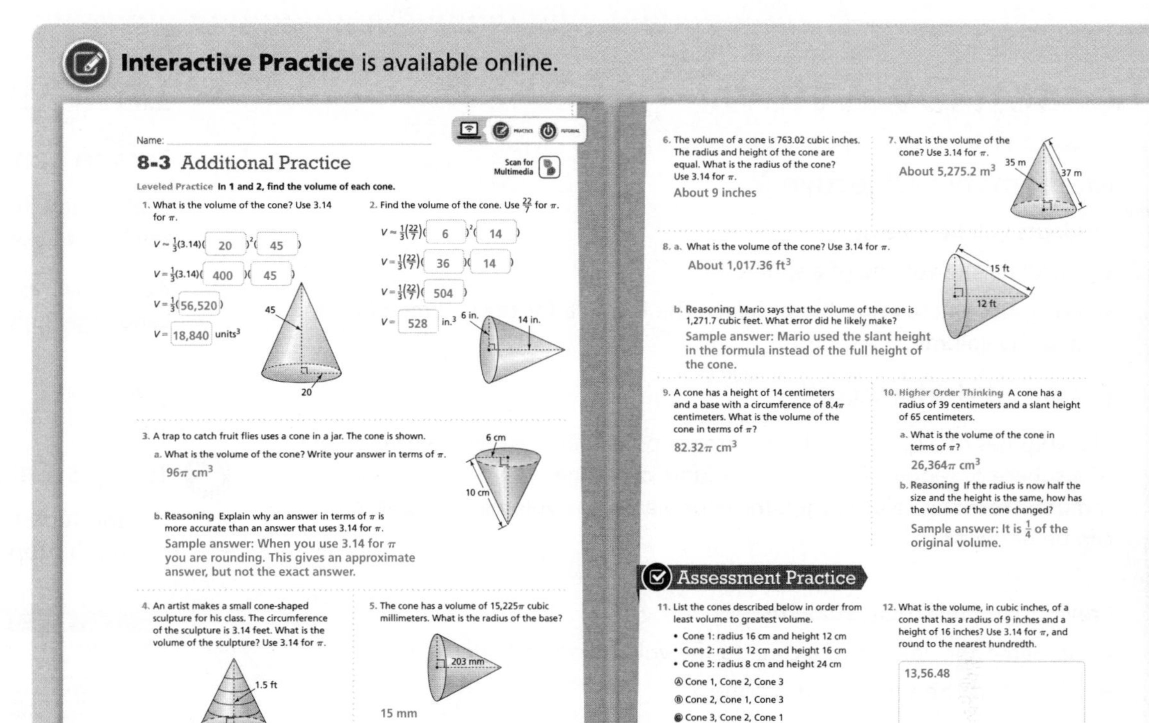

Name:

**8-3** Additional Practice

Scan for Multimedia

Leveled Practice **In 1 and 2, find the volume of each cone.**

1. What is the volume of the cone? Use 3.14 for $\pi$.

$V \approx \frac{1}{3}(3.14)(20)^2(45)$

$V = \frac{1}{3}(3.14)(400)(45)$

$V = \frac{1}{3}(56{,}520)$

$V = 18{,}840$ units$^3$

2. Find the volume of the cone. Use $\frac{22}{7}$ for $\pi$.

$V \approx \frac{1}{3}\left(\frac{22}{7}\right)(6)^2(14)$

$V = \frac{1}{3}\left(\frac{22}{7}\right)(36)(14)$

$V = \frac{1}{3}\left(\frac{22}{7}\right)(504)$

$V = 528$ in.$^3$

3. A trap to catch fruit flies uses a cone in a jar. The cone is shown.

a. What is the volume of the cone? Write your answer in terms of $\pi$.

$96\pi$ cm$^3$

b. **Reasoning** Explain why an answer in terms of $\pi$ is more accurate than an answer that uses 3.14 for $\pi$.

Sample answer: When you use 3.14 for $\pi$ you are rounding. This gives an approximate answer, but not the exact answer.

4. An artist makes a small cone-shaped sculpture for his class. The circumference of the sculpture is 3.14 feet. What is the volume of the sculpture? Use 3.14 for $\pi$.

About 0.3925 ft$^3$

5. The cone has a volume of $15{,}225\pi$ cubic millimeters. What is the radius of the base?

15 mm



8-3 Find Volume of Cones 101

6. The volume of a cone is 763.02 cubic inches. The radius and height of the cone are equal. What is the radius of the cone? Use 3.14 for $\pi$.

About 9 inches

7. What is the volume of the cone? Use 3.14 for $\pi$.

About 5,275.2 m$^3$

8. a. What is the volume of the cone? Use 3.14 for $\pi$.

About 1,017.36 ft$^3$

b. **Reasoning** Mario says that the volume of the cone is 1,271.7 cubic feet. What error did he likely make?

Sample answer: Mario used the slant height in the formula instead of the full height of the cone.

9. A cone has a height of 14 centimeters and a base with a circumference of $8.4\pi$ centimeters. What is the volume of the cone in terms of $\pi$?

$82.32\pi$ cm$^3$

10. **Higher Order Thinking** A cone has a radius of 39 centimeters and a slant height of 65 centimeters.

a. What is the volume of the cone in terms of $\pi$?

$26{,}364\pi$ cm$^3$

b. **Reasoning** If the radius is now half the size and the height is the same, how has the volume of the cone changed?

Sample answer: It is $\frac{1}{4}$ of the original volume.

Assessment Practice

11. List the cones described below in order from least volume to greatest volume.

- Cone 1: radius 16 cm and height 12 cm
- Cone 2: radius 12 cm and height 16 cm
- Cone 3: radius 8 cm and height 24 cm

Ⓐ Cone 1, Cone 2, Cone 3

Ⓑ Cone 2, Cone 1, Cone 3

Ⓒ Cone 3, Cone 2, Cone 1

Ⓓ Cone 3, Cone 1, Cone 2

12. What is the volume, in cubic inches, of a cone that has a radius of 9 inches and a height of 16 inches? Use 3.14 for $\pi$, and round to the nearest hundredth.

13,56.48



102 8-3 Find Volume of Cones

# Differentiated Intervention

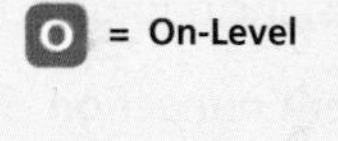
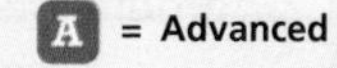

I = Intervention O = On-Level A = Advanced

## Enrichment O A

Presents engaging problems and activities that extend the lesson concepts.

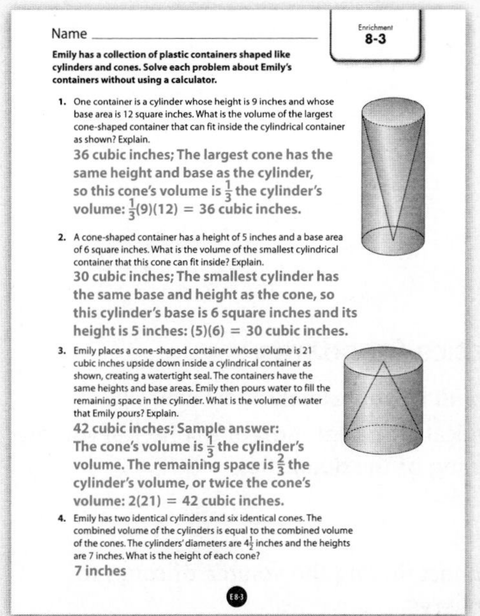

Name

Enrichment 8-3

**Emily has a collection of plastic containers shaped like cylinders and cones. Solve each problem about Emily's containers without using a calculator.**

1. One container is a cylinder whose height is 9 inches and whose base area is 12 square inches. What is the volume of the largest cone-shaped container that can fit inside the cylindrical container as shown? Explain.

36 cubic inches; The largest cone has the same height and base as the cylinder, so this cone's volume is $\frac{1}{3}$ the cylinder's volume: $\frac{1}{3}(9)(12) = 36$ cubic inches.

2. A cone-shaped container has a height of 5 inches and a base area of 6 square inches. What is the volume of the smallest cylindrical container that this cone can fit inside? Explain.

30 cubic inches; The smallest cylinder has the same base and height as the cone, so this cylinder's base is 6 square inches and its height is 5 inches: $(5)(6) = 30$ cubic inches.

3. Emily places a cone-shaped container whose volume is 21 cubic inches upside down inside a cylindrical container as shown, creating a watertight seal. The containers have the same heights and base areas. Emily then pours water to fill the remaining space in the cylinder. What is the volume of water that Emily pours? Explain.

42 cubic inches; Sample answer: The cone's volume is $\frac{1}{3}$ the cylinder's volume. The remaining space is $\frac{2}{3}$ the cylinder's volume, or twice the cone's volume: $2(21) = 42$ cubic inches.

4. Emily has two identical cylinders and six identical cones. The combined volume of the cylinders is equal to the combined volume of the cones. The cylinders' diameters are $4\frac{1}{2}$ inches and the heights are 7 inches. What is the height of each cone?

7 inches

E8-3

## Math Tools and Games I O A

Offers additional activities and games to build understanding and fluency.

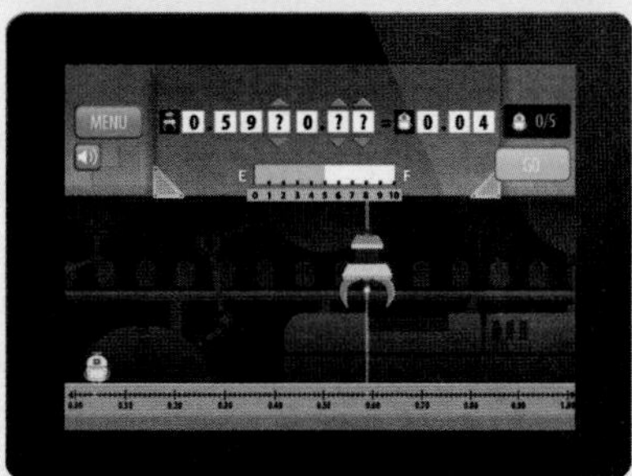


## Pick a Project and STEM Project I O A

Provides an additional opportunity for students to demonstrate understanding of key mathematical concepts.

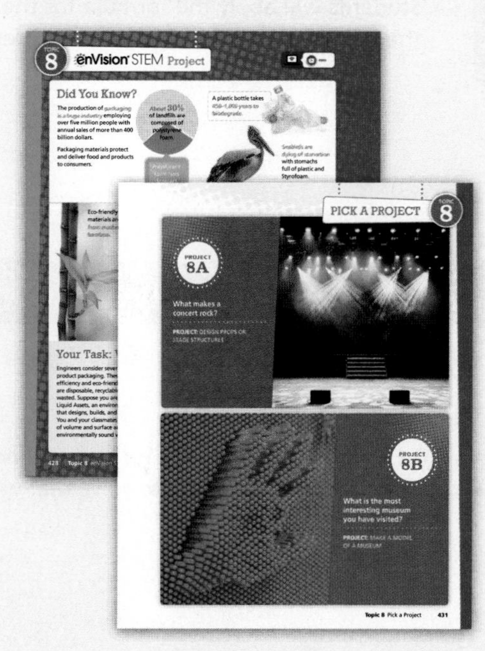

Go Online

# Lesson 8-4 Find Volume of Spheres

## Lesson Overview

FOCUS

### Mathematics Objective

**Students will be able to:**

- ✔ calculate the volume of a sphere.
- ✔ recognize the relationship between the formula for the volume of a cone and the volume of a sphere.

### Essential Understanding

The volumes of a sphere and cone are proportionally related. The volume of a sphere of radius r is twice the volume of a cone with height 2r and radius r. From this relationship, the formula for the volume of a sphere can be deduced.

COHERENCE

**Previously in this topic, students:**

- compared the volume of a cone to the volume of a cylinder.
- calculated the volume of a cone.

**In this lesson, students:**

- calculate the volume of spheres.
- identify the relationship between the volume of a cone and the volume of a sphere.

**In Grade 10, students will:**

- justify the volume formulas they have learned with more sophisticated arguments, including an informal limit approach.

**Cross-Cluster Connection** Students apply previous work solving linear equations (8.EE.2) from Topic 2 when finding volume of cylinders (8.G.3).

RIGOR

This lesson emphasizes a blend of **procedural skill and fluency** and **application.**

- Students will become fluent in calculating the volume of a sphere.
- Students will apply the formula for the volume of a sphere to determine the volume of spherical objects in different scenarios.

## Language Support

### Lesson Language Objective

Explain how to find the volume of a sphere and tell how to use it to solve problems.

Additional resources are available in the **Language Support Handbook**.

## Math Anytime

### Today's Challenge

Use the Topic 8 problems any time during this topic.

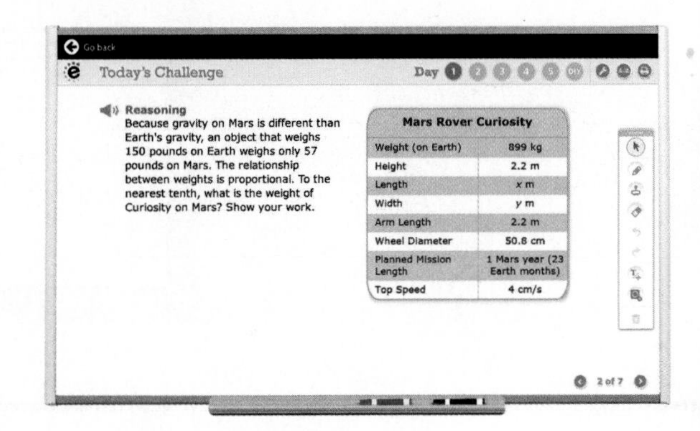


## Mathematics Overview | Common Core Standards

### Content Standards

This lesson focuses on **8.G.C.9.**

- **8.G.C.9** Know the formulas for the volumes of cones, cylinders, and spheres and use them to solve real-world and mathematical problems.

### Mathematical Practice Standards

**MP.2 Reason Abstractly and Quantitatively**
Students will create a logical representation of a spherical volume problem and make meaning of the quantities.

**MP.8 Generalize**
Students will look to connect finding the volume of cones to finding the volume of spheres.

# STEP 1 | Problem-Based Learning

15-20 min

Go Online

Activity

## Explore It! Formative Assessment

**Purpose** Students write an equation for the volume of a spherical object and connect it to the volumes of cones and spheres in the Visual Learning Bridge.

### ETP Before — WHOLE CLASS

**1 Introduce the Problem**

Provide compasses, as needed.

**2 Check for Understanding of the Problem**

Engage students with the problem by asking: What objects in the real world are shaped like a cone? Like a sphere?

### ETP During — SMALL GROUP

**3 Observe Students at Work**

Look for students to draw and label a cone for the beaker and a sphere for the bowl. Given the information, they might reason that the volume of the bowl is twice the volume of the beaker, and since the beaker is a cone, an equation for the volume of the bowl is $V = 2\left(\frac{1}{3}\pi r^2 h\right)$, or $V = \frac{2}{3}\pi r^2 h$. Students might also realize they can simplify the formula using the fact that the height of a sphere is the diameter. By substituting $h = 2r$ into $V = \frac{2}{3}\pi r^2 h$, they can get $V = \frac{2}{3}\pi r^2(2r)$ and ultimately $V = \frac{4}{3}\pi r^3$. If needed, ask Is there anything you learned in the previous lesson that can help you solve the problem?

**Early Finishers**

How would the problem change if the height of the cone was 2 inches? [Sample answer: You would have to fill the beaker 4 times to completely fill the bowl. The equation for the volume of the bowl remains the same.]

### ETP After — WHOLE CLASS

**4 Discuss Solution Strategies and Key Ideas**

Have students discuss what they observe about the dimensions of the cone and sphere; the radius of the sphere and the cone are the same, and the height of the cone is the same as the diameter of the sphere. Have them discuss the relationship between the volume of the cone and the volume of the sphere; the volume of the sphere, $V = \frac{2}{3}\pi r^2 h$, is twice the volume of the cone, $V = \frac{1}{3}\pi r^2 h$. Have students share and explain any numerical expressions they wrote for the volume of the sphere, for example $\frac{32}{3}\pi$.

**5 Consider Instructional Implications**

After presenting Example 1, discuss with students how the problem relates to the problem in the Explore It; both problems have a cone and a sphere with the same height and radius. Have students use volume formulas to calculate the volume of the beaker and the bowl if they were a true cone and sphere; about 50.24 in.$^3$ and 100.48 in.$^3$.

## Analyze Student Work

**Explore It!** Activity is available online.

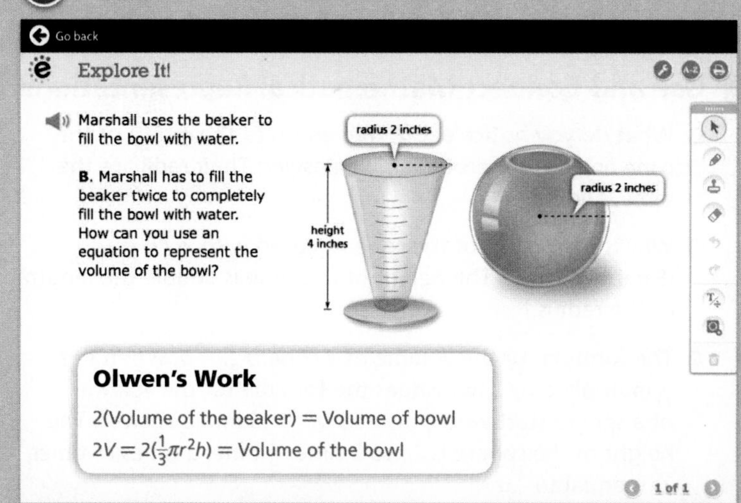


**Olwen** writes an equation she can use to find the volume of the cone in terms of $\pi$ and doubles it to show how she can find the volume of the sphere.

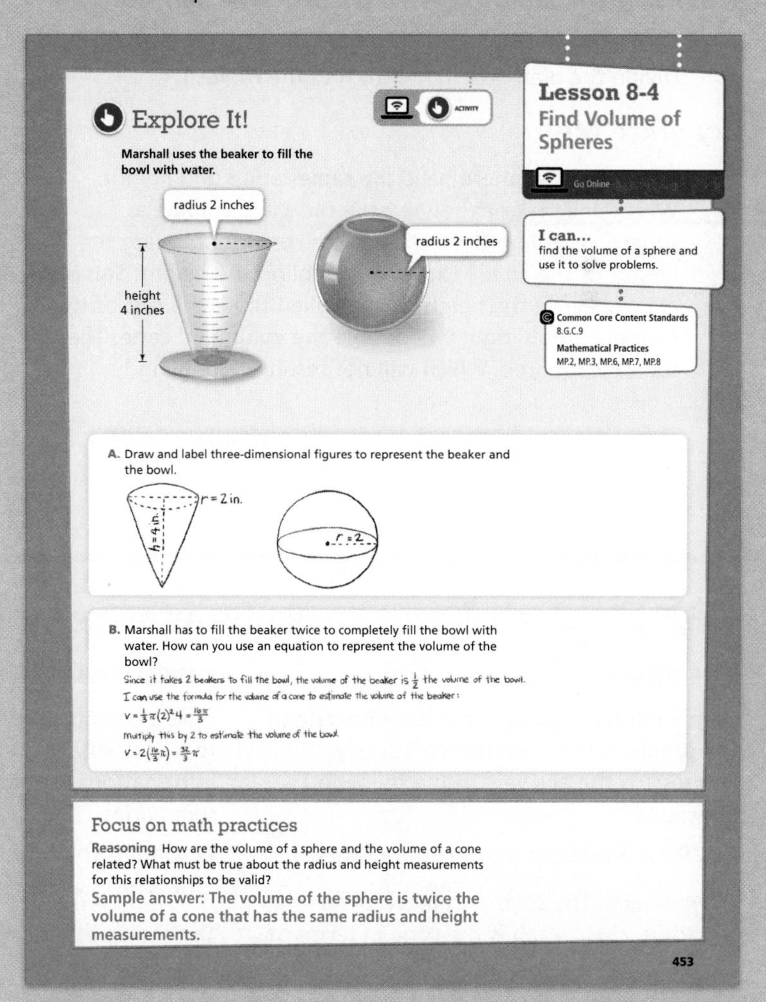


**Rico** estimates the volume of the cone using the formula for the volume of a cone and doubles it to estimate the volume of the sphere.

Go Online

Visual Learning

Assess

# STEP 2 | Visual Learning

## ETP Establish Mathematics Goals to Focus Learning

Engage students in a discussion about the ***Essential Question***. Make sure students know how to identify the radius of a sphere.

## EXAMPLE 1  Relate Volumes of Cones and Spheres

### ETP Use and Connect Mathematical Representations

**Q:** What do you notice about the length of the radius of the cone and the sphere? [Sample answer: Their radii are the same length.]

**Q:** Why is the height of the cone replaced with $2r$? [Sample answer: The height of the cone is double the length of the radius.]

**Q:** The formula for the volume of a cone is $\frac{1}{3}\pi r^2 h$. When this is multiplied by 2, why does the formula for the volume of a sphere start with $\frac{3}{4}$ instead of $\frac{2}{3}$? [Sample answer: The height of the sphere is $2r$, so 2 times $\frac{1}{3}$ times $\pi$ times $r^2$ times $2r$ is equal to $\frac{4}{3}\pi r^3$.]

##  Try It!  Formative Assessment

###  Elicit and Use Evidence of Student Thinking

**Q:** How can you find the length of the radius? [Sample answer: Divide the diameter in half to find the radius.]

### Convince Me!

**Q:** A cone and a sphere have the same radius and height. Which will make the cone have the same volume as the sphere, doubling the radius of the cone or doubling the height of the cone? Explain. [Doubling the height; Sample answer: Since the height is multiplied times the rest of the formula, doubling it will double the volume of cone. The radius is squared, which will not result in doubling.]

**Visual Learning Animation Plus** is available online.

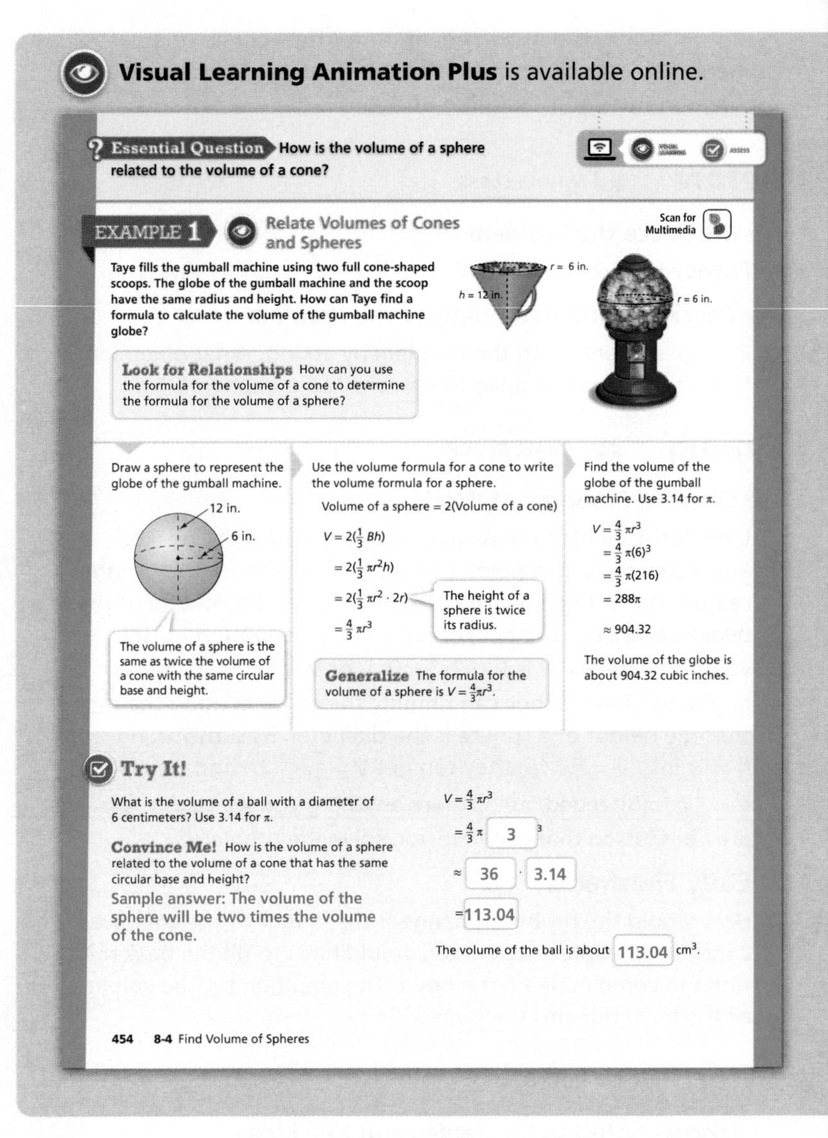

Students can access the ***Visual Learning Animation Plus*** by using the **BouncePages app** to scan this page. Students can download the app for free in their mobile devices' app store.

## ELL English Language Learners

**EMERGING** Use with Example 1.

Help English Language Learners understand the problem. Focus on the vocabulary and discuss the answers to the following questions.

**Q:** Which is taller, the cone or the sphere?

**Q:** How tall is the sphere in terms of its radius, $r$? How tall is the cone in terms of its radius, $r$?

**Q:** Which has the greater volume, the cone or the sphere?

**DEVELOPING** Use with Example 1.

Have students read the problem aloud to a partner and summarize the known information. Ask students to share their summaries.

**Q:** What is the formula for the volume of a cone?

**Q:** What is the formula for the volume of a sphere?

**Q:** How is the formula for the volume of a sphere related to the formula for the volume of a cone?

**EXPANDING** Use with Example 1.

Have students read the problem and then explain to a partner the steps taken to find the volume formula for a sphere. Have students decide together the best way to explain the steps.

Have partners share their steps with the class.

**Q:** What is the formula for the volume of a cone and a sphere?

**Q:** How is the formula for the volume of a sphere related to the formula for the volume of a cone?

## EXAMPLE 2  Find the Volume of a Sphere Given the Surface Area

### Pose Purposeful Questions

**Q:** What information are you not given that you need to know to find the volume of the soccer ball? [The radius]

**Q:** Why can you use the surface area of the soccer ball to find its radius? [Sample answer: The formula for the surface area, $4\pi r^2$, uses the radius.]

## EXAMPLE 3  Find the Volume of a Composite Figure

ETP

### Pose Purposeful Questions

**Q:** How can you write a formula for the volume of a hemisphere? Explain. What is this formula? [$\frac{2}{3}\pi r^2$; Sample answer: The formula for the volume of a hemisphere is $\frac{1}{2}$ times the formula for the volume of a sphere; $\frac{1}{2} \cdot \frac{4}{3}\pi r^3$.]

## Try It! 

### Elicit and Use Evidence of Student Thinking

**Q:** Is the volume of the hemisphere equal to the volume of the cone? Explain. [No; Sample answer: The cone has a height of 6 inches. If it had a height of 4 inches, the diameter of the hemisphere, then they would have equal volume.]

**Examples and Try Its!** are available online.

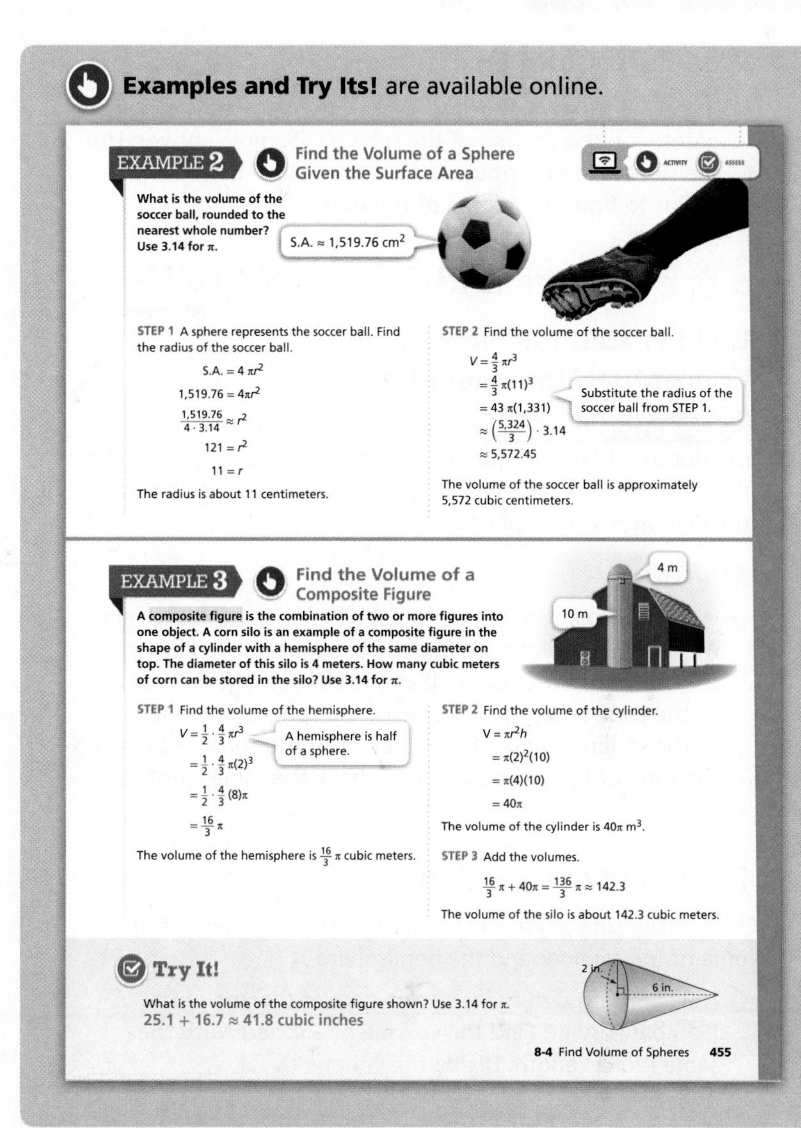

**ADDITIONAL EXAMPLES**

**For additional examples go online.**

## Response to Intervention

**USE WITH EXAMPLE 2** Some students may need help finding the radius using the surface area formula.

- Ask the following.

**Q:** Why are both sides of the equation divided by (4)(3.14)? [Sample answer: You need to isolate the variable. You can use the Division Property of Equality to do this. The 4 is part of the formula, and 3.14 is what you substituted for pi.]

**Q:** What operation is the inverse of squaring a number? How is this used to help solve for the radius, $r$? Explain. [Square root; Sample answer: To find the radius, $r$, you need to find the square root of $r^2$.]

## Enrichment

**USE WITH EXAMPLE 3** Challenge interested students to create their own composite figure and determine its volume. Have these students create a composite figure using at least two of the following: cylinder, cone, sphere, and hemisphere. Have them assign all necessary lengths to their figure and calculate the volume of their composite figure. Have them explain the steps they used.

Go Online

Key Concept

Assess

Activity

# STEP 2 | Visual Learning *continued*

## KEY CONCEPT 

### ETP Pose Purposeful Questions

**Q:** If you are given the surface area of a sphere, how can you determine the volume of the sphere? [Sample answer: Use the surface area formula to find the radius. Then use the radius to find the volume of the sphere.]

Available Online

KEY CONCEPT 

The volume of a sphere is twice the volume of a cone that has the same circular base and height. The formula for the volume of a sphere with radius $r$ is $V = \frac{4}{3}\pi r^3$.

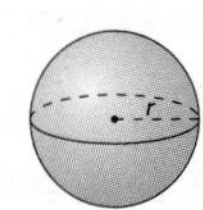

**Do You Understand?**

1. **Essential Question** How is the volume of a sphere related to the volume of a cone?
Sample answer: The volume of a sphere is equal to two times the volume of a cone that has the same circular base and height.

2. **Critique Reasoning** Kristy incorrectly says that the volume of the sphere below is $144\pi$ cubic units. What mistake might Kristy have made?

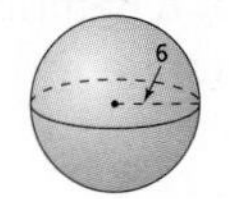


Sample answer: Kristy found the surface area, not the volume of the sphere. She used the formula S.A. $= 4\pi r^2$ instead of $V = \frac{4}{3}\pi r^3$.

3. **Generalize** Mehnaj has a set of blocks that are all the same height. The cone-shaped block has a volume of 125 cubic inches. The sphere-shaped block has a volume of 250 cubic inches. What do you know about the radius of the base of the cone-shaped block? Explain.
Sample answer: The radius of the base of the cone-shaped block is the same as the radius of the sphere-shaped block. The volume of a cone is half the volume of a sphere with the same height (diameter) and radius.

**Do You Know How?**

4. Clarissa has a decorative bulb in the shape of a sphere. If it has a radius of 3 inches, what is its volume? Use 3.14 for $\pi$.
About 113 cubic inches

5. A sphere has a surface area of about 803.84 square centimeters. What is the volume of the sphere? Use 3.14 for $\pi$ and round to the nearest whole number.
The volume of the sphere is about 2,144 cubic centimeters.

6. A water pipe is a cylinder 30 inches long, with a radius of 1 inch. At one end of the cylinder there is a hemisphere. What is the volume of the water pipe? Explain.
$30\frac{2}{3}\pi$ in.$^3$ or about 96.3 in.$^3$; Sample answer: In cubic inches, the volume of the cylinder is $\pi r^2 h$ or $30\pi$, and the total volume of the hemisphere is $\frac{2}{3}\pi r^3$ or $\frac{2}{3}\pi$. or . Add the volumes.

456 **8-4** Find Volume of Spheres

## Do You Understand/Do You Know How?

Formative Assessment

### ETP Build Procedural Fluency from Conceptual Understanding

**Essential Question** Students should know that the relationship between spheres and cones is true only when the radii are the same and the height of the cone is the same as the diameter of the sphere.

**ITEM 3**

**Q:** What information in the problem allows you to determine the relationship of the radius of the cone-shaped block to the radius of the sphere? [Sample answer: The volume of the cone is half the volume of the sphere. The diameter of the sphere is equal to the height of the cone. That means the radii of the cone and sphere have the same length.]

### Prevent Misconceptions

**ITEM 6** Make sure students remember to find the sum of the volume of the cylinder and the hemisphere.

**Q:** How will you determine the volume of the end piece? [Sample answer: Find the volume of a sphere with the same radius length. Divide the volume by 2.]

## ADDITIONAL EXAMPLE 3 

Help students transition from solving a problem involving one cylinder and one-half sphere to solving a problem involving one cylinder and a sphere split in half.

**Q:** What shapes make up the time capsule? [Sample answer: A cylinder and two hemispheres, or one sphere.]

**Q:** How do you determine the radius of the time capsule? [Sample answer: The radius is half the diameter, so it is 3 inches.]

**Q:** If the time capsule had concave ends, ends that are hemispheres whose heights go into the cylinder, instead of convex ends, what would be different about finding the solution? [Sample answer: You would subtract the volumes of the hemispheres from the volume of the cylinder instead of adding these volumes.]

**Additional Examples** are available online.

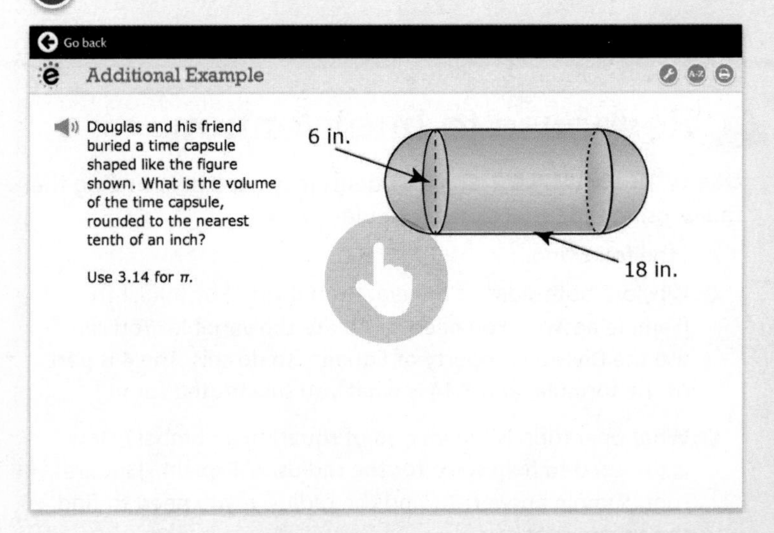


**Answer:** About 621.7 cubic inches.

Go Online

Practice

Tutorials

Math Tools

# Practice & Problem Solving

**Interactive Practice** and **Virtual Nerd Tutorials** are available online.

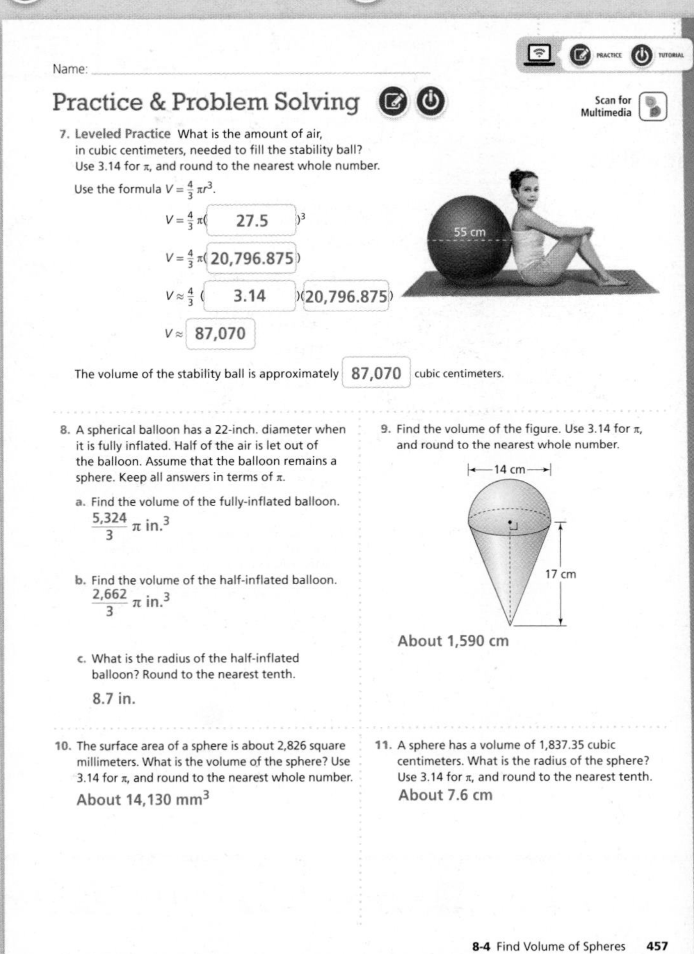

Name: ______

## Practice & Problem Solving

Scan for Multimedia

7. **Leveled Practice** What is the amount of air, in cubic centimeters, needed to fill the stability ball? Use 3.14 for $\pi$, and round to the nearest whole number.

Use the formula $V = \frac{4}{3}\pi r^3$.

$V = \frac{4}{3}\pi(27.5)^3$

$V = \frac{4}{3}\pi(20{,}796.875)$

$V \approx \frac{4}{3}(3.14)(20{,}796.875)$

$V \approx 87{,}070$



The volume of the stability ball is approximately 87,070 cubic centimeters.

8. A spherical balloon has a 22-inch. diameter when it is fully inflated. Half of the air is let out of the balloon. Assume that the balloon remains a sphere. Keep all answers in terms of $\pi$.

a. Find the volume of the fully-inflated balloon.
$\frac{5{,}324}{3}\pi$ in.$^3$

b. Find the volume of the half-inflated balloon.
$\frac{2{,}662}{3}\pi$ in.$^3$

c. What is the radius of the half-inflated balloon? Round to the nearest tenth.
8.7 in.

9. Find the volume of the figure. Use 3.14 for $\pi$, and round to the nearest whole number.



About 1,590 cm

10. The surface area of a sphere is about 2,826 square millimeters. What is the volume of the sphere? Use 3.14 for $\pi$, and round to the nearest whole number.
About 14,130 mm$^3$

11. A sphere has a volume of 1,837.35 cubic centimeters. What is the radius of the sphere? Use 3.14 for $\pi$, and round to the nearest tenth.
About 7.6 cm



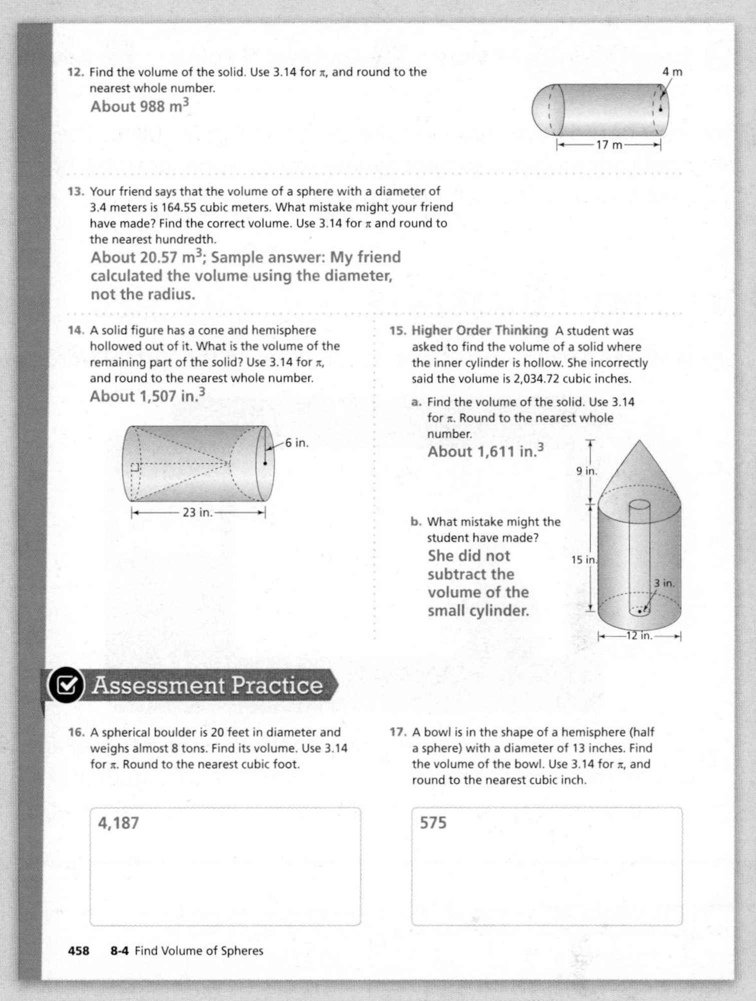

12. Find the volume of the solid. Use 3.14 for $\pi$, and round to the nearest whole number.
About 988 m$^3$



13. Your friend says that the volume of a sphere with a diameter of 3.4 meters is 164.55 cubic meters. What mistake might your friend have made? Find the correct volume. Use 3.14 for $\pi$ and round to the nearest hundredth.
About 20.57 m$^3$; Sample answer: My friend calculated the volume using the diameter, not the radius.

14. A solid figure has a cone and hemisphere hollowed out of it. What is the volume of the remaining part of the solid? Use 3.14 for $\pi$, and round to the nearest whole number.
About 1,507 in.$^3$



15. **Higher Order Thinking** A student was asked to find the volume of a solid where the inner cylinder is hollow. She incorrectly said the volume is 2,034.72 cubic inches.

a. Find the volume of the solid. Use 3.14 for $\pi$. Round to the nearest whole number.
About 1,611 in.$^3$

b. What mistake might the student have made?
She did not subtract the volume of the small cylinder.



### Assessment Practice

16. A spherical boulder is 20 feet in diameter and weighs almost 8 tons. Find its volume. Use 3.14 for $\pi$. Round to the nearest cubic foot.

4,187

17. A bowl is in the shape of a hemisphere (half a sphere) with a diameter of 13 inches. Find the volume of the bowl. Use 3.14 for $\pi$, and round to the nearest cubic inch.

575



## Error Intervention

**ITEM 9** Students may have difficulty understanding how to find the volume of a composite figure.

**Q:** What is the volume of the hemisphere? [About 718 cubic centimeters]

**Q:** What is the volume of the cone? [About 872 cubic centimeters]

**Q:** What is the sum of the volumes? [About 1,590 cubic centimeters]

## Challenge

Challenge students to create their own composite figure that has space removed from it by another figure. Then have them calculate the volume.

**ITEM 14**

**Q:** Create your own composite figure with a figure that removes space. Use at least two of the following shapes: cylinder, cone, rectangular prism, sphere, and hemisphere. What is the volume of your figure? [Check student responses.]

You may opt to have students complete the automatically scored Practice & Problem Solving items online.

### Item Analysis

| Example | Items | DOK |
|---|---|---|
| 1 | 7 | 1 |
| | 8, 11, 16, 17 | 2 |
| | 13 | 3 |
| 2 | 10 | 2 |
| 3 | 9, 12 | 2 |
| | 14, 15 | 3 |

STEP 3 | Assess & Differentiate

Go Online

Assess

Tutorials

Worksheets

# Lesson Quiz

**Formative** Assessment

Use the student scores on the Lesson Quiz to prescribe differentiated assignments.

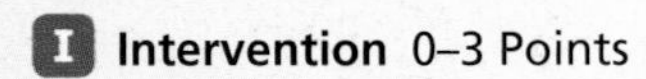

**I Intervention** 0–3 Points **O On-Level** 4 Points **A Advanced** 5 Points

You may opt to have students take the Lesson Quiz online. The Lesson Quiz will be automatically scored, and appropriate remediation, practice, or enrichment will be assigned based on student performance.

# Video Tutorials

Students can access instructional tutorials using the **Virtual Nerd app**.

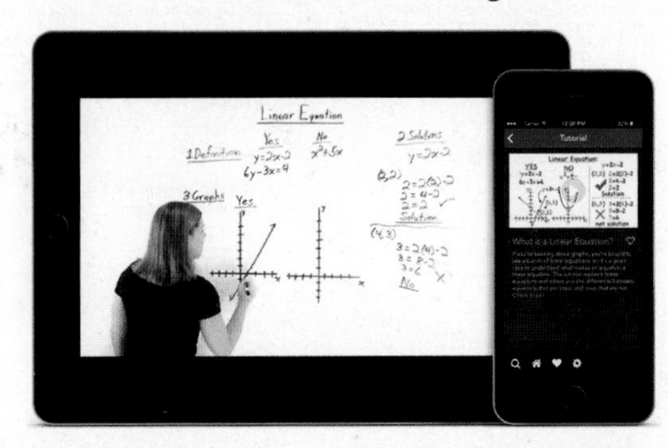

Students can also access the videos using the **BouncePages app** to scan exercise pages marked with this icon. Students can download both apps for free in their mobile devices' app store.

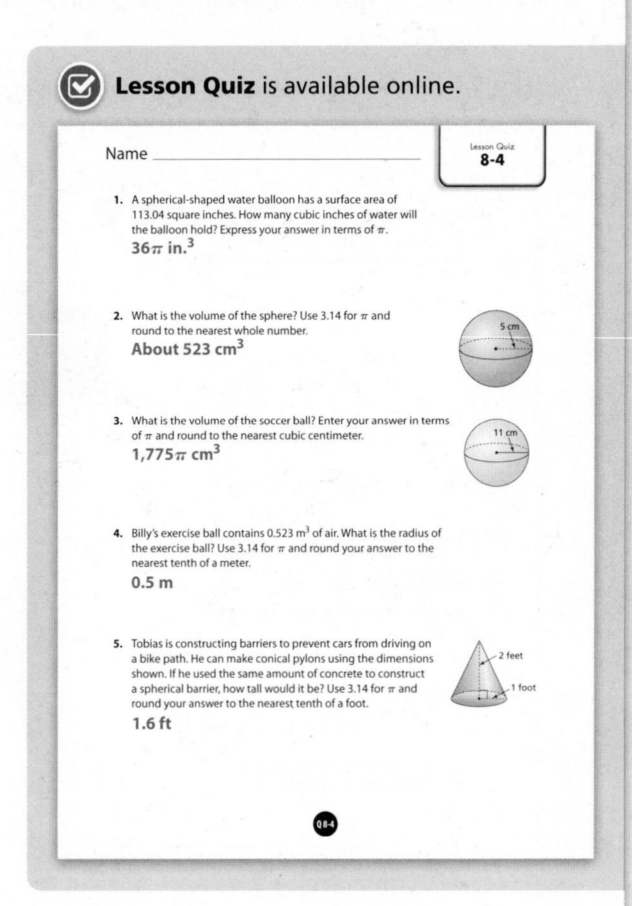

**Lesson Quiz** is available online.

Name ______________________

Lesson Quiz
**8-4**

1. A spherical-shaped water balloon has a surface area of 113.04 square inches. How many cubic inches of water will the balloon hold? Express your answer in terms of $\pi$.
   **$36\pi$ in.$^3$**

2. What is the volume of the sphere? Use 3.14 for $\pi$ and round to the nearest whole number.
   **About 523 cm$^3$**

3. What is the volume of the soccer ball? Enter your answer in terms of $\pi$ and round to the nearest cubic centimeter.
   **$1{,}775\pi$ cm$^3$**

4. Billy's exercise ball contains 0.523 m$^3$ of air. What is the radius of the exercise ball? Use 3.14 for $\pi$ and round your answer to the nearest tenth of a meter.
   **0.5 m**

5. Tobias is constructing barriers to prevent cars from driving on a bike path. He can make conical pylons using the dimensions shown. If he used the same amount of concrete to construct a spherical barrier, how tall would it be? Use 3.14 for $\pi$ and round your answer to the nearest tenth of a foot.
   **1.6 ft**



Q8-4

# Differentiated Intervention

**I** = Intervention **O** = On-Level **A** = Advanced

## Reteach to Build Understanding I

Provides scaffolded reteaching for the key lesson concepts.

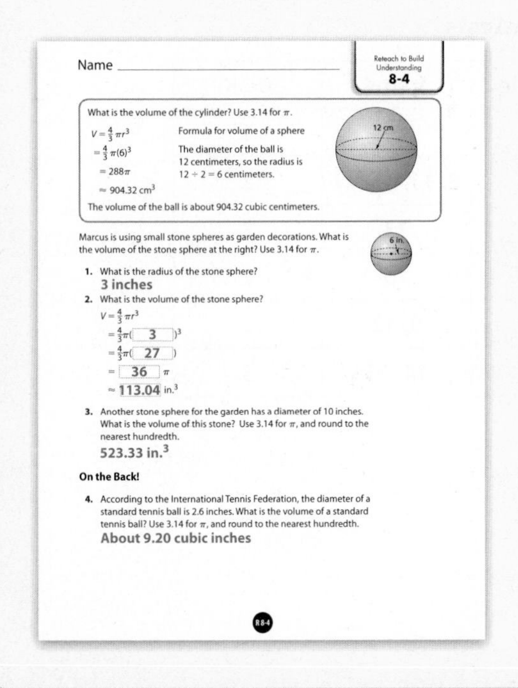

Name ______________________

Reteach to Build Understanding
**8-4**

What is the volume of the cylinder? Use 3.14 for $\pi$.

$V = \frac{4}{3}\pi r^3$ Formula for volume of a sphere

$= \frac{4}{3}\pi(6)^3$ The diameter of the ball is 12 centimeters, so the radius is $12 \div 2 = 6$ centimeters.

$= 288\pi$

$\approx 904.32$ cm$^3$

The volume of the ball is about 904.32 cubic centimeters.

Marcus is using small stone spheres as garden decorations. What is the volume of the stone sphere at the right? Use 3.14 for $\pi$.

1. What is the radius of the stone sphere?
   **3 inches**
2. What is the volume of the stone sphere?
   $V = \frac{4}{3}\pi r^3$
   $= \frac{4}{3}\pi(\ \mathbf{3}\ )^3$
   $= \frac{4}{3}\pi(\ \mathbf{27}\ )$
   $= \mathbf{36}\ \pi$
   $\approx \mathbf{113.04}$ in.$^3$
3. Another stone sphere for the garden has a diameter of 10 inches. What is the volume of this stone? Use 3.14 for $\pi$, and round to the nearest hundredth.
   **523.33 in.$^3$**

**On the Back!**

4. According to the International Tennis Federation, the diameter of a standard tennis ball is 2.6 inches. What is the volume of a standard tennis ball? Use 3.14 for $\pi$, and round to the nearest hundredth.
   **About 9.20 cubic inches**



R8-4

## Additional Vocabulary Support I O

Helps students develop and reinforce understanding of key terms and concepts.

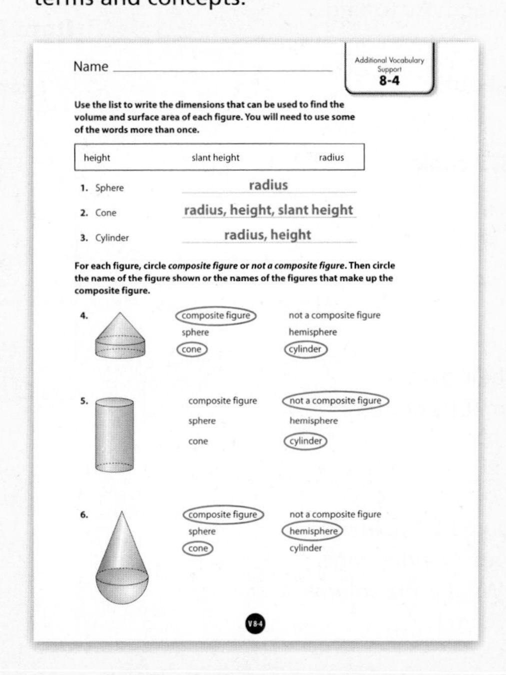

Name ______________________

Additional Vocabulary Support
**8-4**

**Use the list to write the dimensions that can be used to find the volume and surface area of each figure. You will need to use some of the words more than once.**

| height | slant height | radius |
|---|---|---|

1. Sphere **radius**
2. Cone **radius, height, slant height**
3. Cylinder **radius, height**

**For each figure, circle *composite figure* or *not a composite figure*. Then circle the name of the figure shown or the names of the figures that make up the composite figure.**

4. (composite figure) not a composite figure; sphere, hemisphere; (cone) (cylinder)
5. composite figure (not a composite figure); sphere, hemisphere; cone (cylinder)
6. (composite figure) not a composite figure; sphere (hemisphere); (cone) cylinder

V8-4

## Build Mathematical Literacy I O

Provides support for struggling readers to build mathematical literacy.

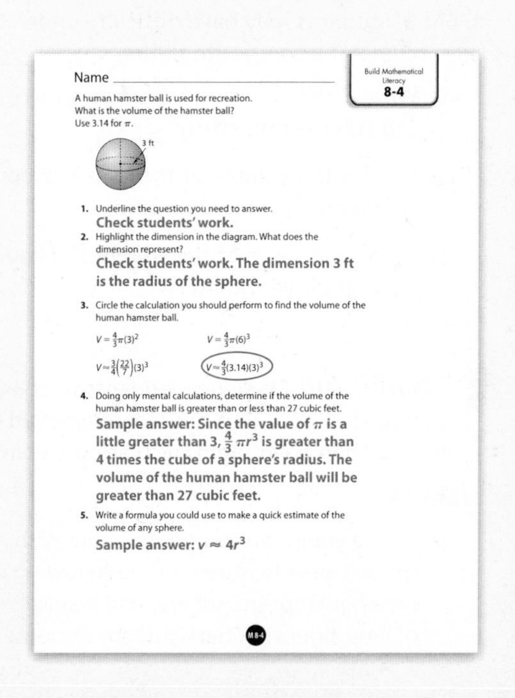

Name ______________________

Build Mathematical Literacy
**8-4**

A human hamster ball is used for recreation. What is the volume of the hamster ball? Use 3.14 for $\pi$.

1. Underline the question you need to answer.
   **Check students' work.**
2. Highlight the dimension in the diagram. What does the dimension represent?
   **Check students' work. The dimension 3 ft is the radius of the sphere.**
3. Circle the calculation you should perform to find the volume of the human hamster ball.
   $V = \frac{4}{3}\pi(3)^2$ $V = \frac{4}{3}\pi(6)^3$
   $V \approx \frac{3}{4}\left(\frac{22}{7}\right)(3)^3$ ($V \approx \frac{4}{3}(3.14)(3)^3$)
4. Doing only mental calculations, determine if the volume of the human hamster ball is greater than or less than 27 cubic feet.
   **Sample answer: Since the value of $\pi$ is a little greater than 3, $\frac{4}{3}\pi r^3$ is greater than 4 times the cube of a sphere's radius. The volume of the human hamster ball will be greater than 27 cubic feet.**
5. Write a formula you could use to make a quick estimate of the volume of any sphere.
   **Sample answer: $v \approx 4r^3$**



M8-4

Go Online

Practice

Worksheets

Math Tools

Math Games

# Additional Practice

You may opt to have students complete the automatically scored Additional Practice items online.

### Item Analysis

| Example | Items | DOK |
|---|---|---|
| 1 | 1 | 1 |
| | 2, 5 | 2 |
| 2 | 4 | 2 |
| | 7 | 3 |
| 3 | 3 | 2 |
| | 6, 8 | 3 |

**Interactive Practice** is available online.

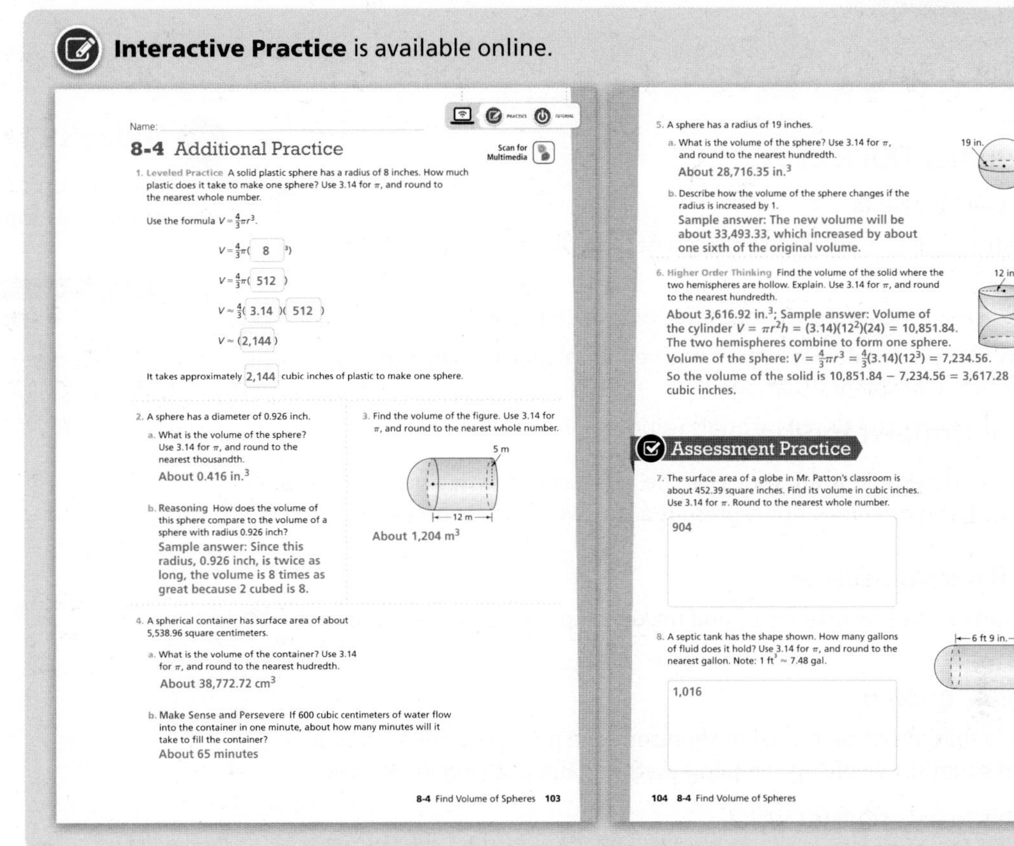

Name:

**8-4** Additional Practice

Scan for Multimedia

1. Leveled Practice A solid plastic sphere has a radius of 8 inches. How much plastic does it take to make one sphere? Use 3.14 for $\pi$, and round to the nearest whole number.

Use the formula $V = \frac{4}{3}\pi r^3$.

$V = \frac{4}{3}\pi(\ 8\ )^3$

$V = \frac{4}{3}\pi(\ 512\ )$

$V = \frac{4}{3}(\ 3.14\ )(\ 512\ )$

$V \approx (\ 2{,}144\ )$

It takes approximately 2,144 cubic inches of plastic to make one sphere.

2. A sphere has a diameter of 0.926 inch.
   a. What is the volume of the sphere? Use 3.14 for $\pi$, and round to the nearest thousandth.
   About 0.416 in.$^3$
   b. Reasoning How does the volume of this sphere compare to the volume of a sphere with radius 0.926 inch?
   Sample answer: Since this radius, 0.926 inch, is twice as long, the volume is 8 times as great because 2 cubed is 8.

3. Find the volume of the figure. Use 3.14 for $\pi$, and round to the nearest whole number.
   5 m; 12 m
   About 1,204 m$^3$

4. A spherical container has surface area of about 5,538.96 square centimeters.
   a. What is the volume of the container? Use 3.14 for $\pi$, and round to the nearest hudredth.
   About 38,772.72 cm$^3$
   b. Make Sense and Persevere If 600 cubic centimeters of water flow into the container in one minute, about how many minutes will it take to fill the container?
   About 65 minutes

8-4 Find Volume of Spheres 103

5. A sphere has a radius of 19 inches.
   a. What is the volume of the sphere? Use 3.14 for $\pi$, and round to the nearest hundredth.
   About 28,716.35 in.$^3$
   b. Describe how the volume of the sphere changes if the radius is increased by 1.
   Sample answer: The new volume will be about 33,493.33, which increased by about one sixth of the original volume.

6. Higher Order Thinking Find the volume of the solid where the two hemispheres are hollow. Explain. Use 3.14 for $\pi$, and round to the nearest hundredth.
   12 in.; 24 in.
   About 3,616.92 in.$^3$; Sample answer: Volume of the cylinder $V = \pi r^2 h = (3.14)(12^2)(24) = 10{,}851.84$. The two hemispheres combine to form one sphere. Volume of the sphere: $V = \frac{4}{3}\pi r^3 = \frac{4}{3}(3.14)(12^3) = 7{,}234.56$. So the volume of the solid is $10{,}851.84 - 7{,}234.56 = 3{,}617.28$ cubic inches.

Assessment Practice

7. The surface area of a globe in Mr. Patton's classroom is about 452.39 square inches. Find its volume in cubic inches. Use 3.14 for $\pi$. Round to the nearest whole number.
   904

8. A septic tank has the shape shown. How many gallons of fluid does it hold? Use 3.14 for $\pi$, and round to the nearest gallon. Note: 1 ft$^3$ ≈ 7.48 gal.
   6 ft 9 in.; 4 ft 3 in.
   1,016

104 8-4 Find Volume of Spheres

# Differentiated Intervention

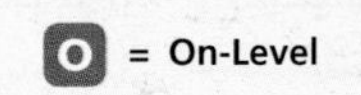
I = Intervention
O = On-Level

A = Advanced

## Enrichment O A

Presents engaging problems and activities that extend the lesson concepts.

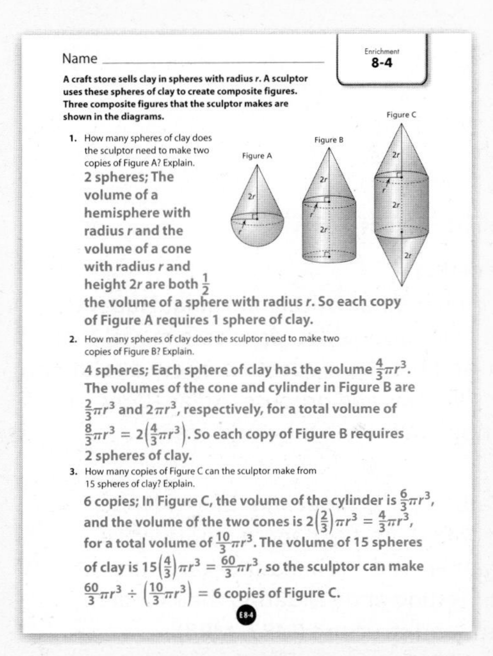

Name

Enrichment 8-4

A craft store sells clay in spheres with radius $r$. A sculptor uses these spheres of clay to create composite figures. Three composite figures that the sculptor makes are shown in the diagrams.

Figure A; Figure B; Figure C

1. How many spheres of clay does the sculptor need to make two copies of Figure A? Explain.
   2 spheres; The volume of a hemisphere with radius $r$ and the volume of a cone with radius $r$ and height $2r$ are both $\frac{1}{2}$ the volume of a sphere with radius $r$. So each copy of Figure A requires 1 sphere of clay.
2. How many spheres of clay does the sculptor need to make two copies of Figure B? Explain.
   4 spheres; Each sphere of clay has the volume $\frac{4}{3}\pi r^3$. The volumes of the cone and cylinder in Figure B are $\frac{2}{3}\pi r^3$ and $2\pi r^3$, respectively, for a total volume of $\frac{8}{3}\pi r^3 = 2\left(\frac{4}{3}\pi r^3\right)$. So each copy of Figure B requires 2 spheres of clay.
3. How many copies of Figure C can the sculptor make from 15 spheres of clay? Explain.
   6 copies; In Figure C, the volume of the cylinder is $\frac{6}{3}\pi r^3$, and the volume of the two cones is $2\left(\frac{2}{3}\right)\pi r^3 = \frac{4}{3}\pi r^3$, for a total volume of $\frac{10}{3}\pi r^3$. The volume of 15 spheres of clay is $15\left(\frac{4}{3}\right)\pi r^3 = \frac{60}{3}\pi r^3$, so the sculptor can make $\frac{60}{3}\pi r^3 \div \left(\frac{10}{3}\pi r^3\right) = 6$ copies of Figure C.

## Math Tools and Games I O A

Offers additional activities and games to build understanding and fluency.

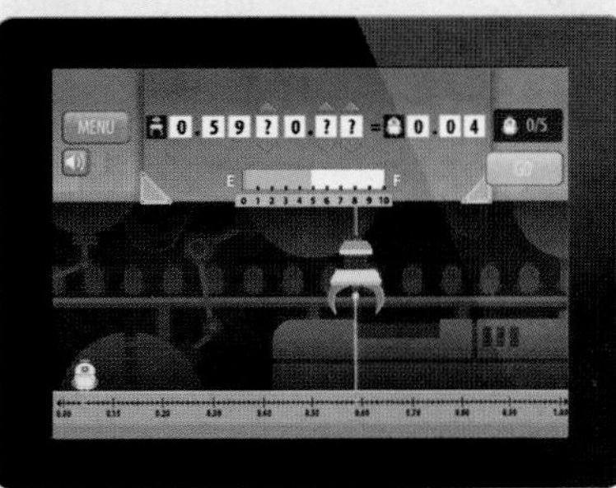


## Pick a Project and STEM Project I O A

Provides an additional opportunity for students to demonstrate understanding of key mathematical concepts.

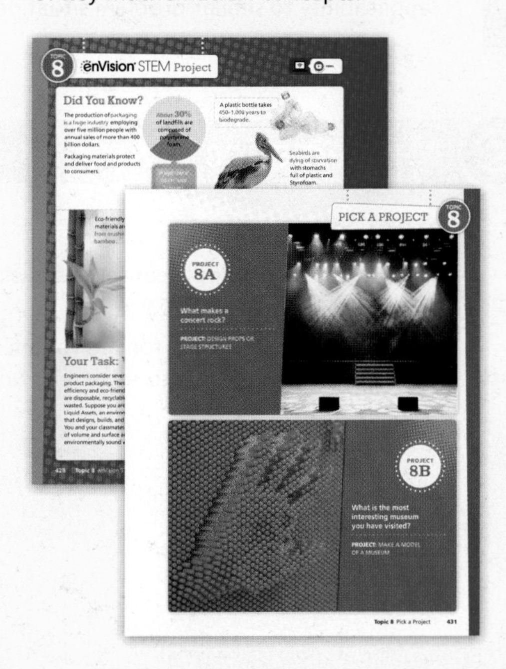

3-ACT MATH

# 3-Act Mathematical Modeling: Measure Up

## Lesson Overview

FOCUS

### Mathematics Objectives

**Students will be able to:**

- ✔ use mathematical modeling to represent a problem situation and to propose a solution.
- ✔ test and verify the appropriateness of their math models.
- ✔ explain why the results from their mathematical models may not align exactly to the problem situation.

### Essential Understanding

Many real-world problem situations can be represented with a mathematical model, but that model may not represent a real-world situation exactly.

COHERENCE

**Earlier in this topic, students:**

- used samples to draw inferences and make comparative inferences about populations.

**In this lesson, students:**

- develop a mathematical model to represent and propose a solution to a problem situation involving sampling methods and drawing inferences.

**Later in this course, students will:**

- refine their mathematical modeling skills.

**Cross-Cluster Connection** Students apply previous work solving linear equations (8.EE.2) from Topic 2 when finding volume of three-dimensional figures (8.G.3).

RIGOR

This mathematical modeling lesson focuses on **application** of both **math content** and **math practices and processes.**

- Students draw on their understanding of sampling and statistical concepts to develop a representative model.
- Students apply their mathematical model to test and validate its applicability to similar problem situations.

## Math Anytime

### Today's Challenge

Use the Topic 8 problems any time during this topic.

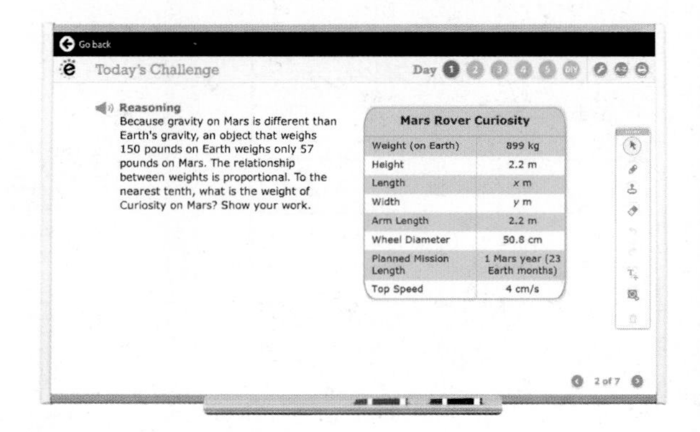


## Mathematics Overview

Common Core Standards

### Content Standards

In this lesson, students apply concepts and skills related to Common Core Standard **8.G.C.9**.

- **8.G.C.9** Know the formulas for the volumes of cones, cylinders, and spheres and use them to solve real-world and mathematical problems.

### Mathematical Practice Standards

**MP.4 Model with Mathematics**

The focus of this lesson is on mathematical modeling. Students identify the relationship among variables, develop a model that represents the situation, and use the model to propose a solution. Students interpret their solutions and propose explanations for why their answers may not match the real-world answer.

As students carry out mathematical modeling, they will also engage in sense-making **(MP.1)**, abstract and quantitative reasoning **(MP.2)**, and mathematical communication and argumentation **(MP.3)**. In testing and validating their models, students look for patterns and structure **(MP.7, MP.8)**.

# 3-Act Mathematical Modeling

Go Online

Video

## ACT 1 The Hook

Students will be tasked with determining whether liquid in one container will fit in a differently shaped container.

### Play the Video and Brainstorm Questions

Have students complete **Question 1**. Encourage them to consider the situation and ask any questions that arise. Listen for interesting mathematical and non-mathematical questions. Ask students what makes each question interesting.

**Q:** What questions do you have? [Sample questions: Why is she transferring the liquid? What is that liquid? How much liquid is there?]

### Pose the Main Question

After the question brainstorming, pose the Main Question students will be tasked with answering. Have students complete **Question 2**.

**Main Question**

**Q:** Will the liquid fit?

### Ask about Predictions

Have students complete **Questions 3–5**. If students unanimously predict the correct answer, ask them to think about what would happen if you add or subtract liquid until there is uncertainty.

You can survey the class for the range of predictions.

**Q:** Why do you think your prediction is the answer to the Main Question?

**Q:** Who had a similar prediction?

**Q:** How many of you agree with that prediction?

**Q:** Who has a different prediction?

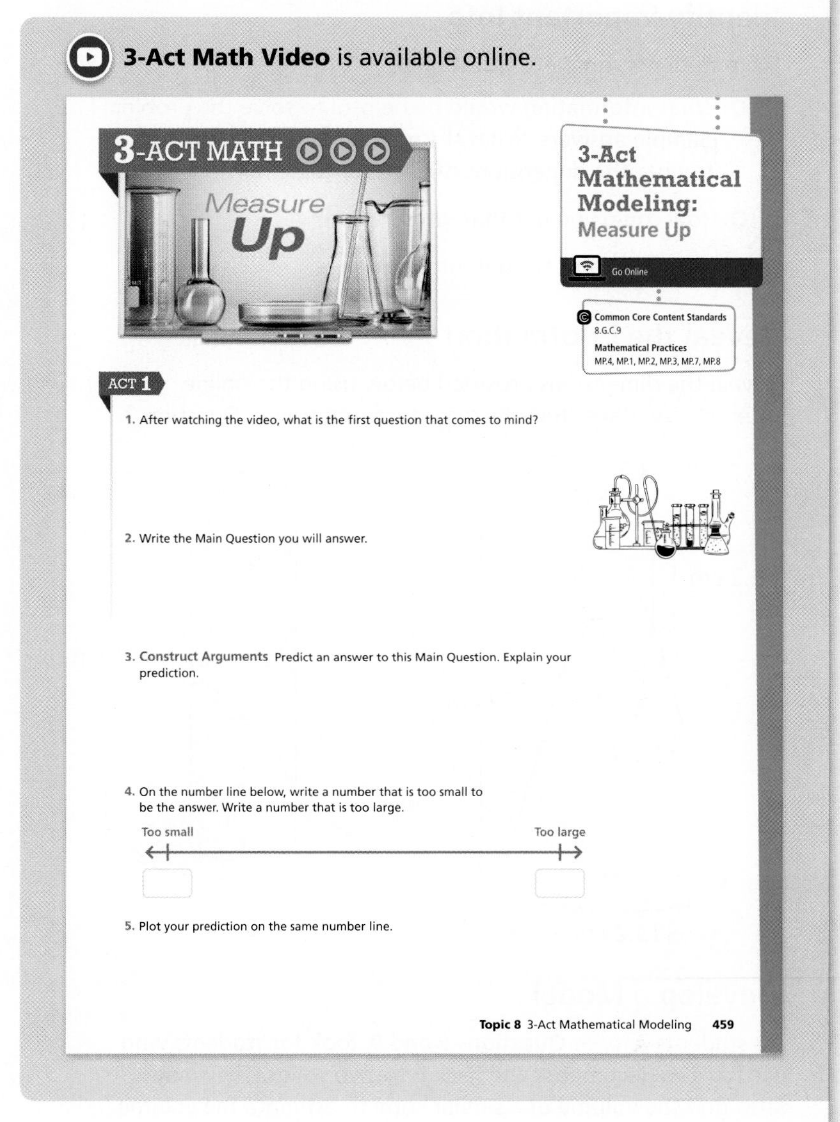

**3-Act Math Video** is available online.

3-ACT MATH

Measure Up

**3-Act Mathematical Modeling:** Measure Up

Go Online

Common Core Content Standards
8.G.C.9

Mathematical Practices
MP.4, MP.1, MP.2, MP.3, MP.7, MP.8

ACT 1

1. After watching the video, what is the first question that comes to mind?

2. Write the Main Question you will answer.

3. **Construct Arguments** Predict an answer to this Main Question. Explain your prediction.

4. On the number line below, write a number that is too small to be the answer. Write a number that is too large.

Too small    Too large

5. Plot your prediction on the same number line.

**Topic 8** 3-Act Mathematical Modeling **459**

# 3-Act Mathematical Modeling *continued*

## ACT 2 The Model

### Identify Important Info

Have students complete **Question 6**.

**Q:** What information would be helpful to solve the problem? [Sample answers: What the volume of each container is; what the dimensions of each container are]

**Q:** How could you get that information?

**Q:** Why do you need that information?

### Reveal the information

Reveal the dimensions provided below using the online interactivity. Have students record information in **Question 7**.

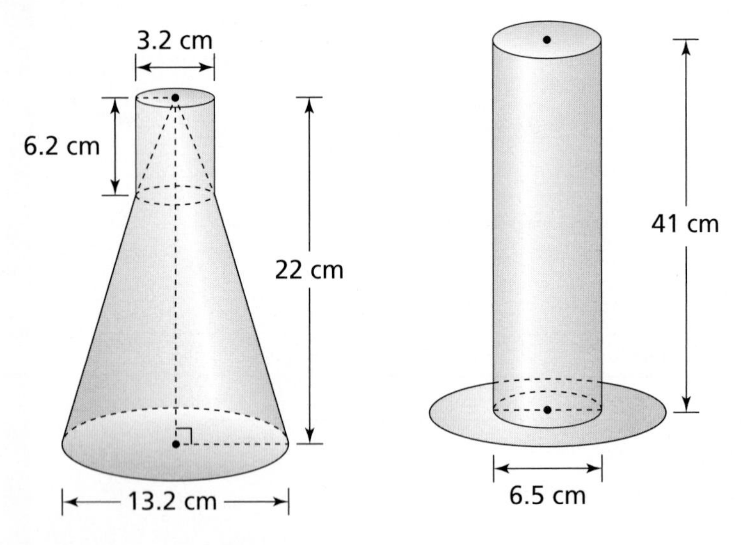


### Develop a Model

As students answer **Questions 8 and 9**, look for students who struggle to decompose the flask into two solids. They may also find the volume of a similar cone to estimate the volume.

**Q:** How can you find the volume of the bottom part of the cone? [Sample answer: Subtract the volume of the top of the cone from the volume of the entire cone.]

**3-Act Math Activity** is available online.

ACT 2

6. What information in this situation would be helpful to know? How would you use that information?

7. **Use Appropriate Tools** What tools can you use to solve the problem? Explain how you would use them strategically.

8. **Model with Math** Represent the situation using mathematics. Use your representation to answer the Main Question.

9. What is your answer to the Main Question? Is it higher or lower than your prediction? Explain why.

460 **Topic 8** 3-Act Mathematical Modeling

### Use the Model to Propose a Solution

After students answer **Questions 8 and 9**, facilitate a discussion about solution methods. If needed, project the possible student solutions (shown below).

### Possible Student Solutions

**Walt's Work**

volume of big cone + volume of cylinder − volume of small cone

$\frac{1}{3}\pi R^2H + \pi r^2h - \frac{1}{3}\pi r^2h$

$= \frac{1}{3}\pi(6.6)^2(22) + \pi(1.6)^2(6.2) - \frac{1}{3}\pi(1.6)^2(6.2)$

$= 1{,}003.55 + 49.86 - 16.62$

$= 1{,}036.79 \text{ cm}^3$

volume of cylinder

$\pi r^2h$

$= \pi(3.25)^2(41)$

$= 1{,}360.51 \text{ cm}^3$

The flask is smaller than the cylinder.

**Walt** finds the volume of each solid and compares them. He uses different variables for the radius and height of the different objects.

**Kiara's Work**

It fits if volume of flask is less than volume of cylinder.

$\frac{1}{3}\pi R^2H + \pi r^2h - \frac{1}{3}\pi r^2h \le \pi r^2h$

$\frac{1}{3}\pi R^2H + \frac{2}{3}\pi r^2h \le \pi r^2h$

$\frac{1}{3}\pi(6.6)^2(22) + \frac{2}{3}\pi(1.6)^2(6.2) \le \pi(3.25)^2(41)$

$1{,}003.55 + 33.24 \le 1{,}360.51$

It will fit in the cylinder.

**Kiara** considers that the volume of the flask needs to be less than or equal to the volume of the cylinder. She combines like terms to simplify the flask volume.

Go Online

Video

# ACT 3 The Solution and Sequel

**3-Act Math Video** is available online.

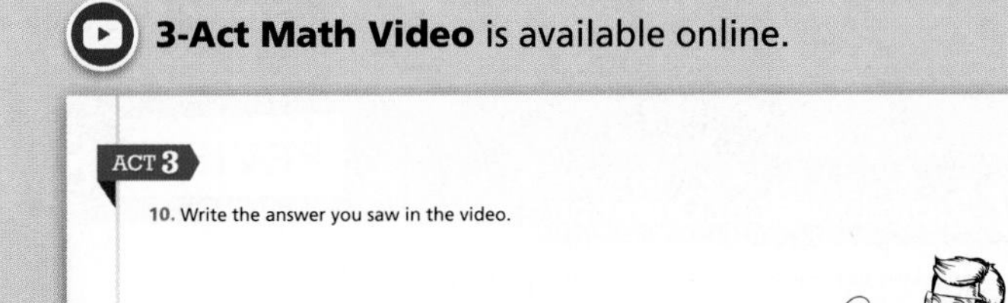

ACT 3

10. Write the answer you saw in the video.

11. **Reasoning** Does your answer match the answer in the video? If not, what are some reasons that would explain the difference?

12. **Make Sense and Persevere** Would you change your model now that you know the answer? Explain.

Topic 8 3-Act Mathematical Modeling 461

ACT 3 Extension

Reflect

13. **Model with Math** Explain how you used a mathematical model to represent the situation. How did the model help you answer the Main Question?

14. **Make Sense and Persevere** When did you struggle most while solving the problem? How did you overcome that obstacle?

SEQUEL

15. **Generalize** Suppose you have a graduated cylinder half the height of the one in the video. How wide does the cylinder need to be to hold the liquid in the flask?

462 Topic 8 3-Act Mathematical Modeling

## Use the Video to Reveal the Answer

The final part of the video shows the entire process of pouring from the flask to the cylinder. Have students complete **Question 10**. Congratulate the students who were closest to the actual answer.

**Main Question Answer**

**The liquid fits in the cylinder.**

## Validate Conclusions

After students complete **Questions 11 and 12**, encourage them to discuss possible sources of error inherent in using math to model real-world situations. Look for students to point out that their models are still useful even though they are not perfect.

**Q:** Why does your answer not match the answer in the video? [Sample answer: The flask was not full, so the volume does not match the volume of the liquid.]

**Q:** How useful was your model at predicting the answer?

**Q:** How could your model better represent the situation?

## Reflect on Thinking

**Make Sense and Persevere** If time allows, have students complete **Questions 13 and 14** as an extension. Use this opportunity to discuss how students incorporate mathematical processes during the task.

## Pose the Sequel

**Generalize** Use **Question 15** to present a similar problem situation involving volume. You can assign to early finishers or as homework so students can test the usefulness of their models.

**Q:** Suppose you have a graduated cylinder half the height of the one in the video. How wide does the cylinder need to be to hold the liquid in the flask?

Using their models and the answer in the video, look for students to point out that the width (or diameter) does not double. (The actual scale factor is $\sqrt{2}$ since volume depends on $r^2$, but knowing it is less than double is sufficient.)

**Q:** When might you use each container in a laboratory? [Sample answer: A flask is easier to pour liquid and to store it. A cylinder is easier to estimate the volume of the liquid inside it.]

Go Online

Glossary

# Solve Problems Involving Surface Area and Volume

## ? Topic Essential Question

**How can you find volumes and surface areas of three-dimensional figures?**

As students answer the Essential Question in writing, encourage them to include definitions, examples, non-examples, models, and other representations that support their answers.

Be sure the following are made explicit while discussing students' answers.

- The areas of polygons can be used to find the surface areas of cylinders, cones, and spheres.
- The volumes of a rectangular prism and a cylinder can both be determined by finding the product of the area of the base and the height of the shape.
- The volume of a cone is $\frac{1}{3}$ the volume of a cylinder with the same base and height.
- The volume of a sphere is twice the volume of a cone with the same circular base and height.

## Vocabulary Review

**ORAL LANGUAGE** Before students complete the page, reinforce oral language by using one or more of the following activities.

- Play a game where the formula for the surface area or volume of a three-dimensional figure is given. Have students guess the name of the three-dimensional figure the formula matches.
- Students work in pairs to discuss the terms *cone*, *cylinder*, and *sphere*. Have the students describe a composite figure that is made up of more than one of these shapes.

**WRITING IN MATH** After students complete the page, you can further reinforce writing in math by doing the following activity.

- Have students work in groups to create a real-world problem that involves using the formula for surface area or volume of a cone, cylinder, or sphere.

Available Online

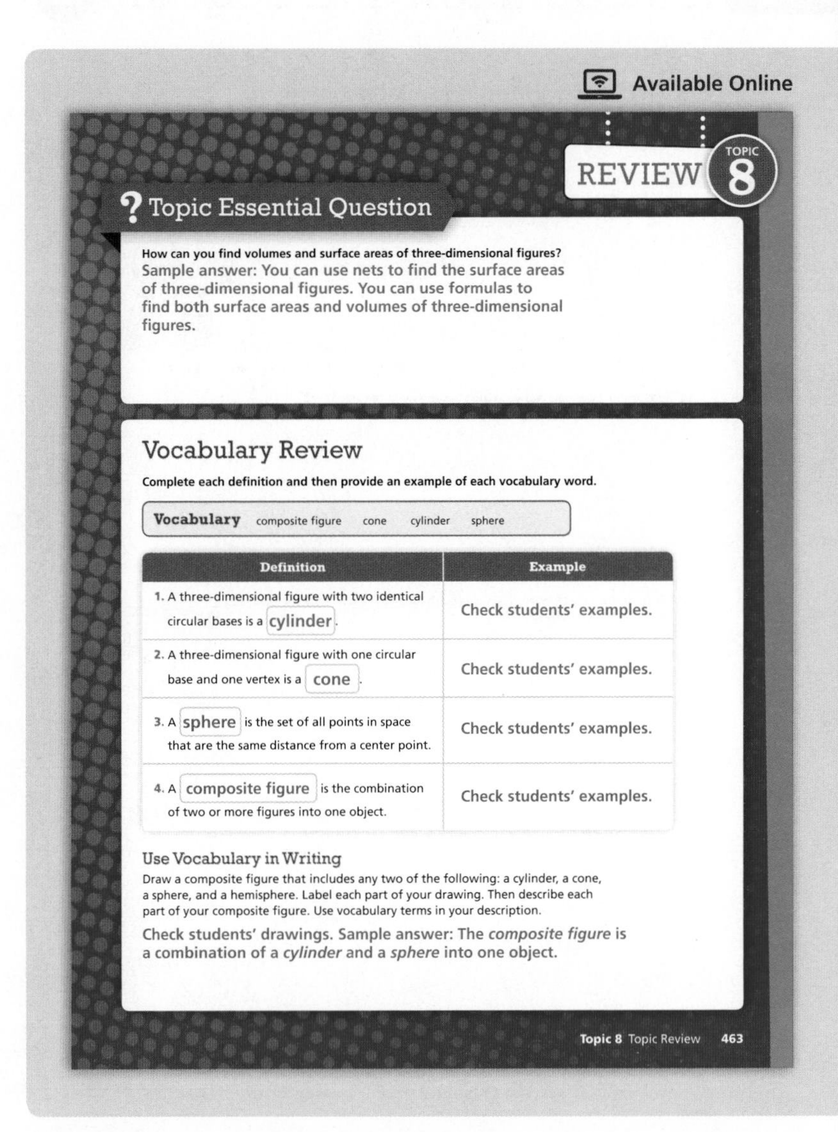

REVIEW TOPIC 8

? Topic Essential Question

How can you find volumes and surface areas of three-dimensional figures?

Sample answer: You can use nets to find the surface areas of three-dimensional figures. You can use formulas to find both surface areas and volumes of three-dimensional figures.

Vocabulary Review

Complete each definition and then provide an example of each vocabulary word.

**Vocabulary** composite figure cone cylinder sphere

| Definition | Example |
|---|---|
| 1. A three-dimensional figure with two identical circular bases is a cylinder. | Check students' examples. |
| 2. A three-dimensional figure with one circular base and one vertex is a cone. | Check students' examples. |
| 3. A sphere is the set of all points in space that are the same distance from a center point. | Check students' examples. |
| 4. A composite figure is the combination of two or more figures into one object. | Check students' examples. |

Use Vocabulary in Writing

Draw a composite figure that includes any two of the following: a cylinder, a cone, a sphere, and a hemisphere. Label each part of your drawing. Then describe each part of your composite figure. Use vocabulary terms in your description.

Check students' drawings. Sample answer: The *composite figure* is a combination of a *cylinder* and a *sphere* into one object.

Topic 8 Topic Review 463

# Concepts and Skills Review

Available Online

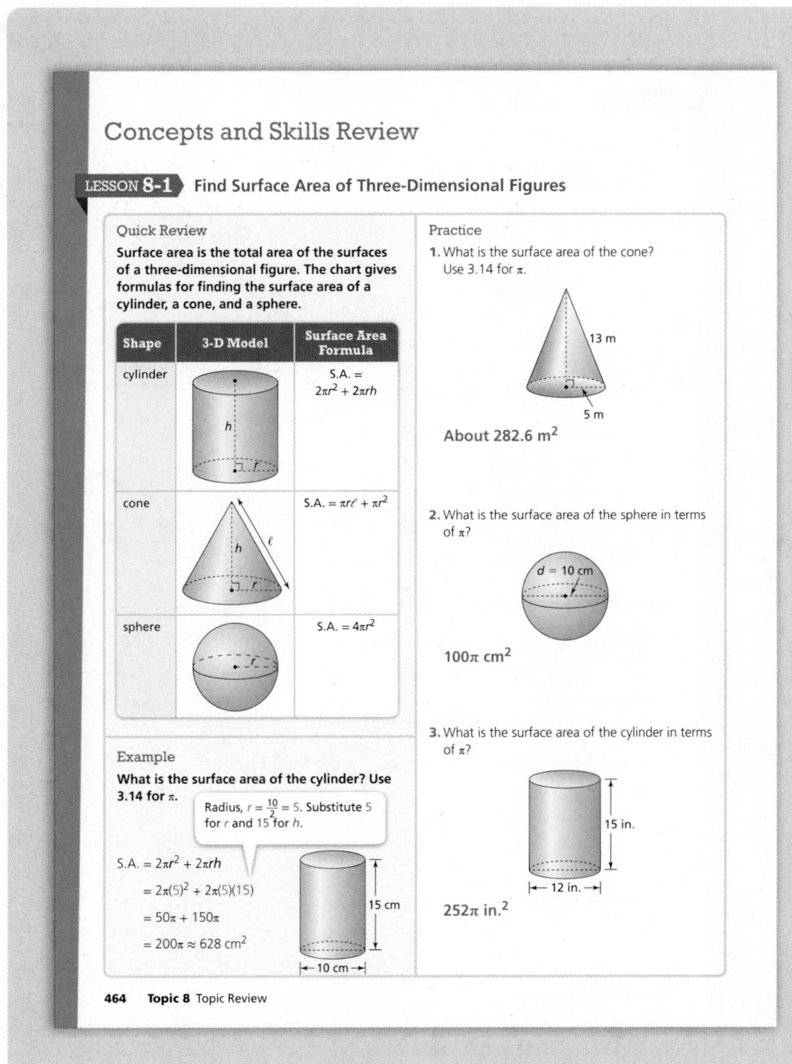

## Concepts and Skills Review

### LESSON 8-1 Find Surface Area of Three-Dimensional Figures

**Quick Review**

**Surface area is the total area of the surfaces of a three-dimensional figure. The chart gives formulas for finding the surface area of a cylinder, a cone, and a sphere.**

| Shape | 3-D Model | Surface Area Formula |
|---|---|---|
| cylinder | | S.A. = $2\pi r^2 + 2\pi rh$ |
| cone | | S.A. = $\pi r\ell + \pi r^2$ |
| sphere | | S.A. = $4\pi r^2$ |

**Example**

**What is the surface area of the cylinder? Use 3.14 for $\pi$.**

Radius, $r = \frac{10}{2} = 5$. Substitute 5 for $r$ and 15 for $h$.

S.A. $= 2\pi r^2 + 2\pi rh$

$= 2\pi(5)^2 + 2\pi(5)(15)$

$= 50\pi + 150\pi$

$= 200\pi \approx 628$ cm$^2$

**Practice**

1. What is the surface area of the cone? Use 3.14 for $\pi$.

About 282.6 m$^2$

2. What is the surface area of the sphere in terms of $\pi$?

$100\pi$ cm$^2$

3. What is the surface area of the cylinder in terms of $\pi$?

$252\pi$ in.$^2$





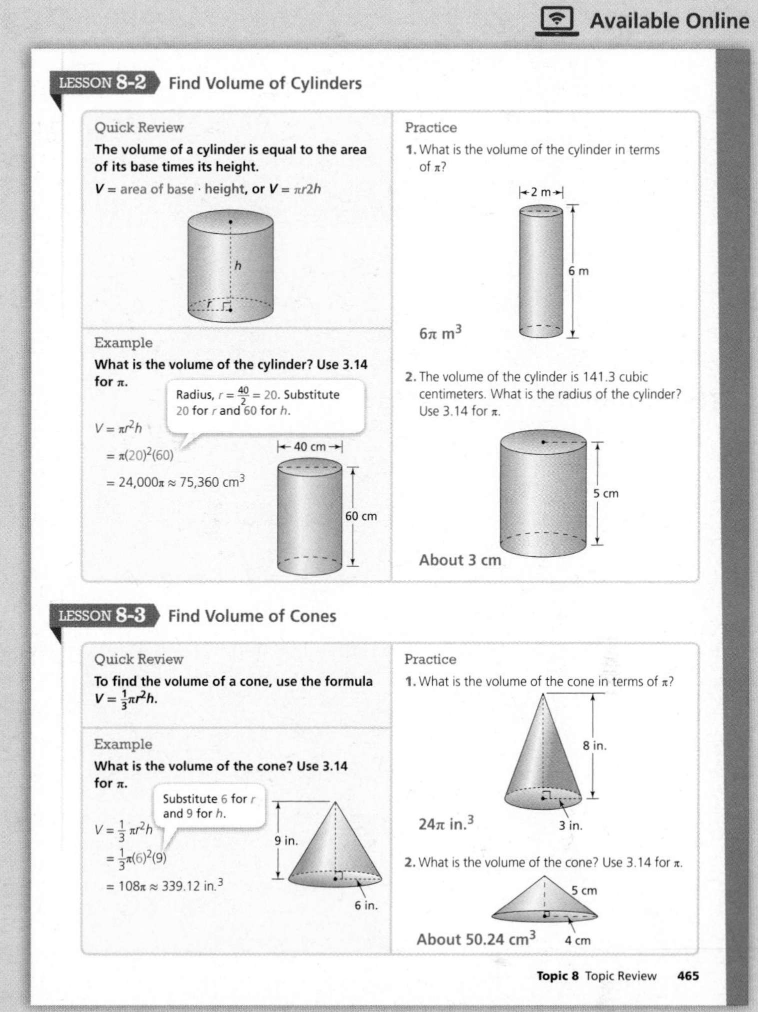

### LESSON 8-2 Find Volume of Cylinders

**Quick Review**

**The volume of a cylinder is equal to the area of its base times its height.**

***V* = area of base · height, or *V* = $\pi r2h$**

**Example**

**What is the volume of the cylinder? Use 3.14 for $\pi$.**

Radius, $r = \frac{40}{2} = 20$. Substitute 20 for $r$ and 60 for $h$.

$V = \pi r^2h$

$= \pi(20)^2(60)$

$= 24{,}000\pi \approx 75{,}360$ cm$^3$

**Practice**

1. What is the volume of the cylinder in terms of $\pi$?

$6\pi$ m$^3$

2. The volume of the cylinder is 141.3 cubic centimeters. What is the radius of the cylinder? Use 3.14 for $\pi$.

About 3 cm

### LESSON 8-3 Find Volume of Cones

**Quick Review**

**To find the volume of a cone, use the formula $V = \frac{1}{3}\pi r^2h$.**

**Example**

**What is the volume of the cone? Use 3.14 for $\pi$.**

Substitute 6 for $r$ and 9 for $h$.

$V = \frac{1}{3}\pi r^2h$

$= \frac{1}{3}\pi(6)^2(9)$

$= 108\pi \approx 339.12$ in.$^3$

**Practice**

1. What is the volume of the cone in terms of $\pi$?

$24\pi$ in.$^3$

2. What is the volume of the cone? Use 3.14 for $\pi$.

About 50.24 cm$^3$

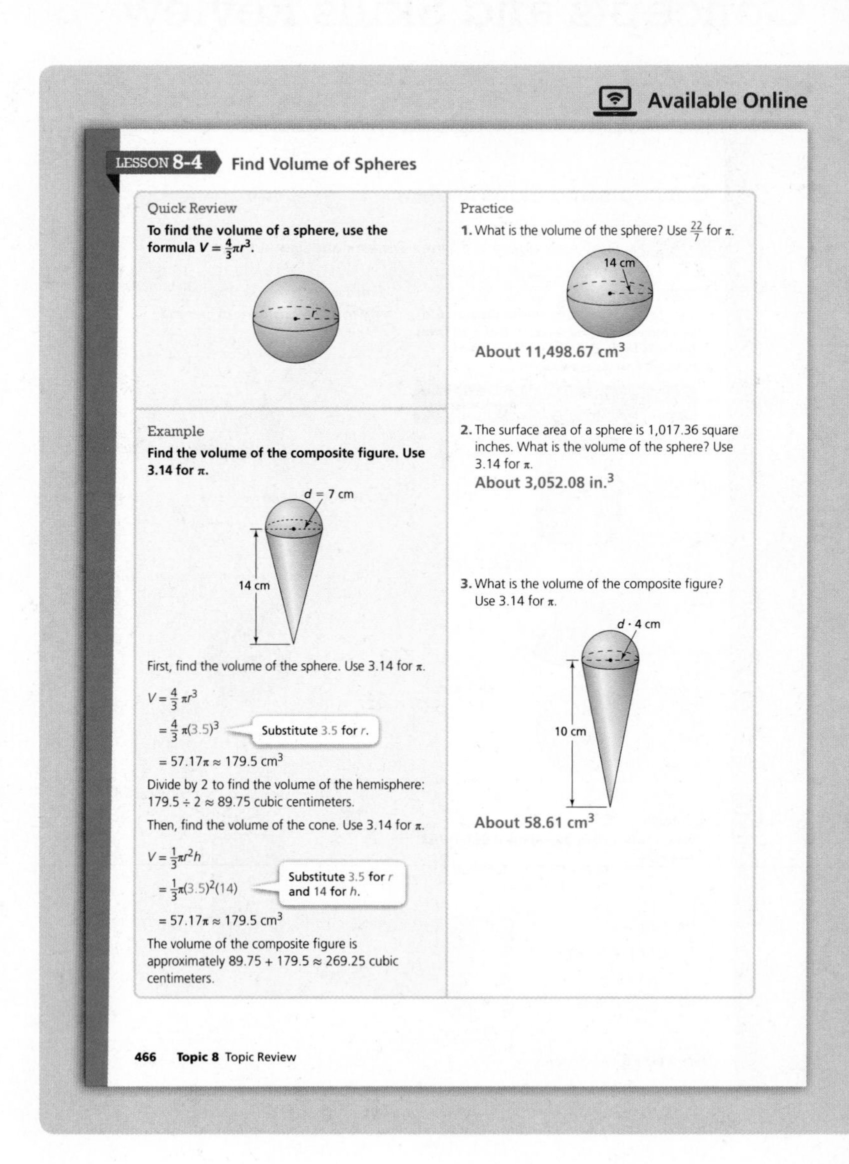

Available Online

LESSON 8-4 **Find Volume of Spheres**

**Quick Review**

**To find the volume of a sphere, use the formula $V = \frac{4}{3}\pi r^3$.**



**Example**

**Find the volume of the composite figure. Use 3.14 for $\pi$.**



First, find the volume of the sphere. Use 3.14 for $\pi$.

$V = \frac{4}{3}\pi r^3$

$= \frac{4}{3}\pi(3.5)^3$ — Substitute 3.5 for $r$.

$= 57.17\pi \approx 179.5 \text{ cm}^3$

Divide by 2 to find the volume of the hemisphere: $179.5 \div 2 \approx 89.75$ cubic centimeters.

Then, find the volume of the cone. Use 3.14 for $\pi$.

$V = \frac{1}{3}\pi r^2 h$

$= \frac{1}{3}\pi(3.5)^2(14)$ — Substitute 3.5 for $r$ and 14 for $h$.

$= 57.17\pi \approx 179.5 \text{ cm}^3$

The volume of the composite figure is approximately $89.75 + 179.5 \approx 269.25$ cubic centimeters.

**Practice**

1. What is the volume of the sphere? Use $\frac{22}{7}$ for $\pi$.



**About 11,498.67 cm$^3$**

2. The surface area of a sphere is 1,017.36 square inches. What is the volume of the sphere? Use 3.14 for $\pi$.

**About 3,052.08 in.$^3$**

3. What is the volume of the composite figure? Use 3.14 for $\pi$.



**About 58.61 cm$^3$**

466 **Topic 8** Topic Review

# Fluency Practice

Go Online

## Hidden Clue

Students maintain fluency with solving multistep equations as they find missing coordinates in an activity that reinforces mathematical practices.

**Getting Started** Students may work independently or with a partner. Go over the directions. Point out that students should combine like terms to simplify equations before solving.

Students should solve each problem and complete their own graph. Encourage students to record their work on a separate sheet of paper.

**As Students Do the Activity** Remind students that they must connect the points in alphabetical order.

Some students may find all of the answers first and then locate the points on the graph. Allow this strategy as it provides the same fluency practice.

**Another Activity** Have students work together to write a new set of equations that results in the same coordinates on the graph. Ask them to record the new equations on a separate sheet of paper.

Extra Challenge Create your own Hidden Clue puzzle activity. Write a new equation for each clue and use graph paper to create the puzzle. Then trade your activity with a partner and complete your partner's activity.

Available Online

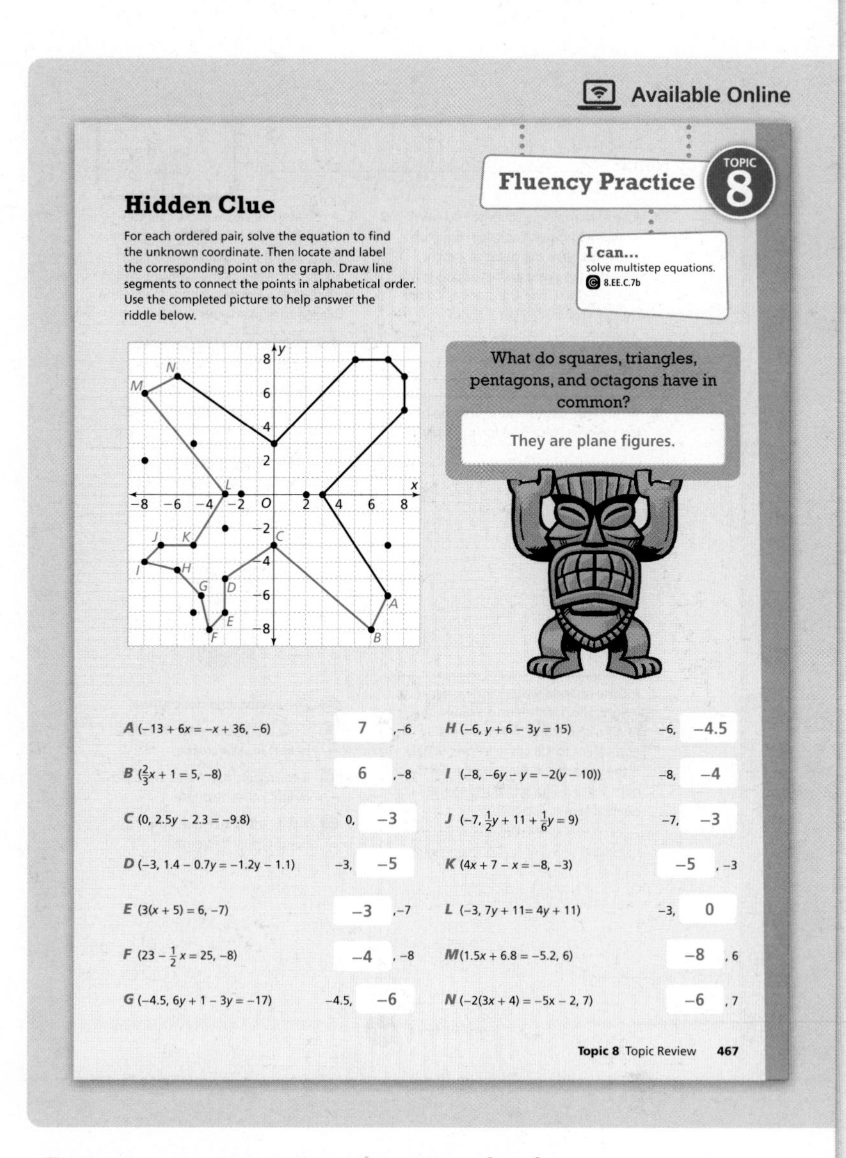

Fluency Practice TOPIC 8

**Hidden Clue**

For each ordered pair, solve the equation to find the unknown coordinate. Then locate and label the corresponding point on the graph. Draw line segments to connect the points in alphabetical order. Use the completed picture to help answer the riddle below.

I can… solve multistep equations. 8.EE.C.7b

What do squares, triangles, pentagons, and octagons have in common?

They are plane figures.

| Point | Answer | Point | Answer |
|---|---|---|---|
| A $(-13 + 6x = -x + 36, -6)$ | 7, −6 | H $(-6, y + 6 - 3y = 15)$ | −6, −4.5 |
| B $(\frac{2}{3}x + 1 = 5, -8)$ | 6, −8 | I $(-8, -6y - y = -2(y - 10))$ | −8, −4 |
| C $(0, 2.5y - 2.3 = -9.8)$ | 0, −3 | J $(-7, \frac{1}{2}y + 11 + \frac{1}{6}y = 9)$ | −7, −3 |
| D $(-3, 1.4 - 0.7y = -1.2y - 1.1)$ | −3, −5 | K $(4x + 7 - x = -8, -3)$ | −5, −3 |
| E $(3(x + 5) = 6, -7)$ | −3, −7 | L $(-3, 7y + 11 = 4y + 11)$ | −3, 0 |
| F $(23 - \frac{1}{2}x = 25, -8)$ | −4, −8 | M $(1.5x + 6.8 = -5.2, 6)$ | −8, 6 |
| G $(-4.5, 6y + 1 - 3y = -17)$ | −4.5, −6 | N $(-2(3x + 4) = -5x - 2, 7)$ | −6, 7 |

Topic 8 Topic Review 467

## Common Core Content Standards

**8.EE.C.7b** Solve linear equations with rational number coefficients, including equations whose solutions require expanding expressions using the distributive property and collecting like terms.

## Mathematical Practices

MP.1, MP.2, MP.6

# Assessment

Go Online

Assess

Available Online

Name ______________________

Topic 8 Assessment Form A

1. Jose is wrapping a stack of 100 coins in a paper holder. Each coin is $\frac{1}{8}$ inch thick and has a diameter of 1 inch. How many square inches of paper will Jose need to cover the stack of coins? Use 3.14 for $\pi$. **1 point**

**About 40.82 in.$^2$**

2. What is the approximate volume of the cylinder? Use 3.14 for $\pi$. **1 point**

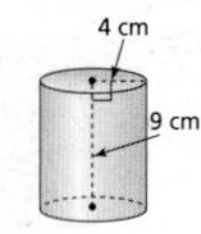


Ⓐ 324 $cm^3$
Ⓑ 452.16 $cm^3$
Ⓒ 734.76 $cm^3$
Ⓓ 1,017.36 $cm^3$

3. A cone-shaped water cup has a height of 3.3 inches and a diameter of 2.7 inches. One fluid ounce is equivalent to 1.8 cubic inches. What is the capacity, in fluid ounces, of the cup? Use 3.14 for $\pi$. Round to the nearest tenth. **1 point**

**About 3.5 fluid ounces**

4. A rectangular prism and a cylinder have the same height. The length of each side of the prism base is equal to the diameter of the cylinder. Which shape has a greater volume? Fill in the blanks to explain your answer.

The **rectangular prism** has the greater volume because the **cylinder** fits within the **rectangular prism** with extra space between the two figures.

5. Suppose the radius of a cylinder changes, but its volume stays the same. How must the height of the cylinder change? **1 point**

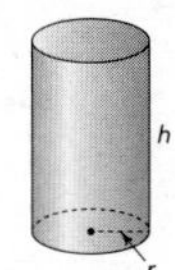


Ⓐ The height does not change.
Ⓑ If the radius increases, then the height must increase.
Ⓒ If the radius decreases, then the height must decrease.
Ⓓ If the radius increases, then the height must decrease.

Assessment, Form A 1 of 2

6. What is the approximate volume of the cone? Use $\frac{22}{7}$ for $\pi$. **1 point**

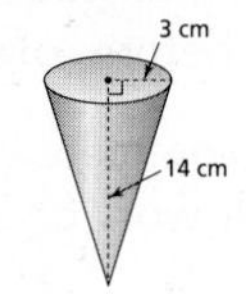


**About 132 $cm^3$**

7. Rover's dog bowl is pictured below. Approximately how much water does it hold? Use 3.14 for $\pi$ and round your answer to the nearest cubic inch.

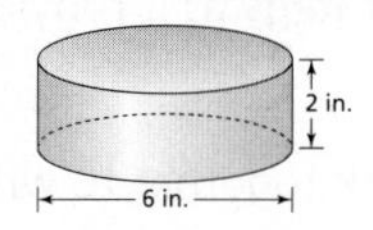


**57 in.$^3$**

8. A cylinder has a volume of 400 cubic feet. If the height of the cylinder is 25 feet, what is the radius of the cylinder? Use 3.14 for $\pi$ and round to the nearest hundredth. **1 point**

**About 2.26 ft**

9. An artist forms a spherical glass ornament that has a diameter of 6 cm. What is the volume of the ornament? Use 3.14 for $\pi$.

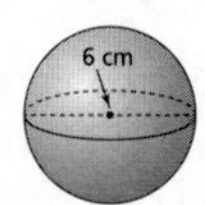


Ⓐ 113.04 $cm^3$
Ⓑ 18 $cm^3$
Ⓒ 11.46 $cm^3$
Ⓓ 39.14 $cm^3$

10. The volume of a cone is 113.04 $mm^3$. What is the approximate volume of the sphere that has the same height and a circular base with the same diameter? Use 3.14 for $\pi$ and round to the nearest hundredth. **1 point**

Ⓐ 113.04 $mm^3$
Ⓑ 226.08 $mm^3$
Ⓒ 904.32 $mm^3$
Ⓓ 3,052 $mm^3$

11. A laser pointer in the shape of a cylinder is 13 centimeters long with a radius of 0.75 centimeter. What is the volume of the laser pointer? Express your answer in terms of $\pi$ and round to the nearest cubic centimeter. **1 point**

**$7\pi$ $cm^3$ or about 23 $cm^3$**

Assessment, Form A  2 of 2

Assess students' understanding of the topic concepts and skills using the Topic Assessments found online.

Use the Item Analysis Chart on the facing page to assign intervention to students based on their scores on the paper and pencil version of the Topic Assessments.

You may opt to have students take the Topic Assessment online. The online assessment is auto-scored, with differentiated intervention automatically assigned to students based on their scores.

You can use ExamView to generate additional Topic Assessments.

There are two versions of the Topic Assessment, Form A and Form B. These parallel versions assess the same content item for item. The Item Analysis chart on the next page can be used with both versions.

## Scoring Guide: Forms A and B

| Score | Recommendations |
|---|---|
| Greater Than 85% | Assign the corresponding MDIS for items answered incorrectly. Use Enrichment activities with the student. |
| 70%–85% | Assign the corresponding MDIS for items answered incorrectly. You may also assign Reteach to Build Understanding and Virtual Nerd Video assets for the lessons correlated to the items the student answered incorrectly. |
| Less Than 70% | Assign the corresponding MDIS for items answered incorrectly. Assign appropriate intervention lessons available online. You may also assign Reteach to Build Understanding, Additional Vocabulary Support, Build Mathematical Literacy, and Virtual Nerd Video assets for the lessons correlated to the items the student answered incorrectly. |

Available Online

Name ______________________

Topic 8
Assessment
Form B

1. Khalil is wrapping a cylindrical candle for a gift. The candle is 10 inches tall and has a diameter of 1.5 inches. How many square inches of wrapping paper will Khalil need to cover the candle? Use 3.14 for $\pi$. **1 point**

**About 50.63 in.$^2$**

2. What is the approximate volume of the cylinder? Use 3.14 for $\pi$. **1 point**

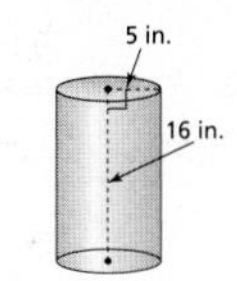


Ⓐ 126 in.$^3$
Ⓑ 153.86 in.$^3$
● 1,256 in.$^3$
Ⓓ 7,121.52 in.$^3$

3. A cone-shaped snow cone cup has a height of 3.38 inches and a diameter of 4.25 inches. One fluid ounce is equivalent to 1.8 cubic inches. What is the capacity, in fluid ounces, of the cup? Use 3.14 for $\pi$ and round to the nearest hundredth. **1 point**

**8.88 ounces**

4. A sphere and a cylinder have the same diameter. The height of the cylinder is equal to its diameter. Which shape has a greater volume? Fill in the blanks to explain your answer.

The **cylinder** has the greater volume because the **sphere** fits within the **cylinder** with extra space between the two figures.

5. A cylinder has a height of $h$ and a diameter of $d$. Which of the following changes would result in twice the volume? **1 point**

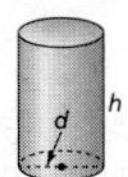


Ⓐ Double the diameter
Ⓑ Double the radius
Ⓒ Double the circumference
● Double the height



6. What is the approximate volume of the cone? Use $\frac{22}{7}$ for $\pi$. **1 point**

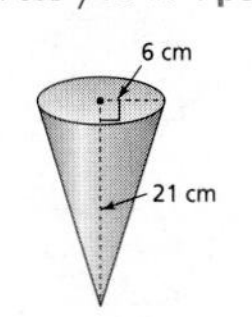


**About 792 cm$^3$**

7. Julia's candle mold is pictured below. Approximately how much wax does it take to make one candle? Use 3.14 for $\pi$ and round your answer to the nearest cubic inch.

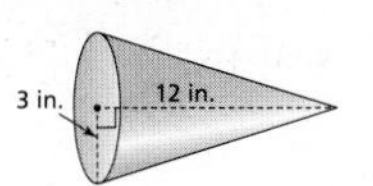


**113 in.$^3$**

8. A cylinder has a volume of 200 cubic centimeters. If the height of the cylinder is 10 centimeters, what is the radius of the cylinder? **1 point**

**About 2.52 cm**

9. A small plastic ball has a diameter of 8 centimeters. What is the volume of the ball? Use 3.14 for $\pi$.

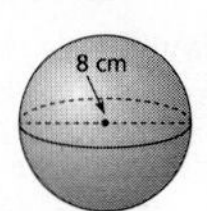


Ⓐ 16.76 cm$^3$
Ⓑ 33.51 cm$^3$
● 267.95 cm$^3$
Ⓓ 134.04 cm$^3$

10. The volume of a sphere is 904.32 mm$^3$. What is the approximate volume of a cone that has the same height and a circular base with the same diameter? Use 3.14 for $\pi$ and round to the nearest hundredth. **1 point**

Ⓐ 301.44 mm$^2$
● 452.16 mm$^2$
Ⓒ 904.32 mm$^2$
Ⓓ 1,808.64 mm$^2$

11. A giant pencil, in the shape of a cylinder, has a length of 36 inches and a diameter of 6 inches. What is the volume of the pencil? Express your answer in terms of $\pi$ and round to the nearest cubic inch. **1 point**

**$324\pi$ in.$^3$ or 1,017 in.$^3$**



## Item Analysis for Diagnosis and Intervention: Forms A and B

| Item | Points | DOK | MDIS | Standard |
|---|---|---|---|---|
| 1 | 1 | 2 | N49 | 8.G.C.9 |
| 2 | 1 | 2 | N49 | 8.G.C.9 |
| 3 | 1 | 2 | N50 | 8.G.C.9 |
| 4 | 1 | 3 | N52, N55 | 8.G.C.9 |
| 5 | 1 | 2 | N53 | 8.G.C.9 |
| 6 | 1 | 2 | N57 | 8.G.C.9 |

| Item | Points | DOK | MDIS | Standard |
|---|---|---|---|---|
| 7 | 1 | 2 | N57 | 8.G.C.9 |
| 8 | 1 | 2 | N55 | 8.G.C.9 |
| 9 | 1 | 2 | N55 | 8.G.C.9 |
| 10 | 1 | 2 | N49 | 8.G.C.9 |
| 11 | 1 | 2 | N53 | 8.G.C.9 |

# Performance Task

Go Online

Assess

Assess students' ability to apply the topic concepts and skills using the Topic Performance Tasks found online.

Available Online

Name ______________________

Topic 8 Performance Task Form A

Cole is building a model rocket in science class. He selects the rocket parts from a set of solid cylinders and cones made from metal.

**1.** Cole wants to build a rocket with the dimensions shown at right. For safety purposes, the maximum lift-off weight of each rocket is 10 pounds. Will Cole's rocket meet the requirement for launch?

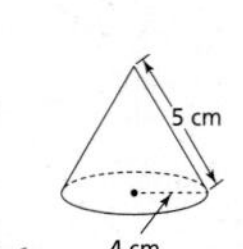


**Part A**

What will be the total length of the assembled rocket? Explain how you found your answer. **2 points**

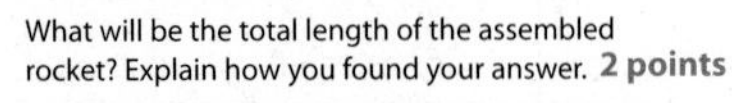
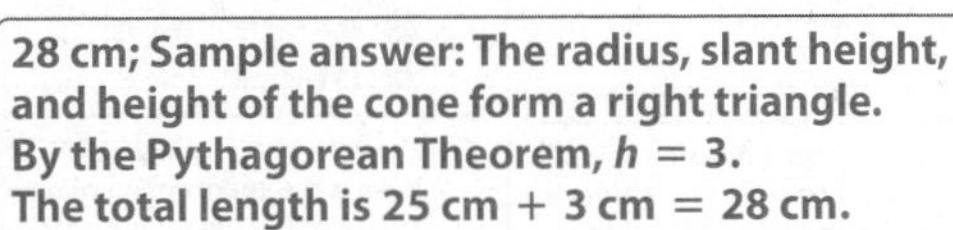

**28 cm; Sample answer: The radius, slant height, and height of the cone form a right triangle. By the Pythagorean Theorem, $h = 3$. The total length is 25 cm + 3 cm = 28 cm.**

**Part B**

What is the approximate volume of the rocket? Use 3.14 for $\pi$. Explain. **2 points**

**About 1,306.24 cm$^3$; Sample answer: Volume of cone + volume of cylinder = $\frac{1}{3}\pi(4^2) \cdot 3 + \pi(4^2) \cdot 25$; $V \approx 50.24 + 1{,}256 \approx 1{,}306.24$.**

**Part C**

If Cole's rocket parts are made of aluminum weighing 0.006 pound per cubic centimeter, will Cole be able to launch his rocket? Explain. **2 points**

**Yes; Sample answer: The weight of Cole's rocket is about 1,306.24 cm$^3$ $\cdot$ 0.006 $\frac{\text{lb}}{\text{cm}^3} \approx 7.84$ lb, which is less than 10 pounds.**

Performance Task, Form A 1 of 2

**2.** If the heights of the cone and cylinder remain the same, what is the maximum radius that will allow for lift-off of a rocket? Round to the nearest hundredth. Explain. **3 points**

**About 4.52 cm; Sample answer: The maximum volume is 10 lb $\div$ 0.006 $\frac{\text{lb}}{\text{cm}^3}$ = 1,666.67 cm$^3$. The volume of the rocket is the sum of the volumes of the cylinder and cone.**
**Cone: $V = \frac{1}{3}Bh = \frac{1}{3}(\pi r^2) \cdot 3 = \pi r^2$;**
**Cylinder: $V = \pi r^2 h = 25\pi r^2$;**
**The total volume is $V = \pi r^2 + 25\pi r^2 = 26\pi r^2$.**
**Using the maximum volume: $1{,}666.67 = 26\pi r^2$; $64.10 \approx (3.14)r^2$; $20.41 \approx r^2$; $4.52 \approx r$.**

**3.** Cole designs a vinyl decal to cover the part of the cone that is visible on his rocket. How much vinyl does Cole need for his decal? Round to the nearest hundredth. Explain. **2 points**

**About 62.86 cm$^2$; Sample answer: The surface area of the visible portion of the cone is $A = \pi r\ell$. $A \approx (3.14 \cdot 4 \cdot 5) \approx 62.86$.**

**4.** Suppose the rocket separates into its original parts before falling to Earth. How does the combined surface areas of the parts compare to the surface area of the assembled rocket?

**Sample answer: The combined surface area is greater by $2 \cdot \pi(4)^2 = 32\pi$ cm$^2$.**

Performance Task, Form A 2 of 2

## Item Analysis for Diagnosis and Intervention: Form A

| Item | DOK | MDIS | Standard |
|---|---|---|---|
| 1A | 3 | N54 | 8.G.C.9, MP.2 |
| 1B | 2 | N57 | 8.G.C.9, MP.6 |
| 1C | 3 | N57 | 8.G.C.9, MP.3 |
| 2 | 4 | N57 | 8.G.C.9, MP.6 |
| 3 | 1 | N50 | 8.G.C.9, MP.4 |
| 4 | 3 | N50 | 8.G.C.9, MP.6 |

## Scoring Rubric: Forms A and B

| Item | Points (Form A) | Points (Form B) |
|---|---|---|
| 1 | A/B/C 2: Correct response<br>1: Partially correct response | 2: Correct answer and explanation<br>1: Correct answer or explanation |
| 2 | 3: Correct maximum volume, maximum radius and explanation<br>2: Correct maximum volume or maximum radius and explanation<br>1: Some correct work shown and explained | 2: Correct answer and explanation<br>1: Correct answer or explanation |
| 3 | 2: Correct surface area and explanation<br>1: Correct drawing of net or explanation | A 1: Correct drawing and labels<br>B 3: Correct answer and explanation<br>2: Correct answer or explanation<br>1: Partially correct answer or explanation |
| 4 | 1: Correct response | 2: Correct answer and explanation<br>1: Correct answer or explanation |

Available Online

Name ______________________

Topic 8
Performance Task
Form B

A company packs spherical glass ornaments that fit snugly into boxes as shown.

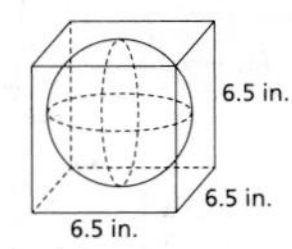


1. What is the volume of the ornament? Use 3.14 for $\pi$. Explain. **2 points**

**About 143.7 in.$^3$; Sample answer: The diameter of the ornament is the edge length of the cube, or 6.5 inches. The radius is equal to $\frac{1}{2} \cdot 6.5$, or 3.25 inches. The volume is $V = \frac{4}{3}\pi r^3 \approx \frac{4}{3}(3.14)(3.25)^3 \approx 143.7$.**

2. To protect the ornament, the company fills the box with packing material. What is the volume of packing material needed? Explain. **2 points**

**About 130.9 in.$^3$; Sample answer: Subtract the volume of the sphere from the volume of the cube; $6.5^3 - 143.7 \approx 130.9$.**

Performance Task, Form B 1 of 2

3. As the company grows, they consider shipping the ornaments in a cylindrical container that snugly fits 4 ornaments.

**Part A**

Draw a sketch of the package and label its dimensions. **1 point**

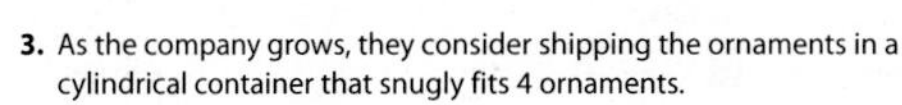

**Sample answer:**

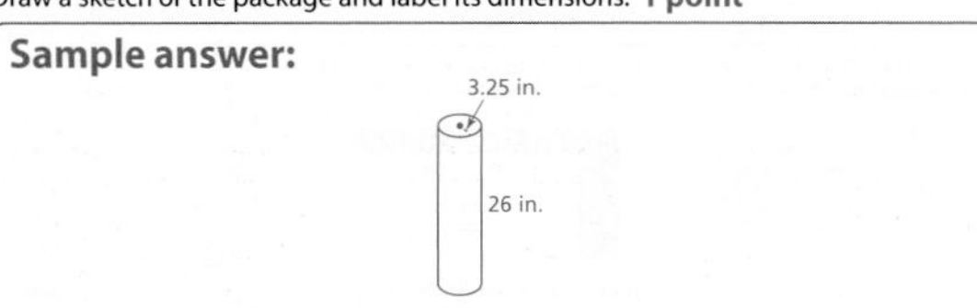


**Part B**

The cylindrical package is cardboard, and it has thin cardboard inserts that separate the ornaments. How much cardboard is needed to construct the package? Use 3.14 for $\pi$. Explain. **3 points**

**About 696.5 in.$^2$; Sample answer: The height of the cylinder is $4(6.5) = 26$ in., so the surface area of the curved surface is $2(3.14)(3.25) \cdot 26 \approx 530.7$. With the two ends, there are 5 circular cardboard pieces with combined area $5(3.14)(3.25^2) \approx 165.8$; $530.7 + 165.8 = 696.5$.**

4. Monique designs a new ornament that has the shape of a cone. She is told that the ornament should use the same amount of glass and have the same radius as the spherical ornament. What is the slant height of the conical ornament? Use 3.14 for $\pi$. Explain. **3 points**

**About 9.75 in.; Sample answer: The surface area of the spherical ornament is $4(3.14)(3.25)^2 \approx 132.67$ in.$^2$. The surface area of the cone is $3.14(3.25)^2 + 3.14(3.25)\ell \approx 33.17 + 10.21\ell$. Set these equal and solve for $\ell$; $\ell \approx 9.75$.**

Performance Task, Form B 2 of 2

## Item Analysis for Diagnosis and Intervention: Form B

| Item | DOK | MDIS | Standard |
|---|---|---|---|
| 1 | 3 | N55 | 8.G.C.9, MP.7 |
| 2 | 2 | N55 | 8.G.C.9, MP.7 |
| 3A | 1 | N49 | 8.G.C.9, MP.1 |
| 3B | 4 | N49 | 8.G.C.9, MP.2 |
| 4 | 3 | N50 | 8.G.C.9, MP.7 |

## Scoring Guide: Forms A and B

| Score | Recommendations |
|---|---|
| Greater Than 85% | Assign the corresponding MDIS for items answered incorrectly. Use Enrichment activities with the student. |
| 70%–85% | Assign the corresponding MDIS for items answered incorrectly. You may also assign Reteach to Build Understanding and Virtual Nerd Video assets for the lessons correlated to the items the student answered incorrectly. |
| Less Than 70% | Assign the corresponding MDIS for items answered incorrectly. Assign appropriate intervention lessons available online. You may also assign Reteach to Build Understanding, Additional Vocabulary Support, Build Mathematical Literacy, and Virtual Nerd Video assets for the lessons correlated to the items the student answered incorrectly. |

# TOPICS 1-8 PROGRESS MONITORING ASSESSMENT FORM A

Available Online

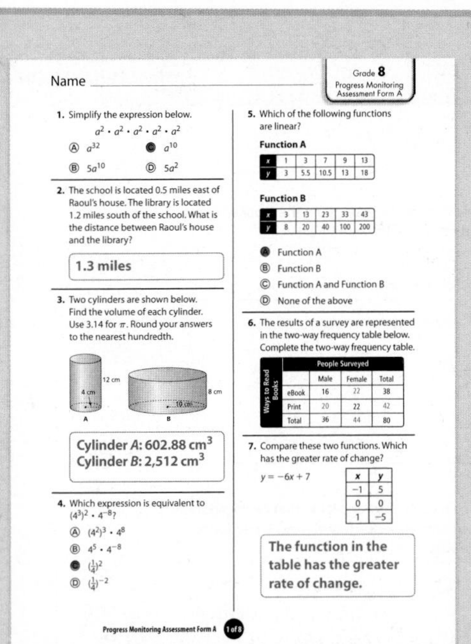
Name ______  Grade 8 Progress Monitoring Assessment Form A

1. Simplify the expression below.
$a^2 \cdot a^2 \cdot a^2 \cdot a^2 \cdot a^2$
Ⓐ $a^{32}$ ● $a^{10}$
Ⓑ $5a^{10}$ Ⓓ $5a^2$

2. The school is located 0.5 miles east of Raoul's house. The library is located 1.2 miles south of the school. What is the distance between Raoul's house and the library?
1.3 miles

3. Two cylinders are shown below. Find the volume of each cylinder. Use 3.14 for $\pi$. Round your answers to the nearest hundredth.
Cylinder $A$: 602.88 $cm^3$
Cylinder $B$: 2,512 $cm^3$

4. Which expression is equivalent to $(4^3)^2 \cdot 4^{-8}$?
Ⓐ $(4^2)^3 \cdot 4^8$
Ⓑ $4^5 \cdot 4^{-8}$
● $(\frac{1}{4})^2$
Ⓓ $(\frac{1}{4})^{-2}$

5. Which of the following functions are linear?
Function A

| x | 1 | 3 | 7 | 9 | 13 |
|---|---|---|---|---|---|
| y | 3 | 5.5 | 10.5 | 13 | 18 |

Function B

| x | 3 | 13 | 23 | 33 | 43 |
|---|---|---|---|---|---|
| y | 8 | 20 | 40 | 100 | 200 |

● Function A
Ⓑ Function B
Ⓒ Function A and Function B
Ⓓ None of the above

6. The results of a survey are represented in the two-way frequency table below. Complete the two-way frequency table.

| Ways to Read Books | Male | Female | Total |
|---|---|---|---|
| eBook | 16 | 22 | 38 |
| Print | 20 | 22 | 42 |
| Total | 36 | 44 | 80 |

7. Compare these two functions. Which has the greater rate of change?
$y = -6x + 7$

| x | y |
|---|---|
| −1 | 5 |
| 0 | 0 |
| 1 | −5 |

The function in the table has the greater rate of change.

Progress Monitoring Assessment Form A 1 of 8

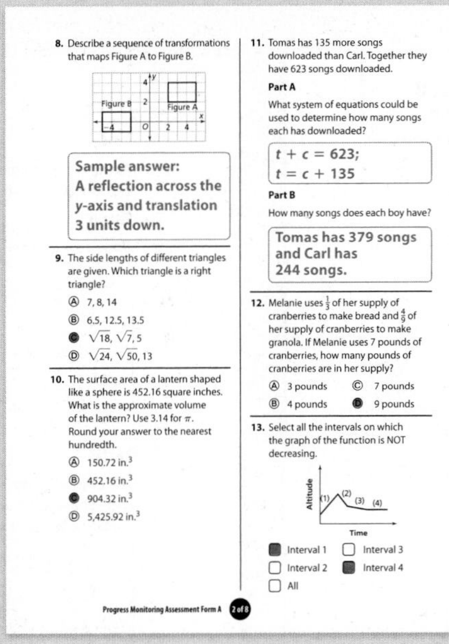
8. Describe a sequence of transformations that maps Figure A to Figure B.
Sample answer: A reflection across the $y$-axis and translation 3 units down.

9. The side lengths of different triangles are given. Which triangle is a right triangle?
Ⓐ 7, 8, 14
Ⓑ 6.5, 12.5, 13.5
● $\sqrt{18}, \sqrt{7}, 5$
Ⓓ $\sqrt{24}, \sqrt{50}, 13$

10. The surface area of a lantern shaped like a sphere is 452.16 square inches. What is the approximate volume of the lantern? Use 3.14 for $\pi$. Round your answer to the nearest hundredth.
Ⓐ 150.72 $in.^3$
Ⓑ 452.16 $in.^3$
● 904.32 $in.^3$
Ⓓ 5,425.92 $in.^3$

11. Tomas has 135 more songs downloaded than Carl. Together they have 623 songs downloaded.
Part A
What system of equations could be used to determine how many songs each has downloaded?
$t + c = 623$; $t = c + 135$
Part B
How many songs does each boy have?
Tomas has 379 songs and Carl has 244 songs.

12. Melanie uses $\frac{1}{5}$ of her supply of cranberries to make bread and $\frac{4}{5}$ of her supply of cranberries to make granola. If Melanie uses 7 pounds of cranberries, how many pounds of cranberries are in her supply?
Ⓐ 3 pounds Ⓒ 7 pounds
Ⓑ 4 pounds ● 9 pounds

13. Select all the intervals on which the graph of the function is NOT decreasing.
■ Interval 1 □ Interval 3
□ Interval 2 ■ Interval 4
□ All

Progress Monitoring Assessment Form A 2 of 8

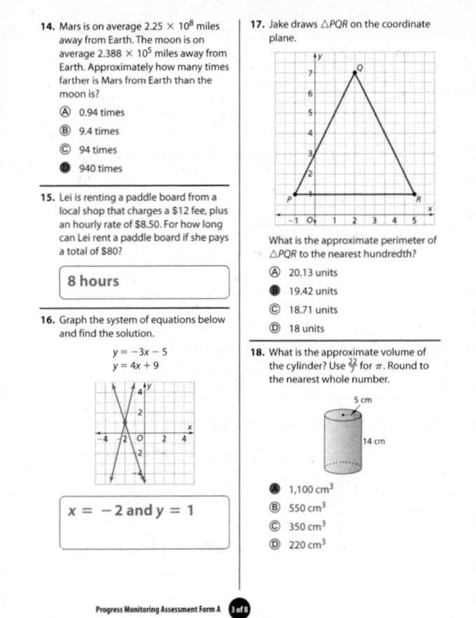
14. Mars is on average $2.25 \times 10^8$ miles away from Earth. The moon is on average $2.388 \times 10^5$ miles away from Earth. Approximately how many times farther is Mars from Earth than the moon is?
Ⓐ 0.94 times
Ⓑ 9.4 times
Ⓒ 94 times
● 940 times

15. Lei is renting a paddle board from a local shop that charges a \$12 fee, plus an hourly rate of \$8.50. For how long can Lei rent a paddle board if she pays a total of \$80?
8 hours

16. Graph the system of equations below and find the solution.
$y = -3x - 5$
$y = 4x + 9$
$x = -2$ and $y = 1$

17. Jake draws $\triangle PQR$ on the coordinate plane.
What is the approximate perimeter of $\triangle PQR$ to the nearest hundredth?
Ⓐ 20.13 units
● 19.42 units
Ⓒ 18.71 units
Ⓓ 18 units

18. What is the approximate volume of the cylinder? Use $\frac{22}{7}$ for $\pi$. Round to the nearest whole number.
● 1,100 $cm^3$
Ⓑ 550 $cm^3$
Ⓒ 350 $cm^3$
Ⓓ 220 $cm^3$

Progress Monitoring Assessment Form A 3 of 8

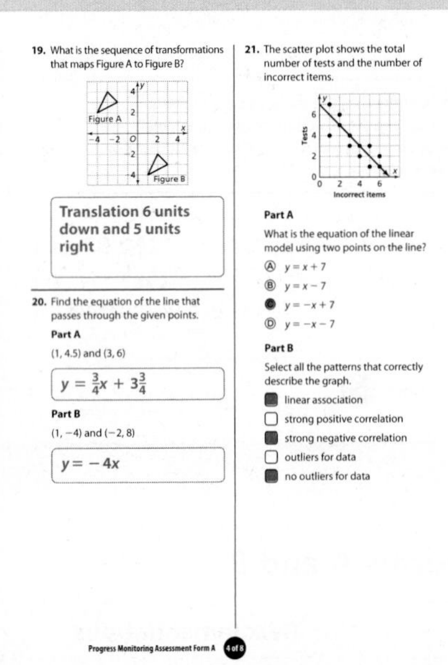
19. What is the sequence of transformations that maps Figure A to Figure B?
Translation 6 units down and 5 units right

20. Find the equation of the line that passes through the given points.
Part A
(1, 4.5) and (3, 6)
$y = \frac{3}{4}x + 3\frac{3}{4}$
Part B
(1, −4) and (−2, 8)
$y = -4x$

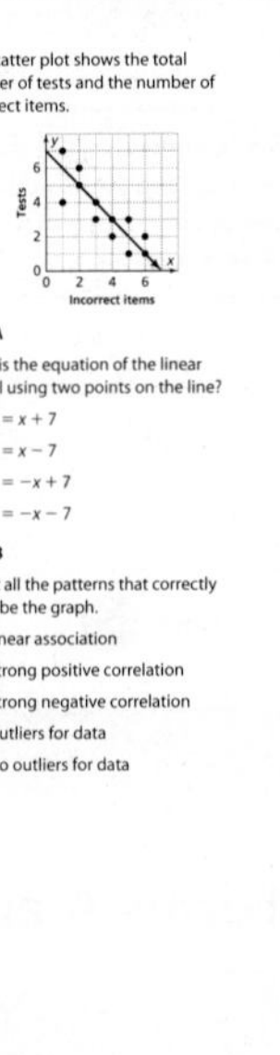
21. The scatter plot shows the total number of tests and the number of incorrect items.
Part A
What is the equation of the linear model using two points on the line?
Ⓐ $y = x + 7$
Ⓑ $y = x - 7$
● $y = -x + 7$
Ⓓ $y = -x - 7$
Part B
Select all the patterns that correctly describe the graph.
■ linear association
□ strong positive correlation
■ strong negative correlation
□ outliers for data
■ no outliers for data

Progress Monitoring Assessment Form A 4 of 8

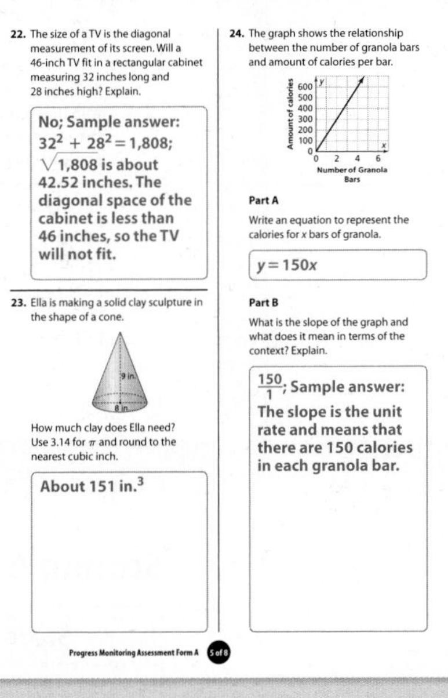
22. The size of a TV is the diagonal measurement of its screen. Will a 46-inch TV fit in a rectangular cabinet measuring 32 inches long and 28 inches high? Explain.
No; Sample answer: $32^2 + 28^2 = 1{,}808$; $\sqrt{1{,}808}$ is about 42.52 inches. The diagonal space of the cabinet is less than 46 inches, so the TV will not fit.

23. Ella is making a solid clay sculpture in the shape of a cone.
How much clay does Ella need? Use 3.14 for $\pi$ and round to the nearest cubic inch.
About 151 $in.^3$

24. The graph shows the relationship between the number of granola bars and amount of calories per bar.
Part A
Write an equation to represent the calories for $x$ bars of granola.
$y = 150x$
Part B
What is the slope of the graph and what does it mean in terms of the context? Explain.
$\frac{150}{1}$; Sample answer: The slope is the unit rate and means that there are 150 calories in each granola bar.

Progress Monitoring Assessment Form A 5 of 8

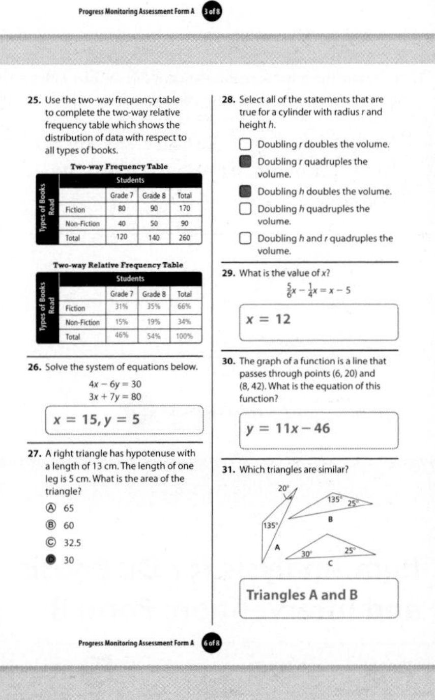
25. Use the two-way frequency table to complete the two-way relative frequency table which shows the distribution of data with respect to all types of books.

Two-way Frequency Table

| Types of Books Read | Grade 7 | Grade 8 | Total |
|---|---|---|---|
| Fiction | 80 | 90 | 170 |
| Non-Fiction | 40 | 50 | 90 |
| Total | 120 | 140 | 260 |

Two-way Relative Frequency Table

| Types of Books Read | Grade 7 | Grade 8 | Total |
|---|---|---|---|
| Fiction | 31% | 35% | 66% |
| Non-Fiction | 15% | 19% | 34% |
| Total | 46% | 54% | 100% |

26. Solve the system of equations below.
$4x - 6y = 30$
$3x + 7y = 80$
$x = 15, y = 5$

27. A right triangle has hypotenuse with a length of 13 cm. The length of one leg is 5 cm. What is the area of the triangle?
Ⓐ 65
Ⓑ 60
Ⓒ 32.5
● 30

28. Select all of the statements that are true for a cylinder with radius $r$ and height $h$.
□ Doubling $r$ doubles the volume.
■ Doubling $r$ quadruples the volume.
■ Doubling $h$ doubles the volume.
□ Doubling $h$ quadruples the volume.
□ Doubling $h$ and $r$ quadruples the volume.

29. What is the value of $x$?
$\frac{5}{6}x - \frac{1}{3}x = x - 5$
$x = 12$

30. The graph of a function is a line that passes through points (6, 20) and (8, 42). What is the equation of this function?
$y = 11x - 46$

31. Which triangles are similar?
Triangles A and B

Progress Monitoring Assessment Form A 6 of 8

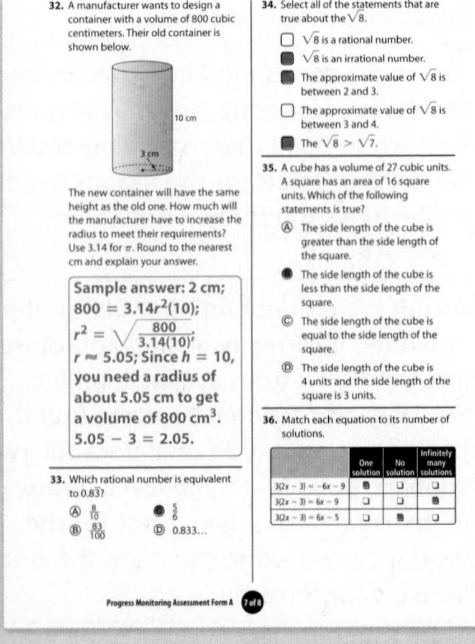
32. A manufacturer wants to design a container with a volume of 800 cubic centimeters. Their old container is shown below.
The new container will have the same height as the old one. How much will the manufacturer have to increase the radius to meet their requirements? Use 3.14 for $\pi$. Round to the nearest cm and explain your answer.
Sample answer: 2 cm; $800 = 3.14r^2(10)$; $r^2 = \sqrt{\frac{800}{3.14(10)}}$; $r \approx 5.05$; Since $h = 10$, you need a radius of about 5.05 cm to get a volume of 800 $cm^3$. $5.05 - 3 = 2.05$.

33. Which rational number is equivalent to $0.8\overline{3}$?
Ⓐ $\frac{8}{10}$ ● $\frac{5}{6}$
Ⓑ $\frac{83}{100}$ Ⓓ 0.833…

34. Select all of the statements that are true about the $\sqrt{8}$.
□ $\sqrt{8}$ is a rational number.
■ $\sqrt{8}$ is an irrational number.
■ The approximate value of $\sqrt{8}$ is between 2 and 3.
□ The approximate value of $\sqrt{8}$ is between 3 and 4.
■ The $\sqrt{8} > \sqrt{7}$.

35. A cube has a volume of 27 cubic units. A square has an area of 16 square units. Which of the following statements is true?
Ⓐ The side length of the cube is greater than the side length of the square.
● The side length of the cube is less than the side length of the square.
Ⓒ The side length of the cube is equal to the side length of the square.
Ⓓ The side length of the cube is 4 units and the side length of the square is 3 units.

36. Match each equation to its number of solutions.

| | One solution | No solution | Infinitely many solutions |
|---|---|---|---|
| $3(2x - 3) = -6x - 9$ | ■ | □ | □ |
| $3(2x - 3) = 6x - 9$ | □ | □ | ■ |
| $3(2x - 3) = 6x - 5$ | □ | ■ | □ |

Progress Monitoring Assessment Form A 7 of 8

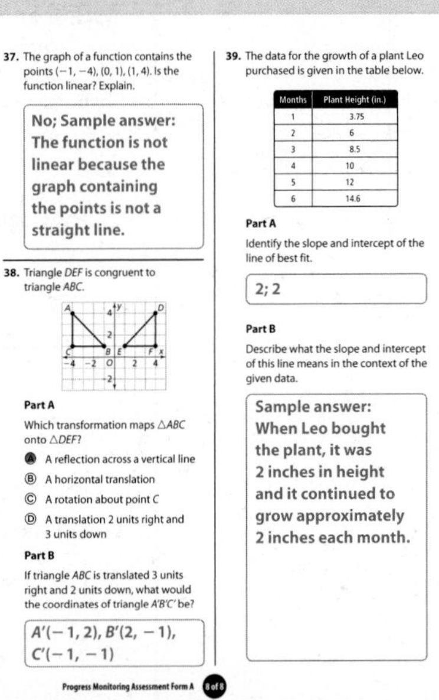
37. The graph of a function contains the points (−1, −4), (0, 1), (1, 4). Is the function linear? Explain.
No; Sample answer: The function is not linear because the graph containing the points is not a straight line.

38. Triangle $DEF$ is congruent to triangle $ABC$.
Part A
Which transformation maps $\triangle ABC$ onto $\triangle DEF$?
● A reflection across a vertical line
Ⓑ A horizontal translation
Ⓒ A rotation about point $C$
Ⓓ A translation 2 units right and 3 units down
Part B
If triangle $ABC$ is translated 3 units right and 2 units down, what would the coordinates of triangle $A'B'C'$ be?
$A'(-1, 2), B'(2, -1), C'(-1, -1)$

39. The data for the growth of a plant Leo purchased is given in the table below.

| Months | Plant Height (in.) |
|---|---|
| 1 | 3.75 |
| 2 | 6 |
| 3 | 8.5 |
| 4 | 10 |
| 5 | 12 |
| 6 | 14.6 |

Part A
Identify the slope and intercept of the line of best fit.
2; 2
Part B
Describe what the slope and intercept of this line means in the context of the given data.
Sample answer: When Leo bought the plant, it was 2 inches in height and it continued to grow approximately 2 inches each month.

Progress Monitoring Assessment Form A 8 of 8

## Item Analysis for Diagnosis and Intervention

| Item | DOK | MDIS | Standard(s) |
|---|---|---|---|
| 1 | 1 | L83 | 8.EE.A.1 |
| 2 | 2 | N64 | 8.G.B.8 |
| 3 | 2 | N53 | 8.G.C.9 |
| 4 | 1 | L83 | 8.EE.A.1 |
| 5 | 2 | K51 | 8.F.A.1 |
| 6 | 3 | N89 | 8.SP.A.4 |
| 7 | 2 | K50, K52 | 8.F.A.2 |
| 8 | 2 | N59, N61 | 8.G.A.4 |
| 9 | 2 | N65 | 8.G.B.6, 8.G.B.7 |
| 10 | 3 | N50, N55 | 8.G.C.9 |
| 11A | 2 | K35 | 8.EE.C.8b |
| 11B | 2 | K35 | 8.EE.C.8b |
| 12 | 2 | K29 | 8.EE.C.7b |
| 13 | 2 | K54 | 8.F.B.5 |
| 14 | 2 | L84 | 8.EE.A.3. 8.EE.A.4 |
| 15 | 2 | K26 | 8.EE.C.7b |
| 16 | 2 | K34 | 8.EE.C.8a |
| 17 | 3 | N66 | 8.G.B.8 |
| 18 | 2 | N53 | 8.G.C.9 |
| 19 | 2 | N59 | 8.G.A.4 |
| 20A | 2 | K50 | 8.EE.B.6 |
| 20B | 2 | K50 | 8.EE.B.6 |
| 21A | 2 | N71 | 8.SP.A.2 |

| Item | DOK | MDIS | Standard(s) |
|---|---|---|---|
| 21B | 2 | N71 | 8.SP.A.1 |
| 22 | 2 | N64 | 8.G.B.7 |
| 23 | 2 | N50 | 8.G.C.9 |
| 24A | 2 | K50 | 8.EE.B.5 |
| 24B | 2 | K50 | 8.EE.B.5 |
| 25 | 3 | N90 | 8.SP.A.4 |
| 26 | 2 | K36 | 8.EE.C.8b |
| 27 | 2 | N66 | 8.G.B.7 |
| 28 | 2 | N57 | 8.G.C.9 |
| 29 | 2 | K29 | 8.EE.C.7b |
| 30 | 3 | K50 | 8.F.B.4 |
| 31 | 2 | N63 | 8.G.A.1b, 8.G.A.5 |
| 32A | 2 | N53, N54 | 8.G.C.9 |
| 32B | 2 | N57 | 8.G.C.9 |
| 33 | 2 | M23, L80 | 8.NS.A.1 |
| 34 | 2 | L81 | 8.NS.A.2 |
| 35 | 2 | N41, N52 | 8.EE.A.2 |
| 36 | 2 | K32 | 8.EE.C.7a |
| 37 | 2 | K52, K53 | 8.F.A.3 |
| 38A | 2 | N59, N60 | 8.G.A.1a, 8.G.A.2 |
| 38B | 2 | N59, N60 | 8.G.A.3 |
| 39A | 2 | N72 | 8.SP.A.3 |
| 39B | 2 | N72 | 8.SP.A.3 |

Monitor the progress students make throughout the year using the Progress Monitoring Assessments Forms A, B, and C. The three forms assess the same content item for item. The Item Analysis chart can be used with all three forms.

One way to use the Progress Monitoring Assessments is to assign them at the beginning, middle, and end of the year.

You can find the Progress Monitoring Assessments online. The online assessments are auto-scored.

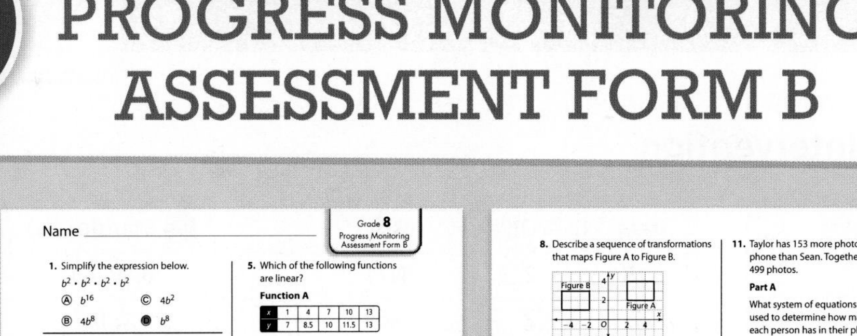
TOPICS 1-8

# PROGRESS MONITORING ASSESSMENT FORM B

Available Online

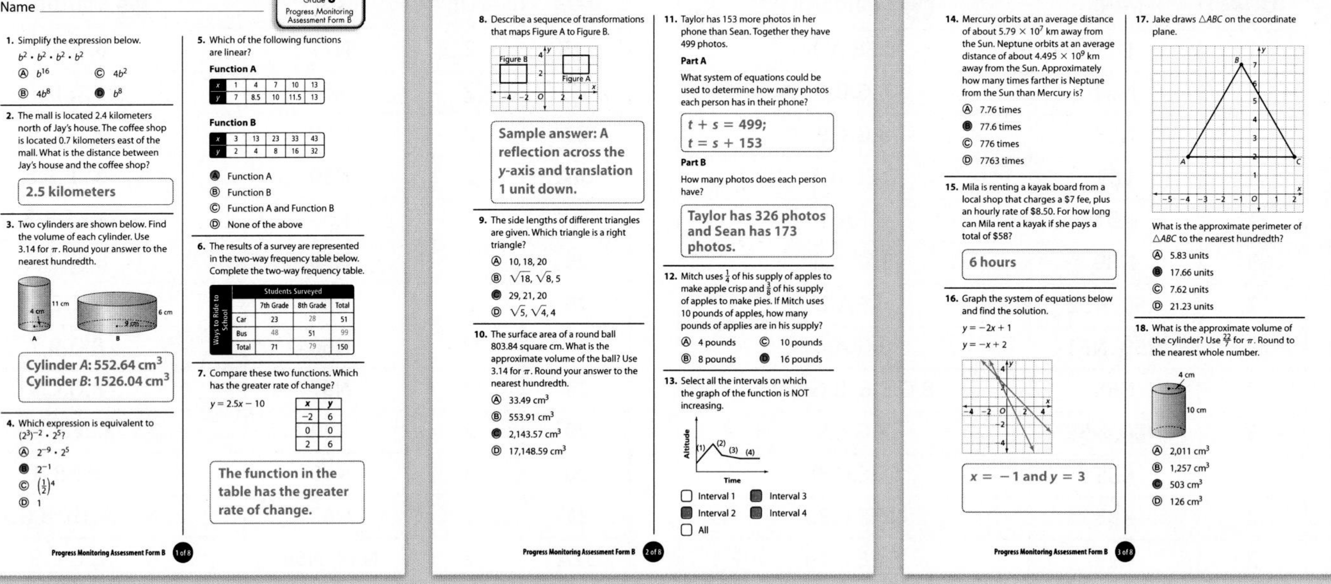
Name

Grade 8
Progress Monitoring Assessment Form B

**1.** Simplify the expression below.
$b^2 \cdot b^2 \cdot b^2 \cdot b^2$
Ⓐ $b^{16}$ Ⓒ $4b^2$
Ⓑ $4b^8$ ● $b^8$

**2.** The mall is located 2.4 kilometers north of Jay's house. The coffee shop is located 0.7 kilometers east of the mall. What is the distance between Jay's house and the coffee shop?
2.5 kilometers

**3.** Two cylinders are shown below. Find the volume of each cylinder. Use 3.14 for $\pi$. Round your answer to the nearest hundredth.
Cylinder *A*: 552.64 $cm^3$
Cylinder *B*: 1526.04 $cm^3$

**4.** Which expression is equivalent to $(2^3)^{-2} \cdot 2^5$?
Ⓐ $2^{-9} \cdot 2^5$
● $2^{-1}$
Ⓒ $(\frac{1}{2})^4$
Ⓓ 1

**5.** Which of the following functions are linear?
Function A

| x | 1 | 4 | 7 | 10 | 13 |
|---|---|---|---|---|---|
| y | 7 | 8.5 | 10 | 11.5 | 13 |

Function B

| x | 3 | 13 | 23 | 33 | 43 |
|---|---|---|---|---|---|
| y | 2 | 4 | 8 | 16 | 32 |

● Function A
Ⓑ Function B
Ⓒ Function A and Function B
Ⓓ None of the above

**6.** The results of a survey are represented in the two-way frequency table below. Complete the two-way frequency table.

| Ways to Ride to School | 7th Grade | 8th Grade | Total |
|---|---|---|---|
| Car | 23 | 28 | 51 |
| Bus | 48 | 51 | 99 |
| Total | 71 | 79 | 150 |

**7.** Compare these two functions. Which has the greater rate of change?
$y = 2.5x - 10$

| x | y |
|---|---|
| −2 | 6 |
| 0 | 0 |
| 2 | 6 |

The function in the table has the greater rate of change.

Progress Monitoring Assessment Form B 1 of 8

**8.** Describe a sequence of transformations that maps Figure A to Figure B.
Sample answer: A reflection across the *y*-axis and translation 1 unit down.

**9.** The side lengths of different triangles are given. Which triangle is a right triangle?
Ⓐ 10, 18, 20
Ⓑ $\sqrt{18}, \sqrt{8}, 5$
● 29, 21, 20
Ⓓ $\sqrt{5}, \sqrt{4}, 4$

**10.** The surface area of a round ball 803.84 square cm. What is the approximate volume of the ball? Use 3.14 for $\pi$. Round your answer to the nearest hundredth.
Ⓐ 33.49 $cm^3$
Ⓑ 553.91 $cm^3$
● 2,143.57 $cm^3$
Ⓓ 17,148.59 $cm^3$

**11.** Taylor has 153 more photos in her phone than Sean. Together they have 499 photos.
Part A
What system of equations could be used to determine how many photos each person has in their phone?
$t + s = 499;$
$t = s + 153$
Part B
How many photos does each person have?
Taylor has 326 photos and Sean has 173 photos.

**12.** Mitch uses $\frac{1}{4}$ of his supply of apples to make apple crisp and $\frac{3}{8}$ of his supply of apples to make pies. If Mitch uses 10 pounds of apples, how many pounds of apples are in his supply?
Ⓐ 4 pounds Ⓒ 10 pounds
Ⓑ 8 pounds ● 16 pounds

**13.** Select all the intervals on which the graph of the function is NOT increasing.
☐ Interval 1 ■ Interval 3
■ Interval 2 ■ Interval 4
☐ All

Progress Monitoring Assessment Form B 2 of 8

**14.** Mercury orbits at an average distance of about $5.79 \times 10^7$ km away from the Sun. Neptune orbits at an average distance of about $4.495 \times 10^9$ km away from the Sun. Approximately how many times farther is Neptune from the Sun than Mercury is?
Ⓐ 7.76 times
● 77.6 times
Ⓒ 776 times
Ⓓ 7763 times

**15.** Mila is renting a kayak board from a local shop that charges a $7 fee, plus an hourly rate of $8.50. For how long can Mila rent a kayak if she pays a total of $58?
6 hours

**16.** Graph the system of equations below and find the solution.
$y = -2x + 1$
$y = -x + 2$
$x = -1$ and $y = 3$

**17.** Jake draws $\triangle ABC$ on the coordinate plane.
What is the approximate perimeter of $\triangle ABC$ to the nearest hundredth?
Ⓐ 5.83 units
● 17.66 units
Ⓒ 7.62 units
Ⓓ 21.23 units

**18.** What is the approximate volume of the cylinder? Use $\frac{22}{7}$ for $\pi$. Round to the nearest whole number.
Ⓐ 2,011 $cm^3$
Ⓑ 1,257 $cm^3$
● 503 $cm^3$
Ⓓ 126 $cm^3$

Progress Monitoring Assessment Form B 3 of 8

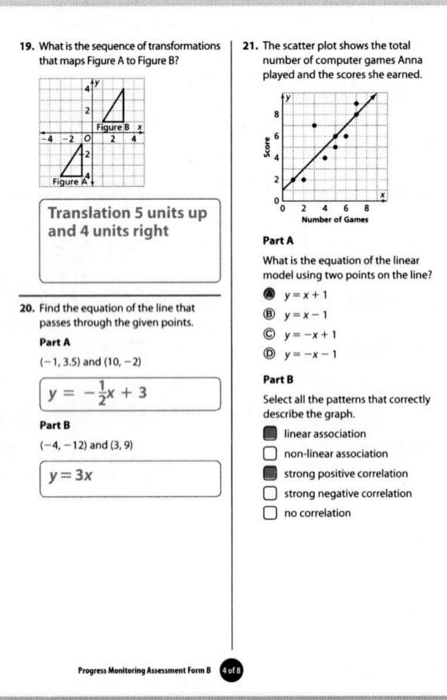
**19.** What is the sequence of transformations that maps Figure A to Figure B?
Translation 5 units up and 4 units right

**20.** Find the equation of the line that passes through the given points.
Part A
(−1, 3.5) and (10, −2)
$y = -\frac{1}{2}x + 3$
Part B
(−4, −12) and (3, 9)
$y = 3x$

**21.** The scatter plot shows the total number of computer games Anna played and the scores she earned.
Part A
What is the equation of the linear model using two points on the line?
● $y = x + 1$
Ⓑ $y = x - 1$
Ⓒ $y = -x + 1$
Ⓓ $y = -x - 1$
Part B
Select all the patterns that correctly describe the graph.
■ linear association
☐ non-linear association
■ strong positive correlation
☐ strong negative correlation
☐ no correlation

Progress Monitoring Assessment Form B 4 of 8

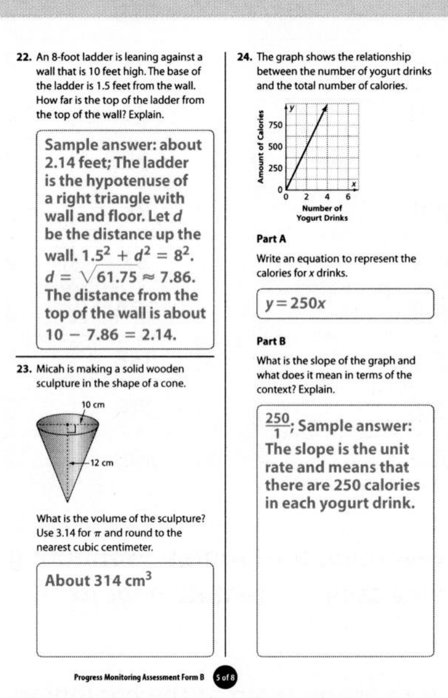
**22.** An 8-foot ladder is leaning against a wall that is 10 feet high. The base of the ladder is 1.5 feet from the wall. How far is the top of the ladder from the top of the wall? Explain.
Sample answer: about 2.14 feet; The ladder is the hypotenuse of a right triangle with wall and floor. Let *d* be the distance up the wall. $1.5^2 + d^2 = 8^2$. $d = \sqrt{61.75} \approx 7.86$. The distance from the top of the wall is about $10 - 7.86 = 2.14$.

**23.** Micah is making a solid wooden sculpture in the shape of a cone.
What is the volume of the sculpture? Use 3.14 for $\pi$ and round to the nearest cubic centimeter.
About 314 $cm^3$

**24.** The graph shows the relationship between the number of yogurt drinks and the total number of calories.
Part A
Write an equation to represent the calories for *x* drinks.
$y = 250x$
Part B
What is the slope of the graph and what does it mean in terms of the context? Explain.
$\frac{250}{1}$; Sample answer: The slope is the unit rate and means that there are 250 calories in each yogurt drink.

Progress Monitoring Assessment Form B 5 of 8

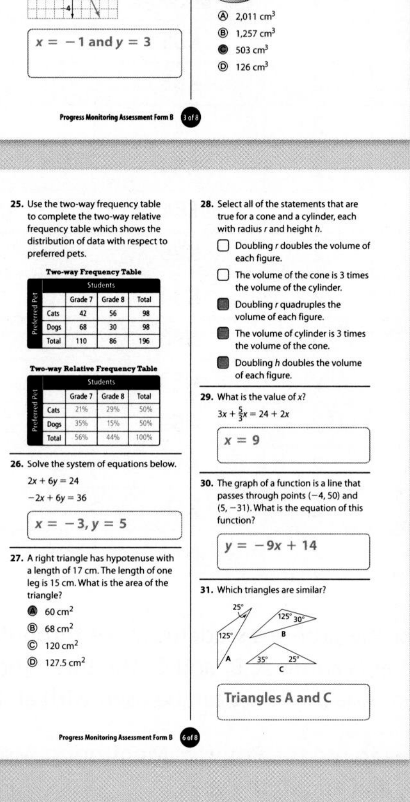
**25.** Use the two-way frequency table to complete the two-way relative frequency table which shows the distribution of data with respect to preferred pets.

Two-way Frequency Table

| Preferred Pet | Grade 7 | Grade 8 | Total |
|---|---|---|---|
| Cats | 42 | 56 | 98 |
| Dogs | 68 | 30 | 98 |
| Total | 110 | 86 | 196 |

Two-way Relative Frequency Table

| Preferred Pet | Grade 7 | Grade 8 | Total |
|---|---|---|---|
| Cats | 21% | 29% | 50% |
| Dogs | 35% | 15% | 50% |
| Total | 56% | 44% | 100% |

**26.** Solve the system of equations below.
$2x + 6y = 24$
$-2x + 6y = 36$
$x = -3, y = 5$

**27.** A right triangle has hypotenuse with a length of 17 cm. The length of one leg is 15 cm. What is the area of the triangle?
● 60 $cm^2$
Ⓑ 68 $cm^2$
Ⓒ 120 $cm^2$
Ⓓ 127.5 $cm^2$

**28.** Select all of the statements that are true for a cone and a cylinder, each with radius *r* and height *h*.
☐ Doubling *r* doubles the volume of each figure.
☐ The volume of the cone is 3 times the volume of the cylinder.
■ Doubling *r* quadruples the volume of each figure.
■ The volume of cylinder is 3 times the volume of the cone.
■ Doubling *h* doubles the volume of each figure.

**29.** What is the value of *x*?
$3x + \frac{5}{3}x = 24 + 2x$
$x = 9$

**30.** The graph of a function is a line that passes through points (−4, 50) and (5, −31). What is the equation of this function?
$y = -9x + 14$

**31.** Which triangles are similar?
Triangles A and C

Progress Monitoring Assessment Form B 6 of 8

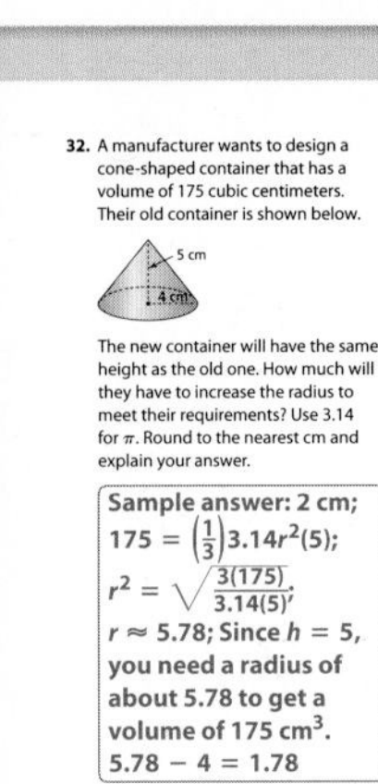
**32.** A manufacturer wants to design a cone-shaped container that has a volume of 175 cubic centimeters. Their old container is shown below.
The new container will have the same height as the old one. How much will they have to increase the radius to meet their requirements? Use 3.14 for $\pi$. Round to the nearest cm and explain your answer.
Sample answer: 2 cm; $175 = (\frac{1}{3})3.14r^2(5)$; $r^2 = \sqrt{\frac{3(175)}{3.14(5)}}$, $r \approx 5.78$; Since $h = 5$, you need a radius of about 5.78 to get a volume of 175 $cm^3$. $5.78 - 4 = 1.78$

**33.** Which rational number is equivalent to $0.\overline{63}$?
Ⓐ 0.63
● $\frac{7}{11}$
Ⓒ $\frac{63}{100}$
Ⓓ $\frac{7}{110}$

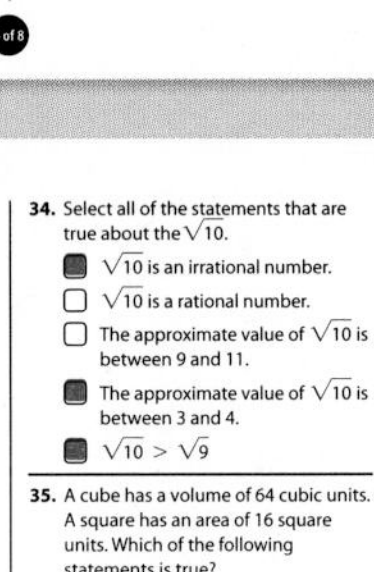
**34.** Select all of the statements that are true about the $\sqrt{10}$.
■ $\sqrt{10}$ is an irrational number.
☐ $\sqrt{10}$ is a rational number.
☐ The approximate value of $\sqrt{10}$ is between 9 and 11.
■ The approximate value of $\sqrt{10}$ is between 3 and 4.
■ $\sqrt{10} > \sqrt{9}$

**35.** A cube has a volume of 64 cubic units. A square has an area of 16 square units. Which of the following statements is true?
Ⓐ The side length of the cube is greater than the side length of the square.
Ⓑ The side length of the cube is less than the side length of the square.
● The side length of the cube is equal to the side length of the square.
Ⓓ The side length of the cube is 4 units and the side length of the square is 8 units.

**36.** Match each equation to its number of solutions.

| | One solution | No solution | Infinitely many solutions |
|---|---|---|---|
| $2(4x + 3) = 8x + 8$ | ☐ | ■ | ☐ |
| $2(4x + 3) = -8x + 6$ | ■ | ☐ | ☐ |
| $2(4x + 3) = 8x + 6$ | ☐ | ☐ | ■ |

Progress Monitoring Assessment Form B 7 of 8

**37.** The graph of a function contains the points (−5, 1), (0, 3), (5, 5). Is the function linear? Explain.
Yes; Sample answer: The function is linear because the graph containing the points is a straight line.

**38.** Triangle *DEF* is congruent to triangle *ABC*.
Part A
Which transformation maps $\triangle ABC$ onto $\triangle DEF$
Ⓐ a rotation about point *B*
● a translation 5 units right and 1 unit up
Ⓒ a reflection across a horizontal line
Ⓓ a reflection across a vertical line
Part B
If $\triangle ABC$ is reflected across the *y*-axis, what would the coordinates of $\triangle A'B'C'$ be?
$A'(4, 4), B'(1, 1), C'(4, 1)$

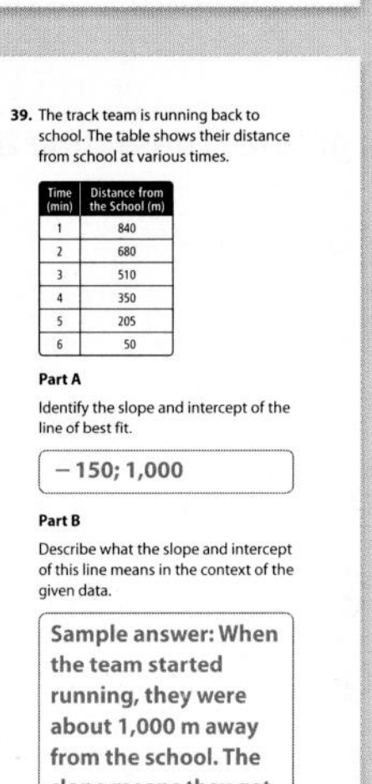
**39.** The track team is running back to school. The table shows their distance from school at various times.

| Time (min) | Distance from the School (m) |
|---|---|
| 1 | 840 |
| 2 | 680 |
| 3 | 510 |
| 4 | 350 |
| 5 | 205 |
| 6 | 50 |

Part A
Identify the slope and intercept of the line of best fit.
−150; 1,000
Part B
Describe what the slope and intercept of this line means in the context of the given data.
Sample answer: When the team started running, they were about 1,000 m away from the school. The slope means they get about 150 m closer to the school each minute.

Progress Monitoring Assessment Form B 8 of 8

## Item Analysis for Diagnosis and Intervention

| Item | DOK | MDIS | Standard(s) |
|---|---|---|---|
| 1 | 1 | L83 | 8.EE.A.1 |
| 2 | 2 | N64 | 8.G.B.8 |
| 3 | 2 | N53 | 8.G.C.9 |
| 4 | 1 | L83 | 8.EE.A.1 |
| 5 | 2 | K51 | 8.F.A.1 |
| 6 | 3 | N89 | 8.SP.A.4 |
| 7 | 2 | K50, K52 | 8.F.A.2 |
| 8 | 2 | N59, N61 | 8.G.A.4 |
| 9 | 2 | N65 | 8.G.B.6, 8.G.B.7 |
| 10 | 3 | N50, N55 | 8.G.C.9 |
| 11A | 2 | K35 | 8.EE.C.8b |
| 11B | 2 | K35 | 8.EE.C.8b |
| 12 | 2 | K29 | 8.EE.C.7b |
| 13 | 2 | K54 | 8.F.B.5 |
| 14 | 2 | L84 | 8.EE.A.3. 8.EE.A.4 |
| 15 | 2 | K26 | 8.EE.C.7b |
| 16 | 2 | K34 | 8.EE.C.8a |
| 17 | 3 | N66 | 8.G.B.8 |
| 18 | 2 | N53 | 8.G.C.9 |
| 19 | 2 | N59 | 8.G.A.4 |
| 20A | 2 | K50 | 8.EE.B.6 |
| 20B | 2 | K50 | 8.EE.B.6 |
| 21A | 2 | N71 | 8.SP.A.2 |

| Item | DOK | MDIS | Standard(s) |
|---|---|---|---|
| 21B | 2 | N71 | 8.SP.A.1 |
| 22 | 2 | N64 | 8.G.B.7 |
| 23 | 2 | N50 | 8.G.C.9 |
| 24A | 2 | K50 | 8.EE.B.5 |
| 24B | 2 | K50 | 8.EE.B.5 |
| 25 | 3 | N90 | 8.SP.A.4 |
| 26 | 2 | K36 | 8.EE.C.8b |
| 27 | 2 | N66 | 8.G.B.7 |
| 28 | 2 | N57 | 8.G.C.9 |
| 29 | 2 | K29 | 8.EE.C.7b |
| 30 | 3 | K50 | 8.F.B.4 |
| 31 | 2 | N63 | 8.G.A.1b, 8.G.A.5 |
| 32A | 2 | N53, N54 | 8.G.C.9 |
| 32B | 2 | N57 | 8.G.C.9 |
| 33 | 2 | M23, L80 | 8.NS.A.1 |
| 34 | 2 | L81 | 8.NS.A.2 |
| 35 | 2 | N41, N52 | 8.EE.A.2 |
| 36 | 2 | K32 | 8.EE.C.7a |
| 37 | 2 | K52, K53 | 8.F.A.3 |
| 38A | 2 | N59, N60 | 8.G.A.1a, 8.G.A.2 |
| 38B | 2 | N59, N60 | 8.G.A.3 |
| 39A | 2 | N72 | 8.SP.A.3 |
| 39B | 2 | N72 | 8.SP.A.3 |

Monitor the progress students make throughout the year using the Progress Monitoring Assessments Forms A, B, and C. The three forms assess the same content item for item. The Item Analysis chart can be used with all three forms.

One way to use the Progress Monitoring Assessments is to assign them at the beginning, middle, and end of the year.

You can find the Progress Monitoring Assessments online. The online assessments are auto-scored.

Available Online

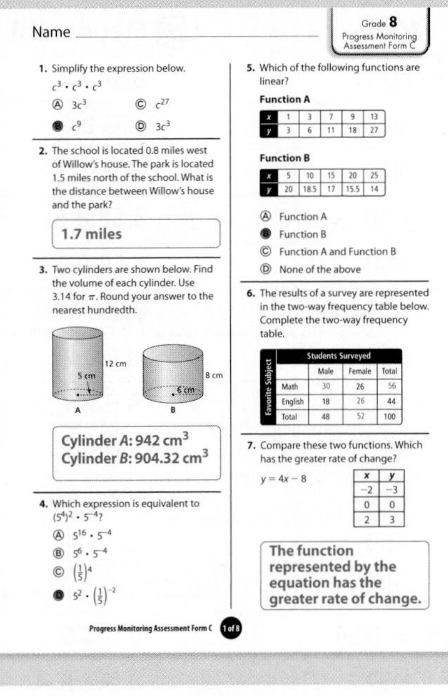

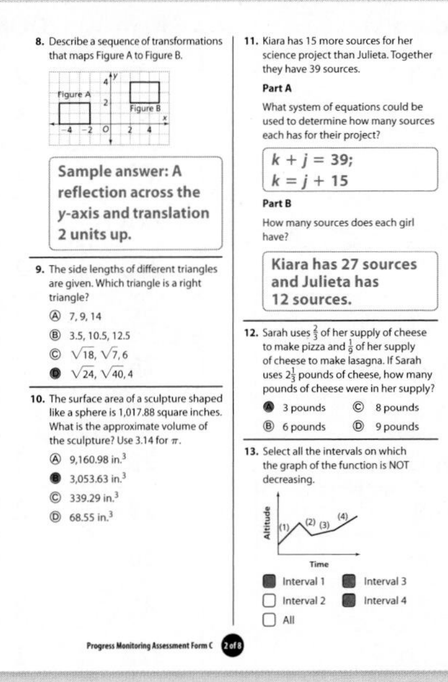

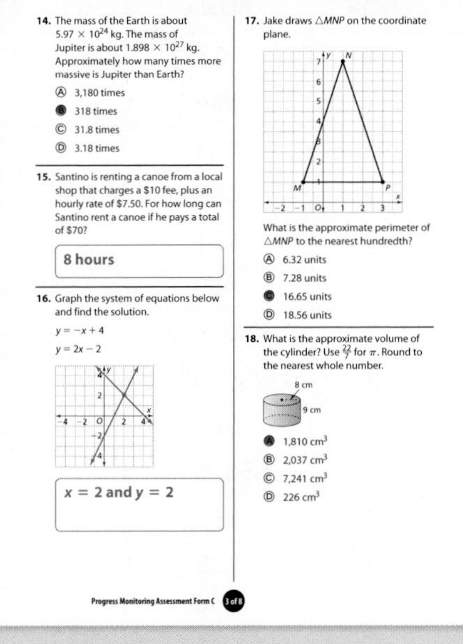

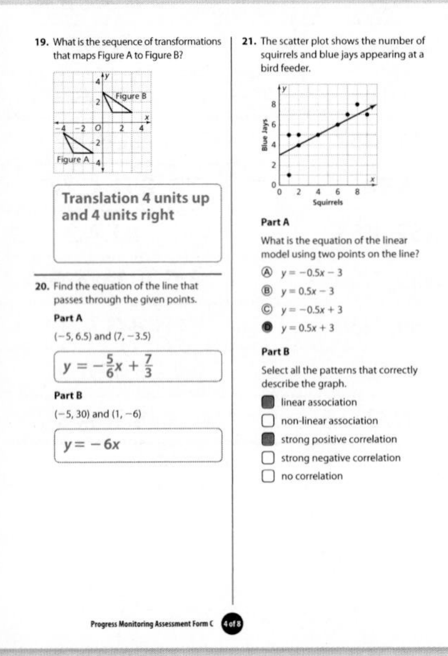

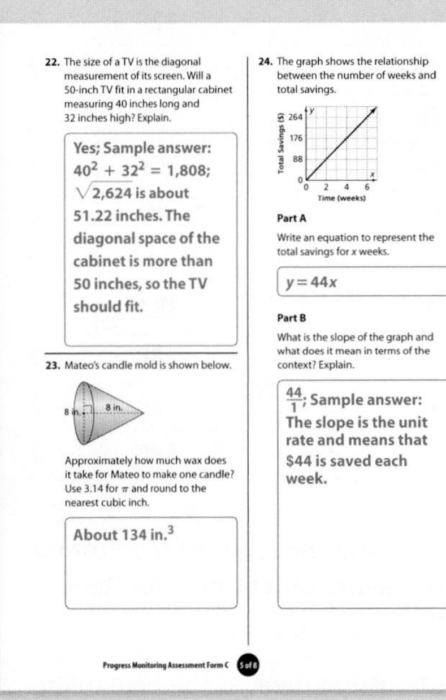

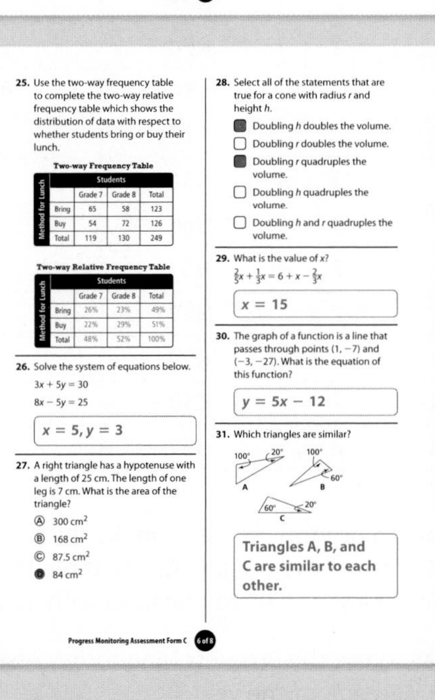

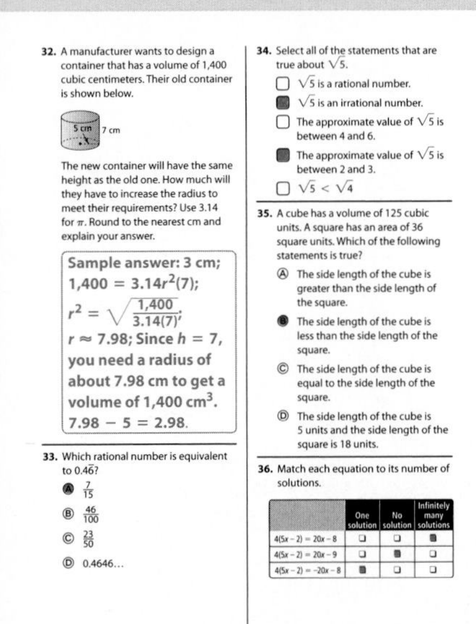

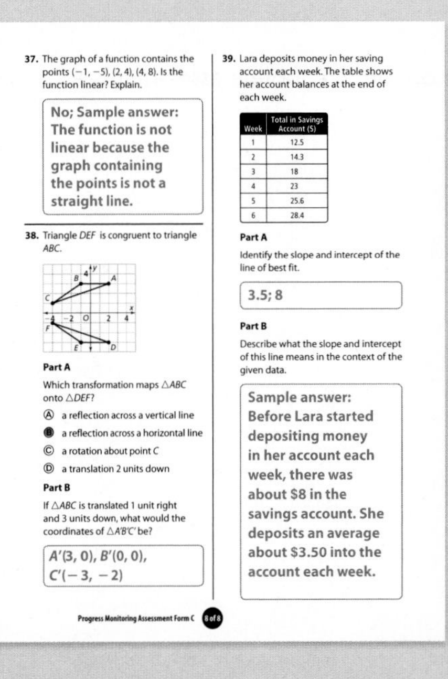

Go Online

Assess

## Item Analysis for Diagnosis and Intervention

| Item | DOK | MDIS | Standard(s) |
|---|---|---|---|
| 1 | 1 | L83 | 8.EE.A.1 |
| 2 | 2 | N64 | 8.G.B.8 |
| 3 | 2 | N53 | 8.G.C.9 |
| 4 | 1 | L83 | 8.EE.A.1 |
| 5 | 2 | K51 | 8.F.A.1 |
| 6 | 3 | N89 | 8.SP.A.4 |
| 7 | 2 | K50, K52 | 8.F.A.2 |
| 8 | 2 | N59, N61 | 8.G.A.4 |
| 9 | 2 | N65 | 8.G.B.6, 8.G.B.7 |
| 10 | 3 | N50, N55 | 8.G.C.9 |
| 11A | 2 | K35 | 8.EE.C.8b |
| 11B | 2 | K35 | 8.EE.C.8b |
| 12 | 2 | K29 | 8.EE.C.7b |
| 13 | 2 | K54 | 8.F.B.5 |
| 14 | 2 | L84 | 8.EE.A.3. 8.EE.A.4 |
| 15 | 2 | K26 | 8.EE.C.7b |
| 16 | 2 | K34 | 8.EE.C.8a |
| 17 | 3 | N66 | 8.G.B.8 |
| 18 | 2 | N53 | 8.G.C.9 |
| 19 | 2 | N59 | 8.G.A.4 |
| 20A | 2 | K50 | 8.EE.B.6 |
| 20B | 2 | K50 | 8.EE.B.6 |
| 21A | 2 | N71 | 8.SP.A.2 |

| Item | DOK | MDIS | Standard(s) |
|---|---|---|---|
| 21B | 2 | N71 | 8.SP.A.1 |
| 22 | 2 | N64 | 8.G.B.7 |
| 23 | 2 | N50 | 8.G.C.9 |
| 24A | 2 | K50 | 8.EE.B.5 |
| 24B | 2 | K50 | 8.EE.B.5 |
| 25 | 3 | N90 | 8.SP.A.4 |
| 26 | 2 | K36 | 8.EE.C.8b |
| 27 | 2 | N66 | 8.G.B.7 |
| 28 | 2 | N57 | 8.G.C.9 |
| 29 | 2 | K29 | 8.EE.C.7b |
| 30 | 3 | K50 | 8.F.B.4 |
| 31 | 2 | N63 | 8.G.A.1b, 8.G.A.5 |
| 32A | 2 | N53, N54 | 8.G.C.9 |
| 32B | 2 | N57 | 8.G.C.9 |
| 33 | 2 | M23, L80 | 8.NS.A.1 |
| 34 | 2 | L81 | 8.NS.A.2 |
| 35 | 2 | N41, N52 | 8.EE.A.2 |
| 36 | 2 | K32 | 8.EE.C.7a |
| 37 | 2 | K52, K53 | 8.F.A.3 |
| 38A | 2 | N59, N60 | 8.G.A.1a, 8.G.A.2 |
| 38B | 2 | N59, N60 | 8.G.A.3 |
| 39A | 2 | N72 | 8.SP.A.3 |
| 39B | 2 | N72 | 8.SP.A.3 |

Monitor the progress students make throughout the year using the Progress Monitoring Assessments Forms A, B, and C. The three forms assess the same content item for item. The Item Analysis chart can be used with all three forms.

One way to use the Progress Monitoring Assessments is to assign them at the beginning, middle, and end of the year.

You can find the Progress Monitoring Assessments online. The online assessments are auto-scored.

TOPICS 1-8

# CUMULATIVE/BENCHMARK ASSESSMENT

Available Online

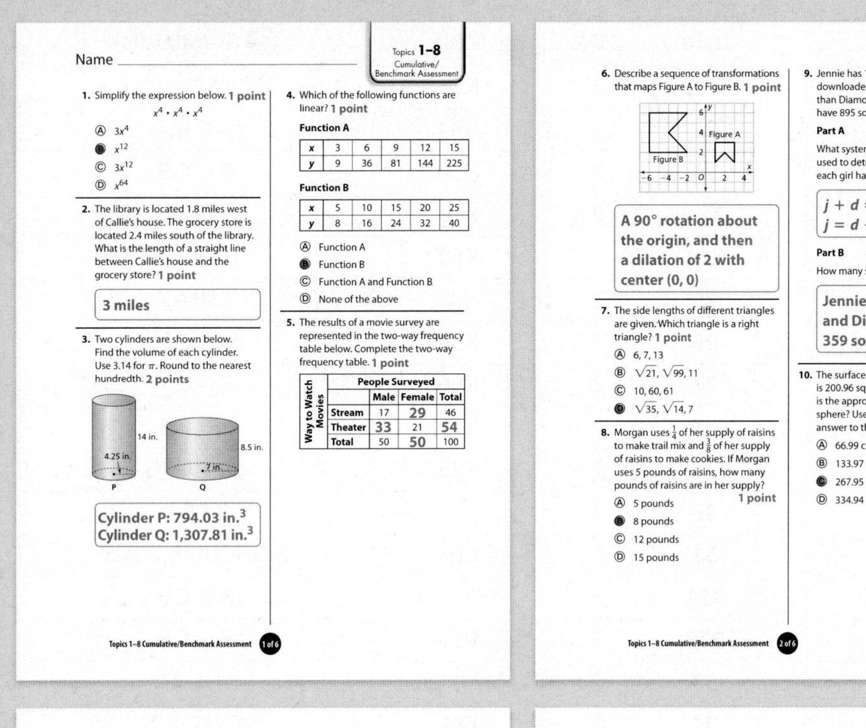

Name

Topics 1–8 Cumulative/Benchmark Assessment

1. Simplify the expression below. 1 point
$x^4 \cdot x^4 \cdot x^4$
- Ⓐ $3x^4$
- Ⓑ $x^{12}$
- Ⓒ $3x^{12}$
- Ⓓ $x^{64}$

2. The library is located 1.8 miles west of Callie's house. The grocery store is located 2.4 miles south of the library. What is the length of a straight line between Callie's house and the grocery store? 1 point

3 miles

3. Two cylinders are shown below. Find the volume of each cylinder. Use 3.14 for $\pi$. Round to the nearest hundredth. 2 points

Cylinder P: 794.03 $in.^3$
Cylinder Q: 1,307.81 $in.^3$

4. Which of the following functions are linear? 1 point

**Function A**

| x | 3 | 6 | 9 | 12 | 15 |
|---|---|---|---|---|---|
| y | 9 | 36 | 81 | 144 | 225 |

**Function B**

| x | 5 | 10 | 15 | 20 | 25 |
|---|---|---|---|---|---|
| y | 8 | 16 | 24 | 32 | 40 |

- Ⓐ Function A
- Ⓑ Function B
- Ⓒ Function A and Function B
- Ⓓ None of the above

5. The results of a movie survey are represented in the two-way frequency table below. Complete the two-way frequency table. 1 point

| Way to Watch Movies | Male | Female | Total |
|---|---|---|---|
| Stream | 17 | 29 | 46 |
| Theater | 33 | 21 | 54 |
| Total | 50 | 50 | 100 |

Topics 1–8 Cumulative/Benchmark Assessment 1 of 6

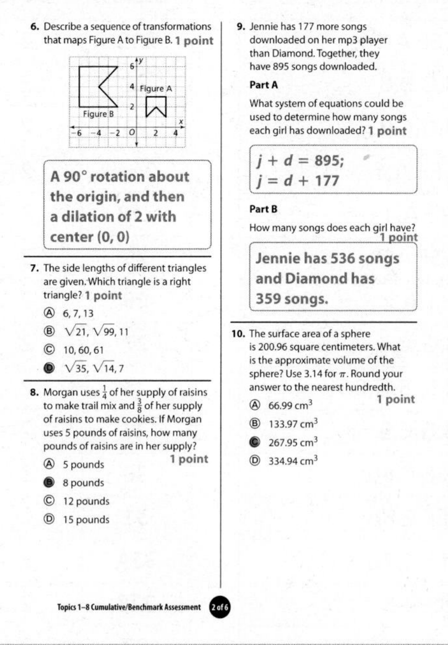

6. Describe a sequence of transformations that maps Figure A to Figure B. 1 point

A 90° rotation about the origin, and then a dilation of 2 with center (0, 0)

7. The side lengths of different triangles are given. Which triangle is a right triangle? 1 point
- Ⓐ 6, 7, 13
- Ⓑ $\sqrt{21}$, $\sqrt{99}$, 11
- Ⓒ 10, 60, 61
- Ⓓ $\sqrt{35}$, $\sqrt{14}$, 7

8. Morgan uses $\frac{1}{4}$ of her supply of raisins to make trail mix and $\frac{3}{8}$ of her supply of raisins to make cookies. If Morgan uses 5 pounds of raisins, how many pounds of raisins are in her supply? 1 point
- Ⓐ 5 pounds
- Ⓑ 8 pounds
- Ⓒ 12 pounds
- Ⓓ 15 pounds

9. Jennie has 177 more songs downloaded on her mp3 player than Diamond. Together, they have 895 songs downloaded.

**Part A**

What system of equations could be used to determine how many songs each girl has downloaded? 1 point

$j + d = 895;$
$j = d + 177$

**Part B**

How many songs does each girl have? 1 point

Jennie has 536 songs and Diamond has 359 songs.

10. The surface area of a sphere is 200.96 square centimeters. What is the approximate volume of the sphere? Use 3.14 for $\pi$. Round your answer to the nearest hundredth. 1 point
- Ⓐ 66.99 $cm^3$
- Ⓑ 133.97 $cm^3$
- Ⓒ 267.95 $cm^3$
- Ⓓ 334.94 $cm^3$

Topics 1–8 Cumulative/Benchmark Assessment 2 of 6

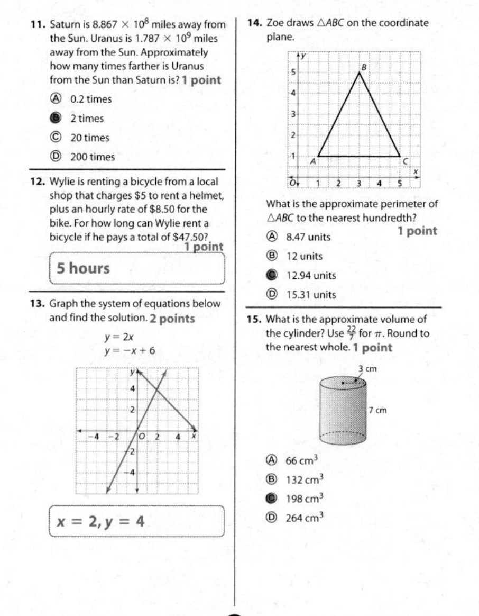

11. Saturn is $8.867 \times 10^8$ miles away from the Sun. Uranus is $1.787 \times 10^9$ miles away from the Sun. Approximately how many times farther is Uranus from the Sun than Saturn is? 1 point
- Ⓐ 0.2 times
- Ⓑ 2 times
- Ⓒ 20 times
- Ⓓ 200 times

12. Wylie is renting a bicycle from a local shop that charges \$5 to rent a helmet, plus an hourly rate of \$8.50 for the bike. For how long can Wylie rent a bicycle if he pays a total of \$47.50? 1 point

5 hours

13. Graph the system of equations below and find the solution. 2 points
$y = 2x$
$y = -x + 6$

$x = 2, y = 4$

14. Zoe draws $\triangle ABC$ on the coordinate plane.

What is the approximate perimeter of $\triangle ABC$ to the nearest hundredth? 1 point
- Ⓐ 8.47 units
- Ⓑ 12 units
- Ⓒ 12.94 units
- Ⓓ 15.31 units

15. What is the approximate volume of the cylinder? Use $\frac{22}{7}$ for $\pi$. Round to the nearest whole. 1 point
- Ⓐ 66 $cm^3$
- Ⓑ 132 $cm^3$
- Ⓒ 198 $cm^3$
- Ⓓ 264 $cm^3$

Topics 1–8 Cumulative/Benchmark Assessment 3 of 6

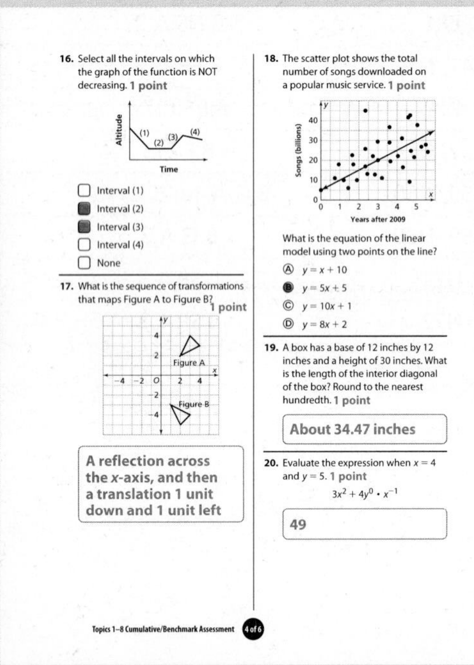

16. Select all the intervals on which the graph of the function is NOT decreasing. 1 point
- ☐ Interval (1)
- ☐ Interval (2)
- ☐ Interval (3)
- ☐ Interval (4)
- ☐ None

17. What is the sequence of transformations that maps Figure A to Figure B? 1 point

A reflection across the x-axis, and then a translation 1 unit down and 1 unit left

18. The scatter plot shows the total number of songs downloaded on a popular music service. 1 point

What is the equation of the linear model using two points on the line?
- Ⓐ $y = x + 10$
- Ⓑ $y = 5x + 5$
- Ⓒ $y = 10x + 1$
- Ⓓ $y = 8x + 2$

19. A box has a base of 12 inches by 12 inches and a height of 30 inches. What is the length of the interior diagonal of the box? Round to the nearest hundredth. 1 point

About 34.47 inches

20. Evaluate the expression when $x = 4$ and $y = 5$. 1 point
$3x^2 + 4y^0 \cdot x^{-1}$

49

Topics 1–8 Cumulative/Benchmark Assessment 4 of 6

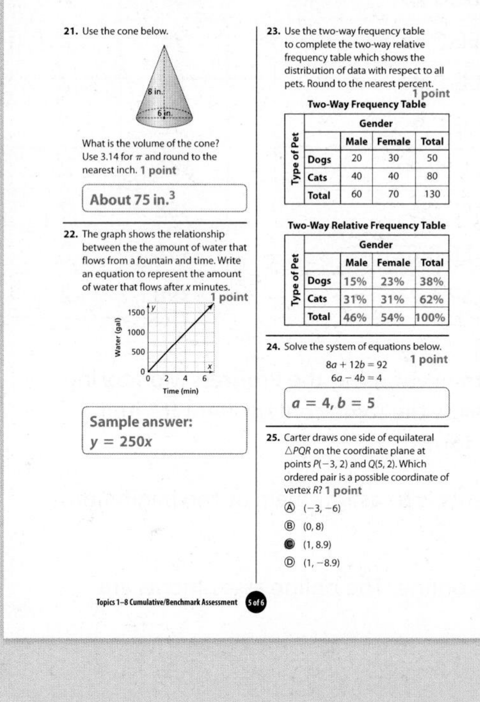

21. Use the cone below.

What is the volume of the cone? Use 3.14 for $\pi$ and round to the nearest inch. 1 point

About 75 $in.^3$

22. The graph shows the relationship between the the amount of water that flows from a fountain and time. Write an equation to represent the amount of water that flows after $x$ minutes. 1 point

Sample answer: $y = 250x$

23. Use the two-way frequency table to complete the two-way relative frequency table which shows the distribution of data with respect to all pets. Round to the nearest percent. 1 point

**Two-Way Frequency Table**

| Type of Pet | Male | Female | Total |
|---|---|---|---|
| Dogs | 20 | 30 | 50 |
| Cats | 40 | 40 | 80 |
| Total | 60 | 70 | 130 |

**Two-Way Relative Frequency Table**

| Type of Pet | Male | Female | Total |
|---|---|---|---|
| Dogs | 15% | 23% | 38% |
| Cats | 31% | 31% | 62% |
| Total | 46% | 54% | 100% |

24. Solve the system of equations below. 1 point
$8a + 12b = 92$
$6a - 4b = 4$

$a = 4, b = 5$

25. Carter draws one side of equilateral $\triangle PQR$ on the coordinate plane at points $P(-3, 2)$ and $Q(5, 2)$. Which ordered pair is a possible coordinate of vertex $R$? 1 point
- Ⓐ (−3, −6)
- Ⓑ (0, 8)
- Ⓒ (1, 8.9)
- Ⓓ (1, −8.9)

Topics 1–8 Cumulative/Benchmark Assessment 5 of 6

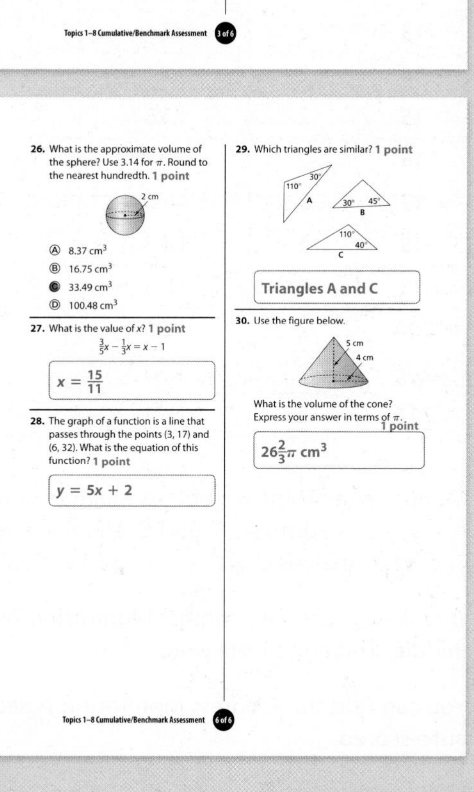

26. What is the approximate volume of the sphere? Use 3.14 for $\pi$. Round to the nearest hundredth. 1 point
- Ⓐ 8.37 $cm^3$
- Ⓑ 16.75 $cm^3$
- Ⓒ 33.49 $cm^3$
- Ⓓ 100.48 $cm^3$

27. What is the value of $x$? 1 point
$\frac{3}{5}x - \frac{1}{2}x = x - 1$

$x = \frac{15}{11}$

28. The graph of a function is a line that passes through the points (3, 17) and (6, 32). What is the equation of this function? 1 point

$y = 5x + 2$

29. Which triangles are similar? 1 point

Triangles A and C

30. Use the figure below.

What is the volume of the cone? Express your answer in terms of $\pi$. 1 point

$26\frac{2}{3}\pi\ cm^3$

Topics 1–8 Cumulative/Benchmark Assessment 6 of 6

## Item Analysis for Diagnosis and Intervention

| Item | Points | DOK | MDIS | Standard |
|---|---|---|---|---|
| 1 | 1 | 1 | L83 | 8.EE.A.1 |
| 2 | 1 | 2 | N64 | 8.G.B.8 |
| 3 | 1 | 2 | N53 | 8.G.C.9 |
| 4 | 1 | 2 | K51 | 8.F.A.1 |
| 5 | 1 | 3 | N89 | 8.SP.A.4 |
| 6 | 1 | 2 | N59, N61 | 8.G.A.4 |
| 7 | 1 | 2 | N65 | 8.G.B.7 |
| 8 | 1 | 2 | K29 | 8.EE.C.7b |
| 9 | 2 | 2 | K35 | 8.EE.C.8b |
| 10 | 1 | 3 | N50, N55 | 8.G.C.9 |
| 11 | 1 | 2 | L84 | 8.EE.A.4 |
| 12 | 1 | 2 | K26 | 8.EE.C.7b |
| 13 | 1 | 2 | K34 | 8.EE.C.8a |
| 14 | 1 | 3 | N66 | 8.G.B.8 |
| 15 | 1 | 2 | N53 | 8.G.C.9 |
| 16 | 1 | 2 | K54 | 8.F.B.5 |

| Item | Points | DOK | MDIS | Standard |
|---|---|---|---|---|
| 17 | 1 | 2 | N59 | 8.G.A.4 |
| 18 | 1 | 2 | N71 | 8.SP.A.2 |
| 19 | 1 | 2 | N64 | 8.G.B.7 |
| 20 | 1 | 1 | L83 | 8.EE.A.1 |
| 21 | 1 | 2 | N54 | 8.G.C.9 |
| 22 | 1 | 2 | K50 | 8.EE.B.5 |
| 23 | 1 | 3 | N90 | 8.SP.A.4 |
| 24 | 1 | 2 | K36 | 8.EE.C.8b |
| 25 | 1 | 2 | N66 | 8.G.B.8 |
| 26 | 1 | 2 | N55 | 8.G.C.9 |
| 27 | 1 | 2 | K29 | 8.EE.C.7b |
| 28 | 1 | 3 | K50 | 8.F.B.4 |
| 29 | 1 | 2 | N63 | 8.G.A.5 |
| 30 | 1 | 2 | N54 | 8.G.C.9 |

You may opt to have students take the Cumulative/Benchmark Assessment online. The online assessment is auto-scored.

### Scoring Rubric

| Item | Points | End-of-Year Assessment |
|---|---|---|
| **3** | 2<br>1 | Correct answer and explanation<br>Correct answer or explanation |
| **13** | 2<br>1 | Correct graph and solution<br>Correct graph or correct solution |

### Scoring Guide

| Score | Recommendations |
|---|---|
| Greater Than 85% | Assign the corresponding MDIS for items answered incorrectly. |
| 70%–85% | Assign the corresponding MDIS for items answered incorrectly. Monitor the student during Step 1 and Try It! parts of the lessons for personalized remediation needs. |
| Less Than 70% | Assign the corresponding MDIS for items answered incorrectly.<br>Assign appropriate intervention lessons available online. |

# ACKNOWLEDGEMENTS


## Photographs

**CVR:** Phonlamai Photo/Shutterstock, ESOlex/Shutterstock, Picsfive/Shutterstock, Laborant/Shutterstock, Onchira Wongsiri/Shutterstock, Christianto/Shutterstock, Peangdao/Shutterstock, Tortoon/Shutterstock, D and D Photo Sudbury/Shutterstock, Grasycho/Shutterstock, Christian Bertrand/Shutterstock/Shutterstock; **261**: kalafoto/ Fotolia; **262** (BCR) yossarian6/Fotolia, (BR) makieni/Fotolia, (C) vicgmyr/Fotolia, (CL) akepong/Fotolia, (CR) travelphotos/Fotolia, (TL) patrimonio designs/Fotolia, (TR) vikpit74/Fotolia; **265** (T) Akira Kaelyn/Shutterstock, (BL) Esin Deniz/Shutterstock, (BR) Ammit Jack/Shutterstock; **266** (T) Dean Drobot/Shutterstock, (B) Kynamuia/ Shutterstock; **267**: Bedrin/Fotolia; **272**: iadams/Shutterstock; **273** (CL) Elnur/Fotolia, (CR) Alliance/Fotolia, (T) btmedia/Shutterstock; **281**: Rawpixel.com/Fotolia; **283**: anton_lunkov/Fotolia; **285** (T) Tolgatezcan/Fotolia, (TCR) Richard Kane/Fotolia, (TR) Paul Yates/Fotolia; **286**: Lilli Jemska/Shutterstock; **288**: Ant Clausen/Shutterstock; **303**: keytoken/Fotolia; **304** (BCR) sapgreen/Fotolia, (BR) yossarian6/Fotolia, (C) murgvi/Fotolia, (CR) Alexander Potapov/Fotolia, (TC) Kletr/Fotolia, (TCR) sveta/Fotolia, (TR) volff/Fotolia, (CL) Mart/Shutterstock; **307** (T) Paolo De Gasperis/Shutterstock, (B) Maksim Narushevich/Shutterstock; **308** (T) Berthuznago/Shutterstock, (B) Ian Dyball/Shutterstock; **309** (C) Goir/Fotolia, (CL) Photka/Fotolia, (CR) Photka/Fotolia; **321**: Tarchyshnik Andrei/ Fotolia; **351** (C): Africa Studio/Fotolia; **357** (C) Veniamin Kraskov/Fotolia, (CL) Studio KIWI/Shutterstock, (CR) Ruslan Ivantsov/Fotolia, (TR) Goir/Fotolia; **370** (CR): Dmitry Chulov/Fotolia; **383**: RapidEye/iStock/ Getty Images Plus/Getty Images; **385**; **397**: Marek/Fotolia; **386** (BCR) yossarian6/Fotolia, (C) BirgitKorber/ Fotolia, (CL) kub_21212/Fotolia, (CR) kubais/Fotolia, (TCR) andrew_rybalko/Fotolia, (TR) andrew_rybalko/ Fotolia, (BR) Tamara321/Shutterstock; **389** (T) Dragon Images/Shutterstock, (B) Tom_Sanderson/ Shutterstock; **390** (T) Oleksandr Kavun/Shutterstock, (B) Boumen Japet/Shutterstock; **391**: tab62/Fotolia; **401** (C) goodween123/Fotolia, (CL) Renewer/Fotolia; **408** (C) vladimirfloyd/Fotolia, (R) Big Face/Fotolia; **412**: Dashadima/Shutterstock; **414**: 3dmavr/Fotolia; **427**: Pinkomelet/Shutterstock; **428** (B) yossarian6/Fotolia, (BC) Natis/Fotolia, (BCR) Zonda/Fotolia, (BR) Natbasil/Fotolia, (CL) Subbotina Anna/Fotolia, (TC) Maxal Tamor/ Fotolia, (TR) Yeko Photo Studio/Fotolia, (TCR) Narupon Nimpaiboon/Shutterstock; **431** (T) Oleksandr Nagaiets/ Shutterstock, (B) Zyabich/Shutterstock; **432** (T) NetVideo/Shutterstock, (B) Jonas Petrovas/Shutterstock; **433** (C) Silkstock/Fotolia, (CL) Ekarin/Fotolia, (TC) Nagel's Blickwinkel/Fotolia; **455**: Anekoho/Fotolia; **F16** (CL) Aurielaki/Fotolia, (TR) Taras Livyy/Fotolia; **F17**: piai/Fotolia; **F18**: kues1/Fotolia; **F19**: FedotovAnatoly/Fotolia; **F20** (BKGRD) totallypic/Fotolia, (CL, CR) abert84/Fotolia; **F21** (CL) Eyematrix/Fotolia, (CR) totallypic/Fotolia; **F22**: darnell_vfx/Fotolia; **F23**: blueringmedia/Fotolia; Gemenacom/Shutterstock; Goir/Fotolia; yossarian6/Fotolia; Svinkin/Shutterstock.